CONCORDIA UNIVERSITY CHICAGO

3 4211 00186 9067

S0-BJP-225

WITHDRAWN

KLINCK MEMORIAL LIBRARY
Concordia University
River Forest, IL 60305-1499

ANNUAL REVIEW OF PHYSIOLOGY

EDITORIAL COMMITTEE (1994)

ROBERT J. ALPERN

BRUCE P. BEAN

DAVID C. DAWSON

PAUL DE WEER

ROBERT F. FURCHGOTT

DARYL K. GRANNER

JOSEPH F. HOFFMAN

DONALD MASSARO

CHRISTINE SEIDMAN

GEORGE N. SOMERO

Responsible for the organization of Volume 56
(Editorial Committee, 1992)

ARTHUR M. BROWN

JOHN A. CLEMENTS

DAVID C. DAWSON

PAUL DE WEER

CLARA FRANZINI-ARMSTRONG

DARYL K. GRANNER

JOSEPH F. HOFFMAN

DONALD C. JACKSON

JIM NELSON (GUEST)

CHRISTINE SEIDMAN

RICHARD TSIEN (GUEST)

ERICH E. WINDHAGER

Production Editor   SANDRA H. COOPERMAN
Subject Indexer   STEVEN M. SORENSEN

ANNUAL REVIEW OF PHYSIOLOGY

VOLUME 56, 1994

JOSEPH F. HOFFMAN, *Editor*

Yale University School of Medicine

PAUL De WEER, *Associate Editor*

University of Pennsylvania School of Medicine

ANNUAL REVIEW INC.   4139 EL CAMINO WAY,   P.O. BOX 10139   PALO ALTO, CALIFORNIA 94303-0897

KLINCK MEMORIAL LIBRARY
Concordia University
River Forest, IL 60305-1499

⟨R⟩ ANNUAL REVIEWS INC.
Palo Alto, California, USA

COPYRIGHT © 1994 BY ANNUAL REVIEWS INC., PALO ALTO, CALIFORNIA, USA. ALL
RIGHTS RESERVED. The appearance of the code at the bottom of the first page of an
article in this serial indicates the copyright owner's consent that copies of the
article may be made for personal or internal use, or for the personal or internal use
of specific clients. This consent is given on the condition, however, that the copier
pay the stated per-copy fee of $5.00 per article through the Copyright Clearance
Center, Inc. (222 Rosewood Drive, Danvers, MA 01923) for copying beyond that
permitted by Sections 107 or 108 of the US Copyright Law. The per-copy fee of
$5.00 per article also applies to the copying, under the stated conditions, of articles
published in any *Annual Review* serial before January 1, 1978. Individual readers,
and nonprofit libraries acting for them, are permitted to make a single copy of an
article without charge for use in research or teaching. This consent does not extend
to other kinds of copying, such as copying for general distribution, for advertising
or promotional purposes, for creating new collective works, or for resale. For such
uses, written permission is required. Write to Permissions Dept., Annual Reviews
Inc., 4139 El Camino Way, P.O. Box 10139, Palo Alto, CA 94303-0897 USA.

International Standard Serial Number: 0066-4278
International Standard Book Number: 0-8243-0356-3
Library of Congress Catalog Card Number: 39-15404

Annual Review and publication titles are registered trademarks of Annual Reviews Inc.

∞ The paper used in this publication meets the minimum requirements of
American National Standard for Information Sciences—Permanence of Paper
for Printed Library Materials, ANSI Z39.48-1984.

Annual Reviews Inc. and the Editors of its publications assume no responsibility for the
statements expressed by the contributors to this *Review*.

Typesetting by Kachina Typesetting Inc., Tempe, Arizona; John Olson, President;
Marty Mullins, Typesetting Coordinator; and by the Annual Reviews Inc. Editorial Staff

PRINTED AND BOUND IN THE UNITED STATES OF AMERICA

PREFACE

This preface considers first, a commentary about research publications in physiology and second, some special aspects of the articles presented in this volume.

It should be evident that what shapes the current content of physiology research is what shapes the *Annual Review of Physiology*. The issue is not the extent to which we are successful in reporting on or critically evaluating the advancing fronts of our science. The issue is what shapes the research literature in physiology? Although this question has no simple answer, it is nevertheless clear that most of the research in our science is, with input from the research community, directed or set by government-defined choices or priorities (mainly the National Institutes of Health in the United States). Therefore, the advancing fronts essentially reflect these decisions, and what is "new" was selected or predetermined at the time the priorities were circumscribed.

It is this new research that forms the substance of what is reviewed in ARP. While the selection of fields (priorities) has many desirable features that provide new understanding, foster change, and stimulate major developments, the system also promotes conformity. The shape of content is now defined less by the unusual, by investigator interests and tastes, than by the priorities of area chosen for funding. In emphasizing that the prime research resources reside in the imaginations of individuals, the future constructs of priorities (and the design and orientation of study sections) should make provision for some enlightened slippage in their set points.

This volume of ARP contains, as is customary, articles surveying advances in the various sectionalized fields of physiology. The articles in each section are interrelated and attempt to be thematic in the subjects covered. There is also a special topic section that deals with excitation/contraction coupling in muscle. The special topic section is intended to bring to the attention of our readership substantive developments in specialized areas that they may not otherwise see. In addition, there is an interdisciplinary theme on signal transduction mechanisms that is complementary to the subjects covered in any one section. A discerning reader would also detect a secondary theme in the use of models in systems analyzed. Obviously the subjects and topics vary from year to year, and we repeat our open invitation to the research community to contact any member of the Editorial Committee with suggestions for subjects/topics, criticisms, and/or comments.

We note with sadness the death of J. Murray Luck, professor emeritus of chemistry, Stanford University, on August 26, 1993. Dr. Luck was not only the founding Editor of the *Annual Review of Physiology* (1939), but also the founder of many other Annual Reviews. His lasting contributions to our series were gratefully acknowledged in the preface to Volume 10. With great respect and admiration for his enduring legacies, the Editorial Committee dedicates this volume to his memory.

JOSEPH F. HOFFMAN
EDITOR

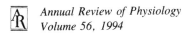

Annual Review of Physiology
Volume 56, 1994

CONTENTS

viii   CONTENTS   (*Continued*)

OTHER REVIEWS OF INTEREST TO PHYSIOLOGISTS

From the *Annual Review of Biochemistry*, Volume 63 (1994):

Functional Significance of GTPases in Vesicular Trafficking, W. Balch
A Molecular Description of Synaptic Vesicle Membrane Trafficking, M. K. Bennett, R. H. Scheller
Signal Transduction in T Cells, G. Crabtree
Structure and Function of G-Protein-Coupled Receptors, C. D. Strader, T. M. Fong, M. R. Tota, D. Underwood, R. A. F. Dixon
Intermediate Filaments: Structure, Dynamics, Function and Disease, E. Fuchs, K. Weber
Genetic and Biochemical Studies of Protein N-Myristoylation, J. I. Gordon
Nitrogenase: A Nucleotide-Dependent Molecular Switch, J. B. Howard, D. C. Rees
The Biochemistry of Regulation of Synaptic Transmission in the Central Nervous System, M. B. Kennedy
Structures and Functions of Multiligand Lipoprotein Receptors: Macrophage Scavenger Receptors and LDL Receptor-Related Protein (LRP), M. Krieger, J. Herz
Endocytosis, I. Mellman
Steroid Hormone Receptors, B. W. O'Malley
Omega-Conotoxins, Omega-Agatoxins, and their Calcium Channel Targets, B. Olivera
Nitric Oxide: A Physiologic Messenger Molecule, D. S. Bredt, S. H. Snyder
Energy Transduction by Cytochrome Complexes in Mitochondrial and Bacterial Respiration: The Enzymology of Coupling Electron Transfer Reactions to Trans-membrane Proton Translocation, B. L. Trumpower, R. B. Gennis

From the *Annual Review of Medicine*, Volume 45 (1994):

Gonadotropin-Releasing Hormone and Its Analogs, M. Conn, W. F. Crowley, Jr.
Metabolic Interactions of Diabetes and Pregnancy, J. L. Kitzmiller, T. A. Buchanan
Biologic andd Clinical Aspects of Hematopoietic Stem Cells, G. J. Spangrude
Malaria, the Red Cell, and the Endothelium, B. L. Pasloske, R. Howard
Thalassemia: Pathophysiology of Red Cell Changes, S. Schrier
Male Sex Determination: Current Concepts of Male Sexual Differentiation, P. K. Donohoe, M. Gustafson
Modulation of the Ionic Milieu of the Airway in Health and Disease, P. G. Noone, K. N. Olivier, M. R. Knowles

From the *Annual Review of Neuroscience*, Volume 17 (1994):

Cloned Glutamate Receptors, M. Hollmann, S. Heinemann
Nitric Oxide and Synaptic Function, E. M. Schuman, D. V. Madison

ANNUAL REVIEWS INC. is a nonprofit scientific publisher established to promote the advancement of the sciences. Beginning in 1932 with the *Annual Review of Biochemistry*, the Company has pursued as its principal function the publication of high quality, reasonably priced *Annual Review* volumes. The volumes are organized by Editors and Editorial Committees who invite qualified authors to contribute critical articles reviewing significant developments within each major discipline. The Editor-in-Chief invites those interested in serving as future Editorial Committee members to communicate directly with him. Annual Reviews Inc. is administered by a Board of Directors, whose members serve without compensation.

1994 Board of Directors, Annual Reviews Inc.

Joshua Lederberg, Chairman of Annual Reviews Inc.
  University Professor, The Rockefeller University
Richard N. Zare, Vice Chairman of Annual Reviews Inc.
  Professor of Physical Chemistry, Stanford University
Winslow R. Briggs, *Director, Carnegie Institution of Washington, Stanford*
W. Maxwell Cowan, *Howard Hughes Medical Institute, Bethesda*
Sidney D. Drell, *Deputy Director, Stanford Linear Accelerator Center*
Sandra M. Faber, *Professor of Astronomy, University of California, Santa Cruz*
Eugene Garfield, *President, Institute for Scientific Information*
William Kaufmann, *President, William Kaufmann, Inc.*
Daniel E. Koshland, Jr., *Professor of Biochemistry, University of California, Berkeley*
Donald A. B. Lindberg, *Director, National Library of Medicine*
Gardner Lindzey, *Director Emeritus, Center for Advanced Study in the Behavioral Sciences, Stanford*
Charles Yanofsky, *Professor of Biological Sciences, Stanford University*
Harriet A. Zuckerman, *Vice President, The Andrew W. Mellon Foundation*

Management of Annual Reviews, Inc.

William Kaufmann, Editor-in-Chief and President
John S. McNeil, Publisher and Secretary-Treasurer
Donald Svedeman, Business Manager
Richard L. Burke, Technology Applications Manager
Richard A. Peterson, Advertising and Marketing Manager

ANNUAL REVIEWS OF

Anthropology
Astronomy and Astrophysics
Biochemistry
Biophysics and Biomolecular Structure
Cell Biology
Computer Science
Earth and Planetary Sciences
Ecology and Systematics
Energy and the Environment
Entomology
Fluid Mechanics
Genetics
Immunology

Materials Science
Medicine
Microbiology
Neuroscience
Nuclear and Particle Science
Nutrition
Pharmacology and Toxicology
Physical Chemistry
Physiology
Phytopathology
Plant Physiology and
    Plant Molecular Biology
Psychology

Public Health
Sociology

SPECIAL PUBLICATIONS

Excitement and Fascination of Science, Vols. 1, 2, and 3

Intelligence and Affectivity, by Jean Piaget

For the convenience of readers, a detachable order form/envelope is bound into the back of this volume.

Knut Schmidt-Nielsen

Annu. Rev. Physiol. 1994. 56:1–12
Copyright © 1994 by Annual Reviews Inc. All rights reserved

ABOUT CURIOSITY AND BEING INQUISITIVE

Knut Schmidt-Nielsen

J. B. Duke Professor of Physiology, Emeritus, Department of Zoology, Duke University, Durham, North Carolina 27708-0325

INTRODUCTION

A sarcastic soul once observed that the primary function of our schools is to impart sufficient facts to make the children stop asking questions. Those with whom the schools do not succeed become scientists. I never made good grades in school, at times I nearly failed, and I never stopped asking questions.

Perhaps curiosity is in the genes. My grandfather, an engineer who built railroads in Norway, did the first experiment in osmoregulation I know about. He was curious about the flounders that occasionally were caught in fresh water upriver from my home town, Trondheim. He wanted to know if this saltwater fish could survive for any length of time in freshwater, so he released over 1000 flounder hatchlings in a large inland lake. The fish survived, and for years afterwards surprised fishermen occasionally caught a grown flounder in the lake. However, the fish were unable to reproduce in fresh water and did not become permanently established in the lake.

My father, a chemistry professor, once measured the osmotic concentration in a large number of saltwater fish and found that they are hyposmotic to seawater; their osmotic concentration is only about one third of the surrounding seawater. There was one exception, the hagfish or slime eel, *Myxine*. This animal is unique among vertebrates in having salt concentrations in its body fluids as high as in seawater. My father also measured the concentration of salt in whale urine to find out how these mammals manage to excrete the salts ingested with their food.

In contemplating my own life and skimming through what I have written, I find that I have been curious about similar problems —more than anything else—how animals meet the challenges of their environment, how they

1

0066-04278/94/0315-0001$02.00

adapt to life in the sea and on dry land. At first glance, these environments may seem extremely different. However, from a physiological viewpoint, water in the sea is not freely available, and on land and especially in deserts, lack of water is an important challenge to survival.

In addition to genes, I have had a great deal of luck. My mother, who was a physicist and a student of Arrhenius, had a knack for explaining things so that a curious boy understood. Hanging out in the kitchen when she worked there, I learned simple things about heat, boiling, eggs and coagulation, emulsions such as cream and butter and mayonnaise, and what causes an emulsion to break down. She gave me factual answers and did not resort to glib explanations. What luck I had to grow up with easy access to information and all sorts of odd facts, such as cream being an emulsion of fat droplets in water and butter an emulsion of water in fat!

I was also fortunate in getting a good education. After switching from a start in engineering, I read chemistry and zoology in Oslo, and then I spent almost ten years in Denmark, where I obtained my doctorate and had the privilege of working in the laboratory of the brilliant Nobel Laureate, August Krogh, one of this century's most versatile physiologists.

WHERE IS PHYSIOLOGY HEADED?

At times I have been asked about the future of physiology and what important discoveries I foresee. I have no idea what the future may bring, except that we will have more answers and even more questions to answer. During the fifty or sixty years since I was a student, I have lived through more "future" in physiology than most of my readers, and I can safely say that nobody would have predicted much of what has taken place. Who could have known, for example, that we would study single ion channels and their molecular configuration? We didn't know about channels, and not even a genius can predict the clarification of phenomena whose very existence we don't know about.

What I can do is to mention some of the problems that have intrigued me and show how the solutions have raised new fundamental questions that, I hope, some day will be better understood than they are now. Judging from what I have seen in the past, physiological discoveries will become more and more interesting, but what discoveries will be made I cannot predict.

DRINKING SEA WATER

A problem that intrigued me when I was a student was how marine birds obtain water— do they drink seawater, which is toxic and lethal to humans who drink it in place of fresh water? I reasoned that if birds do drink seawater, they would have to excrete the ingested salts, which would be revealed by a determination of the salt concentration in the urine. The high magnesium content in seawater could also be used as a tracer. Most food has a low magnesium content, and since about one tenth of the salts in seawater is magnesium, any substantial ingestion of seawater should be revealed by the presence of magnesium in the digestive tract.

In the summer of 1939, when I was 23, I set out for a group of small islands off the coast of Norway. I had assembled equipment for chloride and magnesium analyses that could be used under primitive field conditions, and I had the necessary bird permits. When I arrived at the island of Röst, a kind fisherman permitted me to work in his empty boathouse. Sitting on the rough, wooden floor, I tested my analytical methods and satisfied myself that they worked. I caught a few arctic gulls, which I kept caged in old packing crates, feeding them fish that they greedily devoured. The urine of these birds had a low salt content, in accord with the relatively low salt content of the fish. This suggested that the birds obtained sufficient water in their food and might not need to drink seawater.

To find out what effect seawater had on salt excretion, I gave one of the gulls a liberal amount of seawater by stomach tube and collected the copious amounts of urine the bird produced. To my amazement the salt concentration in the urine was low and seemed to decrease after a salt load. My first thought was to suspect my methods, so I carefully re-checked every step of my procedures without finding anything wrong. Nevertheless, no matter how much seawater I gave the birds, very little salt appeared in the urine, and mysteriously, the blood concentrations did not increase. Testing the contents of the digestive tract gave no exciting leads, and at the end of the brief summer I returned to Copenhagen without any answer to the problem I had set out to solve.

I described what I had done to senior investigators in the laboratotry, but nobody had much to say. I suggested that, if salts do not come out one end of the bird, they must come out the other. I had a hypothesis that I kept to myself. Could the gastric epithelium, which normally secretes hydrochloric acid, in marine birds be specialized to secrete a more concentrated solution of chloride ions, and could the sodium ions be excreted in the urine, bound to insoluble urates? I wanted to return to the problem, but World War II intervened and then other projects took all my time.

It was not until 17 years later, in 1956, that I returned to the problems of marine birds. I worked at the Mount Desert Island Biological Laboratory in Maine with a Japanese colleague and a friend from student days in Denmark. We first repeated my old experiment from Norway, this time with a cormorant. I gave the bird a considerable amount of seawater by stomach tube and placed it in a carefully cleaned plastic container. Almost immediately I noticed droplets appearing on the plastic wall. I sampled the clear liquid with a micropipette; it showed a massive precipitate with silver nitrate, which revealed a high concentration of chloride. The droplets came from the bird's beak, confirming my conviction that what does not come out one end must come out the other.

I now understood why I never saw the secretion while working in Norway. The primitive conditions, working on a rough wooden floor, had made me disregard droplets that the birds occasionally shook from their beaks, thinking that it was merely regurgitated seawater.

The following year I was joined by my good friend Ragnar Fänge from Sweden. All the marine birds we tested, pelicans, gulls, gannets, eiderducks, and petrels, secreted highly concentrated salt solutions. Fänge's anatomical expertise helped establish that the secretion came from glands, known as nasal glands, in the heads of the birds. The concentration of the secreted fluid was up to twice as high as in seawater, and it seemed obvious that all marine birds would be able to tolerate a load of seawater. However, I should add that the presence of a mechanism for extra-renal salt excretion does not necessarily mean that marine birds under natural conditions do drink seawater; the answer to this question may be negative, for much of their food has a relatively low salt content.

After we knew the mechanism for salt excretion in marine birds, it was logical to ask about marine reptiles. We found that both marine turtles and marine iguanas are capable of extra-renal salt excretion. The iguana has a nasal gland that appears homologous to the bird gland, but in turtles a gland in the orbit of the eye is modified for salt excretion and produces very salty tears. To simplify matters, we therefore decided to refer to all the salt secreting glands as salt glands.

Other investigators have found extra-renal salt excretion in sea snakes, in which a sub-lingual gland is responsible, and in saltwater crocodiles, where groups of glands on the tongue are responsible for salt secretion. To a comparative physiologist it is intriguing that in each of the four groups of marine reptiles, the mechanism for extra-renal salt excretion has a different anatomical origin.

Fänge and I wrote a brief note about salt excretion in marine reptiles. Our opening line was a quotation from *Alice In Wonderland,* citing the Mock Turtle's tears, followed by a quote from Kipling's *Just So Stories,* referring to the Crocodile who wept real crocodile tears. We didn't expect that the editor of a serious scientific journal would let us get away with such light-hearted quotations, but to our amazement, our note was accepted by *Nature* without any suggestion for change or revision.

While working on problems of seawater and salt excretion, I came across a report that one species of frog, the crab-eating frog of Southeast Asia, lives and feeds in seawater in coastal mangrove swamps. This excited me; could it really be true? It sounded unbelievable; the skin of frogs is permeable to water, and a frog in seawater would encounter severe osmotic problems and rapidly become dehydrated.

I spent a summer studying the saltwater frogs in collaboration with Malcolm Gordon from the University of California at Los Angeles. We found that the frogs indeed tolerate seawater, but their solution to the osmotic problems is different from the mechanism used by reptiles. Like other vertebrates, the frogs keep their salt concentrations at a fraction of that in seawater, but like sharks, they make up the difference by adding large amounts of urea to the body fluids. In one important respect they differ from sharks; shark kidneys are capable of active reabsorption of urea, an ability lacking in the crab-eating frog.

TEMPERATURE AND WATER MATTERS

From discussing seawater, I wish to turn to problems of life on land. More than 30% of the world's land area is considered arid or semi-arid, and in the driest regions, the deserts, frequent high temperatures magnify the physiological problems of water shortage. I had been interested in desert problems since my student days in Oslo, when I eagerly read Richard Hesse's book on ecological animal geography, *Tiergeographie auf Oekologischer Grundlage*. This fascinating book described innumerable problems in what we today call environmental physiology. However, how I came to spend many years in studies of desert animals was not directly related to that book.

After the war, in 1946, my wife Bodil and I left Denmark to take up post-doctoral positions with Laurence Irving and Pete Scholander at Swarthmore College. I was supposed to help develop simple methods for physiological measurements that would be independent of laboratory facilities and suitable for field work. I had several years' experience in analytical microchemistry and rapidly developed a simple method for chloride analysis.

The method worked well in the laboratory, but Dr. Irving remarked that this was irrelevant, the method might be useless in the field and it needed to be tested under field conditions. He gave me the choice of considering a marine environment or a desert area for a test. Being from Norway I was familiar with the sea, but I had never seen a desert, so the choice was easy.

Action followed quickly, and a few days later Pete Scholander, a friend of his from Norway, and I found ourselves on the way to Arizona in Irving's jeep. We chose to drive on the Pennsylvania turnpike, where we ran into a severe blizzard with heavy winds and drifting snow. We saw a few stranded cars and an abandoned bus at the wayside; then a police car blocked the road and several patrolmen waved us down. Scholander put the jeep in four-wheel drive and swerved around the patrol car, smiling broadly as he waved to the men who were on duty to save our lives. We continued to Arizona.

Once there I was fascinated to learn that virtually nothing was known about the physiology of the common desert animals. With Irving's help we made arrangements to spend the summer studying rodents that were reputed not to need to drink. This beginning led to several years of work during which we examined all components in the water balance of kangaroo rats. My wife became especially interested in their extremely high urine concentrations, and for many years she continued doing innovative research in renal physiology.

One reason kangaroo rats manage to live on an extremely tight water budget is that they are nocturnal. They remain in their burrows during the day and do not use water for temperature regulation. But what about camels, which have no burrows and cannot escape from the daytime heat? How do they manage for days without drinking in hot deserts where humans could survive without water for no more than a day? Anecdotal reports about camels and their ability to store water and go for days or weeks without drinking were plentiful, but physiological measurements were non-existent.

To study camel physiology under desert conditions, I needed financial support, which was not easy to find. I approached a number of agencies and foundations, which politely expressed interest and regretted that they could not be of help. I contacted oil companies, which replied that they had converted to power vehicles for prospecting in desert areas and were no longer interested in camels. However, UNESCO had a program for arid zone research and awarded me $1500, an encouraging beginning, but only a fraction of what I needed. I turned to the National Science Foundation and enthusiastically explained to the program director my plans for camel studies. He expressed no interest whatsoever and remarked, "What is so interesting about camels anyway?" My application was turned down.

The project was rescued by D. H. K. Lee, professor of physiological climatology at Johns Hopkins University. He introduced me to the Offices of the Surgeon General and the Quartermaster General, which granted funds and other support for an expedition to the Sahara Desert in 1953–1954.

One important finding in our study was that, during a severe heat load, a camel deprived of drinking water does not seek to resist a rise in body temperature the way humans do. On a hot day humans attempt to maintain the body temperature at about 37°C by sweating—a thirsty camel will instead conserve water by permitting its body temperature to increase to as much as 41°C. This means that heat is stored in the body during the day, and the excess heat is then dissipated during the cooler night without the use of water. The camel's morning temperature may drop to below 34°C, which gives it an extra margin for storage of heat during the day.

The wide fluctuations in body temperature are characteristic of camels deprived of water. While a well-watered camel maintains a body temperature of about 37°C with diurnal variations of some two degrees, the temperature of a water-deprived camel may vary by more than seven degrees. These variations are essential in the animal's water economy; they are well regulated, and they are in no way a sign of failing temperature regulation.

Although we know that the changes in the temperature regulation of the dehydrated camel are advantageous to its water economy, we do not understand how the changes are achieved. By what mechanism does increasing dehydration affect the thermoregulatory centers in the hypothalamus? How do the centers receive instructions about what level is to be maintained, and most important, what is the nature of these signals? I hope that some day we will have answers to these intriguing questions.

MORE QUESTIONS ABOUT TEMPERATURE

There are many questions about the body temperature of mammals that I wish I could answer. We often refer to mammals as warm-blooded, meaning that they maintain a high and fairly constant body temperature. Why is it important to maintain a high body temperature? It is commonly assumed that a high temperature is an advantage in that it keeps an animal ready for quick action. A predator is ready to pounce quickly on its dinner, and an alert animal is ready to escape from becoming that dinner. But the temperature must not be too high; a body temperature around 43°C, or about six degrees above the resting level, is lethal.

However, it is a curious fact that each of the several major groups of mammals, the eutherian placentals, the marsupials, and the monotremes, maintains the body temperature at a different level. Most eutherian placentals, like humans, maintain their resting body temperature around 37°C with regular diurnal fluctuations of a degree or two. We do not know why these animals seem tied to this uniformity in body temperature. Why do arctic and tropical animals maintain their body temperature at the same level, although the demands on their temperature regulation mechanisms differ widely? Likewise, how is it that large and small mammals maintain the same body temperature, although the heat production per unit body mass in a mouse is about 20 times higher than in an elephant.

Turning to the marsupials, kangaroos and their relatives, we find that these also maintain a reasonably constant body temperature, although at a lower level than the eutherians, around 35°C. Their lethal body temperature is also lower, around 41°C, again about six degrees above the resting temperature. Is this because marsupials are less advanced than eutherians? To consider marsupials primitive would be a mistake. They are different, but not necessarily less advanced. For example, in regard to reproductive physiology, many biologists consider marsupials far more sophisticated than eutherians.

Consider also the monotreme mammals, the egg-laying echidna and platypus, which maintain their body temperature at about 30 to 31°C. It has been said that these mammals are very primitive and almost reptilian, for they lay eggs and are unable to maintain their body temperature at the mammalian level. In fact, in my laboratory Peter Bentley found that the echidna is far from reptilian; it is an excellent temperature regulator and maintains its body temperature constant over a wide range of ambient temperatures. However, the echidna has a poor tolerance for high body temperatures; a body temperature of about 37°C is lethal. Why is a temperature that is normal in one group of mammals lethal in another? We could also ask, why is the latitude for an increase in body temperature, roughly six degrees, so similar in the different groups?

There is another fundamental question: why do animals of each of the major groups of mammals maintain their normal body temperatures at their own characteristic levels? The eutherian placentals, often thought of as the highest among mammalian orders, have the highest normal body temperature. Is a higher temperature somehow better or more desirable? The monotremes have a longer evolutionary history and have presumably had more time to evolve towards a higher temperature, should this be desirable. If a higher temperature is better, why don't eutherians have body temperatures as high as birds, which have normal body temperatures around 40°C and lethal temperatures above 46°C? What we fail to understand is why the characteristic levels of the different orders of mammals are maintained so conservatively.

We could ask, how do the neurons of the temperature regulation center "know" the precise level that should be maintained? We accept that the control is based in genetic mechanisms, but there are other problems we fail to understand. For example, what is the nature of the signals that causes the centers to regulate the body temperature at a different level in exercise or in fever?

When I was a student, I was intrigued by the work of one of Krogh's collaborators, Marius Nielsen, who found that during steady state exercise the body temperature of humans gradually increases and then stabilizes at a level directly related to the magnitude of the work load. To show whether the higher temperature was a result of a failure to dissipate the increased heat production, he increased the heat loss by opening the windows on a cold winter day. The level at which the body temperature stabilized remained unchanged. The conclusion was obvious, the increase in body temperature during exercise is a carefully controlled change in the regulation of body temperature.

The resetting to a higher level is a characteristic response to exercise, not only in mammals, but also in birds. Torre-Bueno, working in my laboratory, found the core temperature of starlings in steady state flight increased by 2 to 4°C above the resting temperature, independent of variations in the ambient temperature from 2 to 26°C.

This raises a question to which we have no adequate answer. How do the cells of the temperature regulation center "know" that, when leg muscles, lungs, and heart work harder, the temperature of the body core should be reset to a level a couple of degrees higher? What is the signal that causes this resetting of the regulating center?

I am intrigued by the question of how the cells of the temperature regulation center receive the instruction to maintain a higher body temperature during exercise, and what the nature of the signal is? I am unwilling to predict that answers will soon be found to these fundamental questions.

In a more general sense, we know the mechanism of many regulatory feedback mechanisms, such as the regulation of respiration and of body temperature. However, our knowledge of the signals that determine the "normal" level to be maintained for the most part remains inadequate.

A FORTUNATE AWARD

In the early 1960s the National Institutes of Health awarded a small number of personal stipends, known as NIH Research Career Awards, to selected research scientists. These awards paid all or a substantial fraction of the academic salaries of the recipients and were lifetime grants, that is, they were expected to be continued until the recipient's retirement. The intent was to allow productive scientists more time for their research by relieving them of administrative duties and excessive teaching obligations.

In 1964 I was fortunate to receive one of these awards, which continued until I retired in 1985. It gave me greater freedom than I had before to pursue my research interests. Until then I had been expected to teach a course every semester; now I chose to teach a course in animal physiology in one semester and have no teaching obligation in the other. Even better, I could in good conscience decline administrative duties and avoid serving as chairman of my department. The best aspect of the award was that I had a great deal of freedom to undertake research projects in other parts of the world without needing to apply for a leave of absence from Duke, as I had done for the camel studies in 1953–1954. However, the Career

Award did not free me from the need to apply for research grants for my projects.

I was eager to study ostriches, desert birds that inevitably must face some of the same physiological problems as camels. Ostriches are common in the deserts of southern Africa and once were abundant in the Sahara, where I had often found fragments of ostrich egg shells. Adult ostriches weigh about one hundred kilograms and are said to be able to eviscerate a man with a single stroke of their powerful feet. I was more interested in their heat tolerance.

One of my students at Duke, Gene Crawford, had worked with a tame ostrich, which we had named Pete in honor of Pete Scholander. He had found that under laboratory conditions, the bird was exceptionally tolerant to heat, but I was interested in studying a greater number of ostriches under more natural conditions. In 1966 I obtained support for taking a group of four scientists to South Africa, where we carried out detailed studies of the temperature regulation of ostriches. When we exposed them to temperatures as high as 50°C, which they tolerated for hours on end, their respiratory rate increased from about 5 cycles per minute to 50, and amazingly, in spite of the increased ventilation, they did not develop alkalosis.

The normally slow breathing rate of the ostrich, one full cycle in about 12 seconds, made it possible to carry out a simple study of how the respiratory system works. We allowed an ostrich to inhale a single breath of pure oxygen and used an oxygen electrode to follow the appearance of oxygen in the various parts of the respiratory system. It was evident that the inhaled gas did not move in and out of the lungs as in mammals; our evidence made us conclude that the gas moved first to the large abdominal air sacs, from which it passed across the respiratory surfaces of the lungs and to the anterior air sacs before it was exhaled.

These encouraging results helped us understand how the complex respiratory system of birds operates, a long-standing enigma. We continued these studies after returning to our home laboratory, where we could develop more sophisticated techniques than we could under field conditions. This work clarified further details of bird respiration and eventually helped explain the exceptional tolerance of birds to high altitude.

WHY COMPARATIVE PHYSIOLOGY?

I have been interested in finding out how animals manage to live in environments that seem to pose severe problems to survival, but I don't know why this is called comparative physiology. All sorts of studies that involve animals other than the usual laboratory animals, such as diving of seals or learning in sea slugs, are readily lumped together as comparative physiology.

Why comparative? The word implies that something is being compared. When C. R. Taylor joined my laboratory in the late 1960s, we started a study of the cost of locomotion in animals of different body sizes. We found that there is a regular relationship between the cost of running and the body size of the animal; the larger the animal, the lower the cost of moving one kilogram of animal over one kilometer.

Size has other profound consequences for function, and comparing animals of different sizes can reasonably be referred to as comparative physiology. Body size relationships are often referred to as scaling, a term commonly used in engineering, where scaling is an important sub-discipline. Think only of the problems of building bigger structures, longer bridges, higher buildings, and so on. The importance of body size and problems of scaling have not always been fully appreciated in physiology, such as when using the effects of drugs or carcinogenic substances in mice to extrapolate to humans.

THE GOLDEN YEARS OF RESEARCH SUPPORT

I was fortunate to live through a couple of decades when it was relatively easy to obtain support for research. Projects that were reasonably well conceived and planned were likely to find support, in contrast to the present situation where the competition for funds has become extremely keen. Today a substantial fraction of a scientist's time is spent on composing grant applications, only to have them unfunded although recommended for revision and resubmission. Then more effort is spent on honing every detail finer and finer, and more time is spent away from the laboratory.

The thought that goes into planning and providing detailed research plans and schedules is not all wasted. Knowing that a plan will be scrutinized and criticized by one's peers is undoubtedly helpful in crystallizing one's thoughts and clarifying the prose. But if every step is circumscribed and outlined in detail, where is the freedom to explore new ideas as they come up? If our scientists could spend more time on science and less on writing applications, their ideas might be more innovative and their lives more creative.

The peer review system has been heavily criticized, but we have to live with it. As long as research funds are in short supply, I see no better way. I am inclined to paraphrase Winston Churchill by saying that the peer review system is the worst possible system—except all the others.

I was lucky to live through the golden years of research funding. Without the freedom to pursue new ideas and without the help of my many gifted research students and postdoctoral associates, I could never have achieved much.

Today I can in good conscience advise only those young persons to become scientists who possess an irresistible curiosity and an overwhelming urge to devote all their efforts to solving problems. In addition, they must possess a high degree of tolerance for frustration and discouragement.

At times I wonder what made me a physiologist and not an engineer or a carpenter or a physician? I could probably have done reasonably well in any of those fields (about carpentry I feel certain). I was always curious about animals, and because my father permitted me to choose my own ways, I have enjoyed the excitement of a life spent in finding out how animals work. It is a privilege to express the gratitude I feel to my parents for the opportunity they gave me to continue to seek my own answers when new problems challenged my curiosity.

Annu. Rev. Physiol. 1994. 56:13–45
Copyright © 1994 by Annual Reviews Inc. All rights reserved

EPITHELIAL-MESENCHYMAL INTERACTIONS IN LUNG DEVELOPMENT

Parviz Minoo and Richard J. King

Department of Pediatrics, Los Angeles County and University of Southern California Medical Center, Los Angeles, California; Southwest Foundation for Biomedical Research, San Antonio, Texas; and Department of Physiology, The University of Texas Health Science Center, San Antonio, Texas

KEY WORDS: lung development, extracellular matrix, cytokines, pattern formation, cell-cell and cell-ECM communication

INTRODUCTION

Biological communication through cellular interactions is central to development (83). The most characterized class of morphogenetic cellular interactions are embryonic inductions that involve the instructive impact of an "inducing" tissue on a "responding" one (63). Primary induction occurs early in development, leads to the emergence of the three germ layers, ectoderm, mesoderm, and endoderm, and sets the stage for pattern formation (89). Pattern formation is a process by which the developmental fates of cells within the embryo are established. These events are followed by secondary induction, known as epithelial-mesenchymal interactions, that controls cellular proliferation and differentiation during organ and tissue development.

The term epithelial-mesenchymal interaction is widely used in developmental biology. In the present review, however, this term is used in its broadest connotation to refer to biological communications, either of an instructive or permissive nature, that occur between epithelially and mesenchymally derived cells and their progenitors during lung development, and in the maintenance (or repair after injury) of the functional status of the lung. A number of critical players have been identified in these interactions, the most studied of which are the extracellular matrix (ECM)

13

0066–4278/94/0315–0013$05.00

components, the cytokines, and cell-cell adhesion and cell-ECM receptors. As in other biological systems, a mechanism to link the extracellular signals to intracellular reactions such as gene expression (signal transduction) is also required, but neither the components nor their specific functions are well understood.

Interactions between the mesenchyme and the epithelium are required for the development of many organs including those of the gastrointestinal, integumental, urogenital, and respiratory systems (63). The accumulated data are consistent with a model by which, during early embryogenesis, the anlage of the lung is formed within the primitive esophagus (136). Little is known about this very early event, but the mechanism by which it occurs may be analogous to that responsible for pattern formation in *Drosophila*. If so, the activity of homeotic genes such as the *Hox* loci, whose products as transcription factors can regulate the expression of other genes, may be intimately involved (see below). Beyond this point, development of the lung primordium occurs by the growth and branching of the primitive respiratory epithelium (the endodermal tubule) into the surrounding mesenchyme to form the bronchial tree. This process is known as branching morphogenesis and is considered the most active period of epithelial-mesenchymal interactions. Evidence for regulation of branching morphogenesis by cell-cell interactions exists; in the absence of the bronchial mesenchyme, branching morphogenesis does not occur, and morphogenesis is altered depending on the source of the inducing mesenchyme (for a review of functionally different mesenchymes, see 144a). Thus branching morphogenesis may be called an instructive biological interaction.

Subsequent to branching morphogenesis, lung development centers around cellular differentiation with the appearance of columnar epithelial cells, which will form the bronchial portion of the fully developed lung, and cuboidal cells, which form distally to give rise to terminal sacs. Throughout morphogenesis, development and regional specification of the respiratory system is dependent on a complex network of interactions among cells and their products such as cytokines, ECM components, and cell surface receptors. Each of these components affects others and each is itself the target of their physiological impact. For example, the ECM, which is synthesized and secreted by epithelial and mesenchymal cells, also controls their proliferation, movement, and differentiation. Thus normal morphogenesis of the lung is accomplished by fine tuning between cell proliferation, migration, and differentiation, using cell-cell and cell-ECM interactions. Although postnatal lung development is not addressed in this review, cell-cell and cell-ECM interactions may be vital in the maintenance of the differentiated phenotype of lung cell populations such as the alveolar type II cells (122). This process may be called a permissive interaction.

Table 1 Chronology of landmarks in murine and human lung development and their correlation with the expression of a sample of known genes

| Human | 5 wks | 16 wks | 24 wks | 36 wks |
Mouse	10 days	15 days	17 days	20 days
Stage	Embryonic →	pseudoglandular →	cannalicular →	saccular
Genes	Hox 5.1 and 1.3 FGF	Hox 1.4 and 2.6 FGF-R2 IGFs SP-B, SP-C EGF, EGF-R N-myc epimorphin cadherins VLA-5, VLA-3 TGF-β syndecans wnt-2	IGFBP-2 SP-B, SP-C	ros −1 SP-A SP-B, EGF, EGF-R
Physiological events	Cell lineage determination: pattern formation	Branching morphogenesis	Differentiation of epithelial cells, synthesis of surfactant, vascularization	Establishment of blood-gas interface

This review is not intended to be a discussion of the general mechanisms of epithelial-mesenchymal interactions. Consequently, some areas are briefly touched on and some not discussed (e.g. collagens). The focus, however, remains on presentation of what is new and relevant to epithelial-mesenchymal interactions in lung development. Where applicable, we also discuss the role of these interactions in lung injury and repair. The organization of this review follows the chronology of events in lung development (Table 1); pattern formation is discussed first, followed by the role of ECM, the cell surface receptors, cytokines, and signal transduction.

PATTERN FORMATION AND THE EXPRESSION OF HOMEOBOX GENES

The development of the lung and the respiratory tract results in the formation of a patterned structure. Through the process of pattern formation (133), the anlage of the respiratory system, a morphologically uniform structure, emerges from the primitive esophagus and develops into a tissue with significant cellular diversity. Accomplishment of this task requires that the identity of each dividing cell is determined and passed on to its daughter cells. Assignment of identity can depend on the relative position of individual cells. In *Drosophila*, homeotic genes whose protein products contain a highly conserved, 60 amino acid long domain known as the homeobox are thought to be involved in the assignment of positional identity. By analogy, the mammalian homologues of the *Drosophila* homeotic genes are also thought to play a similar role.

Genes containing a homeobox domain encode nuclear proteins, some of which are known to act as transcription factors (1) with the ability to regulate batteries of developmental genes. In *Drosophila*, the first evidence for such genes came from the study of homeotic mutants, which mapped to two genomic regions called the antennapedia and bithorax complexes (36). The search for homologous genes in higher vertebrates uncovered four such clusters, termed *Hox* loci (48). Each cluster consists of a number of genes whose expression is spatio-temporally regulated. *Hox* genes appear to cooperate in providing positional information along the anterior-posterior axis of animals with bilateral symmetry and perhaps even in the metazoans (36). Manipulations of *Hox* genes by transgenic approaches suggest that these genes may also provide positional information in tissue development (17, 148). In the mouse, as in *Drosophila*, the strict correspondence between the relative position of *Hox* genes within a given cluster and that of their transcript domains within the developing embryo (or tissue) has been evolutionarily conserved (25). Thus, the 3′ to 5′ position of each gene within the cluster corresponds to its anterior-posterior site of expression within the developing tissues. Several *Hox* genes have been investigated in lung tissue. Specific genes from the four clusters of the *Hox* complex have been shown to be expressed in the mesenchyme of the embryonic lung (34). Spatial distribution of individual *Hox* transcripts in the lung follows the anterior-posterior position of the genes within the chromosomal clusters, in that more anterior genes are expressed in the proximal and more posterior genes are expressed in distal respiratory structures (35, 34).

There are four clusters of antennapedia-like homeogenes in the mouse genome, *Hox* 1, 2, 3, and 5 (25). These genes are thought to be involved in pattern formation during mouse embryogenesis (34). Homeobox-containing genes in the mouse are expressed in different domains along the body axis. These domains are first established before organogenesis within the ectoderm and mesoderm germ layers at 7.5 days of gestation. Strong stage- and tissue-specific differences in the relative abundance of the *Hox* gene clusters have been reported (34). For example, *Hox* 5.1 mRNA was abundant within the mesoderm and ectoderm of early stages (8.5 and 9.5 days), yet were detected only weakly in mesenchyme of the lung at 10.5 days and disappeared completely by 12.5 days. In contrast, *Hox* 1.4 and 2.6 mRNA were relatively weak in early days, but increased within the lung by 12.5 days (34). This corresponds to the period of active branching morphogenesis in the mouse lung (Table 1). Wolgemuth et al (148) overexpressed the mouse *Hox* 1.4 gene in transgenic mice and found that adult expression of this gene in the lung was low, as had been previously described (34). However, in the 12.5 day embryos, where the transgene was overexpressed by at least twofold, no morphological abnormalities were observed in the lung (minute abnormalities, however, may have been missed), although gut development was abnormal in those animals with high levels of transcription.

Retinoic acid (RA) has long been known to play a key role in vertebrate development (133). Excess or deficiency of vitamin A causes an array of embryonic abnormalities in a number of species including human (74). RA may play a role in the regulation of mesenchymal-epithelial interactions in tissues by influencing the expression of growth factors and the ECM genes in both epithelial and mesenchymal cells. However, the discovery that RA mimics the effects of homeotic mutations (67) raised the possibility that it could affect the regulation of homeotic genes. Expression of the *Hox* 1.3 gene in human lung fibroblasts has been found to be induced by RA in culture (8). Induction was specific to bronchial fibroblasts and did not occur when dermal fibroblasts were similarly treated. *Hox* 1.3 is expressed in the developing mouse nervous system and in various embryonic mesodermal tissues and has recently been described in the intestine of adult mouse with regional specificity of expression (64). Induction of *Hox* 1.3 may be the beginning of a cascade of gene expression that results in the expression of

ECM components and paracrine growth factors and their receptors. Changes in these components would inevitably lead to changes in the epithelial cells. Thus the studies described above demonstrate a possible role for the products of *Hox* genes in periods of lung development that corresponds to the formation of the lung anlage and branching morphogenesis. We speculate that further investigation will uncover other homeobox-containing genes that may also be involved in these early developmental events.

N-MYC IN LUNG DEVELOPMENT

Another family of genes whose expression may be involved in the control of normal development is the cellular oncogenes. All members of the *myc* family of oncogenes are expressed at high levels in the early embryo (120, 153). While the expression of *c-myc* appears to be ubiquitous, *N-myc* and *L-myc* gene expression is restricted by tissue and stage specificity in the newborn mouse (120, 153). Although oncogenes are normally thought of as being involved in the control of cell growth, spatial and temporal specificity of *N-myc* transcripts in several embryonic tissues has suggested that *N-myc* expression during development correlates more with the process of differentiation than cell proliferation (60, 88). In the lung, *N-myc* mRNA expression has been detected by Northern analysis in day 12 mouse embryos (88). This expression decreased with advancing age. In a separate study, in situ hybridization demonstrated that the major site of *N-myc* expression in the lung of day 12 mouse embryos is the bronchial epithelium (60). Consistent with these observations, disruptions of the *N-myc* locus by gene targeting in transgenic mice result in morphogenetic abnormalities specifically in regions of the developing lung that correspond to areas of most active *N-myc* gene expression during normal development.

Using homologous recombination in embryonic stem cells together with a neomycin-resistance gene, Moens et al (86) created an insertional mutation in the *N-myc* locus. This recombination event did not completely eliminate, but resulted in the formation of truncated *N-myc* transcripts. Mice homozygous for this insertion died at birth because of an inability to oxygenate their blood, a phenotype that apparently arises from a defect in branching morphogenesis in the lung. This phenotype suggests a possible role for *N-myc* in the epithelial-mesenchymal interactions that are the basis for lung morphogenesis. In homozygous mice, the abnormalities were restricted to the developing airways. The pulmonary epithelium that lines the airways and airspaces of the developing lung, which normally expresses *N-myc*, failed to proliferate and branch normally. In contrast, the number and distribution of the more proximal bronchi were normal. This finding is consistent with the observed normal pattern of *N-myc* expression in the lung with low levels of *N-myc* in the trachea and primary and secondary bronchi and higher levels in the tips of the developing airways (60).

Recently, gene targeting strategies were used to produce null mutations in the *N-myc* locus (114). In this study, development of homozygous embryos was not affected up to day 10.5 of embryogenesis. In later stages of morphogenesis however, mutant embryos showed developmental abnormalities in a number of tissues (114). In contrast to the earlier study, where the expression of *N-myc* was rendered leaky (86), development of the lung in the null mutants showed no signs of branching on day 11.5, and structures distal to the tracheal branching were absent. Again, these areas corresponded to regions of intense *N-myc* expression during normal lung morphogenesis (60). Lungs from day 11.5 mutant embryos, explanted in medium containing fetal calf serum, but not in serum-free medium, showed recovery by undergoing bronchial morphogenesis. This observation indicates that serum contains factor(s) that can replace the missing activities of the *N-myc* null mutation in the lung. Expression of *N-myc* therefore, may not be necessary for normal lung morphogenesis and, instead, it appears that the role of *N-myc* in this process can be by-passed by extracellular factors.

EXTRACELLULAR MATRIX IN EPITHELIAL-MESENCHYMAL INTERACTIONS

Branching morphogenesis is dependent on epithelial-mesenchymal interactions on a functional extracellular matrix. This process does not occur in the absence of an ECM (73). Cell-cell and cell-ECM interactions occur through cell-surface receptors and components of the ECM. A number of ECM components have been implicated in lung branching morphogenesis and these are listed in Table 2. The epithelial and the mesenchymal cells interact with the ECM through the binding of various receptor proteins, the best studied of which with possible role(s) in lung development are listed in Table 3.

Dependence of lung branching morphogenesis on the ECM has been examined by a number of investigators. Most studies to date are confined to descriptions of what ECM components are present during lung development. Few studies have attempted to localize functional domains on these molecules (119). One study has demonstrated directly the independence of lung morphogenesis from a component of the ECM, collagen type I; lung development occurs normally in mice carrying an insertional null mutation in the type I collagen gene (73). Furthermore, the composition of the ECM can affect the maintenance of the differentiated phenotype of alveolar type II cells in culture (122). Both cell shape and the expression of surfactant protein genes were found to be dependent on the nature of the substratum

Table 2 ECM components in lung epithelial mesenchymal interactions

ECM	Composition	Function in the lung	Reference
Laminin	3 subunits	Cell attachment and proliferation	72
	B1 = 222 kd	Cell migration	99
	B2 = 210 kd	Anti-laminin antibodies inhibit branching morpho-	118, 119
	A = 400 kd	genesis	
Fibronectin	2 subunits of	Chemotactic activity for fibroblasts and epithelial	82
	≃ 250 kd	cells	123
		Regulated by lung injury, hyperoxia	124
		pulmonary fibrosis	140
		BPD	38
		Positional information	101
Tenascin	3 subunits	Expressed in embryonic tissue	20
	220 kd	Becomes reactivated in injury	80
	230 kd	May guide cell migration on fibronectin	76, 28
	320 kd	Gene targeting (deletion) has no effect on embryonic	106
		lung development	
	EGF-like domains		

used. Because cell shape is related to the organization of the cytoskeleton, it is possible that the "correct" ECM may impart the appropriate signals through cell surface receptors such as integrins (see below), whose end result is the maintenance of the in vivo cell shape and the retention of the differentiated phenotype. In this section, we present a discussion of relevant findings regarding specific components of the ECM. A number of reviews on other major components of the ECM, such as elastin, are available (32).

Components of the ECM

LAMININ   A multidomain glycoprotein component of the ECM, laminin can be detected as early as in the preimplantation embryo (19). Laminin is present during all stages of development and is principally localized in the basement membrane of a variety of tissues (150). Laminin is composed of three polypeptides: B1 (222 kd), B2 (210 kd), and a 400-kd polypeptide known as the A subunit (137). The amino acid sequences of all three polypeptides are known (111–115). These polypeptide chains are held together by disulfide bridges to form the characteristic cross-shaped molecule (137). The different laminin chains are not coordinately expressed during kidney morphogenesis, which suggests that molecular isoforms of laminin may be assembled from different subunits (26). Laminin is a multifunctional protein that can affect growth, differentiation, migration, and adhesion of a variety of cells. In addition to domain-specific antibodies, proteolytically

Table 3 Cell surface receptors in lung epithelial-mesenchymal interactions

Receptor	Binding site	Distribution	References
Integrins			
Beta-1			
VLA5 (α_5,β_1)	Fibronectin	Epithelial and mesenchymal cells, large vessels, airways and primary bronchioles. May be related to airway maturation	2 100
VLA3 (α_3,β_1)	Laminin, fibronectin, collagen	Airway columnar epithelia. May be involved in cell-cell adhesion	100
Beta-3:			
β_3 (α_v,β_3)	Vitronectin	Epithelial cells, airway mesenchyme, and vessels	100 39
Syndecans	bFGF, thrombospondin fibro-nectin collagens I, III, and IV	Mesenchymal and epithelial cells in the embryo. Exclusively epithelial cells in adults	10 15
Cadherins			
E-cadherin	Possibly vinculin and other cadherins	Cell-cell adhesion junctions. Epithelial cells in both embryo and adults	134 58
P-cadherin	Possibly vinculin and other cadherins	Both epithelial and nonepithelial distribution. In lung: early epithelial rudiment. Later found in distal bronchial tree	52
Epimorphin	?	Mesenchymal cells of embryonic lung. May be crucial in pattern formation and polarity of epithelial cells	59
Wnt-2	?	Lung fibroblasts in both adult and fetal lung	78

derived peptide fragments of laminin have been used to localize domains of function on this molecule. Two sites necessary in cell binding activity have been localized to the cross intersection (69) and at the terminal end of the long arm (135).

Cell proliferation and migration are critical steps during embryogenesis and during the process of wound healing in epithelial cell injury (30). Laminin, type IV collagens, and fibronectin have been found to stimulate the migration of bovine bronchial epithelial cells in vitro (99). Furthermore, polyclonal anti-laminin antibodies were used to determine the biological role of laminin in lung branching morphogenesis (118). Anti-laminin antibodies inhibited branching morphogenesis of the lung primordium in vitro. In contrast, antibodies to thrombospondin and entactin, two other components of the ECM, failed to inhibit branching (118). In a more recent study, monoclonal antibodies to different laminin domains were tested for their ability to inhibit branching morphogenesis (119). Of an array of five, two monoclonal antibodies, AL1 and AL5, were found to inhibit branching. Alterations in the pattern of branching caused by exposure to AL5 antibody were more severe than those caused by AL1 antibody. This observation implies that different laminin functions reside at the epitopes recognized by the two monoclonal antibodies. The AL1 epitope was localized to near the cross region of the laminin structure, and the AL5 epitope was specific to the lateral short arms at the globular end regions of the B chain of laminin. These domains are the same as those reported to be involved in cell attachment and heparin-binding activities of laminin (72). Although it is possible that these domains may facilitate the attachment, proliferation, and migration of embryonic lung cells during branching morphogenesis, the exact mechanisms by which these roles are played remains a subject of intense interest and investigation.

FIBRONECTIN   A major component of the ECM, fibronectin is produced by a variety of cells and is found throughout the pulmonary connective tissue (104). Fibronectin consists of two subunits of approximately 250 kd each, attached to each other via disulfide bonds. The structure of individual fibronectin subunits is modular, consisting of a number of domains, each specialized for binding different moieties (104). Subunit heterogeneity has been observed in fibronectin from various sources (94). Thus assembly of different subunits into fibronectin dimers can generate structurally different forms of fibronectin. Genomic and cDNA sequences of fibronectin have revealed that the various subunits arise from the same gene by alternative splicing of the same pre-mRNA (104).

Fibronectin is a cell adhesive glycoprotein that plays an important role during development (57) and in repair of tissue following injury (143). Increased fibronectin has been reported in lungs of patients with idiopathic pulmonary fibrosis (140). Similarly, bronchoalveolar lavage fluid from children with respiratory distress syndrome, who progress to bronchopulmonary dysplasia, contains increased levels of fibronectin (38). Using in situ hybridization, Sinkin et al (124) recently found increased fibronectin mRNA in alveolar macrophages following in vivo hyperoxia in rabbits.

It has long been known that fibronectin may play a major role during morphogenesis by promoting cell attachment (57). Fibronectin may also facilitate cell movement by providing a scaffolding structure over which cells can migrate (76). Shoji et al (123) demonstrated that bronchial epithelial cells produce fibronectin with chemotactic activity for fibroblasts. Recruitment of lung fibroblasts by epithelially produced fibronectin may be crucial during development and in repair of lung injury. In addition, fibronectin and other ECM proteins exhibit a concentration-dependent chemotactic activity for bovine bronchial epithelial cells (99). The ability of various functional domains of the fibronectin molecule, with known cell-binding activity, to affect cell migration has been examined by the use of tryptic fragments of fibronectin (82). Despite the presence of both heparin and cell-binding domains, two fragments of 40 kDa and 60 kDa from the carboxyl terminus of fibronectin had little chemotactic potential. In contrast, an RGD (see below) containing fragment of 120 kDa stimulated the migration of bronchial epithelial cells. Because the RGD motif mediates fibronectin-integrin interactions, these experiments suggest an integrin-mediated role for fibronectin in cell migration during lung morphogenesis.

Distribution of fibronectin and the $\alpha 5$ subunit of its receptor, the $\alpha_5 \beta 1$ integrin, has been studied during the morphogenesis of murine lungs (101). Fibronectin staining was found in the mesenchyme and the parabronchial cells of day 11 mouse embryonic lung. Staining increased on day 13 concomitant with branching morphogenesis and subsequently decreased after day 16. Fibronectin was localized to areas of airway bifurcation, thus indicating a possible role in cleft formation. The $\alpha 5$ subunit of fibronectin receptor appeared later on day 13 and became colocalized with fibronectin only in developed primary bronchioles. Although these data may have functional implications for the increased fibronectin found in day 13 embryonic lung, the mechanism by which this increase could affect lung development is not understood. It has been suggested that the increased level of fibronectin may be involved in transmission of positional information through the $\alpha_5 \beta 1$ integrin to embryonic lung cells, which regulates their migration and differentiation (101).

TENASCIN   Tenascin is an oligomeric glycoprotein component of the ECM (28). In most species, tenascin consists of one large and two small subunits that assemble into a structure termed a hexabrachion, which consists of two trimers (28). The three subunits have virtually identical peptide maps, and primary sequence data suggest that they are derived by alternative splicing (42). A striking feature of the primary sequences is the existence of peptide domains that resemble other known proteins. For example, there are fibronectin type III domains as well as an EGF-like domain that is repeated 13 times (42). Through a cell adhesion RGD motif found in the fibronectin type III domain, tenascin binds some but not all cells (13). When cells are cultured on tenascin, they do not flatten nor spread, but remain rounded, which suggests a different role for tenascin compared to other cell adhesion molecules such as laminin or fibronectin. It has been suggested that tenascin may modulate cell behavior on fibronectin (28).

Tenascin is expressed with a high degree of temporal and spatial specificity during embryonic development (20). Expression of tenascin is repressed subsequent to cellular differentiation, but becomes reactivated near growing epithelial cells during wound healing and in a variety of tumor cells (79, 80). It is thought that epithelial cells can induce the expression of tenascin in mesenchymal cells surrounding a wound (80). Oyama et al (91) showed that transformed fibroblasts and fetal lung tissue express more of a tenascin mRNA species that contains an extra fibronectin type III sequence repeat (result of alternative splicing) compared to normal cells or adult lung tissue. Aufderheide & Ekblom (5) found that gut mesenchyme from day 13 mouse embryos, when cultured alone, expressed trace amounts of tenascin. However, when the same mesenchyme was cultured with an epithelial cell line, MDCK, it secreted substantial amounts of tenascin. Neither temporal nor spatial distribution and expression of tenascin during lung development have been studied. Disruption of the gene for tenascin by gene targeting produces no abnormal phenotype during mouse development (106). Although one explanation is that the essential role of tenascin may be duplicated by other redundant genes, it has also been argued that tenascin expression may simply be superfluous in certain tissues (29).

Cell-Cell and Cell-ECM Receptors

Interactions among cells and between cells and various components of the ECM are mediated by specialized cell surface receptors. Properties of these molecules and their potential role in mediating lung development are discussed in this section.

INTEGRINS   The binding of cells to each other and to the ECM proteins is mediated, in part, by members of the integrin family of matrix receptors (2). Integrins are heterodimeric cell surface glycoproteins that interact intracellularly with the cytoskeletal proteins. Integrins are composed of α and β subunits that assemble into heterodimeric transmembrane complexes. Heterogeneity arises by combining different β and α subunits. To date, six β and eleven α subunits have been identified (2). Originally, based on their β subunit association, three subfamilies of integrins were defined. The β1 subfamily includes receptors for laminin, fibronectin, and collagen (2), and its members are found on a variety of cells. Members of the β2 subfamily are found exclusively in leukocytes (4), and the β3 subfamily is found on platelets, endothelial cells, and some cancer cells (39). The latter include the receptors for vitronectin, fibrinogen, fibronectin, thrombospondin, and von Wildebrand's factor (39).

Many ECM proteins contain the amino acid sequence motif, Arg-Gly-Asp (the RGD motif) through which the binding with integrins occurs (105). This tri-peptide is used in binding of integrins to fibronectin, thrombospondin, fibrinogen, vitronectin, laminin, and type I collagen (same as above).

Distribution of two members of the β1 integrin subfamily, VLA 3 and VLA 5, and the integrin receptors to vitronectin (β3 subfamily) has been recently examined during the pseudoglandular stage of murine lung development (100). The VLA 5 epitope appeared to be coexpressed with α-smooth muscle actin, making it likely that it was associated with smooth muscle cells in the developing lung. VLA 5 was found to be localized to the airways and primary bronchioles, but less developed bronchioles were either scant or negative. The authors suggest that VLA 5 expression may be related to the state of maturation of the airways. Detectable expression of VLA 5 epitopes was not found in epithelial cells. VLA 3 staining, in contrast, was weak and localized at the apical surface of cells and in between columnar epithelial cells facing the lumen of airways. This observation suggests that VLA 3 epitopes may be involved in cell-cell adhesion during airway development. No VLA 3 staining was detectable in the mesenchyme. In search of a functional correlate, a hexapeptide containing the RGD triple peptide sequence was used in lung explant cultures (100). This peptide diminished, but did not abolish, branching and resulted in morphologically abnormal structures. Since branching was not abolished, non-RGD mechanisms may also be involved in branching morphogenesis. Obviously, one way in which the RGD peptides can affect lung morphogenesis is by competing with the cell-ECM interactions, thus resulting in abnormal cell adhesion and/or migration. Alternatively, by analogy with fibronectin matrix assembly (21), it has been suggested that deposition of specific ECM components, and therefore its composition, may be affected by these peptides (100).

CADHERINS   Cadherins are a family of calcium-dependent glycoproteins of approximately 124 kd (134). Cadherins are cell-cell adhesion molecules which, based on immunological criteria and tissue distribution, can be divided into at least three subclasses, E-, P-, and N-cadherins (90, 134). Expression of E-cadherin is confined to epithelial cells from a variety of embryonic and adult sources (90). P-cadherin is expressed in both epithelial and nonepithelial tissues (90), and N-cadherin has been detected in nonepithelial tissues such as neural tissue and muscle (52). Expression of each cadherin subclass is temporally and spatially regulated during development of various tissues (134).

Distribution and possible role(s) of E- and P-cadherins in the morphogenesis of the lung epithelium was studied by the use of specific antibodies (58). Expression of E- and P-cadherins was detected in all epithelial cells of the lung. Other studies have reported transient expression of N-cadherin in chicken embryonic lung epithelium (52). During lung development, P-cadherin was found to be spatially and temporally regulated. In contrast, expression of E-cadherin occurred constitutively. Neutralizing antibodies to

E- an P-cadherins in culture induced abnormal morphogenesis and branching of the epithelium, which displayed crushed and deformed lobules or tubules (58). Inhibition of E-cadherin resulted in more dramatic abnormalities than inhibition of P-cadherin. This is in contrast to other tissues where P-cadherin appears to play a more crucial role compared to E-cadherin (52). However, a synergistic effect was noted when both antibodies were used. In this case, arrangement of the epithelial cells in the lung primordium was disrupted, and the epithelium was not capable of branching (58). These results suggest a role played by cadherins in establishing intercellular junctions among epithelial cells. Interference by antibodies in cadherin-mediated cell adhesion, leads to abnormal epithelial morphogenesis, perhaps by disrupting cell-cell communication.

SYNDECANS   Syndecans are a family of cell surface proteoglycans. These molecules are transmembrane receptor proteins whose extracellular domains contain chondroitin sulfate and heparan sulfate chains. The core proteins of the syndecan family are structurally alike (10). Syndecans are involved in cell adhesion and cell-ECM interactions (10). One possible role for syndecans may be in modulating cellular activity by binding and providing a depot for growth factors as well as by affecting the ECM. For example, syndecans bind basic fibroblast growth factor (bFGF), thrombospondin, fibronectin, and collagens I, II, and V through their heparan sulfate moiety (9). In adult mouse tissues, syndecans are found nearly exclusively in epithelial cells (54). In the embryo, syndecans are expressed on all cell surfaces in the condensed mesenchyme (132). Syndecan expression in the developing embryo is spatially and temporally regulated (141). For example, syndecan is expressed transiently in the condensing mesenchyme under the influence of the epithelial-mesenchymal interaction during limb development (126). Furthermore, syndecans from different tissues exhibit heterogeneity in their number and length of the glycosaminoglycan chains (109). The size and number of glycosaminoglycan chains on syndecans appear to be dictated by the mesenchyme (14). Because the mesenchyme induces differentiation of the epithelium, this suggests a correlation between cellular organization and syndecan structure. Branching morphogenesis during development of the salivary gland is dependent on synthesis and deposition of proteoglycans such as syndecans (128). These observations have prompted the hypothesis that these molecules play a crucial role in the morphogenesis of various tissues. For example, it is known that cell surface heparan sulfate proteoglycans may be required for the activity of basic fibroblast growth factor (bFGF) (68). Mutations of the heparin/heparan sulfate binding site on bFGF reduces its biological activity (121). The activity of acidic FGF may also require cell surface heparan sulfate proteoglycan (107). Furthermore, CHO cells defective in synthesis of heparan sulfate cannot bind bFGF even in the presence of the FGF high affinity receptor, FGFR-1 (152). Therefore, binding and activation of transduction are dependent on heparan sulfate.

The structure and cellular distribution of syndecan-1 change during lung development (15). Syndecan is found in both the mesenchyme and the epithelium of the day 12 mouse lung. The level of this protein, however, is low in the mesenchyme compared to the epithelium. As development proceeds, the staining is lost from the mesenchyme, but is retained in the epithelium until the alveolar type II cells undergo terminal differentiation. Syndecan staining then disappears, and the terminally differentiated alveolar type II cells do not contain detectable amounts of this protein. Furthermore, during lung development, the size of the glycosaminoglycan chains on syndecan is reduced (15). As lung development proceeds from day 12 to 18 of gestation, the apparent molecular mass of mouse syndecan is reduced from greater than 100 kd to approximately 69 kd. This reduction is due to the reduced size of the heparan sulfate moieties and, to a lesser extent, to changes in the chondroitin sulfate chains. Although the functional implication of these structural changes is not clear, they may affect the interaction of cells with the ECM, thereby affecting cellular shape and organization as well as cell mobility in any given tissue during morphogenesis. Embryonic day 12 lung mesenchyme expresses TGF-β, and this expression decreases upon further development (55). Since TGF-β is known to affect syndecan size in cell cultures of differentiating epithelial cells (97), it is possible that the change in size of syndecan during lung development may be mediated through TGF-β.

OTHER CELL SURFACE RECEPTORS   Epimorphin is a protein of 150 kd expressed on the surface of mesenchymal cells of mouse embryonic tissues (59). Lung epithelial tubular formation in vitro is inhibited by monoclonal antibodies to epimorphin. Normal tubular morphogenesis of lung epithelial cells can be accomplished by co-culturing with transfected (and not un-transfected) NIH 3T3 cells engineered to express epimorphin from a cDNA. Because epithelial morphogenesis of a number of tissues is disrupted by antibodies to epimorphin, it is suggested that this molecule may be required as a general factor in inductive processes of mesenchyme to epithelium. Epimorphin is localized heavily to the areas on mesenchymal cells adjacent to the epithelium. Therefore, epithelial cells may be physically in contact with epimorphin. During the development of the lung, epithelial cells normally differentiate to form tubules with large lumens when induced by the underlying mesenchyme. In the presence of anti-epimorphin antibodies, this process is strongly inhibited and apical-basal polarity of these cells, as assessed by staining for E-cadherin, is disturbed. Thus, epimorphin may provide morphogenetic signals crucial for establishment of proper pattern formation (cell arrangement) or polarity during lung development.

The *wnt* gene family encodes a group of 11 proteins implicated in intercellular communication and signaling in a number of organs during different stages of development (37). Members of this family have been shown to be temporally and spatially regulated during mouse and *Xenopus* development and may be involved in early pattern formation (18). Many of the *wnt* genes are expressed in the lung (37). *Wnt-2* is expressed in lung fibroblasts of both adult and fetal lung, but recent data suggest differential expression of this gene in fetal vs adult lung tissue (78). Expression of *wnt-2* in lung fibroblasts is regulated by growth factors. Basic fibroblast growth factor and epidermal growth factor (EGF) both decrease the expression of *wnt-2* mRNA in fetal lung fibroblasts (78). Expression of *wnt-2* mRNA in epithelial cells results in cellular transformation (12), which suggests a role in controlling cellular proliferation. The specific role of *wnt-2* in the lung and whether it stimulates proliferation or differentiation of epithelial cells remains to be elucidated. However, presentation of *wnt-2* to epithelial cells by fibroblasts is a potential mechanism by which the process of epithelial-mesenchymal communication in lung development could be mediated.

GROWTH FACTORS IN LUNG EPITHELIAL-MESENCHYMAL INTERACTIONS

Growth factors complement ECM proteins and their receptors in a number of ways during pattern formation and organogenesis. First, many growth factors bind and are active on the ECM. Examples of this purported co-dependence are TGF-β and fibronectin (31), and heparin-binding growth factors and proteoglycans (47). Second, some growth factors (e.g. bFGF) have no signal peptide and are probably co-secreted bound to ECM proteins (47). Third, growth factors can stimulate the synthesis of ECM proteins and their receptors and can thereby establish interacting systems between mesenchyme and epithelium through the ECM (87). Finally, soluble growth factors may directly induce physiological actions (103). Direct evidence for a role of growth factors in the transfer of information between mesenchyme and epithelium of vertebrates is just emerging. However, circumstantial evidence placing growth factors at places where developmental processes are accelerating (142) makes the prospect of their involvement highly likely.

In this section we present a focused discussion of only those growth factors with purported roles in epithelial-mesenchymal communication during lung development. For a more general appreciation of this topic in other organ systems, there are other relatively recent reviews (116).

EGF and TGF-α

EGF is a small peptide growth factor consisting of 53 amino acids with a molecular weight of 6,045 kDa. Although EGF mRNA is found primarily in the submandibular gland and kidney, a number of other tissues, including the lung, contain lesser amounts of EGF mRNA (93, 125). The presence of EGF mRNA in these tissues suggests a local source of EGF that may function in a paracrine or autocrine manner. TGF-α has a 35% homology with EGF and was first detected in murine sarcoma virus-transformed cells (138). The activity of TGF-α is similar to that of EGF, and it binds to the EGF receptor (93). TGF-α is expressed during mouse fetal development (146), in neonatal and adult epidermal cells, and in the brain (147). TGF-α mRNA is increased in the lungs of prematurely delivered baboons with hyaline membrane disease (84). The temporal increase in the expression of TGF-α precedes the hyperproliferation of epithelial cells in the premature lung and coincides with the expression of collagenase and tissue inhibitor of metalloproteinases, TIMP (85), both of which could potentially affect remodeling of tissue in lung injury.

EGF accelerates lung development and maturation. Exposure to EGF induces DNA synthesis and formation of supernumerary tracheal and bronchial buds in embryonic chick lung (43). By in situ hybridization and immunolocalization, EGF mRNA and EGF precursor protein have been localized to clusters of cells in the embryonic mouse lung primordia (125). EGF precursor protein, but not mRNA, was found in bronchial epithelial cells, but EGF mRNA and protein were found in a few mesenchymal cells of the developing lung (13–16 day gestation). One possible explanation for these observations is that the EGF protein may be synthesized in the mesenchymal cells and rapidly transported to the epithelial cells, the site of the immunodetection. Thus these studies demonstrate that localized and spatially restricted production of growth factors occurs during lung development and may be crucial in regulating cell proliferation and differentiation. In addition to localized production of EGF, modulations in the number of EGF receptor (EGF-R) molecules may provide the means by which the activity of EGF can be regulated during lung development. An abundance of EGF-R was found in the mesenchyme surrounding the epithelium during the most active period of epithelial branching of the lung primordium (93). Upon further morphogenesis, EGF binding decreased significantly and was localized to distal epithelial branches and the neighboring mesenchyme (93). In a separate study (7), the pattern of EGF binding appeared to resemble that of the glucocorticoid binding in the mouse embryonic lung, which suggests that the mesenchyme is the primary target for both cytokine and hormonal responses during early lung development.

EGF induces the expression of pulmonary surfactant proteins in cultured late gestation pulmonary type II cells (145). Raaberg et al (96) extended this finding to show that rat alveolar type II cells express EGF protein and functional EGF receptor. Translation arrest of endogenous EGF, using antisense strategies, demonstrated a striking association between EGF and branching morphogenesis (121a). Collectively these data suggest that alveolar type II cells may be capable of autoregulating their own growth and proliferation. What has not been studied, however, is how EGF may be involved in the inductive mechanisms that result in the emergence of the differentiated pulmonary type II cells during lung morphogenesis, and how mature EGF may be mediating epigenetic instructive or permissive signaling during epithelial-mesenchymal interactions in lung morphogenesis. EGF-like motifs have been detected in the ECM protein, laminin (92). If the EGF mature protein (or its precursor) is bound by the ECM, then it could provide the functional substratum for cell-cell and cell-ECM interactions that play an important role in the development of the tissues and terminal differentiation of the lung cells. Expression or activation of ECM-degrading enzymes, such as collagenase, which we have found in the premature baboon lung with hyaline membrane disease (P Minoo, unpublished results), could result in the local release of growth factors such as EGF and the stimulation of proliferation of specific cell populations in the lung. Hydrolysis of the ECM components and consequent proliferation of cells during morphogenetic events have been previously reported (46).

TGF-β

TGF-β is a potent regulatory protein for both cellular proliferation and differentiation (81). The TGF-β gene family consists of many members and related genes, however, only three TGF-β isoforms have been identified in humans and all three are expressed in lung tissue (33, 56). The three TGF-β isoforms have similar biological activities in vitro, but a well-defined and characteristic pattern of expression during murine development (33). Depending on the cell type and specific physiological conditions, TGF-β can exert a variety of effects on mammalian cells (81). A major physiological role of TGF-β is the stimulation of ECM components and their deposition (61). TGF-β also positively regulates the expression of integrins and, by so doing, may increase cell-ECM interactions (62). Conversely, it has been shown that the expression of TGF-β1 can be regulated by the ECM (131). Expression of TGF-β1 is high in mammary epithelial cells cultured on plastic petri dishes, but is strongly downregulated when cells are placed on a reconstituted basement membrane matrix. In contrast, TGF-β2 mRNA levels are unchanged. These data suggest that TGF-β1, but not TGF-β2, may play a role in regulating the ECM synthesis.

Spatial and temporal patterns of expression of TGF-β2 and TGF-β3 isoforms were studied in human embryos of 32 to 57 days post-coitus (pc) by in situ localization of their transcripts (33). TGF-β2 transcripts were detectable in the primitive lung epithelium of 43 day pc human embryos. By day 57 pc, however, TGF-β2 expression was confined to epithelial cells in the growing tips of the developing bronchioles. TGF-β2 was also co-expressed with TGF-β3 in the terminal growing buds. TGF-β3 transcripts were localized to the proximal respiratory tract from the presumptive larynx downwards to the junction of bronchi and bronchioles. Epithelial lining of the bronchioles distal to this position were also found to contain TGF-β3 transcripts. The spatially distinct pattern of TGF-β2 and TGF-β3 transcript distribution suggests that the two isoforms of TGF-β may play different role(s) during lung morphogenesis. TGF-β1 was expressed in both mesenchymal and epithelial cells of the lung primordial tubules. As in other tissues (e.g. mammary glands), TGF-β1 was secreted into and sequestered by the ECM. This pattern was most prominent at sites where branching of the lung primordium occurs. TGF-β1 was not apparent in areas around the terminal epithelial buds (33).

TGF-β is an effective inducer of collagen and fibronectin synthesis (61). Immunolocalization with antibodies to peptide domains of TGF-β1 was used to examine the distribution of this growth factor during the morphogenesis of the mouse lung primordium (56). The extracellular form of TGF-β was found to be expressed with spatial and temporal specificity during branching morphogenesis and cleft formation during lung development. TGF-β1 was found to be co-localized with the components of the ECM, collagen I and II, fibronectin, and glycosaminoglycans at the epithelial-mesenchymal interfaces of stalks and clefts of the branching lung. Endodermal branching in the lung depends on the interaction between the epithelium and the mesenchyme and the formation of an ECM at the interface of these tissue layers. Temporally, this co-localization is coincident with the time when the ECM proteins can first be visualized in these areas (56). Because TGF-β1 participates in the development of the ECM, it may be important in providing the basic architectural framework that is necessary for lung morphogenesis. Co-localization was most pronounced during the period of primordial tubule differentiation into alveolar and bronchial ducts. Whether there is a cause-effect relationship in this phenomenon is unknown since TGF-β accumulation may be secondary to matrix accumulation. In vitro results support the contention that TGF-β is the inducer of collagen I and III and fibronectin in lung fibroblasts (61). Furthermore, the finding that TGF-β can induce the expression of cell adhesion molecules (62) also supports the scheme whereby its expression facilitates the stabilization of the newly formed lung tissue at the clefts and ducts at the interphase of the mesenchymal-epithelial layers. These are sites where the adjacent stromal cells are actively producing collagens and fibronectin to facilitate pattern formation.

Torday & Kourembanas (139) studied the effects of lung fibroblasts on maturation of fetal alveolar type II cells in a set of in vitro recombination experiments using lung fibroblasts derived from a number of mouse fetuses at different gestational ages. In these studies, mature lung fibroblasts of day 21 gestation stimulated the maturation of fetal alveolar type II cells. However, this stimulation was blocked by the presence of immature (day 17) lung fibroblasts, or conditioned media from such cells. The inhibitory activity was neutralized by anti-TGF-β antibodies. TGF-β was found in culture media of day 15 to day 19 lung fibroblasts and decreased rapidly between days 19 and 21, although mRNA for TGF-β was detected in fibroblasts throughout fetal development. These observations demonstrate that TGF-β may play a role in the maturation of alveolar type II cells as a soluble factor involved in mesenchymal-epithelial interactions during lung development (145).

Insulin-like Growth Factors

The insulin like growth factors, IGF-I and IGF-II, are peptides with potential roles in both proliferation and differentiation of a number of cell types (129). IGFs are expressed predominantly by mesenchymal cells and can be detected in most organs and tissues. The two IGFs are encoded by distinct genes and share approximately 64% homology in their primary structure (22). Two distinct cell surface receptors, designated type 1 IGF receptor and type 2 IGF receptor (identical to mannose-6-phosphate receptor) bind IGF-I and IGF-II, respectively (102). However, their biological actions have not as yet been directly linked to interactions with these receptors. Expression of IGFs is developmentally regulated, with IGF-II expression occurring primarily during fetal development and IGF-I during postnatal development (23).

Using immunocytochemisty with an antibody that recognizes epitopes in common between IGF-I and IGF-II, distribution and cell type specificity of IGFs were studied in the lung of mid-gestation human fetuses (51). These investigators found that immunostaining was confined to the columnar epithelium of both large and small airways. In a separate study, it was shown by in situ hybridization that these epithelial cells do not express detectable amounts of IGF mRNA (130). Taken together, these data suggest that lung epithelial cells accumulate but do not synthesize IGFs. Because the mesenchyme of the lung was found to express IGF mRNA, these data also suggest that IGFs may be produced in the mesenchymal cells and act on the nearby epithelium. Primary cultures of lung epithelial cells that can be induced to proliferate by IGF-I also express the type 1 IGF receptor, which is capable of binding this cytokine (98).

IGF-I and IGF-II bind to a large family of binding proteins designated IGFBPs (75). These proteins may regulate the activity of IGFs by, for example, binding to the cell surface (149). Six IGFBPs have been identified, of which IGFBP 2 expression predominates during fetal development. Recently, the expression of IGFBP 2 mRNA and its relationship to location of IGF-I and IGF-II protein and IGF-II mRNA have been examined in fetal rat lung (70). IGFBP 2 transcripts were localized mainly on the alveolar and airway structures during late fetal development on days 16 and 18. By day 20, however, IGFBP 2 mRNA was also localized to the mesenchyme. In contrast, IGF-II mRNA was found throughout the lung tissue. Unlike the previous studies (51), the use of specific antibodies in these experiments had the advantage of distinguishing between IGF-I and IGF-II. Immunolocalization revealed that the two cytokines are not co-localized during late fetal development of the rat lung. However, the pattern of staining for IGF-II correlated with the pattern of localization of IGFBP 2 mRNA in epithelial cells. These data suggest that IGF-II, which is synthesized by the mesenchyme, may act on epithelial cells to mediate cell-cell interactions during lung development. In addition, these data suggest that local control of growth regulation during lung development may, in addition to IGF receptors, be specified by selective and localized expression of IGFBP 2.

Fibroblast Growth Factors

Fibroblast growth factors (FGFs) are multipotential protein mediators of a variety of physiological processes including cellular proliferation and differentiation, cell migration, angiogenesis, and development (45). There are two closely related forms of FGF: acidic (aFGF) and basic (bFGF). During embryogenesis, FGF is distributed throughout the embryo and is responsible for mesoderm induction and the establishment of embryonic pattern formation (44). Members of the FGF gene family as well as high affinity binding sites for FGFs can be detected late in development during periods of organogenesis (53). Depending on cell type, the biological activity of FGF can be modulated by TGF-β (41). This observation suggests that the effects of FGF on cellular proliferation and differentiation could be determined locally by the relative concentration of FGF and TGF-β (45). Furthermore, neither aFGF nor bFGF possesses an obvious conventional signal peptide, and bFGF has been found in the form of bFGF-heparan sulfate proteoglycan complexes incorporated into the ECM (108). A discussion of the association between the ECM and bFGF was presented in the section under syndecans.

Questions regarding the distribution and possible role(s) of FGF during lung development are just beginning to be addressed. Using monoclonal antibodies specific to aFGF and bFGF, the distribution of these cytokines in the postnatal development of rat lungs has been examined (110). The immunolocalization pattern of aFGF was suggestive of a local source for this cytokine in normal lung cell turnover. In contrast, bFGF immunoreactivity, which was possible only after treatment of lung tissue with hyaluronidase, was primarily localized to the basement membranes beneath developing epithelium and the endothelium of vessel wall intima and in the adventitia. These data are consistent with a potential role for bFGF in the morphogenesis of lung tissue.

Cellular and developmental responses affected by FGFs are mediated by a family of at least four specific receptor tyrosine kinases (45). In the developing lung, one FGF receptor, FGFR1, is expressed primarily with a mesenchymal distribution, whereas another, FGFR2, is localized to the lung bud epithelium (95). FGFR2 is also expressed in tracheal epithelium throughout tracheal development and FGFR1 is expressed in the tracheal mesenchyme. Further lung development (16.5 days pc) is accompanied by expression of FGFR2 in terminal bronchioles and not in the more proximal airways, and expression of FGFR1 is decreased in lung bud mesenchyme. The functional significance of the differential distribution of the two FGF receptors is not known. A number of studies have suggested that both aFGF and bFGF bind FGFR1 and FGFR2 with equal affinity (24). However, some isoforms of both FGF receptors, derived by alternative splicing, display binding specificity different from the original receptor (27). Therefore, it is possible that upon binding FGF, the different receptors may elicit different responses in mesenchymal and epithelial cells. In *Drosophila*, deletional mutations for the FGF receptor result in abnormal epithelial morphogenesis (40). By extrapolation, it is possible that FGFR2 may play an important role in the development of the lung and other organs whose morphogenesis is dependent on epithelial branching.

Expression of bFGF and the FGF receptor (FGF-R) has been studied during fetal rat lung development (50). These studies were performed with a monoclonal antibody to bFGF and antisera raised against a synthetic peptide that cross reacts with both FGFR1 and FGFR2. bFGF was localized to fetal tracheal, bronchial, and airway epithelial cells and their ECM. The exact functional consequence of these observations is not known. Fetal rat lung epithelial cells are known to respond to bFGF (16), and bFGF is a mitogen for adult pulmonary type II cells in vitro (77). It is therefore possible that bFGF may be involved in control of lung epithelial cell proliferation. FGF-R was detected in airway epithelial cells, as early as day 13, especially in the branching areas and in the interstitial cells. The number of cells expressing FGF-R increased during the pseudoglandular stages of lung development and were followed by fluctuations during the canalicular stages. No FGF-R was detected in the saccular stage of lung development. FGF itself appears to be sequestered by the ECM and released at times of physiologic need. Interaction between FGF and the ECM may provide a critical regulatory mechanism by which the activity of this cytokine is controlled and utilized during development and in tissue injury. In addition, differential expression of FGF-R may further regulate the biological activity of bFGF during lung development. For example, increased expression of FGF-R during the pseudoglandular stages of lung development, a period of branching morphogenesis that is dependent on epithelial-mesenchymal interactions, may be the mechanism by which these processes are regulated by the locally available FGF.

SIGNAL TRANSDUCTION IN EPITHELIAL-MESENCHYMAL INTERACTIONS

Communication among cells and between cells and the ECM is essential during embryonic development. The underlying molecular and biochemical mechanisms involved in these processes remain largely undeciphered. As in other biological systems, mechanisms must exist by which the signals from the cells or the ECM are received and transduced into specific physiological responses. This mechanism is known as signal transduction and is generally mediated by receptor-type tyrosine kinases and their specific ligands.

A number of genes that encode such receptors have been defined through the ability of their mutated forms to induce malignant transformation (151). Many receptor tyrosine kinases and their ligands function in growth control and in the maintenance of normal homeostasis. However, recent data point to the importance of their expression during development. For example, in the mouse, tyrosine kinase receptors, such as the product of the *W* locus (c-Kit receptor tyrosine kinase), are required for the proliferation and migration of various stem cells (3). In *Drosophila*, the products of a number of such genes with transmembrane tyrosine kinase activity, such as *sevenless,* are known to have critical roles in development. Development of the omatidia (the eye equivalents) in *Drosophila* is dependent on the expression of *sevenless* and its role in the establishment of cell fate (6).

Analysis of a transmembrane tyrosine kinase receptor, *ros*-1, cDNA indicates that this gene encodes a cell surface receptor with an unusually large extracellular domain closely related to *sevenless* in *Drosophila* (11). Sonnenberg and colleagues (127) found transient and locally restricted expression of *ros*-1 during the development of the mouse in parenchymal tissues such as kidney, intestine, and lung. Expression of *ros*-1 was low throughout development of the lung compared to that of kidney and intestine, but was nevertheless developmentally regulated. Specific *ros*-1 mRNAs were detectable on day 18 (compared to day 14 for kidney and day 16 for intestine) of embryogenesis. The level of transcripts increased slightly after birth and declined thereafter. Low level expression of *ros*-1 was detected throughout adulthood in the lung, although kidneys and intestine showed no detectable levels of this gene transcript. Unfortunately, in the lung, attempts to localize the transcript by in situ hybridization were not successful, and therefore the source of *ros*-1 expression is not known. However, in situ hybridization localized *ros*-1 transcripts specifically to the growing tip of the ureter during the development of the kidney. The same cells that stain for *ros*-1 are known to be involved in two inductive events: the mesenchymally induced branching of the ureter and the ureter-induced conversion of mesenchyme to epithelium (115). It is of interest to know the relationship between branching morphogenesis of the lung tissue and the expression of *ros*-1. Perturbations in the expression of this gene in transgenic animals may provide the opportunity to answer this important question.

Integrins play a critical role in the interactions that occur between cells and the ECM. In this capacity, integrins may be involved in the mechanisms of signal transduction by affecting the organization of the cellular cytoskeleton through their cytoplasmic domains. The results from a number of recent studies suggest that integrins may play the role of a true receptor with the ability to induce biochemical signals within target cells (65). Kornberg et al (71) demonstrated that clustering of integrins by anti-integrin antibodies, which mimics the lateral association of integrins during adhesive contact, results in integrin-specific enhanced tyrosine phosphorylation of a complex of proteins ranging between 120 and 130 kd. One component of this complex bears immunological similarity with a 125 kd substrate for the *src* family of tyrosine kinases (66). Integrin stimulates tyrosine phosphorylation of this protein in mouse fibroblasts (49). This protein, designated pp125 focal adhesion kinase, pp125^{fak}, is a novel tyrosine kinase molecule (117). pp125^{fak} appears to be a cytoplasmic kinase lacking transmembrane and growth factor receptor domains. These exciting findings raise the possibility that early steps in signal transduction from the ECM to the intracellular machinery through integrins may be mediated by activation of pp125^{fak}.

CONCLUSIONS

Morphogenesis of the lung is a complex process, initiated early in embryonic development with the establishment of what can be called a morphogenetic field, determined to form the lung bud in the primitive esophagus. The exact mechanism for establishing this morphogenetic field remains obscure, but may involve localized expression of genes, such as *Hox* loci, known to regulate positional identity. This contention is supported by detection of *Hox* mRNAs during the embryonic and pseudoglandular periods of lung development (Table 1). Further structural and functional development of the lung depends on epithelial-mesenchymal interactions on a suitable ECM. Among numerous factors, these interactions occur via cellular receptors, various components of the ECM, and specific cytokines, a select sample of which has been highlighted in this review. Formation of the lung requires both cellular proliferation and differentiation. These events occur in concert with regional specification. For example, the morphogenetic history of the bronchial tubes is distinct from that of the terminal alveoli, although both are regulated by cell-cell and cell-ECM interactions. The complexity of the processes involved is underscored by the fact that the composition of the ECM, which regulates many cellular activities, is itself determined by the proliferating and differentiating cells themselves. Interactions between cells and groups of cells also occur via cell surface receptor molecules and morphogens, such as cytokines, that are being made locally by the participating cells. These observations suggest that development results not so much from the ingredients that make up the lung, but rather from the ongoing combination and interaction of the ingredients whose composition may constantly change. Figure 1 represents an attempt to simplify and integrate specific examples of interactions and their mediators during the process of lung development. In the end, our task will be to gain an understanding of how cellular and cell-ECM interactions can be related to cellular proliferation and the expression of the differentiated phenotype. In the lung, this requires a mechanistic knowledge of how differentiation-specific genes, such as *SP-C*, whose expression is detectable in early lung epithelial progenitors (144), is activated or maintained in alveolar epithelial cells and silenced in other epithelial cells during regional specification.

Since the discovery of embryonic induction, significant advances have been made in understanding the role of intercellular communication in organ development. Although these biological processes remain obscure at the molecular and mechanistic levels, the identification and characterization of their many components hold much promise. The exciting challenge facing us now is the seminal information that is needed to connect intercellular communication with its final outcome, cellular differentiation and activation of tissue- and cell-type-specific gene expression.

ACKNOWLEDGMENTS

The research in our laboratories is supported by HL 48298, the American Lung Association RG-109-N (PM), HL 40986 and HL 43704 (RJK). Our

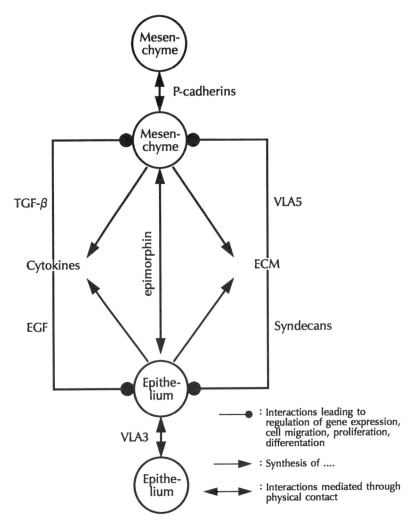

Figure 1   A schematic diagram of epithelial-mesenchymal interactions during lung development. Examples of genes or gene products mediating specific interactions are given for each case.

thanks go to Robert deLemos, John McCarrey and Tom Dooley, who read the manuscript and made valuable suggestions for its improvement. PM extends special thanks to Hal Slavkin and Jim Weston, who took the time to make me appreciate some of the finer aspects of cell-cell interactions during development. We also thank the members of the word processing department at SFBR for excellent secretarial assistance.

Literature Cited

1. Affolter M, Schier A, Gehring WJ. 1990. Homeodomain proteins and the regulation of gene expression. *Cell Biol.* 2:485–95
2. Albelda SM, Buck CA. 1990. Integrins and other cell adhesion molecules. *FASEB J.* 4:2868–80
3. Anderson DM, Lyman SD, Baird A, Wignall JM, Eisenman J, et al. 1990. Molecular cloning of mast cell growth factor, a hematopoietin that is active in both membrane bound and soluble forms. *Cell* 63:235–43
4. Arnaout MA. 1990. Structure and function of the leukocyte adhesion molecules CD11/CD18. *Blood* 75:1037–50
5. Aufderheide E, Ekblom P. 1988. Tenascin during gut development: appearance in the mesenchyme, shift in molecular forms, and dependence on epithelial-mesenchymal interactions. *J. Cell Biol.* 107:2341–49
6. Basler K, Christen B, Hafen E. 1991. Ligand-independent activation of the sevenless receptor tyrosine kinase changes the fate of cells in the developing Drosophila eye. *Cell* 64:1069–81
7. Beer DG, Butley MS, Cunha GR, Malkinson AM. 1984. Autoradiographic localization of specific [³H] dexamethasone binding in fetal lung. *Dev. Biol.* 105:351–64
8. Bernacki SH, Nervi C, Vollberg TM, Jetten AM. 1992. Homeobox 1.3 expression: Induction by retinoic acid in human bronchial fibroblasts. *Am. J. Respir. Cell Mol. Biol.* 7:3–9
9. Bernfield M, Hooper KC. 1991. Possible regulation of FGF activity by syndecan, an integral membrane heparan sulfate proteoglycan. *Ann. NY Acad. Sci.* 638:182–94
10. Bernfield M, Kokenyesi R, Kato M, Hinkes MT, Spring J, et al. 1992. Biology of the syndecans: A family of transmembrane heparan sulfate proteoglycans. *Annu. Rev. Cell Biol.* 8: 365–93
11. Birchmeier C, O'Neill K, Riggs M, Wigler M. 1990. Characterization of ROS1 cDNA from a human glioblastoma cell line. *Proc. Natl. Acad. Sci. USA* 87:4799–803
12. Blasband A, Schryver B, Papkoff J. 1992. The biochemical properties and transforming potential of human wnt-2 are similar to wnt-1. *Oncogene* 7:153–61
13. Bourdon MA, Ruoslahti E. 1989. Tenascin mediates cell attachment through an RGD-dependent receptor. *J. Cell Biol.* 108:1149–55
14. Boutin EL, Sanderson RD, Bernfield M, Cunha GR. 1991. Epithelial-mesenchymal interactions in uterus and vagina alter the expression of the cell surface proteoglycan, snydecan. *Dev. Biol.* 148(1):63–74
15. Brauker JH, Trautman MS, Bernfield M. 1991. Syndecan, a cell surface proteoglycan, exhibits a molecular polymorphism during lung development. *Dev. Biol.* 147(2):285–92
16. Caniggia I, Tseu I, Han RNN, Smith BT, Tanswell K, et al. 1991. Spatial and temporal differences in fibroblast behavior in fetal rat lung. *Am J. Physiol.* 261:L424–33
17. Chisaka O, Capecchi MR. 1991. Regionally restricted developmental defects resulting from targeted disruption of the mouse homeobox gene *hox-1.5*. *Nature* 35:473–79
18. Christial JL, McMahon JA, McMahon AP, Moon RT. 1991. *Xwnt-8*, a *Xenopus Wnt-1/int-1*-related gene responsive to mesoderm-including growth factors, may play a role in ventral mesodermal patterning during embryogenesis. *Development* 111:1045–55
19. Cooper AR, MacQueen HA. 1983. Subunits of laminin are differentially synthesized in mouse eggs and early embryos. *Dev. Biol.* 96:467–71
20. Crossin KL, Hoffman S, Grumet M, Thiery JP, Edelman GM. 1986. Site-restricted expression of cytotactin during development of the chicken embryo. *J. Cell Biol.* 102:1917–30
21. Darribere T, Guida K, Larjava H, Johnson KE, Yamada K, et al. 1990. In vivo analysis of integrin β-1 subunit function in fibronectin matrix assembly. *J. Cell Biol.* 110:1813–23
22. Daughaday WH, Rotwein P. 1989. Insulin-like growth factors I and II. Peptide, messenger ribonucleic acid and gene structures, serum, and tissue concentrations. *Endocrinol. Rev.* 10:68–91
23. Davenport JL, D'Ercole AJ, Azizkhan JC, Lund, PK. 1987. Somatomedin-C/insulin-like growth factor I (Sm-C/IGF-I) and insulin-like growth factor II (IGF-II) mRNAs during lung development in the rat. *Exp. Lung Res.* 14:607–18
24. Dionne C, Crumley G, Bellot F, Kaplow J, Searfoss G, et al. 1990. Cloning and expression of two distinct

high-affinity receptors cross-reacting with acidic and basic fibroblast growth factors. *EMBO J.* 9:2685–92

25. Duboule D, Dolle P. 1989. The structural and functional organization of the murine *Hox* gene family resembles that of *Drosophila* homeotic genes. *EMBO J.* 8:1497–505

26. Ekblom M, Klein G, Mugraver G, Fecker L, Deutzmann R, et al. 1990. Transient and locally restricted expression of laminin A chain mRNA by developing epithelial cells during kidney organogenesis. *Cell* 60:337–46

27. Elsemann A, Ahn J, Graziani G, Tronick S, Ron D. 1991. Alternative splicing generates at least five different isoforms of the human basic-FGF receptor. *Oncogene* 6:1195–202

28. Erickson HP. 1989. Tenascin: an extracellular matrix protein prominent in specialized embryonic tissues and tumors. *Annu. Rev. Cell Biol.* 5:71–92

29. Erickson HP. 1993. Gene knockouts of c-src, transforming growth factor β1, and tenascin suggest superfluous, nonfunctional expression of proteins. *J. Cell Biol.* 120:1079–81

30. Evans MJ, Shami SG, Cabral-Anderson LJ, Dekker NP. 1986. Role of nonciliated cells in renewal of the bronchial epithelium of rats exposed to NO_2. *Am. J. Pathol.* 123:126–33

31. Fava RA, McClure DB. 1987. Fibronectin-associated transforming growth factors. *J. Cell Physiol.* 131: 184–89

32. Foster JA, Curtiss SW. 1990. The regulation of lung elastin synthesis. *Am. J. Physiol.* 259:L13–23

33. Gatherer D, Dijke PT, Baird DT, Akhurst RJ. 1990. Expression of TGF-β isoforms during first trimester human embryogenesis. *Development* 110:445–60

34. Gaunt SJ, Krumlauf R, Duboule D. 1989. Mouse homeo-genes within a subfamily, *Hox-1.4, -2.6* and *-5.1*, display similar anteroposterior domains of expression in the embryo, but show stage- and tissue-dependent differences in their regulation. *Development* 107:131–41

35. Gaunt SJ, Sharpe PT, Duboule D. 1988. Spatially restricted domains of homeo gene transcripts in mouse embryos: relation to segmented body plan. *Development* 104(Suppl.):169–79

36. Gaunt SJ, Singh PB. 1990. Homeogene expression patterns and chromosomal imprinting. *Trends Gene* 6:208–12

37. Gavin BJ, McMahon JA, McMahon AP. 1990. Expression of multiple novel *Wnt-1/int-1*-related genes during fetal

and adult mouse development. *Genes Dev.* 4:2319–32

38. Gerdes JS, Yoder MC, Douglas SD, Harris PMC, Polin RA. 1986. Tracheal lavage and plasma fibronectin: relationship to respiratory distress syndrome and development of bronchopulmonary dysplasia. *J. Pediatr.* 108: 601–6

39. Ginsberg M, Lofius J, Plow E. 1988. Cytoadhesins, integrins, and platelets. *Thromb. Haemost.* 59:1–6

40. Glazer L, Shilo B. 1991. The *Drosophila* FGF-R homolog is expressed in the embryonic tracheal system and appears to be required for directed tracheal cell extension. *Genes Dev.* 5:697–705

41. Globus R, Patterson-Buckendahl P, Gospodarowlez D. 1988. Regulation of bovine bone cell proliferation by fibroblast growth factor and transforming growth factor-β. *Endocrinology* 123:93–105

42. Glucher JR, Nies DE, Marton LS, Stefansson K. 1989. An alternatively spliced region of the human hexabrachion contains a novel repeat of potential N-glycosylation sites. *Proc. Natl. Acad. Sci. USA* 86:1588–92

43. Goldin GV, Opperman LA. 1980. Induction of supernumerary tracheal buds and the stimulation of DNA synthesis in the embryonic chick lung and trachea by epidermal growth factor. *J. Embryol. Exp. Morphol.* 60:235–43

44. Gonzalez A, Buscaglia M, Ong M, Baird A. 1990. Distribution of basic fibroblast growth factor in the 18-day rat fetus: Localization in the basement membranes of diverse tissues. *J. Cell Biol.* 110:753–65

45. Gospodarowicz D. 1990. Fibroblast growth factor and its involvement in developmental processes. *Curr. Top. Dev. Biol.* 24:57–93

46. Gospodarowicz D, Neufeld G, Schweigerer L. 1986. Molecular and biological characterization of fibroblast growth factor, an angiogenic factor which also controls the proliferation and differentiation of mesoderm and neuroectoderm derived cells. *Cell Differ.* 9:1–17

47. Gospodarowicz D, Neufeld G, Schweigerer L. 1987. Fibroblast growth factor: structural and biological properties. *J. Cell Physiol.* (Suppl.) 5:15–26

48. Graham A, Papolopulu N, Krumlauf R. 1989. The murine and Drosophila homeobox gene complexes have com-

mon features of organization and expression. *Cell* 57:367–78

49. Guan JL, Trevethick JE, Hynes RO. 1991. Fibronectin/integrin interaction induces tyrosine phosphyorylation of a 120KD protein. *Cell Regul.* 2:951–64

50. Han RNN, Liu J, Tanswell AK, Post M. 1992. Expression of basic fibroblast growth factor and receptor: immunolocalization studies in developing rat fetal lung. *Pediatr. Res.* 31(5):435–40

51. Han VK, Hill DJ, Strain AJ. 1987. Identification of somatomedin/insulin-like growth factor immunoreactive cells in the human fetus. *Pediatr. Res.* 22:245–49

52. Hatta K, Takagi S, Fujisawa H, Takeichi M. 1987. Spatial and temporal expression pattern of N-cadherin cell adhesion molecules correlated with morphogenetic processes of chicken embryos. *Dev. Biol.* 120:215–27

53. Haub O, Goldfarb J. 1991. Expression of the fibroblast growth factor-5 gene in the mouse embryo. *Development* 112:397–406

54. Hayashi K, Hayashi M, Jalkaner M, Firestone JH, Trelstad R, et al. 1987. Immunocytochemistry of cell surface heparan sulfate proteoglycan in mouse tissues. A light and electron microscopic study. *J. Histochem. Cytochem.* 35(10):1079–88

55. Heine UI, Munoz EF, Flanders KC, Ellinsworth LR, Lam HYP, et al. 1987. Role of transforming growth factor-β in the development of the mouse embryo. *J. Cell Biol.* 105:2861–76

56. Heine UI, Munoz EF, Flanders KC, Roberts AB, Sporn MB. 1990. Colocalization of TGF-β 1 and collagen I and III, fibronectin and glycosaminoglycans during lung branching morphogenesis. *Development* 109:29–36

57. Hilfer SRR, Rayner RM, Brown JW. 1985. Mesenchymal control of branching pattern in the fetal mouse lung. *Tissue Cell* 17:523–38

58. Hirai Y, Nose A, Kobayashi S, Takeichi M. 1989. Expression and role of E- and P-cadherin adhesion molecules in embryonic histogenesis. *Development* 105:263–70

59. Hirai Y, Takebe K, Takashina M, Kobayash S, Takeichi M. 1992. Epimorphin: A mesenchymal protein essential for epithelial morphogenesis. *Cell* 69:471–81

60. Hirning U, Schmid P, Schultz WA, Rettenberger G, Hameister H. 1991. A comparative analysis of N-*myc* and c-*myc* expression and cellular prolifer-ation in mouse organogenesis. *Mech. Dev.* 33:119–26

61. Ignotz RA, Endo T, Massagué J. 1987. Regulation of fibronectin and type 1 collagen mRNA levels by transforming growth factor-β. *J. Biol. Chem.* 262:6443–46

62. Ignotz RA, Massagué J. 1987. Cell adhesion protein receptors as targets for transforming growth factor-β action. *Cell* 51:189–97

63. Jacobson AG, Sater AK. 1988. Features of embryonic induction. *Development* 104:341–59

64. James R, Kazenwadel J. 1991. Homeobox gene expression in the intestinal epithelium of adult mice. *J. Biol. Chem.* 5:3246–51

65. Juliano RL, Haskill S. 1993. Signal transduction from the extracellular matrix. *J. Cell Biol.* 120(3):577–85

66. Kanner SB, Reynolds AB, Vines RR, Parsons JT. 1990. Monoclonal antibodies to individual tyrosine kinase phosphorylated protein substrates of oncogene encoded tyrosine kinases. *Proc. Natl. Acad. Sci. USA* 87:3328–32

67. Kessel M, Gruss P. 1991. Homeotic transformations of murine vertebrae and concomitant alteration of Hox codes induced by retinoic acid. *Cell* 67:89–104

68. Klagsbrun M, Baird A. 1991. A dual receptor system is required for basic fibroblast growth factor activity. *Cell* 67(2):229–31

69. Kleinman HK, Graf J, Iwamoto Y, Sasaki M, Schasteen CS, et al. 1989. Identification of a second active site in laminin for promotion of cell adhesion and migration and inhibition of in vivo melanoma lung colonization. *Arch. Biochem. Biophys.* 272:39–45

70. Klempt M, Hutchins A-M, Gluckman PD, Skinner SJM. 1992. IGF binding protein-2 gene expression and the location of IGF-I and IGF-II in fetal rat lung. *Development* 115:765–72

71. Kornberg I, Earp HS, Turner C, Prokop C, Juliano RL. 1991. Signal transduction by integrins: increased protein tyrosine phosphorylation caused by clustering of beta integrins. *Proc. Natl. Acad. Sci. USA* 88:8392–96

72. Kouzi-Koliakos K, Koliakos GG, Tsilibary EC, Furcht LT, Charonis AS. 1989. Mapping of three major heparin-binding sites on laminin and identification of a novel heparin-binding site on the B1 chain. *J. Biol. Chem.* 264:17,971–78

73. Kratochwil K, Dziadek M, Loheer J, Harbirs K, Jaenisch R. 1986. Normal

epithelial branching morphogenesis in the absence of collagen 1. *Dev. Biol.* 117:596–606

74. Lammer GJ, Chen DT, Hoar RM, Agnish, ND, Benke PJ, et al. 1985. Retinoic acid embryopathy. *N. Engl. J. Med.* 313:837–41

75. Lamson G, Giudice LC, Rosenfeld RG. 1991. Insulin-like growth factor binding proteins: Structural and molecular relationships. *Growth Factors* 5:19–28

76. Le Douarin NM. 1984. Cell migration in embryo. *Cell* 38:358–60

77. Leslie CC, McCormick-Shannon KK, Mason RJ. 1990. Heparin binding growth factors stimulate DNA synthesis in rat alveolar type II cells. *Am. J. Respir. Cell Mol. Biol.* 2:99–106

78. Levay-Young BK, Navre M. 1992. Growth and developmental regulation of *wnt-2 (irp)* gene in mesenchymal cells of fetal lung. *Am. J. Physiol.* 262:L672–83

79. Mackie EJ, Chiquet-Ehrismann R, Pearson CA, Inaguma Y, Taya K. 1987. Tenascin is a stromal marker for epithelial malignancy in the mammary gland. *Proc. Natl. Acad. Sci. USA* 84:4621–25

80. Mackie EJ, Halfter W, Liverani D. 1988. Induction of tenascin in healing wounds. *J. Cell Biol.* 107:2757–67

81. Massagué J. 1990. The transforming growth factor-β family. *Annu. Rev. Cell Biol.* 6:597–641

82. McCarthy JB, Skubitz APN, Zhao Q, et al. 1990. RGD-independent cell adhesion to the carboxy-terminal heparin-binding fragment of fibronectin involves heparin-dependent and -independent activities. *J. Cell Biol.* 110: 777–87

83. Melton DA. 1991. Pattern formation during animal development. *Science* 252:234–40

84. Minoo P, Lin A, King R, deLemos R. 1991. Expression of TGF-α in fetal and premature lung. *Pediatr. Res.* 29:325A

85. Minoo P, Penn R, Coalson J, deLemos D, deLemos R. 1993. Tissue inhibitor of metalloproteinases (TIMP) mRNA is specifically induced in lung tissue following birth. *Pediatr. Res.* In press

86. Moens, CB, Auerbach, AB, Conlon, RA, Joyner, AL, Rossant J. 1992. A targeted mutation reveals a role for N-myc in branching morphogenesis in the embryonic mouse lung. *Gen. Dev.* 6:691–704

87. Moses HL, Yang EY, Pietenpol JA.

1990. TGF-β stimulation and inhibition of cell proliferation: new mechanistic insights. *Cell* 63:245–47

88. Mugrauer G, Alt FW, Ekblom P. 1988. N-myc proto-oncogene expression during organogenesis in the developing mouse as revealed by in situ hybridization. *J. Cell Biol.* 107:1325–35

89. Nieuwkoop PD, Johnen AG, Albers B. 1985. *The Epigenetic Nature of Early Chordate Development.* Cambridge: Cambridge Univ. Press

90. Nose A, Takeichi M. 1986. A novel cadherin adhesion molecule: Its expression patterns associated with implantation and organogenesis of mouse embryos. *J. Cell Biol.* 103:2649–58

91. Oyama F, Hirohashi S, Shimosato Y, Titani K, Sekiguchi K. 1991. Qualitative and quantitative changes of human tenascin expression in transformed lung fibroblast and lung tumor tissues: comparison with fibronectin. *Cancer Res.* 51:4876–81

92. Panayotou G, End P, Aumailley M, Timpi R, Engel J. 1989. Domains of laminin with growth-factor activity. *Cell* 56:93–101

93. Partanen A-M. 1990. Epidermal growth factor and transforming growth factor-α in the development of epithelial-mesenchymal organs of the mouse. *Curr. Top. Dev. Biol.* 24:31–55

94. Paul JL, Hynes, RO. 1984. Multiple fibronectin subunits and their post-translational modifications. *J. Biol. Chem.* 259:13477–88

95. Peters KG, Werner S, Chen G, Williams LT. 1992. Two FGF receptor genes are differentially expressed in epithelial and mesenchymal tissues during limb formation and organogenesis in the mouse. *Development* 114:233–43

96. Raaberg L, Nexo E, Buckley S, Luo W, Snead ML, et al. 1991. Epidermal growth factor transcription, translation and signal transduction by rat type II pneumocytes in culture. *Am. J. Resp. Cell Mol. Biol.* 6:44–49

97. Rapraeger A. 1989. Transforming growth factor (Type β) promotes the addition of chondroitin sulfate chains to the cell surface proteoglycan (syndecan) of mouse mammary epithelia. *J. Cell Biol.* 109:2509–18

98. Retsch-Bogart GZ, Stiles AD, Moats-Staats MM, Van Scott MR, Boucher RC, et al. 1990. Canine tracheal epithelial cells express the type 1 insulin-like growth factor receptor and proliferate in response to insulin-like

growth factor I. *Am. J. Respir. Cell Mol. Biol.* 3:227–34

99. Rickard KA, Taylor J, Rennard SI, Spurzem JR. 1993. Migration of bovine bronchial epithelial cells to extracellular matrix components. *Am. J. Respir. Cell Mol. Biol.* 8:63–68

100. Roman J, McDonald JA. 1991. Potential role of RGD-directed integrins in mammalian lung branching morphogenesis. *Development* 112:551–58

101. Roman J, McDonald JA. 1992. Expression of fibronectin, the integrin α5, and α-smooth muscle actin in heart and lung development. *Am. J. Respir. Cell Mol. Biol.* 6:472–80

102. Roth RA. 1988. Structure of the receptor for insulin-like growth factor II: the puzzle amplified. *Science* 239:1269–71

103. Ruiz A, Melton DA. 1989. Interaction between peptide growth factors and homeobox genes in the establishment of antero-posterior polarity in frog embryos. *Nature* 341:33–38

104. Ruoslahti E. 1988. Fibronectin and its receptors. *Annu. Rev. Biochem.* 57:375–413

105. Ruoslahti E, Pierschbacher MD. 1987. New perspectives in cell adhesion: RGD and integrins. *Science* 238:491–97

106. Saga Y, Yagi T, Ikawa Y, Sakakura T, Alzawa S. 1992. Mice develop normally without tenascin. *Genes Dev.* 6:1821–31

107. Sakaguchi K, Yanagishita M, Takeuchi Y, Aurbach GD. 1991. Identification of heparan sulfate proteoglycan as a high affinity receptor for acidic fibroblast growth factor (aFGF) in a parathyroid cell line. *J. Biol. Chem.* 266(11):7270–78

108. Saksela O, Moscatelli D, Sommer A, Rifkin DB. 1988. Endothelial cell-derived heparan sulfate binds basic fibroblast growth factor and protects it from proteolytic degradation. *J. Cell Biol.* 107:743–51

109. Sanderson RD, Bernfield M. 1988. Molecular polymorphism of a cell surface proteoglycan: distinct structures on simple and stratified epithelia. *Proc. Natl. Acad. Sci. USA* 85(24):9562–66

110. Sannes PL, Burch KK, Khosla J. 1992. Immunohistochemical localization of epidermal growth factor and acidic and basic fibroblast growth factors in postnatal developing and adult rat lungs. *Am. J. Respir. Cell Mol. Biol.* 7:230–37

111. Sasaki M, Kato S, Kohno K, Martin GR, Yamada Y. 1987. Sequence of the cDNA encoding the laminin B1 chain reveals a multidomain protein containing cysteine-rich repeats. *Proc. Natl. Acad. Sci. USA* 84:935–39

112. Sasaki M, Kleinman HK, Huber H, Deutzmann R, Yamada Y. 1988. Laminin, a multidomain protein. The A chain has a unique domain and homology with the basement membrane proteoglycan and the laminin B chains. *J. Biol. Chem.* 263:16,536–44

113. Sasaki M, Yamada Y. 1987. The laminin B2 chain has a multi-domain structure homologous to the B1 chain. *J. Biol. Chem.* 262:17,111–17

114. Sawai S, Shimono A, Wakamatsu Y, Palmes C, Hanaoka K, et al. 1993. Defects of embryonic organogenesis resulting from targeted disruption of the N-*myc* gene in the mouse. *Development* 117:1445–55

115. Saxen L. 1987. *Organogenesis of the Kidney.* Cambridge: Cambridge Univ. Press

116. Saxen L, Thesleff I. 1992. Epithelial-mesenchymal interactions in murine organogenesis. In *Postimplantation Development in the Mouse. Ciba Found. Symp.* 165:183–98

117. Schaller MD, Borgman A, Cobb BS, Vines RR, Reynolds AB, Parsons JT. 1992. pp125[fak] a structurally unique protein tyrosine kinase associated with focal adhesions. *Proc. Natl. Acad. Sci. USA* 89:5192–96

118. Schuger L, O'Shea S, Rheinheimer J, Varani J. 1990. Laminin in lung development: Effects of anti-laminin antibody in murine lung morphogenesis. *Dev. Biol.* 137:26–32

119. Schuger L, Skubitz APN, O'Shea KS, Chang JF, Varani J. 1991. Identification of laminin domains involved in branching morphogenesis: Effects of anti-laminin monoclonal antibodies on mouse embryonic lung development. *Dev. Biol.* 146:531–41

120. Sejersen T, Björklund H, Sümegi J, Ringertz NR. 1986. N-*myc* and c-*src* genes are diffentially regulated in PCC7 embryonal carcinoma cells undergoing neutromal differentiation. *J. Cell. Physiol.* 127:274–80

121. Seno M, Sasada R, Kurokawa T, Igarishi K. 1990. Carboxyl-terminal structure of basic fibroblast growth factor significantly contributes to its affinity for heparin. *Eur. J. Biochem.* 188(2):239–45

121a. Seth R, Shum L, Wu F, Waenschell C, Slavkin HC. 1993. Role of epidermal growth factor expression in early mouse embryo lung branching morphogenesis in culture: antisense oligodeoxynucleotide inhibitory strategy. *Dev. Biol.* In press

122. Shannon JM, Emrie PA, Fisher JA, Kuroki Y, Jennings SD, et al. 1990. Effect of a reconsituted basement membrane on expression of surfactant apoproteins in cultured adult rat alveolar type II cells. *Am. J. Respir. Cell Mol. Biol.* 2:183–92

123. Shoji S, Rickard KA, Ertl RF, Robbins RA, Linder J, et al. 1989. Bronchial epithelial cells produce lung fibroblast chemotactic factor: Fibronectin. *Am. J. Respir. Cell Mol. Biol.* 1:13–20

124. Sinkin RA, LoMonaco MB, Finkelstein JN, Watkins RH, Cox C, et al. 1992. Increased fibronectin mRNA in alveolar macrophages following in vivo hyperoxia. *Am. J. Respir. Cell Mol. Biol.* 7:548–55

125. Snead ML, Luo W, Oliver P, Nakamura M, Don-Wheeler G, et al. 1989. Localization of epidermal growth factor precursor in tooth and lung during embryonic development. *Dev. Biol.* 134:420–29

126. Solursh M, Reiter RS, Jensen KL, Kato M, Bernfield M. 1990. Transient expression of a cell surface heparan sulfate proteoglycan (syndecan) during limb development. *Dev. Biol.* 140(1): 83–92

127. Sonnenberg E, Gödecke A, Walter B, Bladt F, Birchmeier C. 1991. Transient and locally restricted expression of *ros* 1 protooncogene during mouse development. *EMBO J.* 10(12):3693–3702

128. Spooner SB, Bassett K, Stokes B. 1985. Sulfated glycosaminoglycan deposition and processing at the basal epithelial surface in branching and β-D-xyloside-inhibited embryonic salivary glands. *Dev. Biol.* 109:177–83

129. Stiles AD, D'Ercole AJ. 1990. The insulin-like growth factors and the lung. *Am. J. Respir. Cell Mol. Biol.* 3:93–100

130. Stiles AD, Smith BT, Post M. 1986. Reciprocal autocrine and paracrine regulation of growth of mesenchymal and alveolar epithelial cells from fetal lung. *Exp. Lung Res.* 11:165–77

131. Streuli CH, Schmidhauser C, Kobrin M, Bissell MJ, Derynck R. 1993. Extracellular matrix regulates expression of the TGF-β1 gene. *J. Cell Biol.* 120(1):253–60

132. Sutherland AE, Sanderson RD, Mayes M, Seibert M, Calarco PG. 1991. Expression of syndecan, a putative low affinity fibroblast growth factor receptor, in the early mouse embryo. *Development* 113(1):339–51

133. Tabin CJ. 1991. Retinoids, homeoboxes, and growth factors: Toward molecular models for limb development. *Cell* 66:199–217

134. Takeichi M. 1988. The cadherins: cell-cell adhesion molecules controlling animal morphogenesis. *Development* 102: 639–55

135. Tashiro K, Sephel GC, Weeks B, Sasaki M, Martin GR, et al. 1989. A synthetic peptide containing the IKVAV sequence from the A chain of laminin mediates cell attachment, migration and neuritic outgrowth. *J. Biol. Chem.* 264:16,174–82

136. Ten Have-Opbroek, AAW. 1981. The development of the lung in mammals: An analysis of concepts and findings. *Am. J. Anat.* 162:201–19

137. Timpl R, Rhode J, Gehron-Robey P, Rennard ST, Foidart JM, et al. 1979. Laminin—A glycoprotein from basement membranes. *J. Biol. Chem.* 254: 9933–37

138. Todaro GJ, Fryling C, De Larco JE. 1980. Transforming growth factors produced by certain human tumor cells: polypeptides that interact with epidermal growth factor receptors. *Proc. Natl. Acad. Sci. USA* 77:5258–62

139. Torday JS, Kourembanas S. 1990. Fetal rat lung fibroblasts produce a TGF-β homolog that blocks alveolar type II cell maturation. *Dev. Biol.* 139:35–41

140. Torikata C, Villiger B, Kuhn C III, McDonald JA. 1985. Ultrastructural distribution of fibronectin in normal and fibrotic lung. *Lab. Invest.* 52:399–408

141. Trautman MS, Kimelman J, Bernfield M. 1991. Developmental expression of syndecan, an integral membrane proteoglycan, correlates with cell differentiation. *Development* 111(1):213–20

142. Vaahtokari A, Vainio S, Thesleff I. 1991. Associations between transforming growth factor β1 RNA expression and epithelial-mesenchymal interactions during tooth morphogenesis. *Development* 113:985–94

143. Vartio T, Laitinen L, Narvanen O, Cutolo M, Thornell L. 1987. Differential expression of the ED sequence-containing form of cellular fibronectin in embryonic and adult human tissues. *J. Cell Sci.* 88:419–30

144. Wert SE, Glasser SW, Korfhagen TR, Whitsett JA. 1993. Transcriptional elements from the human SP-C gene

direct expression in the primordial respiratory epithelium of transgenic mice. *Dev. Biol.* 156:426–43

144a. Weston JA. 1984. The embryonic neural crest: migration and differentiation and possible contributions to the developing lung. In *The Endocrine Lung in Health and Disease,* ed. KL Becker, AF Gazdar. Philadelphia: Saunders

145. Whitsett JA, Weaver TE, Lieberman MA, Clark JC, Daugherty C. 1987. Differential effects of epidermal growth factor and transformation growth factor-β on synthesis of M_r 35,000 surfactant-associated protein in fetal lung. *J. Biol. Chem.* 262:7908–13

146. Wilcox JN, Derynck R. 1988. Developmental expression of transforming growth factors alpha and beta in mouse fetus. *Mol. Cell Biol.* 8:3415–22

147. Wilcox JN, Derynck R. 1988. Localization of cells synhesizing transforming growth factor-α mRNA in the mouse brain. *J. Neurosci.* 8:1901–4

148. Wolgemuth DJ, Behringer RR, Mostoller MP, Brinster RL, Palmiter RD. 1989. Transgenic mice over-expressing the mouse homeobox containing gene *Hox-1.4* exhibit abnormal gut development. *Nature* 337:464–67

149. Wood TL, Streck RD, Pintar JE. 1992. Expression of the *IGFBP-2* gene in post-implantation rat embryos. *Development* 114:59–66

150. Wu TC, Wan YJ, Chung AE, Damajonov I. 1983. Immunohistochemical localization of entactin and laminin in mouse embryos and fetuses. *Dev. Biol.* 100:496–505

151. Yarden Y, Ullrich A. 1988. Growth factor receptor tyrosine kinases. *Annu. Rev. Biochem.* 57:443–78

152. Yayon A, Klagsbrun M, Esko JD, Leder P, Ornitz DM. 1991. Cell surface, heparin-like molecules are required for binding of basic fibroblast growth factor to its high affinity receptor. *Cell* 64(4):841–848

153. Zimmerman KA, Yancopoulos GD, Collum RG, Smith RK, Kohl NE, et al. 1986. Differential expression of myc family genes during murine development. *Nature* 319:780–83

Annu. Rev. Physiol. 1994. 56:47–67
Copyright © 1994 by Annual Reviews Inc. All rights reserved

PULMONARY INTRAVASCULAR MACROPHAGES

Norman C. Staub

Department of Physiology and Cardiovascular Research Institute, University of California, San Francisco, California 94143-0130

KEY WORDS: mononuclear phagocytes, pulmonary circulation, acute lung injury, comparative physiology, endotoxin response, thromboxane

INTRODUCTION

The existence of pulmonary intravascular macrophages was conclusively proven by Rybicka and her associates (65) in 1974. Our laboratory did not become aware of this remarkable cell line until Albertine (1) noted the pulmonary arterial pressure rise following injections of what were assumed to be innocuous pigment particles (colloidal carbon or Monastral blue) to mark sites of vascular injury and leakage. We then found several reports, mostly by veterinary pathologists that described these new cells (9, 84, 90, 94, 97).

Now, twenty years after the definitive description of these cells, a number of anatomists and physiologists are still unaware of the existence of pulmonary intravascular macrophages. A recent treatise on comparative biology of the normal lung does not even mention the intravascular macrophages, except for two sentences in one chapter (81). However, papers are appearing that deal, if not directly with the macrophages, at least with mentioning them as the cells probably responsible for a variety of pulmonary vascular responses in several species widely used as experimental models of acute lung microvascular injury. This issue alone justifies studying the intravascular macrophages.

This review is directed primarily to new physiologic and pathophysiologic data that have accumulated since 1988. The anatomical description or the quantitative histology of this mononuclear phagocyte population will not be

47

described, although several of the earlier references will be noted to provide continuity.

A symposium volume exists (72) that contains both anatomical detail, some physiological and pathophysiological data, and considerable speculation about the significance of the macrophages. Because the number of studies on macrophages is accelerating, some in press abstracts or papers are referred to wherever they might address important questions or offer new insights. Two reviews have appeared concerning the macrophages; an extensive anatomical study (93), and a brief summary of their immunologic functions (17).

THE MONONUCLEAR PHAGOCYTIC SYSTEM IN THE LUNG

Figure 1 schematically represents the lung mononuclear phagocytes as a dynamic system. Monocytes constitute 3–8% (average 5%) of circulating leukocytes in most species (38). Further, according to Van Furth (82), a large fraction of the total accessible monocyte pool is marginated or

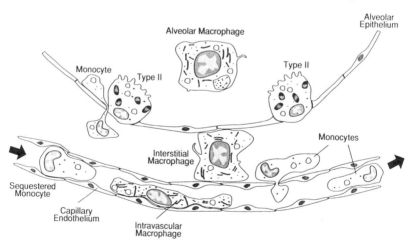

Figure 1   The extent of the mononuclear phagocyte system in the lung is suggested in this scheme. Large numbers of monocytes are sequestered (*inflow arrow*) in the microcirculation because they are too large to pass readily through the pulmonary capillaries into the systemic circulation. They remain stuck for several seconds until their shape is passively molded by the upstream vascular pressure. They then flow through into the systemic circulation (*exit arrow*). An unknown number of the sequestered monocytes migrate into the interstitium or alveoli, differentiating in either location into macrophages. Not shown are monocytes that may become temporarily adherent and activated to become phagocytic in the capillaries, as for example after acute or chronic endotoxin infusions. In animals of the mammalian orders Artiodactyla and Perissodactyla, some monocytes become permanently adherent to the endothelium and differentiate into intravascular macrophages.

sequestered, as are other leukocytes. The major site of sequestration is probably the pulmonary microcirculation, for not only is the pulmonary arterial pressure relatively low, but the spherical leukocytes with their high effective viscosity must change shape in order to slide through the capillaries, which in life are somewhat flattened in cross-section. Doerschuk (28) showed a correlation between first pass extraction of various labeled leukocytes in the rabbit lung and the cell volume or diameter.

Although most lung sequestration studies have dealt with neutrophils (35, 75), large numbers of lymphocytes (61) and monocytes are also sequestered (24, 53, 58). Ohgami studied [111]Indium-labeled monocyte kinetics in the rabbit. On the first pass through the lung 86% of the cells were delayed relative to labeled erythrocytes. After 10 min, 30–35% of the injected monocytes were still sequestered in the lung compared to 5–7% circulating. From this Ohgami deduced that the sequestered lung pool was five times the size of the circulating pool. That appears to be an overestimate. If the 27% of monocytes sequestered in the liver at 10 min are added, one calculates that up to 90% of monocytes are sequestered. Van Furth (82) reported 50–75% sequestration, that is, two to three times the circulating pool.

In our abstract on lung leukocyte washout in goats, we estimated that 25–30% of the circulating pools of neutrophils, lymphocytes, monocytes, and eosinophils were sequestered in excess of those in the residual lung blood (76). We have been justifiably criticized by J Hogg (personal communication) for not determining how many leukocytes were left in the lung in the above experiment. Interestingly, at 24 hr, Ohgami found lung retention to be 27% of the circulating pool (58).

While there is still uncertainty about the absolute size of the sequestered lung monocyte pool, this key point should be remembered; there is a large sequestered monocyte population in the pulmonary capillaries at any moment, from which lung intravascular, interstitial, and alveolar mononuclear phagocytes can be recruited.

While the majority of the monocytes are only sequestered transiently, a few may adhere more tightly to the capillary endothelium and migrate, by mechanisms unknown, into the lung interstitium or alveoli (Figure 1) where they differentiate into interstitial or alveolar macrophages, respectively. To what extent such migration occurs is controversial; Blusse Van Oud Alblas (13) presented data indicating it is the usual mechanism of alveolar macrophage renewal, but Shellito (68) found that local mitosis was more likely to explain alveolar macrophage renewal. Sibille & Reynolds, in their recent review of alveolar macrophages, opined that both mechanisms participated in replacement (69). Whatever the mechanism of interstitial and alveolar macrophage renewal is, the process or sequestration and migration occur independently of the intravascular macrophages.

POSTNATAL DEVELOPMENT OF LUNG MACROPHAGES

At birth, there are few intravascular or alveolar macrophages (43, 63, 89, 94, 98). Coincident with the onset of air breathing, colonization of the lung by circulating monocytes begins. According to Winkler, at birth piglets have few intravascular cells that can be identified by morphologic criteria as mature intravascular macrophages. By 1 month of age, however, piglets have a large population of resident intravascular macrophages.

Longworth (43) determined the time course of the functional development of pulmonary intravascular macrophages in the newborn lamb. She showed that within 1 to 3 days after birth the number of intravascular cells phagocytizing the tracer Monastral blue or retaining radioactively labeled liposomes was only 10 to 20% of the number at 2–3 weeks of age. Even more important, the cells did not function as mature intravascular macrophages because uptake of tracer particles did not lead to increased pulmonary arterial pressure or thromboxane production. In a subsequent study, Longworth showed that 1-day old lambs had minimal pulmonary hemodynamic or lymph dynamic responses to *E. coli* endotoxin infusions, whereas by 2 to 3 weeks of age, lambs responded in a similar manner to adult sheep (44).

Since every mammalian species examined has alveolar and interstitial lung macrophages, whereas only a limited number of species have intravascular macrophages (73), it is clear that there is no necessary relationship between these two populations. On the other hand, in those species that do have intravascular macrophages, their development after birth parallels that of the alveolar macrophages. Beyond that, nothing is known about the relationship between these populations.

DISTRIBUTION AMONG MAMMALIAN SPECIES

All species with macrophages belong to two orders, with one exception—the cat. Following the definitive identification of resident pulmonary intravascular macrophages in the bovine (65), similar resident macrophages were shown to exist in other mammalian species of the order Artiodactyla (even-toed), including pigs (9, 20), sheep (85, 90), goats (29, 52); llama (73), and reindeer (74).

It was recently shown that pulmonary intravascular macrophages also exist in the order Perissodactyla (odd-toed), horse and pony, (5, 33, 42, 73). In fact, based on particle retention, the horse has as many intravascular macrophages as any other species tested; further, its pulmonary vascular reactivity is extraordinary (42).

The cat is an outlier, and it is difficult to develop a consistent theory to explain the existence of pulmonary intravascular macrophages that includes the cat. Macrophages have not been found in the pulmonary capillaries of two other species of the order carnivore [dog (20, 52); ferret (K Longworth, personal communication)].

It has been known since the early part of this century that cats were different from other laboratory animals because they retained infused colloidal tracer particles within the lung (37). Wislocki (96) introduced the concept of activated endothelium to describe the phenomenon. At that time, the phagocytizing cells could not be identified, mainly because neither thin sectioning techniques nor transmission electron microscopy had been invented. In 1970, Schneeberger-Keeley (66) described intravascular macrophages in the cat. She concluded that they were displaced liver macrophages. However, there can no longer be any doubt that the cat possesses resident mononuclear phagocytic cells in its pulmonary capillaries (52, 93, 72). Whether they are to be classified as true intravascular macrophages depends in large part on how one defines that population.

The existence of pulmonary intravascular macrophages in other mammalian species is controversial. We are not convinced that true resident pulmonary intravascular macrophages have been conclusively demonstrated in any species of any other order. Our approach to this question is chiefly from the functional point of view; others approach it via a morphological definition. The morphologist view must not be casually dismissed, since it was veterinary anatomists and pathologists who first described the pulmonary intravascular macrophages, whereas physiologists such as myself had plenty of opportunity to discover them, but did not.

Niehaus (25, 55) claims a small intravascular macrophage population exists in the rat. Carrasco (15) claims they can be found in the normal rabbit. Fracica (31) reported them in the baboon. The last finding is important, of course, because if intravascular macrophages are present in primates, they may be present in humans. Only one relevant paper has been published. Dehring & Wismar (22) examined human surgical specimens and, after exhaustive sectioning, found what they interpreted to be examples of intravascular macrophages within the human lung. They concluded that such cells must be rare.

Thus an important question remains unresolved. Is it likely that all mammalian species have at least a few pulmonary intravascular macrophages? On the other hand, there is obviously a large sequestered pool of monocytes in the lungs of all mammals that may become phagocytic when stimulated in various ways. Therefore, by anatomical criteria, they may be considered to be true resident intravascular macrophages (59).

According to the classical teaching about the mononuclear phagocytic system (82), there are liver (Kupffer cells), splenic, and bone marrow intravascular macrophages. The lung was not thought to have morphologically or functionally recognizable intravascular macrophages. In part, this was because the common laboratory animals (dog, rat, mouse, rabbit) and humans do not have intravascular macrophages, and in part because no one was looking for them in any animal. The latter explains why the intravascular macrophages in the cat were not identified until 1970 (66, 93, 96). The discovery of intravascular macrophages in the placental mammalian orders Artiodactyla and Perissodactyla raises the question, why do these animals have macrophages?

One of the first clues may have been found in the studies by Bertram (8, 9) concerning the response of the intravascular macrophages in pigs to pulmonary infection with *Haemophilus pleuropneumoniae*. He reported that following infection, the pulmonary intravascular macrophages increased dramatically in number in the infected portion of the lung. Whiteley (91, 92) inoculated calves with live or killed *Pasteurella haemolytica A*. He reported that the pulmonary intravascular macrophages may be involved in the early intravascular inflammatory events.

Carrasco and his associates (14, 70) have studied the lung pathology of pigs infected with African swine fever virus strains of differing virulence. African swine fever is an acute or chronic process characterized by pulmonary edema or pneumonia, respectively. Carrasco's light and electron microscopic analysis showed that the pulmonary intravascular macrophages were the lung cells most involved in the replication of the more virulent strain, together with the cytopathic effects, which they thought might account for the abundant masses of cell debris found in the alveolar wall capillaries. However, even the attenuated virus strain stimulated the intravascular macrophages. In the later course of the infection, they found that the intravascular macrophages were decreased in number, whereas the alveolar macrophages were increased. Thus one could speculate that the intravascular macrophages are an early line of defense against inhaled pathogens. At the very least, the intravascular macrophages can be stimulated from the alveolar compartment. These several studies are morphologic, as indeed are the majority of reports about intravascular macrophages. However, they suggest a role for the macrophages in early lung inflammation.

Most investigators have concentrated on the role of intravascular macrophages in blood clearance (15, 20, 29, 51, 85). For example, Carrasco (15) reported on the effects of rabbit hemorrhagic disease, a newly emerging parvovirus disease that has been devastating rabbit populations since 1984, spreading from China to North Africa and southern Europe. The virus infection carries with it a high mortality, and the disease is characterized by pulmonary hemorrhage, congestion, and edema, as well as abdominal organ involvement. Using homogenates of infected rabbit liver, the authors inoculated rabbits intraperitoneally or by mouth. Thus the virus particles reached the lung capillaries via the vascular compartment. Carrasco states that he detected a few cells morphologically identical to intravascular macrophages in control animals, but especially after the hemorrhagic disease inoculum. In the experimental animals, he found the intravascular macrophage-like cells were involved in the removal of cellular debris. Some of the intravascular phagocytes reacted positively to antisera against rabbit hemorrhagic fever or other parvoviruses; however, no virus particles were detected in any cells.

There can be no doubt that infusions of bacterial endotoxin and test particles are usually followed by remarkable pulmonary responses in animals with intravascular macrophages; namely, prolonged lung retention of the test particles, an early (1 min or less) rise in pulmonary arterial pressure and calculated pulmonary vascular resistance, and production and secretion of thromboxane into the pulmonary circulation.

This has led to an interesting hypothesis to account for the existence of pulmonary intravascular macrophages; namely, that animals can be divided into two groups according to whether they have a liver-oriented (strong) intravascular macrophage system or a lung-oriented (weak) system (23, 39, 56). The concept is based on the fact that animals such as dogs and rats will eat almost anything, and therefore their liver macrophage system is highly developed to remove all manner of absorbed toxic substances, bacteria, or particles. However, animals such as sheep and bovine, which are herbivores, are not generally exposed to high doses of ingested pathogenic bacteria and toxins. Therefore, their liver phagocytic system is not as well-developed, and the pulmonary intravascular macrophage system has developed as compensation. This hypothesis, however, fails to account for pigs, which will eat anything and which have a large pulmonary intravascular population (95). Further, the weak and strong liver macrophage theory has been neatly disposed of by DeCamp (21), who showed that in sheep, it is the route of delivery and dose of substances, such as bacteria, particles, or endotoxin, that determines the main site of extraction; that is, given intravenously the pulmonary intravascular macrophages remove most of the test materials, but given into the portal vein, the liver macrophages remove most of them. Endotoxin was a partial exception because about half of the portal vein dose entered the pulmonary vascular bed.

Another theory is that the number of pulmonary intravascular macrophages is related to the extent of collateral ventilation (39). This is frank speculation and dependent on the notion that the intravascular macrophages are precursors of alveolar macrophages, a notion for which no evidence exists.

A third theory to account for the peculiar distribution of reactive pulmonary intravascular macrophages is that they are present only in domesticated farm animals (73, 74). We suggest that the functional value of these cells has to do with the removal of some constituent of the inspired air (dust, spores, parasite eggs, bacteria, viruses, etc) that has been deposited in the alveolar region and has for some reason escaped the mucociliary clearance system and the alveolar macrophages. This hypothesis also fits with the veterinary pathology studies of Bertram, Whiteley, and Carrasco described above.

To test the domesticated farm animal hypothesis, we studied four Norwegian wild reindeer (74). Reindeer belong to the order Artiodactyla and therefore should have pulmonary intravascular macrophages, but they are not domesticated farm animals, and thus we hypothesized that their pulmonary intravascular macrophages would be unreactive. My associates and I demonstrated a large population of pulmonary intravascular macrophages, but three of the four animals tested had a significant pulmonary arterial pressure rise and produced thromboxane following intravenous infusion of our test particles (Monastral blue pigment suspension or microspheres). Clearly the reindeer is not unreactive, although it is relatively insensitive, and required larger doses of test particles to achieve responses comparable to sheep. Thus the hypothesis that only domesticated farm animals have reactive macrophages was disproved. Recently, we also found reactive intravascular macrophages in llamas (73; K Longworth, unpublished data).

We have not abandoned the inhaled agent concept, however. Based on the accumulating evidence, a modified hypothesis is that pulmonary intravascular macrophages are present because of inhaled pathogens peculiar to these animals. The unifying concept is that the pathogens somehow bypass or overwhelm the alveolar macrophage defense line and penetrate the alveolar-capillary barrier. Pulmonary intravascular macrophages are, therefore, an evolutionary development of what is, in most animals, a nonexistent or minimally existent population. Since this hypothesis is readily testable, it may even prove useful.

Finally, there is that persistent question already mentioned. Do all species have at least a few latent pulmonary intravascular macrophages that possess the potential to expand into a significant population upon demand? The attractiveness of this notion is that it could explain why some investigators find macrophage-like cells in the lungs of species (human, 22; baboon, 31; rabbit, 15; rat, 55) that other workers claim do not have them. We do not think the theory of latency is of much value, mainly because it is difficult to test, and there appears to be no absolute criterion that will differentiate between a small population of true intravascular macrophages and sequestered, activated monocytes.

DEVELOPMENT IN SPECIES THAT DO NOT HAVE PULMONARY MACROPHAGES

One important aspect of the societal value of studying pulmonary intravascular macrophages is whether there are clinical conditions that may lead to the development of pulmonary intravascular macrophages in humans or in experimental animals that do not normally have them. Thus far, three approaches have been tried. Unfortunately, these approaches are described only in abstracts (16, 31, 60, 80, 87). The experimental approaches used are (*a*) induction of chronic liver injury by bile duct ligation (16), (*b*) repeated low dose endotoxin infusions (59, 80, 87), and (*c*) inhalation of 100% oxygen for 3 days (31).

In humans or dogs, technetium-labeled sulfur colloid infused to image the liver is not ordinarily detectable in the lung. However, in chronic liver injury (tumors, cirrhosis), the lung may develop significant retention of the colloid particles (40, 71). Chang (16) ligated the bile duct in rats and found after 2–4 weeks that the lungs retained significant quantities of fluorescent microspheres or radioactively-labeled albumin macroaggregates. Microscopically, he found a large number of mononuclear phagocytes that he believes fill most of the criteria essential to intravascular macrophages.

Warner and colleagues (87) gave rabbits and rats intravenous injections of endotoxin daily for 1–28 days. One day after the final dose each animal was injected with iron oxide particles intravenously. One hour later the iron content of lung, liver, and spleen was analyzed by magnetometry; one lung was fixed by intratracheal glutaraldehyde. The rabbit lungs showed a doubling of iron particle retention; the rats a fivefold increase. By electron microscopy large mononuclear cells containing iron particles were seen in the lung capillaries. The authors concluded that endotoxin may promote adhesion of circulating mononuclear phagocytes and their differentiation into resident macrophages.

Doerschuk's group (60, 80) infused endotoxin daily into rabbits for 7 days, at which time they showed significant retention of colloidal carbon particles by large mononuclear phagocytic cells in the lung capillaries. Initially, they thought that they had induced pulmonary intravascular macrophages. However, in spite of continued daily infusions of endotoxin, the phagocytic cells in the capillaries left the lung in 24–48 hr. Their conclusion was that they had activated monocytes that temporarily adhered to the lung endothelium.

Fracica (31) reported that biopsies of normal baboon lungs showed a few intravascular macrophage-like cells. When eight baboons were exposed to 100% inspired oxygen until death or termination, quantitative electron microscopic histology showed a threefold increase in the relative volume of such cells in the lung capillaries. The authors did not state whether there were more or larger mononuclear phagocytes.

The investigators for these studies agree that with suitable stimulation, mononuclear phagocytes accumulate in the lung capillaries. Are these true intravascular macrophages arising from a minimal preexisting population, are they induced by the disease process itself, or are they sequestered monocytes that have developed their phagocytic capability?

We think that the cells in the capillaries are activated monocytes. The critical identification may lie in the recovery experiment. The observed intravascular phagocytes could also be macrophages displaced from the liver, especially in the bile duct ligation experiment, but that hypothesis can be fairly readily tested.

Is it important to distinguish between true pulmonary intravascular macrophages and sequestered, activated monocytes. The difference is important in terms of physiologic function, cell biology, and genetics. The pulmonary intravascular macrophages are a resident population, tightly adherent to the endothelium, not readily displaced, and capable of specific actions beyond those attributable to activated monocytes.

In the first place, the emphasis in most of the experimental models on intravascular particle clearance may be misplaced, especially if the primary evolutionary value in having pulmonary intravascular macrophages is for defense against inhaled agents. Secondly, little convincing data exists showing that various putative mononuclear phagocytes, which accumulate in the lung capillaries under experimental conditions, function in the same manner as true intravascular macrophages. For example, where are the data to demonstrate that phagocytosis of particles by activated monocytes causes pulmonary hemodynamic changes or the production of thromboxane—signal phenotypic characteristics of true pulmonary intravascular macrophages?

We believe that if the survival of humans, baboons, dogs, or rats required pulmonary intravascular macrophages as a defense against some inhaled invader, a permanent population of intravascular macrophages would develop shortly after birth, just as in the species that have them. An important direction for investigation would be to determine the immunologic specificity of the pulmonary intravascular macrophages for respiratory viruses (such as parvoviruses) in species in the order Artiodactyla or Perissodactyla.

PULMONARY INTRAVASCULAR MACROPHAGE PHYSIOLOGY

Studies of intravascular macrophage function are few. The first physiological study of which we are aware was that of Halmagyi (34) (at least a decade before intravascular macrophages were identified), who reported that sheep had marked pulmonary hemodynamic and ventilatory responses to infusions of small quantities of foreign blood. Halmagyi did not determine the mechanism of this specificity, but concluded that the lung was the primary organ of transfusion reaction in the sheep. Nearly twenty years passed before another significant study was done. In a comparison between the dog and the pig, Crocker (20) showed that sepsis caused a steep rise in pulmonary arterial pressure in sheep, but not in the dog. Crocker's group was the first to correlate the presence of pulmonary intravascular macrophages with the hemodynamic response.

Later Albertine and I (1), while using particulate tracers to localize lung microvascular barrier injury at the ultrastructural level, found that sheep were remarkably sensitive to colloidal carbon and a new pigment particle, Monastral blue. We found that the pigment particles had been phagocytized by mononuclear cells in the pulmonary capillaries. The hemodynamic response was blocked by the cyclooxygenase inhibitor, indomethacin. It had already been reported by Ogletree & Brigham (57) that the pulmonary hemodynamic response to endotoxin infusions in sheep could be blocked by cyclooxygenase inhibitors, but the subsequent microvascular injury could not be inhibited. Meyrick & Brigham (48) reported mononuclear phagocytes in the lung capillaries of sheep injured by endotoxin, but they believed they were activated monocytes and did not attribute the acute lung injury to them, concentrating instead on neutrophils. Miyamoto (51) published the first systematic study of the physiologic responses to foreign particles and the retention of particles by pulmonary intravascular macrophages in sheep.

Phagocytosis

As endocytosis or phagocytosis of foreign particles is a major function of intravascular macrophages in the liver and (as it turns out also in the lung), many studies on macrophage phagocytosis have been done. The basic work, of course, was done on liver macrophages, in which it was shown in the common laboratory species (mouse, rat, rabbit, dog) that a variety of test particles including bacteria, lipopolysaccharide, plastic microspheres, colloidal pigment particles, etc are rapidly and efficiently cleared (46). Quantification shows that 85–90% of intravenously or intra-arterially infused particulate loads, including endotoxin, end up in the liver; the remainder in the spleen or bone marrow. A small quantity may be retained in the circulation, possibly associated with circulating leukocytes (45). Further, by direct visualization of liver sinusoids, the liver macrophages can effectively internalize test particles in 20–30 sec (46). When we infuse Monastral blue particles into normal sheep to label intravascular macrophages, they are completely cleared from arterial plasma within 1 min (N Staub, unpublished).

In regard to the pulmonary intravascular macrophages, a large fraction of test particles (50% or more) is removed in a single pass through the lung and retained there for long periods (43, 51, 85). Likewise, the physiological responses to an intravenous liposome infusion begin in approximately 30 sec, and reach a peak in 1–2 min (51).

Atwal and his associates (2–5) have studied the endocytosis/phagocytosis process of the pulmonary intravascular macrophages by transmission electron microscopy. They preserved the lungs of bovine, goat, sheep, and pony by tracheal instillation of glutaraldehyde-paraformaldehyde within 2–5 min of intravenous infusions of test particles. Even at the earliest fixation times, they found tracer particles in linear arrays of globules on the glycocalyx of the pulmonary intravascular macrophages in all species tested. Further, some of the particles and the surface globules were already internalized in endosomes or phagolysosomes.

Following standard airway fixation, Atwal applied block staining with tannic acid, which has an affinity for lipoprotein molecules. He reports that the globules on the glycocalyx are separated from the cell membrane by a lucent space. The globules are usually in the range of 25–90 nm in diameter, although in ponies he found globules of up to 1 μm in diameter. As the globular coat was removed by intravenous heparin or by the enzyme lipoprotein lipase, he concluded that the external surface coat on the pulmonary intravascular macrophages contains lipids or lipoproteins. Interestingly, he finds the surface coat to be unique to the pulmonary intravascular macrophages. It does not occur on any other lung leukocytes nor on liver intravascular macrophages (Kupffer cells). In his most recent study, Atwal found that Monastral blue (a copper phthalocyanine pigment particle) and cationized ferritin (but not neutral ferritin) interact with the globular surface arrays.

Atwal reports that the Monastral blue-labeled globules are internalized by receptor-mediated endocytosis, which subsequently fuse with lysosomes. That, however, cannot be the entire story because in our studies, we regularly find large phagosomes in pulmonary intravascular macrophages without any relation to endocytosed globules or lipid droplets. Further, liver intravascular macrophages also readily phagocytize Monastral blue, although these cells do not have a globular surface array.

Why have not other anatomists and pathologists (85, 93) mentioned the surface globules? Atwal argues (personal communication) that without tannic acid staining, the globular surface coat is not easily seen. My colleague K Albertine (personal communication) does see surface beading on the pulmonary intravascular macrophages occasionally, even though our animals are anticoagulated with heparin and the lungs are perfusion-fixed.

Atwal has implicated the pulmonary intravascular macrophages in lipid or lipoprotein metabolism, possibly in surfactant metabolism. He has demonstrated lamellar bodies in some intravascular macrophages. However, he has not determined whether there is any difference in lipoprotein or lung surfactant metabolism between species with or without pulmonary intravascular macrophages. Thus his intriguing morphological findings must wait until suitable experiments can be done to correlate his results with physiologic function.

Monastral blue infusions also lead to extensive platelet aggregation, with phagocytosis of these aggregates by the intravascular macrophages (O Atwal, personal communication). Why Monastral blue would lead to platelet aggregation is not clear, although it is possible that it interacts with plasma protein components, such as complement. In a possibly related phenomenon, Binder (12) and Miyamoto (50) have reported transient pulmonary arterial pressure rises in sheep after infusions of antiplatelet serum. The response is not due to the serum because after the platelets are depleted, additional infusions of antiplatelet serum evoke no response.

Miyamoto (49) reported that inhibition of platelet-activating factor (PAF) attenuates the pulmonary hemodynamic response to foreign particles in sheep. The inhibition is partial, whereas that following a cyclooxygenase inhibitor is complete. He speculates that the macrophages may be producing PAF in addition to thromboxane.

Because of the reaction of the surface globular coat of the pulmonary intravascular macrophages with cationized ferritin (positively charged), but not with neutral ferritin, Atwal believes the surface charge on particles is important. Goats receiving 200 mg of cationized ferritin showed clinical effects (rapid breathing), whereas those receiving neutral ferritin did not.

Miyamoto and his associates (49, 50, 54) studied the effect of surface charge and phospholipid composition of liposomes on pulmonary intravascular macrophage reactivity. Initially, they reported that both positively and negatively charged liposomes had similar effects on pulmonary arterial pressure in sheep. The neutral liposomes caused little response, which was in agreement with Atwal's ferritin experiments.

However, in further experiments, Nakano (54) changed the phospholipid composition of the liposomes and showed that two different species of liposomes with neutral surface charge caused different responses, one giving a marked rise in pulmonary arterial pressure and the other none. The Miyamoto group conclude that the composition of the liposome is more important for macrophage recognition and reactivity than is the surface charge.

Macrophage Secretions

Although the standard texts about macrophages indicate that they are capable of secreting a large array of biologically important substances, there is little data detailing what the pulmonary intravascular macrophages produce.

In sheep (51), goats (29) and newborn lambs (43) an important secretory product of the pulmonary intravascular macrophages is thromboxane. Not only can large increases in the stable metabolite, TxB_2 be found in arterial blood, but when simultaneous samples are taken from the pulmonary artery and the aorta, their difference—indicating pulmonary production—correlates with the rise in pulmonary arterial pressure or calculated pulmonary vascular resistance.

Interestingly, in animals that lack reactive pulmonary intravascular macrophages, including 1-day old lambs (43), no increase in thromboxane production occurs. Miyamoto (49) measured thromboxane production in two cats and found no significant increase in arterial thromboxane production. Enzan (29) compared thromboxane production in the rabbit and in the goat following foreign red cell infusions and found that there was a good dose-response relationship in the goat between the rise of pulmonary arterial pressure and the increase in thromboxane production, but not in the rabbit. Likewise, it is well known from studies of liver intravascular macrophages (Kupffer cells) that thromboxane is not their major product following stimulation by a variety of agents (41, 79). The data support two conclusions: (a) in animals without reactive intravascular macrophages, there is no significant pulmonary production of thromboxane, (b) liver intravascular macrophages do not make thromboxane following their stimulation. These conclusions mean that there is a significant phenotypic difference between pulmonary intravascular macrophages and liver intravascular macrophages.

Bertram and his associates (10, 11) isolated putative pig lung intravascular macrophages, which they proceeded to culture and compare with lavaged alveolar macrophages. By feeding arachidonic acid to the cultured cells, they showed that the intravascular macrophages produced mainly hydroxy-heptadecatrienoic (HHT) acid, together with small amounts of thromboxane, prostaglandins $F_{2\alpha}$, D_2, E_2, and hydroxyeicosatetraenoic (HETE) acids, whereas the isolated alveolar macrophages produced mainly prostaglandin $F_{2\alpha}$ with lesser amounts of HHT and various HETEs.

Continuing their study of isolated mononuclear phagocytes, Bertram stimulated them with glass microspheres, asbestos particles, or the calcium ionophore A23187. Again, the putative intravascular macrophages produced a wider variety of eicosanoids (both cyclooxygenase and lipoxygenase products) than did the alveolar macrophages. They confirmed that the major cyclooxygenase metabolite from the intravascular macrophages was HHT, whereas that from the alveolar macrophages was $PGF2_\alpha$. Taken at face value, there seems to be a difference in the secretion of arachidonate metabolites between the isolated intravascular and alveolar macrophages. In addition, there appears to be a significant difference in thromboxane production between intravascular macrophages in the intact lung and the isolated mononuclear phagocytes washed out of the lung.

Other Immune Properties of Intravascular Macrophages

Chitko-McKown and associates (17–19) studied some of the immunological functions of pulmonary intravascular macrophages. They used pigs and obtained mononuclear phagocytes (putative macrophages) by wash out of the pulmonary circulation. They compared these phagocytes with alveolar macrophages obtained by lavage of the same animal. Their initial data suggested that alveolar macrophages were more phagocytic than intravascular macrophages, but the latter appeared to be more cytotoxic against ingested bacteria. In a repeat study, however, they concluded that both had similar phagocytic and bactericidal activities. The tumoricidal activity and antibody-dependent cellular cytotoxicity were also similar, and both cell types produced interleukins 1 and 2 and tumor necrosis factor alpha at similar concentrations. The investigators found that the intravascular macrophages were more cytotoxic than were alveolar macrophages against virally infected target cells, and after endotoxin stimulation the intravascular macrophages produced more T cell proliferative cytokines. However, the alveolar macrophages produced more tumor necrosis factor and nitric oxide.

The intravascular macrophages immunological properties have been reviewed by Chitko-McKown & Blecha (17). They produced an extensive table in which all of the immune properties or activities claimed for pulmonary intravascular macrophages in various species have been listed. The results, unfortunately, have not been analyzed.

Although it is likely that the pulmonary intravascular macrophages have important immunologic properties, which may or may not be similar to those of alveolar macrophages or other intravascular macrophages, a great deal more work needs to be done, including comparing responses between macrophages in the pulmonary capillaries with those of isolated macrophages.

ISOLATION OF INTRAVASCULAR MACROPHAGES

Several attempts have been made to isolate the pulmonary intravascular macrophages in order to study their properties in vitro. All of the early attempts have been to obtain the macrophages by vascular washout. This, of course, would be the most desirable and simplest procedure, since the macrophages obtained would be contaminated only by blood leukocytes, which can be readily separated.

However, removal of macrophages permanently adherent to endothelial cells has not been very successful. Rous (64) made the first attempt to obtain liver intravascular macrophages, but was unable to obtain a significant number by perfusion. Later workers have abandoned the idea of detaching the Kupffer cells from the sinusoid endothelial cells by perfusion alone (67).

In the lung, attempts at isolation by perfusion have been made by Staub (77), Morton (53), Fowler (30), and Chitko-McKown (18). The data are summarized in Table 1. Whether the mononuclear phagocytes recovered are true pulmonary intravascular macrophages or activated monocytes is not certain, but for the purposes of this review, we have used the results more or less as the authors claimed. Based on our experience (77), the recovery of true macrophages is low. See also Rogers' (62) recovery estimate by washout.

Although the above studies differed in procedural details, all of the washout protocols follow the same pattern. With or without vasodilators, the pulmonary vascular bed is perfused to remove the residual blood, followed by perfusion with calcium and magnesium-free solutions, usually with added chelating agents. Finally, the lung is perfused with an enzyme solution, generally collagenase.

While some macrophages have been recovered and placed in culture for comparative biochemical or functional studies, in general the washouts are disappointing, containing about 1% of the total estimated number of intra-vascular macrophages.

Because of these limitations, the next round of isolation attempts will probably require lung disruption techniques, such as are used to obtain other alveolar epithelial or interstitial cells (24, 27, 36). Indeed, Rogers (62) and Warner (83) have reported improved recoveries by chopping sheep lungs into tiny fragments, then digesting them using collagenase or elastase for 1 hr. Rogers states that he recovered about 200,000 iron-oxide-labeled intravascular macrophages/gram of lung. The recovered iron oxide was about 30–50% of that in the lung mince, which yields a total of 0.4–.6 million intravascular macrophages/gram.

Table 1 Recovery of mononuclear leukocytes from lung[a]

Species	Total mononuclear (millions)	Mononuclear phagocytes (millions)	References
Pig	93	51	53
Pig	380	95	30
Pig	160	66	18
Sheep, pig	—	0.2/gram	62

[a] Abstracts of Staub (77) and Warner (83) do not provide data to calculate recoveries.

These results differ from Warner's earlier calculation of 19 billion intravascular macrophages in adult sheep lungs (85). Her numbers, obtained by quantitative histology, are calculated at an estimated 40–50 million intravascular macrophages/gram of lung. That number seems very high. In a later review, Warner & Brain (86) revised the estimate of the total population downward to 8 million/gram. By way of comparison, the number of liver intravascular macrophages in the rat is 8–10 million/gram (82, 88), although recoveries by digestion are much less.

Eventually, when the nature of the macrophage-endothelial adhesion is understood, vascular perfusion with macrophage washout will be the method of choice, but current use favors lung disruption.

MACROPHAGE/ENDOTHELIAL ADHESION

The morphology of the adhesion plaques that permanently bind macrophages and endothelial cells appears to be similar between the lung intravascular macrophages and the liver intravascular macrophages (93). The junction consists of closely opposed cell surfaces (15 nm space) with subplasmalemmal densities on both sides of the junction. Franke (32) calls them non-desmosomal adherens junctions.

The adhesion molecules involved have not yet been identified. One of the limiting factors is the lack of specific labels for junctional proteins in the animals that have pulmonary intravascular macrophages. However, mouse or rat liver, for which junctional tracer molecules are available, could be used as a model.

There is some information about the adhesion of monocytes to isolated, activated endothelium. While this may be a false lead, it does offer a starting place. Mentzer (47) identified the integrin LFA-1 in the junctions. DiCorleto and de la Motte (26) were able to partially block monocyte adherence to cultured endothelial cells by using the lectin wheat germ agglutinin, lactose-1-PO_4 or octylglucoside. However, once the adhesion had occurred, they were unable to detach the monocytes with any of these sugars, which suggests that while endothelial cell surface glycoproteins may be essential for the initial attachment, they are not involved in the permanent adhesion. Beekhuisen and associates (6, 7) analyzed the adhesion of monocytes to normal and to cytokine-stimulated cultured endothelia. They found partial blockade of adhesion by a monoclonal antibody against the common beta 2 subunit of integrins and by MAC-1. Further, CD14 on the surface of peripheral blood monocytes may participate in their adhesion to cytokine-stimulated endothelium (6). Interestingly, CD14 is also the ligand for lipopolysaccharide binding protein on elicited peritoneal macrophages (78).

Literature Cited

1. Albertine KH, Staub NC. 1986. Vascular tracers alter hemodynamics and airway pressure in anesthetized sheep. *Microvasc. Res.* 32:279–88

2. Atwal OS, Minhas KJ, Ferenczy BG, Jassal DS, Milton D, Mahadevappa VG 1989. Morphology of pulmonary intravascular macrophages (PIMs) in ruminants: ultrastructural and cytochemical behavior of dense surface coat. *Am. J. Anat.* 186:285–99

3. Atwal OS, Minhas KJ, Gill BS, Sanhu PS. 1992. In vivo monastral blue-induced lamellar-bodies in lysosomes of pulmonary intravascular macrophages (PIMs) of bovine lung: implications of the surface coat. *Anat. Rec.* 234:223–39

4. Atwal OS, Saldanha KA. 1985. Erythrophagocytosis in alveolar capillaries of goat lung: ultrastructural properties of blood monocytes. *Acta Anat.* 124:245–54

5. Atwal OS, Singh B, Staempfli H, Minhas K. 1992. Presence of pulmonary intravascular macrophages in the equine lung: some structuro-functional properties. *Anat. Rec.* 234:530–40

6. Beekhuizen H, Blokland I, Corsel-van Tilburg AJ, Koning F, van Furth R. 1991. CD14 contributes to the adherence of human monocytes to cytokine-stimulate endothelial cells. *J. Immunol.* 147:3761–67

7. Beekhuizen H, Corsel-van Tilburg AJ, van Furth R. 1990. Characterization of monocyte adherence to human macrovascular and microvascular endothelial cells. *J. Immunol.* 145:510–18

8. Bertram TA. 1985. Quantitative morphology of peracute pulmonary lesions in swine induced by *Haemophilus pleuropneumoniae*. *Vet. Pathol.* 22:598–609

9. Bertram TA. 1986. Intravascular macrophages in lungs of pigs infected with *Haemophilus pleuropneumoniae*. *Vet. Pathol.* 23:681–91

10. Bertram TA, Overby LH, Brody AR, Eling TE. 1989. Comparison of arachidonic acid metabolism by pulmonary intravascular and alveolar macrophages exposed to particulate and soluble stimuli. *Lab. Invest.* 61:457–66

11. Bertram TA, Overby LH, Danilowicz R, Eling TE, Brody AR. 1988. Pulmonary intravascular macrophages metabolize arachidonic acid in vitro: comparison with alveolar macrophages. *Am. Rev. Respir. Dis.* 138:936–44

12. Binder AS, Kageler W, Perel A, Flick MR, Staub NC. 1980. Effect of platelet depletion on lung vascular permeability after microemboli in sheep. *J. Appl. Physiol.* 48:414–40

13. Blusse Van Oud Alblas A, van Furth R. 1979. Origin, kinetics, and characteristics of pulmonary macrophages in the normal steady state. *J. Exp. Med.* 149:1504–18

14. Carrasco L, Fernandez A, Gomez-Villamandos JC, Mozos E, Mendez A, Jover A. 1992. Kupffer cells and PIMs in acute experimental African swine fever. *Histol. Histopathol.* 7:421–25

15. Carrasco L, Rodriguez F, Martin de las Mulas J, Sierra MA, Gomez-Villamandos JC, Fernandez A. 1991. Pulmonary intravascular macrophages in rabbits experimentally infected with rabbit haemorrhagic disease. *J. Comp. Path.* 105:345–52

16. Chang S, Wang X, Kamp D, Henson J, Ohara N. 1990. Induction of pulmonary intravascular macrophages in rats with chronic cholestasis: morphologic and functional evidence. *Am. Rev. Respir. Dis.* 141:A644

17. Chitko-McKown CG, Blecha F. 1992. Pulmonary intravascular macrophages: a review of immune properties and functions. *Ann. Rech. Vet.* 23:201–14

18. Chitko-McKown CG, Chapes SK, Brown RE, Phillips RM, McKown RD, Blecha F. 1991. Porcine alveolar and pulmonary intravascular macrophages: comparison of immune functions. *J. Leuko. Biol.* 50:364–72

19. Chitko-McKown CG, Reddy DN, Chapes SK, McKown RD, Blecha F. 1992. Immunological characterization of pulmonary intravascular macrophages. *Regional Immunol.* 4:236–44

20. Crocker SH, Eddy DO, Obenauf RN, Wismar BL, Lowery BD. 1981. Bacteremia: host-specific lung clearance and pulmonary failure. *J. Trauma* 21:215–20

21. DeCamp MM, Warner AE, Molina RM, Brain JD. 1992. Hepatic versus pulmonary uptake of particles injected into the portal circulation in sheep. Endotoxin escapes hepatic clearance causing pulmonary inflammation. *Am. Rev. Respir. Dis.* 146:224–31

22. Dehring DJ, Wismar BL. 1989. Intravascular macrophages in pulmonary capillaries of humans. *Am. Rev. Respir. Dis.* 139:1027–29

23. Dehring DJ, Wismar BL. 1989. Animal

models of sepsis. See Ref. 72, pp. 79–100

24. Dethloff LA, Lehnert BE. 1988. Pulmonary interstitial macrophages: Isolation and flow cytometric comparisons with alveolar macrophages and blood monocytes. *J. Leuko. Biol.* 43: 80–90

25. DiBattiste D, Niehaus GD. 1988. Rat pulmonary vascular macrophages. *FASEB J.* 2:A1167

26. DiCorleto PE, de la Motte CA. 1989. Role of surface carbohydrate moieties in monocytic cell adhesion to endothelium in vitro. *J. Immunol.* 143: 3666–72

27. Dobbs LG, Mason RJ. 1979. Pulmonary alveolar type II cells isolated from rat. *J. Clin. Invest.* 63:378–87

28. Doerschuk CM, Downey GP, Dohery DE, English D, Gie RP, et al. 1990. Leukocyte and platelet margination within the microvasculature of rabbit lungs. *J. Appl. Physiol.* 68: 1956–61

29. Enzan K, Wang Y, Schultz E, Stravos F, Mitchell MD, Staub NC. 1991. Pulmonary hemodynamic reaction to foreign blood in goats and rabbits. *J. Appl. Physiol.* 71:2231–37

30. Fowler AA, Carey PD, Walsh CJ, Sessler CN, Mumaw VR, et al. 1991. In situ pulmonary vascular perfusion for improved recovery of pulmonary intravascular macrophages. *Microvasc. Res.* 41:328–44

31. Fracica PJ, Bertram T, Knapp M, Crapo JD. 1988. Pulmonary intravascular macrophages in normal and oxygen injured baboon lung tissue. *Clin. Res.* 36:A591

32. Franke WW. 1988. The endothelial junction: the plaque and its components. In *Endothelial Cell Biology in Health and Disease,* ed. N Simionescu, M Simionescu, pp. 147–66. New York: Plenum

33. Frevert CW, Warner AE, Adams ET, Brain JD. 1991. Pulmonary intravascular macrophages are important parts of the mononuclear phagocyte system in the horse. *J. Vet. Intern. Med.* 5:145 (Abstr.)

34. Halmagyi DFJ, Starzecki B, McRae M, Horner GJ. 1963. The lung as the main target organ in the acute phase transfusion reaction in sheep. *J. Surg. Res.* 3:418–29

35. Hogg JC. 1987. Neutrophil kinetics and lung injury. *Physiol. Rev.* 67: 1249–95

36. Holt PG, Degebrodt A, Venaille T, O'Leary C, Krska K, et al. 1985. Preparation of interstitial cells by enzymatic digestion of tissue slices. *Immunology* 54:139–47

37. Hopkins JG, Parker JT. 1918. The effect of injections of hemolytic streptococci on susceptible and insusceptible animals. *J. Exp. Med.* 27:1–26

38. Jain NC, ed. 1986. *Schalm's Veterinary Hematology.* Philadelphia: Lea & Febiger

39. King LS, Newman JH. 1989. Clinical importance of macrophages. See Ref. 72, pp. 141–56

40. Klingensmith WC II, Ryerson TW. 1973. Lung uptake of ^{99m}Tc-sulfur colloid. *J. Nucl. Med.* 14:201–4

41. Kuiper J, Zijlstra FL, Kamps JAAM, van Berkel TJC. 1988. Identification of prostaglandin D_2 as the major eicosanoid from liver endothelial and Kupffer cells. *Biochim. Biophys. Acta* 959:143–52

42. Longworth K. 1992. Comparative physiology of pulmonary intravascular macrophage function in ponies and calves. *FASEB J.* 6:A1242

43. Longworth KE, Lei D, Schultz EL, Westgate A, Grady MK, Staub NC. 1992. Development of pulmonary intravascular macrophages in lambs: hemodynamics and uptake of particles. *J. Appl. Physiol.* 73:2608–15

44. Longworth KE, Serikov V, Staub NC. 1993. Maturation of pulmonary vascular reactivity to endotoxin in the newborn lamb. *Am. Rev. Respir. Dis.* 142(Prt. 2):A248

45. Mathison JC, Ulevitch R. 1979. The clearance, tissue distribution, and cellular localization of intravenously injected lipopolysaccharide in rabbits. *J. Immunol.* 123:2133–43

46. McCuskey PA, McCuskey RS, Urbaschek R, Urbaschek B. 1984. Species differences in Kupffer cells and endotoxin sensitivity. *Infect. Immunol.* 45:278–80

47. Mentzer SJ, Crimmins MAV, Burakoff SJ, Faller DV. 1987. Alpha and beta subunits of the LFA-1 membrane molecule are involved in human monocyte-endothelial cell adhesion. *J. Cell Physiol.* 130:410–15

48. Meyrick B, Brigham KL. 1983. Acute effects of *E. coli* endotoxin on the pulmonary microcirculation of anesthetized sheep: structure-function relationships. *Lab. Invest.* 48:267–74

49. Miyamoto K. 1989. Comparative hemodynamic and lymph dynamic reactions to particles. See Ref. 72, pp. 59–78

50. Miyamoto K, Nakano T, Aoi K, Kawakami Y. 1991. Effects of differ-

entially composed liposomes on pulmonary arterial pressure in sheep—involvement of pulmonary intravascular macrophages. *Jpn. J. Thorac. Dis.* 29:1268–74 (in Japanese)

51. Miyamoto K, Schultz E, Heath T, Mitchell M, Albertine K, Staub NC. 1988. Pulmonary intravascular macrophages and hemodynamic effects of liposomes in sheep. *J. Appl. Physiol.* 64:1143–52

52. Miyamoto K, Schultz E, Staub NC. 1986. Pulmonary vascular response and lung uptake of liposomes in 7 animal species. *Physiologist* 29:177

53. Morton D, Bertram TA. 1988. Isolation and preliminary in vitro characterization of the porcine pulmonary intravascular macrophage. *J. Leuko. Biol.* 43:403–10

54. Nakano T, Miyamoto K, Aida A, Aoi K, Kishi F, Kawakami Y. 1991. Effects of antiplatelet serum on the pulmonary intravascular macrophage. *Jpn. J. Thorac. Dis.* 29:1104–10 (in Japanese)

55. Niehaus GD. 1989. Role in host defense. See Ref. 72, pp. 123–40

56. Niehaus GD, Schumacker PR, Saba TM. 1980. Reticuloendothelial clearance of blood-borne particles in sheep: relevance to experimental lung microembolization and vascular injury. *Ann. Surg.* 191:479–87

57. Ogletree ML, Brigham KL. 1982. Effects of cyclooxygenase inhibitors on pulmonary vascular responses to endotoxin in unanesthetized sheep. *Prostaglandin Leukotrienes Med.* 8:489–502

58. Ohgami M, Doerschuk CM, Gie RP, English D, Hogg JC. 1991. Monocyte kinetics in rabbits. *J. Appl. Physiol.* 70:152–57

59. Ohgami M, Doerschuk CM, Gie RP, English D, Hogg JC. 1992. Late effects of endotoxin on the accumulation and function of monocytes in rabbit lungs. *Am. Rev. Respir. Dis.* 146:190–55

60. Ohgami M, Doerschuk CM, Hogg JC. 1990. Leukocyte kinetics in chronic endotoxemia in NZW rabbits. *Am. Rev. Respir. Dis.* 141:A651

61. Pabst R, Binns RM, Licence ST, Peter M. 1987. Evidence of a major vascular marginal pool of lymphocytes in the lung. *Am. Rev. Respir. Dis.* 136:1213–18

62. Rogers RA, Tasat DR, Warner AE, Brain JD. 1991. Isolation of pulmonary intravascular macrophages requires proteolytic lung digestion. *J. Leuko. Biol. Suppl.* 2:64 (Abstr.)

63. Rothlein R, Galilly R, Kim YB. 1981.

Development of alveolar macrophages in specific pathogen-free and germ-free Minnesota miniature swine. *J. Reticuloendothel. Soc.* 30:483–95

64. Rous P, Beard JW. 1934. Selection with the magnet and cultivation of reticulo-endothelial cells (Kupffer cells). *J. Exp. Med.* 59:577–91

65. Rybicka K, Daly BDT, Migliore JJ, Norman JC. 1974. Intravascular macrophages in normal calf lung. An electron microscopic study. *Am. J. Anat.* 139:353–68

66. Schneeberger-Keeley EE, Burger EJ. 1970. Intravascular macrophages in cat lungs after open chest ventilation. *Lab. Invest.* 22:361–69

67. Seglen PO. 1976. Preparation of isolated rat liver cells. In *Methods in Cell Biology*, ed. DM Prescott, XIII:29–82. New York: Academic

68. Shellito J, Esparza C, Armstrong C. 1987. Maintenance of the normal rat alveolar macrophages cell population: the roles of monocyte influx and alveolar macrophages proliferation in situ. *Am. Rev. Respir. Dis.* 135:78–82

69. Sibille Y, Reynolds HY. 1990. Macrophages and polymorphonuclear neutrophils in lung defense and injury. *Am. Rev. Respir. Dis.* 141:471–501

70. Sierra MA, Carrasco L, Gomez-Villamandos JC, Martin de las Mulas J, Mendez A, Jover A. 1990. Pulmonary intravascular macrophages in lungs of pigs inoculated with African swine fever virus of differing virulence. *J. Comp. Pathol.* 102:323–34

71. Stadalnik R. 1980. Diffuse lung uptake of Tc^{99m}-sulfur colloid. *Sem. Nucl. Med.* 10:106–7

72. Staub NC. ed. 1989. *The Pulmonary Intravascular Macrophage.* Mt. Kisco: Futura. 180 pp.

73. Staub NC. 1989. Pulmonary vascular reactivity: a status report. See Ref. 72, pp. 123–40

74. Staub NC, Nicolaysen A, Nicolaysen G. 1992. Pulmonary intravascular macrophages in reindeer. *FASEB J.* 6:A1242

75. Staub NC, Schultz EL, Albertine KH. 1982. Leukocytes and pulmonary microvascular injury. *Ann. NY Acad. Sci.* 384:332–42

76. Staub NC, Schultz EL, Longworth K, Wang Y. 1989. Quantification of leukocytes washed from the pulmonary circulation. *Am. Rev. Respir. Dis.* 136:A297

77. Staub NC, Schultz EL, Milligan S, Wang Y, Enzan K, et al. 1987. Isolation, primary culture and properties

of pulmonary intracapillary macrophages from goats and sheep. *Fed. Proc.* 46:329

78. Tobias PS, Mathison J, Mintz D, Kravchenko V, Kato K, et al. 1992. Participation of lipopolysaccharide-binding protein in lipopolysaccharide-dependent macrophage activation. *Am. J. Respir. Cell Mol. Biol.* 7:239–45

79. Tran-Thi TA, Gyufko K, Dieter P, Reinke M, Decker K. 1989. Stimulation of Kupffer cells in the perfused rat liver: a study on release and effects of eicosanoids. In *Cells of the Hepatic Sinusoid*, ed. E Wisse, DL Knook, K Decker, 2:186–89. Rijswijk, The Netherlands: Kupffer Cell Foundation

80. Tsubouchi T, English D, Doerschuk CM. 1991. Monocyte accumulation in the lung after chronic endotoxemia in rabbits. *Am. Rev. Respir. Dis.* 143: A329

81. Valberg PA, Blanchard JD. 1992. Pulmonary macrophage physiology: origin, motility endocytosis. In *Comparative Biology of the Normal Lung*, ed. RA Parent, 1:681–723. Boca Raton, Fla.: CRC Press

82. van Furth R. 1989. Origin and turnover of monocytes and macrophages. *Curr. Top. Pathol.* 79:125–50

83. Warner A, Tasat T, Brain JD. 1992. Sheep pulmonary intravascular macrophages isolated by lung digestion show normal phagocytic activity and intracellular motility. *J. Leuko. Biol. Suppl.* 3:15 (Abstr.)

84. Warner AE, Brain JD. 1984. Intravascular pulmonary macrophages in ruminants participate in reticuloendothelial clearance of particles. *Fed. Proc.* 43: 1001A

85. Warner AE, Brain JD. 1986. Intravascular pulmonary macrophages: a novel cell removes particles from blood. *Am. J. Physiol.* 250:R728-R732

86. Warner AE, Brain JD. 1990. The cell biology and pathogenic role of pulmonary intravascular macrophages. *Am. J. Physiol.* 258:L1-12

87. Warner AE, DeCamp MM, Bellows CF, Brain JD. 1989. Endotoxemia enhances lung uptake of circulating particles in species lacking pulmonary intravascular macrophages. *Am. Rev. Respir. Dis.* 139:A158

88. Weibel ER, Staeubli W, Gnaegi HR, Hess FA. 1969. Correlated morphometric and biochemical studies on the liver cell. *J. Cell Biol.* 42:68–91

89. Weiss RA, Chanana AD, Joel DD. 1986. Postnatal maturation of pulmonary antimicrobial defense mechanisms in conventional and germ-free lambs. *Pediatr. Res.* 20:496–504

90. Wheeldon EB, Hansen-Flaschen J. 1986. Intravascular macrophages in the sheep lung. *J. Leuko. Biol.* 40:657–61

91. Whiteley LO, Maheswaran SK, Weiss DL, Ames TR. 1991. Alterations in pulmonary morphology and peripheral coagulation profiles caused by intratracheal inoculation of live and ultraviolet light-killed pasteurella haemolytica A in calves. *Vet. Pathol.* 28:275–85

92. Whiteley LO, Maheswaran SK, Weiss DL, Ames TR. 1991. Morphological and morphometrical analysis of the acute response of the bovine alveolar wall to pasteurella haemolytica A1-derived endotoxin and leucotoxin. *J. Comp. Pathol.* 104:23–32

93. Winkler GC. 1988. Pulmonary intravascular macrophages in domestic animal species: review of structural and functional properties. *Am. J. Anat.* 181:217–34

94. Winkler GC, Cheville NF. 1985. Monocytic origin and postnatal mitosis of intravascular macrophages in the porcine lung. *J. Leuko. Biol.* 38:471–80

95. Winkler GC, Cheville NF. 1987. Postnatal colonization of porcine lung capillaries by intravascular macrophages: an ultrastructural morphometric analysis. *Microvasc. Res.* 33:224–32

96. Wislocki GB. 1924. On the fate of carbon particles into the circulation with especial reference to the lungs. *Am. J. Anat.* 32:423–45

97. Wismar BL. 1981. Intravascular phagocytes of the lung: a new cell type? *Anat. Rec.* 199:280A

98. Zeligs BJ, Zeligs JD, Nerurkar LS, Bellanti JA. 1977. Maturation of rabbit alveolar macrophages during animal development. I. Perinatal influx into alveoli and ultrastructural differentiation. *Pediatr. Res.* 11:197–205

Annu. Rev. Physiol. 1994. 56:69–91
Copyright © 1994 by Annual Reviews Inc. All rights reserved

PULMONARY REFLEXES:
Neural Mechanisms of Pulmonary Defense

H. M. Coleridge and J. C. G. Coleridge

Cardiovascular Research Institute, University of California San Francisco, San Francisco, California 94143–0130

KEY WORDS: airway C-fibers, respiratory chemoreflexes, vagal nociceptors

INTRODUCTION

In his 1954 Harvey lecture on the functions of the lung, Comroe divided pulmonary reflexes into regulatory and defensive or protective (18). Characteristically, regulatory reflexes are subject to a continuous input from low-threshold afferent endings whose impulse frequency waxes and wanes as their effective stimulus (e.g. volume or pressure) varies around a control or resting setpoint. Reflexes of this type exert a continuous control of ventilatory events (11) and promote the smooth interaction of the ventilatory and cardiovascular systems (13), their predominant function being to maintain the status quo. Defensive reflexes are a broader constellation of reflex responses evoked by stimuli that threaten lung function. These reflexes are the subject of the present review. Both regulatory and defensive reflexes are mediated predominantly by afferent fibers traveling to the medullary centers in the vagus nerves. The sensory innervation of the lower airways includes a component whose cell bodies are in the upper thoracic dorsal root ganglia and whose fibers travel to the spinal cord with branches of the sympathetic nerves. However, these so-called sympathetic afferents appear to play a relatively minor part in pulmonary defensive reflexes, and even powerful chemical stimuli applied to their endings cause little more than a brief disturbance of breathing (14, 19). Pulmonary defensive reflexes (or effects indistinguishable from them) are not only triggered by extrinsic agents such as irritant gases that pose a threat to the airways, but can be

69

0066–4278/94/0315–0069$05.00

initiated internally by locally released autacoids, some of which stimulate sensory nerve endings and engage reflex pathways.

Our understanding of the properties of the sensory nerve endings involved in airway defense, the central connections of their reflex arcs, and the multiplicity of effects included under the general heading of defensive reflexes has increased on a number of fronts. Information about the neurotransmitters released in pulmonary defensive reflexes and about their binding to membrane receptors on smooth muscle and glands has increased enormously. The explosion of information has sometimes tended to obscure the fact that these biochemical end-points have their beginning in stimulation of sensory nerves and activation of reflex pathways with powerful effects in the airways and beyond.

MANIFESTATIONS OF PULMONARY DEFENSIVE REFLEXES

In discussing pulmonary defensive reflexes, Comroe chose as an example the "profound reflex effects... produced by chemicals injected into the pulmonary circulation," giving them the general title of pulmonary chemoreflexes, and citing the effects of injection of serotonin as being typical (18). Comroe listed apnea, bradycardia (often to the point of cardiac arrest), systemic arterial hypotension, constriction of pulmonary vessels, and bronchoconstriction as being the primary reflex effects, although in his example, only the initial triad of apnea, bradycardia, and hypotension was solely of reflex origin, for serotonin has direct excitatory actions on vascular and airway smooth muscle. Other chemicals, including phenyl diguanide and biguanide, which are structurally related to serotonin but have the advantage of having little direct effect on the airways, have been used in experiments of this type, but their effects are often limited to certain species. The chemical engaging most interest at the present time is capsaicin, the active principal of hot peppers. Use of capsaicin (38) has been central to studies of somatic and visceral sensory neurophysiology because in low doses it stimulates the smallest sensory nerve fibers (nonmyelinated or C-fibers) in a relatively selective fashion, and produces intense sensations of itching and burning without causing tissue damage. In high doses, it acts as a neurotoxin with selective effects on chemosensitive C-fibers throughout the body, damaging them irreversibly and blunting the normal aversive reactions to chemical irritants (38). The importance of vagal C-fibers as the afferent pathway for pulmonary chemoreflexes was established in early studies, because although the pulmonary chemoreflex effects of capsaicin were abolished when the vagus nerves were cut, they could still be evoked when the nerves were cooled to a temperature at which saltatory conduction in myelinated fibers was blocked (16). Interest in the contribution of vagal C-fibers to pulmonary defense remains high because, like their counterparts in the somatic nervous system, they contain neuropeptides (23, 56, 59, 60). When stimulated by capsaicin, these sensory C-fibers, which are a major component of bronchial and pulmonary vagal branches, can release neuropeptides, some of which have powerful effects on airway function. The release is brought about by a peripheral axon-reflex mechanism (38) that is likely to be important in airway disease and must now be included under the general heading of pulmonary defensive reflexes.

If pulmonary defensive reflexes are defined as responses that act to limit access of harmful agents to the respiratory exchange region, then cough is in the forefront, being the most immediately effective of the defensive reactions. Bronchoconstriction and bronchosecretion appear to be useful mainly in increasing the expulsive effectiveness of coughing. Other components of the pulmonary defensive reflex constellation are of less obvious utility, however. The ventilatory changes other than cough include apnea, gasping, and closure of the glottis, followed by rapid shallow breathing (11). Airway changes include a marked increase in blood flow to the bronchial mucosa (12, 71). Cardiovascular effects include bradycardia, a decrease in cardiac contractility and output, and systemic hypotension with vasodilation of skeletal muscle, diaphragm, and myocardium (7, 9, 10). Finally, in their most dramatic form, pulmonary defensive reflexes include a brief but profound loss of skeletal muscle tone, which is thought by some investigators to represent a primitive "sham death" response to an overwhelming visceral stimulus (13).

AFFERENT PATHWAYS

Electroneurographic studies of impulse activity in individual afferent units have, over the last 10–20 years, significantly changed our perception of the pulmonary defensive role of vagal sensory endings. Chemosensitive C-fibers, once dismissed as a nociceptive system of relatively minor importance— activated only by exotic foreign chemicals and powerful inhaled irritants—are now acknowledged to be a major afferent pathway to the medullary centers. Such recognition stems from an appreciation of the range of stimuli to which airway C-fiber endings are sensitive, and from the realization that many of these stimuli are encountered under natural circumstances. Input in the myelinated fibers of rapidly adapting receptors, although no longer thought to be paramount in initiating pulmonary defensive reflexes, also makes an important contribution to airway defense.

Pulmonary and Bronchial C-Fibers

The relatively insignificant and low-frequency action potentials of afferent C-fibers are most easily identified by their response to injection of chemical stimulants such as capsaicin into their blood supply (16). Serial injection of capsaicin into the arterial supply to the lungs and airways of dogs made possible a distinction between pulmonary and bronchial C-fibers, and most of the studies directed to distinguishing the properties of the afferents have been in the dog. Pulmonary C-fiber endings, which are located in the lung parenchyma, are directly accessible to capsaicin injected into the pulmonary artery, and the onset of their evoked discharge coincides with the onset of the pulmonary chemoreflex. Bronchial C-fiber endings are located further downstream, innervating the airway mucosa (16); they are accessible to capsaicin injected into the left atrium and, at shorter latency, to capsaicin injected directly into the bronchial artery.

Although the distinction between pulmonary and bronchial C-fibers was based initially on the location and vascular accessibility of their sensory endings, the two have now been found to differ somewhat in their afferent properties. Pulmonary C-fiber endings are sensitive to increases in lung volume of a magnitude similar to those stimulating rapidly adapting receptors (11, 16); bronchial C-fiber endings are less sensitive, being relatively unpredictable in their response to inflation (11, 16). Inhalation of irritant vapors such as cigarette smoke (57) and sulfur dioxide (16), and concentrations of volatile anesthetics sufficient to inhibit the firing of myelinated lung afferents (16), stimulates the endings of both pulmonary and bronchial C-fibers (16), but only bronchial C-fibers are stimulated when ozone is added to the inspired air (17). Effective stimuli are not necessarily harmful, and non-isosmotic sodium chloride solutions that are unlikely to cause tissue damage stimulate the endings of both pulmonary and bronchial C-fibers (75).

The endings of pulmonary and bronchial C-fibers differ in their response to lung autacoids. Pulmonary C-fiber endings are relatively insensitive to autacoids. They are sensitized by the serotonin released in pulmonary embolism (11) and are stimulated by high doses of prostaglandins injected intravenously (78); they are not stimulated by either histamine or bradykinin, and neither of these autacoids, injected intravenously, evokes a typical pulmonary chemoreflex (11, 15). By contrast, bronchial C-fiber endings are sensitive to a wide range of intrinsic chemicals, and like chemosensitive afferents in the skin, they signal the presence of autacoids released in immune reactions and in response to pathogenic agents. They are stimulated by histamine, bradykinin, and the prostaglandins, either injected into the bronchial artery or administered as aerosol (16, 50, 78). This differential sensitivity may explain why bradykinin fails to cause irritant airway sensations or reflexes when injected intravenously, but evokes cough, bronchoconstriction, and irritant airway sensations in humans (27), and tachypnea and bronchoconstriction in dogs (14), when inhaled as aerosol.

Rapidly Adapting Receptors

The presence of rapidly adapting mechanoreceptors in the airways was recognized in early single fiber studies. Their functional importance remained obscure, however, until Widdicombe and colleagues found that the input of these receptors increased markedly in histamine-induced bronchoconstriction, pulmonary congestion, pneumothorax, and pulmonary embolism, and named them irritant receptors (63, 90). Measurement of conduction velocities in a small sample of rapidly adapting receptor fibers in rabbits suggested that, although myelinated, the fibers were of small diameter (63)—a characteristic often associated with chemosensitive afferent fibers. Measurements in larger samples of rapidly adapting receptors, however, indicated that the conduction velocities overlapped those of slowly adapting receptor fibers and that relatively few of the fibers conducted sufficiently slowly to belong to the category of chemosensitive afferents (3, 81).

It is now clear that, although rapidly adapting receptors are more chemically sensitive than their slowly adapting counterparts and are stimulated by anisosmotic solutions (75), as a group they respond most readily to changes in the mechanical properties of the lungs and airways, and their functional importance in airway defense probably lies in this direction. In general, the chemicals to which they respond cause bronchoconstriction, and stimulation is probably secondary to changes in lung mechanics. The gasps or augmented breaths occasionally evoked when irritants such as cigarette smoke are inhaled are characteristic of stimulation of rapidly adapting receptors (58), in contrast to the apnea and rapid shallow breathing evoked by stimulation of airway C-fibers (11). Rapidly adapting receptors are sensitive to small decreases in lung compliance, and the resultant increase in their discharge is probably responsible for the augmented breaths or sighs seen from time to time during quiet breathing, as lung compliance decreases spontaneously (42, 73). The augmented breaths act to restore compliance to its original level and are frequent in pneumothorax.

The contribution of rapidly adapting receptors to the reflex bronchoconstriction, increased secretion, and bronchial vasodilation of airway defense has been difficult to establish, because the inhaled irritants used to evoke these effects also stimulate airway C-fibers. However, two measures have recently been shown to stimulate rapidly adapting receptors without increasing the activity of airway C-fibers: namely, reducing lung compliance (42, 73), and cooling the pulmonary blood (28). Use of these stimuli has now confirmed that rapidly adapting receptors do indeed evoke reflex increases in bronchial secretion (99) and blood flow (72). Rapidly adapting receptors have no influence on cardiac function, however.

Slowly Adapting Pulmonary Stretch Receptors

There can be little argument that, in general, slowly adapting stretch receptors are of regulatory rather than defensive significance. They have little chemical sensitivity (11), and their input depresses vagal bronchomotor output (15). Nevertheless their activity seems essential to the cough reflex (35, 82) (see below), that most obviously useful of all pulmonary defensive responses.

Unclassified Vagal Afferents

Our knowledge of the vagal sensory innervation of the lower airways is not complete. Nonmyelinated axons, which account for 80–90% of the vagal input from the lower airways, have generally inconspicuous activity. Those studied systematically and characterized probably represent only a fraction of the total, particularly since some airway C-fibers are unresponsive to procedures usually employed to identify nonmyelinated vagal fibers. For example, previously unidentified vagal fibers whose small spikes barely rose above the baseline were activated by lung congestion and edema (77). They were stimulated by probing or pinching the lungs, but responded neither to injection of capsaicin nor to lung hyperinflation, and hence did not belong to an established category of pulmonary afferent. In another study, units unresponsive to capsaicin and hyperinflation, and with potentials of extremely low amplitude, were also activated by addition of 2–3 ppm ozone to the inspired air (17). In neither case were these unclassified vagal afferents examined in single fiber studies, and speculation as to their significance seems premature.

STIMULI THAT EVOKE DEFENSIVE REFLEXES

A wide variety of stimuli evoke pulmonary defensive reflexes. Three examples illustrate the different modes of action of stimuli commonly encountered by human subjects. Ozone is a potentially harmful chemical stimulus with irritant effects on the airways. Small volumes of water and hypertonic saline, although apparently innocuous, are surprisingly powerful stimuli. Pulmonary congestion and edema provide stimuli of intrinsic origin that are largely mechanical in their effects.

Acute Inhalation of Ozone

Rapid shallow breathing, cough, inspiratory chest pain, and bronchoconstriction are major sources of discomfort in human subjects breathing ozone for even relatively short periods (2, 37). The first three symptoms clearly arise from stimulation of sensory nerves. Moreover, tachypnea and respiratory discomfort are relieved by local anesthetic aerosol, and bronchoconstriction by anesthetic and atropine aerosols (2, 37). Some investigators have attributed the respiratory effects to stimulation of airway C-fibers (37), others to sensitization of slowly adapting stretch receptors (83). The vagal afferents responsible for the respiratory effects of acute exposure to ozone have been examined in a combined reflex (86) and electroneurographic (17) study. When dogs inhaled 2–3 ppm ozone into the lower trachea, tidal volume and dynamic lung compliance decreased and breathing frequency, total lung resistance, and tracheal smooth muscle tension increased (86). Ozone still evoked significant effects when conduction in myelinated vagal axons was blocked selectively by cooling the nerves to 7°C, but when vagal conduction was blocked completely by cooling to 0°C, the pattern of breathing and lung mechanics resembled those during air breathing at 0°C. These results suggest that vagal C-fibers are major contributors to the tachypnea and bronchoconstriction induced by ozone.

In a parallel afferent study in artificially ventilated dogs, bronchial C-fiber endings were stimulated by ozone, their activity increasing more than 40-fold within 1–7 min of the exposure (17)—a latency of onset that agreed well with that of the reflex effects (86). Pulmonary C-fibers were not significantly affected. Stimulation of bronchial C-fibers was relatively slow to reach its peak, which suggests that autacoids such as prostaglandins released in the airway mucosa, rather than ozone itself, contributed to their stimulation, and there is indirect evidence from human studies that this may be the case (85). Two thirds of rapidly adapting receptors were stimulated by ozone, an effect that was abolished by hyperinflation of the lungs, and hence appeared to be secondary to the ozone-induced changes in lung mechanics.

Taken together, the results of these reflex and afferent studies indicate that bronchial C-fibers contribute to the changes in breathing and bronchomotor tone evoked by short-term exposure to ozone and to the vagally-mediated tachypnea that survives vagal cooling to 7°C. Rapidly adapting receptors undoubtedly contribute to the ozone-induced increase in bronchomotor tone.

Changes in Airway Surface Osmolarity

Injection of hyperosmotic sodium chloride solution into the pulmonary artery evokes classical pulmonary chemoreflex effects (74), an observation providing yet another example of the powerful reflex responses to injection of chemicals into the pulmonary circulation, but in itself probably of little additional significance. Of more interest is the observation that airway C-fibers and rapidly adapting receptors are sensitive to changes in surface osmolarity of the airways and are stimulated when small volumes of distilled water or hyperosmotic saline at body temperature are introduced into the bronchus supplying the lobe in which the endings are located (75). Similar volumes of normal saline have little effect. Stimulation of airway C-fibers and rapidly adapting receptors by water appears to result from hyposmolarity rather than to an absence of sodium or chloride ions because isosmotic glucose solution is ineffective. The response to hyperosmotic saline is concentration-dependent. Rapidly adapting receptors differ from airway C-fibers in their response to non-isosmotic solutions, the former being stimulated more strongly. by water than by even the most hyperosmotic saline, whereas the reverse is true for the latter (75).

Injection of water or hyperosmotic saline into a lobar bronchus evokes apnea followed by rapid shallow breathing, bradycardia, systemic arterial hypotension, and bronchoconstriction (75). The afferent and reflex responses have similar latencies, and all effects are abolished by vagal section. Like the afferent responses, the reflex effects increase in amplitude with greater deviation of the injected solution from isosmolarity. The observation that the apnea and depressor cardiovascular effects were greatest with the most hyperosmotic solutions is consistent with the notion that afferent C-fibers play the major part in the reflex response. Rapidly adapting receptors increase inspiratory efforts rather than reduce them (11) and appear to have no effect on the general systemic circulation. Contraction of airway smooth muscle probably resulted from stimulation of both types of afferent.

Stimulation of airway afferents by changes in airway surface osmolarity probably accounts for the reflex apnea, coughing, bronchoconstriction, and cardiovascular depression that occur when anisosmotic fluids are inhaled, for example, during fresh water or salt water drowning, or when liquids are accidentally inhaled during drinking (75). Increases in the osmolarity of airway fluid are theoretically possible in other circumstances, hyperventilation with cold, dry air being one of them; hence osmotic stimulation of airway afferents could contribute to exercise-induced asthma.

Pulmonary Congestion and Edema

Acute congestion of the lungs stimulates pulmonary and bronchial C-fiber endings and rapidly adapting receptors (16, 76, 77). Paintal has suggested that the situation of pulmonary C-fiber endings (Type J receptors) in the most peripheral divisions of the airways and their sensitivity to distortion allows them to function as interstitial stretch receptors in the lung parenchyma and believes that their response to pulmonary congestion is their most important afferent function (65, 66). In dogs and cats, pulmonary C-fiber activity increases progressively with elevation of left atrial pressure (16, 65, 76), and many continue to discharge irregularly at relatively high frequency during the resultant interstitial pulmonary edema, after congestion has been relieved and pressures in the pulmonary circulation restored to normal (77). Bronchial C-fibers are stimulated when congestion becomes severe and results in peribronchial cuffing (77). The increased activity of pulmonary and bronchial C-fibers may account for the rapid shallow breathing in patients with pulmonary edema. This pattern of breathing can be demonstrated in unanesthetized cats with pulmonary vascular congestion (36), although slow, rather than rapid, breathing was found to be more frequent in experimental lobar congestion in unanesthetized dogs (29). Studies in cats indicate that an increase in airway C-fiber activity induced by acute lung congestion is also responsible for an inhibition of somatic motor activity (see below). This viscero-somatic reflex may contribute to the fatigue and weakness of human patients with congestive heart failure. The increased activity of airway C-fibers and rapidly adapting receptors may be implicated in the bronchoconstriction of cardiac asthma.

COUGH AND IRRITANT AIRWAY SENSATIONS

Cough is the most common presenting symptom of lower airway disease and is certainly the most immediately effective of the defensive mechanisms; in human subjects it is almost always associated with irritant airway sensation. The cough reflex is blunted by anesthesia (64), and because it cannot be evoked with any degree of regularity in anesthetized animals, its mechanisms are not easy to examine. The afferent pathways for the cough reflex are carried in the vagus nerves, and the same is true for the afferent pathways for pain and irritant sensations from the lung (33). Information regarding the cough reflex and irritant airway sensations rests on human studies of inhalation of irritant aerosols, some of which, such as capsaicin, prostaglandin E_2, and bradykinin, appear to have their major actions on lower airway afferents. There is still no consensus about the identity of the lower airway afferents that initiate cough; however, it seems likely that all the classified lower airway afferents described in this chapter contribute to the fully developed response (49).

In the forefront of the putative cough receptors is a group of rapidly adapting receptors with thick myelinated fibers that innervate the airway mucosa in the carinal region. They were called cough receptors by Widdicombe because they appeared to be responsible for the cough elicited by even the lightest touch to the carinal mucosa (97). Cough evoked by chemical irritants is initiated most readily from the more peripheral airways, however, and does not seem to depend upon the stimulation of rapidly adapting receptors in the peripheral airways (49, 97). The possibility that airway C-fibers initiate chemically-evoked cough is still debated (49). The pulmonary chemoreflex is not associated with coughing, even in conscious animals (8, 12), the only ventilatory response being apnea followed by tachypnea. In humans, however, cough and intense, retrosternal burning sensations have been evoked within the pulmonary circulation time when lobeline (which is known to stimulate pulmonary C-fibers) was injected into the pulmonary artery (41), and intense burning sensations in the thorax and elsewhere were evoked in each of three subjects, with paroxysmal coughing in one of them, when small doses of capsaicin were injected intravenously (98). In addition, chemicals known to stimulate airway C-fibers (bronchodilator prostaglandins, bradykinin, and capsaicin) evoke cough and irritant retrosternal sensations in humans when inhaled as aerosols (26, 27, 91).

Retrosternal sensations of a tickling or burning character are common in inflammation of the airways and produce an urge to cough. When the sensations are relatively weak, cough is often initiated voluntarily; alternatively the urge to cough can be suppressed. Like somatic irritant sensations, therefore, sensations of airway irritation have a defensive function. They are relieved by coughing in much the same way as tickling in the skin is relieved by scratching. The cough receptors described by Widdicombe (97) probably contribute to these sensations, being stimulated mechanically if mucus and cellular debris collect in the carinal region.

Although slowly adapting pulmonary stretch receptors have a largely regulatory role, their afferent input is now thought to be an essential component of the cough reflex. Cough can no longer be evoked in rabbits when pulmonary stretch receptor input is selectively abolished by a few breaths of a high concentration of sulfur dioxide (35, 82), a procedure that leaves input from lung C-fibers and rapidly adapting receptors intact. The mounting input from slowly adapting stretch receptors during inspiration inhibits central inspiratory neurons and excites central expiratory neurons and may be essential to facilitate the expulsive expiratory act of coughing. It seems reasonable to conclude, therefore, that all the established categories of lower airway afferent participate in the cough reflex, and any suggestion that tussigenic effectiveness is confined to certain specific categories of lower airway afferent is probably incorrect (49).

Cough depends on a complex neural mechanism involving several types of afferent pathway and the integration of output to the diaphragm and muscles of the body wall. Its effectiveness as a defense mechanism is increased by the supporting reflex responses of bronchoconstriction and increased airway secretion (49), which appear to depend on simpler reflex arcs. More is known about the mechanisms of these supporting airway responses because, unlike the cough reflex, they are relatively unaffected by anesthesia.

DEFENSIVE REFLEX EFFECTS ON THE LOWER AIRWAYS

Defensive reflex effects on the lower airways have, for the most part, both sensory and motor pathways in the vagus nerves. The motor pathways themselves are highly complex systems and are responsible for bronchoconstriction, increased airway secretion, and vasodilation, which may be sufficient to double or treble bronchial blood flow. Although acetylcholine is the principal parasympathetic neurotransmitter for these effects, two potential peptide nonadrenergic, noncholinergic (NANC) transmitters have been identified in the vagus and its branches, vasointestinal polypeptide (VIP) and peptide histidine-leucine (PHI) (59). VIP, which is believed to be an important neurotransmitter in the parasympathetic motor pathway (80), is present not only in preganglionic efferent vagal fibers but also in airway ganglia, and in postganglionic nerve terminals on airway smooth muscle, blood vessels, and glands (23, 56). A further complexity is added to the neural mechanisms of airway defense by the release of tachykinins from the endings of airway C-fibers. These tachykinins, substance P (SP), neurokinin A (NKA) and neurokinin B (NKB), together with calcitonin gene-related peptide (CGRP), are manufactured by the chemosensitive C-fiber neurons of the nodose ganglion of the vagus and transported peripherally to the sensory terminals (59). Stimulation of airway C-fibers is thought to have dual effects, not only activating central reflex arcs, but also causing axon-reflex release of neuropeptides with local airway effects (38, 59). The regulatory role of neuropeptide neurotransmitters, whether of parasympathetic or sensory origin, is complex, and varies between species. The role of axon reflexes in airway defense is prominent in rodents, but less easily demonstrated in larger animals.

Effects on Bronchial Smooth Muscle

The function of airway smooth muscle contraction in airway defense is hard to imagine, except as a means of stabilizing the airways during coughing. Nevertheless an atropine-sensitive, parasympathetically mediated bronchoconstriction was among the first of the airway components of pulmonary defensive reflexes to be clearly recognized. Its association with coughing has been reviewed (49).

Parasympathetic pathways play the paramount role in controlling the smooth muscle of the airways, and in animals and normal human subjects (but not in asthmatics), pharmacological blockade of sympathetic β-adrenergic bronchodilator pathways does not cause any increase in baseline muscarinic bronchomotor tone (15). When parasympathetic pathways to bronchial smooth muscle are activated in pulmonary defensive reflexes, not only acetylcholine, but also the peptidergic neurotransmitters VIP and PHI are released at postganglionic terminals. The two peptides probably have similar actions, but VIP has been studied more extensively (59, 80). VIP relaxes airway smooth muscle, an effect that is normally masked by the excitatory effects of cholinergic pathways, but if smooth muscle tone is first increased by a bronchoconstrictor agent, the relaxant effects of VIP can be demonstrated after pharmacological blockade of muscarinic and β-adrenergic pathways. Pulmonary defense reflexes elicited under these conditions evoke relaxation rather than contraction of airway smooth muscle (39). The hypothesis that a defect in production of a parasympathetic bronchodilator neuropeptide is a causative factor in asthma is attractive—especially since VIP has anti-inflammatory as well as smooth muscle relaxant effects (80). Investigation of this hypothesis has been hampered, however, by a lack of antagonists to VIP and PHI.

A role for axon reflexes in the bronchoconstrictor response to airway irritants such as capsaicin may be difficult to demonstrate (12, 71). The neurokinins released by chemosensitive C-fibers in the airways are potent bronchoconstrictors in guinea pigs, and in some, but not all strains of rats (60). In larger mammals their potency may be small compared with that of acetylcholine. Studies of axon reflex bronchoconstriction involving stimulation of chemosensitive C-fibers by capsaicin are often carried out in guinea pigs, whose airways, unlike those of humans (25), are constricted by substance P, but direct extrapolation of the results to other mammalian species is probably unjustified. NKA is the most potent of the tachykinins in its excitatory effects on human airway smooth muscle and can cause bronchoconstriction in humans when inhaled or infused (25, 43). Indirect evidence that axon reflexes cause bronchoconstriction in asthmatic humans has been obtained recently (40). Thus the bronchoconstriction evoked in a group of asthmatics by administration of aerosolized bradykinin was reduced by inhalation of a novel competitive tachykinin antagonist, FK-224. Although, in guinea pigs, FK-224 bound specifically to tachykinin receptors, and not to bradykinin receptors, in the asthmatic subjects it also reduced the incidence of cough evoked by bradykinin aerosol. This suggests that both the bronchoconstriction and the cough were evoked, not by bradykinin per se, but by a secondary release of tachykinins. The possibility that stimulation of airway C-fiber endings in asthmatics releases tachykinins that act as a major sensory feedback, thereby stimulating the endings further and evoking a centrally mediated reflex such as cough seems unlikely, but not inconceivable. However, in normal human subjects, aerosolized brady-kinin evokes cough, irritant airway sensations, and a bronchoconstriction abolished by atropine (27). In normal subjects, therefore, there seems no reason to attribute either the cough or the bronchoconstriction evoked by bradykinin to secondary release of tachykinins.

Effects on Airway Secretion

Reflex airway secretion plays an obvious role in pulmonary defense, facil-itating the expulsive efficiency of the cough reflex. Although it is a matter of general observation that coughing is usually accompanied by an increase in lower airway secretion, methods for quantifying the secretory output of the lower airways have not yet been developed in animals or humans. Studies of the reflex regulation of secretion have been limited to secretion in the cervical trachea. Secretion hillocks from individual tracheal submu-cosal glands have been visualized and counted in dogs (21, 88, 89), and the amount of secretory product collected in a tracheal pouch has been measured in cats (68). Tracheal submucosal gland secretion increases rapidly in dogs when airway C-fibers are stimulated by right atrial injection of capsaicin (89) and bronchial arterial injection of bradykinin (21). Secretion also increases when airway C-fibers (57) and rapidly adapting receptors (52) are stimulated by a puff of cigarette smoke delivered to the lower airways (88). Tracheal secretion also increases in dogs in response to a reduction in pulmonary compliance (99), which stimulates rapidly adapting receptors, but has no effect on airway C-fibers (42). Tracheal secretion increases in cats in response to chemical stimulation of lung afferents sufficient to cause cough (68). One may conclude, therefore, that sensory inputs from pulmo-nary and bronchial C-fibers, rapidly adapting receptors and carinal cough receptors, are all capable of stimulating airway secretion. Although release of VIP may contribute to the tracheal vasodilation evoked in dogs when vagal motor pathways are stimulated electrically (55), the reflex secretory effects described above are abolished by atropine (21, 88), and hence are wholly muscarinic in nature. The neuropeptides released by chemosensitive C-fibers are powerful salivary and nasal secretogogues (59), but methods have not yet been developed to determine whether secretion in the lower airways can be evoked locally by an axon-reflex.

Bronchovascular Effects

Activation of parasympathetic pathways dilates the resistance vessels of the trachea and bronchi; atropine diminishes the vasodilation but does not abolish it (12, 55, 70, 71, 79). The results of antidromic stimulation of the vagus nerves led some investigators to conclude that vasodilation in the bronchial mucosa results entirely from release of tachykinins from sensory C-fibers

(61, 62). In general, however, the investigators employed a low frequency of stimulation, and it is possible that higher frequencies, comparable to those evoked in vagal bronchomotor fibers during reflex activation (96), would have demonstrated a parasympathetic component more effectively.

Studies in sheep and dogs suggest that an increase in bronchial blood flow is one of the components of the pulmonary defensive reflexes. It is evoked in sheep (12) and dogs (71), together with other manifestations of the pulmonary chemoreflex, when airway C-fibers are stimulated by right atrial injection of capsaicin. It is also evoked in dogs when airway C-fibers and rapidly adapting receptors are stimulated by injection of small volumes of water into a lobar bronchus (70). In sheep the increase in blood flow is greatly diminished by atropine, and the small component that remains usually seems to depend on the integrity of the central reflex arc. In dogs, the increase is more dramatic, bronchial blood flow increasing three- to fourfold, even though cardiac output and mean arterial pressure decrease. Although the effects are reduced by atropine, a component remains that is usually abolished by vagotomy (70, 71). In some dogs, however, capsaicin still evokes a small increase in bronchial blood flow after the vagus nerves have been sectioned. In these dogs, it seems clear that stimulation of C-fibers causes a local axon reflex independent of sensory input to the central nervous system (71). Undoubtedly, therefore, airway axon reflex effects are not confined to rodents, but can operate in the airways of larger mammals. The factors influencing the operation of such axon reflexes in larger mammals have still to be determined, and a plea could be made that the present emphasis on rodents as the preferred species for investigation of airway axon reflexes should give way to a more general approach embracing other species. Moreover, interest in what has been called the efferent function of C-fiber afferents in the airways (38) should not be allowed to obscure the well established role of these nonmyelinated afferents in triggering conventional centrally mediated reflex changes in bronchomotor, bronchosecretory, and bronchovascular function.

CENTRAL ASPECTS OF PULMONARY DEFENSIVE REFLEXES

Our understanding of the medullary pathways and the ascending and descending central connections of the pulmonary defensive reflexes is still fragmentary. Progress has been made in tracing the primary afferent projections in the brainstem using neuroanatomical and neurophysiological methods, but the techniques are difficult and advances are necessarily slow. The first order interneurons subserving pulmonary defensive reflexes occupy an area of the solitary tract nucleus caudal to that involved in regulatory reflexes (5, 6). The central processes of both rapidly adapting receptors and airway C-fibers have been traced to this caudal area by an antidromic mapping technique based on the identification of cell bodies of airway afferents in the nodose ganglion of cats (20, 53). The cell bodies of rapidly adapting receptors were first identified by their response to hyperinflation; they were then activated antidromically by stimulation of their central terminals within the tractus and nucleus solitarius (20). These central terminals branched widely and partially overlapped those of slowly adapting stretch receptors, but their contralateral projections were more extensive and prominent than those of the latter. The terminals of rapidly adapting receptors projected most densely in a caudal direction, away from those of slowly adapting receptors, to end within the commissural subnucleus of the solitary tract nucleus (20), an observation confirmed by others using a combination of neurophysiological and neuroanatomical tracing methods (48).

The cell bodies of airway C-fibers were identified in the nodose ganglion by their response to right atrial injection of capsaicin and phenyldiguanide (53). Those stimulated at short latency, within the pulmonary circulation time, were identified as the cell bodies of pulmonary C-fibers; those stimulated at longer latency were assumed to be the cell bodies of bronchial C-fibers and appeared more numerous, although they may have included units innervating the heart, great vessels, and other viscera. The central branches of both groups of C-fibers were distributed densely in a caudal direction along the borders of the parvicellular (gelatinosus) subnucleus, a region showing strong substance P-like immunoreactivity (53). Their terminals branched within the dorsal portion of the commissural subnucleus. Since this subnucleus receives input from both rapidly adapting receptors and bronchopulmonary C-fibers, it probably contains first order interneurons for pulmonary defensive reflexes. Indeed, injection of picomolar quantities of excitatory amino acid into this region in rats evokes ventilatory and cardiovascular effects characteristic of the pulmonary chemoreflex, whereas injection of cobalt causes a reversible blockade of the pulmonary chemoreflex evoked by phenyldiguanide (5).

On the motor side of the reflex arc, the general distribution and connections of vagal bronchomotor and cardiomotoneurons are clear (46), but little is known about the medullary motoneurons influencing airway secretion and blood flow.

The medullary pathways for the ventilatory components of the pulmonary defensive reflexes have not been investigated fully. The inspiratory inhibition involved in the initial apnea of the pulmonary chemoreflex differs from that of the Hering Breuer inflation-inhibitory reflex (51, 87). Whereas the latter is reciprocal in character, involving inhibition of α motor fibers to inspiratory muscles and excitation of those to expiratory muscles, the apnea of the pulmonary chemoreflex involves an initial suppression of α motoneuron activity to both inspiratory and expiratory muscles and a suppression of γ motoneuron activity to intercostal muscles. Paintal took the view that the abrupt and intense stimulation of pulmonary C-fibers by a bolus injection of chemical had no counterpart in nature and was likely to contribute "a strong artifactual element" to the reflex response; he suggested that rapid shallow breathing was the more likely outcome of pulmonary C-fiber (J receptor) stimulation (67). Others held that apnea was the sole ventilatory response to stimulation of pulmonary C-fibers and that the tachypnea of the pulmonary chemoreflex resulted from blood gas changes or from stimulation of vagal C-fibers innervating regions downstream to the pulmonary circulation (16). Nevertheless, pulmonary defensive reflex apneas do not require that chemicals be injected as a bolus; they are also evoked when irritants such as cigarette smoke are inhaled (58). Moreover, prolonged rapid shallow breathing, which may or may not be preceded by apnea, is evoked when pulmonary (32) or bronchial (14) C-fibers, respectively, are activated by chemicals slowly infused into the pulmonary or bronchial arteries. It seems reasonable to conclude, therefore, that curtailment of tidal volume and inspiratory time is characteristic of a tonic increase in firing of airway C-fibers and that apnea is the ultimate extension of this effect. The general complaint of shortness of breath made by patients with chronic lung disease (24) seems an apt description of this central limitation of tidal volume, and in such patients a reduction of breath-holding time is characteristic (34). A preliminary study of the central respiratory components of the rapid shallow breathing of the pulmonary chemoreflex reveals complex changes, not only in inspiratory, but also in expiratory and phase-spanning neuronal discharges (4).

It is clear that pulmonary defensive reflexes involve somatic motor pathways at higher levels of the central nervous system and that the ventilatory aspects of these reflexes are influenced by descending pathways from midbrain and cortical levels. The initial suppression of central respiratory activity characteristic of the pulmonary chemoreflex is thought by some to be merely part of an overall inhibition of somatic motor activity (51), which Paintal called the J reflex (66). This includes, but is not confined to, an inhibition of spinal monosynaptic reflex arcs (22), which requires the participation of forebrain areas including the caudate nucleus and cingulate gyrus (45). Indeed, it has been known for many years that stimulation of regions within the orbitoinsulotemporal and anterior cingulate cortex (regions called vagal zones because they receive projections from the vagus nerve) evokes a similar composite response, including respiratory, cardiovascular, and somatic components (44). Nevertheless, relay areas for the somatic motor inhibition associated with the pulmonary chemoreflex must also be present in the midbrain because the response can be demonstrated in decerebrate cats in which the brain stem is sectioned caudal to these forebrain structures (30, 69). In decerebrate cats activity in α and γ motoneurons to flexor and extensor limb muscles is briefly suppressed (30).

Generalized motor inhibition is an integral part of the pulmonary chemoreflex in both conscious and anesthetized animals (8, 12, 47). The reflex motor inhibition resulting from stimulation of respiratory afferents even has a counterpart in fish, in which chemical stimulation of sensory fibers supplying the gills evokes a cessation of swimming movements accompanied by a chemoreflex triad of bradycardia, hypotension, and an absence of gill movements (84). The J reflex could therefore be regarded as a primitive "sham-death response" that developed relatively early in evolution, but has outlasted its useful function in mammals, and now has little physiological significance. Nevertheless, Paintal's suggestion (66) that the reflex somatic response in mammals is a true pulmonary defensive mechanism that functions to inhibit exercise in the presence of pulmonary congestion has recently been supported by the results of an elegant study of simulated exercise (walking on a treadmill) produced by electrical stimulation of the mesencephalic motor center in decerebrate cats (69). The coordinated movements resulting from this stimulation were inhibited when left atrial pressure was elevated by inflating a balloon. In some cats, the increase in atrial pressure required to inhibit locomotion was moderate and the latency of inhibition was as short as 4–5 sec. The movements were also inhibited at short latency by right or left atrial injection of phenylbiguanide. The relatively large doses of phenylbiguanide injected into the right atrium in these exercising cats did not produce the marked bradycardia (often amounting to a 4–5 sec asystole) that is the accepted hallmark of the pulmonary chemoreflex in most species (16). This raises the possibility that the cardiac component of the pulmonary chemoreflex is to some extent gated in exercise, so that the inhibition of limb muscles operates preferentially. Changes in breathing were not examined in these experiments, but the possibility of a comparable gating of the respiratory components of the chemoreflex merits investigation (see discussion in 16).

The apnea and motor inhibition evoked by right atrial injection of capsaicin or phenylbiguanide in anesthetized cats preempts the cough response to mechanical stimulation of the tracheobronchial tree and larynx—an observation that has been taken to indicate that lung C-fibers do not cause coughing (95). Moreover, if cough is the most important of the respiratory protective mechanisms, the observation might be thought to invalidate the claim that pulmonary C-fibers have an important role in pulmonary defensive reflexes. Such a conclusion implies a narrow definition of pulmonary defensive reflexes, one limited to changes in breathing and excluding bronchoconstriction and increased airway secretion. Although the latter effects on airway function may be ancilliary to cough, and may even lack a major protective function in the absence of cough, they are undoubtedly integral components of the pulmonary defensive response, and there is ample evidence that pulmonary C-fibers play a major part in these responses.

Whether the pulmonary chemoreflex suppression of laryngeal cough is integrated at medullary levels or involves more rostral regions of the brain is unknown. However, the cough reflex is known to be generally more sensitive to descending inhibitory influences than are other components of the pulmonary defensive reflex. Cough is suppressed during slow wave sleep, and in order to evoke cough from the lower airways during sleep, the stimulus must be sufficiently intense to produce cortical arousal (94). Other ventilatory aspects of pulmonary defensive reflexes, including gasps or augmented breaths triggered by stimulation of rapidly adapting receptors, are more resistant to inhibitory influences and are more easily studied in animals. Neither the central pathways for the cough reflex nor those for the gasp reflex have been studied in detail, however. The gasp reflex evoked by stimulation of rapidly adapting receptors is probably quite different from the agonal gasps evoked from a primitive gasping center (93).

CONCLUSIONS

The pulmonary defensive reflexes have as their common end the protection of the respiratory exchange region against inhaled harmful agents and the local effects of lower respiratory disease. But as more is learned about these reflex effects, the label of defensive appears less generally appropriate, and it becomes increasingly difficult to assign a useful function to all components of the defensive responses. Coughing, assisted by increased airway secretion, certainly expels harmful agents and bronchoconstriction stabilizes the airways during the explosive expiratory event; apnea limits the aspiration of inhaled fluid. Even so, arguments for the utility of all the reflex actions that we have described—even the purely ventilatory ones—are hard to sustain, for the neurally-mediated defensive responses are not invariably of physiological benefit. It may be argued that the gasp reflex evoked by inhaled irritants, such as cigarette smoke, is negative in its effects. Reflex changes such as tachypnea, cough, excess bronchial secretion, and bronchoconstriction may lose their initial defensive function and contribute to the morbidity and discomfort associated with lung disease.

Airway defensive reflexes may have dramatic—indeed fatal—consequences. Of all the hazards of inhaling fluids, possibly the greatest immediate threat to life is posed by a sudden reflex bradycardia evoked by stimulation of airway C-fibers when fluids are inhaled. Part of the cardioinhibitory input evoked by inhalation of fluid comes from the upper airways, but it is reinforced by input from the lower airways. The intense vagal bradycardia evoked by aspiration of fluid into the lower airways during fresh or salt water drowning, coupled with hypotension and an increasing hypoxia resulting from the apnea, probably contributes to the ventricular arrhythmias and cardiac arrest that appear to be the immediate cause of death in ~10% of drowning victims (31).

Physical or chemical changes in the lower respiratory tract may trigger reflex responses that aggravate an existing disease, or even initiate major components of a disease. It is conceivable, for example, that stimulation of vagal afferents by changes in airway surface osmolarity resulting from evaporative water loss could contribute to exercise-induced asthma (1, 92). Airway sensory endings in asthmatic individuals may be unusually sensitive to changes in surface osmolarity because of disruption of the epithelium (54). Changes in airway surface osmolarity that are subthreshold in non-asthmatic individuals could be sufficient in asthmatic subjects to stimulate vagal sensory endings and evoke bronchoconstriction, mucous secretion, and mucosal hyperemia through conventional centrally-mediated reflex pathways and by local release of neuropeptides from the C-fiber terminals themselves. In other words, asthmatic attacks evoked by changes in osmolarity could be seen as an exaggerated form of reflexes that normally serve to limit the access of exogenous liquids to the lower airways.

We have already discussed the likelihood that some pulmonary defensive reflexes appear to have outlasted (in an evolutionary sense) their useful function. Indeed one may even speculate that we would be better able to withstand the assaults of disease and the harmful effects of inhaled foreign agents without the intervention of some of the reflex effects triggered by sensory nerves in the lower airways. Useful or not, however, the pulmonary, defensive reflexes are potent neurally-mediated effects that cannot be ignored in health or disease.

Literature Cited

1. Anderson SD, Smith CM. 1991. Osmotic challenges in the assessment of airway hyperresponsiveness. *Am. Rev. Respir. Dis.* 143:S43–46 (Suppl.)
2. Beckett WS, McDonnell WF, Horstman DH, House DE. 1985. Role of the parasympathetic nervous system in acute lung response to ozone. *J. Appl. Physiol.* 59:1879–85
3. Bergren DR, Sampson SR. 1982. Characterization of intrapulmonary rapidly adapting receptors of guinea pigs. *Respir. Physiol.* 47:83–95

4. Bonham AC, Joad JP. 1991. C-fiber evoked rapid shallow breathing: effects on medullary inspiratory and expiratory neurons. *Soc. Neurosci.* 17:103 (Abstr.)
5. Bonham AC, Joad JP. 1991. Neurones in commissural nucleus tractus solitarii required for full expression of the pulmonary C fibre reflex in rat. *J. Physiol.* 441:95–112
6. Bonham AC, McCrimmon DR. 1990. Neurones in a discrete region of the nucleus tractus solitarius are required

for the Breuer-Hering reflex in rat. *J. Physiol.* 427:261–80

7. Cassidy SS, Ashton JH, Wead WB, Kaufman MP, Monsereenusorn Y, Whiteside JA. 1986. Reflex cardiovascular responses caused by stimulation of pulmonary C-fibers with capsaicin in dogs. *J. Appl. Physiol.* 60:949–58

8. Clifford PS, Litzow JT, Coon RL. 1987. Pulmonary depressor reflex elicited by capsaicin in conscious intact and lung-denervated dogs. *Am. J. Physiol.* 252:R394–97

9. Clozel J-P, Roberts AM, Hoffman JIE, Coleridge HM, Coleridge JCG. 1985. Vagal chemoreflex coronary vasodilation evoked by stimulating pulmonary C-fibers in dogs. *Circ. Res.* 57:450–60

10. Coast JR, Romeo RM, Cassidy SS. 1989. Diaphragmatic vasodilation elicited by pulmonary C-fiber stimulation. *Respir. Physiol.* 75:279–88

11. Coleridge HM, Coleridge JCG. 1986. Reflexes evoked from tracheobronchial tree and lungs. In *Handbook of Physiology, Sec. 3, The Respiratory System, Control of Breathing, Part I*, ed. NS Cherniack, JG Widdicombe, 2:395–429. Washington, DC: Am. Physiol. Soc.

12. Coleridge HM, Coleridge JCG, Green JF, Parsons GH. 1992. Pulmonary C-fiber stimulation by capsaicin evokes reflex cholinergic bronchial vasodilation in sheep. *J. Appl. Physiol.* 72:770–79

13. Coleridge HM, Coleridge JCG, Jordan D. 1991. Integration of ventilatory and cardiovascular control systems. In *The Lung: Scientific Foundations*, ed. RG Crystal, JB West, PJ Barnes, NS Cherniack, ER Weibel, 2:1405–18. New York: Raven

14. Coleridge HM, Coleridge JCG, Roberts AM. 1983. Rapid shallow breathing evoked by selective stimulation of airway C fibres in dogs. *J. Physiol.* 340:415–33

15. Coleridge HM, Coleridge JCG, Schultz HD. 1989. Afferent pathways involved in reflex regulation of airway smooth muscle. *Pharmacol. Ther.* 42:1–63

16. Coleridge JCG, Coleridge HM. 1984. Afferent vagal C fibre innervation of the lungs and airways and its functional significance. *Rev. Physiol. Biochem. Pharmacol.* 99:1–110

17. Coleridge JCG, Coleridge HM, Schelegle ES, Green JF. 1993. Acute inhalation of ozone stimulates bronchial C-fibers and rapidly adapting receptors in dogs. *J. Appl. Physiol.* 74:2345–52

18. Comroe JH Jr. 1954. The functions of the lung. *Harvey Lectures NY* 48:110–44

19. Coon RL, Clifford PS, Hopp FA, Zuperku EJ. 1990. Reflex ventilatory effects of KCl stimulation of lung receptors with sympathetic afferents. *Respir. Physiol.* 82:349–58

20. Davies RO, Kubin L. 1986. Projection of pulmonary rapidly adapting receptors to the medulla of the cat: an antidromic mapping study. *J. Physiol.* 373:63–86

21. Davis B, Roberts AM, Coleridge HM, Coleridge JCG. 1982. Reflex tracheal gland secretion evoked by stimulation of bronchial C-fibers in dogs. *J. Appl. Physiol.* 53:985–91

22. Deshpande SS, Devanandan MS. 1970. Reflex inhibition of monosynaptic reflexes by stimulation of type J pulmonary endings. *J. Physiol.* 206:345–57

23. Dey RD, Shannon WA Jr, Said S. 1981. Localization of VIP-immunoreactive nerves in airways and pulmonary vessels of dogs, cats, and human subjects. *Cell Tissue Res.* 220:231–38

24. Elliott MW, Adams L, Cockroft A, Macrae KD, Murphy K, Guz A. 1991. The language of breathlessness: use of verbal descriptors by patients with cardiopulmonary disease. *Am. Rev. Respir. Dis.* 144:826–32

25. Evans TW, Dixon CM, Clarke B, Conradson T-B, Barnes PJ. 1988. Comparison of neurokinin A and substance P on cardiovascular and airway function in man. *Br. J. Clin. Pharmacol.* 25:273–75

26. Fuller RW, Dixon CMS, Barnes PJ. 1985. Bronchoconstrictor response to inhaled capsaicin in humans. *J. Appl. Physiol.* 58:1080–84

27. Fuller RW, Dixon CMS, Cuss FMC, Barnes PJ. 1987. Bradykinin-induced bronchoconstriction in humans. Mode of action. *Am. Rev. Respir. Dis.* 135:176–80

28. Giesbrecht GG, Pisarri TE, Coleridge JCG, Coleridge HM. 1993. Cooling the pulmonary blood in dogs alters activity of pulmonary vagal afferents. *J. Appl. Physiol.* 74:24–30

29. Giesbrecht GG, Younes M. 1993. Respiratory response to pulmonary vascular congestion in intact conscious dogs. *J. Appl. Physiol.* 74:345–53

30. Ginzel KH, Eldred E. 1977. Reflex depression of somatic motor activity from heart, lungs and carotid sinus. In *Krogh Centenary Symposium on Respiratory Adaptations, Capillary Exchange and Reflex Mechanisms*, ed. AS Paintal, P Gill-Kumar, pp. 358–94. Delhi: Vallabhbhai Patel Chest Inst.

31. Golden FStC. 1980. Problems of immersion. *Br. J. Hosp. Med.* 23:371–83
32. Green JF, Schmidt ND, Schultz HD, Roberts AM, Coleridge HM, Coleridge JCG. 1984. Pulmonary C-fibers evoke both apnea and tachypnea of pulmonary chemoreflex. *J. Appl. Physiol.* 57:562–67
33. Guz A. 1977 Respiratory sensations in man. *Br. Med. Bull.* 33:175–77
34. Guz A, Noble MIM, Eisele JH, Trenchard D. 1970. Experimental results of vagal block in cardiopulmonary disease. In *Breathing: Hering-Breuer Centenary Symposium,* ed R Porter, pp. 315–29. London: Churchill
35. Hanacek J, Davies A, Widdicombe JG. 1984. Influence of lung stretch receptors on the cough reflex in rabbits. *Respiration* 45:161–68
36. Hatridge J, Haji A, Perez-Padilla JR, Remmers JE. 1989. Rapid shallow breathing caused by pulmonary vascular congestion in cats. *J. Appl. Physiol.* 67:2257–64
37. Hazucha MJ, Bates DV, Bromberg PA. 1989. Mechanism of action of ozone on the human lung. *J. Appl. Physiol.* 67:1535–41
38. Holzer P. 1991. Capsaicin: cellular targets, mechanisms of action, and selectivity for thin sensory neurons. *Pharmacol. Rev.* 43:143–201
39. Ichinose M, Inoue H, Miura M, Yafuso N, Nogami H, Takishima T. 1987. Possible sensory receptor of nonadrenergic inhibitory nervous system. *J. Appl. Physiol.* 63:923–29
40. Ichinose M, Nakajima N, Takahashi T, Yamauchi H, Inoue H, Takishima T. 1992. Protection against bradykinin-induced bronchoconstriction in asthmatic patients by neurokinin receptor antagonist. *Lancet* 340:1248–51
41. Jain SK, Subramanian S, Julka DB, Guz A. 1972. Search for evidence of lung chemoreflexes in man: study of respiratory and circulatory effects of phenyldiguanide and lobeline. *Clin. Sci.* 42:163–77
42. Jonzon A, Pisarri TE, Coleridge JCG, Coleridge HM. 1986. Rapidly adapting receptor activity in dogs is inversely related to lung compliance. *J. Appl. Physiol.* 61:1990–97
43. Joos G, Pauwels R, van der Straeten M. 1987. Effect of inhaled substance P and neurokinin A on the airways of normal and asthmatic subjects. *Thorax* 42:779–83
44. Kaada BR. 1960. Cingulate, posterior orbital, anterior insular and temporal pole cortex. In *Handbook of Physiology, Section I, Neurophysiology,* ed. J Field, HW Magoun, VE Hall, II:1345–72. Washington, DC: Am. Physiol. Soc.
45. Kalia MP. 1973. Effects of certain cerebral lesions on the J reflex. *Pflügers Arch.* 343:297–308
46. Kalia MP. 1987. Organization of central control of airways. *Annu. Rev. Physiol.* 49:595–609
47. Kalia MP, Koepchen HP, Paintal AS. 1973. Somatomotor and autonomic effects of Type J receptor stimulation in awake freely moving and restrained cats. *Pflügers Arch.* 339:R80 (Abstr.)
48. Kalia MP, Richter D. 1988. Rapidly adapting pulmonary receptor afferents. I. Arborization in the nucleus of the tractus solitarius. *J. Comp. Neurol.* 274:560–73
49. Karlsson J-A, Sant'Ambrogio G, Widdicombe J. 1988. Afferent neural pathways in cough and reflex bronchoconstriction. *J. Appl. Physiol.* 65:1007–23
50. Kaufman MP, Coleridge HM, Coleridge JCG, Baker DG. 1982. Bradykinin stimulates afferent vagal C-fibers in intrapulmonary airways of dogs. *J. Appl. Physiol.* 48:511–17
51. Koepchen HP, Kalia M, Sommer D, Klussendorf D. 1977. Action of Type J afferents on the discharge pattern of medullary respiratory neurons. See Ref. 30, pp. 407–25
52. Kou YR, Lee L-Y. 1990. Stimulation of rapidly adapting receptors in canine lungs by a single breath of cigarette smoke. *J. Appl. Physiol.* 68:1203–10
53. Kubin L, Kimura H, Davies RO. 1991. The medullary projections of afferent bronchopulmonary C fibres in the cat as shown by antidromic mapping. *J. Physiol.* 435:207–28
54. Laitinen LA, Heino M, Laitinen A, Kava T, Haahtela T. 1985. Damage of the airway epithelium and bronchial reactivity in patients with asthma. *Am. Rev. Respir. Dis.* 131:599–606
55. Laitinen LA, Laitinen MVA, Widdicombe JG. 1987. Parasympathetic nervous control of tracheal vascular resistance in the dog. *J. Physiol.* 385:135–46
56. Laitinen A, Partanen M, Hervonen A, Pelto-Huikko M, Laitinen LA. 1985. VIP-like immunoreactive nerves in human respiratory tract. Light and electron microscopic study. *Histochemistry* 82:313–19
57. Lee L-Y, Kou YR, Frazier DT, Beck ER, Pisarri TE, et al. 1989. Stimulation of vagal pulmonary C-fibers by a single

breath of cigarette smoke in dogs. *J. Appl. Physiol.* 66:2032–38

58. Lee L-Y, Morton RF, Hord AH, Frazier DT. 1983. Reflex control of breathing following inhalation of cigarette smoke in conscious dogs. *J. Appl. Physiol.* 54:562–70

59. Lundberg JM, Martling C-R, Hokfelt T. 1988. Airways, oral cavity and salivary glands: classical transmitters and peptides in sensory and autonomic motor neurons. In *Handbook of Chemical Neuroanatomy, The Peripheral Nervous System*, ed. A Bjorklund, T Hokfelt, C Owman, 6:391–444. Elsevier: Amsterdam

60. Lundberg JM, Saria A. 1987. Polypeptide-containing neurons in airway smooth muscle. *Annu. Rev. Physiol.* 49:557–72

61. Martling C-R, Matran R, Alving K, Lacroix JS, Lundberg JM. 1989. Vagal vasodilatory mechanisms in the pig bronchial circulation preferentially involves sensory nerves. *Neurosci. Lett.* 96:306–11

62. Matran R, Alving K, Martling CR, Lacroix JS, Lundberg, JM. 1989. Vagally mediated vasodilatation by motor and sensory nerves in the tracheal and bronchial circulation of the pig. *Acta Physiol. Scand.* 135:29–37

63. Mills JE, Sellick H, Widdicombe JG. 1969. Activity of lung irritant receptors in pulmonary microembolism, anaphylaxis and drug-induced bronchoconstrictions. *J. Physiol.* 203:337–57

64. Nishino T, Hiraga K, Mizuguchi T, Honda Y. 1988. Respiratory reflex responses to stimulation of tracheal mucosa in enflurane-anesthetized humans. *J. Appl. Physiol.* 65:1069–74

65. Paintal AS. 1969. Mechanism of stimulation of type J pulmonary receptors. *J. Physiol.* 203:511–32

66. Paintal AS. 1970. The mechanism of excitation of type J receptors and the J reflex. See Ref. 34, pp. 59–71

67. Paintal AS. 1973. Vagal sensory receptors and their reflex effects. *Physiol. Rev.* 53:159–227

68. Phipps RJ, Richardson PS. 1976. The effects of irritation at various levels of the airway upon tracheal mucus secretion in the cat. *J. Physiol.* 261:563–81

69. Pickar JG, Hill JM, Kaufman MP. 1993. Stimulation of vagal afferents inhibits locomotion in mesencephalic cats. *J. Appl. Physiol.* 74:103–10

70. Pisarri TE, Coleridge HM, Coleridge JCG. 1993. Reflex bronchial vasodilation in dogs evoked by injection of a small volume of water into a bronchus. *J. Appl. Physiol.* In press

71. Pisarri TE, Coleridge JCG, Coleridge HM. 1993. Capsaicin-induced bronchial vasodilation in dogs: central and peripheral neural mechanisms. *J. Appl. Physiol.* 74:259–66

72. Pisarri TE, Giesbrecht GG, Coleridge JCG, Coleridge HM. 1993. Reflex tracheal smooth muscle contraction and bronchial vasodilation evoked by cooling the pulmonary blood in dogs. *FASEB J.* 7:A401 (Abstr.)

73. Pisarri TE, Jonzon A Coleridge HM, Coleridge JCG. 1990. Rapidly adapting receptors monitor lung compliance in spontaneously breathing dogs. *J. Appl. Physiol.* 68:1997–2005

74. Pisarri TE, Jonzon A, Coleridge HM, Coleridge JCG. 1991. Intravenous injection of hypertonic NaCl solution stimulates pulmonary C-fibers in dogs. *Am. J. Physiol.* 260:H1522–530

75. Pisarri TE, Jonzon A, Coleridge HM, Coleridge JCG. 1992. Vagal afferent and reflex responses to changes in surface osmolarity in lower airways of dogs. *J. Appl. Physiol.* 73:2305–13

76. Ravi K, Kappagoda CT. 1992. Responses of pulmonary C-fibre and rapidly adapting receptor afferents to pulmonary congestion and edema in dogs. *Can. J. Physiol. Pharmacol.* 70:68–76

77. Roberts AM, Bhattacharya J, Schultz HD, Coleridge HM, Coleridge JCG. 1986. Stimulation of pulmonary vagal afferent C-fibers by lung edema in dogs. *Circ. Res.* 58:512–22

78. Roberts AM, Schultz HD, Green JF, Armstrong DJ, Kaufman MP, et al. 1985. Reflex tracheal contraction evoked in dogs by bronchodilator prostaglandins E_2 and I_2. *J. Appl. Physiol.* 58:1823–31

79. Sahin G, Webber SE, Widdicombe JG. 1987. Lung and cardiac reflex actions on the tracheal vasculature in anaesthetized dogs. *J. Physiol.* 387:47–57

80. Said SI. 1991. Neuropeptides (VIP) and tachykinins. VIP as a modulator of lung inflammation and airway constriction. *Am. Rev. Respir. Dis.* 143: S22–24

81. Sampson SR. 1977. Sensory neurophysiology of airways. *Am. Rev. Respir. Dis.* 115:107–15

82. Sant'Ambrogio G, Sant'Ambrogio FB, Davies A. 1984. Airway receptors in cough. *Clin. Respir. Physiol.* 20:43–47

83. Sasaki K, Nadel JA, Hahn HL. 1987. Effect of ozone on breathing in dogs:

vagal and nonvagal mechanisms. *J. Appl. Physiol.* 62:15–26

84. Satchell GH. 1977. The J reflex in fish. See Ref. 30, pp. 432–39
85. Schelegle ES, Adams WC, Siefkin AD. 1987. Indomethacin pretreatment reduced ozone-induced pulmonary function decrements in human subjects. *Am. Rev. Respir. Dis.* 136:1350–54
86. Schelegle ES, Carl ML, Coleridge HM, Coleridge JCG, Green JF. 1993. Contribution of vagal afferents to respiratory reflexes evoked by acute inhalation of ozone in dogs. *J. Appl. Physiol.* 74:2338–44
87. Schmidt T, Wellhoner HH. 1970. The reflex influence of a group of slowly conducting vagal afferents on α and γ discharges in cat intercostal nerves. *Pflügers Arch.* 318:335–45
88. Schultz HD, Davis B, Coleridge HM, Coleridge JCG. 1991. Cigarette smoke in lungs evokes reflex increase in tracheal submucosal gland secretion in dogs. *J. Appl. Physiol.* 71:900–9
89. Schultz HD, Roberts AM, Bratcher C, Coleridge HM, Coleridge JCG. 1985. Pulmonary C-fibers reflexly increase secretion by tracheal submucosal glands in dogs. *J. Appl. Physiol.* 58:907–10
90. Sellick H, Widdicombe JG. 1969. The activity of lung irritant receptors during pneumothorax, hyperpnoea and pulmonary vascular congestion. *J. Physiol.* 203:359–81
91. Smith AP, Cuthbert MF. 1976 The response of normal and asthmatic subjects to prostaglandins E_2 and $F_{2\alpha}$ by different routes, and their significance in asthma. In *Advances in Prostaglandin and Thromboxane Research,* ed.

B Samuelsson, R Paoletti, 1:449–59. New York: Raven
92. Smith CM, Anderson SD. 1986. Hyperosmolarity as the stimulus to asthma induced by hyperventilation? *J. Allergy Clin. lmmunol.* 77:729–36
93. St John WW. 1990. Neurogenesis, control, and functional significance of gasping. *J. Appl. Physiol.* 68:1305–15
94. Sullivan CE, Kozar LF, Murphy E, Phillipson EA. 1979. Arousal, ventilatory, and airway responses to bronchopulmonary stimulation in sleeping dogs. *J. Appl. Physiol.* 47:17–25
95. Tatar M, Webber SE, Widdicombe JG. 1988. Lung C-fibre receptor activation and defensive reflexes in anaesthetized cats. *J. Physiol.* 402:411–20
96. Widdicombe JG. 1966. Action potentials in parasympathetic and sympathetic efferent fibres to the trachea and lungs of dogs and cats. *J. Physiol.* 186:56–88
97. Widdicombe JG. 1977. Defensive mechanisms of the respiratory system. In *International Review of Physiology: Respiratory Physiology II,* ed. JG Widdicombe, 14:291–315. Baltimore: Univ. Park Press
98. Winning AJ, Hamilton RD, Shea SA, Guz A. 1986. Respiratory and cardiovascular effects of central and peripheral intravenous injections of capsaicin in man: evidence for pulmonary chemosensitivity. *Clin. Sci.* 71:519–26
99. Yu J, Schultz HD, Goodman J, Coleridge JCG, Coleridge HM, Davis B. 1989. Pulmonary rapidly adapting receptors reflexly increase airway secretion in dogs. *J. Appl. Physiol.* 67: 682–87

Annu. Rev. Physiol. 1994. 56:93–116
Copyright © 1994 by Annual Reviews Inc. All rights reserved

NUCLEUS TRACTUS SOLITARIUS — GATEWAY TO NEURAL CIRCULATORY CONTROL

Michael C. Andresen

Department of Physiology, Oregon Health Sciences University, Portland, Oregon 97201-3098

Diana L. Kunze

Department of Molecular Physiology and Cellular Biophysics, Baylor College of Medicine, Houston, Texas 77030

KEY WORDS: baroreceptor, baroreflex, NTS, autonomic, nodose, glutamate

INTRODUCTION

The neural regulation of the cardiovascular system has been the subject of active investigation for more than a century. Generally, the detailed information available about peripheral mechanisms, both afferent and efferent, far exceeds what we know about the central nervous system (CNS) processing, which gives rise to reflex responses (80). The current picture of the CNS contribution to cardiovascular regulation consists primarily of a loose network schematic including identified cell locations and connections involved in baroreflexes (Figure 1) and is the recent topic of several excellent, comprehensive reviews (80, 88, 132, 144). Much less is known about the functional properties by which these neurons communicate, how they are modulated, or the mechanisms responsible for various features of the reflex.

Over the past ten years considerable research effort has focused on the initial neurons of the baroreceptor reflex, and it is here that work is most rapidly approaching issues of the cellular basis of function. Most cardio-

0066–4278/94/0315–0093$05.00

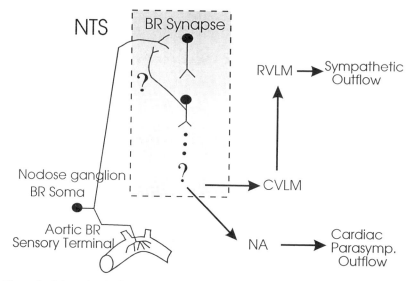

Figure 1 Schematic of afferent baroreceptor (BR) pathway through central nervous system. Shaded box represents nucleus tractus solitarius (NTS). BR sensory endings are embedded in certain major arteries such as the aortic arch and their cell bodies in ganglia outside the central nervous system (e.g. nodose ganglion). Central processes of BR neurons enter the brain at NTS. Two question marks indicate uncertainty as to the number of neurons in the pathway(s) within NTS and the presence of presynaptic feedback at the sensory afferent synapse in NTS. RVLM (rostral ventrolateral medulla), CVLM (caudal ventrolateral medulla), and NA (nucleus ambiguus).

vascular afferents converge initially on the dorsomedial portions of the nucleus of the tractus solitarius (NTS) (80, 88, 144). In the late 1960's, experiments suggested that events in the NTS critically condition afferent baroreceptor (BR) input to the CNS and profoundly shape the performance characteristics of the overall reflex (128). In the following 25 years, a number of clues about the relationship of afferent input to NTS processing have been inferred from looking at blood pressure and heart rate responses. Most recently, however, studies have been directed toward the cellular basis of NTS function. These developments coincide with the general explosion of new and powerful techniques in the neurosciences. Some of these new techniques promise to allow us to build on broad functional questions posed earlier and to approach a more fundamental understanding of the basis for CNS integration.

In the present review, we selectively highlight recent results, using these cellular approaches, to begin to understand the interaction of afferent neurons with the NTS in the first CNS step of cardiovascular regulation. Beyond the specifics of cardiovascular regulation, the rat NTS offers a unique model for many more general neuroscience issues concerning sensory processing. This is afforded by the anatomical presence of a single sensory modality, BR afferent nerve, which is accessible for labeling (the aortic depressor nerve; ADN) and has a clear functional role. Given the space allowed, we limit our discussion to these first two neurons in the baroreflex (the BR neuron and the second order neuron in NTS; Figure 1), the nature of their coupling, and the impact of voltage- and ligand-gated ion channels that are responsible for synaptic communication between cells.

NTS

NTS has a number of unique anatomical and phenotypical features that probably contribute to its pivotal role in neural cardiovascular regulation and integration. The rat NTS contains an estimated 42,000 cells with roughly 10^6 synapses, and perhaps one third of these neurons may be involved in baroreflexes (109). Multiple modalities of visceral afferents distribute synapses across NTS neurons to some extent viscerotopically (88). Thus generally, gustatory afferents are concentrated rostrally, cardiovascular afferents impinge on dorsomedial NTS, respiratory afferent endings are found ventrally and ventrolaterally, and gastrointestinal afferents end in subpostremal NTS, although there is clear overlap across modalities as well. NTS also receives from and sends processes to a number of CNS areas in an interesting pattern of reciprocal connections including paraventricular and lateral nuclei of the hypothalamus, rostral ventrolateral medulla, caudal raphe nuclei, the A5 cell group, and area postrema (88). An undetermined number of synapses within NTS are from interneurons. NTS neurons in turn project their axons to numerous areas within the medulla and beyond to other brain areas and the spinal cord. These projections include the following areas and nuclei: dorsal motor nucleus of vagus, ambiguus nucleus, area postrema, dorsal reticular formation, retrofacial nucleus, prepositus nucleus, intercalatus nucleus, parabracheal nucleus, and the intermediolateral cell column of the spinal cord. Another interesting feature of NTS is the remarkably high rates of solute exchange with the general circulation in medial and medial commissural NTS, which suggests highly localized deficits of the blood brain barrier in areas important to cardiovascular regulation (58–60). The convergence of inputs, synaptic density, and the number of potential transmitters/modulators and their receptors, which have been identified in the NTS region, suggest a site of great potential for neurohumoral integration.

NTS IN BAROREFLEX ACTIVATION

Reflex experiments in conscious and anesthetized animals suggest that NTS, particularly the medial portions, is absolutely essential to baroreflex integrity (119). Lesions or pharmacological blockade of NTS effectively eliminate baroreflex responses. Electrical or pharmacological (e.g. excitatory amino acid) activation of medial NTS mimics baroreflex responses by evoking decreases in heart rate, blood pressure and sympathetic nerve activity similar to electrical stimulation of a major BR-containing nerve trunk, the ADN, or the carotid sinus nerve (CSN).

While these in vivo results are of enormous value in placing NTS functionally within the overall scheme of cardiovascular control, at the same time they present certain difficulties for a mechanistic interpretation. In fact, a major problem for all studies of NTS, whether at the reflex or single neuron level, is the absence of firm information about the local neural circuits within NTS and the identity of which cells are involved in a given response. For reflex studies, for example, discrete effects are difficult to obtain. Injection of the typical 50–100 nL of highly concentrated drugs will initially span a large distance relative to the dimensions of NTS: for 100 nL, a 300μ radius. After diffusing for a few seconds, a concentration gradient centered at the pipette tip will develop, and the extent of the spread, the concentration at any point in time or space, and the area of brain affected are difficult to judge precisely, but the drug, even with these small volumes, is likely to reach beyond any subnucleus of NTS. Within NTS, a heterogenous population of neurons will be affected including those receiving direct afferent input, local interneurons and output neurons. All of these considerations apply to local electrical stimulation as well. Such complications may be responsible for some of the discord in reports of microinjection studies such as those involving the role of glutamate (GLU) in NTS, e.g. (86, 89, 138). To understand these integrated responses, it is essential to examine events more directly and learn the details of the mechanisms responsible for neurotransmission and afferent processing. This will necessarily involve studies at the single neuron level and identification of local circuits in NTS. This cellular approach often severs functional links and will require a careful comparison to reflex results to maintain relevance.

BARORECEPTOR INPUT TO NTS

Horseradish peroxidase (HRP) applied to ADN unilaterally in rat, cat, and rabbit is transported through the sensory ganglion to BR presynaptic terminal fields within NTS (30, 72, 145). Labeling is predominantly ipsilateral in dorsomedial, dorsolateral, and commissural aspects of NTS, but with some contralateral labeling. The lipophilic dye, DiA, partitions into the neural membrane and thus does not require nerve sectioning or an active uptake process. DiA in the rat ADN yields a relatively more restricted distribution of labeled BR terminals than HRP, generally in medial NTS without contralateral labeling (93). While the origin of these distribution differences is unclear, post-axotomy spread of HRP-labeled terminal fields may also contribute (26). Electrophysiological studies stimulating CSN or ADN generally confirm the anatomical work, which suggests that the major areas of BR innervation lie mostly in the medial and dorso-medial NTS in most species (131). The terminal distributions of the two major subclasses of BRs (myelinated, A-type, and unmyelinated, C-type axons), mapped utilizing electrophysiological techniques, generally coincide with these labeling studies of NTS (43). However, there is some evidence of medial-lateral segregation by fiber type. C-fiber aortic BRs in the cat may tend to be located more often medially in NTS, with myelinated fibers more dispersed, especially laterally in NTS (41).

The discharge characteristics of the A- and C-type BRs recorded from the axons innervating the peripheral sensory terminals have been compared in detail in several studies (25, 31, 141). Major features are summarized here. The threshold for the initiation of discharge by the A-type aortic BRs in rats is in the range of 40–120 mm Hg (1, 24). In response to a step increase in pressure, these receptors discharge at a frequency that adapts over 4–5 sec to a steady value that is directly proportional to the amplitude of pressure step. A-type BRs are capable of responding with high frequencies of discharge >100 Hz. In vivo, over most of the physiological range of arterial pressures, A-type BRs exhibit a pulsatile discharge with each arterial pressure wave. Thus the A-type BR discharge pattern is very regular and can generate a fairly high fidelity reflection of the pressure input waveform. The group of C-type aortic BRs in rats has a threshold for discharge that is higher than that of A-type BRs, 60–>200 mmHg (142), and they discharge at a lower frequency than A-type BRs at the same pressure. Maximum sustained frequency is approximately 20–30/sec. While some C-type BRs in rats (142) or in rabbits (151) show a regular discharge frequency in response to step increases in pressure, most C-type BRs exhibit an irregular discharge pattern. Other patterns and rarer subclasses of BRs have been reported (e.g. 117, 127). In vivo C-type BRs either fire a burst of action potentials of lower frequency than the A-fibers with each pulse or, more often, Cs fire only one or two action potentials loosely correlated to the pressure pulse (151). It is reasonable to infer from the differences in the discharge characteristics that the A- and C-type BRs provide different types of information to the central neurons. Unfortunately, despite the effort of several groups of investigators (9, 44, 45, 48, 74, 75, 81, 126, 135), there is not a consensus as to which parameters of the discharge pattern determine the reflex output, nor has there been a clear separation of the role of the A- vs C-type BRs.

Centrally at the cellular level, activation of BR afferents presumably excites NTS neurons with an excitatory postsynaptic potential (EPSP), although a variety of responses have been reported (132). Pure inhibitory responses to BR inputs have been observed relatively rarely and tend to have longer latencies, which perhaps suggests that the connection is polysynaptic (133). More complex EPSP-IPSP (inhibitory postsynaptic potential) responses to afferent stimulation have been reported in NTS neurons both in vivo (e.g. 96, 97) and in vitro (e.g. 22, 46). Electrical or natural stimulation of BR nerves in vivo evoke short latency responses centered on the medial NTS in cat (39, 40, 42, 43). Such in vivo recordings have the clear advantage of being able to use natural stimuli or electrical activation of nerves of defined function such as the ADN. However, a surprisingly small proportion of the NTS neurons recorded in vivo show the cardiac pulse-synchronous pattern that might be expected of neurons receiving phasic afferent input (98, 132). Several explanations may account for this unexpected result. It is possible that, owing to some technical aspect such as neuron size or orientation, most NTS neurons encountered in these experiments are not monosynaptically connected to the afferent neurons, and thus synaptic filtering or local circuitry may modify the primary BR input. Another aspect of the afferent input that is often ignored, however, is the irregularity of discharge often found in the C-type BRs and the fact that C-type BRs far outnumber regularly discharging A-type BRs. Thus the poor correlation of discharge frequency to the arterial pressure wave in electrocardiogram triggered averages (e.g. 151) might be reflected in an asynchronous input to NTS by a majority of BRs.

Even at the single cell level with either extracellular or intracellular recording, it is difficult to determine whether the neuron is connected directly to an afferent synapse or whether the connection is polysynaptic. Several schemes have been employed to test this that rely chiefly on the absolute response latency and its invariance and on responses to paired pulse protocols. Such procedures are often difficult to complete in vivo with relatively short-lasting intracellular recordings. Interestingly, there appears to be a hierarchy of synaptic latencies such that the shortest latencies tend to be EPSPs and the longest are IPSPs with the EPSP-IPSPs in between (96, 97). One possible explanation could be that the NTS neurons receiving monosynaptic afferent input respond with EPSPs and that neurons responding with IPSPs and EPSP-IPSPs are connected through polysynaptic pathways. This view might help explain the differences in NTS responses to solitary tract stimulation between transverse and horizontal medullary brain slices.

In the transverse slice, the site of tract axon stimulation is within a few hundred microns of the recording site, and stimulation evokes prominent EPSP-IPSPs, which are probably recruited from NTS interneurons (e.g. 22). By contrast, in quasi-horizontal medullary slices, tract axons can be stimulated at distances of 1–3 mm from NTS, and EPSP-IPSPs are less common (7). The contributions of afferent axon branching, sensory modality, myelination subclass, or co-neurotransmitters are unknown.

TRANSMITTERS AND MODULATORS

Microinjection, immunocytochemical, and electrophysiological recordings in NTS have implicated the participation of a wide variety of potential transmitters and modulators. In accordance with the array of projections that NTS neurons receive, dozens of neurotransmitters/modulators may be involved in NTS (109, 144). The major classes are (*a*) biogenic amines (dopamine, norepinephrine, epinephrine, histamine, serotonin, acetylcholine); (*b*) amino acids (glutamate, GLU; aspartate, glycine and γ-aminobutyric acid, GABA); and (*c*) neuropeptides [vasopressin, neurophysins, oxytocin, angiotensins, bradykinin, thyrotropin-releasing hormone, somatostatin, substance P, neuropeptide Y (NPY), neurotensin, enkephalins, β-endorphin, adrenocorticotropic hormone, α-melanotropic-stimulating hormone, vasoactive intestinal peptide, and gastrin]. The evidence for most of these potential transmitters is largely anatomical localization or indicated by changes in blood pressure and heart rate on injection into NTS (144).

Some of these substances may be released from the afferent pathway either to modulate the postsynaptic cell, or to act on autoreceptors of the terminals to modulate further release from the afferent pathway itself. The evidence for GLU as the primary transmitter is reviewed below. In addition, it is important to note that immunocytochemical techniques have shown that the sensory afferent soma of the petrosal and nodose ganglia contain a variety of transmitter substances including substance P, neurokinin A, calcitonin gene-related peptide (CGRP), tyrosine hydroxylase (dopamine), cholecystokinin, vasoactive intestinal peptide, and somatostatin (for review, see 65–67, 144)). Furthermore, soma of arterial chemoreceptors or BRs have been shown by in situ hybridization to express the messenger RNA for CGRP, preproenkephalin A, NPY and preprotachykinin and tyrosine hydroxylase. However, studies that show release of these peptides from a BR afferent pathway and a resulting physiological function at the postsynaptic cell have not been done.

The two transmitters that have been investigated in most detail are GLU and GABA. As in other CNS areas, excitatory amino acids appear to be mediate fast excitatory synaptic transmission, and GABA is associated with pre- and postsynaptic inhibition. In addition to these classical neurotransmitters, we discuss angiotensin II, one of many neuropeptides suggested to modulate neuronal function in NTS.

Glutamate

The NTS role of GLU in cardiovascular regulation has been a remarkably contentious issue. Evidence includes (a) removal of the nodose ganglion (location of afferent cell bodies) reduces GLU levels and its high affinity uptake, (b) GLU is released during afferent stimulation, (c) GLU is synthesized, stored and reaccumulated in afferent nerve endings, (d) NTS microinjection of GLU reduces blood pressure and heart rate thus mimicking BR activation (139). The pharmacology of excitatory amino acid receptors, however, has proven to be very complex (104). Excitatory amino acids activate two basic types of response systems: ion channels (ionotropic responses), and second messenger systems (metabotropic responses) (16, 104, 107). Based on agonist preferences, three classes of inotropic receptors are distinguished: N-methyl-D-aspartate (NMDA), and two non-NMDA classes, quisqualate/AMPA (Q/A) and kainate (KA). Concentration-dependent interactions for various agonists and antagonists exist among subtypes with nonspecific effects at high concentrations (104).

Baroreflexes are blocked by injection of broad-spectrum GLU antagonists such as kynurenate into the NTS region (56, 61, 77, 85, 86, 120, 138, 139). With the use of varied and more specific agents, however, several puzzles arose about GLU involvement in the NTS step of the baroreflex pathway. Microinjection of GLU or its receptor-specific analogues (e.g. NMDA, Q/A, and KA) into NTS evoke BP responses (51, 79, 85, 86, 138, 143). Highly specific NMDA antagonists were the first available among subtype-selective GLU antagonists and used in NTS. Responses to ADN stimulation are blocked by selective NMDA receptor antagonists (77, 86, 138). From such results it was suggested that afferent BR synaptic transmission was mediated by postsynaptic NMDA receptors, despite the more generally held concept that NMDA receptors mediate slow or prolonged response functions (34). As discussed above, however, interpretation of microinjection results is complicated because it is difficult to identify the affected neurons with microinjection (e.g., are neurons beyond the first synapse involved?), and antagonists may lose their specificity at locally high concentrations. In fact, subsequent reflex work incorporating non-NMDA selective antagonists concludes that non-NMDA receptors predominate in NTS (56, 79).

In in vitro preparations that permit pharmacological agents to be utilized in controlled concentrations while examining discrete populations of neurons and sensory inputs, electrophysiology provides more conclusive information about transmitter actions on single neurons. These studies support the participation of multiple excitatory amino acid receptors in synaptic transmission within NTS. Extracellular recordings from cardiovascular areas of NTS (101) suggest that both NMDA and non-NMDA receptors are involved. Intracellularly recorded, short-latency EPSP responses to solitary tract stimulation are blocked by non-NMDA antagonists, but are unaffected by NMDA receptor or channel antagonists (7, 8). Thus it appears that BR as well as other sensory afferent fast synaptic transmission is mediated primarily by GLU acting at a non-NMDA receptor (Figure 2).

Postsynaptic NMDA responses are apparent in neurons within NTS. Relatively small NMDA currents (<15 pA) are evoked in most dissociated medial NTS neurons (46, 47, 105), although a small percentage (18%) of cells respond to NMDA with much larger currents. In the presence of non-NMDA antagonist in medullary slices, stimulation of sites medial to the solitary tract elicit a small, slow EPSP in NTS neurons, which is enhanced by extracellular Mg^{2+} omission and blocked by NMDA antagonist (23). These results are consistent with a relative predominance of NMDA

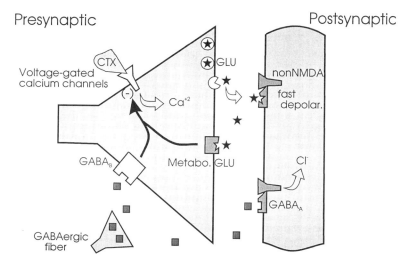

Figure 2   Schematic of the first synapse of the baroreflex. Afferent action potentials depolarize the BR presynaptic ending and activate voltage-gated calcium channels. As presynaptic intracellular calcium concentration rises, glutamate (GLU, *star*) is released into the synaptic clefts and binds to nonNMDA ionotropic receptors on the postsynaptic membrane triggering a fast EPSP. A major portion of the presynaptic calcium channels is blocked by ω-conotoxin (CTX). The presynaptic bouton is a major site of synaptic modulation at receptors such as by GABAB (inhibitory), metabotropic GLU (inhibitory), and angiotensin II (facilitory). GABA (*filled squares*) is released by adjacent fibers onto both pre- and postsynaptic (GABAA) sites. Postsynaptic GABAA increases chloride ion conductance and generally inhibits the NTS neuron.

receptors on interneurons within NTS and their relative absence on cells receiving primary afferent inputs. Such results offer a cellular site of action for NMDA within NTS and a potential explanation for the complexity of blood pressure responses to NMDA microinjection described above.

Interestingly, blood pressure responses to injection of GLU into NTS are still found, however, in the presence of a kynurenate concentration, which effectively blocks reflex responses to natural or electrical activation of BRs (51, 79, 85, 86, 138, 143). This finding suggests that GLU could be acting at receptors that do not fit the NMDA/non-NMDA classification (113). Recent work in in vitro experiments with the metabotropic agonist trans-ACPD (trans-1-aminocyclopentyl-1, 3-decarboxylate) suggests another possible synaptic mechanism (53). Despite blockade of Q-A/KA and NMDA receptors, trans-ACPD, GLU, and tract stimulation elicit small depolarizations in NTS neurons in medullary slices (53). In addition, trans-ACPD depresses $GABA_A$ and AMPA receptor responses (54). Thus both reflex and in vitro electrophysiological results suggest that excitatory amino acids acting at NMDA and non-NMDA ionotropic receptors and at metabotropic receptors are present in NTS. The potential for interactions of excitatory amino acids with other neurotransmitters suggests a possibly complex interrelationship. In all likelihood, non-NMDA receptors provide the main basis for synaptic transmission for the BR afferent synapse with modulation of that transmission provided by NMDA and metabotropic receptors. Clearly, the details of the circuits involved in NTS need to be elucidated before overall transmission and processing of afferent information through NTS can be understood and functional roles can be assigned to these responses.

GABA

The involvement of the inhibitory amino acid neurotransmitter, GABA, in cardiovascular regulation at NTS has also been controversial (144). $GABA_A$ receptors are generally localized postsynaptically and increase chloride conductance (Figure 2), while $GABA_B$ receptors are associated with presynaptic sites that inhibit transmitter release (excitatory amino acids, amines, and neuropeptides) via a reduction in calcium conductance and/or an increase in potassium conductance (20, 108). $GABA_A$ and $GABA_B$ binding sites are found in NTS (144) and both receptor types appear to affect blood pressure control. Microinjection of GABA into NTS increases blood pressure and $GABA_A$ antagonist blocks these pressure increases and enhances responses to ADN stimulation (19, 76). Microinjection of GABA onto NTS neurons inhibits their activation by CSN stimulation, and this inhibitory effect is blocked by a $GABA_A$ antagonist (91). $GABA_A$ antagonist injected into NTS also reduces the efficacy of hypothalamic inhibition of both spontaneous and BR-evoked activity of NTS units (71, 76, 99). Spontaneous release from attached, native boutons evokes prominent GABA-mediated synaptic chloride currents in enzymatically dispersed medial NTS neurons (46). GABA activates chloride currents in dispersed NTS neurons, and these are blocked by a $GABA_A$ antagonist (106). Blockade of the specific uptake of GABA increases resting blood pressure, but this inhibition of apparently ongoing release of GABA is mediated by $GABA_B$ receptors (136). $GABA_B$ agonist, baclofen, injected into NTS increases blood pressure (114) and depresses baroreflex responses (51, 137). Baclofen's two effects in medullary slices are reduction of the amplitude and frequency of spontaneous EPSPs and IPSPs and the amplitude of tract-evoked synaptic events presumably by presynaptic mechanisms, and hyperpolarization of NTS neurons by direct actions (22). This raises the possibility that activation of a GABAergic neuron could excite (disinhibit) NTS neurons by removing a $GABA_A$ergic input (IPSP) via $GABA_B$ receptors. Thus not only is there a $GABA_B$ presynaptic modulation of excitatory amino acid release, but also a $GABA_B$ presynaptic modulation of GABA release onto a $GABA_A$ postsynaptic site. Recent electron microscopic studies, however, failed to resolve presynaptic GABA terminals (70). Thus there is considerable inconsistency between the views of the roles of $GABA_A$ and $GABA_B$ in NTS, and in all probability both mechanisms exist, possibly on different neurons. $GABA_B$ may well act primarily as a presynaptic modulator of a variety of inputs to NTS, while $GABA_A$ mediates postsynaptic inhibition from interneurons and central neurons outside of NTS. The complicated nature of the effects of GABA in the NTS, coupled with the lack of positive identification of the affected neurons, makes it difficult to conceive of unique explanations for blood pressure and baroreflex data.

Angiotensin II

Of the many peptides identified in NTS, angiotensin II (AII) has perhaps one of the most complete dossiers spanning reflex responses to single cell electrophysiology and has the potential for fulfilling criteria for a truly neurohumoral integrative mediator. AII is an important modulator within the CNS (103, 115) and strongly influences the control of blood pressure and fluid homeostasis. Although the components of the renin-angiotensin system have been identified in various CNS areas, less is certain about the cellular mechanisms of action and whether angiotensin acts hormonally and/or as a transmitter. Central AII function may be involved in the development of hypertension in SHR (115), and NTS AII levels and receptor expression are higher in spontaneously hypertensive rats (SHRs) than in Wistar-Kyoto rats(WKY) (95, 118).

NTS contains one of the highest densities of high affinity AII receptors in the brain (94, 146), and much of this appears to be presynaptic (38).

Microinjection of fairly high doses of AII (50–250 ng) directly into NTS evokes pressor responses (115). Injection of saralasin, a competitive AII antagonist, into NTS increases reflex bradycardia to increases in systemic pressure (27), an effect consistent with inhibition of baroreflexes by endogenous AII in NTS. However, other studies suggest that much lower doses of AII (0.1–12.5 ng) in medial NTS produce depressor responses (28, 78). Although AII injected systemically raises blood pressure and decreases discharge in most extracellular NTS units, two thirds of those specifically identified as sensitive to AII increase their discharge (110). Interestingly, only excitatory responses to local AII have been recorded in NTS neurons. In horizontal medullary slices, AII increases extracellular spike frequencies of about half of medial NTS units and involves the AT-1 receptor (14, 15). However, in intracellular slice recordings from medial NTS neurons, which were monosynaptically connected to the solitary tract, AII increases the size of tract-evoked EPSPs in a subpopulation (30%) of neurons without altering postsynaptic conductance or membrane potential (149). This, plus binding studies, suggest that AII may be acting presynaptically to augment transmitter release. By extension, if the AII modulation of calcium currents in aortic BR soma dissociated from the nodose ganglion (11, 12) is indicative of the events at the presynaptic fibers, the primary effect of AII may be to enhance bouton calcium currents (Figure 2) and thereby to increase the release of GLU. How can these single NTS neuron findings be reconciled with an inhibition of the baroreflex at NTS observed in blood pressure data using high doses of AII and antagonists? AII inhibition of the baroreflex under these conditions may not occur at the first (afferent) synapse or on postsynaptic cells directly connected to tract axons. Among the possible alternatives are that AII may act at neurons beyond the first synapse by (a) activating GABAergic interneurons or enhancing their inhibitory synapses onto afferent connected neurons, (b) inhibiting NTS output neurons, or (c) by actions at non-NTS sites such as area postrema neurons, which are synaptically connected to NTS. AII could also be acting to modulate release of another transmitter from an input not activated by tract stimulation. These results suggest that low doses of AII may act within NTS to facilitate the reflex and, at high doses, AII could diffuse out of NTS and/or affect additional neurons beyond NTS. Clearly, much more work needs to be done to eliminate or confirm any of these possibilities.

Other candidates for modulation of presynaptic terminals are suggested by substances that produce changes in the electrical activity of the peripheral soma of the BRs neurons. At the soma, a number of endogenous transmitters have been applied to observe the effects either on the action potentials, or on specific ionic currents. Where it has been possible to characterize the cells as either A-type or C-type (based on conduction velocity measurements or the shape of the action potential), it is clear that the C-type soma are sensitive to more substances than are the A-type. The C-type respond to GABA, serotonin (5-HT), acetylcholine, histamine, catecholamines, and bradykinin (for a review, see 67). Of these, the A type cells are consistently sensitive only to the catecholamines and to GABA. In addition to AII, CGRP, NPY, and GLU are also shown to modify the calcium currents in the isolated nodose soma (64, 147, 148).

TARGETS OF PRESYNAPTIC MODULATION

As discussed above, angiotensin II or other medial NTS transmitters may have as targets presynaptic sites on the BR terminals within medial NTS. These presynaptic receptors may be channels that are opened by ligand binding, such as GLU, GABA, or glycine receptors. Alternatively, ligand-activated receptors may, directly or through second messenger systems, modulate the activity of voltage-dependent channels in the membrane of the central presynaptic terminal. In either case, the final common pathway for presynaptic modulation is via regulation of intracellular calcium and subsequent transmitter release. A key question to understanding the presynaptic modulation of synaptic transmission between the BR afferent fiber and the medial NTS neuron is what ion channels control transmitter release. The central terminals are not currently accessible to electrical recording. However, presynaptic mechanisms can be inferred indirectly from postsynaptic responses measured in NTS neurons. An alternative and, in some ways, more direct approach is to identify and characterize the channels in these same neurons at the cell body of the sensory neurons (87). Channels expressed in the soma (Figure 1) may well be present at the central synaptic terminal. Information about these channels can then used to probe the synaptic terminals with techniques such as localizing labeled high affinity agonists for a particular channel to the synaptic terminal region, or by monitoring the EPSP in the presence of agents that block specific ion channels. For example, changes in membrane potential at the presynaptic terminal should modulate calcium influx and alter the release of transmitter that in turn alters the amplitude of the EPSP recorded at the postsynaptic cell.

Sodium Channels

Potential candidates for synaptic terminal channels have been provided by numerous studies of soma in the nodose and petrosal ganglia (17, 52, 68, 134) and the subgroup of BR neurons of the nodose ganglion in particular (63, 64, 92). Two types of sodium currents have been described in studies of the sensory soma. One is tetrodotoxin (TTX)-sensitive, the other TTX-insensitive. A composite of data suggests that the TTX-sensitive current is present in the A-type cells, while both the TTX-sensitive and insensitive current are present in the soma of neurons with C fibers (13, 68, 134). The presence of the TTX-resistant sodium current contributes to the broad action potential in the soma of C-type nodose neurons (13).

Calcium Channels

Calcium currents are of particular interest as they are often the target of modulation by neurotransmitters. At least three types of calcium channels are present in the BR soma as well as in the more general sensory afferent population. A small component of the total calcium current is contributed by a low threshold T type channel, Ca_T (18, 68, 73, 92). High threshold calcium current has also been described in the unidentified afferent soma population (18, 68, 73, 92). The high threshold component was dissected pharmacologically (11, 92). In the nodose ganglion, an ω-conotoxin- (CTX) sensitive channel (92) and a quiescent pool of dihydropyridine- (DHP) sensitive channels (11) are present. A component of calcium current that remains in the presence of both blockers has not been identified with regard to toxin specificity (92). As mentioned earlier, the CTX-sensitive calcium current is modulated by AII (11, 12). Interestingly, since calcium permeation does not appear to be required for excitation of the peripheral sensory endings of aortic BRs (2, 3, 83, 140), this suggests a selective preferential expression of calcium channels at somal and synaptic terminal membranes.

Potassium Channels

At least three types of potassium channels are present in labeled BR neurons. A transient outward, 4-aminopyridine- (4-AP) sensitive current that inactivates with several time constants is present (84) and is similar to that described in detail in the wider general population of nodose neurons (32, 90). A delayed outwardly rectifying potassium current (84) is also similar to the general population (32, 90). Two calcium-activated potassium channels, $I_{K,Ca}$ (63) have been identified in nodose neurons. One of these is specifically blocked by charybdotoxin and by low concentrations (1 mM) of tetraethylammonium (TEA).

Presynaptic Localization in NTS

Within NTS, the presence of calcium channels at the presynaptic terminal, which are similar to those described at the soma, can be tested by monitoring the amplitude of the EPSP in the postsynaptic cell in response to stimulation of the solitary tract. These studies using selective calcium channel blockers suggest that there is little current flow through DHP-sensitive voltage-dependent calcium channels and that most of the calcium influx responsible for the transmitter release (Figure 2) comes through ω-conotoxin-sensitive calcium channels (4). This is consistent with the channels that are present at identified aortic BR soma (92). Not surprisingly, TTX-sensitive sodium channels are also present and TTX blocks afferent synaptic transmission (149). The presence of TTX-insensitive channels has not been substantiated. The presence of the specific potassium channels identified in the soma has not been investigated in the central terminals.

VOLTAGE-GATED IONIC CURRENTS AND INTEGRATED NTS RESPONSE CHARACTERISTICS

The postsynaptic NTS neurons appear to have a fairly conventional complement of voltage-dependent ion channels (29, 125). TTX eliminates action potentials in most NTS neurons, which indicates the presence of a fast sodium current I_{Na} (29, 82, 116). A residual broad spike and inward calcium current is found in the presence of TTX and is eliminated by cadmium in many NTS neurons (29, 82). Two calcium currents can be resolved, an L-type and a T-type: L-type with a high voltage threshold for activation blocked by DHPs, and T-type, which is largely inactivated at resting potentials, can be activated at negative membrane potentials (82). Several potassium channels have been identified in NTS. A slowly developing, non-inactivating potassium current, I_K, is blocked by TEA (36, 102). A TEA-resistant, transient potassium current, I_A, and a delayed, more slowly inactivating potassium current, I_D, are more variably present across NTS and are blocked by 4-AP (29, 35, 36, 102). An $I_{K,Ca}$ channel is present in medial NTS neurons (29, 36, 102) and is blocked by charybdotoxin (102).

These three major classes of intrinsic time- and voltage-dependent ionic channels, sodium, calcium, and potassium, give rise to a spectrum of response properties in NTS neurons and are capable of transforming the ultimate output of NTS neurons in response to synaptic activation or inhibition (125). No absolute differential distribution of these channels across the subnuclei of NTS is readily apparent, although in the ventral and medial portions of caudal NTS and in rostral parts of NTS there are suggestions of subtypes of neurons based on morphology and/or on discharge characteristics such as spike frequency adaptation and delayed excitation, which depend on these channels (21, 29, 35–37, 62, 111, 112). Short periods of conditioning at hyperpolarized membrane potentials greatly dampen the response to subsequent activation for prolonged intervals and produce the signature delayed excitation response prominently featured in most portions of NTS (21, 29, 37, 125, 150). Potassium channel blockers support a prominent general role of I_A in delayed excitation (35, 36). A recent comprehensive ionic current model of medial NTS neurons suggests that delayed excitation, the sculpting of the action potential waveform, and spike frequency adaptation result from the dynamic interplay between I_A, I_D, $I_{K,Ca}$, and the injected depolarizing current (125). In addition, some of these or other voltage-gated channels are targets for selective modulation by neurotransmitters (10, 116).

FUNCTION OF THE FIRST BAROREFLEX SYNAPSE: Relay or Integration?

Many of the questions most relevant to the overall contribution of NTS to baroreflex performance are broad and highly integrative in nature. An outstanding example is an intriguing report of Seller & Illert (128), who found a pronounced reduction in baroreflex responses in cats at CSN stimulation frequencies beyond 5 Hz, which they attributed to a frequency-dependent depression of afferent synaptic transmission in NTS. This is particularly surprising given that discharge from even a single myelinated BR afferent neuron generates bursts of action potentials of 50–100 Hz or more (e.g. 5, 33). Tests of efferent nerve activity, blood pressure, and heart rate suggest that the reflex outflow becomes similarly attenuated at relatively low input frequencies (69, 131). Bypassing the first synapse and stimulating NTS neurons directly, Seller & Illert (128) found progressive increases in the blood pressure responses to frequencies of up to 120 Hz. These and other experiments clearly suggest a major impact of the frequency trans-mission properties of the first synapse within the NTS on baroreflex function. Frequency-dependent depression appears to be a common feature in the NTS and other nearby regions of the medulla in response to afferent stimulation (e.g. 129, 130). Afferent-NTS synaptic responses recorded intracellularly are depressed at similar frequencies in vivo (97, 98) and in brain slices (6, 100). Frequency-dependent limits of baroreflex responses to ADN stimulation may be more modest in rats, however (57, 77, 121).

Although this and other phenomena must be a function of cellular receptors and channels at this synapse, little is known about the frequency-dependent depression in NTS. Primary afferent depolarization (PAD) appears to con-tribute to this frequency-dependent response depression for pulmonary afferents in other areas of NTS, but the evidence for BRs (including intracellular recordings from afferent BR axons) has been negative for PAD (49, 50, 122–124). The contribution of pre- and/or postsynaptic mechanisms to frequency-dependent synaptic depression in NTS remain uncertain. Frequency-dependent differences reported in the reflex responses to electrical stimulation of the aortic nerve of SHRs compared to controls could con-ceivably be related to NTS synaptic transmission (55). The contribution of voltage-gated conductances to frequency-dependent depression of information transfer from the BR beyond the first NTS neuron is still unclear.

CONCLUSION

Clearly a broad range of information on the nature and mechanisms of cellular function of NTS is not yet available. Fairly systematic studies will be required to examine many critical issues in NTS in order to approach the complexities of overall performance mechanisms such as the frequency transmission within NTS and on to other brain nuclei. There are many pressing needs. Major aspects of local circuitry (secondary neurons, interneurons, and output neurons) need to be defined and studied both in isolation and within an integrative framework. Intra-axonal HRP loading within NTS suggests that BR synaptic terminals arborize over great distances (33), yet how many NTS neurons are innervated by a single BR neuron (single BR divergence)? Convergence from different source nerves (CSN and ADN) and modalities (chemo- and BR) onto single NTS neurons is fairly common (e.g. 42, 43, 49, 96, 97), but how many individual BRs contact a single NTS neuron? It is relatively rare for single NTS neurons to be activated by both A- and C-fiber afferents (41). Is A-type and C-type BR information processed differently, and what are the critical features of these inputs to shaping the reflex responses? How do the many transmitters act and interact and at what cells within NTS? Are ionic channels differentially expressed within NTS, and how do they interact with neurotransmitter and second messenger systems to modulate NTS and reflex performance? How does the system change with development and pathology, especially hypertension?

Pulling all the information becoming available at the cellular level into a framework that can effectively reflect upon what is known about the reflex will be a major challenge requiring novel approaches. Computer modeling may aid this process. Comprehensive mathematical models point the way to a new tool in understanding complex, dynamic interactions of multiple ionic currents in neurons such as NTS. Rigorous models incorporating primary data from the concerned neurons provide a forum for linking dissociated or cultured neuron data with more integrative data from slice or in vivo work. Multidimensional models allow simultaneous assessment of various ionic currents and lend themselves to reasonably realistic feasibility evaluation of trial hypotheses about portions of the system that are only indirectly accessible experimentally. Such modeling may prove to be a practical way to combine essentially unidimensional interventions such as pharmacological blockers or lesions or to formulate ideas about how cellular processes may give rise to facets of the behavior of the more intact system. Using what-if scenarios, these models can suggest more efficient experimental designs. Ultimately though, testing any of these theoretical constructs will require careful evaluation with well designed tests in the intact system.

ACKNOWLEDGMENTS

The authors would like to thank David Mendelowitz and Virginia L. Brooks for their helpful advice in the preparation of this manuscript.

Literature Cited

1. Andresen MC. 1984. Short- and long-term determinants of baroreceptor function in aged normotensive and spontaneously hypertensive rats. *Circ. Res.* 54:750–59
2. Andresen MC, Kunze DL. 1987. Ionic sensitivity of baroreceptors. *Circ. Res.* 61:166–71
3. Andresen MC, Kuraoka S, Brown AM. 1979. Individual and combined actions of calcium, sodium and potassium ions on baroreceptors in the rat. *Circ. Res.* 45:757–63
4. Andresen MC, Mendelowitz D, Yang M. 1993. Dihydropyridine and omega-conotoxin sensitivity of afferent synaptic transmission in rat medial nucleus tractus solitarius. *FASEB J.* 7:A99 (Abstr.)
5. Andresen MC, Yang M. 1990. Dynamic and static conditioning pressures evoke equivalent rapid resetting in rat aortic baroreceptors. *Circ. Res.* 67: 303–11
6. Andresen MC, Yang M. 1990. Frequency dependent excitatory postsynaptic potentials (EPSPs) in neurons of rat medial nucleus tractus solitarius (mNTS) to tract stimulation. *FASEB J.* 4:A1195 (Abstr.)
7. Andresen MC, Yang M. 1990. Non-NMDA receptors mediate sensory afferent synaptic transmission in medial nucleus tractus solitarius. *Am. J. Physiol.* 259:H1307–11
8. Andresen MC, Yang M. 1993. Excitatory amino acid receptors and afferent synaptic transmission in the nucleus tractus solitarius. In *Nucleus of the Solitary Tract,* ed. RA Barraco, pp. 187–92. Boca Raton, Fla.: CRC Press
9. Angell-James JE, Daly MD. 1970. Comparison of the reflex vasomotor responses to separate and combined stimulation of the carotid sinus and aortic arch baroreceptors by pulsatile and non-pulsatile pressure in the dog. *J. Physiol.* 209:257–93
10. Bacal K, Kunze DL. 1991. Calcium and potassium currents in neurons isolated from the nucleus tractus solitarius decrease in response to somatostatin. *FASEB J.* 5:A743 (Abstr.)
11. Bacal K, Kunze DL. 1993. Angiotensin II reversibly reduces calcium currents in neonatal rat nodose neurons. *FASEB J.* 7:A94 (Abstr.)
12. Bacal K, Priddy M, Kunze DL. 1991. Angiotensin II reversibly increases calcium currents in cultured rat nodose neurons. *Physiologist* 34:242 (Abstr.)
13. Baccaglini P, Cooper E. 1982. Electrophysiological studies of new-born rat nodose neurones in cell culture. *J. Physiol.* 324:429–39
14. Barnes KL, Knowles WD, Ferrario CM. 1990. Angiotensin II and angiotensin (1–7) excite neurons in the canine medulla in vitro. *Brain Res. Bull.* 24:275–80
15. Barnes KL, McQueeney AJ, Ferrario CM. 1993. Receptor subtype that mediates the neuronal effects of angiotensin II in the rat dorsal medulla. *Brain Res. Bull.* 31:195–200
16. Baskys A. 1992. Metabotropic receptors and 'slow' excitatory actions of glutamate agonists in the hippocampus. *Trends Neurosci.* 15:92–96
17. Belmonte C, Gallego R. 1983. Membrane properties of cat sensory neurones with chemoreceptor and baroreceptor endings. *J. Physiol.* 342:603–14
18. Bossu JL, Rodeau JL, Feltz A. 1989. Decay kinetics of calcium currents in rat sensory neurones: analysis at two internal free calcium concentrations. *Pflügers Arch.* 414:89–91
19. Bousquet P, Feldman J, Bloch R, Schwartz J. 1982. Evidence for a neuromodulatory role of GABA at the first synapse of the baroreceptor reflex pathway. Effects of GABA derivatives injected into the NTS. *Naunyn-Schmiedeberg's Arch. Pharmacol.* 319: 168–71
20. Bowery N. 1989. GABA$_B$ receptors and their significance in mammalian

pharmacology. *Trends Pharmacol. Sci.* 10:401–7

21. Bradley RM, Sweazey RD. 1992. Separation of neuron types in the gustatory zone of the nucleus tractus solitarii on the basis of intrinsic firing properties. *J. Neurophysiol.* 67:1659–68

22. Brooks PA, Glaum SR, Miller RJ, Spyer KM. 1992. The actions of baclofen on neurones and synaptic transmission in the nucleus tractus solitarii of the rat in vitro. *J. Physiol.* 457:115–29

23. Brooks PA, Spyer KM. 1993. Evidence for NMDA receptor-mediated synaptic events in the rat nucleus tractus solitarii. *J. Physiol.* 467:21P (Abstr.)

24. Brown AM, Saum WR, Tuley FH. 1976. A comparison of aortic baroreceptor discharge in normotensive and spontaneously hypertensive rats. *Circ. Res.* 39:488–96

25. Brown AM, Saum WR, Yasui S. 1978. Baroreceptor dynamics and their relationship to afferent fiber type and hypertension. *Circ. Res.* 42:694–702

26. Cameron AA, Pover CM, Willis WD, Coggeshall RE. 1992. Evidence that fine primary afferent axons innervate a wider territory in the superficial dorsal horn following peripheral axotomy. *Brain Res.* 575:151–54

27. Campagnole-Santos MJ, Diz DI, Ferrario CM. 1988. Baroreceptor reflex modulation by angiotensin II at the nucleus tractus solitarii. *Hypertension 11 (Suppl.)*I:167–71

28. Campagnole-Santos MJ, Diz DI, Santos RAS, Khosla, MC. Brosnihan KB, Ferrario CM. 1989. Cardiovascular effects of angiotensin-(1–7) injected into the dorsal medulla of rats. *Am. J. Physiol.* 257:H324–29

29. Champagnat J, Jacquin T, Richter DW. 1986. Voltage-dependent currents in neurones of the nuclei of the solitary tract of rat brainstem slices. *Pflügers Arch.* 406:372–79

30. Ciriello J. 1983. Brainstem projections of aortic baroreceptor afferent fibers in the rat. *Neurosci. Lett.* 36:37–42

31. Coleridge HM, Coleridge JCG, Schultz HD. 1987. Characteristics of C fibre baroreceptors in the carotid sinus of dogs. *J. Physiol.* 394:291–313

32. Cooper E, Shrier A. 1989. Inactivation of A currents and A channels on rat nodose neurons in culture. *J. Gen. Physiol.* 94:881–910

33. Czachurski J, Dembowsky K, Seller H, Nobling R, Taugner R. 1988. Morphology of electrophysiologically identified baroreceptor afferents and second order neurons in the brainstem of the cat. *Arch. Ital. Biol.* 126:129–44

34. Daw NW, Stein PSG, Fox K. 1993. The role of NMDA receptors in information processing. *Annu. Rev. Neurosci.* 16:207–22

35. Dekin MS, Getting PA. 1984. Firing pattern of neurons in the nucleus tractus solitarius: modulation by membrane hyperpolarization. *Brain Res.* 324:180–84

36. Dekin MS, Getting PA. 1987. In vitro characterization of neurons in the ventral part of the nucleus tractus solitarius. II. Ionic basis for repetitive firing patterns. *J. Neurophysiol.* 58:215

37. Dekin MS, Getting PA, Johnson SM. 1987. In vitro characterization of neurons in the ventral part of the nucleus tractus solitarius. I. Identification of neuronal types and repetitive firing properties. *J. Neurophysiol.* 58:195–96

38. Diz DI, Barnes KL, Ferrario CM. 1986. Contribution of the vagus nerve to angiotensin II binding sites in the canine medulla. *Brain Res. Bull.* 17: 497–505

39. Donoghue S, Felder RB, Gilbey MP, Jordan D, Spyer KM. 1985. Post-synaptic activity evoked in the nucleus tractus solitarius by carotid sinus and aortic nerve afferents in the cat. *J. Physiol.* 360:261–73

40. Donoghue S, Felder RB, Jordan D, Spyer KM. 1984. The central projections of carotid baroreceptors and chemoreceptors in the cat: a neurophysiological study. *J. Physiol.* 347:397–409

41. Donoghue S, Fox RE, Kidd C, McWilliam PN. 1981. The terminations and secondary projections of myelinated and non-myelinated fibres of the aortic nerve in the cat. *Q. J. Exper. Physiol.* 66:405–22

42. Donoghue S, Garcia M, Jordan D, Spyer K. 1982. The brain-stem projections of pulmonary stretch afferent neurones in cats and rabbits. *J. Physiol.* 322:353–63

43. Donoghue S, Garcia M, Jordan D, Spyer K. 1982. Identification and brain-stem projections of aortic baroreceptor afferent neurones in nodose ganglia of cats and rabbits. *J. Physiol.* 322:337–53

44. Douglas W, Ritchie J, Schaumann W. 1956. Depressor reflexes from medullated and nonmedullated fibres in the rabbit's aortic nerve. *J. Physiol.* 132: 187–98

45. Douglas W, Schaumann W. 1956. A study of the depressor and pressor components of the cat's carotid sinus

and aortic nerves using electrical stimuli of different intensities and frequencies. *J. Physiol.* 132:173–86

46. Drewe JA, Childs GV, Kunze DL.
1988. Synaptic transmission between
dissociated adult mammalian neurons
and attached synaptic boutons. *Science*
241:1810–13

47. Drewe JA, Miles R, Kunze DL. 1990.
Excitatory amino acid receptors of
guinea pig medial nucleus tractus
solitarius neurons. *Am. J. Physiol.*
259:H1389–95

48. Ead HW, Green JN, Neil E. 1952. A
comparison of the effects of pulsatile
and non-pulsatile blood flow through
the carotid sinus on the reflexogenic
activity of the sinus baroreceptors in
the cat. *J. Physiol.* 118:509–19

49. Felder RB. 1986. Excitatory and inhibitory interactions among renal and
cardiovascular afferent nerves in dorsomedial medulla. *Am. J. Physiol.* 250:
R580–88

50. Felder RB, Heesch CM. 1987. Interactions in the nucleus tractus solitarius
between right and left carotid sinus
nerves. *Am. J. Physiol.* 253:H1127–
35

51. Florentino A, Varga K, Kunos G.
1990. Mechanism of the cardiovascular
effects of GABAB receptor activation
in the nucleus tractus solitarii of the
rat. *Brain Res.* 535:264–70

52. Gallego R, Eyzaguirre C. 1978. Membrane and action potential characteristics of A and C nodose ganglion cells
studied in whole ganglia and in tissue
slices. *J. Neurophysiol.* 41:1217–32

53. Glaum SR, Miller RJ. 1992. Metabotropic glutamate receptors mediate
excitatory transmission in the nucleus
of the solitary tract. *J. Neurosci.* 12:
2251–58

54. Glaum SR, Miller RJ. 1993. Activation
of metabotropic glutamate receptors
produces reciprocal regulation of ionotropic glutamate and GABA responses
in the nucleus of the tractus solitarius
of the rat. *J. Neurosci.* 13:1636–41

55. Gonzalez E, Krieger AJ, Sapru HN.
1983. Central resetting of baroreflex
in the spontaneously hypertensive rat.
Hypertension 5:346–51

56. Gordon FJ, Leone C. 1991. Non-
NMDA receptors in the nucleus of the
tractus solitarius play the predominant
role in mediating aortic baroreceptor
reflexes. *Brain Res.* 568:319–22

57. Gordon FJ, Mark AL. 1984. Mechanism of impaired baroreflex control in
prehypertensive Dahl salt-sensitive rats.
Circ. Res. 54:378–87

58. Gross PM. 1991. Morphology and
physiology of capillary systems in sub-
regions of the subfornical organ and
area postrema. *Can. J. Physiol. Pharmacol.* 69:1010–25

59. Gross PM, Wall KM, Pang JJ, Shaver
SW, Wainman DS. 1990. Microvascular specializations promoting rapid
interstitial solute dispersion in nucleus
tractus solitarius. *Am. J. Physiol.* 259:
R1131–38

60. Gross PM, Wall KM, Wainman DS,
Shaver SW. 1991. Subregional topography of capillaries in the dorsal vagal
complex of rats: II. Physiological properties. *J. Comp. Neurol.* 306:83–94

61. Guyenet PG, Filz TM, Donaldson SR.
1987. Role of excitatory amino acids
in rat vagal and sympathetic baroreflexes. *Brain Res.* 407:272–84

62. Haddad GG, Getting PA. 1989. Repetitive firing properties of neurons in
the ventral region of nucleus tractus
solitarius. In vitro studies in adult and
neonatal rat. *J. Neurophysiol.* 62:1213–
24

63. Hay M, Kunze DL. 1993. Calcium-
activated potassium currents in rat nodose ganglia neurons. *Am. J. Physiol.*
Submitted

64. Hay M, Kunze DL. 1993. Calcium
current inhibition by L-Glu metabotropic receptor activation in nodose
neurons. *FASEB J.* 7:A99 (Abstr.)

65. Helke CJ, Hill KM. 1988. Immunohistochemical study of neuropeptides
in vagal and glossopharyngeal afferent
neurons in the rat. *Neuroscience* 26:
539–51

66. Helke CJ, Neiderer AJ. 1990. Studies
on the coexistence of substance P with
other putative transmitters in the nodose
and petrosal ganglion. *Synapse* 5:144–
51

67. Higashi H. 1986. Chemosensitivity of
visceral primary afferent neurons: Nodose ganglia. In *Autonomic and Enteric
Ganglia: Transmission and Its Pharmacology,* ed. AG Karczmar, K
Koketsu, S Nishi, pp. 439–55. New
York: Plenum

68. Ikeda SR, Schofield GG, Weight FF.
1986. Na$^+$ and Ca^{2+} currents of acutely
isolated adult rat nodose ganglion cells.
J. Neurophysiol. 55:527–39

69. Ishikawa N, Sagawa K. 1983. Non-
linear summation of depressor effects
of carotid sinus pressure changes and
aortic nerve stimulation in the rabbit.
Circ. Res. 52:401–10

70. Izzo PN, Sykes RM, Spyer KM. 1992.
gamma-Aminobutyric acid immunoreactive structures in the nucleus tractus

solitarius: A light and electron microscopic study. *Brain Res.* 591:69–78

71. Jordan D, Mifflin SW, Spyer KM. 1988. Hypothalamic inhibition of neurons in the nucleus tractus solitarius of the cat is GABA mediated. *J. Physiol.* 399:389–404

72. Kalia M, Welles R. 1980. Brain stem projections of the aortic nerve in the cat: a study using tetramethyl benzidine as the substrate for horseradish peroxidase. *Brain Res.* 188:23–32

73. Kelly KM, Gross RA, Macdonald RL. 1990. Valproic acid selectively reduces the low threshold (T) calcium current in rat nodose neurons. *Neurosci. Lett.* 116:233–38

74. Kendrick JE, Matson GL, Oberg B, Wennergren G. 1973. The effect of stimulus pattern on the pressure response to electrical stimulation of the carotid sinus nerve of cats. *Proc. Soc. Exper. Biol. Med.* 144:412–16

75. Koizumi K, Sato A. 1972. Reflex activity of single sympathetic fibres to skeletal muscle produced by electrical stimulation of somatic and vago-depressor afferent nerves in the cat. *Pflügers Arch.* 332:283–301

76. Kubo T, Kihara M. 1988. Evidence for gamma-aminobutyric acid receptor-mediated modulation of the aortic baroreceptor reflex in the nucleus tractus solitarii of the rat. *Neurosci. Lett.* 89:156–60

77. Kubo T, Kihara M. 1988. Evidence of N-methyl-D-aspartate receptor-mediated modulation of the aortic baroreceptor reflex in the rat nucleus tractus solitarius. *Neurosci. Lett.* 87:69–74

78. Kubo T, Kihara M. 1990. Modulation of the aortic baroreceptor reflex by neuropeptide Y, neurotensin and vasopressin microinjected into the nucleus tractus solitarii of the rat. *Naunyn-Schmiedeberg's Arch. Pharmacol.* 342:182–88

79. Kubo T, Kihara M. 1991. Unilateral blockade of excitatory amino acid receptors in the nucleus tractus solitarii produces an inhibition of baroreflexes in rats. *Naunyn-Schmiedeberg's Arch. Pharmacol.* 343:317–22

80. Kumada M, Terui N, Kuwaki T. 1990. Arterial baroreceptor reflex: its central and peripheral neural mechanisms. *Prog. Neurobiol.* 35:331–61

81. Kunze DL. 1980. Regulation of activity of cardiac vagal motorneurons. *Fed. Proc.* 39:2513–18

82. Kunze DL. 1987. Calcium currents of cardiovascular neurons isolated from adult guinea pigs. *Am. J. Physiol.* 252:H867-H871

83. Kunze DL, Andresen MC, Torres LA. 1986. Do calcium antagonists act directly on calcium channels to alter baroreceptor function? *J. Pharmacol. Exp. Ther.* 239:303–10

84. Kunze DL, Hay M. 1992. Three different potassium channels recorded from cultured nodose ganglia neurons. *Soc. Neurosci. Abstr.* 18:1016 (Abstr.)

85. Le Galloudec E, Merahi N, Laguzzi R. 1989. Cardiovascular changes induced by the local application of glutamate-related drugs in the rat nucleus tractus-solitarii. *Brain Res.* 503:322–25

86. Leone C, Gordon FJ. 1989. Is L-glutamate a neurotransmitter of baroreceptor information in the nucleus of tractus solitarius? *J. Pharmacol. Exp. Ther.* 250:953–62

87. Llinás RR. 1988. The intrinsic electrophysiological properties of mammalian neurons: Insights into central nervous system function. *Science* 242: 1654–64

88. Loewy AD. 1990. Central autonomic pathways. In *Central Regulation of Autonomic Functions*, ed. AD Loewy, KM Spyer, pp. 88–103. New York: Oxford Univ. Press

89. Machado BH, Bonagamba LGH. 1992. Microinjection of L-glutamate into the nucleus tractus solitarii increases arterial pressure in conscious rats. *Brain Res.* 576:131–38

90. McFarlane S, Cooper E. 1991. Kinetics and voltage dependence of A-type currents on neonatal rat sensory neurons. *J. Neurophysiol.* 66:1380–91

91. McWilliam PN, Shepheard SL. 1988. A GABA-mediated inhibition of neurones in the nucleus tractus solitarius of the cat that respond to electrical stimulation of the carotid sinus nerve. *Neurosci. Lett.* 94:321–26

92. Mendelowitz D, Kunze DL. 1992. Characterization of calcium currents in aortic baroreceptor neurons. *J. Neurophysiol.* 68:509–17

93. Mendelowitz D, Yang M, Andresen MC, Kunze DL. 1992. Localization and retention in vitro of fluorescently labeled aortic baroreceptor terminals on neurons from the nucleus tractus solitarius. *Brain Res.* 581:339–43

94. Mendelsohn FAO, Quirion R, Saavedra JM, Aguilera G, Catt KJ. 1984. Autoradiographic localization of angiotensin II receptors in rat brain. *Proc. Natl. Acad. Sci. USA* 81:1575–79

95. Meyer JM, Felten DL, Weyhenmeyer

JA. 1990. Measurement of immuno-reactive angiotensin II levels in micro-dissected brain nuclei from developing spontaneously hypertensive and Wistar Kyoto rats. *Exp. Neurol.* 107:164–69

96. Mifflin SW. 1992. Arterial chemore-ceptor input to nucleus tractus solitarius. *Am. J. Physiol.* 263:R368–75

97. Mifflin SW, Felder RB. 1988. An intracellular study of time-dependent cardiovascular afferent interactions in nucleus tractus solitarius. *J. Neuro-physiol.* 59:1798–813

98. Mifflin SW, Felder RB. 1990. Synaptic mechanisms regulating cardiovascular afferent inputs to solitary tract nucleus. *Am. J. Physiol.* 259:H653–61

99. Mifflin SW, Spyer KM, Withington-Wray DJ. 1988. Baroreceptor inputs to the nucleus tractus solitarius in the cat: modulation by the hypothalamus. *J. Physiol.* 399:369–87

100. Miles R. 1986. Frequency dependence of synaptic transmission in nucleus of the solitary tract in vitro. *J. Neu-rophysiol.* 55:1076–1602

101. Miller BD, Felder RB. 1988. Excit-atory amino acid receptors intrinsic to synaptic transmission in nucleus tractus solitarii. *Brain Res.* 456:333–43

102. Moak JP, Kunze DL. 1993. Potassium currents of neurons isolated from the medial nucleus tractus solitarius. *Am. J. Physiol.* 265:1596–1602

103. Moffett RB, Bumpus FM, Husain A. 1987. Cellular organization of the brain renin-angiotensin system. *Life Sci.* 41:1867–79

104. Monaghan DT, Bridges RJ, Cotman CW. 1989. The excitatory amino acid receptors: Their classes, pharmacol-ogy,and distinct properties in the func-tion of the central nervous system. *Annu. Rev. Pharmacol. Toxicol.* 29:365–402

105. Nakagawa T, Shirasaki T, Tateishi N, Murase K, Akaike N. 1990. Effects of antagonists on N-methyl-D-aspartate response in acutely isolated nucleus tractus solitarii neurons of the rat. *Neurosci. Lett.* 113:169–74

106. Nakagawa T, Wakamori M, Shirasaki T, Nakaye T, Akaike N. 1991. γ-Aminobutyric acid-induced response in acutely isolated nucleus solitarii neu-rons of the rat. *Am. J. Physiol.* 260:C745–49

107. Nicholls DG. 1992. A retrograde step forward. *Nature* 360:106–7

108. Nicoll RA, Malenka RC, Kauer JA. 1990. Functional comparison of neu-rotransmitter receptor subtypes in mam-malian central nervous system. *Physiol. Rev.* 70:513–51

109. Palkovits M. 1981. Neuropeptides and biogenic amines in central cardiovas-cular control mechanisms. In *Central Nervous System Mechanisms in Hyper-tension,* ed. JP Buckley, CM Ferrario, pp. 73–87. New York: Raven

110. Papas S, Smith P, Ferguson AV. 1990. Electrophysiological evidence that sys-temic angiotensin influences rat area postrema neurons. *Am. J. Physiol.* 258:R70–76

111. Paton JFR, Foster WR, Schwaber JS. 1993. Characteristic firing behavior of cell types in the cardiorespiratory re-gion of the nucleus tractus solitarii of the rat. *Brain Res.* 604:112–25

112. Paton JFR, Rogers WT, Schwaber JS. 1991. Tonically rhythmic neurons with-in a cardiorespiratory region of the nucleus tractus solitarii of the rat. *J. Neurophysiol.* 66:824–38

113. Pawloski-Dahm C, Gordon FJ. 1992. Evidence for a kynurenate-insensitive glutamate receptor in nucleus tractus solitarii. *Am. J. Physiol.* 262:H1611–15

114. Persson B. 1981. A hypertensive re-sponse to baclofen in the nucleus tractus solitarii in rats. *J. Pharmacol.* 33:226–31

115. Phillips MI. 1987. Functions of angio-tensin in the central nervous system. *Annu. Rev. Physiol.* 49:413–35

116. Priddy M, Drewe JA, Kunze DL. 1992. L-glutamate inhibition of an inward potassium current in neonatal neurons from the nucleus of the solitary tract. *Neurosci. Lett.* 136:131–35

117. Qu L, Stuesse SL. 1991. Low-pres-sure-sensitive baroreceptor fibers re-corded from rabbit carotid sinus nerves. *Circ. Res.* 69:1608–15

118. Raizada MK, Sumners C, Lu D. 1993. Angiotensin II type 1 receptor mRNA levels in the brains of normotensive and spontaneously hypertensive rats. *J. Neurochem.* 60:1949–52

119. Reis DJ. 1984. The brain and hy-pertension: reflections on 35 years of inquiry into the neurobiology of the circulation. *Circulation* 70(SIII):31–45

120. Reis DJ, Granata AR, Perrone M, Talman W. 1981. Evidence that glu-tamic acid is the neurotransmitter of baroreceptor afferents terminating in the nucleus tractus solitarius (NTS). *J. Auton. Nerv. Syst.* 3:321–34

121. Reynolds PJ, Andresen MC. 1993. Frequency dependence of baroreflex

responses to aortic nerve stimulation in the rat. *FASEB J.* 7:A100 (Abstr.)

122. Richter DW, Jordan D, Ballantyne D, Meesmann M, Spyer KM. 1986. Presynaptic depolarization in myelinated vagal afferent fibres terminating in the nucleus of the tractus solitarius in the cat. *Pflügers Arch.* 406:12–19

123. Rudomin P. 1967. Presynaptic inhibition induced by vagal afferent volleys. *J. Neurosci.* 30:964–81

124. Rudomin P. 1968. Excitability changes of superior laryngeal, vagal and depressor afferent terminals produced by stimulation of the solitary tract nucleus. *Exp. Brain Res.* 6:156–70

125. Schild JH, Khushalani S, Clark JW, Andresen MC, Kunze DL, Yang M. 1993. An ionic current model for neurons in the rat medial nucleus tractus solitarius receiving sensory afferent input. *J. Physiol.* 469:341–63

126. Seagard JL, Hopp FA, Drummond HA, Van Wynsberghe DM. 1993. Selective contribution of two types of carotid sinus baroreceptors to the control of blood pressure. *Circ. Res.* 72:1011–22

127. Seagard JL, Van Brederode JFM, Dean C, Hopp FA, Gallenberg LA, Kampine JP. 1990. Firing characteristics of single-fiber carotid sinus baroreceptors. *Circ. Res.* 66:1499–509

128. Seller H, Illert M. 1969. The localization of the first synapse in the carotid sinus baroreceptor reflex pathway and its alteration of the afferent input. *Pflügers Arch.* 306:1–19

129. Sessle BJ. 1973. Excitatory and inhibitory inputs to single neurons in the solitary tract nucleus and adjacent reticular formation. *Brain Res.* 53:319–31

130. Sessle BJ. 1973. Presynaptic excitability changes induced in single laryngeal primary afferent fibers. *Brain Res.* 53:333–42

131. Spyer KM. 1981. Neural organisation and control of the baroreceptor reflex. *Rev. Physiol. Biochem. Pharmacol.* 88:24–124

132. Spyer KM. 1990. The central nervous organization of reflex circulatory control. See Ref. 88, pp. 168–88

133. Spyer KM, Donoghue S, Felder RB, Jordan D. 1984. Processing of afferent inputs in cardiovascular control. *Clin. Exp. Hypertens. A. Theory Pract.* A6: 173–84

134. Stansfeld CE, Wallis DI. 1985. Properties of visceral primary afferent neurons in the nodose ganglion of the rabbit. *J. Neurophysiol.* 54:245–60

135. Stegemann J, Tibes U. 1967. Sinus-oidal stimulation of carotid sinus baroreceptors and peripheral blood pressure in dogs. *Ann. NY Acad. Sci.* 156:787–95

136. Sved AF, Sved JC. 1990. Endogenous GABA acts on $GABA_B$ receptors in the nucleus tractus solitarius to increase blood pressure. *Brain Res.* 526:235–40

137. Sved AF, Tsukamoto K. 1992. Tonic stimulation of $GABA_B$ receptors in the nucleus tractus solitarius modulates the baroreceptor reflex. *Brain Res.* 592:37–43

138. Talman WT. 1989. Kynurenic acid microinjected into the nucleus tractus solitarius of rat blocks the arterial baroreflex but not responses to glutamate. *Neurosci. Lett.* 102:247–52

139. Talman WT, Perrone MH, Reis DJ. 1980. Evidence for L-glutamate as the neurotransmitter of baroreceptor afferent nerve fibers. *Science* 209:813–15

140. Thoren PN, Andresen MC, Brown AM. 1982. Effects of changes in extracellular ionic concentrations on aortic baroreceptors with nonmyelinated afferent fibers. *Circ. Res.* 50:413–18

141. Thoren PN, Jones J. 1977. Characteristics of aortic baroreceptor C-fibers in the rabbit. *Acta Physiol. Scand.* 99: 448–56

142. Thoren PN, Saum WR, Brown AM. 1977. Characteristics of rat aortic baroreceptors with nonmedullated afferent nerve fibers. *Circ. Res.* 40:231–37

143. Urbanski RW, Sapru HN. 1988. Putative neurotransmitters involved in medullary cardiovascular regulation. *J. Auton. Nerv. Syst.* 25:181–93

144. Van Giersbergen PLM, Palkovits M, De Jong W. 1992. Involvement of neurotransmitters in the nucleus tractus solitarii in cardiovascular regulation. *Physiol. Rev.* 72:789–824

145. Wallach J, Loewy A. 1980. Projections of the aortic nerve to the nucleus tractus solitarius in the rabbit. *Brain Res.* 188:247–51

146. Wamsley JK, Herblin WF, Alburges ME, Hunt M. 1990. Evidence for the presence of angiotensin II-type 1 receptors in brain. *Brain Res. Bull.* 25:397–400

147. Wiley JW, Gross RA, Lu Y, Macdonald RL. 1990. Neuropeptide Y reduces calcium current and inhibits acetylcholine release in nodose neurons via a pertussis toxin-sensitive mechanism. *J. Neurophysiol.* 63:1499–507

148. Wiley JW, Gross RA, Macdonald RL. 1992. The peptide CGRP increases a high-threshold Ca^{2+} current in rat no-

dose neurones via a pertussis toxin-sensitive pathway. *J. Physiol.* 455: 367–81

149. Yang M, Andresen MC. 1991. Angiotensin enhances sensory afferent synaptic transmission in neurons of rat medial nucleus tractus solitarius in vitro. *FASEB J.* 5:A677 (Abstr.)

150. Yang M, Andresen MC. 1992. Delayed excitation is uniformly present in medial nucleus tractus solitarius neurons activated by tract stimulation. *FASEB J.* 6: (Abstr.)

151. Yao T, Thoren PN. 1983. Characteristics of brachiocephalic and carotid sinus baroreceptors with non-medullated afferents in rabbit. *Acta Physiol. Scand.* 117:1–8

Annu. Rev. Physiol. 1994. 56:117–40
Copyright © 1994 by Annual Reviews Inc. All rights reserved

CONTROL OF THE GASTROINTESTINAL TRACT BY ENTERIC NEURONS

Annmarie Surprenant

Glaxo Institute for Molecular Biology, 1228 Plan-les-Ouates, Geneva, Switzerland

KEY WORDS: enteric nervous system, synaptic transmission, ligand-gated ion channels,
             potassium channels, reflex vasodilation, microcirculation

INTRODUCTION

The gastrointestinal (GI) tract is host to three physiological effector systems: visceral smooth muscle, which is responsible for motility; intestinal musosa, which is responsible for fluid and electrolyte homeostasis; and the vasculature. The three divisions of the autonomic nervous system (sympathetic, parasympathetic, and enteric) contribute to the neural control of each of these effector systems although it seems fair to say that the enteric nervous system plays the predominant role in neuronal modulation of GI function. Complex reflex activities involving GI motility, intestinal ion transport, and mucosal blood flow occur in the absence of extrinsic autonomic and sensory input. Thus sensory, motor, and interneuronal elements mediating these types of reflex loops are contained within the two neural networks of the enteric nervous system: the myenteric (Auerbach's), and the submucosal (Meissner's) plexus (Figure 1). The major function of myenteric neurons is to control GI motility, while the submucosal neurons are primarily involved with modulation of GI blood flow and intestinal ion transport. Modern studies concerning the structure and function of synaptic transmission within the enteric nervous system essentially began in the early 1970's, and mushroomed through the 1980's to provide extensive and detailed information that Furness & Costa brought together in 1987 in their elegant and comprehensive treatise (37). More recently, Mihara (76) has provided a major update on the chemical coding and electrophysiological properties of enteric neurons. This chapter focuses on recent contributions to our under-

117

0066–4278/94/0315–0117$05.00

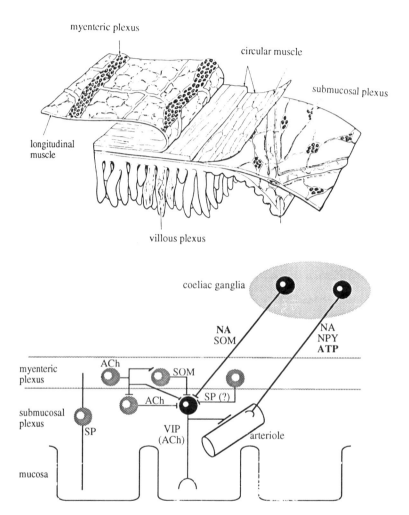

Figure 1 The drawing (*upper*) of the enteric plexuses shows arrangement of myenteric and submucosal plexuses as present in the guinea pig small intestine (drawing by M Costa from Reference 40, with permission). The diagram (*lower*) of the neuronal circuitry described in the text indicates known synaptic pathways. Acetylcholine (ACh) mediates fast EPSPs; noradrenaline (NA) and somatostatin (SOM) from myenteric neurons evoke IPSPs in VIP-containing submucosal neurons; transmitters (SP ?) underlying the slow EPSP have not been elucidated. Distinct populations of sympathetic neurons innervate enteric neurons (those that co-localize NA and SOM) and submucosal blood vessels (those that co-localize NA, NPY and ATP); sympathetic substances in bold-face are responsible for synaptic transmission. See text for further description.

standing of synaptic transmission within the enteric nervous system; it summarizes work concerning the cellular mechanisms of this synaptic transmission, and then describes one of the reflex mechanisms involving some of these synaptic pathways.

Immunohistochemical techniques, many of which were pioneered by investigators of the enteric nervous system, have been combined with selective denervations to provide a detailed picture of the neuronal projections within the enteric nervous system of the guinea pig small intestine (6, 19, 35–41). Overviews of the neural pathways described in this chapter are illustrated in Figure 1; complete descriptions can be found in previous reviews (6, 19, 38, 40, 41, 76) and the text of Furness & Costa (37).

SYNAPTIC TRANSMISSION IN ENTERIC NEURONS

Fast Excitatory Transmission

SYNAPTIC POTENTIALS AND TRANSMITTER CANDIDATES   Approximately 50% of all myenteric neurons and 85–90% of submucosal neurons in guinea pig small intestine are S/Type I neurons; that is, they receive fast nicotinic synaptic input (52, 53, 88). [The other main type of neuron, AH/Type 2, lacks fast excitatory synaptic potentials and has a prominent afterhyperpolarization following an action potential (52, 88).] Cholinergic interneurons provide almost all of the nicotinic input into myenteric S neurons (37, 108), although a small number of extrinsic vagal fibers innervate a distinct subpopulation of these neurons (60). In the submucosal plexus about half the nicotinic input originates from myenteric neurons and the remainder from other submucosal neurons (6–9); vagal or other extrinsic cholinergic fibers do not appear to reach this plexus (60). The molecular species of nicotinic channel(s) present in enteric neurons have not been determined. Such information is of particular interest because the pharmacology of synaptic nicotinic receptors in enteric neurons differs from other autonomic neurons; for example, 10 to 100-fold higher concentrations of antagonists such as hexamethonium and curare are required to block the fast synaptic potential (121). Measurements of unitary currents from outside-out membrane patches of submucosal neurons have resolved at least two distinct nicotinic receptor-channel types that show unitary conductances of about 12 and 35 pS (25), but detailed pharmacological characterization of these nicotinic receptors has not been carried out.

Two other ligand-gated cationic receptor-channels that mediate fast excitatory responses are presesent in enteric S/Type 1 neurons, the $5\text{-}HT_3$ receptor and the P_{2X}-type ATP purinoceptor (24, 25, 45, 121). Whole-cell and single-channel recordings of these receptor-channels have been carried out in submucosal neurons (24, 25; K-Z Shen et al, unpublished observations). Nicotinic, 5-HT$_3$, and P$_{2X}$ purinoceptor inward currents can be evoked in the same cell; ion replacement studies and reversal potential measurements have demonstrated that the ionic mechanism of each response is similar, but responses to the three agonists can be distinguished by sensitivity to selective antagonists (24, 25, 27, 121). Nicotinic- and 5-HT$_3$-induced currents show only slight rectification in their current-voltage relations, while there is marked inward rectification of the ATP-induced current in whole cell recordings (24, 25, 27).

Acetylcholine, 5-HT, and ATP all induce single channel openings in excised outside-out membrane patches of submucosal neurons; unitary currents activated by each of these agonists can be distinguished by selective receptor antagonists, as well as by distinct unitary conductances and open channel kinetics. Unitary conductances have been measured for nicotinic, 5-HT, and ATP currents in the same membrane patch with an internal solution of 160 mM K-gluconate and an external solution of 160 mM NaCl. As is the case for nicotinic single channels recorded from excised submucosal membranes, both 5-HT and ATP induce openings of at least two distinct channels; 5-HT$_3$ receptor activation opens channels having unitary conductances of approximately 10 and 17 pS (24, 25), while ATP-P$_{2X}$ receptor activation opens channels showing unitary conductances of 9 and 50 pS (24). As expected from ligand-gated ion channels, the latency to onset of channel activity is less than a few ms from time of agonist application, and internal GTP is not required for activation of any of these receptors (24, 25, 27, 121).

A subpopulation of 5-HT-containing myenteric neurons innervates other myenteric neurons as well as submucosal neurons; indeed, in many instances 5-HT-containing nerve terminals can be seen to envelop a submucosal cell body in a dense basket-like web (21, 32, 36, 37, 45; S Vanner et al, unpublished observations). However, 5-HT-mediated fast synaptic potentials have not been recorded from such neurons, even when they readily respond to exogenously applied 5-HT with fast cationic currents (111, 121). Electron microscopic evidence suggests that 5-HT nerve terminals do make tight synaptic contact through which fast synaptic transmission might be expected to occur (26). It is possible that postsynaptic 5-HT$_3$ receptors are not present in the synaptic zone, but are dispersed throughout extra-synaptic locales. Similarly, there is no evidence to suggest that neurally released ATP mediates a fast synaptic potential in enteric neurons, although fast excitatory synaptic potentials resulting from ATP release onto P$_{2X}$ purinoceptors have been demonstrated in neuronal cultures of the sympathetic neurons that provide innervation to the submucous plexus (27).

Slow Excitatory Transmission

SYNAPTIC POTENTIALS AND TRANSMITTER CANDIDATES Slow excitatory postsynaptic potentials (slow EPSPs) can be recorded from the majority of all enteric neurons in response to single or multiple nerve stimuli (37, 76, 78, 109). In myenteric neurons in which a single nerve stimulus is sufficient to evoke a slow excitatory response, the slow EPSP can be attributed to the release of acetylcholine acting on muscarinic receptors (91), but in the majority of cases the transmitter underlying the slow EPSP cannot be identified unequivocally. A large number of other substances that mimic the slow EPSP are present in, and released from, enteric nerve fibers; these include the tachykinins (substance P, neurokinin A, and neuropeptide B), 5-HT, vasoactive intestinal polypeptide (VIP), cholecystokinin (CCK), calcitonin gene-related peptide (CGRP), gastrin-releasing peptide (GRP), and ATP (33, 37, 38). No receptor antagonists consistently inhibit the non-cholinergic slow EPSP in enteric neurons. The major source of slow excitatory input to submucosal ganglia is from myenteric projections because the slow EPSP in these neurons is markedly reduced after myectomy, which removes all but the 5-HT-containing projections from myenteric plexus into submucosal plexus (6–9). The much reduced submucosal slow EPSP remaining after a combined myectomy and extrinsic sensory denervation can thus be attributed to submucosal interneurons.

Simultaneous intracellular recordings made from pairs of myenteric neurons located within the same ganglion have revealed that AH/Type 2 neurons, which are known to subserve sensory transduction (10, 34, 37), synapse directly onto other AH neurons as well as onto S neurons to produce slow EPSPs (67). No fast EPSPs were produced in these synaptic pairs even though all AH neurons contain acetylcholine. Thus sensory neurons of the myenteric plexus can synapse onto other myenteric neurons located within the same ganglion and release slow excitatory transmitters. Similar experiments in dissociated myenteric neurons maintained in tissue culture for several days revealed that both fast nicotinic and non-cholinergic slow EPSPs can be evoked between pairs of cells (124, 125). These two separate studies provide direct evidence that peptides can be released during action potential propagation in a single neuron and that this physiological release of peptide can evoke a slow EPSP in an output neuron.

IONIC MECHANISMS It was realized very early on that the slow EPSP recorded from enteric neurons is primarily the result of a decrease in a potassium conductance (gK) of the membrane (45, 57) and that both the voltage-independent background (or linear leak) gK_{leak} and the voltage-dependent, calcium-activated potassium conductance (gK$_{Ca}$) were the main targets for inhibition by slow excitatory transmitters (1, 47, 83, 109, 111, 113). This slow gK$_{Ca}$ in myenteric AH and submucosal neurons exhibits similar voltage-dependence, pharmacology, and agonist sensitivity (1, 83, 92, 119) as does the M-current, which is a primary target for modulation by slow excitatory agonists in other neuronal systems (15, 58, 117). The slow gK$_{Ca}$ in enteric neurons and the M-current in many other autonomic neurons make significant contributions to the resting conductance of the cell. Based on changes in conductance that occur during application of maximum concentrations of slow excitatory agonist, it is estimated that some 20–70% of the total membrane conductance at rest is due to the presence of these currents (1, 15, 92, 117). The main differences between these currents are the relatively smaller calcium dependence and somewhat faster kinetics of the M-current compared to the slow gK$_{Ca}$ (see 119).

More recent studies carried out in submucosal neurons have demonstrated that other conductances also can be modulated during slow excitatory synaptic transmission and/or during application of many of the slow excitatory substances listed above. Steady-state current-voltage curves obtained from the majority of submucosal neurons demonstrate an inwardly rectifying potassium conductance (gK$_{IR}$) similar to that described in many excitable and non-excitable cells (50); this type of gK$_{IR}$ in mammalian central neurons, such as rat locus coerulus and striatum, is reduced by the application of substance P and muscarine (97, 98). Several studies have investigated whether agonists modify this potassium conductance in enteric neurons; all results have demonstrated that neither slow excitatory synaptic transmission nor the application of substance P, muscarine and other slow excitatory agonists alters this resting inward rectification of the membrane (1, 76, 79, 101, 117). However, the slow excitatory agonists can inhibit an inwardly rectifying potassium conductance that is increased by the inhibitory agonists noradrenaline and somatostatin (gK$_{agonist}$; 101 and see below). These results may indicate that the gK$_{agonist}$ in these neurons is not identical to the resting gK$_{IR}$, or it may be that the potassium conductance coupled to the inhibitory agonists must be in an activated state before the slow excitatory agonists are able to produce an inhibition.

In many submucosal neurons, substance P, muscarine, and VIP evoke an inward current associated with an increased membrane conductance under conditions where gK$_{leak}$ and gK$_{Ca}$ are absent or minimal (e.g. calcium and potassium-free external solution). The agonist-induced current recorded under these conditions reverses at approximately 0 mV and is dependent on external sodium concentration, which implies that the slow excitatory agonist activates a predominantly sodium-selective cationic current (101). This pattern of dual potassium conductance decrease/sodium conductance increase by muscarine and other slow excitatory agonists is paralleled in many other excitable cells. A similar type of slow cationic current is well known to be activated by muscarine in amphibian sympathetic neurons (65, 116) and in cardiac and smooth muscle (4, 54, 75); more recently, results similar to these have been demonstrated for the actions of substance P and muscarine in mammalian central locus coeruleus neurons (97, 98). The contribution each makes to the excitatory response depends on the potassium conductance available at the resting potential. For example, in rat locus coeruleus neurons, where muscarine and SP increase a cationic conductance and inhibit a gK_{IR}, the gK_{IR} contributes little to the resting potential of the cell and consequently the excitation is primarily from the cation conductance increase (97). In submucosal neurons, the primary conductance available for modulation at the resting potential is the slow gK_{Ca}, and it is only at hyperpolarized levels that the cationic conductance becomes significant (1, 101).

As mentioned, nerve stimulation and agonist application generally produce identical actions in a given neuron. An exception is a recent study by Mihara & Nishi (79) in which the actions of substance P, neurokinin A, and slow excitatory synaptic transmission were compared in submucosal neurons. As expected, substance P inhibited both gK_{leak} and gK_{Ca} and also increased a distinct membrane conductance, but the excitatory actions of neurokinin A and the slow EPSP were found to be solely the result of the inhibition of gK_{leak} and gK_{Ca}. This finding suggests that neurokinin A rather than substance P may be the primary transmitter underlying the slow EPSP in these enteric neurons.

SIGNAL TRANSDUCTION   There is a substantial body of indirect evidence obtained from electrophysiological studies to suggest that the potassium conductance decreases produced by substance P, muscarine, 5-HT, VIP, and other slow excitatory agonists in enteric neurons may result from stimulation of the adenylate cyclase pathway (1, 86, 94, 95, 101). This evidence is based primarily upon mimicry of responses and is only briefly summarized here because it has been reviewed in detail recently (76). The decreased gK_{leak}, gK_{Ca}, and $gK_{agonist}$, as well as the increased cation conductance caused by muscarine or substance P, can all be mimicked by the application of forskolin, dibutyryl cyclic AMP, and other membrane-permeable cyclic AMP analogues, and phosphodiesterase inhibitors such as 3-isobutyl-1-methylxanthine (IBMX). Cholera toxin, which catalyses the ADP ribosylation of the stimulatory guanine nucleotide-binding protein of the adenylyl cyclase system ($G_{s\alpha}$) and consequently stimulates the adenylate cyclase-cyclic AMP pathway (46), also mimics all of the actions of slow excitatory agonists in a single cell (55, 101). On the other hand, results obtained from other electrophysiological and biochemical studies do not support this notion (45, 95). For example, 5-HT has been shown to increase cyclic AMP levels in dissociated myenteric ganglia, but this response is not inhibited by selective 5-HT$_{1P}$ receptor antagonists, which do inhibit a slow EPSP in myenteric neurons (45). In any event, further experiments will be required to provide direct evidence for involvement of the cyclic AMP cascade in transduction of the slow EPSP in enteric neurons. It is expected that cultures of myenteric neurons should prove most amenable to these types of experiments because it has been demonstrated that slow EPSPs occur in these cultures (125). Substantive tests of this hypothesis would include intracellular injections of antisense oligonucleotides directed toward the G$_s$ subunit of the G protein known to be linked to receptor-adenylate cyclase coupling (45), intracellular injections of the catalytic subunits of protein kinase A (3, 5, 49), and biochemical measurements of cyclic AMP levels during electrical stimulation of a population of enteric neurons uncontaminated with visceral smooth muscle (45).

Inhibitory Synaptic Transmission

SYNAPTIC POTENTIALS AND TRANSMITTER CANDIDATES   The first demonstration of an inhibitory postsynaptic potential (IPSP) in a mammalian nerve cell that resulted from an increased potassium conductance was the IPSP recorded from submucosal neurons (53). The hyperpolarizing IPSP in these neurons is a powerful synaptic event lasting approximately 1 sec, during which time the membrane potential is often hyperpolarized from a typical resting potential of -50 mV to about -85 mV (53, 77–79, 90). There is now unequivocal evidence that activation of postsynaptic α_2-adrenoceptors on submucosal cell bodies by the release of noradrenaline from sympathetic nerves accounts for the IPSP evoked in response to single and low frequency nerve stimuli and in response to short trains of high frequency stimulation (76, 78, 90, 102). In addition, a much slower, smaller amplitude non-adrenergic, non-cholinergic IPSP (2–10 mV, 4–15 sec duration) can be demonstrated during prolonged trains of high frequency stimulation (8, 80, 102); its ionic and signal transduction mechanisms are identical to the adrenergic IPSP (see below). In an impressive display of synaptic plasticity, within 5–7 days after removal of the extrinsic sympathetic nerves, single and low frequency nerve stimuli now evoke the non-adrenergic IPSP whose time course and amplitude have become the same as the adrenergic IPSP (102). There is fairly convincing evidence that this non-adrenergic IPSP arises from the release of somatostatin from myenteric neurons. Dense networks of somatostatin-containing nerve terminals, which originate from a distinct population of myenteric neurons, normally surround submucosal neurons (22, 35, 37); the non-adrenergic IPSP cannot be recorded after surgical removal of the myenteric plexus and extrinsic nerves, which results in the disappearance of all somatostatin-containing nerve terminals in the submucosal plexus (8, 102). The non-adrenergic IPSP is selectively abolished in the presence of desensitizing concentrations of somatostatin, which does not alter the adrenergic IPSP or the response to α_2-adrenoceptor and δ-opioid receptor agonists (102). These agonists act at their own receptors to activate the same potassium conductance (89, 93; see below).

Adrenergic and somatostatinergic IPSPs are present in a distinct population of submucosal neurons, those that are immunoreactive for VIP. This represents approximately 50% of all submucosal neurons in the guinea pig small intestine (22, 35, 37). Immunohistochemical studies have shown that only these submucosal neurons receive an extrinsic sympathetic innervation (6, 20, 40), and electrophysiological studies have demonstrated that only these neurons possess δ-opioid, α_2-adrenoceptor, and somatostatin receptors that mediate membrane hyperpolarization (9, 28, 93). The cause-and-effect of this interesting correlation is unknown.

Little information is available concerning IPSPs in myenteric neurons. This is because inhibitory synaptic transmission in myenteric neurons is rare; IPSPs have been recorded in less than 5% of all cells, generally are of small amplitude, and require long trains of high frequency stimulation for their initiation (see 76). Although there is abundant data concerning substances that hyperpolarize myenteric neurons (43, 44, 95), there are no data concerning possible transmitters that may mediate the IPSP in myenteric neurons.

IONIC MECHANISM   The mechanism of inhibitory synaptic transmission in submucosal neurons through G protein activation of a family of K channels is one of the best characterized in the mammalian nervous system and is similar in most respects to that described subsequently in parts of the central nervous system (87, 89, 110). Each of the three known inhibitory agonists activate distinct receptors: noradrenaline acts on α_{2A}-adrenoceptors (96), opiates activate δ-opioid receptors (81), and somatostatin appears to activate the pharmacologically defined SRIF$_1$ receptor [which corresponds to the cloned SRIF$_2$-R (70, 102, 126)]. Outward currents produced by supramaximal concentrations of each of the inhibitory agonists are not additive, and single potassium channels recorded from an outside-out membrane patch can be activated by application of all three agonists in a receptor-specific manner (82, 99, 112, 115). These results provide direct evidence that activation of these three distinct membrane receptors results in activation of the same population of potassium channels.

Activation of these receptors increases an inwardly rectifying potassium conductance, $gK_{agonist}$; there are striking similarities between the kinetic and pharmacological properties of this $gK_{agonist}$ and the resting gK_{IR} in the absence of agonist (82, 112, 115). That is, both $gK_{agonist}$ and gK_{IR} are activated virtually instantaneously when step hyperpolarizing pulses are applied; they are equally sensitive to blockade by low micromolar concentrations of barium, show the same voltage-dependent block by cesium and a similar dependence on extracellular potassium concentration (76, 82, 112).

When outside-out membrane patches are pulled from submucosal neurons (99), at least three distinct sets of unitary potassium currents can be recorded at the usual resting potential of the cell (i.e. -50 mV). The three sets of potassium channels show unitary conductances in equal potassium concentrations of 30–50 pS for the small conductance channel, 100–140 pS for the intermediate conductance channel, and 220–260 pS for the large conductance channel. None of these channels is likely to be a calcium-activated potassium channel because the recordings were carried out in the absence of calcium and the presence of high concentrations of calcium buffers. The current-voltage relations, kinetics, dependence on potassium concentration, and blockade by cesium and barium of each of these potassium channels appear to be identical. Noradrenaline, somatostatin, and/or enkephalin increase the activity (e.g. frequency of opening) of each of the unitary potassium currents that are active in the absence of agonist. Agonists do not appear to activate channels that are not already active in the absence of agonist, and agonists do not cause the opening of any channels in membrane patches in which no channel activity is present prior to agonist application. Thus results obtained from whole cell and single-channel recordings support the conclusion that the inhibitory agonists act by increasing the activity of a set of background or resting potassium channels in the membrane rather than by activating a unique potassium channel, as is the case for the acetylcholine-activated potassium conductance in cardiac tissue (14, 66, 118). These results also suggest that agonists produce an outward current (or hyperpolarization) at the resting potential by shifting the voltage dependence of activation of these resting inwardly rectifying potassium channels.

A major discrepancy between whole cell and single-channel potassium currents recorded from submucosal neurons is that the single-channel properties do not exhibit inward rectification. The probability of opening appears to increase with positive potentials, a result opposite to that required to account for whole cell rectification, and decreasing the extracellular potassium to more physiological concentrations (e.g. 20 mM) does not cause unitary currents to exhibit inward rectification (99). It is difficult to compare these observations in submucosal neurons to those obtained from single-channel recordings of the resting gK_{IR}, or the acetylcholine-activated inwardly rectifying gK_{ACh} of cardiac tissue (66) because the cardiac currents have not been studied in the outside-out patch configuration (118). In cardiac tissue these two inwardly rectifying potassium currents continue to show single-channel rectification in both cell-attached and inside-out membrane patches; the rectification results from block of outward currents by cytoplasmic magnesium ions (50, 74). Alterations in internal or external magnesium concentrations from zero to 2 mM do not appreciably alter the properties of potassium currents recorded from outside-out patches of submucosal neurons (99). Therefore, it is possible that the whole cell inward rectification results from current through other sets of potassium channels that may not have been detected because of very small unitary conductances, or through washing out after patch excision.

SIGNAL TRANSDUCTION   Intracellular injection or dialysis with the non-hydrolyzable GTP analogue, GTP-γ-S, produces an irreversible hyperpolarization or outward current upon application of inhibitory agonists. Agonist-induced outward currents are abolished after pertussis toxin pretreatment, or when pertussis is added directly into the cell by means of whole cell patch-pipette dialysis. Agonist-activated outward currents can be reconstituted after pertussis treatment by intracellular dialysis with pipettes containing purified G_i or G_o proteins (76, 77, 82, 112, 115). Agonist activation of potassium channel activity in excised outside-out membrane patches requires GTP on the inner surface of the membrane, and after pertussis treatment agonists no longer alter unitary currents in excised membrane patches (99). Thus one or more pertussis-toxin-sensitive G proteins are involved in inhibitory signal transduction in enteric neurons. It is not known which G proteins are involved but, by analogy with results obtained in other G protein-coupled systems (62-64), it seems likely that a distinct α-β-γ G protein complex may be uniquely associated with each receptor-ion channel coupling. Such an arrangement would provide for a specificity in the pathways of the otherwise promiscuous couplings between inhibitory receptor and potassium channel families described above.

The minimum latency to onset of the noradrenaline or somatostatin-induced outward current in submucosal neurons is 25–40 ms (76, 82, 112), which is intermediate between the rapid (< 2 ms) activation of ligand-gated ionic channels and the slow (> 100 ms) onset of channel modulation by cytoplasmic second messenger systems (89), and one that is in keeping with a more direct receptor-G protein coupling mechanism. Much additional evidence suggests the transduction between inhibitory receptor, G protein, and potassium channel does not require cytoplasmic messengers. Possible involvement of adenylyl cyclase has been tested in some detail because of biochemical studies showing that activation of α_2-adrenoceptors, somatostatin receptors, and δ-opioid receptors is associated with an inhibition of adenylyl cyclase activity provided this enzyme has first been turned on by activators of this second messenger cascade (68, 69). However, none of the electrophysiological properties (e.g. amplitude, time course, concentration-response relations, or current-voltage relations) of the somatostatin, noradrenaline or enkephalin responses is altered in the presence of activators of the protein kinase A cascade (1, 77, 82, 112). Tests of the involvement of other transduction cascades also have been negative or equivocal; that is, phorbol esters, arachidonic acid and its metabolites, nitroprussides, and inhibitors of nitric oxide synthase neither mimic, enhance, nor inhibit agonist-induced outward currents in submucosal neurons (1, 30, 82, 112). Prolonged exposure to calcium-free extracellular solution and intracellular injections of EGTA or BAPTA can reduce the agonist-induced response, and direct injection of IP_3 activates a potassium conductance (76, 77); however, these results are more in keeping with a generalized modulatory effect of intracellular calcium than with a direct activation of agonist-activated potassium channels. Finally, results from single-channel recordings of potassium channels in outside-out membrane patches provide the strongest evidence for a direct coupling between receptor, G protein, and potassium channel. Noradrenaline, somatostatin, and enkephalin continue to increase activity of single potassium channels on repeated applications for up to 2 hr after patch excision when GTP is included in the pipette solution bathing the internal membrane; in the absence of internal GTP, resting potassium channel activity shows no obvious differences, but agonist application is without effect (99).

Summary of Ion Channels in Enteric Neurons

Table 1 summarizes the presence of the major classes of ion channels in enteric neurons, their role in synaptic transmission in the enteric nervous system, and their modulation by agonists known to be present in enteric neurons. Noteworthy absences in intracellular microelectrode and whole cell recordings are the apamin-sensitive "fast" gK_{Ca}, which is wide-spread in other autonomic and central neurons (58), and the M-current (15, 58). Large sodium currents are recorded from all enteric neurons; many enteric neurons exhibit both TTX-sensitive and TTX-insensitive sodium currents (114). There is little information concerning possible synaptic or agonist modulation of sodium currents in enteric neurons.

Both whole cell and single-channel calcium currents have been recorded in submucosal neurons (100, 114), with the N-type calcium current being the major, or sole, current recorded from either type of experiment. The L-type calcium current does not appear to be present in either myenteric or submucosal neurons, in that no dihydropyridine-sensitive calcium current is

Table 1 Ligand and voltage-gated ion channels in enteric neurons

Current	Presence (n)	Involved in synaptic transmission	Modulated
Nicotinic	All S	Yes: fast EPSP	—
5-HT$_3$	All SMP many MP	No	—
ATP-P$_{2X}$	most SMP many MP	No	—
TTX-sensitive Na$^+$	All	—	—
TTX insensitive Na$^+$	Most SMP	—	—
N-type Ca^2	All	—	Decreased by inhibitory agonists
L-type Ca^{2+}	Not detected	—	—
T-type Ca^{2+}	Some MP/ SMP	—	??
Delayed rectifier K$^+$	All	—	??
A-current K$^+$	Most SMP/MP	—	No
Apamin-sensitive K$^+$ (calcium-activated)	Not detected		
TEA-sensitive (maxi) K$^+$ (calcium-activated)	AH	—	??
M-current K$^+$	Not present		
Slow calcium-activated K$^+$	Most SMP All MP AH	Yes: slow EPSP	Decreased by slow excitatory agonists
Resting (linear leak) K$^+$	All	Yes: slow EPSP	Decreased by slow excitatory agonists
Resting (inward rectifier) K$^+$	Most SMP Many MP	Yes: IPSP (SMP)	Increased by inhibitory agonists
Slow cationic	Most SMP ?? MP	Yes: slow EPSP (SMP)	Activated by slow excitatory agonists
Hyperpolarization-activated Cationic (H-current)	All MP AH rare SMP	No	??

Abbreviations are S/type 1 cell (S); AH/type 2 cell (AH); myenteric plexus (MP); submucosal plexus (SMP); neuron (n.). Inhibitory agonists are those acting at somatostatin, α_2-adrenoceptor, and δ-opioid receptors. Slow excitatory agonists are tachykins, 5-HT (non-5-HT$_3$), VIP, and muscarine.

observed in whole cell recordings, nor is the calcium action potential altered by dihydropyridine agonists or antagonists in either submucosal or myenteric AH neurons (76, 114). But the L-type calcium channel agonist, BAYK 8644, occasionally induces the appearance of a voltage-activated unitary calcium current in outside-out membrane patches of submucosal neurons whose properties are similar to L-type unitary conductances described in other neurons (K-Z Shen, unpublished observations). As in numerous other excitable tissues (14, 110), the calcium current in enteric neurons is a prime target for inhibitory agonists. Activation of α_2-adrenoceptors, δ-opioid receptors, and somatostatin receptors inhibits the calcium current in submucosal neurons through a pertussis toxin-sensitive G protein (114). It is most likely that G proteins distinct from those that couple these receptors to potassium channel activation are involved in receptor coupling to calcium currents. This assumption is based on results obtained in cardiac tissue, sensory neurons, and endocrine cell lines, which generally have shown that α_o subunits of the G proteins couple to calcium current inhibition while α_i subunits couple to potassium current activation (14, 62-64). Circumstantial evidence in support of the notion that distinct G proteins couple inhibitory receptors in enteric neurons to calcium and potassium channels is the observation that 10 to 30-fold higher concentrations of noradrenaline are required to inhibit calcium currents than to activate potassium currents and that the latency to onset of calcium current inhibition by agonist is approximately three times slower than the latency to potassium conductance activation (76, 114).

NEURAL CONTROL OF GI MICROCIRCULATION

The remainder of this chapter focuses on the neural control of only one of the three physiological effectors that comprise the GI tract: intestinal blood flow (see Introduction). A major aim is to relate the preceding discussion on synaptic transmission in the enteric nervous system to the control of GI blood flow. A comprehensive summary of recent work on the neural control of the other two physiological systems in the GI tract, motility and mucosal function, is outside the scope of this chapter. The intimate role of enteric neurons in the control of GI motility has been appreciated for over a century; the involvement of myenteric neurons in the peristaltic reflex was accepted by some scientists as early as the 1850's (72, see 37). There is now a wealth of information concerning the neural circuitry involved in, and cellular mechanisms underlying, reflex control of gut motility; interesting historical perspectives and comprehensive summaries of work to date in this area can be found in the reviews and recent publications by Furness (10, 11, 103, 104, 127) and Costa (12, 13, 105). Work carried out over the past 20 years also has demonstrated convincingly that enteric neurons are involved in the reflex control of intestinal ion transport with distinct populations of submucosal neurons being shown to subserve secretomotor efferent activity (16–18, 31, 59, 61). Over this same two decades, Lundgren and colleagues have marshalled much evidence from in vivo experiments to suggest that enteric nerves play a role in the control of the GI microcirculation (56), but it is only in the past five years that details of this neuronal circuitry have emerged.

Rates of blood flow, oxygen consumption, and transcapillary fluid and solute transport in the GI microcirculation are higher than any other peripheral vascular bed: intestinal mucosa receive the highest vascular perfusion of any peripheral organ (48, 56). The contractile state of the submucosal arteriolar network primarily determines the rate of vascular perfusion of the mucosa. The influence of nerves on submucosal arteriolar diameter had been little characterized until the recent introduction of techniques to measure contractility in these very small resistance vessels [outside diameters 10–80 μm (84)]. Such studies have shown that submucosal neurons subserve a vasomotor role, their excitation leads to vasodilation of submucosal arterioles, which increases blood flow to the intestinal mucosa (42, 85, 122). Reflex vasodilation in response to mechanical or chemical stimulation of the intestinal mucosa appears to involve the particular neuronal group that receive inhibitory synaptic innervation from sympathetic and myenteric ganglia described in the preceding sections (i.e. VIP-immunoreactive neurons). Sympathetic nerves originating from the same paravertebral ganglia also provide vasoconstrictor innervation to submucosal arterioles, thus forming an important link in this autonomic reflex pathway (see Figure 1).

Control of Intestinal Arterioles by Sympathetic Nerves

Sympathetic nerves from the coeliac ganglia supply the vasoconstrictor innervation to submucosal arterioles of the guinea pig small intestine; these vasoconstrictor nerves possess a distinct chemical code whereby noradrenaline co-exists with ATP and NPY in only those sympathetic nerves that innervate vasculature (Figure 1; 71, 73). There is no evidence to suggest that enteric neurons can play a vasoconstrictor role in the normal or the extrinsically denervated intestine (42, 85). Stimulation of the sympathetic nerves to submucosal arterioles evokes excitatory junction potentials (EJPs) in the vascular smooth muscle. EJPs are not recorded in sympathetically denervated arterioles and are abolished by the sympatholytic antagonist, guanethidine; these procedures also abolish all nerve-evoked arteriolar vasoconstrictions (29, 51). Thus in submucosal arterioles, as in most peripheral vasculature, vasoconstriction clearly results from the release of neurotransmitter from sympathetic nerves. However, adrenoceptor antagonists do not inhibit submucosal arteriolar EJPs, nor does reserpine treatment, which reduces noradrenaline content in sympathetic nerves by more than 95% (29, 51). Adrenoceptor antagonists and reserpine pretreatment also do not inhibit the neurogenic vasoconstriction in these arterioles, even when very long trains of high frequency nerve stimulation are applied (29).

There now is little doubt that neurogenic EJPs and vasoconstrictions in submucosal arterioles result from ATP released onto P_{2X}-purinoceptors. The selective P_2-purinoceptor antagonist, suramin, abolishes both EJPs and neurogenic vasoconstriction; it also blocks vasoconstrictions to exogenously applied ATP, but not to applied noradrenaline or the α_1-adrenoceptor agonist phenylephrine (29). Additionally, EJPs, as well as the neurogenic and ATP-mediated vasoconstrictions, are abolished selectively during the desensitization that occurs during applications of the P_{2X}-selective agonist, α,β-methylene ATP (29). Thus in contrast to the vast majority of peripheral vessels in which both ATP and noradrenaline account for neurally evoked vasoconstrictions (123), it appears that ATP is the sole sympathetic vasoconstrictor in submucosal arterioles.

Noradrenaline is apparently released from sympathetic neurons innervating submucosal arterioles because α_2-adrenoceptor antagonists significantly increase both EJPs and neurogenic vasoconstrictions (29); these results indicate that noradrenaline acts through prejunctional α_2-adrenoceptors to depress the release of ATP (106, 107). Therefore, the physiological role of neurally released noradrenaline in submucosal arterioles appears to be restricted to its presynaptic modulation of ATP release. These results are in accord with structural studies showing synaptic specializations in these arterioles (51) and support the notion that there are distinct junctional ATP receptors, but no postsynaptic adrenoceptors, at these synaptic sites.

Control of Intestinal Arterioles by Enteric Neurons

A vasodilator innervation from autonomic nerves to the GI vasculature was first demonstrated in 1913 by Henry Dale (23); but the submucosal plexus origin of these vasodilator nerves has only recently been elucidated (85). Electrical stimulation of the interganglionic nerve fibers in the submucosal plexus produces arteriolar vasodilation of submucosal arterioles that is abolished by TTX, or by cutting the interganglionic connectives. This neurogenic vasodilation is not altered by extrinsic denervation of both sympathetic and spinal sensory nerves, nor is it significantly altered by myectomy, which indicates that submucosal neurons provide the vasodilator innervation to these arterioles. Muscarinic receptor antagonists generally block these responses in the guinea pig small intestine (2, 85), although there is an additional large non-cholinergic component to the neurogenic vasodilation in the large intestine (122). Pharmacological results indicate that the muscarinic receptors activated by neurally released acetylcholine are located on the endothelium and their activation leads to the release of nitric oxide from the endothelial cell and subsequent vessel relaxation (2). This is an important physiological finding because it is the first demonstration that neurally released acetylcholine can indeed reach the endothelium to cause nitric oxide release.

Individual submucosal vasodilator neurons have been identified by simultaneous intracellular recordings (with dye-filled microelectrodes) and video-monitoring of arteriolar diameter; initiation of action potentials by intracellular injection of depolarizing pulses is directly associated with arteriolar vasodilation in a number of neurons, thus confirming their vasodilator role. To date, these experiments have shown that all vasodilator neurons are immunoreactive for VIP (JC Bornstein et al, A Surprenant et al, unpublished observations). These results are quite unexpected and pose an interpretive dilemma because immunohistochemical studies have demonstrated that submucosal neurons form two distinct and mutually exclusive populations; about half the neurons are VIP-containing and the remainder are immunoreactive for choline acetyltransferase (ChAT), which is a marker for cholinergic neurons (19, 37, 39). Yet, the direct physiological experiment shows that VIP-containing cells are actually cholinergic. Currently available ChAT antibodies stain only cell bodies in the enteric nervous system and not their processes; therefore, it has not been possible to trace cholinergic vasodilator neuronal projections using these antibodies. One explanation that might resolve the conflicting physiological and immunohistochemical results would be if acetylcholine does co-exist with VIP in VIP-containing submucosal neurons, but levels of ChAT are too low in these somata to be detected by the available antibodies.

Mucosa-Submucosal Neuron-Blood Vessel Reflex

Vascular perfusion to the intestinal mucosa increases by up to 100% during digestion, mostly because of increased blood flow in the submucosal arterioles (48, 56). In vivo studies have demonstrated that local mechanical and chemical stimulation of the mucosa produces a reflex vasodilation in the submucosal vascular network that accounts for the increased mucosal blood flow (56). A reflex vasodilation of submucosal arterioles also can be demonstrated in an isolated preparation of submucosal plexus in which the underlying mucosa is left attached (Figure 2A, 120). Mechanical and chemical stimulation of the mucosa results in a neurogenic vasodilation (Figure 2B); this reflex is stimulated by the activity of the cholinergic submucosal neurons because it is blocked by muscarinic receptor antagonists and does not require the integrity of extrinsic or myenteric synaptic transmission (120). Mucosal stimulation also induces synaptic activity in a population of VIP-containing submucosal neurons (Figure 2C); both fast and slow EPSPs are elicited by mucosal stimulation. When these stimulus-induced EPSPs reach threshold for action potential discharge, vasodilation occurs. Further, the axons of many VIP-containing neurons bifurcate shortly after leaving the somata with one process passing over or around, and occasionally appearing to terminate in an arteriole, and the other process

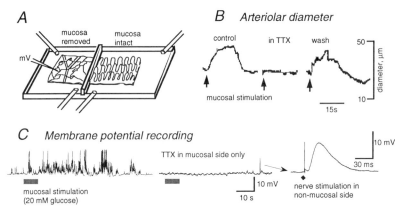

Figure 2 Reflex pathways mediating vasodilation in an isolated preparation of submucosa-mucosa in guinea pig small intestine. (*A*) Schematic drawing of preparation in which separate superfusion of solutions can be carried out; on one side intracellular recordings from submucosal neurones and monitoring of arteriolar diameter are carried out and on the other side chemical or mechanical stimulation is applied to the intestinal mucosa. (*B*) Arteriolar diameter recordings showing neurogenic basis (i.e. TTX sensitivity) of vasodilation in response to mechanical stimulation of the mucosa; records from Reference 120, with permission. (*C*) Membrane potential recorded from submucosal neuron in response to application of high glucose solution to the mucosal side of the bath. Mucosal stimulation results in barrage of fast EPSPs that produce vasodilation when threshold for action potential is reached. Mucosal stimulation no longer elicits synaptic activity when TTX is applied to mucosal side of the bath. Fast EPSP (shown on fast time scale) can still be evoked when nerves are stimulated on the non-mucosal side of the bath, which indicates that synaptic transmission is blocked only on the mucosal side of the bath.

terminating in the intestinal mucosa (28, 55). These results led to the proposal that the cholinergic (but VIP-immunoreactive) vasodilator neurons in the submucosal plexus are true sensorimotor neurons. That is, these neurons dually innervate submucosal arterioles and intestinal mucosa; they provide an afferent limb to the mucosa and an efferent vasodilator limb to the arterioles. The neurons are sensory because their mucosal terminals can be activated by mechanical or chemical stimuli, and they are motor because action potential initiation in their cell bodies produces vasodilation. This reflex is similar to the classic axon collateral reflex in dorsal horn neurons that project to both skin and skin vessels. However, these submucosal sensorimotor neurons cannot be considered to be solely sensory neurons possessing an efferent axon collateral because these neurons receive multiple excitatory and inhibitory synaptic input from both intrinsic enteric and extrinsic sympathetic nerves (described in detail above). Moreover, it is to be expected that synaptically driven activity in the cell body of this sensorimotor neuron will release transmitter from terminals in the intestinal mucosa as well as in the vasculature. Both acetylcholine and VIP are known to increase intestinal fluid and ion transport in mucosal epithelia by neuronal and non-neuronal processes (16–18, 59). Thus acetylcholine released from vascular terminals will produce vasodilation, while acetylcholine and/or VIP released from mucosal terminals will enhance intestinal secretory activity. A final consequence of this proposal is that the mucosal process of the submucosal sensorimotor neuron may serve either a sensory or a motor function depending on the means by which it is activated.

Literature Cited

1. Akasu T, Tokimasa T. 1989. Potassium currents in submucous neurones of guinea-pig caecum and their synaptic modification. *J. Physiol.* 416:571–88
2. Andriantsitohaina N, Surprenant A. 1992. Acetylcholine released from guinea-pig submucosal neurones dilates arterioles by releasing nitric oxide from endothelium. *J. Physiol.* 453:493–502
3. Bacskai BJ, Hochner B, Mahaut-Smith M, Adams SR, Kaang BK, et al. 1993. Spatially resolved dynamics of cAMP and protein kinase A subunits in *Aplysia* sensory neurons. *Science* 260:222–26
4. Benham CD, Bolton TB, Lang RJ. 1985. Acetylcholine activates an inward current in single mammalian smooth muscle cells. *Nature* 316:345–47
5. Benz I, Frobe U, Kohlhardt M. 1991. Single cardiac outwardly rectifying K^+ channels modulated by protein kinase A and a G-protein. *Eur. Biophys. J.* 20:281–86
6. Bornstein JC. 1988. Correlated electrophysiological and histochemical studies of submucous neurons and their contribution to understanding neural circuits. *J. Auton. Nerv. Syst.* 25:1–13
7. Bornstein JC, Costa M, Furness JB. 1986. Synaptic input to immunohistochemically identified neurons in the submucous plexus of the guinea-pig small intestine. *J. Physiol.* 281:465–82
8. Bornstein JC, Costa M, Furness JB. 1988. Intrinsic and extrinsic inhibitory inputs to submucous neurones of the guinea-pig small intestine. *J. Physiol.* 398:371–90
9. Bornstein JC, Furness JB, Costa M. 1987. Sources of excitatory synaptic inputs to neurochemically identified submucous neurones of guinea-pig small intestine. *J. Auton. Nerv. Syst.* 18:83–91
10. Bornstein JC, Furness JB, Smith TK, Trussell DC. 1991. Synaptic responses evoked by mechanical stimulation of the mucosa in morphologically characterized myenteric neurons of the guinea-pig ileum. *J. Neurosci.* 11:505–18
11. Bornstein JC, Hendriks R, Furness JB, Trussell DC. 1991. Ramifications of the axons of AH-neurons injected with intracellular marker biocytin in the myenteric plexus of the guinea pig small intestine. *J. Comp. Neurol.* 313:1–15
12. Brookes SJ, Song ZM, Steele PA, Costa M. 1992. Identification of motor neurons to the longitudinal muscle of the guinea pig ileum. *Gastroenterology* 103:961–73
13. Brookes SJ, Steele PA, Costa M. 1991. Identification and immunohistochemistry of cholinergic and non-cholinergic circular muscle motor neurons in the guinea-pig small intestine. *Neuroscience* 42:863–78
14. Brown AM, Birnbaumer L. 1990. Ionic channels and their regulation by G protein subunits. *Annu. Rev. Physiol.* 52:197–213
15. Brown DA. 1988. M-currents. In *Ion Channels*, ed. T Narahasi, 1:55–94. New York: Plenum
16. Cooke HJ. 1986. Neurobiology of the intestinal mucosa. *Gastroenterology* 90:1057–81
17. Cooke HJ. 1992. Neuromodulation of ion secretion by inflammatory mediators. *Ann. NY Acad. Sci.* 664:346–52
18. Cooke HJ. 1987. Neural and hormonal regulation of small intestinal electrolyte transport. In *Physiology of the Gastrointestinal Tract*, ed. LR Johnson, pp. 1307–50. New York: Raven. 1780 pp. 2nd ed.
19. Costa M, Brooks SJ, Steele PA, Vickers J. 1991. Chemical coding of

neurons in the gastrointestinal tract. *Adv. Exp. Med. Biol.* 298:17–27

20. Costa M, Furness JB. 1984. Somatostatin is present in a subpopulation of noradrenergic nerve fibres supplying the intestine. *Neuroscience* 13:911–19

21. Costa M, Furness JB, Cuello AC, Verhofstad AAJ, Steinbusch HWM, Elde RP. 1982. Neurones with 5-hydroxytryptamine-like immunoreactivity in the enteric nervous system: their visualization and reactions to drug treatment. *Neuroscience* 7:341–49

22. Costa M, Furness JB, Llewellyn-Smith IJ, Davies B, Oliver J. 1980. An immunohistochemical study of the projections of somatostatin-containing neurons in the guinea-pig intestine. *Neuroscience* 5:841–52

23. Dale HH. 1913. On the action of ergotoxine: with special reference to the existence of sympathetic vaso-dilators. *J. Physiol.* 46:291–300

24. Derkach V, Surprenant A. 1992. Purinergic P_2 receptor channel coupling in celiac ganglia neurons. *Biophys. J.* 64:A326 (Abstr.)

25. Derkach V, Surprenant A, North RA. 1989. 5-HT_3 receptors are membrane ion channels. *Nature* 339:706–9

26. Erde SM, Sherman D, Gershon MD. 1985. Morphology and serotonergic innervation of physiologically identified cells of the guinea pig's myenteric plexus. *J. Neurosci.* 5:617–33

27. Evans RJ, Derkach V, Surprenant A. 1992. ATP mediates fast synaptic transmission in mammalian neurons. *Nature* 357:503–5

28. Evans RJ, Jiang MM, Surprenant A. 1994. Morphological properties and projections of electrophysiologically characterised neurones in the guinea-pig submucosal plexus. *Neuroscience.* In press

29. Evans RJ, Surprenant A. 1992. Vasoconstriction of guinea-pig submucosal arterioles following sympathetic nerve stimulation is mediated by the release of ATP. *Br. J. Pharmacol.* 106:242–49

30. Evans RJ, Surprenant A. 1993. Effects of phospholipase A_2 inhibitors on coupling of $\alpha 2$-adrenoceptors to inwardly rectifying potassium currents in guinea-pig submucosal neurones. *Br. J. Pharmacol.* 110:591–96

31. Frieling T, Wood JD, Cooke HJ. 1992. Submucosal reflexes: distension-evoked ion transport in the guinea-pig distal colon. *Am. J. Physiol.* 263:G91–96

32. Furness JB, Bornstein JC. 1991. The enteric nervous system and its extrinsic connections. In *Textbook of Gastroen-*terology, ed. T Yamada, pp. 2–24. Philadelphia: Lippincott

33. Furness JB, Bornstein JC, Murphy R, Pompolo S. 1992. Role of peptides in transmission in the enteric nervous system. *Trends Neurosci.* 15:66–71

34. Furness JB, Bornstein JC, Smith TK, Murphy R, Pompolo S. 1989. Correlated functional and structural analysis of enteric neural circuits. *Arch. Histol. Cytol.* 52:161–66

35. Furness JB, Costa M. 1980. Types of nerves in the enteric nervous system. *Neuroscience* 5:1–20

36. Furness JB, Costa M. 1982. Neurones with 5-hydroxytryptamine-like immunoreactivity in the enteric nervous system: their projections in the guinea-pig small intestine. *Neuroscience* 7:351–63

37. Furness JB, Costa M. 1987. *The Enteric Nervous System.* London/New York: Churchill Livingston. 290 pp.

38. Furness JB, Costa M. 1989. Identification of transmitters of functionally defined enteric neurons. In *Handbook of Physiology*, Sect. 6: *The Gastrointestinal System. Motility and Circulation* ed. SG Schultz, JD Wood, BB Rauner, pp. 387–402. Bethesda: Am. Physiol. Soc. 1777 pp.

39. Furness JB, Costa M, Keast JR. 1984. Choline acetyltransferase and peptide immunoreactivity of submucous neurones in the small intestine of the guinea-pig. *Cell Tissue Res.* 237:328–36

40. Furness JB, Costa M, Llewellyn-Smith IJ. 1987. Histochemistry of the enteric nervous system. See Ref. 18, pp. 1–40

41. Furness JB, Llewellyn-Smith IJ, Bornstein JC, Costa M. 1988. Chemical neuroanatomy and the analysis of neuronal circuitry in the enteric nervous system. In *Handbook of Chemical Neuroanatomy. The Peripheral Nervous System*, ed. A Bjorklund, T Hokfelt, C Owman, 6:161–218. Amsterdam: Elsevier

42. Galligan JJ, Jiang MM, Shen KZ, Surprenant A. 1990. Substance P mediates neurogenic vasodilation in extrinsically denervated guinea-pig submucosal arterioles. *J. Physiol.* 420:267–80

43. Galligan JJ, North RA. 1991. Opioid, 5-HT_{1A} and $\alpha 2$ receptors localized to subsets of guinea-pig myenteric neurons. *J. Auton. Nerv. Syst.* 32:1–11

44. Galligan JJ, Surprenant A, Tonini M, North RA. 1988. Differential localization of 5-HT_1 receptors on myenteric and submucosal neurons. *Am. J. Physiol.* 255:G603–11

45. Gershon MD, Wade PR, Fiorica-Howells E. 1992. Serotonin (5-HT) and its receptors in the bowel. In *Advances in the Innervation of the Gastrointestinal Tract,* ed. GE Holle, JD Wood, pp. 317–25. London/New York: Excerpta Medica

46. Gilman AG. 1987. G proteins: transducers of receptor-generated signals. *Annu. Rev. Biochem.* 56:615–49

47. Grafe P, Mayer CJ, Wood JD. 1980. Synaptic modulation of calcium-dependent potassium conductance in myenteric neurones in the guinea-pig. *J. Physiol.* 305:235–48

48. Granger DN, Kvietys PR, Korthuis RJ, Premen AJ. 1989. Microcirculation of the intestinal mucosa. See Ref. 38, pp. 1405–74

49. Gross RA, Uhler MD, Macdonald RL. 1990. The cyclic AMP-dependent protein kinase catalytic subunit selectively enhances calcium currents in rat nodose neurones. *J. Physiol.* 429:483–96

50. Hille B. 1992. *Ionic Channels of Excitable Membranes.* Sunderland, MA: Sinauer. 607 pp. 2nd ed.

51. Hirst GDS. 1989. Neuromuscular transmission in intramural blood vessels. See Ref. 38, pp. 1635–65

52. Hirst GDS, Holman ME, Spence I. 1974. Two types of neurones in the myenteric plexus of duodenum in the guinea-pig. *J. Physiol.* 236:303–26

53. Hirst GDS, McKirdy HC. 1975. Synaptic potentials recorded from neurones of the submucous plexus of guinea-pig small intestine. *J. Physiol.* 249:369–85

54. Inoue R, Kitamura K, Kuriyama K. 1987. Acetylcholine activates single sodium channels in smooth muscle cells. *Pflügers Arch.* 410:69–74

55. Jiang MM, Kirchgessner AL, Gershon MD, Surprenant A. 1993. Cholera toxin sensitive neurons in guinea-pig submucosal plexus. *Am. J. Physiol.* 264:G86–94

56. Jodal M, Lundgren O. 1989. Neurohormonal control of gastrointestinal blood flow. See Ref. 38, pp. 1667–1711

57. Johnson SM, Katayama Y, North RA. 1980. Slow synaptic potentials in neurones of the myenteric plexus. *J. Physiol.* 301:505–16

58. Jones SW, Adams PR. 1987. The M-current and other potassium currents of vertebrate neurons. In *Neuromodulation, the Biochemical Control of Neuronal Excitability,* ed. LK Kaczmarek, IB Levitan, pp. 159–86. New York: Oxford Univ. Press

59. Keast JR. 1987. Mucosal innervation and control of water and ion transpot in the intestine. *Rev. Physiol. Biochem. Pharmacol.* 109:1–59

60. Kirchgessner AL, Gershon MD. 1989. Identification of vagal and submucosal inputs to the myenteric plexus by retrograde and anterograde transport. In *Nerves and the Gastrointestinal Tract,* ed. MV Singer, H Goebell, pp. 69–78. Boston: MTP Press. 815 pp.

61. Kirchgessner AL, Tamir H, Gershon MD. 1992. Identification and stimulation by serotonin of intrinsic sensory neurons of the submucosal plexus of the guinea pig gut: activity induced expression of Fos immunoreactivity. *J. Neurosci.* 12:235–48

62. Kleuss C, Hescheler J, Ewel C, Schultz G, Wittig B. 1991. Assignment of G-protein subtypes to specific receptors inducing inhibition of calcium currents. *Nature* 353:43–48

63. Kleuss C, Scherubl H, Hescheler J, Schultz G, Wittig B. 1992. Different β-subunits determine G-protein interaction with transmembrane receptors. *Nature* 358:424–26

64. Kleuss C, Scherubl H, Hescheler J, Schultz G, Wittig B. 1993. Selectivity in signal transduction determined by γ-subunits of heterotrimeric G proteins. *Science* 259:832–34

65. Kuba K, Koketsu K. 1977. Synaptic events in sympathetic ganglia. *Prog. Neurobiol.* 11:77–169

66. Kubo Y, Reuveny E, Slesinger P, Jan YN, Jan LY. 1993. Primary structure and functional expression of a rat G-protein-coupled muscarinic potassium channel. *Nature* 364:802–6

67. Kunze WAA, Furness JB, Bornstein JC. 1993. Stimultaneous intracellular recordings from enteric neurons reveal that myenteric AH neurons transmit via slow excitatory postsynaptic potentials. *Neuroscience* 55:685–94

68. Lefkowitz RJ, Caron MG. 1987. Molecular and regulatory properties of adrenergic receptors. *Recent Prog. Hormone Res.* 43:469–97

69. Lefkowitz RJ, Caron MG. 1988. Adrenergic receptors. *J. Biol. Chem.* 263:4993–96

70. Li X-J, Forte M, North RA, Ross CA, Snyder SH. 1992. Cloning and expression of a rat somatostatin receptor enriched in brain. *J. Biol. Chem.* 267:21307–12

71. Lindh B, Hokfelt T, Elfvin LG, Terenius L, Fahrenkrug J, et al. 1986. Topography of NPY-, somatostatin- and VIP-immunoreactive neuronal subpopulations in the guinea-pig celiac-

superior mesenteric ganglion and their projections to the pylorus. *J. Neurosci.* 6:2371–83

72. Lister J. 1858. Preliminary account of an inquiry into the functions of the visceral nerves, with special reference to the so-called "inhibitory system". *Proc. R. Soc. London Ser. B* 9:367–80

73. Macrae IM, Furness JB, Costa M. 1986. Distribution of subgroups of noradrenaline neurons in the coeliac ganglion of the guinea-pig. *Cell Tissue Res.* 244:173–80

74. Matsuda H, Saigusa A, Irisawa H. 1987. Ohmic conductance through the inwardly rectifying K channels and blocking by internal Mg^{2+}. *Nature* 325:156–59

75. Matsumoto K, Pappano AJ. 1989. Sodium-dependent membrane current induced by carbachol in single guinea-pig ventricular myocytes. *J. Physiol.* 415:487–502

76. Mihara S. 1993. Intracellular recordings from neurones of the submucous plexus. *Prog. Neurobiol.* 40: 529–72

77. Mihara S, Hirai K, Katayama Y, Nishi S. 1991. Mechanisms underlying intracellular signal transduction of the slow IPSP in submucous neurones of the guinea-pig caecum. *J. Physiol.* 436:621–41

78. Mihara S, Katayama Y, Nishi S. 1986. Slow postsynaptic potentials in neurones of the submucous plexus of guinea-pig caecum and their mimickry by noradrenaline and various peptides. *Neuroscience* 16:1057–66

79. Mihara S, Nishi S. 1993. Neurokinin A mimics the slow EPSC in submucous neurones of the guinea-pig caecum. *Symp. Auton. Neuroeffec. Mech. II, Oxford, England.* p. 23

80. Mihara S, Nishi S, North RA, Surprenant A. 1987. A non-adrenergic, non-cholinergic slow inhibitory postsynaptic potential in neurones of the guinea-pig submucous plexus. *J. Physiol.* 390:357–66

81. Mihara S, North RA. 1986. Opioids increase potassium conductance in submucous neurones of guinea-pig caecum by activating δ-receptors. *Br. J. Pharmacol.* 88:315–22

82. Mihara S, North RA, Surprenant A. 1987. Somatostatin increases an inwardly rectifying potassium conductance in guinea-pig submucous neurones. *J. Physiol.* 390:335–56

83. Morita K, North RA. 1985. Significance of slow synaptic potentials for transmission of excitation in guinea-pig myenteric neurones. *Neuroscience* 14: 661–72

84. Neild TO. 1989. Measurement of arteriole diameter changes by analysis of television images. *Blood Vessels* 26:48–52

85. Neild TO, Shen KZ, Surprenant A. 1990. Vasodilation of arterioles by acetylcholine released from single neurones in the guinea-pig submucosal plexus. *J. Physiol.* 420:247–65

86. Nemeth PR, Palmer JM, Wood JD, Zafirov DH. 1986. Effects of forskolin on electrical behaviour of myenteric neurones in guinea-pig small intestine. *J. Physiol.* 376:439–50

87. Nicoll RA, Malenka RC, Kauer JA. 1989. Functional comparison of neurotransmitter receptor subtypes in the mammalian nervous system. *Physiol. Rev.* 70:513–65

88. Nishi S, North RA. 1973. Intracellular recording from the myenteric plexus of the guinea-pig ileum. *J. Physiol.* 231:471–91

89. North RA. 1989. Drug receptors and inhibition of nerve cells. *Br. J. Pharmacol.* 98:13–28

90. North RA, Surprenant A. 1985. Inhibitory synaptic potentials resulting from α_2-adrenoceptor activation in guinea-pig submucous plexus neurones. *J. Physiol.* 358:17–32

91. North RA, Tokimasa T. 1982. Muscarinic synaptic potentials in guinea-pig myenteric plexus neurones. *J. Physiol.* 333:151–56

92. North RA, Tokimasa T. 1987. Persistent calcium-sensitive potassium current and the resting properties of guinea-pig myenteric neurones. *J. Physiol.* 386: 333–53

93. North RA, Williams JT, Surprenant A, Christie MJ. 1987. $\alpha 2$ and μ receptors both belong to a family of receptors which couple to a potassium conductance. *Proc. Natl. Acad. Sci. USA* 84:5487–91

94. Palmer JM, Wood JD, Zafirov DH. 1986. Elevation of adenosine $3'5'$-phosphate mimicks slow synaptic excitation in myenteric neurones of guinea-pig. *J. Physiol.* 376:451–60

95. Palmer JM, Wood JD, Zafirov DH. 1987. Transduction of aminergic and peptidergic signals in enteric neurones of the guinea-pig. *J. Physiol.* 387:371–83

96. Shen K-Z, Barajas-Lopez C, Surprenant A. 1990. Functional characterization of neuronal pre and postsynaptic α_2-adrenoceptor subtypes in guinea-pig

submucosal plexus. *Br. J. Pharmacol.* 101:925–31

97. Shen K-Z, North RA. 1992. Muscarine increases cation conductance and decreases potassium conductance in rat locus coeruleus neurones. *J. Physiol.* 455:471–85

98. Shen K-Z, North RA. 1993. Excitation of rat locus coeruleus neurons by adenosine 5'-triphosphate: ionic mechanism and receptor characterization. *J. Neurosci.* 13:894–99

99. Shen K-Z, North RA, Surprenant A. 1992. Potassium channels opened by noradrenaline and other transmitters in excised membrane patches of guinea-pig submucosal neurones. *J. Physiol.* 445:581–99

100. Shen K-Z, Surprenant A. 1991. Noradrenaline, somatostatin and opioids inhibit activity of single HAV/N-type calcium channels in excised neuronal membranes. *Pflügers Arch.* 418:614–16

101. Shen K-Z, Surprenant A. 1993. Common ionic mechanisms of excitation by substance P and other transmitters in guinea-pig submucosal neurones. *J. Physiol.* 462:483–501

102. Shen K-Z, Surprenant A. 1993. Somatostatin mediates an inhibitory synaptic potential in sympathetically denervated submucosal neurones of the guinea-pig. *J. Physiol.* In press

103. Smith TK, Bornstein JC, Furness JB. 1991. Interactions between reflexes evoked by distension and mucosal stimulation: electrophysiological studies of guinea-pig ileum. *J. Autonom. Nerv. Syst.* 34:69–76

104. Smith TK, Bornstein JC, Furness JB. 1992. Convergence of reflex pathways excited by distension and mechanical stimulation of the mucosa onto the same myenteric neurons of the guinea-pig small intestine. *J. Neurosci.* 12:1502–10

105. Song ZM, Brookes SJ, Steele PA, Costa M. 1992. Projections and pathways of submucous neurons to the mucosa of the guinea-pig small intestine. *Cell Tissue Res.* 269:87–98

106. Starke K. 1981. Presynaptic receptors. *Annu. Rev. Pharmacol. Toxicol.* 21:7–30

107. Starke K. 1987. Presynaptic α-autoreceptors. *Rev. Physiol. Biochem. Pharmacol.* 107:73–146

108. Steele PA, Brookes SJ, Costa M. 1991. Immunohistochemical identification of cholinergic neurons in the myenteric plexus of guinea-pig small intestine. *Neuroscience* 45:227–39

109. Surprenant A. 1984. Slow excitatory synaptic potentials recorded from neurones of guinea-pig submucosal plexus. *J. Physiol.* 351:343–62

110. Surprenant A. 1989. The neurotransmitter noradrenaline and its receptors. *Sem. Neurosci.* 1:125–36

111. Surprenant A, Crist J. 1988. Electrophysiological characterization of functionally distinct 5-HT receptors on guinea-pig submucous plexus neurones. *Neuroscience* 24:283–95

112. Surprenant A, North RA. 1988. Mechanisms of synaptic inhibition by noradrenaline acting at α_2 adrenoceptors. *Proc. R. Soc. London Ser. B* 234:85–114

113. Surprenant A, North RA, Katayama Y. 1987. Observations on the actions of substance P and [D-Arg[1],D-Pro[2],D-Trp[7,9],Leu[11]] substance P on single neurones of the guinea-pig submucous plexus. *Neuroscience* 20:189–99

114. Surprenant A, Shen KZ, North RA, Tatsumi H. 1990. Inhibition of calcium currents by noradrenaline, somatostatin and opioids in guinea-pig submucosal neurones. *J. Physiol.* 431:585–608

115. Tatsumi H, Costa M, Schimerlik M, North RA. 1990. Potassium conductance increased by noradrenaline, opioids, somatostatin and G-proteins: whole-cell recording from guinea pig submucous neurones. *J. Neurosci.* 10:1675–82

116. Tsuji S, Kuba K. 1988. Muscarinic regulation of two ionic currents in the bullfrog sympathetic neurones. *Pflügers Arch.* 411:361–70

117. Tokimasa T, Akasu T. 1993. Biochemical gating for voltage-gated channels: mechanisms for slow synaptic potentials. In *Autonomic Ganglia*, ed. EM McLachlan, pp. 1–19. Berkshire: Harwood

118. Trube G, Hescheler J. 1984. Inward-rectifying channels in isolated patches of the heart cell membrane: ATP dependence and comparison with cell-attached patches. *Pflügers Arch.* 401:17–84

119. Vanner S, Evans RJ, Matsumoto SG, Surprenant A. 1993. Potassium currents and their modulation by muscarine and substance P in neuronal cultures from adult guinea-pig coeliac ganglia. *J. Neurophysiol.* 69:1632–44

120. Vanner S, Jiang MM, Surprenant A. 1993. Mucosal stimulation evokes vasodilation in submucosal arterioles by neuronal and nonneuronal mechanisms. *Am. J. Physiol.* 264:G202–12

121. Vanner S, Surprenant A. 1990. Effects

of 5-HT$_3$ receptor antagonists on 5-HT and nicotinic depolarizations in guinea-pig submucosal neurones. *Br. J. Pharmacol.* 99:840–44

122. Vanner S, Surprenant A. 1991. Cholinergic and noncholinergic submucosal neurons dilate arterioles in the guinea-pig colon. *Am. J. Physiol.* 261:G136–44

123. VonKugelgen I, Starke K. 1991. Noradrenaline-ATP co-transmission in the sympathetic nervous system. *Trends Pharmacol. Sci.* 12:319–24

124. Willard AL, Nishi R. 1985. Neurons dissociated from rat myenteric plexus retain differentiated properties when grown in cell culture. III Synaptic interactions and modulatory effects of neurotransmitter candidates. *Neuroscience* 16:213–21

125. Willard AL, Nishi R. 1989. Enteric neurons in culture. See Ref. 38, pp. 331–48

126. Yamada Y, Post SR, Wang K, Tager HS, Bell GI, Seino S. 1992. Cloning and functional characterization of a family of human and mouse somatostatin receptors expressed in brain, gastrointestinal tract and kidney. *Proc. Natl. Acad. Sci. USA* 89:251–55

127. Yuan SY, Furness JB, Bornstein JC. 1992. Post-stimulus depression of reflex changes in circular muscle activity in the guinea-pig small intestine. *J. Auton. Nerv. Syst.* 40:171–80

Annu. Rev. Physiol. 1994. 56:141–68
Copyright © 1994 by Annual Reviews Inc. All rights reserved

SYNAPTIC TRANSMISSION IN THE OUTER RETINA

Samuel M. Wu

Cullen Eye Institute, Baylor College of Medicine, Houston, Texas 77030

KEY WORDS: chemical synapses, receptive field, on and off pathways, rods and cones, synaptic plasticity

INTRODUCTION

The primary function of the retina is to detect light and to process visual images. Light is absorbed by photoreceptors, and its energy is transduced into electrical signals in the form of membrane hyperpolarization (165). Signals in rod and cone photoreceptors are transmitted to higher order retinal neurons through a complex and highly organized network of electrical and chemical synapses. Photoreceptors make electrical synapses with other photoreceptors nearby (12, 14, 22, 44, 47, 70, 134, 135), and they make chemical synapses on dendrites of second-order retinal neurons, the horizontal cells (HCs) and bipolar cells (BCs) (33, 56, 57, 59, 92, 98, 99, 165). Horizontal cells make feedback chemical synapse on cones (22, 121, 122, 186) and feedforward chemical synapse on bipolar cells (56, 57, 59, 201); they also make electrical synapses with other HCs (84, 172). Bipolar cells relay visual signals from the outer retina to the inner retina, where they make electrical synapses with other bipolar cells (95, 110, 173) and make chemical (and occasional electrical) synapses with amacrine cells and ganglion cells (33, 57, 59, 173, 177). Ganglion cells send retinal signals to the brain.

Information processing in the retina is, in great part, mediated by its synapses. Synaptic interactions within the retina, for example, are responsible for contrast enhancement, center-surround antagonism, movement and directional sensitivity, and color perception (18, 20, 56, 62, 83, 154, 170). Retinal synapses also maximize useful signals and minimize unwanted noise (31). Moreover, many retinal synapses exhibit a high degree of plasticity that allows modification of retinal function under various adaptational

141

0066–4278/94/0315–0141$05.00

conditions (185). Each synapse in the retina is responsible for certain visual tasks. It is extremely useful, therefore, to examine not only the fundamental mechanisms of synaptic transmission in the retina, but also their roles in visual information processing. The vertebrate retina is a unique preparation in this respect. It is advantageous over many other preparations because its natural input, light, is known and accurately controllable. One can study synaptic responses to light stimuli of various brightness, color, and shapes that human or animals see naturally in their living environments. One can also study synaptic plasticity in the retina induced by natural adaptational inputs, such as prolonged darkness or background light. Knowledge we obtain from studying retinal synapses provides useful information not only for vision researchers, but also for neuroscientists who are interested in synaptic function and plasticity.

ELECTRICAL SYNAPSES BETWEEN PHOTORECEPTORS

Photoreceptor Coupling

Electrical coupling between photoreceptors was first discovered by Baylor, Fourtes, and O'Bryan in 1971 (22). Electron microscopic studies reveal that gap junctions exist between photoreceptors in many vertebrate species (47, 71, 134, 135, 153), although the pattern of coupling varies from animal to animal. In the turtle retina, couplings are found between cones of the same spectral sensitivity (22, 44, 45, 50) and between rods (138); whereas in amphibians, rods are strongly coupled to each other (12, 65, 70, 71), but cones are not (14). Coupling between rods and cones has been observed in turtles and tiger salamanders, but the coupling resistance is higher than that between cones (in turtles) and between rods (in tiger salamander) (14, 70, 71, 139). In the primate retina, anatomical data show large gap junctions between cones and smaller junctions between rods and cones (134, 135, 166), which suggests that cone-cone coupling is stronger than rod-cone coupling.

In the tiger salamander retina, the coupling resistances between photoreceptors have been determined by dual microelectrode recording technique (one electrode for current injection and the other for recording voltage response from another photoreceptor nearby) in conjunction with a photoreceptor network model. The rod-rod coupling resistance is about 300 MΩ, whereas the rod-cone coupling resistance is about 5000 MΩ (12, 14). The ratio of these two resistance values is similar to the ratio of the numbers of junctional particles (recorded with the freeze fracture technique) between rods and between rods and cones in the toad retina (71), which suggests that the gap junction particles in both synapses have similar conductance. Although most rods are weakly coupled with cones in the tiger salamander retina, a small fraction of rods (10–15%), nevertheless, are strongly coupled with adjacent cones (180, 184, 190). Voltage responses of these rods (named rod$_c$s) to current injection into a next-neighbor cone is about three to four times larger than those of the other rods (190). Rod$_c$s behave like hybrids of rods and cones, and their function is not completely understood.

Photoreceptor Coupling and Visual Function

At first glance, photoreceptor coupling is a counter-intuitive arrangement—it decreases resolution (visual acuity) of the visual system by spatially averaging photoreceptor signals over some lateral distance in the retina (64, 97). However, the advantage of this arrangement is that it improves the signal-to-noise ratio of the photoreceptor output when the retina is uniformly illuminated (67, 97, 147). This is important for the retina, especially for the rods, detecting dim images under dark-adapted conditions when the voltage noise (mediated by three different sources of fluctuations in photoreceptors) (see below) is high (24, 147). It can be shown mathematically, however, that photoreceptor coupling decreases the signal-to-noise ratio of the photoreceptor output if the number of illuminated photoreceptors is less than the square root of the number of photoreceptors that are effectively coupled (6). This and the spatial averaging effect of coupling suggest that the size of the retinal image coupled photoreceptors can resolve is substantially larger than the diameters of individual photoreceptors. Photoreceptors mediating high visual acuity (e.g. foveal cones) are unlikely to be electrically coupled (49).

Rod and cone photoreceptors operate in different ranges of illuminance, and they exhibit different spectral sensitivities (23, 162, 163). Electrical coupling between rods and cones broadens the operating ranges and spectral sensitivity spans of both photoreceptors by mixing their light-evoked signals. Additionally, under conditions when the signal in one type of photoreceptor is suppressed (e.g. rod response in the presence of background light), its output synapse can be used to transmit signal from the other type of photoreceptor (e.g. cones) (129, 185). In fact, evidence described in this review suggests that rod-cone coupling in the tiger salamander retina is enhanced by background light (198). This allows transmission of cone signals through the rod output synapses. Such "synapse sharing" minimizes the amount of neural hardware and facilitates cone inputs in second-order retinal cells (152, 185).

The effects of photoreceptor coupling go beyond what it is described above, when one takes the voltage- and time-dependent current in the photoreceptor inner segments into consideration. Membrane hyperpolarization in rods and cones activates a time-dependent inward current that results in more transient voltage responses in these cells at the onset of a light step (10, 12, 14, 27, 51). It has been shown by mathematical simulation that this current and photoreceptor coupling make the response of the photoreceptor network depend on the speed of moving light stimuli. The time-dependent current and photoreceptor coupling also change the modulation transfer function (spatial contrast) of the photoreceptor network (6, 13).

CHEMICAL SYNAPSES BETWEEN PHOTORECEPTORS AND SECOND-ORDER CELLS

General Morphology of Photoreceptor Output Synapses

In the vertebrate retina, rod and cone photoreceptors make synaptic contacts with dendrites of second-order retinal neurons, the horizontal cells (HCs) and bipolar cells (BCs), in the outer plexiform layer (OPL). Two morphological types of synapses are often observed. The first is the invaginated ribbon synapse, which consists of a synaptic ribbon surrounded by precisely arranged arrays of synaptic vesicles; the second is the superficial basal junction, which consists of smoothly indented membrane with prominent electron-dense materials, but often shows no synaptic vesicles near the contact area (56, 57, 92). The ribbon synapse is believed to be associated with vesicular neurotransmitter release, whereas the basal junctions are associated with non-vesicular release of photoreceptor transmitter (56). The outputs of these two types of synaptic contacts vary from species to species. In primates, there seems to be a rule: basal junctions contact off-bipolar cells and ribbon synapses contact on-bipolar cells and horizontal cells (56). This rule breaks down in lower vertebrate species (100, 153). In the tiger salamander retina, for example, off-bipolar cells are predominately associated with ribbon synapses, whereas on-bipolar cells are predominately associated with basal junctions (100).

Rod and Cone Synaptic Pathways

Rods are responsible for vision under conditions of dim illumination when cones are not responsive. Cones operate under conditions of bright illumination, and they mediate color vision and provide high spatial resolution, features that rods do not handle (49, 56). It is of great interest to examine how rod and cone signals are transmitted along the visual pathway. Are rod and cone signals segregated or mixed in higher-order visual neurons? If they are mixed, at what stage and what synaptic mechanisms are involved in the mixing?

Strictly speaking, rod and cone signals start to mix through the gap junctions between them even before reaching their output synapses (see last section). However, rod-cone coupling is relatively weak (it may not exist everywhere in the retina, e.g. foveal cones), and thus the primary sites of signal mixing are post-receptor (73, 124). Synaptic organization of the rod and cone pathways in the outer retina varies from species to species. In mammals, rod and cone signals are transmitted separately to rod and cone bipolar cells, which send the segregated signals to the higher-order visual cells (124). HCs in the fish retina also receive rod and cone signals separately. There is one type of rod-driven HC and three types of cone-driven HCs, and each type of the cone HCs exhibits a distinct pattern of color responses (153, 154, 162). Bipolar cells in the fish retina, on the other hand, receive mixed inputs from rods and cones (85, 153). The second-order neurons in the amphibian retinas are thought to receive mixed inputs from rods and cones (59, 73, 99, 100, 103, 113, 200). However, recent evidence suggests that bipolar cells in the tiger salamander, either on-center or off-center, fall into two groups. One is rod-dominated and the other is cone-dominated (77, 78, 203). These two types of bipolar cells relay rod- or cone-dominated (though not exclusively rod- or cone-driven) signals to higher order visual neurons (77). It seems that the tiger salamander retina adopts a compromised strategy between mixing and segregating the rod and cone signals at the bipolar cell level.

Center-Surround Antagonistic Receptive Field Organization

Center-surround antagonistic receptive field (CSARF) is the basic alphabet for encoding spatial information in the visual system. It was first discovered by Kuffler in 1953, who demonstrated that light falling on the central region of the receptive field of cat retinal ganglion cells elicited a response of opposite sign as that elicited by light falling on the surround region of the receptive field (94). Later studies showed that such CSARF also exist upstream in retinal bipolar cells (83, 170) and downstream in cells in the lateral geniculate nucleus and the primary visual cortex (80, 81). Furthermore, complex receptive fields of neurons in higher visual centers are probably mediated by arrays of upstream neurons that exhibit CSARF organizations (81).

The first neuron along the visual pathway that exhibits CSARF organization is retinal bipolar cells. Bipolar cells may be "on" center with "off" surround, or "off" center with "on" surround (see below). The center input of a bipolar cell is mediated by direct photoreceptor output synapses made on its dendrites (and the dendrites of adjacent bipolar cells electrical coupled with it) (32, 59, 74). The surround input is mediated by the horizontal cells in the outer plexiform layer and by amacrine cells in the inner plexiform layer (59, 170). Horizontal cells make sign-inverting feedback synapse on cones (22) and feedforward synapses on bipolar cells (59). The feedback synapse is responsible for mediating the surround responses of bipolar cells in the outer retina (148, 170). Recent studies from the tiger salamander retina reveals that the feedforward synapses are also involved (although contributing only about one fourth to one third of the surround response) in generating bipolar cell surround responses (187, 201).

CSARF organization is ubiquitous in all vertebrate species. According to the computational theory of Marr (115), it is essential for detecting edges in visual images. Marr and colleagues pointed out that the CSARF of retinal bipolar cells, for example, acts like a filter for visual images, and the filter constitutes an approximation of taking the second spatial derivative of the light intensity ($\nabla^2 I$). At the edge of an image, $\nabla^2 I$ gives a large positive value on one side of the edge and a large negative value on the other side, and a zero-crossing in the middle. This type of filter (e.g. CSARF) can register intensity changes efficiently and therefore is an excellent edge detector. Additionally, Marr's theory also suggests that CSARF plays a crucial role in the detection of moving edges in visual images (116, 117).

Spatial frequency analysis of retinal cells also suggests that CSARF enhances response amplitudes at the edges of intensity distributions of visual images (13, 38). This approach involves taking the Fourier transform of the CSARF of visual cells, which give rise to the spatial frequency sensitivity function of the cell (38). The two antagonistic inputs of the receptive field result in fall-offs of the spatial frequency sensitivity at both high and low frequencies (6, 13) and thus make the cell a good contrast detector (62).

CSARF is a major vehicle for carrying color information in the visual system. In some species the receptive field of certain bipolar cells and ganglion cells exhibit "double-opponent" organization. For instance, the receptive field center of a bipolar cell is depolarized by red and hyperpolarized by green, while the surround is depolarized by green and hyperpolarized by red (86). In other species bipolar cells have other color coding organizations that include opponent receptive field centers with non-opponent surround, or vice versa (85, 205). These types of color-coded CSARF organizations help the visual system to detect stationary and moving color edges.

Sign-Preserving and Sign-Inverting Synapses—Initiation of the On and Off Pathways

Signals in the visual system are segregated into on and off channels. On cells respond to illumination in the center of their receptive field with membrane depolarization, or increase in action potential frequency, whereas off cells respond to center illumination with membrane hyperpolarization, or decrease in action potential frequency (18–20, 62, 94). The segregation of on and off channels is initiated at the bipolar cell level in the outer retina, and it persists throughout the entire visual pathway (80, 81). The on bipolar cells are depolarized by center illumination (therefore they are also named depolarizing bipolar cells, or DBCs), but hyperpolarized by surround illumination. The off bipolar cells (or the hyperpolarizing bipolar cells, HBCs) exhibit opposite center-surround response polarities (83, 170). The center responses of both types of bipolar cells are mediated directly by the photoreceptors, with the on bipolar cells (DBCs) through a sign-inverting synapse, and with the off bipolar cells (HBCs) through a sign-preserving synapse.

It has long been a puzzle how the same photoreceptor output synapses generate two postsynaptic responses of opposite polarities. Photoreceptors continuously release neurotransmitters, presumably glutamate, in darkness. Light hyperpolarizes photoreceptors and suppresses glutamate release. Recent evidence suggests that the two vastly different types of postsynaptic actions of glutamate are mediated by different classes of glutamate receptors (125–127, 149–151), and detailed mechanisms of these receptors are described below.

It is important to recognize that the sign-inverting synapse between photoreceptors and DBC is probably all the visual system needs to segregate the on and off pathways. After sign inversion by this synapse, visual signals in the "on-center" pathway do not need any further changes in response polarities. The synapses between DBC and on ganglion cell and between on ganglion cell and LGN cell, for example, are all sign-preserving (30, 42, 68, 80, 170).

Segregation of visual signals into on and off pathways helps to improve the ability of edge detection by visual cells (6, 115). If there were only one class of visual neurons, for instance, the on cells, then the cells with receptive field center at one side of the edge would give a higher rate of firing than those at the other side of the edge. This would result in a slower transmission of signal from the darker side of the edge because the spike frequency is lower. Consequently, the speed of information transmission from the two sides of the edge would not match. Having two classes of visual cells, the on and off cells, one class at each side of the edge, will give high frequency (or low frequency) responses from both sides, with comparable transmission speed (6).

Mechanisms of Neurotransmitter Release

Vertebrate photoreceptors continuously release glutamate in darkness, which activates postsynaptic receptors in bipolar cells and horizontal cells (43). This tonic release of glutamate is largely calcium-dependent (48, 58, 202), although a calcium-independent component of release has been reported

(140). Anatomical evidence has shown that rod and cone synaptic terminals are filled with synaptic vesicles, and the release site of these vesicles is probably near the ridges of ribbon synapse (134, 135). Physiological evidence of vesicular release, on the other hand, has been sparse until recently when discrete miniature excitatory postsynaptic currents (MEPSCs) were observed in tiger salamander retinal bipolar cells (107). These MEPSCs are Ca^{2+}-dependent vesicular process (168). The amplitudes and durations of individual MEPSCs, however, vary over wide ranges, which suggests that each MEPSC is probably mediated by a cluster of synaptic vesicles of various numbers and varying degrees of synchronization (107). In addition to tiger salamander bipolar cells, discrete and transient voltage changes have also been observed in the turtle bipolar cells (51).

Input-Output Relations of Synaptic Gains

Input-output relations of the photoreceptor output synapses are obtained by plotting the voltage responses of a simultaneously recorded [in retinal slices or flat-mounted isolated retina (169)] photoreceptor and second-order cells to whole field illumination (8, 29, 183). This approach implicitly takes synaptic convergence into consideration: it gives the relationship between voltage response of a second-order cell evoked by synaptic inputs from hundreds (or thousands) of photoreceptors that are uniformly polarized and the voltage response of one of these presynaptic photoreceptors. The voltage gains, derived as the slopes of these input-output relations, therefore represent the gain of all photoreceptor synapses converged to the second-order cell. The input-output relations of the rod output synapses in the tiger salamander and toad retina are nonlinear, with the highest voltage gains near the rod dark membrane potential. The gain (slope of the I/O relations) decreases as the rod becomes more hyperpolarized (8, 29, 39, 183, 187).

There have been considerable variations in the shape and voltage spans of the input-output relations and voltage gains of the rod-HC and rod-BC synapses in the amphibian retinas. For example, some studies indicate that the voltage range of rod outputs to second-order cells is limited to about 1.5–5 mV below the rod dark potentials. Rod responses larger than that are "clipped" by the output synapses (8, 29). Other studies show that the voltage range of rod outputs are as wide as 10–15 mV (178, 183). This discrepancy can be explained, at least partially, by a recent finding that the input-output relations are modulated by light and dark adaptation (91). A dim background light can reduce the rod output voltage range by about 5 mV, and it increases the voltage gain of the rod output synapses. This result suggests that the rod output synapses are probably not static, but exhibit a high degree of plasticity (see below).

Fluctuations and Kinetics of Synaptic Transmission

The membrane potential of bipolar cells fluctuates in darkness, and these fluctuations are reduced by light (1–5, 31, 51, 147). Voltage fluctuations in bipolar cells come from two sources: (*a*) photoreceptor voltage noise, which comprises fluctuations arising from photoisomerization of 11-cis retinal in dark, fluctuations in concentrations of substances involved in the transduction process, and fluctuations coming from random opening and closing of the light-regulated channels in the outer segments (24–26, 28, 72, 97, 147); (*b*) synaptic noise, which comprises fluctuations arising from random release of glutamate, fluctuations in glutamate binding, and fluctuations coming from random opening and closing of postsynaptic channels (1, 2, 41, 55, 107). In photoreceptors, voltage noise in steady light is about four times lower than that in darkness (2, 147). The voltage noise of HBCs in steady light is about six times lower than in darkness; whereas the voltage noise cf DBCs is about two to five times higher in dim light and about two times lower in bright light than in darkness (1). The light-induced changes in bipolar cell voltage noise partially result from the change in photoreceptor voltage noise, and partially from the suppression of glutamate release and changes in opening probabilities of postsynaptic channels (1, 41).

The kinetics of the photoreceptor output synapses have been studied by determining the impulse response functions for signal transmission. In the turtle retina, the impulse response of the rod-HC synapse is about ten times slower than that of the cone-HC synapse (136), whereas the impulse responses of the cone-HC synapse and the cone-HBC synapse are about four times faster than that of the cones-DBC synapse (1, 41). These differences in transmission kinetics may reflect the differences in time- and voltage-dependent behavior of postsynaptic receptors and channels, presynaptic release and uptake of glutamate, or/and the cooperativeness of glutamate binding in various photoreceptor output synapses (41).

Glutamate Receptors and Postsynaptic Conductances

Glutamate is the neurotransmitter used by all vertebrate photoreceptors (40, 43, 60, 108, 109, 118, 120, 199, 202) with a possible exception of blue cones, whose neurotransmitter identity is still unknown (109). At least five types of receptors with significantly distinct functions exist in glutamatergic synapses. These receptors are named after their specific agonists: kainate (KA), α-amino-3-hydroxy-5-methylisoxazole-4-propionic acid (AMPA), N-methyl-D-aspartate (NMDA), L-α-amino-4-phosphonobutyrate (L-AP4), and trans-1-aminocyclopentane-1, 3-dicarboxylic acid (ACPD) receptors (119).

Postsynaptic responses of retinal HBCs horizontal cells (HCs) are mediated primarily by KA and AMPA receptors (104, 149–151, 202). Glutamate released from photoreceptors in darkness binds to the KA/AMPA receptors and opens postsynaptic cation channels (Na^+ and K^+) (9, 40, 82, 104, 146, 157). The reversal potential of the glutamate-gated current in HBCs and HCs is about -10–0 mV in most species (9, 157). Light reduces glutamate release from photoreceptors and closes the postsynaptic channels, which results in hyperpolarizing voltage responses in HBCs and HCs.

The sign-inverting synapses between photoreceptors and DBCs are mediated mainly by the L-AP4 receptors (90, 126, 127, 143–145, 149). Glutamate released from photoreceptors binds to the L-AP4 receptors in DBCs, which results in an increase of cGMP hydrolysis by a G protein-mediated process, thus leading to a fall of intracellular cGMP and closure of cation channels (126, 127, 143–145). Light suppresses glutamate release, which increases intracellular cGMP that opens cation channels and results in membrane depolarization.

Removal of Glutamate by Uptake Transporters

The actions of glutamate in synaptic clefts between photoreceptors and second-order retinal neurons are not terminated by enzymes that convert glutamate into inactive molecules, but by uptake transporters located in photoreceptors and glial cells (Muller cells). Autoradiographic studies have revealed that high-affinity uptake systems in photoreceptor and Muller cells are capable of removing extracellular glutamate effectively, with an approximate K_d of 1–20 μM (108). Recent electrophysiological studies have shown that the uptake transporters in these cells are electrogenic; each glutamate anion is co-transported with perhaps 3 Na^+ into and 1 K^+ out of the cells (17, 142). Therefore, it is possible to study the kinetics of glutamate transporters by measuring the electrogenic current with whole-cell voltage clamp techniques. Results from such studies show that the time constant of glutamate decrease in the extracellular space caused by transporters in cone photoreceptors and Muller cells is approximately 30–50 msec (7, 17, 61, 142). Since the decay time course of the postsynaptic responses to brief presynaptic voltage changes in the photoreceptor output synapses is about 200 msec (1, 136), the decrease of extracellular glutamate induced by photoreceptors and Muller cell transporters seems to be fast enough to account for terminating the synaptic actions of glutamate (7).

HORIZONTAL CELL OUTPUT SYNAPSES

There are two output synapses made by HCs, one on cone photoreceptors (feedback synapse), and the other on bipolar cells (feedforward synapse).

The HC output synapses serve vital functions in information processing in the outer retina. They are responsible for generating the antagonistic surround responses in bipolar cells. Application of γ-aminobutyric acid (GABA), a HC neurotransmitter in cold-blooded vertebrates (96, 111, 141, 171, 179), abolishes the surround response of bipolar cells while leaving the center response unaffected (93, 179). HCs also mediate color opponency and regulate the dynamic range and reliability of photoreceptor output synapses.

Feedback Synapse Between Horizontal Cells and Cones

The sign-inverting (negative) feedback signal from HCs to cones was first recorded in the turtle retina (22), and subsequently in perch (34, 35), carp (121, 122), and tiger salamander (11, 102, 148, 186). Although an electrical model has been proposed (36, 37), it is widely accepted that the feedback signal is mediated by chemical synapses between HCs and cones. In darkness, HCs are depolarized by the continuous flow of photoreceptor neurotransmitter (glutamate), which results in a high rate of HC neurotransmitter release. In many lower vertebrates, GABA released from HCs in darkness opens Cl^- channels in cones, possibly through $GABA_A$ receptors (87, 88, 158, 186). The reversal potential of the $GABA_A$-mediated Cl^- conductances is estimated to be below -50 mV in turtle cones (88, 158), and around -65mV in tiger salamander cones (186). As the resting potential of cones is between -30 and -40 mV (10, 11, 21–23, 186), GABA released from HCs hyperpolarizes the cones tonically in darkness (179, 188). In the presence of light stimuli, HCs are hyperpolarized, and thus GABA release is suppressed. This results in the closure of Cl^- channels and a membrane depolarization in cones. Because of synaptic delays and the relatively slow HC response rise time, the feedback response may sometimes be observed as a delayed depolarizing sag in the cone light response (52, 132, 186). The cone response sag, however, cannot be completely attributed to the feedback signal because a hyperpolarization-activated time-dependent current in cones contributes partially to the slow repolarization in the cone response (10).

INPUT-OUTPUT RELATIONS AND VOLTAGE GAIN OF THE HC-CONE FEEDBACK SYNAPSE   Input-output relations and voltage gains of the HC-cone feedback synapse have been studied by using the truncated cone method (cone outer segment is truncated off to avoid masking effect of photocurrent on feedback signals) in the tiger salamander retina (185). The input-output relation of the HC-cone feedback synapse was obtained by plotting the simultaneous voltage points of the HC and truncated cone responses. Analysis of experimental data leads to the conclusion that the light-evoked feedback response in intact cones (outer segments attached) is controlled by two factors: first, the magnitude of the postsynaptic conductance decrease (due to the reduction of HC neurotransmitter) increases as brighter light gives rise to larger HC hyperpolarization; and second, the driving force (V_{cone}-E_s) of the postsynaptic current decreases as brighter light hyperpolarizes the cone, which brings it closer to the reversal potential of the feedback synapse ($E_s \approx$ –67 mV). These two factors exert opposite effects on the feedback light responses in cones and thus result in a bell-shaped input-output relation (186, 187).

An important implication of the bell-shaped input-output relation for light-evoked feedback signals is that the strength of the feedback signal in a given cone decreases with the intensity of light falling directly onto it, but increases with that falling onto other photoreceptors. This spatial discrimination of light enhances spatial contrast in the retina; the antagonistic response of a cone (and thus bipolar cells and ganglion cells) is greatest when the cone itself is not directly stimulated by light. When cones are directly stimulated by light, the antagonistic response decreases and eventually disappears as the direct light hyperpolarizes the cone to the feedback reversal potential (186–187).

FUNCTIONS OF HORIZONTAL CELL-CONE FEEDBACK SYNAPSE IN THE OUTER RETINA: HORIZONTAL CELL-CONE FEEDBACK SYNAPSE IMPROVES THE PERFORMANCE OF THE PHOTORECEPTOR OUTPUT SYNAPSES   The HC-cone feedback synapse constitutes a negative feedback circuit for the photoreceptor output synapses. Based on the principles of system analysis, negative feedback loops improve the reliability, signal-to-noise ratio, response band width, and stability of the forward signals (114). In the retina, the photoreceptor-bipolar-ganglion cell synapses constitute the direct and express route for signal transmission between the photoreceptor and the brain. The HC-cone feedback synapse helps to improve the performance and accuracy of signal transfer in this pathway.

HORIZONTAL CELL-CONE FEEDBACK SYNAPSE MODULATES DYNAMIC RANGES OF RETINAL BIPOLAR CELLS   In the vertebrate retina, different types of neurons operate within different light intensity (dynamic) ranges. The dynamic ranges for photoreceptors and horizontal cells, for example, are much wider than those of the bipolar cells and ganglion cells (161). As photoreceptor-bipolar synaptic transmission is limited within a window of the photoreceptor voltage (29, 203), a tonic negative feedback signal can shift the dynamic range of bipolar cells towards the right in the intensity axis (161, 187). When a steady background illumination tonically activates the feedback synapses between HCs and cones, the operating range of the bipolar cells shifts to the right so that a brighter light stimulus is required to generate a given bipolar cell response. This synaptic arrangement enhances the simultaneous contrast of the visual system: the brighter the background (ambient) light, the brighter the stimulus is required to generate a given response. Bipolar cells are good contrast detectors because their narrow dynamic ranges allow steep V-log I relations (larger voltage changes per unit change in light intensity). As the feedback synapse can shift the dynamic ranges along the intensity axis, the bipolar cell operation can still cover a wide intensity range while background lights of various intensities are applied to the retina (187).

HORIZONTAL CELL-CONE FEEDBACK SYNAPSE MEDIATES COLOR OPPONENCY IN RETINAL NEURONS   There are three spectrally distinct types of cone photoreceptors in vertebrates that exhibit rich color vision: the red-, green-, and blue-sensitive cones (163). It is a common misconception that cones can distinguish colors. This is not true because although cones have different sensitivities to lights of different color, they cannot distinguish between them. Color encoding in the visual system begins at second-order retinal neurons, which exhibit color opponency: light of certain wavelengths elicits depolarizing responses, whereas light of other wavelengths elicits hyper-polarizing responses. The best-studied color-opponent second-order retinal cells are the fish horizontal cells, and their color opponency is mediated by the feedback synapses between HCs and cones (154). The color opponency of other second-order cells, such as double-opponent bipolar cells, is also mediated at least partially by the feedback synapses between HCs and cones (85, 86).

HORIZONTAL CELL-CONE FEEDBACK SYNAPSE MEDIATES SURROUND RESPONSES IN RETINAL BIPOLAR CELLS   As described above, center-surround antago-nistic receptive field (CSARF) organization is the basic alphabet for encoding spatial information in the visual system. The surround responses of retinal bipolar cells is mediated by HCs primarily through the HC-cone-bipolar cell synaptic pathways (187). These feedback synapses give sign-inverting sur-round signals to HBCs because the HC-cone synapse is sign-preserving, and the cone-HBC synapse is sign-preserving. They give sign-preserving surround signals to DBCs because both the HC-cone and cone-DBC synapses are sign-inverting.

FEEDFORWARD SYNAPSES BETWEEN HORIZONTAL CELLS AND BIPOLAR CELLS Feedforward synaptic contacts between HCs and bipolar cells were first observed anatomically from electron microscopic studies (59, 99, 101). Physiologically it has been difficult to demonstrate that HC signals are transmitted to bipolar cells through direct synapses made between the two cells. HC inputs elicited by light or by current injection have been observed in bipolar cells, but it is difficult to determine whether the inputs are mediated by the feedback (HC-cone-bipolar) pathway or the feedforward (HC-bipolar cell) synapse (112, 123, 164, 182). A recent study in the tiger salamander retina overcame this difficulty by selectively blocking synaptic transmission from photoreceptors to DBCs with L-AP4, while leaving other synapses unaffected (201). Application of 20 μM L-AP4 suppresses the depolarizing light response of DBCs and converts it into a hyperpolarizing response. This hyperpolarizing light response in DBCs in the presence of L-AP4 is probably mediated by the HC input transmitted through the HC-DBC feedforward synapse, but not through the HC-DBC feedback pathway because the cone-DBC synapse is blocked.

Although the HC-HBC feedforward synapse observed from anatomical studies (59, 101) may be also functional, it is not yet possible to demonstrate it physiologically because there are no known pharmacological agents that can effectively block the photoreceptor-HBC synapse without affecting the photoreceptor-HC synapse (both HBCs and HCs receive photoreceptor inputs through KA/AMPA receptors).

One implication of the direct HC-bipolar feedforward synapses is that HCs must be capable of making two distinct types of synaptic outputs: the one on DBC must be sign-preserving and the one on the HBC must be sign-inverting, according to the polarities of the bipolar cell responses to annulus light and current injections into HCs (83, 112, 123, 164, 170). In darkness, HCs are tonically depolarized, and they release neurotransmitter on bipolar cells. The HC neurotransmitter must result in membrane depolarization in DBCs but membrane hyperpolarization in HBCs. Light hyperpolarizes the HCs and suppresses the release of HC neurotransmitter, which results in hyperpolarizing responses in DBCs (sign-preserving) and depolarizing responses in HBCs (sign-inverting). The question is how does the HC neurotransmitter depolarize the DBCs but hyperpolarize the HBCs. One possible answer is that the HC neurotransmitter opens postsynaptic channels in one type of bipolar cell and closes channels in the other. This resembles the actions of the photoreceptor neurotransmitter glutamate, which opens channels in HBCs but closes channels in DBCs (see above). Another possibility is that HC neurotransmitter may exert the same action on both types of bipolar cells (e.g. Cl^- channels), but the reversal potentials (E_r) of the permeable ion of the neurotransmitter-gated channels in the two bipolar cells are on opposite sides of the respective dark membrane potentials (V_d). From the study of the tiger salamander retina, the voltage gain of the HC-DBC feedforward synapse is much lower than that of the HC-cone-DBC feedback pathway. The slope gain of the feedforward synapse near the HC dark potential is about 0.15, whereas that of the feedback pathway is about 0.58 (obtained as the product of the gains of the HC-cone (-0.33) and cone-DBC (-1.75) synapses) (187). Therefore, the HC inputs in DBCs is predominately mediated by the feedback pathway (which contributes about 70–80% of the HC input), although the feedforward synapse is clearly functional (which contributes 20-30% of the HC input) (187).

ELECTRICAL SYNAPSES BETWEEN HORIZONTAL CELLS AND BETWEEN BIPOLAR CELLS

Horizontal cells in the vertebrate retina are electrically coupled to one another. In fishes especially, the electrical (gap) junctions between HCs are very extensive. Gap junctions are observed between HC perikarya or between HC processes, but the couplings are only made between HC of homologous types. For example, the H1 cone HCs in the fish couple only with other H1 cells, H2 couple only with other H2 cells, and HC axon terminals couple only with other HC axon terminals (172).

The primary function of HC coupling is to increase the receptive field size of these cells. The dendritic diameter of the fish HCs typically range from 30–150 µm (137, 153, 172), but the receptive field of these cells range from 2 to 10 mm in diameter (84, 124). Electrical synapses between HCs therefore greatly increase the lateral integration of HC signals. Consequently, the HCs provide broad field antagonistic inputs to cones and bipolar cells that are important for spatial information processing and edge detection in the retina (115).

Electrical coupling between bipolar cells has been reported in several vertebrate retinas. Electron microscopic studies have revealed that gap junctions are made between bipolar cell axon terminals in the inner plexiform layer (110, 173). Current injection into fish bipolar cells elicits sign-preserving responses in adjacent bipolar cells (95). In the tiger salamander retina, the diameter of the bipolar cell receptive field center is about 10–20 times larger than the diameter of the dendritic arbors of these cells (32). These results suggest that bipolar cells of the same type are extensively coupled to one another at least in certain species or certain areas of the retina. The primary function of bipolar cell coupling is to increase the receptive field center of these cells. Additionally, bipolar cell coupling also improves the signal-to-noise ratio of the bipolar cell output signals. The disadvantage of bipolar cell coupling, however, is that it reduces the spatial resolution of bipolar cell outputs. Coupling does not occur between foveal bipolar cells in primates, thus high visual acuity is preserved (49).

MODULATION OF SYNAPTIC FUNCTIONS

In the previous sections, the synaptic organization and mechanisms of synaptic transmission in the outer retina have been reviewed. Although synaptic parameters, such as voltage gains, have been characterized quantitatively, they are by no means static. Recent evidence has shown that retinal synapses exhibit high degrees of plasticity; their function can be modulated by prolonged darkness, background light, and a number of neuromodulatory substances (185). It is evident that synapses in the retina are designed to accommodate large degrees of adjustability so that they can function effectively under a wide range of conditions. In this section, studies on synaptic modulations in the outer retina are reviewed. Changes in synaptic efficacy and kinetics induced by dark or light adaptation, or by various neuromodulatory agents, are examined.

Modulation of Electrical Synapses Between Photoreceptors

In the tiger salamander retina, three lines of evidence suggest that rod-cone coupling is stronger under light-adapted conditions than under dark-adapted conditions (198). (*a*) Rods or cones in prolonged dark-adapted retinas obey the principle of univariance (200, 124), which is indicative of weak interaction between the two photoreceptor types. Under moderately light-adapted conditions, the principle of univariance does not hold in either rods or cones, which indicates signal mixing of the two photoreceptors. (*b*) Increment threshold measurements reveal that rods receive increasing inputs from cones as background light becomes brighter. (*c*) Voltage response in rods to current injection into adjacent cones is larger in the presence of background light than in darkness. This again is consistent with the notion that light enhances rod-cone coupling in the tiger salamander retina. Voltage response in rods to current injection into adjacent rods, on the other hand, is not affected by background illumination, which indicates that rod-rod coupling is not modulated by light or dark adaptation (15).

Modulation of Electrical Coupling Between Horizontal Cells

Overwhelming evidence has shown that dopamine alters electrical coupling between horizontal cells in fish and other cold-blooded vertebrates (54, 56, 105, 106, 128). Application of dopamine, dibutyryl-cAMP (a cAMP analogue) and compounds that increase the intracellular levels of cAMP all narrow the receptive fields of HCs and suppress dye diffusion between HCs in the fish and turtle retinas (159). Destruction of the interplexiform cells, the only source of dopamine in the fish retina, broadens the receptive fields of HCs and facilitates dye diffusion across gap junctions (160). Dopamine and cAMP decrease the conductance of the electrical synapses between pairs of coupled fish HCs in culture (105). These results suggest that dopamine acts on HCs and raises the intracellular levels of cAMP, which closes gap junction channels between HCs. cAMP activates protein kinases that phosphorylate gap junction channel proteins, thus leading to closure of the channels (167).

In addition to dopamine, GABA has been found to uncouple HCs in the turtle retina (133). In the mudpuppy retina, APB, a glutamate receptor agonist, also uncouples HCs. However, this action is thought to be indirect: APB facilitates the release of dopamine, which uncouples the HCs (53, 54). The uncoupling effect of dopamine (and perhaps GABA) on retinal HCs suggests that the receptive fields of HCs can be adjusted. This implies that under certain conditions, when extracellular concentration of dopamine is low, HCs exhibit a broad receptive field, and thus lateral inhibition in the outer retina extends for long distances. Under conditions when extracellular dopamine level is high, HCs narrow their receptive fields and the extent of lateral inhibition is reduced. Such modulation of the electrical synapses between HCs allows flexibility of lateral inhibition and adjustability of the strength of the antagonistic surround responses in retina neurons (19).

Modulation of Efficacy of the Photoreceptor Output Synapses

LIGHT ALTERS INPUT-OUTPUT RELATIONS AND ENHANCES SYNAPTIC GAIN Recent evidence from the tiger salamander retina has demonstrated that the voltage gain of the rod-HC and rod-HBC synapses can be modulated by background light. A dim background light shifts the input-output relations of the rod output synapses to the more hyperpolarized rod potentials and enhances the slope gains of these synapses by a factor of 10 (191). The mechanisms of this light-elicited synaptic modulation is not known, although several hypothesis appear reasonable (181, 185). It is possible, for example, that background light alters the extracellular levels of neuromodulatory substances such as GABA, zinc, and dopamine (175, 178, 189, 197), which change either the Ca^{2+} influx in the rod terminal (16, 46), or the binding efficacy of glutamate receptors and/or postsynaptic conductances in second-order neurons. Evidence of modulatory actions of GABA on Ca^{2+} influx in synaptic terminals has been recently reported (75, 76), and evidence of modulation of glutamate receptors by dopamine is described below.

DOPAMINE ALTERS SYNAPTIC EFFICACY BETWEEN CONES AND HCS   In the fish retina, dopamine decreases the light response of cone HCs to full-field illumination (106, 194, 195). Application of dopamine or cAMP enhances the glutamate- or kainate-induced conductance changes in dissociated cone HCs, but not in dissociated rod HCs (91). The decrease of light responsiveness of the cone HCs is thought to be mediated by the dopamine-induced enhancement of glutamate potency. Light-elicited reduction of glutamate release is less effective, and thus the response amplitude is smaller (194).

Modulation of Rod-Cone Balance in Second-Order Cells

Second-order retinal neurons in many species receive mixed inputs from rods and cones. It appears from recent studies that the relative rod and cone inputs (rod-cone balance) in HCs and bipolar cells can be altered by several classes of neuroactive substances (174–176, 192) and by the state of adaptation (63, 193). The mechanisms of modulation of rod and cone balance is complex, especially because many modulatory agents interact and thus the action of one agent can be changed by another agent (192, 193).

MODULATION OF ROD-CONE BALANCE BY DOPAMINE   In the *Xenopus* retina, application of D_1 and D_2 dopamine agonists increases the amplitude and kinetics of the cone input, but reduces the amplitude of the rod input in HCs (176). Similar results have been observed in the tiger salamander HCs when dopamine is applied (193). Although no dopaminergic interplexiform cells have been found in these amphibian species (56), dopaminergic amacrine cells may be the source of dopamine that diffuses from the inner plexiform layer to the outer retina and regulates the efficacies of the rod and cone output synapses. At least in the *Xenopus,* the extracellular concentration of dopamine is thought to be high in the presence of background light (photopic condition) and low in darkness (scotopic condition) (176). Therefore, the rod input in HCs is stronger under scotopic condition where low luminous vision is important, and cone input is stronger under photopic condition where high luminous vision or color vision is more critical (130, 131).

MODULATION OF ROD-CONE BALANCE BY GLUTAMATE UPTAKE TRANSPORTERS In the tiger salamander, application of dihydrokainate (DHK), a glutamate uptake transporter blocker, mimics flickering light and suppresses HC responses to 500 nm light and the response voltage "tails," which are indicative of selective reduction of rod inputs in these cells (192). D-aspartate, another glutamate uptake transporter blocker, suppresses both the rod and cone inputs in HCs. It is thought that DHK is more effective in blocking the glutamate uptake transporters in the rod synaptic cleft, whereas D-aspartate is probably less selective in that it blocks glutamate uptake in both the rod and cone output synapses. The physiological factors that control the activity and affinity of the glutamate transporters in the rod and cone synapses are not clear. Preliminary evidence suggests that dopamine, H^+, and adenosine may interact with the glutamate uptake systems (192).

Modulation of Response Waveform of Photoreceptors and Second-Order Cells

The waveform and kinetics of light responses in photoreceptors and second-order cells in the retina vary with the state of adaptation. In the tiger salamander retina, adaptation alters at least two aspects of response waveforms in the outer retinal neurons. (a) Background light speeds up the HC response rise time (HCRRT) and darkness slows it down (185, 196, 197). (b) An off-overshoot response can be observed in photoreceptors and second-order cells under light-adapted conditions, but not under dark-adapted conditions (69, 180, 184, 185). Detailed analysis has shown that the HCRRT is modulated by at least two mechanisms: (a) short-term modulation (STM), the HCRRT becomes faster immediately after the onset of background light, and it reaches steady state about 2 sec after the background light onset; (b) long-term modulation (LTM), the HCRRT becomes faster after the offset of prolonged light exposure, and the time to reach steady state is about 6–8 min. STM has been shown to be closely related to the rod voltage, and it is probably mediated by suppressive rod-cone interaction in HCs. In darkness, while rods are depolarized, they may release modulators that slow down the kinetics of the postsynaptic receptor-channel complexes in HCs. Background light hyperpolarizes the rods and reduces the release of modulators, and thus speeds up the HC responses (196). Application of GABA and glycine mimics prolonged darkness and slows down the HCCRT (156, 197). Application of bicuculline mimics light adaptation and speeds up HCRRT (197). These results suggest that LTM may be mediated by GABA-ergic and glycinergic pathways. It is possible that GABA is released continuously in darkness from HCs and that it opens chloride channels in HCs (89, 155). Light hyperpolarizes HCs, suppresses GABA release, and closes chloride channels. Since the chloride equilibrium potential is near the HC dark voltage, and the suppression of GABA release or closure of Cl^- channels is a slow process, the onset of HC is slow (89, 196, 204). Under light-adapted conditions, the Cl^- channels are closed and the HC light response is mediated primarily by closure of glutamate-gated cation channels, which have fast kinetics, thus the HCRRT is faster. Glycine may diffuse from amacrine cells to the HC synapses and act as a GABA agonist, or it may be released from the interplexiform cells onto HCs and somehow facilitate GABA release from the latter cells (197). Additionally, vesicular zinc has been localized in photoreceptor synaptic terminals of the tiger salamander, and application of micromolar zinc blocks the actions of GABA on horizontal cells (189). It is possible that zinc may be co-released with glutamate in darkness, which modulates the HCRRT through its actions on GABA receptors.

The second aspect of adaptation-induced change in response waveform occurs at the offset of the light stimulus. Rod_cs (a population of rods that are strongly coupled with cones) exhibit a mixed response waveform of rods and cones under dark-adapted condition and a cone-mediated response under light-adapted condition (180, 184, 190). The cone-mediated responses in rod_cs abruptly repolarize to the baseline at the termination of the light step, and this enables rod_cs to activate regenerative potentials in the anode break fashion (79). Anode break calcium spikes have been observed in toad rods (66), and similar conductances may exist in the tiger salamander rods. Other rods (non-rod_cs) do not exhibit off-overshoot responses probably because they never have the opportunity to perform anode break excitation since their light response returns to the baseline slowly under dark-adapted conditions and their response becomes small under light-adapted conditions.

The off-overshoot response observed in light-adapted cones is probably mediated by the off-overshoot spikes in rod_cs through the electrical synapses between them. As discussed above, rod-cone coupling is stronger under light-adapted conditions, and this facilitates the cone-mediated light responses to rods (and rod_cs) as well as the rod_cs-mediated off-overshoot responses to cones. The off-overshoot responses in HCs and bipolar cells are probably mediated by the postsynaptic responses to the off-overshoot potentials in rod_cs and cones.

PERSPECTIVE

Vertebrate retina is probably the most ideal model system for studying the brain. Its complex but highly organized synaptic network exemplifies how synapses in the brain work and how various brain functions may be accomplished by its synapses. From the materials covered in this review, it is evident that synapses in the outer retina are cleverly arranged so that visual tasks can be effectively, reliably, and economically accomplished. There are a number of ingenious strategies of synaptic arrangements in the retina. In order to achieve high acuity, the retina makes discrete photoreceptors, each of which covers a tiny area in the visual field. However, in some animals, or in some part of the retina where high acuity is less important than reliability, photoreceptors are connected by electrical synapses so that higher signal-to-noise ratio can be accomplished. Similar rules appear to be applicable to bipolar cells and perhaps other higher order neurons. In order to achieve high spatial contrast, the retina uses lateral neurons, such as HCs, to make inhibitory synapses with central neurons, such as bipolar cells, to form the CSARF. In order to increase the edge and motion detecting capabilities, the retina forms on and off pathways. This segregation is achieved by using different types of glutamate receptors in the on and off bipolar cells so that one gives rise to depolarizing response and the other gives rise to hyperpolarizing response to the same photoreceptor input. In order to improve transmission stability, mediate color opponency, and regulate dynamic ranges of visual neurons, retinal HCs make feedback synapses with cone photoreceptors, in addition to feedforward lateral synapses with bipolar cells. Moreover, in order to achieve high adaptability, retinal synapses are made to be highly susceptible to modulation. Light or neuromodulatory agents can alter the efficacies of both electrical and chemical synapses in the retina. Consequently, the receptive fields of retinal neurons, synaptic gains, and response waveforms in the retina can be altered. The strategies of synaptic organization we have learned apply not only to the retina, but may also apply to the rest of the brain. By using the retina as a model, we can ask questions on how synapses in the brain work and what is the meaning of their arrangement.

ACKNOWLEDGMENTS

The preparation of this review and some of the work presented herein is supported by National Institutes of Health EY04446, the Retina Research Foundation (Houston), Research to Prevent Blindness, Inc., and the Human Frontier Science Program.

Literature Cited

1. Ashmore JF, Copenhagen DR. 1980. Different postsynaptic events in two types of retinal bipolar cell. *Nature* 288:84–86
2. Ashmore JF, Falk G. 1977. Dark noise in retinal bipolar cells and stability of rhodopsin in rods. *Nature* 270:69–71
3. Ashmore JF, Falk G. 1979. Transmission of visual signals to bipolar cells near absolute threshold. *Vision Res.* 19:419–23
4. Ashmore JF, Falk G. 1980. Responses of rod bipolar cells in the dark-adapted retina of the dogfish, *Scyliorhinus canicula. J. Physiol.* 300:115–50
5. Ashmore JF, Falk G. 1980. The single-photon signal in rod bipolar cells of the dog fish retina. *J. Physiol.* 300:151–66
6. Attwell D. 1986. Ion channels and signal processing in the outer retina. *J. Exp. Physiol.* 71:497–536
7. Attwell D. 1990. The photoreceptor output synapse. *Prog. Retin. Res.* 9: 337–62
8. Attwell D, Borges S, Wu SM, Wilson M. 1987. Signal clipping by the rod output synapse. *Nature* 328:522–24
9. Attwell D, Mobbs P, Tessier-Lavigne M, Wilson M. 1987. Neurotransmitter-induced currents in retinal bipolar cells of the axolotl, *Ambystoma mexicanum. J. Physiol.* 387:125–61
10. Attwell D, Werblin FS, Wilson M. 1982. The properties of single cones isolated from the tiger salamander retina. *J. Physiol.* 328:259–83
11. Attwell D, Werblin FS, Wilson M, Wu SM. 1983. A sign-reversing pathway from rods to double and single cones in the retina on the tiger salamander. *J. Physiol.* 336:313–33
12. Attwell D, Wilson M. 1980. Behaviour of the rod network in the tiger salamander retina mediated by membrane properties of individual rods. *J. Physiol.* 309:287–315
13. Attwell D, Wilson M. 1983. The spatial frequency sensitivity of bipolar cells. *Biol. Cybern.* 47:131–40
14. Attwell D, Wilson M, Wu SM. 1984. A quantitative analysis of interactions between photoreceptors in the salaman-

der *(Ambystoma)* retina. *J. Physiol.* 352:703–37

15. Attwell D, Wilson M, Wu SM. 1985. The effect of light on the spread of signals through the rod network of the salamander *(Ambystoma)* retina. *Brain Res.* 343:79–88

16. Bader CR, Bertrand D, Schwartz EA. 1982. Voltage-activated and calcium-activated currents studied in solitary rod inner segments from the salamander retina. *J. Physiol.* 331:253–84

17. Barbour B, Brew H, Attwell D. 1991. Electrogenic uptake of glutamate and aspartate into glial cells isolated from the salamander *(Ambystoma)* retina. *J. Physiol.* 436:169–93

18. Barlow HB. 1981. The Ferrier Lecture, 1980: Critical limiting factors in the design of the eye and the visual cortex. *Proc. R. Soc. London Ser. B* 212:1–34

19. Barlow HB, Fitzhugh R, Kuffler SW. 1957. Change of organization in the receptive field of the cat's retina during dark adaptation. *J. Physiol.* 137:338–54

20. Barlow HB, Levick WR. 1965. The mechanisms of directionally selective units in rabbit's retina. *J. Physiol.* 178:477–504

21. Baylor DA, Fuortes MGF. 1970. Electrical responses of single cones in the retina of the turtle. *J. Physiol.* 207:77–92

22. Baylor DA, Fuortes MGF, O'Bryan PM. 1971. Receptive fields of single cones in the retina of the turtle. *J. Physiol.* 24:265–94

23. Baylor DA, Hodgkin AL, Lamb TD. 1974. The electrical response of turtle cones to flashes and steps of light. *J. Physiol.* 242:685–727

24. Baylor DA, Lamb TD, Yau KW. 1979. The membrane current of single rod outer segments. *J. Physiol.* 288:589–612

25. Baylor DA, Lamb TD, Yau KW. 1979. Responses of retinal rods to single photons. *J. Physiol.* 288:613–34

26. Baylor DA, Matthews G, Yau KW. 1980. Two components of electrical dark noise in toad retinal rod outer segments. *J. Physiol.* 309:591–621

27. Baylor DA, Nunn BJ. 1986. Electrical properties of the light-sensitive conductance of rods of the salamander *Ambystoma tigrinum*. *J. Physiol.* 371:115–45

28. Baylor DA, Nunn BJ, Schnapf JL. 1984. The photocurrent noise, and spectral sensitivity of rods of the monkey *Macaca fascicularis*. *J. Physiol.* 357:575–607

29. Belgum JH, Copenhagen DR. 1988. Synaptic transfer of rod signals to horizontal and bipolar cells in the retina of the toad. *J. Physiol.* 396:225–45

30. Belgum JH, Dvorak DR, McReynolds JS. 1982. Sustained synaptic input to ganglion cells of mudpuppy retina. *J. Physiol.* 326:91–108

31. Bialek WS, Owen WG. 1990. Temporal filtering in retinal bipolar cells: Elements of an optional computation? *Biophys. J.* 58:1227–33

32. Borges S, Wilson M. 1987. Structure of the receptive fields of bipolar cells in the salamander retina. *J. Neurophysiol.* 58(6):1275–91

33. Boycott BB, Dowling JE. 1969. Organization of the primate retina: light microscopy. *Philos. Trans. R. Soc. London Ser. B* 255:109–84

34. Burkhardt DA. 1974. Sensitization and center-surround antagonism in necturus retina. *J. Physiol.* 236:593–610

35. Burkhardt DA. 1977. Responses and receptive-field organization of cones in perch retinas. *J. Neurophysiol.* 40:53–62

36. Byzov AL. 1977. Models of mechanism of feedback between horizontal cells and photoreceptors in vertebrate retina. *Neurophysiology* 9:86–94

37. Byzov AL, Shura-Bura TM. 1986. Electrical feedback mechanisms in the processing of signals in the outer plexiform layer of the retina. *Vision Res.* 26:33–44

38. Campbell FW, Robson JG. 1968. Application of Fourier analysis to the visibility of gratings. *J. Physiol.* 197:551–56

39. Capovilla M, Hare WA, Owen WG. 1987. Voltage gain of signal transfer from retinal rods to bipolar cells in the tiger salamander. *J. Physiol.* 391:125–40

40. Cervetto L, MacNichol EF Jr. 1972. Inactivation of horizontal cells in turtle retina by glutamate and aspartate. *Science* 178:767–68

41. Copenhagen DR, Ashmore JF, Schnapf JK. 1983. Kinetics of synaptic transmission from photoreceptors to horizontal and bipolar cells in turtle retina. *Vision Res.* 23:363–69

42. Copenhagen DR, Hemila S, Reuter T. 1990. Signal transmission through dark-adapted retina of the toad *(Bufo marinus)*. *J. Gen. Physiol.* 95:717–32

43. Copenhagen DR, Jahr CE. 1988. Release of endogenous excitatory amino acids from turtle photoreceptors. *Nature* 341:536–39

44. Copenhagen DR, Owen WG. 1976. Functional characteristics of lateral in-

teractions between rods in the retina of the snapping turtle. *J. Physiol.* 259:251–82

45. Copenhagen DR, Owen WG. 1980. Current-voltage relations in the rod photoreceptor network of the turtle retina. *J. Physiol.* 308:159–84

46. Corey DP, Dubinsy JM, Schwartz EA. 1984. The calcium current in inner segments of rods from the salamander *(Ambystoma tigrinum)* retina. *J. Physiol.* 354:557–75

47. Custer NV. 1973. Structurally specialized contacts between the photoreceptors of the retina of the axolotl. *J. Comp. Neurol.* 151:35–56

48. Dacheux FF, Miller RF. 1976. Photoreceptor-bipolar cell transmission in the perfused retina eyecup of the mudpuppy. *Science* 191:963–64

49. Davson H. 1990. *Physiology of the Eye,* pp. 203–445. New York: Pergamon. 5th ed.

50. Detwiler PB, Hodgkin AL. 1979. Electrical coupling between cones in the turtle retina. *J. Physiol.* 291:75–100

51. Detwiler PB, Hodgkin AL, Lamb TD. 1984. A note on the synaptic events in hyperpolarizing bipolar cells of the turtle's retina. In *Photoreceptors,* ed. A Borsellino, L Cervetto. New York: Plenum

52. Detwiler PB, Hodgkin AL, McNaughton PA. 1980. Temporal and spatial characteristics of the voltage response of rods in the retina of the snapping turtle. *J. Physiol.* 300:213–501

53. Dong CJ, McReynolds JS. 1989. APB increases apparent coupling between horizontal cells in mudpuppy retina. *Vision Res.* 29:541–44

54. Dong CJ, McReynolds JS. 1991. The relationship between light, dopamine release, and horizontal cell coupling in the mudpuppy retina. *J. Physiol.* 440:291–309

55. Donner K, Copenhagen DR, Reuter T. 1990. Weber and noise adaptation in the retina of the toad *(Bufo marinus). J. Gen. Physiol.* 95:733–53

56. Dowling JE. 1987. *The Retina, an Approachable Part of the Brain.* Boston: Harvard Univ. Press

57. Dowling JE, Boycott BB. 1966. Organization of the primate retina: electron microscopy. *Proc. R. Soc. London Ser. B* 166:80–111

58. Dowling JE, Ripp H. 1973. Effects of magnesium on horizontal cell activity in the skate retina. *Nature* 242:101–3

59. Dowling JE, Werblin FS. 1969. Organization of the retina of the mudpuppy *(Necturus maculosus).* 1. Synaptic structure. *J. Neurophysiol.* 32:315–88

60. Ehinger B, Dowling JE. 1987. Retinal neurocircuitry and transmission. In *Handbook of Chemical Neuroanatomy,* ed. AA Bjorklund, T Hokfelt, LW Swanson, 5:389–446. Amsterdam/Lausanne/New York: Elsevier

61. Eliasof S, Werblin FS. 1993. Characterization of glutamate transporter in retinal cones of the tiger salamander. *J. Neurosci.* 13:402–11

62. Enroth-Cugell C, Robson JG. 1966. The contrast sensitivity of retinal ganglion cells of the cat. *J. Physiol.* 187:517–52

63. Eysteinsson T, Frumkes TE. 1989. Physiology and pharmacological analysis of suppressive rod-cone interaction in *Necturus* retina. *J. Neurophysiol.* 61:866–73

64. Fain GL. 1975. Quantum sensitivity of rods in the toad retina. *Science* 187:838–41

65. Fain GL. 1975. Interactions of rod and cone signals in the mudpuppy retina. *J. Physiol.* 252:735–69

66. Fain GL, Gerschenfeld HM, Quandt FN. 1980. Calcium spikes in toad rods. *J. Physiol.* 303:495–513

67. Falk G, Fatt P. 1972. Physical changes induced by light in the rod outer segments of vertebrates. In *Handbook of Sensory Physiology,* Vol. VII/1: *Photochemistry of Vision,* ed. HJA Dartnall, pp. 235–39. Berlin: Springer-Verlag

68. Friedlander MJ, Lin CS, Stanford LR, Sherman SM. 1981. Morphology of functionally identified neurons in lateral geniculate nucleus of the cat. *J. Neurophysiol.* 46:80–129

69. Frumkes TE, Wu SM. 1990. Independent influences of rod adaptation upon cone-mediated responses to light onset and offset in distal retinal neurons. *J. Neurophysiol.* 64:1043–54

70. Gold GH. 1979. Photoreceptor coupling in the retina of the toad *(Bufo marinus).* II. Physiology. *J. Neurophysiol.* 42:311–28

71. Gold GH, Dowling JE. 1979. Photoreceptor coupling in the retina of the toad *(Bufo marinus).* I. Anatomy. *J. Neurophysiol.* 42:292–310

72. Gray P, Attwell D. 1985. Kinetics of light-sensitive channels in vertebrate photoreceptors. *Proc. R. Soc. London Ser. B* 223:379–88

73. Hanani M, Vallerga S. 1980. Rod and cone signals in the horizontal cells of the tiger salamander retina. *J. Physiol.* 298:397–405

74. Hare WA, Owen WG. 1990. Spatial organization of the bipolar cells receptive fields in the retina of the tiger salamander. *J. Physiol.* 421:223–45

75. Heidelberger R, Mathews G. 1991. Inhibition of Ca^{+2} current by α-aminobutyric acid in single synaptic terminals. *Proc. Natl. Acad. Sci. USA* 88:7135–39

76. Heidelberger R, Mathews G. 1992. Calcium influx and calcium current in single synaptic terminals of goldfish retinal bipolar neurons. *J. Physiol.* 447:235–56

77. Hensley SH, Yang XL, Wu SM. 1993. Relative contribution of rod and cone inputs to bipolar and ganglion cells in the tiger salamander retina. *J. Neurophysiol.* 69:2086–98

78. Hensley SH, Yang XL, Wu SM. 1993. Identification of glutamate receptor subtypes mediating inputs to bipolar cells and ganglion cells in the tiger salamander retina. *J. Neurophysiol.* 69:2099–2107

79. Hodgkin AL, Huxley AF. 1952. A quantitative description of membrane current and its application to conduction and excitation in nerve. *J. Physiol.* 117:500–44

80. Hubel DH, Wiesel TN. 1961. Integrative action in the cat's lateral geniculate body. *J. Physiol.* 155:385–98

81. Hubel DH, Wiesel TN. 1962. Receptive fields, binocular interaction and functional architecture in the cat's visual cortex. *J. Physiol.* 160:106–54

82. Ishida AT, Kaneko A, Tachibana M. 1984. Responses of solitary retinal horizontal cells from *Carassias auratus* to L-glutamate and related amino acids. *J. Physiol.* 348:255–78

83. Kaneko A. 1970. Physiological and morphological identification of horizontal cells, bipolar cells, and amacrine cells in the goldfish retina. *J. Physiol.* 207:623–33

84. Kaneko A. 1971. Electrical connections between horizontal cells in the dogfish retina. *J. Physiol.* 213:95–105

85. Kaneko A. 1973. Receptive field organization of bipolar and amacrine cells in the goldfish retina. *J. Physiol.* 235:133–53

86. Kaneko A, Tachibana M. 1981. Retinal bipolar cells with double colour-opponent receptive fields. *Nature* 293:220–23

87. Kaneko A, Tachibana M. 1986. Blocking effects on cobalt and related ions on gamma-aminobutyric acid-induced current in turtle retinal cones. *J. Physiol.* 373:463–79

88. Kaneko A, Tachibana M. 1986. Effects of gamma-aminobutyric acid on isolated cone photoreceptors of the turtle retina. *J. Physiol.* 373:443–61

89. Karmermans M, Werblin F. 1992. GABA-mediated positive autofeedback loop controls horizontal cell kinetics in tiger salamander retina. *J. Neurosci.* 12(7):2451–63

90. Karschin A, Wassle H. 1990. Voltage- and transmitter-gate currents in isolated rod bipolar cells of retina. *J. Neurophysiol.* 63:860–76

91. Knapp AG, Dowling JE. 1987. Dopamine enhances excitatory amino acid-gated conductances in cultured retinal horizontal cells. *Nature* 325:437–39

92. Kolb H. 1970. Organization of the outer plexiform layer of the primate retina: electron microscopy of Golgi-impregnated cells. *Philos. Trans. R. Soc. London Ser. B* 258:261–83

93. Kondo H, Toyoda J-I. 1982. GABA and glycine effects on bipolar cells of the carp retina. *Vision Res.* 23:1259–64

94. Kuffler SW. 1953. Discharge patterns and functional organization of mammalian retina. *J. Neurophysiol.* 16:37–68

95. Kujiraoka T, Saito T. 1986. Electrical coupling between bipolar cells in carp retina. *Proc. Natl. Acad. Sci. USA* 83:4063–66

96. Lam DMK, Steinman L. 1971. The uptake of ^{3}H-GABA in the goldfish retina. *Proc. Natl. Acad. Sci. USA* 68:2777–81

97. Lamb TD, Simon EJ. 1976. The relation between intracellular coupling and electrical noise in turtle photoreceptors. *J. Physiol.* 263:257–86

98. Lasansky A. 1971. Synaptic organization of cone cells in the turtle retina. *Philos. Trans. R. Soc. London Ser. B* 262:365–81

99. Lasansky A. 1973. Organization of the outer synaptic layer in the retina of the larval tiger salamander. *Philos. Trans. R. Soc. London Ser. B* 265:471–89

100. Lasansky A. 1978. Contacts between receptors and electrophysiologically identified neurons in the retina of the larval tiger salamander. *J. Physiol.* 285:531–42

101. Lasansky A. 1980. Lateral contacts and interactions of horizontal cell dendrites in the retina of the larval tiger salamander. *J. Physiol.* 301:59–68

102. Lasansky A. 1981. Synaptic action mediating cone responses to annular

illumination in the retina of the larval tiger salamander. *J. Physiol.* 210:205–14

103. Lasansky A, Vallerga S. 1975. Horizontal cell responses in the retina of the larval tiger salamander. *J. Physiol.* 251:145–65

104. Lasater EM, Dowling JE. 1982. Carp horizontal cells in culture respond selectively to L-glutamate and its agonists. *Proc. Natl. Acad. Sci. USA* 79:936–40

105. Lasater EM, Dowling JE. 1985. Dopamine decreases conductance of the electrical junction between cultured retinal horizontal cells. *Proc. Natl. Acad. Sci. USA* 82:3025–29

106. Mangel SC, Dowling JE. 1985. Responsiveness and receptive field size of carp horizontal cells are reduced by prolonged darkness and dopamine. *Science* 229:1107–9

107. Maple B, Werblin FS, Wu SM. 1993. The subunit structure of quantal transmission from photoreceptors to off-center bipolar cells. *Assoc. Res. Vision Ophthalmol. Abstr.* 3116

108. Marc RE, Lam DMK. 1981. Uptake of aspartic and glutamic acids by photoreceptors in the goldfish retina. *Proc. Natl. Acad. Sci. USA* 78:7185–89

109. Marc RE, Liu W-LS, Kalloniatis M, Raiguel SF, Van Haesendonck E. 1990. Patterns of glutamate immunoreactivity in the goldfish retina. *J. Neurosci.* 10(12):4006–34

110. Marc RE, Liu W-LS, Muller JF. 1988. Gap junctions in the inner plexiform layer of the goldfish retina. *Vision Res.* 28:9–24

111. Marc RE, Stall WK, Bok D, Lam DMK. 1978. GABAergic pathways in the goldfish retina. *J. Comp. Neurol.* 182:221–46

112. Marchiafava PL. 1978. Horizontal cells influence membrane potential of bipolar cells in the retina of the turtle. *Nature* 275:141–42

113. Mariani AP. 1986. Photoreceptors of the larval tiger salamander retina. *Proc. R. Soc. London Ser. B* 227:483–92

114. Marmarelis PZ, Marmarelis VZ. 1978. *Analysis of Physiological Systems, the White-Noise Approach.* New York: Plenum

115. Marr D. 1982. *Vision.* San Francisco: Freeman

116. Marr D, Hildreth EC. 1980. Theory of edge detection. *Proc. R. Soc. London Ser. B* 207:187–217

117. Marr D, Ullman S. 1981. Directional selectivity and its use in early visual processing. *Proc. R. Soc. London Ser. B* 211:151–80

118. Miller RF, Slaughter MM. 1985. Excitatory amino-acid receptors in the vertebrate retina. In *Retinal Transmitters and Modulators: Models of the Brain,* ed. WW Morgan, pp. 123–60. Boca Raton: CRC Press

119. Monaghan DT, Bridges RJ, Cotman CW. 1989. The excitatory amino acid receptors: their classes, pharmacology, and distinct properties in the function of the central nervous system. *Annu. Rev. Pharmacol. Toxicol.* 29:365–402

120. Murakami M, Ohtsuka T, Shimazaki H. 1975. Effects of aspartate and glutamate on the bipolar cells in the carp retina. *Vision Res.* 15:456–58

121. Murakami M, Shimoda Y, Nakatani K, Miyachi E, Watanabe S. 1982. GABA-mediated negative feedback from horizontal cells to cones in carp retina. *Jpn. J. Physiol.* 32:911–26

122. Murakami M, Shimoda Y, Nakatani K, Miyachi E, Watanabe S. 1982. GABA-mediated negative feedback and color opponency in carp retina. *Jpn. J. Physiol.* 32:927–35

123. Naka KI. 1972. The horizontal cell. *Vision Res.* 12:573–88

124. Naka KI, Rushton WAH. 1966. S-potentials from colour units in the retina of fish *(Cyprinidae). J. Physiol.* 185:536–55

125. Nawy S, Copenhagen DR. 1990. Intracellular cesium separates two glutamate conductances in retinal bipolar cells of goldfish. *Vision Res.* 30:967–72

126. Nawy S, Jahr CE. 1990. Suppression by glutamate of cGMP-activated conductance in retinal bipolar cells. *Nature* 346:269–71

127. Nawy S, Jahr CE. 1991. cGMP-gated conductances in retinal bipolar cells is suppressed by photoreceptor transmitter. *Neuron* 7:677–83

128. Negishi K, Drujan B. 1979. Reciprocal changes in center and surrounding S-potentials of fish retina in response to dopamine. *Neurochem. Res.* 4:313–18

129. Nelson R. 1977. Cat cones have rod input: a comparison of the response properties of cone-horizontal cell bodies in the retina of the cat. *J. Comp. Neurol.* 172:109–36

130. Normann RA, Perlman I. 1979. Signal transmission from red cones to horizontal cells in the turtle retina. *J. Physiol.* 286:509–24

131. Normann RA, Perlman I. 1990. Background and bleaching adaptation in

luminosity type of horizontal cells in the isolated turtle retina. *J. Physiol.* 421:321–41

132. Piccolino M, Neyton J, Gerschenfeld H. 1981. Centre-surround antagonism in small-field luminosity horizontal cells of turtle retina. *J. Neurophysiol.* 45:363–75

133. Piccolino M, Neyton J, Witkovsky P, Gerschenfeld HM. 1982. γ-Aminobutyric acid antagonists decrease junctional communication between L-horizontal cells of the retina. *Proc. Natl. Acad. Sci. USA* 79:3671–75

134. Raviola E, Gilula NB. 1973. Gap junctions between photoreceptor cells in the vertebrate retina. *Proc. Natl. Acad. Sci. USA* 70:1677–81

135. Raviola E, Gilula NB. 1975. Intermembrane organization of specialized contacts in the outer plexiform layer of the retina: a freeze-fracture study in monkeys and rabbits. *J. Cell Biol.* 65:192–222

136. Schnapf JL, Copenhagen DR. 1982. Differences in the kinetics of rod and cone synaptic transmission. *Nature* 296: 862–64

137. Scholes JH. 1975. Colour receptors and their synaptic connexions in the retina of a cyprinid fish. *Philos. Trans. R. Soc. London Ser. B* 270:61–68

138. Schwartz EA. 1975. Rod-rod interaction in the retina of the turtle. *J. Physiol.* 246:617–38

139. Schwartz EA. 1975. Cones excite rods in the retina of the turtle. *J. Physiol.* 246:639–51

140. Schwartz EA. 1986. Synaptic transmission in amphibian retinal during conditions unfavorable for calcium entry into presynaptic terminals. *J. Physiol.* 376:411–28

141. Schwartz EA. 1987. Depolarization without calcium can release γ-aminobutyric acid from a retinal neuron. *Science* 238:350–55

142. Schwartz EA, Tachibana M. 1990. Electrophysiology of glutamate and sodium co-transport in a glial cell of the salamander retina. *J. Physiol.* 426:43–80

143. Shiells RA, Falk G. 1990. Glutamate-receptor cyclic GMP cascade via a G-protein. *Proc. R. Soc. London Ser. B* 242:91–94

144. Shiells RA, Falk G. 1992. The glutamate-receptor linked cGMP cascade of retinal on-bipolar cells is pertussis and cholera toxin-sensitive. *Proc. R. Soc. London Ser. B* 247:17–20

145. Shiells RA, Falk G. 1992. Properties of the cGMP-activated channel of retinal on-bipolar cells. *Proc. R. Soc. London Ser. B* 247:21–25

146. Shiells RA, Falk G, Naghshineh S. 1981. Action of glutamate and aspartate analogues on rod horizontal and bipolar cells. *Nature* 294:592–94

147. Simon EL, Lamb TD, Hodgkin AL. 1975. Spontaneous voltage fluctuations in retinal cones and bipolar cells. *Nature* 256:661–62

148. Skrzypek J, Werblin FS. 1983. Lateral interactions in absence of feedback to cones. *J. Neurophysiol.* 49:1007–16

149. Slaughter MM, Miller RF. 1981. 2-Amino-4-phosphonobutyric acid: a new pharmacological tool for retina research. *Science* 211:182–85

150. Slaughter MM, Miller RF. 1983. An excitatory amino-acid antagonist blocks cone input to sight-conserving second-order retinal neurons. *Science* 219: 1230–32

151. Slaughter MM, Miller RF. 1983. Bipolar cells in the mudpuppy retina use an excitatory amino-acid neurotransmitter. *Nature* 303:537–38

152. Srinivasan MV, Laughlin SB, Dubs A. 1982. Predictive coding a fresh view of inhibition in the retina. *Proc. R. Soc. London Ser. B* 216:459–72

153. Stell WK. 1967. The structure and relationships of horizontal cells and photoreceptor-bipolar synaptic complexes in goldfish retina. *Am. J. Anat.* 121:401–24

154. Stell WK, Lightfoot DO. 1975. Color-specific interconnections of cones and horizontal cells in the retina of the goldfish. *J. Comp. Neurol.* 159:473–502

155. Stockton RA, Slaughter MM. 1991. Depolarizing actions of GABA and glycine on amphibian retinal horizontal cells. *J. Neurophysiol.* 65:680–92

156. Stone S, Witkovsky P. 1984. The actions of γ-aminobityric acid glycine and their antagonists upon horizontal cells of the *Xenopus* retina. *J. Physiol.* 353:249–64

157. Tachibana M. 1985. Permeability changes induced by L-glutamate in solitary retinal horizontal cells isolated from *Carassius auratus*. *J. Physiol.* 358:153–67

158. Tachibana M, Kaneko A. 1984. Gamma-aminobutyric acid acts at axon terminals of turtle photoreceptors: difference in sensitivity among cell types. *Proc. Natl. Acad. Sci. USA* 81:7961–64

159. Teranishi T, Negishi K, Kato S. 1983. Dopamine modulates S-potential am-

plitude and dye-coupling between external horizontal cells in carp retina. *Nature* 301:243–46

160. Teranishi T, Negishi K, Kato S. 1984. Regulatory effect of dopamine on spatial properties of horizontal cells in carp retina. *J. Neurosci.* 4:1271–80

161. Thibos LN, Werblin FS. 1978. The response properties of the steady antagonistic surround in the mudpuppy retina. *J. Physiol.* 278:79–99

162. Tomita T. 1965. Electrophysiological study of the mechanisms subserving color coding in the fish retina. *Cold Spring Harbor Symp. Quant. Biol.* 30:559–66

163. Tomita T, Kaneko A, Murakami M, Paulter EL. 1967. Spectral response curves of single cones in the carp. *Vision Res.* 7:519–31

164. Toyoda J-I, Tonosaki K. 1978. Effect of polarization of horizontal cells on the on-center bipolar cells of the carp retina. *Nature* 276:399–400

165. Trifonov YA. 1968. Study of synaptic transmission between the photoreceptor and the horizontal cell using electrical stimulation of the retina. *Biofizika* 13: 809–17

166. Uga S, Nakas F, Mimura M, Ikui H. 1970. Some new findings on the fine structure of human photoreceptor cells. *J. Electron Microsc.* 19:71–84

167. Van Buskirk R, Dowling JE. 1981. Isolated horizontal cells from carp retina demonstrate dopamine-dependent accumulation of cyclic AMP. *Proc. Natl. Acad. Sci. USA* 78:7825–29

168. Weakly JNC. 1973. The action of cobalt ions on neuromuscular transmission in the frog. *J. Physiol.* 234:597–612

169. Werblin FS. 1978. Transmission along and between rods in the tiger salamander. *J. Physiol.* 280:449–70

170. Werblin FS, Dowling JE. 1969. Organization of the retina of the mudpuppy, *Necturus maculosus*. II. Intracellular recording. *J. Neurophysiol.* 32:339–55

171. Werblin FS, Maguire G, Lukasiewicz P, Eliasof S, Wu SM. 1988. Neural interactions mediating detection of motion in the retina of the tiger salamander. *Vision Neurosci.* 1:317–29

172. Witkovsky P, Owen WG, Woodworth M. 1983. Gap junctions among the perikaya, dendrites and axon terminals of L-type horizontal cells of the turtle retina. *J. Comp. Neurol.* 216:359–68

173. Witkovsky P, Stell WK. 1973. Retinal structure in the smooth dogfish *Mustelus canis*: electron microscopy of serially sectioned bipolar cell terminals. *J. Comp. Neurol.* 150:147–68

174. Witkovsky P, Stone S. 1987. GABA and glycine modify the balance of rod and cone inputs to horizontal cells in the *Xenopus* retina. *Exp. Biol.* 47:13–22

175. Witkovsky P, Stone S, Besharse J. 1987. Dopamine mimics light adaptation in horizontal cells of the *Xenopus* retina. *Soc. Neurosci.* 12:24

176. Witkovsky P, Stone S, Tranchina D. 1989. Photoreceptor to horizontal cell synaptic transfer in the *Xenopus* retina: Modulation by dopamine ligands and a circuit model for interactions of rod and cone inputs. *J. Neurophysiol.* 62: 864–81

177. Wong-Riley MTT. 1974. Synaptic organization of the inner plexiform layer in the retina of the tiger salamander. *J. Neurocytol.* 3:1–33

178. Wu SM. 1985. Synaptic transmission from rods to bipolar cells in the salamander retina. *Proc. Natl. Acad. Sci. USA* 82:3944–47

179. Wu SM. 1986. Effects of gamma-aminobutyric acid on cones and bipolar cells of the tiger salamander retina. *Brain Res.* 365:70–77

180. Wu SM. 1987. Changes in response waveform of retinal horizontal cells during dark and light adaptation. *Vision Res.* 27:143–50

181. Wu SM. 1987. Light-dependent synaptic delay between photoreceptors and horizontal cells in the tiger salamander retina. *Vision Res.* 27: 363–67

182. Wu SM. 1987. Synaptic connections among retinal neurons in living slices of the tiger salamander retina. *J. Neurosci. Methods* 20:139–49

183. Wu SM. 1988. Synaptic transmission from rods to horizontal cells in dark-adapted tiger salamander retina. *Vision Res.* 28:1–8

184. Wu SM. 1988. The depolarizing off-responses of photoreceptors and horizontal cells in light-adapted retina of the larval tiger salamander. *Exp. Eye Res.* 47:261–68

185. Wu SM. 1991. Signal transmission and adaptation-induced modulation of photoreceptor synapses in the retina. *Prog. Retinal Res.* 10:27–44

186. Wu SM. 1991. Input-output relations of the feedback synapse between horizontal cells and cones in the tiger salamander retina. *J. Neurophysiol.* 65: 1197–1206

187. Wu SM. 1992. Feedback connections

and operation of outer plexiform layer of the retina. *Curr. Opin. Neurobiol.* 2:462–68

188. Wu SM, Dowling JE. 1980. Effects of GABA and glycine on the distal cells of the cyprinid retina. *Brain Res.* 199:401–14

189. Wu SM, Qiao X, Noebels JL, Yang XI. 1993. Localization and modulatory actions of zinc in vertebrate retina. *Vision Res.* In press

190. Wu SM, Yang XL. 1988. Electrical coupling between rods and cones in the tiger salamander retina. *Proc. Natl. Acad. Sci. USA* 85:275–78

191. Wu SM, Yang XL. 1992. Modulation of synaptic gain by light. *Proc. Natl. Acad. Sci. USA* 89:11755–58

192. Yang JH, Wu SM. 1993. Effects of dihydrokainate on rod and cone inputs of horizontal cells in the tiger salamander retina. *Assoc. Res. Vision Ophthamol. Abstr.* 2904

193. Yang JH, Wu SM. 1992. Physiological factors influencing the horizontal cell tail responses in the tiger salamander retina. *Assoc. Res. Vision Ophthamol. Abstr.* 3175

194. Yang XL, Tornqvist K, Dowling JE. 1988. Modulation of cone horizontal cell activity in the teleost fish retina. I. Effects of prolonged darkness and background illumination on light responsiveness. *J. Neurosci.* 8:2259–68

195. Yang XL, Tornqvist K, Dowling JE. 1988. Modulation of cone horizontal cell activity in the teleost fish retina. II. Role of interplexiform cells and dopamine in regulating light responsiveness. *J. Neurosci.* 8:2269–78

196. Yang XL, Wu SM. 1989. Effects of background illumination on horizontal cell responses in the tiger salamander retina. *J. Neurosci.* 9(3):815–27

197. Yang XL, Wu SM. 1989. Effects of prolonged light exposure, gamma-aminobutyric acid and glycine on the HC responses in the tiger salamander retina. *J. Neurophysiol.* 61:1025–35

198. Yang XL, Wu SM. 1989. Modulation of rod-cone coupling by light. *Science* 244:352–54

199. Yang XL, Wu SM. 1989. Effects of CNQX, APB, PDA and kynurenate on horizontal cells in the tiger salamander retina. *Vision Neurosci.* 3:207–12

200. Yang XL, Wu SM. 1990. Synaptic inputs from rods and cones to horizontal cells in the tiger salamander retina. *Sci. China* 33:32–40

201. Yang XL, Wu SM. 1991. Feedforward lateral inhibition: input-output relation of the horizontal cell to bipolar cell synapse in the tiger salamander retina. *Proc. Natl. Acad. Sci. USA* 88:3310–13

202. Yang XL, Wu SM. 1991. Coexistence and functions of multiple types of glutamate receptors in horizontal cells of the tiger salamander retina. *Vision Neurosci.* 7:377–82

203. Yang XL, Wu SM. 1993. Synaptic transmission from rods to rod-dominated bipolar cells in the tiger salamander retina. *Brain Res.* 613:275–80

204. Yang XL, Wu SM. 1993. Effects of GABA on horizontal cells in the tiger salamander retina. *Vision Res.* 33:1339–44

205. Yazulla S. 1976. Cone input to bipolar cells in the turtle retina. *Vision Res.* 16:737–44

Annu. Rev. Physiol. 1994. 56:169–91
Copyright © 1994 by Annual Reviews Inc. All rights reserved

PHOSPHOINOSITIDES AND CALCIUM AS REGULATORS OF CELLULAR ACTIN ASSEMBLY AND DISASSEMBLY

Paul A. Janmey

Experimental Medicine Division, Brigham and Women's Hospital, Department of Biological Chemistry and Molecular Pharmacology, Harvard Medical School, Boston Massachusetts 02115

KEY WORDS: actin, phosphoinositide, PIP_2, Ca^{2+}, cytoskeleton, polymerization, actin-binding proteins

INTRODUCTION

Cell locomotion and changes in cell structure initiated by the binding of extracellular ligands to transmembrane receptors are generally accompanied by a transient increase in cytoplasmic Ca^{2+} concentration, $[Ca^{2+}]$, and by the synthesis and hydrolysis of phosphorylated phosphatidylinositol lipids, or polyphosphoinositides (PPIs). These two potential signals to the cytoskeleton are not necessarily the immediate consequence of receptor stimulation, but are themselves modulated by upstream signals that include GTPases, protein kinases, ion channels, and probably other agents (reviewed in 118). Cell motility and changes in morphology also require spatially and temporally coordinated changes in the mechanical properties of the cell cortex, and these changes are brought about by transitions between gel (solid) and sol (liquid) states of the cytoskeleton (32, 119, 120). A link between Ca^{2+} and phospholipids, on the one hand, and changes in cell rigidity, on the other, was apparent enough to suggest nearly 40 years ago (52) that "the rigidity of the cortex depends on the fact that it contains

169

0066–4278/94/0315–0169$05.00

calcium bound to protein (and also to lipid). Chemical and physical agents which are able to free calcium in the cortex from its bound state cause a liquefaction of the cortex." Since that time there have been challenges to the concept that cell mechanics is necessarily governed by cytoplasmic Ca^{2+} and phospholipid messengers, but also a great deal of evidence that Ca^{2+} and PPIs alter the functions of many proteins that affect the protein polymers of the cytoskeleton in ways that are likely to cause the molecular changes necessary for the gel-sol transitions observed in the living cell. It has also become clear from alterations of different cytoskeletal polymers in vivo and from the viscoelastic properties of each system in vitro that changes in actin microfilaments, rather than microtubules or intermediate filaments, are likely to be primarily responsible for the mechanical changes initiated by Ca^{2+} and PPIs.

The physical properties of actin networks depend on the length and concentration of the filaments and on the number and geometry of crosslinks between them. Actin-binding proteins that regulate each of these properties and that promote or prevent filament formation have been identified and, in many cases, their interactions with actin are altered by molecules implicated in cell signaling, which include Ca^{2+} and PPIs. Tracing the pathway from the production of a single messenger molecule to a change in the state of actin is difficult because multiple steps may be required to achieve the change and because messengers such as Ca^{2+} and PPIs influence each other's production and activate other signaling pathways. This review focuses on the direct effects of Ca^{2+} and polyphosphoinositide lipids on proteins or protein complexes that affect the state of actin assembly and attempts to integrate the data on individual proteins to suggest a possible set of coordinated reactions that could produce gel-sol transitions in vivo.

Ca^{2+} SIGNALING

Among the earliest effects of chemotactic factors on motile cells such as leukocytes are transient increases in intracellular Ca^{2+} and polymerized actin (92), which suggests that increasing Ca^{2+} from the 100 nM level of resting cells to μM levels may be the signal for initiating actin polymerization. In contrast, increased intracellular Ca^{2+} induces degradation of the lens cytoskeleton (90), reduces polymeric actin in permeabilized chromaffin cells in a manner probably related to their mechanism of exocytosis (12, 96a), and destabilizes the actin cytoskeleton in the periphery of neurons as may be required for neurite extension (95). Whether Ca^{2+} is a signal for strengthening or weakening the cell cortex probably depends on the cell type and on other activating factors, but an effect on the actin cytoskeleton is a frequent consequence of altering cytoplasmic Ca^{2+}. The effects of Ca^{2+}

depend on the time course of elevation as well as the levels of concentration generated. The recent demonstration that the diffusion of Ca^{2+} in cytoplasmic extracts is greatly constrained and that its effective range, before it binds to some targets, is only 100 nm (4) reinforces the concept that signaling by Ca^{2+} may relate more to spatial gradients and transients of $[Ca^{2+}]$ than to its bulk concentration (10). Furthermore, the $[Ca^{2+}]$ required to affect many purified actin-binding proteins in vitro is much higher than the levels thought to occur globally in vivo, which suggests that other factors are involved or that local variations in intracellular Ca^{2+} are important.

On the other hand, many of the changes in actin assembly associated with increased Ca^{2+} can also be achieved in cells loaded with sufficient Ca^{2+} chelators to maintain bulk intracellular Ca^{2+} concentration at or below resting cell levels. Actin polymerization in neutrophils can occur without detectable Ca^{2+} increases (28, 116), and a reorganization of the actin system of neural cells (61) can be achieved without increased concentration of either IP$_3$ or Ca^{2+}. A further complication to determining whether there is a strict relation between Ca^{2+} and F-actin is that actin polymerization is probably initiated near the interface between cytoplasm and membranes (36, 119). Intracellular Ca^{2+} chelators and fluorescent reporters may not alter or detect Ca^{2+} concentrations at these interfaces. Therefore, a role for membrane-associated Ca^{2+} in the regulation of actin assembly cannot be ruled out (9).

The concept that emerges from studies relating intracellular $[Ca^{2+}]$ to F-actin content is that the state of actin is not simply predicted from the instantaneous average $[Ca^{2+}]$. Equally important are the time course of the $[Ca^{2+}]$ change, the spatial distribution, and the nature of other signaling pathways that are activated in concert with the Ca^{2+} flux. The crucial importance of Ca^{2+} for cytoskeletal structure is indicated by the number of actin-binding proteins whose function is regulated by Ca^{2+} in vitro. These proteins are listed in Table 1.

Ca^{2+} REGULATED ACTIN-BINDING PROTEINS

Actin Filament-Severing Proteins

The family of structurally related proteins that sever actin filaments currently includes gelsolin (131, 132), villin (35, 43, 123), severin (31, 128), fragmin (39, 49), adseverin (87, 115), scinderin (113), and fragmin 60 (40). The first of these proteins was discovered because it led to gel-sol transitions in cytoplasmic extracts when Ca^{2+} was added in micromolar concentrations (131). All known actin-severing proteins with similar potency also require Ca^{2+} under physiologic conditions. The concentration of Ca^{2+} needed to

Table 1 Actin-binding proteins regulated by calcium

Protein	Effect	Reference
Direct effect of Ca^{2+}		
Alpha-actinin	Some isoforms dissociate from F-actin and crosslinking between filaments is reversed	101, 125b
Gelsolin	Filament severing activity and nucleation of actin	132
Villin	polymerization activated by $[Ca^{2+}] > 10 \ \mu M$	123
Severin	Barbed filament end uncapped with villin, but not	31
Fragmin	gelsolin or severin	49
Adseverin		87
Scinderin		113
30-kd bundling protein	Dissociates from F-actin in 0.1 $\mu M \ Ca^{2+}$, and bundling activity is reversed	34
gCap-39/MCP	Binds to actin monomers and barbed filament ends in $>\mu M \ Ca^{2+}$; uncaps barbed end when Ca^{2+} decreases	137 20
Annexins	Bind F-actin and cause either bundling or association	57
lipocortin	with phospholipids in presence of Ca^{2+}	58
calpactin		
Fimbrin	Contain EF-hand structures. Some but not all experiments show inhibition of actin filament bundling by Ca^{2+}	24
plastin		140
Sac6		
Effect of calcium/calmodulin		
MARCKS	Dissociated from side of F-actin by calcium/calmodulin	48
Myosin	ATPase activity of some isoforms increased by calcium/calmodulin. Phosphorylation by Ca-dependent pathways may activate or inhibit acto-myosin	17
HSP100	Dissociated from F-actin by calcium/calmodulin	73
Squid retina proteins	Dissociated from F-actin by calcium/calmodulin	121
Caldesmon	Dissociates from sides of F-actin, removing inhibition of myosin and gelsolin. Mediated by calcium/calmodulin or other accessory proteins	94
Spectrin/4.1	Actin crosslinking by 4.1 inhibited by calcium/calmodulin	121

activate severing proteins in vitro is often quite high: 10–100 μM for gelsolin at neutral pH (77), and up to 1 mM for villin (102). Furthermore, very rapid transients of $[Ca^{2+}]$ may be unable to activate gelsolin (70). Some severing proteins also promote actin assembly by forming complexes with two actin monomers that serve as nuclei for filament formation. In all cases reported, nucleation activity also requires Ca^{2+}. The net effect of Ca^{2+} on this family of proteins would appear to be cleavage of the actin network system into filament fragments and formation of new nuclei that would grow in response to further signals to polymerize.

Proteins in this family are composed of three (fragmin, severin) to six (gelsolin, villin) weakly homologous domains, all of which might contact actin in the complex. The Ca^{2+}-sensitive domains have been identified in some cases (11, 16, 55, 75, 93, 125), and differences within this group have been found (35, 65). In both gelsolin and villin, the C-terminal half of the protein, which is missing in severin/fragmin, depends on Ca^{2+} for actin-binding, but the N-terminal half of gelsolin functions independently of Ca^{2+} (16, 125), whereas the homologous fragment of villin requires Ca^{2+} for activity (65). These proteins do not contain EF-hand structures or any obvious sequence homology with other Ca^{2+}-binding proteins. After severing the actin filament, these proteins remain bound to the fast-growing (barbed, as defined by heavy meromyosin-labeling) end of F-actin. Reduction of Ca^{2+} below μM levels releases villin from the filament end (123), but chelation of free Ca^{2+} does not dissociate gelsolin from the end of actin filaments or from the complexes with actin monomers that serve as (pointed end) nuclei for filament assembly (62, 63, 74). In some cases, Ca^{2+} binding is dissociated from functional regulation. For example, severin, like gelsolin, loses the requirement for Ca^{2+} to sever actin filaments when a slightly smaller truncate of the recombinant protein is expressed, but this severin derivative still binds Ca^{2+} (30).

Filament End-Blocking Proteins

Different classes of end-blocking proteins, also called F-actin capping proteins (125a) exist, and some are regulated by Ca^{2+}. Proteins (39 kd) with limited homology to the N-terminal half of gelsolin and villin have been isolated from macrophages and other cell types and are variously called gCap39 (137) or MCP (20). A closely related protein of unknown function was isolated as a nuclear protein containing a basic helix-loop-helix motif (110). Unlike gelsolin, gCap39/MCP does not sever actin filaments, or nucleate their assembly, but it does bind actin monomers and the barbed end of actin filaments with high affinity in the presence of Ca^{2+}. Also unlike gelsolin, the binding of gCap39/MCP to the filament end is completely reversible when Ca^{2+} levels are lowered to resting cell levels (100 nM), and this protein may function in part by exposing barbed ends to nucleate actin assembly after a transient rise in $[Ca^{2+}]$.

F-Actin Side-Binding or Crosslinking Proteins

Non-muscle alpha-actinin was the first actin-binding protein shown to contain EF-hand structures required for Ca^{2+}-sensitive actin binding (101). *Dictyostelium* alpha-actinin contains two EF-hand structures with different affinities for Ca^{2+} and distinct regulatory effects on actin crosslinking (125b). There are differing reports of the efficiency of alpha-actinin as an actin gelation factor that forms high-angle branches between actin filaments, and as a bundling protein that forms links between parallel filaments. In part these functional differences result from subtle structural differences in alpha-actinin isoforms (96). The calcium-dependence of alpha-actinin's function is not universally observed, and some isoforms are unaffected by Ca^{2+} (105) perhaps because of small but crucial differences in sequence in the putative Ca^{2+}-regulatory sites. The importance of alpha-actinin for cytoskeletal structure is suggested by the disruption caused by microinjected alpha-actinin fragments (106), but cells genetically altered to prevent alpha-actinin expression retain many normal cytoskeletal functions (126).

A family of related proteins called fimbrin, isolated from chicken intestinal epithelial cells (24), plastin from macrophages (82), p65 from T lymphocytes (140), and Sac-6 (1) from yeast, have homologous structures with two EF-hand sequences and two potential actin-binding sites (140) based on homology with other F-actin-binding proteins. These proteins bind to the filament side with apparent stoichiometry of approximately 8 actin to 1 fimbrin/plastin (99) and cause bundle formation of actin under some conditions. At least some members of this family of proteins, for example L-plastin, are inactivated at $[Ca^{2+}] > 10^{-6}$ M (99). Since these proteins are also targets for protein kinases, for example after T-cell stimulation by IL2 (140), alternate mechanisms for regulating their activity are also likely.

Villin (43) and a 30-kd protein from *Dictyostelium* (34) also can bundle actin filaments in vitro, and this activity is reversed by micromolar $[Ca^{2+}]$. This rise of Ca^{2+} converts villin from a bundling protein to a filament end-binding or severing protein and dissociates the 30-kd protein from F-actin.

Proteins that Link F-Actin to Other Structures

Annexins are a superfamily of Ca^{2+} and phospholipid-binding proteins that include lipocortin and calpactin (annexin II), which were described as Ca^{2+}-dependent actin-binding proteins (12, 29, 58). Several other annexin isoforms such as annexin VI (68-kd protein) (57) also bind actin. In contrast to fimbrin and alpha-actinin, annexins bind F-actin more strongly in the presence than in the absence of $[Ca^{2+}]$ (57), and the filament bundling activity can be inhibited by a nine residue peptide derived from the annexin II sequence (69). The localization of annexins to cell membranes and the membranes of organelles suggests a role for these proteins in Ca^{2+}-stimulated exocytosis (12, 29).

MARCKS, the myristoylated C-kinase substrate and its homologues undergo a cycling between plasma membrane and cytosol following stimulation of macrophages or neuronal cells by agents that also alter the cytoskeleton. MARCKS also binds to the side of F-actin, which causes actin-bundling in vitro (48). Increased Ca^{2+} promotes binding of calcium/calmodulin to MARCKS and prevents the binding of MARCKS to F-actin.

Caldesmon binds to the sides of F-actin and inhibits the interaction between actin and myosin at low $[Ca^{2+}]$. At greater than micromolar concentrations, calcium/calmodulin binds to caldesmon and reverses the inhibition (94, 111, 124). In addition to calmodulin, a number of other proteins isolated from different cell types also reverse the inhibition of acto-myosin by caldesmon (83, 89, 111). Some of these proteins require Ca^{2+} to reverse inhibition, and some are Ca^{2+}-independent. Caldesmon/F-actin binding is enhanced by tropomyosin, which also binds the side of F-actin. In this ternary complex, caldesmon and tropomyosin together partially inhibit the ability of gelsolin to sever actin filaments and promote reannealing of filament fragments by removing gelsolin bound to the barbed filament end (60).

Recently a number of other Ca^{2+} or calcium/calmodulin-dependent actin-binding activities have been identified. For example, the binding of the spectrin-band 4.1 complex to F-actin, which is essential for linking the two-dimensional protein cytoskeleton to the lipid membrane of erythrocytes and probably other cells types, is disrupted by a soluble factor in red cell extracts that appears to be calmodulin. Purified calcium/calmodulin also suppresses the crosslinking of F-actin by spectrin/4.1 (121). Calcium/calmodulin may also disrupt this connection indirectly by activating a specific protease that cleaves the alpha and beta chains of fodrin, the non-erythrocyte spectrin homologue (46). Another calcium/calmodulin-regulated actin-binding protein is HSP100, a protein isolated from mouse lymphoma cells that binds to F-actin and is dissociated by calcium/calmodulin (73). A number of calcium/calmodulin-dependent actin-binding proteins with molecular weights ranging from 92 to 135 K have also been identified in squid retina and may participate in light-induced cytoskeletal restructuring (6).

Motor Proteins

Regulation by Ca^{2+} of acto-myosin interactions involved in force generation in skeletal muscle has been extensively studied and only a few aspects relevant to non-muscle myosin (17, 18, 71, 109) are addressed here. Cells lacking the classical actin/tropomyosin/troponin regulatory system alter myosin activity by several methods. The effects of caldesmon/calmodulin/tropomyosin have some similarity to those of tropomyosin/troponin (25), and myosin activity is affected by Ca^{2+}-dependent phosphorylation of myosin light chains by either myosin light chain kinase, or protein kinase C. Actin-filament severing and crosslinking proteins regulated by Ca^{2+}(3, 68, 70, 103) also affect acto-myosin ATPase activity and contraction, and gelsolin enhances acto-myosin ATPase in the presence, but not the absence, of Ca^{2+} (3, 103). Some non-muscle myosin isoforms, notably the 110-kd protein in microvilli (97) and myosin-V from chicken brain (33), bind multiple calmodulin subunits in a calcium-dependent manner. In addition to potentially regulating active movement of actin filaments, binding of calcium/calmodulin to non-muscle myosin isoforms may also participate in regulated binding of actin filaments to cell membranes, where some of these myosin isoforms are localized (38).

SUMMARY OF Ca^{2+} EFFECTS

Proteins with diverse effects on actin assembly are regulated by Ca^{2+}. These effects include filament severing, capping, nucleation, bundling, and linkage to cell membranes, organelles, or other proteins. Notably missing from the list are actin monomer-sequestering proteins and, with the exception of alpha-actinin, proteins involved in forming the focal contacts linking actin filament assemblies (stress fibers) to the extracellular matrix. In some cases, actin binding is activated by Ca^{2+}, and in other cases it is inhibited or reversed. From the many different effects of Ca^{2+} on individual proteins, a pattern appears to emerge: proteins such as gelsolin, gCap39, or scinderin, which lead to disruption of actin networks by filament fragmentation or end-blocking, are activated by Ca^{2+}, whereas filament crosslinking proteins such as alpha-actinin, MARCKS, or fimbrin are inhibited by Ca^{2+}. There are also other functions such as regulation of acto-myosin or linkage by annexins or myosin to organelles that do not themselves weaken the actin network, but may cooperate with the solation of the cortical actin gel during, for example, exocytosis. The cumulative effect of increased Ca^{2+} in the absence of other signals would appear to be a solubilization of the actin cytoskeleton, which would allow for such effects as myosin-based contraction, osmotic expansion (104), secretion (96a), and preparing the cytoskeleton for reformation in response to a subsequent signal.

It is significant that several of the effects of calcium on actin-binding protein function can also be achieved by other signals without increased Ca^{2+}. For example, caldesmon dissociates from F-actin after binding calcium/calmodulin, or after phosphorylation by CDC-kinase (88, 129). Similarly, binding of MARCKS to F-actin is reversed either by calcium/calmodulin or by phosphorylation by PKC (48). In the latter case, there is evidence that calmodulin binding on MARCKS occurs at a small site of 20 amino acids that also contains four PKC-sensitive serine residues. The activation of gelsolin by Ca^{2+} can also be achieved by lowered pH (77), or by limited proteolysis (16). Alternative pathways to produce the same effect as increased Ca^{2+} may explain, in part, the changes in actin assembly produced in cells that have been loaded with Ca^{2+} chelators.

PHOSPHOINOSITIDE SIGNALING

Soon after the discovery of the phosphoinositide cycle more than 30 years ago, it was evident that some of these acidic phospholipids such as triphosphoinositide (PIP$_2$) formed complexes with certain proteins (22, 23) that had many characteristics of specific interactions. Contributions of electrostatic and hydrophobic interactions were observed in various instances, and the binding depended on divalent cations in some cases but not others. The possible biologic significance of such protein/lipid interactions for the cytoskeleton was not proposed until the mid 1980's, when three potentially important interactions were discovered. The linkage of the actin cytoskeleton of red cells to the cell membrane, which depends primarily on the binding of band 4.1 to the transmembrane protein glycophorin (band 3), was shown to be strengthened by PIP$_2$ (5). Alpha-actinin was found associated with fatty acids and diacylglycerol in the cell membrane (14). Since diacylglycerol derives partly from the hydrolysis of PIP$_2$, a potential link between alpha-actinin function or localization and the PPI cycle was suggested (13). Perhaps the most compelling evidence that PPIs might regulate actin assembly was the demonstration that complexes of actin with the monomer-sequestering protein profilin were dissociated by PIP$_2$, thus leading to actin polymerization (80, 81). This work also established the importance of the physical state of PIP$_2$ for its interaction with proteins and led to the idea of a direct link between the PI cycle and actin cytoskeletal remodeling in vivo (78, 79). Since that time, numerous other actin-binding proteins, listed in Table 2, have been shown to bind PPIs, and a recent review summarizes many of the earlier observations (59).

The best-characterized signaling role for PPIs is as a source for IP$_3$ and diacylglycerol through the hydrolysis of PI(4,5)P$_2$ by phospholipase C. However, there are a large number of kinases and phosphatases that add or remove phosphates on the inositol ring to create PPIs that have no generally accepted function and that, in some cases, are not substrates for PLC. Figure 1 summarizes some of these reactions and the PPIs that are implicated in regulating actin polymerization.

Table 2 Actin-binding proteins regulated by phosphoinositides

Protein	Effect of phosphoinositide	Reference
Profilin	Sequestered actin released from profilin/actin complexes	80
Gelsolin	Severing activity inhibited more strongly than	67
Villin	nucleating activity. Actin/gelsolin complexes dis-	65
Severin	sociated. Barbed ends uncapped under some con-	31
Adseverin	ditions. Multiple PPI-binding sites	115
Cofilin	Binding to actin inhibited, PPI-binding site identified	136
Destrin		
gCap39	Dissociated from actin monomers and barbed filament ends	137
Alpha actinin	F-actin crosslinking activity increased	37
Filamin	F-actin crosslinking activity diminished	41
MAP-2C	F-actin bundling activity diminished	130
Myosin-I	Links F-actin to acidic phospholipid bilayer	2
Talin	Links F-actin to acidic phospholipid bilayer	53
CapZ	Released from barbed filament end	50
Cap 32/34		54
Cap 100	Released from barbed filament end	56

PHOSPHOINOSITIDE-REGULATED ACTIN-BINDING PROTEINS

Monomer-Sequestering Proteins

Profilin was the first G actin-binding protein described (15) and was originally thought to account for the large amount of actin that was unpolymerized in resting cells, a role now attributed in part to profilin and mainly to thymosin β-4 and its homologues (114). When cells such as platelets or neutrophils are activated, their F-actin content increases, and the fraction of profilin bound to actin decreases (84, 91, 117). The search for a regulator of profilin/actin binding, which is insensitive to Ca^{2+}, led to the finding that PIP and PIP_2 specifically dissociate actin from the complex (78, 80, 81). Furthermore, this actin retains the ability to polymerize. The

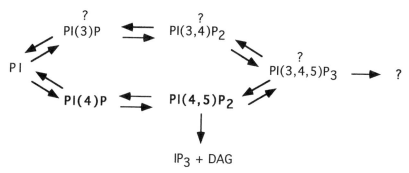

Figure 1   Phosphoinositides produced during cell activation by the actions of phosphoinositide kinases. The species listed in boldface have been demonstrated to regulate actin-binding proteins in vitro. The ? denotes that this species has not yet been tested.

combination of localizing the profilin/actin complex to the cell membrane and providing a means to trigger sub-membrane actin polymerization in response to a specific signal (the activation of PI or PIP kinases) suggests an attractive model to explain the rapid polymerization of actin in the cell cortex following cell activation. In addition to the regulation of actin-profilin interactions by PPIs, the binding of profilin to PIP$_2$ also affects the hydrolysis of PIP$_2$ by phospholipase C-γ (45). The potential biologic importance of this interaction is suggested by the finding that PLC-γ, which is constitutively active on PIP$_2$ in the absence of profilin, is strongly inhibited by profilin, but that tyrosine phosphorylation of PLC-γ by the epidermal growth factor receptor overcomes this inhibition (44). The importance of the profilin/PIP$_2$ binding is further suggested by the finding that yeast mutants that lack the cyclase-associated protein (CAP) and exhibit altered actin filament structure are rescued by overexpression of either their endogenous profilin, or *Acanthamoeba* profilin (122). *Acanthamoeba* express several profilin isoforms that differ in affinity for actin and PIP$_2$ (86). Only profilin isoforms that retain PPI-binding activity rescue the CAP mutation defect, which suggests that the PPI-binding is more important than the actin-binding properties of profilin in this setting. The recent finding that the platelet homologue of yeast CAP is itself an actin-binding protein (42) provides additional evidence for a link between profilin and CAP.

Filament-Severing Proteins

All of the Ca^{2+}-sensitive F-actin filament-severing proteins examined to date—gelsolin (26, 27, 63, 66, 67, 133), villin (65), severin (31, 134), adseverin (87, 115)—are also regulated by the polyphosphoinositides PIP and PIP_2 in vitro and, in all cases, the effects are antagonistic to those of Ca^{2+}: inhibiting severing, nucleation, and actin monomer binding. In cases where these different activities have been directly compared, the severing function is most strongly inhibited by PPIs, with 50% inhibition of gelsolin occurring at approximately equal molar amount of gelsolin and PIP_2 micelles (66). PIP is approximately as active as PIP_2, whereas PI and other acidic phospholipids have little or no inhibitory effect on gelsolin (66), although they somewhat inhibit other severing proteins (31, 87). In vitro, 90% inhibition of gelsolin can be achieved with less than 100 μM PIP_2. Since the concentration of PIP_2 in cells such as platelets is around 300 μM when averaged over the whole cell volume (112), and since there is usually more PIP than PIP_2, the levels of these lipids in cells are potentially sufficient to produce inhibition. Inhibition of nucleation by gelsolin requires approximately ten times as much PIP_2 (67) compared with inhibition of severing activity, and dissociation of gelsolin complexed to actin monomers or filament ends may require even higher levels in vitro. Nevertheless, barbed ends that have been capped by gelsolin in Ca^{2+} can be uncapped by addition of PIP_2 and calcium chelators under some conditions in vitro (63).

Gelsolin, severin, and probably the other related proteins contain at least two PPI-binding sites, as defined by the PPI sensitivity of individual protein domains and by the activities of synthetic peptides. Peptides mimicking residues 135–149 from domain 1 of human plasma gelsolin (CKSGLKY-KKGGVASKF) (138), and residues 150–169 (KHVVPNEVVVQRLFQV-KGRR) from domain 2 (64) bind to both PIP vesicles and PIP_2 micelles with affinity equal to that of gelsolin, and the 150–169 peptide can displace gelsolin from PPIs and reverse the inhibition of gelsolin's severing function by the lipid. The interaction of these basic peptides with the acidic PPIs is not simply electrostatic, since neither they nor the parent proteins require divalent cations or a narrow range of pH for binding PPIs. Furthermore, the even more strongly basic peptide KRFSFKKSFKLSGFSFKKN, which mimics the calmodulin-binding site of MARCKS, binds to PPIs two orders of magnitude more weakly than does the gelsolin 150–169 peptide (64). Since the PPI-binding sites occur at junctions between gelsolin domains that are highly accessible to proteases (75, 76), they may have an open structure in the native protein, and the synthetic peptides undergo a transition from random coil to alpha-helix in aqueous solution when exposed to PIP_2 (127). Such a rearrangement of structure in the parent molecule could disorient actin-binding sites and thereby prevent severing even under conditions where actin binding was not entirely eliminated.

Binding of PPIs to actin-severing proteins appears to require the clustering of multiple PPIs or PPIs and other acidic phospholipids (66). PIP_2 molecules dispersed in a PC bilayer do not inhibit gelsolin regardless of the total amount of lipid unless the PIP$_2$/PC molar ratio exceeds some threshold. The molar ratio of PIP$_2$ to PC required for interaction can be lowered by addition of PI, which is also acidic but inactive by itself, or raised by addition of sphingosine or cholesterol. Monomeric PIP$_2$ derivatives such as IP$_3$ or glycerophosphatidylinositol 4,5 bisphosphate do not affect gelsolin activity (67), and severing activity can be restored to gelsolin/PIP$_2$ by treatment with triacylglycerol lipase (JA Lamb, unpublished data). These data suggest that the physical packing, or lipid demixing, of PIP or PIP$_2$ in the inner leaflet of the plasma bilayer may be more significant for regulating gelsolin and other actin-binding proteins than the bulk level of PIP$_2$. Therefore, it is not surprising that the formation of IP$_3$ may not directly relate to gelsolin activity in vivo (9, 21).

All biochemical assays of actin-binding protein or protein/PPI binding to date have used either PI(4)P or PI(4,5)P$_2$, since only these isoforms are currently available in sufficient quantities. The similar activities of PIP and PIP$_2$ in some cases implies that the phosphomonoester in the 4' position is of primary importance in forming the lipid/protein contact. Since activation of PI-3 kinase to form PIP, PIP$_2$, and PIP$_3$ containing phosphomonoesters on the 3' position is associated with activation of thrombin or growth factor receptors and with remodeling of the platelet cytoskeleton (139), it will be of interest to determine how such PPIs phosphorylated on the 3' position interact with gelsolin and other proteins.

Like profilin, gelsolin and gelsolin-actin complexes also inhibit PLC-γ-mediated hydrolysis of PIP$_2$, and the gelsolin-actin complex copurifies with some, but not all, PLC isoforms in platelet extracts (8). Gelsolin, profilin, and the PPI-binding peptides derived from gelsolin also inhibit phosphorylation of PI(4)P by PI(4)P-5 kinase (L Ling, unpublished experiments), which confirms that inhibition of these enzymatic activities probably results from the ability of gelsolin, profilin, and related proteins to sequester the lipid substrate.

In addition to the gelsolin family of F-actin severing proteins, there are also smaller, less efficient severing proteins that appear to disrupt F-actin by extracting monomers from the filament interior, but do not bind tightly to the barbed end. These proteins, which are highly homologous, include ADF (7), depactin (85), destrin (98, 136), actophorin (19), and cofilin (98, 135, 136). Destrin and cofilin are both inhibited by PIP or PIP$_2$ (135, 136), and given the similarity in primary structure, this regulation is likely to be observed in ADF, actophorin, and depactin as well. A small peptide (WAPECAPLKSKM) with sequence distinct from that of the gelsolin peptides binds PIP$_2$ and competes with cofilin for binding to actin (135). This peptide also inhibits phospholipase C-mediated hydrolysis of PIP$_2$, as does cofilin.

Filament End-Blocking Proteins

As discussed in the previous section, PPIs have the potential to release severing proteins from the barbed ends of filaments. Other proteins that bind the barbed end, but do not sever, are also dissociated by PPIs. The calcium-activated capping proteins, gCap39 and MCP, dissociate from the barbed end when PPIs are added and create sites for elongation of filaments. Ca^{2+}-insensitive barbed end blocking proteins also are removed by PPIs. CapZ, which blocks the ends of thin filaments in the Z-disk of sarcomeres, and is also found in non-muscle cells (54), and the Cap32/34 complex of *Dictyostelium discoideum* (50) bind the barbed end with very high affinity $(K_a > 10^{10} \text{ M}^{-1})$, but are efficiently released from F-actin by modest (100 μM) concentrations of PIP_2 in vitro. The site of PPI binding has not yet been localized in these proteins, but it may be significant that CapZ and Cap32/34 contain a site of sequences similar to one of the PPI-binding sites of gelsolin (138). Another PPI-inhibited barbed end-capping protein is Cap100 isolated from *Dictyostelium* (56). This protein has primary structure homology to villin, but has not been demonstrated to be either Ca^{2+}-sensitive or capable of severing actin. However, its end-blocking activity is of high affinity and inhibited by PPIs in a manner similar to villin and gelsolin.

F-Actin Side-Binding or Crosslinking Proteins

The ability of alpha-actinin to crosslink actin filaments into viscoelastic networks is enhanced by the binding of either PIP or PIP_2 to alpha-actinin (37). This enhancement is eliminated or reversed by adding triton micelles to the alpha-actinin-PIP_2 mixture, which supports the concept derived from studies of actin-severing proteins that the physical packing of PPIs is crucial to their interaction with proteins. Alpha-actinin isolated from skeletal muscle copurifies with PIP_2, whereas alpha-actinin purified by similar methods from different tissues is isolated free of phospholipids. This differential copurification of alpha-actinin with lipid may relate to the differential abilities of alpha-actinin to crosslink or bundle F-actin reported in different studies. Two unusual aspects of alpha-actinin/PIP_2 binding are that the protein/lipid binding can be detected by immunofluorescence at sites such as the Z-band of the sarcomere, which are thought not to contain lipid bilayers, and that the protein-lipid binding is sufficiently tight that it remains intact during electrophoresis in SDS. It has been suggested that this tight binding may involve covalent linkage of PIP_2 to the protein because of oxidation of the unsaturated fatty acyl chain of the lipid (100), but a non-covalent component of this tight association has also been demonstrated (37). If the finding of protein/PPI complexes in regions of the cytoplasm devoid of membranes is confirmed, it would alter the understanding of how PPIs are distributed and transported in the cell, and might provide a valuable insight into the function of the more highly phosphorylated PPIs such as PIP$_3$, which might be relatively unstable in a planar lipid bilayer because of their large head-group charge.

In contrast to the PIP$_2$-enhanced binding of alpha-actinin to actin, PIP$_2$ inhibits the actin crosslinking activity of gizzard filamin (41). The contrasting effects of PIP$_2$ on crosslinking of actin by different proteins observed under similar conditions provide an important clue that PPIs act specifically on the actin-binding proteins rather than non-specifically on F-actin. One limitation to interpretation of these in vitro results is that the binding of proteins to PIP$_2$ micelles probably produces protein/lipid complexes with multiple binding sites for actin, and the gelation efficiency of such clusters depends critically on the spatial distribution of actin-binding sites, which may vary from one preparation to another.

A third actin-crosslinking protein affected by PPIs is MAP2, a protein generally thought to be a microtubule-associated protein, but one whose biologic function is unknown. It also binds F-actin (72). In vitro, MAP2 and its smaller homologue Map2c can form actin filament bundles. Bundle formation is inhibited by PI and perhaps also by phosphorylated PIs (130). Such a regulation of actin binding may participate in the segregation of Map2c and tau in neurons since the actin-binding activity of tau, which is otherwise similar to that of Map2c, is not affected by PI (130).

Linkage by Motors and Other Proteins Between Actin and Membranes

In addition to providing a functional regulation, PPI-binding of proteins can also target them to particular regions in the cell where PPIs are abundant or are being synthesized. One possible function is suggested by the binding of acidic phospholipids, including PPIs, to some myosin isoforms at a site distinct from their actin-binding site (2, 51). This binding could allow myosins to anchor at specific sites at the membrane of the cell or organelles and determine where the force of the acto-myosin interaction is directed. By analogy with this proposed linkage, proteins involved in linking actin to focal contacts such as vinculin and talin also bind with some specificity to bilayers containing acidic phospholipids (53, 59). Although it has not yet been shown that PPIs specifically mediate such binding, the large negative charge on the PPI headgroups makes them good candidates for stabilizing such contacts.

SUMMARY OF PPI EFFECTS

The effects of PPIs on actin-binding proteins are approximately opposite to those of Ca^{2+} and generally disposed to promote actin polymerization and strengthen the cortical actin gel, especially near the plasma membrane. The link between the spectrin/actin network and the cell membrane mediated by band 4.1/glycophorin is strengthened by PIP_2 and weakened by Ca^{2+}; actin filament-severing proteins are inhibited by PPIs and activated by Ca^{2+}. F-actin barbed ends are liberated by PPIs, whereas Ca^{2+} causes their occlusion by capping proteins. The crosslinking activity of alpha-actinin can be enhanced by PPIs and decreased by Ca^{2+}. There are some exceptions to this general picture, such as the inhibition of filamin activity by PIP_2, but on the whole, formation or appropriate rearrangement of PPIs in the membrane or perhaps elsewhere leads to increased actin polymerization and activation of factors that favor the gel state. Decreased PPIs along with increased Ca^{2+} favor solation of the actin network and depolymerization of filaments.

INTEGRATION OF PHOSPHOINOSITIDE AND Ca^{2+} SIGNALS

The roughly opposite effects of Ca^{2+} and PPIs had led to a two-step model for the reorganization of the cytoskeleton when cells are activated to spread or crawl (118, 119). The initial phase of this process involves activation of Ca^{2+}-sensitive actin-binding proteins to release actin filaments from their link to the membrane and to sever filaments forming the elastic actin network. The net effect of this action is to solate the cell cortex and allow for deformation in response to mechanical forces generated either by motor proteins or by hydrostatic or osmotic pressures. At least some of these solating activities, such as filament severing, can also be activated by Ca^{2+}-independent mechanisms such as lowered pH. Solation of the cytoskeleton is not sufficient for locomotion or cell protrusion, and a second phase, in which actin repolymerizes, is required. The second phase could be triggered by synthesis or rearrangement of polyphosphoinositides. This second signal would inactivate severing proteins, liberate the ends of actin nuclei formed by the severing or nucleating activities initially activated by Ca^{2+}, and enhance some actin crosslinking activities. It would also provide a fresh pool of actin monomers by dissociating them from profilin-actin complexes, probably at the plasma membrane, where actin assembly occurs in living cells. This second phase does not depend on PLC activity, and therefore would not necessarily be reflected by changes in IP_3 (9), but depends on the reordering of PPIs within the lipid bilayer or the activation of PI and PIP kinases (108). There is evidence that such kinase activities occur early in the course of processes such as platelet activation (79) and that specific PI(4)P and PI-3 kinases (107, 139) are bound to the cytoskeleton at sites where they could produce lipid products that directly affect actin-binding proteins. Experimental evidence of the separate influences of Ca^{2+} and PPIs on the restructuring of the platelet actin cytoskeleton has recently been reported (47).

It is likely that the pattern of cytoskeletal remodeling depends on the balance between the two opposing influences of Ca^{2+} and PPIs and especially depends on the time course of changes rather than simply the concentration of a single messenger. The subtle interrelationships between Ca^{2+} and PPI signaling pathways are likely to account for the versatility in responses that cells require in vivo.

ACKNOWLEDGMENT

I am grateful to Thomas Stossel, Walter Witke, and Philip Allen for valuable discussions.

Literature Cited

1. Adams AE, Botstein D, Drubin DG. 1991. Requirement of yeast fimbrin for actin organization and morphogenesis in vivo. *Nature* 354:404–8
2. Adams RJ, Pollard TD. 1989. Binding of myosin I to membrane lipids. *Nature* 340:565–68
3. Albanesi JP, Coue M, Fujisaki H, Korn ED. 1985. Effect of actin filament length and filament number concentration on the actin-activated ATPase activity of *Acanthamoeba* myosin I. *J. Biol. Chem.* 260:13276–80
4. Allbritton NL, Meyer T, Stryer L. 1992. Range of messenger action of calcium ion and inositol 1,4,5-trisphosphate. *Science* 258:1812–15
5. Anderson RA, Marchesi VT. 1985. Regulation of the association of membrane skeletal protein 4.1 with glycophorin by a polyphosphoinositide. *Nature* 318:295–98
6. Asai H, Arai T, Fujii T, Matsumoto G. 1989. Purification and characterization of Ca^{2+}/calmodulin-dependent actin-binding proteins from squid retina. *FEBS Lett.* 247:377–80
7. Bamburg J, Bray D. 1987. Distribution and cellular localization of actin depolymerizing factor. *J. Cell Biol.* 105: 2817–25
8. Banno Y, Nakashima T, Kumada T, Ebisawa K, Nonomura Y, et al. 1992. Effects of gelsolin on human platelet cytosolic phosphoinositide-phospholipase C isozymes. *J. Biol. Chem.* 267: 6488–94
9. Bengtsson T, Rundquist I, Stendahl O,

Wymann MP, Andersson T. 1988. Increased breakdown of phosphatidylinositol 4,5-bisphosphate is not an initiating factor for actin assembly in human neutrophils. *J. Biol. Chem.* 263:17385–89
10. Brundage RA, Fogarty KE, Tuft RA, Fay FS. 1991. Calcium gradients underlying polarization and chemotaxis of eosinophils. *Science* 254:703–6
11. Bryan J. 1988. Gelsolin has three actin-binding sites. *J. Cell Biol.* 106: 1553–62
12. Burgoyne RD, Handel SE, Morgan A, Rennison ME, Turner MD, et al. 1991. Calcium, the cytoskeleton and calpactin (annexin II) in exocytotic secretion from adrenal chromaffin and mammary epithelial cells. *Biochem. Soc. Trans.* 19:1085–90
13. Burn P. 1988. Phosphatidylinositol cycle and its possible involvement in the regulation of cytoskeleton-membrane interactions. *J. Cell. Biochem.* 36:15–24
14. Burn P, Rotman A, Meyer RK, Burger MM. 1985. Diacylglycerol in large alpha-actinin/actin complexes and in the cytoskeleton of activated platelets. *Nature* 314:469–72
15. Carlsson L, Nystrom LE, Sundkvist I, Markey F, Lindberg U. 1976. Profilin, a low molecular weight protein controlling actin polymerisability. In *Contractile Systems in Non-muscle Tissues*, ed. SV Perry, A Margreth, RS Adelstein, pp. 39–49. Amsterdam: Elsevier/North-Holland

16. Chaponnier C, Janmey PA, Yin HL. 1986. The actin filament-severing domain of plasma gelsolin. *J. Cell Biol.* 103:1473–81

17. Cheney RE, Mooseker MS. 1992. Unconventional myosins. *Curr. Opin. Cell Biol.* 4:27–35

18. Collins K, Sellers J, Matsudaira P. 1991. Myosin I: a new insight into the mechanism and cellular significance of actin-based motility. *Adv. Biophys.* 27:221–26

19. Cooper JA, Blum JD, Williams RC, Pollard TD. 1986. Purification and characterization of actophorin, a new 15,000-dalton actin-binding protein from *Acanthamoeba castellanii*. *J. Biol. Chem.* 261:477–85

20. Dabiri GA, Young CL, Rosenbloom J, Southwick FS. 1992. Molecular cloning of human macrophage capping protein cDNA. A unique member of the gelsolin/villin family expressed primarily in macrophages. *J. Biol. Chem.* 267:16545–52

21. Dadabay CY, Patton E, Cooper JA, Pike LJ. 1991. Lack of correlation between changes in polyphosphoinositide levels and actin/gelsolin complexes in A431 cells treated with epidermal growth factor. *J. Cell Biol.* 112:1151–56

22. Dawson RMC. 1965. 'Phosphatido-peptide'-like complexes formed by the interaction of calcium triphosphoinositide with protein. *Biochem. J.* 97:134–38

23. Dawson RMC, Eichberg J. 1965. Diphosphoinositide and triphospho-inositide in animal tissues. Extraction, estimation and changes post mortem. *Biochem. J.* 96:634–43

24. de Arruda M, Watson S, Lin C-S, Leavitt J, Matsudaira P. 1990. Fimbrin is a homologue of the cytoplasmic phosphoprotein plastin and has domains homologous with calmodulin and actin gelation proteins. *J. Cell Biol.* 111:1069–79

25. Dobrowolski Z, Borovikov YS, Nowak E, Galazkiewicz B, Dąbrowska R. 1988. Comparison of Ca^{2+}-dependent effects of caldesmon-tropomyosin-calmodulin and troponin-tropomyosin complexes on the structure of F-actin in ghost fibers and its interaction with myosin heads. *Biochim. Biophys. Acta* 956:140–50

26. Doi Y. 1992. Interaction of gelsolin with covalently cross-linked actin dimer. *Biochemistry* 31:10061–69

27. Doi Y, Hashimoto T, Yamaguchi H, Vertut DA. 1991. Modification of gelsolin with 4-fluoro-7-nitrobenz-2-oxa-1,3-diazole. *Eur. J. Biochem.* 199:277–83

28. Downey GP, Chan CK, Trudel S, Grinstein S. 1990. Actin assembly in electropermeabilized neutrophils: role of intracellular calcium. *J. Cell Biol.* 110:1975–82

29. Drust DS, Creutz CE. 1988. Aggregation of chromaffin granules by calpactin at micromolar levels of calcium. *Nature* 331:88–91

30. Eichinger L, Noegel AA, Schleicher M. 1991. Domain structure in actin-binding proteins: expression and functional characterization of truncated severin. *J. Cell Biol.* 112:665–76

31. Eichinger L, Schleicher M. 1992. Characterization of actin- and lipid-binding domains in severin, a $Ca(2+)$-dependent F-actin fragmenting protein. *Biochemistry* 31:4779–87

32. Elson E. 1988. Cellular mechanics as an indicator of cytoskeletal structure and function. *Annu. Rev. Biophys. Biochem.* 17:397–430

33. Espindola FS, Espreafico EM, Coelho MV, Martins AR, Costa FR, et al. 1992. Biochemical and immunological characterization of p190-calmodulin complex from vertebrate brain: a novel calmodulin-binding myosin. *J. Cell Biol.* 118:359–68

34. Fechheimer M, Furukawa R. 1993. A 27,000-D core of the *Dictyostelium* 34,000-D protein retains $Ca(2+)$-regulated actin cross-linking but lacks bundling activity. *J. Cell Biol.* 120:1169–76

35. Finidori J, Friederich E, Kwiatkowski DJ, Louvard D. 1992. In vivo analysis of functional domains from villin and gelsolin. *J. Cell Biol.* 116:1145–55

36. Forscher P, Smith SJ. 1988. Actions of cytochalasins on the organization of actin filaments and microtubules in a neuronal growth cone. *J. Cell Biol.* 107:1505–16

37. Fukami K, Furuhashi K, Inagaki M, Endo T, Hatano S, et al. 1992. Requirement of phosphatidylinositol 4,5-bisphosphate for alpha-actinin function. *Nature* 359:150–52

38. Fukui Y, Lynch TJ, Brzeska H, Korn ED. 1989. Myosin I is located at the leading edges of locomoting *Dictyostelium* amoebae. *Nature* 341:328–31

39. Furuhashi K, Hatano S. 1992. Actin kinase: a protein kinase that phosphorylates actin of fragmin-actin complex. *J. Biochem.* 111:366–70

40. Furuhashi K, Hatano S. 1989. A fragmin-like protein from plasmodium

of *Physarum* polycephalum that severs F-actin and caps the barbed end of F-actin in a Ca^{2+}-sensitive way. *J. Biochem.* 106:311–18

41. Furuhashi K, Inagaki M, Hatano S, Fukami K, Takenawa T. 1992. Inositol phospholipid-induced suppression of F-actin-gelating activity of smooth muscle filamin. *Biochem. Biophys. Res. Commun.* 184:1261–65

42. Gieselmann R, Mann K. 1992. ASP-56, a new actin sequestering protein from pig platelets with homology to CAP, an adenylate cyclase-associated protein from yeast. *FEBS Lett.* 298: 149–53

43. Glenney JR, Weber K. 1981. Calcium control of microfilaments: uncoupling of the F-actin severing and -bundling activity of villin by limited proteolysis in vitro. *Proc. Natl. Acad. Sci. USA* 78:2810–14

44. Goldschmidt-Clermont PJ, Kim JW, Machesky LM, Rhee SG, Pollard TD. 1991. Regulation of phospholipase C-gamma 1 by profilin and tyrosine phosphorylation. *Science* 251: 1231–33

45. Goldschmidt-Clermont PJ, Machesky LM, Baldassare JJ, Pollard TD. 1990. The actin-binding protein profilin binds to PIP$_2$ and inhibits its hydrolysis by phospholipase C. *Science* 247:1575–78

46. Harris AS, Morrow JS. 1990. Calmodulin and calcium-dependent protease I coordinately regulate the interaction of fodrin with actin. *Proc. Natl. Acad. Sci. USA* 87:3009–13

47. Hartwig JH. 1992. Mechanisms of actin rearrangements mediating platelet activation. *J. Cell Biol.* 118:1421–42

48. Hartwig JH, Thelen M, Rosen A, Janmey PA, Nairn AC, et al. 1992. MARCKS is an actin filament cross-linking protein regulated by protein kinase C and calcium-calmodulin. *Nature* 356:618–22

49. Hasegawa T, Takahashi S, Hayashi H, Hatano S. 1980. Fragmin: a calcium ion sensitive regulatory factor on the formation of actin filaments. *Biochemistry* 19:2677–83

50. Haus U, Hartmann H, Trommler P, Noegel AA, Schleicher M. 1991. F-actin capping by cap32/34 requires heterodimeric conformation and can be inhibited with PIP$_2$. *Biochem. Biophys. Res. Commun.* 181:833–39

51. Hayden SM, Wolenski JS, Mooseker MS. 1990. Binding of brush border myosin I to phospholipid vesicles. *J. Cell Biol.* 111:443–51

52. Heilbrunn LV. 1956. *The Dynamics*

of Living Cytoplasm, p. 275. New York: Academic

53. Heise H, Bayerl T, Isenberg G, Sackmann E. 1991. Human platelet P-235, a talin-like actin binding protein, binds selectively to mixed lipid bilayers. *Biochim. Biophys. Acta* 106 1:121–31

54. Heiss SG, Cooper JA. 1991. Regulation of CapZ, an actin capping protein of chicken muscle, by anionic phospholipids. *Biochemistry* 30:8753–58

55. Hesterberg LK, Weber K. 1986. Isolation of a domain of villin retaining calcium-dependent interaction with G-actin, but devoid of F-actin fragmenting activity. *Eur. J. Biochem.* 154: 135–40

56. Hofmann A, Eichinger L, Andre E, Rieger D, Schleicher M. 1992. Cap100, a novel phosphatidylinositol 4,5-bisphosphate-regulated protein that caps actin filaments but does not nucleate actin assembly. *Cell Motil. Cytoskeleton* 23:133–44

57. Hosoya H, Kobayashi R, Tsukita S, Matsumura F. 1992. Ca(2+)-regulated actin and phospholipid binding protein (68 kD-protein) from bovine liver: identification as a homologue for annexin VI and intracellular localization. *Cell Motil. Cytoskeleton* 22:200–10

58. Ikebuchi NW, Waisman DM. 1990. Calcium-dependent regulation of actin filament bundling by lipocortin-85. *J. Biol. Chem.* 265:3392–400

59. Isenberg G. 1991. Actin-binding protein—lipid interactions. *Cell Motil. Cytoskeleton* 12:136–44

60. Ishikawa R, Yamashiro S, Matsumura F. 1989. Annealing of gelsolin-severed actin fragments by tropomyosin in the presence of Ca^{2+}. Potentiation of the annealing process by caldesmon. *J. Biol. Chem.* 264:16764–70

61. Jalink K, Moolenaar WH. 1992. Thrombin receptor activation causes rapid neural cell rounding and neurite retraction independent of classic second messengers. *J. Cell Biol.* 118:411–19

62. Janmey PA, Chaponnier C, Lind SE, Zaner KS, Stossel TP, et al. 1985. Interactions of gelsolin and gelsolin-actin complexes with actin. Effects of calcium on actin nucleation, filament severing, and end blocking. *Biochemistry* 24:3714–23

63. Janmey PA, Iida K, Yin HL, Stossel TP. 1987. Polyphosphoinositide micelles and polyphosphoinositide-containing vesicles dissociate endogenous gelsolin-actin complexes and promote actin assembly from the fast-growing

end of actin filaments blocked by gelsolin. *J. Biol. Chem.* 262:12228–36

64. Janmey PA, Lamb J, Allen PG, Matsudaira PT. 1992. Phosphoinositide-binding peptides derived from the sequences of gelsolin and villin. *J. Biol. Chem.* 267:11818–23

65. Janmey PA, Matsudaira PT. 1988. Functional comparison of villin and gelsolin. Effects of Ca^{2+}, KCl, and polyphosphoinositides. *J. Biol. Chem.* 263:16738–43

66. Janmey PA, Stossel TP. 1989. Gelsolin-polyphosphoinositide interaction. Full expression of gelsolin-inhibiting function by polyphosphoinositides in vesicular form and inactivation by dilution, aggregation, or masking of the inositol head group. *J. Biol. Chem.* 264:4825–31

67. Janmey PA, Stossel TP. 1987. Modulation of gelsolin function by phosphatidylinositol 4,5-bisphosphate. *Nature* 325:362–64

68. Janson LW, Sellers JR, Taylor DL. 1992. Actin-binding proteins regulate the work performed by myosin II motors on single actin filaments. *Cell Motil. Cytoskeleton* 22:274–80

69. Jones PG, Moore GJ, Waisman DM. 1992. A nonapeptide to the putative F-actin binding site of annexin-II tetramer inhibits its calcium-dependent activation of actin filament bundling. *J. Biol. Chem.* 267:13993–97

70. Kanno K, Sasaki Y. 1989. Smooth muscle gelsolin and a Ca^{2+}-sensitive contractile cell model. *J. Cell. Physiol.* 139:58–67

71. Korn ED, Hammer JA. 1990. Myosin I. *Curr. Opin. Cell Biol.* 2:57–61

72. Kotani S, Nishida E, Kumagai J, Sakai H. 1985. Calmodulin inhibits interaction of actin with MAP2 and tau, two major microtubule-associated proteins. *J. Biol. Chem.* 260:10779–83

73. Koyasu S, Nishida E, Miyata Y, Sakai H, Yahara I. 1989. HSP100, a 100-kDa heat shock protein, is a Ca^{2+}-calmodulin-regulated actin-binding protein. *J. Biol. Chem.* 164:15083–87

74. Kurth MC, Bryan J. 1984. Platelet activation induces the formation of a stable gelsolin-actin complex from monomeric gelsolin. *J. Biol. Chem.* 259:7473–79

75. Kwiatkowski DJ, Janmey PA, Yin HL. 1989. Identification of critical functional and regulatory domains in gelsolin. *J. Cell Biol.* 108:1717–26

76. Kwiatkowski DJ, Yin HL. 1987. Molecular biology of gelsolin, a calcium-regulated actin filament severing protein. *Biorheology* 24:643–47

77. Lamb JA, Allen PG, Tuan BY, Janmey PA. 1993. Modulation of gelsolin function: activation at low pH overrides Ca^{2+} requirement. *J. Biol. Chem.* 268:8999–9004

78. Lassing I, Lindberg U. 1988. Evidence that the phosphatidylinositol cycle is linked to cell motility. *Exp. Cell Res.* 174:1–15

79. Lassing I, Lindberg U. 1990. Polyphosphoinositide synthesis in platelets stimulated with low concentrations of thrombin is enhanced before the activation of phospholipase C. *FEBS Lett.* 262:231–33

80. Lassing I, Lindberg U. 1985. Specific interaction between phosphatidylinositol 4,5-bisphosphate and profilactin. *Nature* 314:472–74

81. Lassing I, Lindberg U. 1988. Specificity of the interaction between phosphatidylinositol 4,5-bisphosphate and the profilin:actin complex. *J. Cell. Biochem.* 37:255–67

82. Lin C-S, Aebersold R, Kent S, Varma M, Leavitt J. 1988. Molecular cloning and characterization of plastin, a human leukocyte protein expressed in transformed human fibroblasts. *Mol. Cell. Biol.* 8:4659–68

83. Lin Y, Ishikawa R, Kohama K. 1992. A novel regulatory protein that affects the functions of caldesmon and myosin light chain kinase. *Biochem. Biophys. Res. Commun.* 184:1212–18

84. Lind SE, Janmey PA, Chaponnier C, Herbert T, Stossel TP. 1987. Reversible binding of actin to gelsolin and profilin in human platelet extracts. *J. Cell Biol.* 105:833–42

85. Mabuchi I. 1983. An actin-depolymerizing protein (depactin) from starfish oocytes: properties and interaction with actin. *J. Cell Biol.* 97:1612–21

86. Machesky LM, Goldschmidt-Clermont PJ, Pollard TD. 1990. The affinities of human platelet and *Acanthamoeba* profilin isoforms for polyphosphoinositides account for their relative abilities to inhibit phospholipase C. *Cell Reg.* 1:937–50

87. Maekawa S, Sakai H. 1990. Inhibition of actin regulatory activity of the 74-kDa protein from bovine adrenal medulla (Adseverin) by some phospholipids. *J. Biol. Chem.* 265:10940–42

88. Mak AS, Watson MH, Litwin CM, Wang JH. 1991. Phosphorylation of caldesmon by cdc2 kinase. *J. Biol. Chem.* 266:6678–81

89. Mani RS, McCubbin WD, Kay CM.

1992. Calcium-dependent regulation of caldesmon by an 11-kDa smooth muscle calcium-binding protein, caltropin. *Biochemistry* 31:11896–901

90. Marcantonio JM, Duncan G. 1991. Calcium-induced degradation of the lens cytoskeleton. *Biochem. Soc. Trans.* 19:1148–50

91. Markey F, Persson T, Lindberg U. 1981. Characterization of platelet extracts before and after stimulation with respect to the possible role of profilactin as microfilament precursor. *Cell* 23: 145–53

92. Marks P, Maxfield F. 1990. Transient increases in cytosolic free calcium appear to be required for the migration of adherent human neutrophils. *J. Cell Biol.* 110:43–52

93. Matsudaira P, Jakes R, Walker JE. 1985. A gelsolin-like Ca^{2+}-dependent actin-binding domain in villin. *Nature* 315:248–50

94. Matsumura F, Yamashiro S. 1993. Caldesmon. *Curr. Opin. Cell Biol.* 5:70–76

95. Mattson MP, Engle MG, Rychlik B. 1991. Effects of elevated intracellular calcium levels on the cytoskeleton and tau in cultured human cortical neurons. *Mol. Chem. Neuropathol.* 15:117–42

96. Meyer R, Aebi U. 1990. Bundling of actin filaments by α-actinin depends on its molecular length. *J. Cell Biol.* 110:2013–24

96a. Miyamoto S, Funatsu T, Ishiwata S, Fujime S. 1993. Changes in mobility of chromaffin granules in actin network with its assembly and Ca(2+)-dependent disassembly by gelsolin. *Biophys. J.* 64:1139–49

97. Mooseker MS, Coleman TR. 1989. The 110-kD protein-calmodulin complex of the intestinal microvillus (brush border myosin I) is a mechanoenzyme. *J. Cell Biol.* 108:2395–400

98. Moriyama K, Yonezawa N, Sakai H, Yahara I, Nishida E. 1992. Mutational analysis of an actin-binding site of cofilin and characterization of chimeric proteins between cofilin and destrin. *J. Biol. Chem.* 267:7240–44

99. Namba Y, Ito M, Zu Y, Shigesada K, Maruyama K. 1992. Human T cell L-plastin bundles actin filaments in a calcium-dependent manner. *J. Biochem.* 112:503–7

100. Niggli V. 1993. Lipid-cytoskeleton interactions. *Nature* 361:214

101. Noegel A, Witke W, Schleicher M. 1987. Calcium-sensitive nonmuscle α-actinin contains EF-hand structures and

highly conserved regions. *FEBS Lett.* 221:391–96

102. Northrop J, Weber A, Mooseker M, Franzini-Armstrong C, Bishop MF, et al. 1986. Different calcium dependence of the capping and cutting activities of villin. *J. Biol. Chem.* 261:9274–81

103. Onji T, Takagi M, Shibata N. 1988. Gelsolin is Ca^{2+}-sensitive regulator of actomyosin system in platelet. *Biochem. Biophys. Res. Commun.* 155:91–99

104. Oster G. 1988. Biophysics of the leading lamella. *Cell Motil. Cytoskeleton* 10:164–71

105. Pacaud M, Harricane MC. 1993. Macrophage alpha-actinin is not a calcium-modulated actin-binding protein. *Biochemistry* 32:363–74

106. Pavalko FM, Burridge K. 1991. Disruption of the actin cytoskeleton after microinjection of proteolytic fragments of alpha-actinin. *J. Cell Biol.* 114:481–91

107. Payrastre B, van Bergen en Henegouwen PM, Breton M, Denhartigh JC, Plantavid M, et al. 1991. Phosphoinositide kinase, diacylglycerol kinase, and phospholipase C activities associated to the cytoskeleton: effect of epidermal growth factor. *J. Cell Biol.* 115:121–28

108. Pike MC, Costello K, Southwick FS. 1991. Stimulation of human polymorphonuclear leukocyte phosphatidylinositol-4-phosphate kinase by concanavalin A and formyl-methionyl-leucyl-phenylalanine is calcium-independent. Correlation with maintenance of actin assembly. *J. Immunol.* 147: 2270–75

109. Pollard TD, Doberstein SK, Zot HG. 1991. Myosin-I. *Annu. Rev. Physiol.* 53:653–81

110. Prendergast GC, Ziff EB. 1991. Mbh 1: a novel gelsolin/severin-related protein which binds actin in vitro and exhibits nuclear localization in vivo. *EMBO J.* 10:757–66

111. Pritchard K, Marston SB. 1993. The Ca(2+)-sensitizing component of smooth muscle thin filaments: properties of regulatory factors that interact with caldesmon. *Biochem. Biophys. Res. Commun.* 190:668–73

112. Rittenhouse S, Sasson J. 1985. Mass changes in myoinositol trisphosphate in human platelets stimulated by thrombin. *J. Biol. Chem.* 260:8657–60

113. Rodriguez Del Castillo A, Lemaire S, Tchakarov L, Jeyapragasan M, Doucet J-P, et al. 1990. Chromaffin cell scinderin, a novel calcium-dependent

actin filament-severing protein. *EMBO J.* 9:43–52

114. Safer D. 1992. The interaction of actin with thymosin beta 4. *J. Muscle Res. Cell. Motil.* 13:269–71

115. Sakurai T, Kurokawa H, Nonomura Y. 1991. The Ca(2+)-dependent actin filament-severing activity of 74-kDa protein (adseverin) resides in its NH2-terminal half. *J. Biol. Chem.* 266: 4581–85

116. Sha'afi R, Shefcyk J, Yassin R, Molski T, Naccache P, et al. 1986. Is a rise in intracellular concentration of free calcium necessary or sufficient for stimulated cytoskeletal-associated actin. *J. Cell Biol.* 102:1459–63

117. Southwick F, Young C. 1990. The actin released from profilin-actin complexes insufficient to account for the increase in F-actin in chemoattractant-stimulated polymorphonuclear leukocytes. *J. Cell Biol.* 110:1965–74

118. Stossel T. 1993. On the crawling of animal cells. *Science* 260:1086–94

119. Stossel TP. 1989. From signal to pseudopod. How cells control cytoplasmic actin assembly. *J. Biol. Chem.* 264:18261–64

120. Stossel TP, Janmey PA, Zaner KS. 1987. The cortical cytoplasmic actin gel. In *Cytomechanics,* ed. J Bereiter-Hahn, OR Anderson, WE Reif, pp. 131–53. Berlin: Springer

121. Tanaka T, Kadowaki K, Lazarides E, Sobue K. 1991. Ca(2+)-dependent regulation of the spectrin/actin interaction by calmodulin and protein 4.1. *J. Biol. Chem.* 266:1134–40

122. Vojtek A, Haarer B, Field J, Gerst J, Pollard TD, et al. 1991. Evidence for a functional link between profilin and CAP in the yeast S. cerevisiae. *Cell* 66:497–505

123. Walsh T, Weber A, Davis K, Bonder E, Mooseker M. 1984. Calcium dependence of villin-induced actin depolymerization. *Biochemistry* 23: 6099–102

124. Wang CL, Wang LW, Xu SA, Lu RC, Saavedra AV, et al. 1991. Localization of the calmodulin- and actin-binding sites of caldesmon. *J. Biol. Chem.* 266:9166–72

125. Way M, Gooch J, Pope B, Weeds AG. 1989. Expression of human plasma gelsolin in *Escherichia coli* and dissection of actin binding sites by segmental deletion mutagenesis. *J. Cell Biol.* 109:593–605

125a. Weeds A, Maciver S. 1993. F-actin capping proteins. *Curr. Opin. Cell Biol.* 5:63–69

125b. Witke W, Hofmann A, Koppel B, Schleicher M, Noegel AA. 1993. The Ca(2+)-binding domains in non-muscle type alpha-actinin: biochemical and genetic analysis. *J. Cell Biol.* 121:599–606

126. Witke W, Schleicher M, Noegel AA. 1992. Redundancy in the microfilament system: abnormal development of Dictyostelium cells lacking two F-actin cross-linking proteins. *Cell* 68:53–62

127. Xian W, Garver TM, Braunlin WH, Janmey PA. 1992. NMR and CD conformational studies of a 20 amino acid PIP2-binding site on gelsolin. *FASEB J.* 6:A87

128. Yamamoto K, Pardee JD, Reidler J, Stryer L, Spudich JA. 1982. Mechanism of interaction of *Dictyostelium* severin with actin filaments. *J. Cell Biol.* 95:711–19

129. Yamashiro S, Yamakita Y, Hosoya H, Matsumura F. 1991. Phosphorylation of non-muscle caldesmon by p34cdc2 kinase during mitosis. *Nature* 349:169–72

130. Yamauchi PS, Purich DL. 1993. Microtubule-associated protein interactions with actin filaments: evidence for differential behavior of neuronal MAP-2 and tau in the presence of phosphatidylinositol. *Biochem. Biophys. Res. Commun.* 190:710–15

131. Yin HL, Stossel TP. 1979. Control of cytoplasmic actin gel-sol transformation by gelsolin, a calcium-dependent regulatory protein. *Nature* 281:583–86

132. Yin HL. 1987. Gelsolin. A calcium-and polyphosphoinositide-regulated actin-modulating protein. *BioEssays* 7: 176–79

133. Yin HL, Iida K, Janmey PA. 1988. Identification of a polyphosphoinositide-modulated domain in gelsolin which binds to the sides of actin filaments. *J. Cell Biol.* 106:805–12

134. Yin HL, Janmey PA, Schleicher M. 1990. Severin is a gelsolin prototype. *FEBS Lett.* 264:78–80

135. Yonezawa N, Homma Y, Yahara I, Sakai H, Nishida E. 1991. A short sequence responsible for both phosphoinositide binding and actin binding activities of cofilin. *J. Biol. Chem.* 266:17218–21

136. Yonezawa N, Nishida E, Iida K, Yahara I, Sakai H. 1990. Inhibition of the interactions of cofilin, destrin, and deoxyribonuclease I with actin by phosphoinositides. *J. Biol. Chem.* 265: 8382–86

137. Yu FX, Johnston PA, Sudhof TC, Yin HL. 1990. gCap39, a calcium ion- and

polyphosphoinositide-regulated actin capping protein. *Science* 250:1413–15

138. Yu FX, Sun HQ, Janmey PA, Yin HL. 1992. Identification of a polyphosphoinositide-binding sequence in an actin monomer-binding domain of gelsolin. *J. Biol. Chem.* 267:14616–21

139. Zhang J, Fry MJ, Waterfield MD, Jaken S, Liao L, et al. 1992. Activated phosphoinositide 3-kinase associates with membrane skeleton in thrombin-exposed platelets. *J. Biol. Chem.* 267: 4686–92

140. Zu YL, Shigesada K, Nishida E, Kubota I, Kohno M, et al. 1990. 65-kilodalton protein phosphorylated by interleukin 2 stimulation bears two putative actin-binding sites and two calcium-binding sites. *Biochemistry* 29: 8319–24

Annu. Rev. Physiol. 1994. 56:193–212
Copyright © 1994 by Annual Reviews Inc. All rights reserved

MODULATION OF ION CHANNELS BY PROTEIN PHOSPHORYLATION AND DEPHOSPHORYLATION

Irwin B. Levitan

Graduate Department of Biochemistry and Center for Complex Systems, Brandeis University, Waltham, Massachusetts 02254

KEY WORDS: protein kinase, phosphoprotein phosphatase, channel gating, channel inactivation, ATP modulation

INTRODUCTION

When an electrode is advanced through a nervous system from one cell to another, to systematically sample the electrical activity of individual neurons, a striking diversity of neuronal electrical properties is observed. For example different neurons may exhibit different endogenous firing patterns; some may be silent in the absence of external stimulus, whereas others may fire action potentials spontaneously, at regular or irregular intervals. Neurons may also vary in the size and shape of their action potentials, which can give rise to large differences in the amplitude and time course of neurotransmitter release from their terminals. Finally, even closely related neurons may respond differently to the same synaptic input. Clearly such diversity of neuronal properties is of fundamental importance in determining the output of the neural circuits in which neurons participate.

Equally important is the fact that patterns of neuronal electrical activity are not static, but are subject to dynamic regulation by a variety of external influences (63). For example, under certain conditions, a neuron that normally is silent might begin to fire action potentials spontaneously, the duration of its action potentials might increase or decrease, or it might change the magnitude and even the direction of its response to a particular

193

0066–4278/94/0315–0193$05.00

synaptic input. Such modulation of neuronal activity, which often can last for a long time, can give rise to long-term plastic changes in neural circuits and higher neural functions.

Because electrical activity in nerve cells—indeed, in all cells—is determined by the movement of ions across the plasma membrane through the specialized class of membrane proteins known as ion channels, a study of how ion channels are modulated is essential for even the most rudimentary understanding of the kinds of modulation of neuronal activity described above (72). Conceptual and technical breakthroughs during the last decade have led to revolutionary advances in our knowledge of structure and function of ion channels. These breakthroughs have included the introduction of single channel recording techniques, in concert with the molecular cloning of genes encoding ion channel proteins and their expression in heterologous expression systems. Among the fundamental properties of many ion channels that are being studied intensively using these approaches are conduction and selectivity, gating behavior (including activation and inactivation kinetics), and modulation.

MODULATION OF ION CHANNELS BY PROTEIN PHOSPHORYLATION

Ion channels are proteins, and there are many mechanisms by which the properties of proteins can be modulated. For example, allosteric effectors may bind to some site on an enzyme, remote from the active site, and influence enzyme activity. The opening and closing of the conduction pathway in a major class of ion channels, the so-called ligand-gated ion channels, are indeed dependent on just such binding of a neurotransmitter to a receptor site on the extracellular side of the ion channel protein. Ion channel activity can also be influenced by such factors as pH (34), intracellular redox state (119), the binding of calcium ions to the intracellular side of the channel (68), and block of the conducting pathway by other ions (80, 96, 135), or by portions of the ion channel protein itself (43, 53, 124, 134, 148).

The mechanism of ion channel modulation that has been most thoroughly studied and appears to be most widespread is protein phosphorylation (20, 71, 72). Phosphorylation of proteins on serine, threonine, and tyrosine residues is an ubiquitous mechanism of regulating the activity of proteins and the cellular processes in which these proteins are involved (26, 27, 48). There is now abundant evidence that a variety of ion channels are among the proteins that are substrates for protein kinases and phosphoprotein phosphatases and that ion channel phosphorylation can influence profoundly the electrical properties of neurons and other cells. In this review I make no attempt at a comprehensive survey of this rapidly expanding field, but rather focus on recent cellular, molecular, and biophysical studies of ion channel modulation by phosphorylation, with emphasis on several specific examples for which the mechanisms and consequences of channel phosphorylation are becoming particularly clear.

MODULATION OF LIGAND-GATED ION CHANNELS BY PROTEIN PHOSPHORYLATION

The ligand-gated ion channels form a super-family, the members of which contain both a neurotransmitter binding site and a closely associated ion channel as part of a single macromolecular complex. They mediate rapid onset and rapidly reversible synaptic transmission in nerve and muscle cells, and thus at first glance might seem to be unlikely targets for longer term modulation by protein phosphorylation. However, one of the earliest examples of ion channel modulation by phosphorylation comes from work on the nicotinic acetylcholine receptor, the prototype of the ligand-gated ion channels. More recent studies implicate phosphorylation in the regulation of other members of this receptor/channel super-family, including the GABA$_A$ and glutamate receptors (reviewed recently in references 107 and 130). Glycine receptors may also be regulated by phosphorylation (107), but the evidence to date is more preliminary and I will not review it here.

Nicotinic Acetylcholine Receptor/Channels

Because of the availability of an excellent source of material—the *Torpedo* electric organ—and a highly specific affinity reagent—the cobra venom component α-bungarotoxin—the nicotinic acetylcholine receptor/channel was the first ion channel protein to be purified and the first for which molecular clones became available. The *Torpedo* nicotinic receptor is a heteropentameric structure containing two α subunits and one each of the β, γ, and δ subunits. The α subunits contain the acetylcholine binding sites, occupation of which leads to opening of a non-selective cation channel. Each of the subunits, which exhibit substantial sequence homology to each other, is believed to span the plasma membrane four times and contribute to the structure of the channel pore. A large intracellular loop between the third and fourth membrane-spanning regions of each subunit contains multiple consensus sites for phosphorylation by several different protein kinases. Early experiments demonstrated that the *Torpedo* nicotinic receptor is indeed a substrate for cyclic AMP-dependent protein kinase (PKA), protein kinase C (PKC), and tyrosine kinase (56, 57, 121). Furthermore, phosphorylation can modulate channel activity by influencing the rate of desensitization in the presence of agonist (51, 55), and this phenomenon appears to be of physiological importance in regulating the properties of various synapses that use nicotinic acetylcholine receptor/channels (36, 40, 83, 91).

Recently it was demonstrated that, in addition to modulating channel activity acutely, phosphorylation can influence the assembly of newly-synthesized nicotinic receptor subunits and the aggregation of receptors at synapses. For example, phosphorylation by PKA appears to promote the stability of receptor subunits and assembly of mature receptors in the plasma membrane (45, 114, 115). In addition, tyrosine phosphorylation may cause nicotinic receptors to accumulate in arrays that resemble postsynaptic receptor aggregates at the vertebrate neuromuscular junction (106, 140). Tyrosine phosphorylation of the receptor can be triggered by agrin (140), a protein in the extracellular matrix of the synaptic cleft that is thought to be involved in formation of postsynaptic specializations at nerve-muscle synapses (82).

Many of these phenomena are also observed with neuronal nicotinic acetylcholine receptor/channels, which differ from their *Torpedo* and muscle counterparts in that they lack γ and δ subunits (47, 75), and are heteropentamers containing several different kinds of α and β subunits (29). Nevertheless their overall structural organization resembles that of their *Torpedo* and muscle cousins, and they contain consensus sequences for protein phosphorylation (see Table 1 in reference 130). Phosphorylation at these sites can regulate the rate of receptor desensitization (36) or the number of functional receptors in the plasma membrane (78, 137), which suggests that these kinds of modulation are common to the different flavors of nicotinic acetylcholine receptor/channels.

$GABA_A$ Receptor/Channels

The $GABA_A$ receptors are ligand-gated chloride-selective ion channels that are responsible for most fast inhibitory synaptic transmission in the mammalian central nervous system. They too are heteropentameric structures, formed from at least five different kinds of homologous subunits (99). There is much evidence that $GABA_A$ receptor subunits are substrates for a variety of protein kinases including PKA, PKC, the type II calcium/calmodulin-dependent protein kinase (CamK II), and an unidentified protein kinase that is closely associated with the purified $GABA_A$ receptor/channel (16, 64, 70, 76, 89, 129). In addition, treatment of intact cells with agents that would be expected to affect $GABA_A$ receptor phosphorylation can influence the amplitude and kinetics of the GABA-evoked chloride current (23, 105, 125).

Recent experiments combining heterologous expression of recombinant $GABA_A$ receptors with site-directed mutagenesis have identified a particular serine residue in the β subunit as an essential site for modulation by phosphorylation. The catalytic subunit of PKA can cause a decrease in the peak amplitude and in the rapid component of desensitization of the GABA-evoked current in cells expressing the α_1 and β_1 subunits of the $GABA_A$ receptor (90). These effects are similar to those seen when the receptor phosphorylation state is manipulated in nerve cells (23, 105, 125) and are reminiscent of the kinds of alterations in nicotinic acetylcholine receptor/channel function that result from phosphorylation (51, 55). Site-directed mutagenesis of the serine residue at position 409 of the β_1 subunit eliminates both of these actions of PKA (90); this result emphasizes that the functional consequences of phosphorylation of a single amino acid residue can be extremely complex. Adding to this complexity is the recent finding that co-expression in mouse fibroblasts of recombinant $GABA_A$ receptor, together with the catalytic subunit of PKA, leads to an enhancement of GABA-evoked currents (7). Thus chronic phosphorylation by PKA may regulate the expression or degradation of $GABA_A$ receptors, and this effect is also eliminated by site-directed mutagenesis of serine^{409} of the γ_1 subunit (7).

An unusual and interesting example of the way phosphorylation may influence the function of ligand-gated ion channels comes from the recent finding that the γ_2 subunit of the $GABA_A$ receptor can be expressed in alternative splice variants, one of which contains a phosphorylation site that is absent from the other (147). This site can be phosphorylated by PKC (89, 147) or CamK II (76). Ethanol, which long has been known to potentiate responses mediated by $GABA_A$ receptors in neurons, is effective only on recombinant receptors that include the γ_2 subunit variant with the phosphorylation site (138). Furthermore, site-directed mutagenesis of the serine that is phosphorylated removes ethanol sensitivity in the recombinant receptor (139). These results raise the intriguing possibility that some actions of ethanol in nerve cells may be mediated via protein phosphorylation.

Glutamate Receptor/Channels

The glutamate receptors mediate most rapid excitatory synaptic transmission in the mammalian brain. They also are found in retina and in nerve and muscle cells in many invertebrates. The glutamate receptors are the most recent members of the ligand-gated ion channel super-family to succumb to the assaults of molecular cloning, and their functional and molecular diversity is daunting (61, 94). They have long been separated into two classes, the N-methyl-D-aspartate (NMDA) and non-NMDA (also known as AMPA/kainate) receptors, on the basis of their binding site pharmacology and the ionic selectivity of their channels. In addition there is a separate class of metabotropic glutamate receptors that produce their effects via intracellular second messengers and are not ligand-gated ion channels. These functional distinctions among the various glutamate receptor classes are consistent with differences in their molecular structures (50, 54, 79, 88, 93). Because glutamate receptors are widely believed to play an important role in certain forms of synaptic plasticity (77), their modulation has been investigated thoroughly.

Increases in cyclic AMP levels, or direct intracellular introduction of the catalytic subunit of PKA, can enhance currents carried by non-NMDA glutamate receptor/channels in several different neuronal cell types. For example, in fish retinal horizontal cells, PKA modulation of non-NMDA receptors is responsible for the increase in kainate-evoked currents seen in the presence of dopamine (74). In addition, exogenous PKA (46, 141) or CamK II (81) can enhance kainate-evoked currents in mammalian hippocampal neurons. Of particular interest is the finding that an inhibitor of PKA depresses (141) the kainate-evoked currents in these neurons, and inhibitors of cellular phosphoprotein phosphatases enhance (81, 141) these currents. These results suggest that endogenous PKA and phosphoprotein phosphatases are involved in normal physiological regulation of the non-NMDA glutamate receptors.

These findings in neurons have recently been extended to recombinant non-NMDA glutamate receptors expressed in heterologous expression systems. One cloned non-NMDA receptor subtype, GluR1, is a substrate for CamK II and (to a lesser extent) for PKC, but is not phosphorylated by PKA (81). GluR6, on the other hand, is phosphorylated by PKA on at least one and possibly two serine residues (108, 142). Phosphorylation of GluR6 with PKA enhances the currents evoked by glutamate or kainate, consistent with the modulatory effects in neurons described above. Thus non-NMDA glutamate receptor function can be modulated by direct phosphorylation of the receptor/channel protein.

The picture is less clear for the NMDA receptors. PKC can phosphorylate several distinct sites on the NR1 NMDA receptor subtype (133), but the functional consequences of this phosphorylation of the recombinant receptor remain to be explored. PKC also enhances glutamate responses mediated by NMDA receptors in a variety of neuronal types, and an intriguing mechanism has recently been proposed to account for this general finding (22). Intracellular injection of PKC into trigeminal neurons causes a decrease in the voltage-dependent block of NMDA receptors by extracellular magnesium (22). Because magnesium block plays an essential role in the functioning of NMDA receptor channels (80, 96), a reduction in the block will greatly influence the amplitude and voltage-dependence of NMDA currents.

MODULATION OF VOLTAGE-GATED ION CHANNELS BY PROTEIN PHOSPHORYLATION

The ion channels whose activity is regulated by the trans-membrane voltage also form a channel super-family, the diversity of which rivals that of the ligand-gated ion channel super-family. Included among the voltage-gated ion channels are channels selective for calcium, sodium, and potassium ions; in spite of their different ionic selectivities, they share common structural features that justify considering them as a group (20, 21, 62, 86). Although the voltage-gated calcium and potassium channels clearly are regulated by protein phosphorylation (e.g. 8, 9, 17, 32, 42, 52, 98 for calcium channels; 49, 100, 102–104 for potassium channels), I concentrate here on recent developments in the modulation of sodium channel activity by several protein kinases.

Sodium channels purified from a variety of sources all have a high molecular weight (approximately 260 K) α subunit, and one or more smaller subunits (20). Heterologous expression of the α subunit alone in *Xenopus* oocytes (12, 127) or mammalian cells (97) is sufficient to form a functional voltage-gated sodium channel, although the co-expression of other subunits can modify the gating kinetics (12, 65). The large α subunit consists of four homologous domains, each containing six putative membrane-spanning sequences (95). There are a number of consensus sequences for phosphorylation by protein kinases, and a series of biochemical experiments have established that the α subunit is an excellent substrate for phosphorylation by both PKA (30, 39, 116–118) and PKC (92).

What are the functional consequences of sodium channel phosphorylation? Treatment of cultured embryonic rat brain neurons with phorbol ester or diacylglycerol activators of PKC reduces the peak sodium current and also markedly slows the time course of inactivation of the macroscopic sodium current (97). Diacylglycerols have similar effects on the amplitude and kinetics of the macroscopic sodium current in Chinese hamster ovary (CHO) cells stably transfected with the α subunit of rat brain type IIA sodium channels; an examination of single channel currents demonstrates that inactivation is largely removed following diacylglycerol treatment, as evidenced by the presence of many more channel reopenings during a depolarizing pulse (97). These effects of diacylglycerol on sodium channel activity are mimicked by the intracellular injection of purified PKC and blocked by a specific peptide inhibitor of PKC (but not by an inhibitor of PKA), which confirms that these effects do indeed result from PKC-mediated protein phosphorylation (97). Site-directed mutagenesis of a single serine residue, in the intracellular loop between the third and fourth homologous domains in the α subunit, eliminates both the decrease in peak current amplitude and the slowing of channel inactivation (144). It is interesting that previous experiments had identified this intracellular loop as playing a critical role in sodium channel inactivation (126, 136).

Phosphorylation by PKA also modulates sodium channel function, but the effects of PKA are different from those of PKC. When the purified catalytic subunit of PKA is applied to the cytoplasmic surface of membrane patches detached from cultured embryonic rat brain neurons, there is a decrease in the activity of single sodium channels in the patch (73). This decrease is exhibited as a reduction in the probability that the channels will open in response to depolarization. In contrast to the actions of PKC, phosphorylation by PKA does not change the kinetics of sodium channel activation or inactivation. A similar result, a reduction in peak sodium current with no change in the voltage dependence or kinetics of activation and inactivation, is observed when the macroscopic sodium current is examined in patches from CHO cells transfected with rat brain type IIA sodium channels (73). These actions of PKA are blocked by a peptide inhibitor specific for this kinase and are reversed by application of phosphoprotein phosphatases.

I have presented these findings on modulation of sodium channel activity by protein phosphorylation in some detail as an example of the complexity of the regulation of members of the voltage-gated ion channel family. It is particularly interesting that neurotransmitters and hormones that act through different signaling pathways can converge on voltage-gated sodium channels as a common target, and it will be a formidable task to decipher how the balance between the PKA and PKC pathways ultimately determines sodium channel activity under various physiological conditions.

MODULATION OF CALCIUM-DEPENDENT POTASSIUM CHANNELS BY PROTEIN PHOSPHORYLATION

This task becomes even more daunting when one considers the regulation of the calcium-dependent potassium (K_{Ca}) channels. The K_{Ca} channels are ubiquitous. There are numerous varieties that differ in such features as single channel conductance, calcium sensitivity, kinetics, and pharmacology (e.g. 67, 101, 110, 113; reviewed in reference 68). Although the diversity revealed by these biophysical, physiological, and pharmacological studies is impressive, recent molecular characterization suggests that the family of K_{Ca} channels may in fact be far more diverse than suspected previously (2, 11, 19). The K_{Ca} channels are highly selective for potassium, and channel opening is dependent on a complex interaction between intracellular calcium and membrane depolarization (68, 87). Thus they provide a link between a major intracellular messenger, calcium, and neuronal electrical activity. Finally, they are important targets for modulation by protein phosphorylation. For example a variety of agents that increase the activity of PKC (e.g. 13, 35, 122) or PKA (e.g. 33, 38, 41, 66, 69, 112, 120, 123) can influence the activity of K_{Ca} channels in neurons and other cells. That is, at least three distinct signaling pathways, those involving calcium, PKA, and PKC, can converge on K_{Ca} channels as a common cellular target.

Biophysical Studies of K_{Ca} Channel Modulation

I focus here on studies of the modulation of K_{Ca} channels reconstituted into artificial phospholipid bilayer membranes. Bilayer reconstitution is far from physiological, but it provides a well-controlled experimental environment for the molecular and biophysical investigation of ion channels and their modulation (84, 85). Among the advantages of the system are the ready access to both sides of the ion channel in the bilayer chamber, for the application and removal of reagents including purified protein kinases and phosphoprotein phosphatases. Another important feature for studies of channel modulation is that ion channel proteins are at essentially infinite dilution in the lipid of the bilayer membrane; thus it is possible to test rigorously the hypothesis that the ion channel protein itself, or some closely associated regulatory protein, is the direct target for protein kinases and phosphatases.

Direct application of the purified catalytic subunit of PKA to the cytoplasmic side of the bilayer membrane can modulate the activity of single K_{Ca} channels reconstituted from plasma membrane fractions derived from snail neurons (41) or rat brain (112). Because the channels are at infinite dilution in the bilayer (see above), these findings demonstrate that the phosphorylation target must be either the ion channel protein itself, or some regulatory protein so intimately associated with the ion channel that it swims with it in the bilayer. The rat brain plasma membrane fractions used for these studies contain at least four distinct K_{Ca} channels (110), and the phosphorylation of two of them has been studied in detail. Although these two channels are similar with respect to their calcium sensitivities and single channel conductances, they can be distinguished on the basis of their gating kinetics, pharmacology, and responses to PKA: the open probability of the faster gating, charybdotoxin-sensitive (Type I) K_{Ca} channel is increased by PKA, whereas that of the slower gating, charybdotoxin-insensitive (Type II) channel is decreased by PKA (112). Both these actions of PKA require ATP and can be reversed by addition of the purified catalytic subunit of phosphoprotein phosphatase 2A (PP2A), which confirms that both result from protein phosphorylation (112). A common feature of modulation of the snail K_{Ca} channel and both rat brain K_{Ca} channels is that in all cases phosphorylation produces a change in channel calcium/voltage sensitivity (41, 112).

The fact that the Type I and Type II K_{Ca} channels from rat brain are modulated in opposite directions by PKA suggests that they contain distinct sites for phosphorylation by this enzyme. In fact, the modulation of the Type II channel is more complex still because its activity can be regulated by ATP in the absence of exogenous protein kinase (25). In the presence of ATP, channel open probability is increased, and the subsequent down-modulation produced by PKA (112) overrides this up-modulation by ATP alone. The action of ATP is not simply the result of its binding to the Type II K_{Ca} channel because the modulation can be mimicked by ATP analogues such as ATPγS that can serve as substrates for protein kinases, but not by non-substrate ATP analogues such as adenylylimidodiphosphate (AMPP[N]P) (25). These findings suggest that the modulation by ATP involves protein phosphoryla-tion, and this is confirmed by the observation that the effect of ATP can be reversed by another specific phosphatase, phosphoprotein phosphatase 1 (PP1) (25). Because no exogenous protein kinase is added in these experiments, the modulation by ATP must be mediated by an endogenous kinase that is either part of the Type II K_{Ca} channel or accompanies it into the artificial bilayer. Furthermore, the channel must contain at least two distinct phosphorylation sites, one specific for PKA, and the other for the endogenous protein kinase, that participate in modulation of channel activity in different directions.

An important conclusion from these experiments, based on the infinite dilution argument advanced above, is that the Type II K_{Ca} channel exists as part of a regulatory complex that contains the ion channel in intimate association with a protein kinase activity that can modulate channel properties (25). More recent evidence suggests that an endogenous phosphoprotein phosphatase activity may also participate in this regulatory complex (111). Other studies indicate that a purified dendrotoxin-binding protein, reconsti-tuted into bilayers, exhibits both voltage-gated potassium channel activity and an apparent endogenous protein kinase activity that can regulate the channel (109). Thus a regulatory complex may be a common feature of other modulatable ion channels.

Cellular Studies of K_{Ca} Channel Modulation

A complementary approach to these biophysical experiments is to investigate the cellular mechanisms and physiological consequences of K_{Ca} channel modulation. For example, in *Aplysia* sensory neurons, activation of K_{Ca} channels by PKC may contribute to the modulation of a simple behavioral response (31). In a mammalian pituitary tumor cell line, the neuropeptide somatostatin inhibits secretion, in part as a result of activation of K_{Ca}

channels (146). The channel modulation in turn results from activation of a cellular phosphoprotein phosphatase, via a pertussis toxin-sensitive G protein that is coupled to the somatostatin receptors (10). It was concluded by analogy with the bilayer data (112) that somatostatin stimulates K_{Ca} channel activity as a result of dephosphorylation of the channel protein itself, or of some closely associated regulatory molecule (146).

Another peptide hormone, atrial natriuretic peptide (ANP), also inhibits secretion from the same pituitary tumor cell line by increasing potassium conductance. Again the inhibition involves an increase in the activity of K_{Ca} channels following stimulation of phosphoprotein phosphatase activity, but in this case the mechanism does not involve a pertussis toxin-sensitive G protein (145). ANP receptors are known to be coupled to guanylate cyclase, and this increase in K_{Ca} channel activity requires cyclic GMP-dependent protein kinase (145). However, the kinase does not appear to modulate the K_{Ca} channels directly; experiments using the phosphoprotein phosphatase inhibitor okadaic acid suggest that the cyclic GMP-dependent protein kinase may instead stimulate the activity of a phosphatase that, in turn, dephosphorylates and modulates the channels (145).

Findings such as these emphasize that the participation of multiple intracellular signaling pathways, together with the intricate regulation of single channels discussed above, can confer enormous complexity on the modulation of cellular electrical activity (27). They also draw attention to the essential role of phosphoprotein phosphatase activity in modulatory phenomena. Although much is known about the regulation of protein kinases and their actions on ion channels, until recently the contributions of phosphatases have largely been neglected. However, the availability of potent and specific phosphoprotein phosphatase inhibitors has led to the demonstration that phosphatases are an important regulatory target in controlling the activity of membrane ion channels (112, 145, 146) and ion currents (59, 60), as well as fundamental physiological processes such as neurotransmitter release (1, 128).

MODULATION OF OTHER CHANNELS BY PROTEIN PHOSPHORYLATION—MIN-K AND CFTR

Modulation of the Min-K Channel

Min-K is a potassium channel that does not fit into the traditional categorization of voltage-gated and K_{Ca} potassium channels described above. It is voltage-dependent, but it requires many seconds to activate following a depolarizing voltage step (15, 132). The cloned cDNA for this channel codes for a protein of only 130 amino acids, containing only a single putative membrane-spanning domain (132); it has no homology with other cloned ion channels. When min-K is expressed in *Xenopus* oocytes, it can be modulated by activation of either the PKA (14) or PKC (18) signaling pathways. Treatments that increase cyclic AMP levels in the oocyte increase the amplitude of the min-K current without changing its kinetics or voltage dependence, and this effect can be blocked by a specific peptide inhibitor of PKA (14). The min-K protein sequence does not contain a canonical consensus sequence for PKA phosphorylation, but it does contain a serine residue, flanked by basic amino acids, that might be a substrate for PKA (132). Interestingly, mutation of this site does not eliminate the modulation of min-K via the PKA pathway (14), thus raising the possibility that the phosphorylatable modulatory site may be on some yet unidentified channel regulatory molecule that is present in the *Xenopus* oocyte.

A different result is obtained by manipulating the PKC pathway. Treatment of oocytes with diacylglycerol or phorbol ester activators of PKC leads to a decrease in min-K current as a result of a change in the voltage dependence of channel activation (18). This effect can be blocked by a PKC inhibitor and is eliminated by mutation of a particular serine residue in the putative intracellular domain of the channel protein (18), which suggests that the min-K protein itself is a substrate for phosphorylation and modulation by PKC.

Modulation of CFTR

Another channel outside the traditional classification is the cystic fibrosis transmembrane regulator, CFTR. Mutations in CFTR are responsible for cystic fibrosis, a prevalent lethal congenital disorder characterized by defective ion transport in epithelial tissues (28, 143). The sequence of CFTR does not exhibit homology to other cloned ion channels, but expression of CFTR in heterologous expression systems produces a chloride conductance that can be modulated by the PKA signaling pathway (5, 131). Thus it appears likely that CFTR itself forms a modulatable chloride channel (4), and it also may participate in the regulation of other chloride channels in epithelial cells (37, 44).

The sequence of CFTR bears a striking resemblance to a family of membrane transporters known as the traffic ATPases (28, 58, 143). The putative structure contains five distinct domains: two membrane-spanning domains, each consisting of six membrane-spanning sequences; two intracellular nucleotide-binding domains; and an intracellular regulatory domain that contains several consensus sequences for phosphorylation by PKA. The mechanism by which CFTR chloride channel activity is modulated is unusual and interesting. Phosphorylation by PKA of one or more sites in the regulatory domain is necessary, but not sufficient, to open the channel (24).

Furthermore ATP binding to the nucleotide-binding domains is also necessary, but not sufficient, for channel activity (3, 6). A series of elegant experiments (summarized in references 28 and 143) have demonstrated that the channel can open only when ATP binds to the nucleotide-binding domains of a previously phosphorylated channel. The physiological significance of this novel and interesting two-stage modulation of CFTR chloride channel activity remains to be determined.

SUMMARY AND CONCLUSIONS

Modulation of the properties of membrane ion channels is of fundamental importance for the regulation of neuronal electrical activity and of higher neural functions. Among the many potential molecular mechanisms for modulating the activity of membrane proteins such as ion channels, protein phosphorylation has been chosen by cells to play a particularly prominent part. This is not surprising given the central role of protein phosphorylation in a wide variety of cellular, metabolic, and signaling processes (26, 27, 48). As summarized here, regulation by phosphorylation is not restricted to one or another class of ion channel; rather, many, and perhaps all, ion channels are subject to modulation by phosphorylation. Similarly, a number of different protein kinase signaling pathways can participate in the regulation of ion channel properties, and it is not unusual to find that a particular channel is modulated by several different protein kinases, each influencing channel activity in a unique way. Finally, the biophysical mechanisms of modulation also exhibit a striking diversity that ranges from changes in desensitization rates to shifts in the voltage dependence and kinetics of channel activation and inactivation.

The convergence of channel molecular biology with patch-clamp technology has been spectacularly productive, even allowing the identification of particular amino acid residues in ion channel proteins that participate in specific modulatory changes in channel biophysical properties. This task is far from complete, and no doubt there remain surprises in store for us, but nevertheless it is appropriate to ask where we go from here. One important direction will be to relate functional modulation, produced by phosphorylation, to changes in the three-dimensional structure of the ion channel protein. Unfortunately, structural studies of membrane proteins are extremely difficult, and to date there is no high resolution structure available for any ion channel protein. A complementary strategy that is more feasible with current technology is to investigate the ways in which channel modulation contributes to the regulation of cellular physiology. Novel computational approaches are being brought to bear on this complex issue, and their combination with channel molecular biology and biophysics should significantly advance our understanding of molecular mechanisms of neuronal plasticity.

ACKNOWLEDGMENT

I am grateful to Drs. M. Browning, W. Catterall, R. Huganir, R. Macdonald, and L. Salkoff for providing me with data and manuscripts prior to publication. Work in my laboratory is supported by grants from the National Institutes of Health.

Literature Cited

1. Abdul-Ghani M, Kravitz EA, Meiri H, Rahamimoff R. 1991. Protein phosphatase inhibitor okadaic acid enhances transmitter release at neuromuscular junctions. *Proc. Natl. Acad. Sci. USA* 88:1803–7

2. Adelman JP, Shen K-Z, Kavanaugh MP, Warren RA, Wu YN, et al. 1992. Calcium-activated potassium channels expressed from cloned complementary DNAs. *Neuron* 9:209–16

3. Anderson MP, Berger HA, Rich DP, Gregory RJ, Smith AE, Welsh MJ. 1991. Nucleoside triphosphates are required to open the CFTR chloride channel. *Cell* 67:775–84

4. Anderson MP, Gregory RJ, Thompson S, Souza DW, Sucharita P, et al. 1991. Demonstration that CFTR is a chloride channel by alteration of its anion selectivity. *Science* 253:202–5

5. Anderson MP, Rich DP, Gregory RJ, Smith AE, Welsh MJ. 1991. Generation of cAMP-activated chloride currents by expression of CFTR. *Science* 251:679–82

6. Anderson MP, Welsh MJ. 1992. Regulation by ATP and ADP of CFTR chloride channels that contain mutant nucleotide-binding domains. *Science* 257:1701–4

7. Angelotti TP, Uhler MD, Madconald RL. 1993. Enhancement of a recombinant $\alpha 1\beta 1\gamma 2S$ GABA$_A$ receptor currents by chronic elevation of cAMP-dependent protein kinase is mediated by phosphorylation of the $\beta 1$ subunit. *J. Neurosci.* In press

8. Armstrong DL. 1989. Calcium channel regulation by calcineurin, a Ca^{2+} activated phosphatase in mammalian brain. *Trends Neuro. Sci.* 12:1–10

9. Armstrong DL, Rossier MF, Shcherbatko AD, White RE. 1991. Enzymatic gating of voltage-activated calcium channels. *Ann. NY Acad. Sci.* 635:26–34

10. Armstrong DL, White RE. 1992. An enzymatic mechanism for potassium channel stimulation through pertussis toxin-sensitive G proteins. *Trends Neuro. Sci.* 15:403–8

11. Atkinson NS, Robertson GA, Ganetzky B. 1991. A component of calcium-activated potassium channels encoded by the *Drosophila slo* locus. *Science* 253:551–55

12. Auld VJ, Goldin AL, Krafte DS, Marshall J, Dunn JM, et al. 1988. A rat brain Na$^+$ channel α subunit with novel gating properties. *Neuron* 1:449–61

13. Baraban JM, Snyder SH, Alger B. 1985. Protein kinase C regulates ionic conductance in hippocampal pyramidal neurons: electrophysiological effects of phorbol esters. *Proc. Natl. Acad. Sci. USA* 82:2538–42

14. Blumenthal EM, Kaczmarek LK. 1992. Modulation by cAMP of a slowly activating potassium channel expressed in *Xenopus* oocytes. *J. Neurosci.* 12:290–96

15. Boyle MB, Azhderian EM, MacLusky NJ, Naftolin F, Kaczmarek LK. 1987. *Xenopus* oocytes injected with rat uterine RNA express very slowly activating potassium currents. *Science* 235:1221–24

16. Browning MD, Bureau M, Dudek EM, Olsen RW. 1990. Protein kinase C and cAMP-dependent protein kinase phosphorylate the β subunit of the purified γ-aminobutyric acid A receptor. *Proc. Natl. Acad. Sci. USA* 87:1315–18

17. Brum G, Flockerzi V, Hofmann F, Osterrieder W, Trautwein W. 1983. Injection of catalytic subunit of cAMP-dependent protein kinase into isolated

cardiac myocytes. *Pflügers Arch.* 398:147–54

18. Busch AE, Varnum MD, North RA, Adelman JP. 1992. An amino acid mutation in a potassium channel that prevents inhibition by protein kinase C. *Science* 255:1705–07

19. Butler AG, Tsunoda SL, McCobb DP, Wei AD, Salkoff LB. 1993. *mSlo,* a complex mouse gene encoding high conductance calcium-activated potassium channels. *Science* 261:221–24

20. Catterall WA. 1988. Structure and function of voltage-sensitive ion channels. *Science* 242:50–61

21. Catterall WA. 1991. Functional subunit structure of voltage-gated calcium channels. *Science* 253:1499–500

22. Chen L, Huang LYM. 1992. Protein kinase C reduced Mg^{2+} block of NMDA-receptor channels as a mechanism of modulation. *Nature* 356:521–23

23. Chen QX, Stelzer A, Kay AR, Wong RKS. 1990. $GABA_A$ receptor function is regulated by phosphorylation in acutely dissociated guinea-pig hippocampal neurones. *J. Physiol.* 420:207–21

24. Cheng SH, Rich DP, Marshall J, Gregory RJ, Welsh MJ, Smith AE. 1991. Phosphorylation of the R domain by cAMP-dependent protein kinase regulates the CFTR chloride channel. *Cell* 66:1027–36

25. Chung SK, Reinhart PH, Martin BL, Brautigan D, Levitan IB. 1991. Protein kinase activity closely associated with a reconstituted calcium-activated potassium channel. *Science* 253:560–62

26. Cohen P. 1988. Protein phosphorylation and hormone action. *Proc. R. Soc. London Ser. B* B234:115–44

27. Cohen P. 1992. Signal integration at the level of protein kinases, protein phosphatases and their substrates. *Trends Biochem. Sci.* 17:408–13

28. Collins FS. 1992. Cystic fibrosis: Molecular biology and therapeutic implications. *Science* 256:774–79

29. Cooper E, Couturier S, Ballivet M. 1991. Pentameric structure and subunit stoichiometry of a neuronal nicotinic acetylcholine receptor. *Nature* 350:235–38

30. Costa MR, Casnellie JE, Catterall WA. 1982. Selective phosphorylation of the α subunit of the sodium channel by cAMP-dependent protein kinase. *J. Biol. Chem.* 257:7918–21

31. Critz SD, Byrne JH. 1992. Modulation of $I_{K,Ca}$ by phorbol ester-mediated activation of PKC in pleural sensory neurons of *Aplysia. J. Neurophysiol.* 68:1079–86

32. Curtis BM, Catterall WA. 1985. Phosphorylation of the calcium antagonist receptor of the voltage-sensitive calcium channel by cAMP-dependent protein kinase. *Proc. Natl. Acad. Sci. USA* 82:2528–32

33. DePeyer JE, Cachelin AB, Levitan IB, Reuter H. 1982. Ca^{2+}-activated K^+ conductance in internally perfused snail neurons is enhanced by protein phosphorylation. *Proc. Natl. Acad. Sci. USA* 79:4207–11

34. Deutsch C, Lee SC. 1989. Modulation of K^+ currents in human lymphocytes by pH. *J. Physiol.* 413:399–413

35. Doerner D, Pitler TA, Alger B. 1988. Protein kinase C activators block specific calcium and potassium current components in isolated hippocampal neurons. *J. Neurosci.* 8:4069–78

36. Downing JEG, Role LW. 1987. Activators of protein kinase C enhance acetylcholine receptor desensitization in sympathetic ganglion neurons. *Proc. Natl. Acad. Sci. USA* 84:7739–43

37. Egan M, Flotte T, Afione S, Solow R, Zeitlin PL, et al. 1992. Defective regulation of outwardly rectifying Cl^- channels by protein kinase A corrected by insertion of CFTR. *Nature* 358:581–84

38. Egan TM, Dagan D, Levitan IB. 1993. Properties and modulation of a calcium-activated potassium channel in rat olfactory bulb neurons. *J. Neurophysiol.* 69:1433–42

39. Emerick MC, Agnew WS. 1989. Identification of phosphorylation sites for adenosine 3′,5′-cyclic phosphate dependent protein kinase on the voltage-sensitive sodium channel from *Electrophorus electricus. Biochemistry* 28:8367–80

40. Eusebi F, Molinaro M, Zani BM. 1985. Agents that activate protein kinase C reduce acetylcholine sensitivity in cultured myotubes. *J. Cell Biol.* 100:1339–42

41. Ewald D, Williams A, Levitan IB. 1985. Modulation of single Ca^{2+}-dependent K^+ channel activity by protein phosphorylation. *Nature* 315:503–6

42. Flockerzi V, Oeken HJ, Hofmann F, Pelzer D, Cavalie A, Trautwein W. 1986. Purified dihydropyridine-binding site from skeletal muscle t-tubules is a functional calcium channel. *Nature* 323:66–68

43. Foster CD, Chung SK, Zagotta WN, Aldrich RW, Levitan IB. 1992. A peptide derived from the *Shaker* B K^+

channel produces short and long blocks of reconstituted Ca^{2+}-dependent K^+ channels. *Neuron* 9:229–36

44. Gabriel SE, Clarke LL, Boucher RC, Stutts MJ. 1993. CFTR and outward rectifying chloride channels are distinct proteins with a regulatory relationship. *Nature* 363:263–66

45. Green WN, Ross AF, Claudio T. 1991. cAMP stimulation of acetylcholine receptor expression is mediated through posttranslational mechanisms. *Proc. Natl. Acad. Sci. USA* 88:854–58

46. Greengard P, Jen J, Nairn AC, Stevens CF. 1991. Enhancement of the glutamate response by cAMP-dependent protein kinase in hippocampal neurons. *Science* 253:1135–38

47. Halvorsen SW, Berg DK. 1990. Subunit composition of nicotinic acetylcholine receptors from chick ciliary ganglia. *J. Neurosci.* 10:1711–18

48. Hemmings HC, Nairn AC, McGuinness TL, Huganir RL, Greengard P. 1991. Role of protein phosphorylation in neuronal signal transduction. *FASEB J.* 3:1582–92

49. Hoger JH, Walter AE, Vance D, Yu L, Lester HA, Davidson N. 1991. Modulation of a cloned mouse brain potassium channel. *Neuron* 6:227–36

50. Hollmann M, O'Shea-Greenfield A, Rogers S, Heinemann S. 1989. Cloning by functional expression of a member of the glutamate receptor family. *Nature* 342:643–48

51. Hopfield JF, Tank DW, Greengard P, Huganir RL. 1988. Functional modulation of the nicotinic acetylcholine receptor by tyrosine phosphorylation. *Nature* 336:677–80

52. Hosey MM, Borsotto M, Lazdunski M. 1986. Phosphorylation and dephosphorylation of dihydropyridine-sensitive voltage-dependent Ca^{2+} channel in skeletal muscle membranes by cAMP-and Ca^{2+}-dependent processes. *Proc. Natl. Acad. Sci. USA* 83:3733–37

53. Hoshi T, Zagotta WN, Aldrich RW. 1990. Biophysical and molecular mechanisms of *Shaker* potassium channel inactivation. *Science* 250:533–38

54. Houamed KM, Kuijper JL, Gilbert TL, Haldeman BA, O'Hara PJ, et al. 1991. Cloning, expression and gene structure of a G protein-coupled glutamate receptor from rat brain. *Science* 252:1318–21

55. Huganir RL, Delcour AH, Greengard P, Hess GP. 1986. Phosphorylation of the nicotinic acetylcholine receptor regulates its rate of desensitization. *Nature* 321:774–76

56. Huganir RL, Greengard P. 1983. cAMP-dependent protein kinase phosphorylates the nicotinic acetylcholine receptor. *Proc. Natl. Acad. Sci. USA* 80:1130–34

57. Huganir RL, Miles K, Greengard P. 1984. Phosphorylation of the nicotinic acetylcholine receptor by an endogenous tyrosine-specific protein kinase. *Proc. Natl. Acad. Sci. USA* 81:6968–72

58. Hyde SC, Emsley P, Hartshorn MJ, Mimmack MM, Gileadi U, et al. 1990. Structural model of ATP-binding proteins associated with cystic fibrosis, multidrug resistance and bacterial transport. *Nature* 346:362–65

59. Ichinose M, Byrne JH. 1991. Role of protein phosphatases in the modulation of neuronal membrane currents. *Brain Res.* 549:146–50

60. Ichinose M, Endo S, Critz SD, Shenolikar S, Byrne JH. 1990. Microcystin-LR, a potent phosphatase inhibitor, prolongs the serotonin- and cAMP-induced currents in sensory neurons of *Aplysia californica. Brain Res.* 533: 137–40

61. Jahr CE, Stevens CF. 1987. Glutamate activates multiple single channel conductances in hippocampal neurons. *Nature* 325:522–25

62. Jan LY, Jan YN. 1989. Voltage-sensitive ion channels. *Cell* 56:13–25

63. Kaczmarek LK, Levitan IB. 1987. *Neuromodulation: the Biochemical Control of Neuronal Excitability*, pp. 3–280. New York: Oxford Univ. Press

64. Kirkness EF, Bovenkerk CF, Ueda T, Turner A. 1989. Phosphorylation of γ-aminobutyrate (GABA)/benzodiazepine receptors by cyclic AMP-dependent protein kinase. *Biochem. J.* 259:613–16

65. Krafte DS, Snutch TP, Leonard JP, Davidson N, Lester HA. 1988. Evidence for the involvement of more than one mRNA species in controlling the inactivation process of rat and rabbit brain Na channels expressed in *Xenopus* oocytes. *J. Neurosci.* 8:2859–68

66. Kume H, Tokuno H, Tomita T. 1989. Regulation of Ca^{2+}-dependent K^+-channels in tracheal myocytes by phosphorylation. *Nature* 341:152–54

67. Lancaster B, Nicoll RA, Perkel DJ. 1991. Calcium activates two types of potassium channels in rat hippocampal neurons in culture. *J. Neurosci.* 11:23–30

68. Latorre R, Oberhauser A, Labarca P, Alvarez O. 1989. Varieties of calcium-activated potassium channels. *Annu. Rev. Physiol.* 51:385–99

69. Lechleiter JD, Dartt DA, Brehm P.

1988. Vasoactive intestinal peptide activates Ca^{2+}-dependent K^+ channels through a cAMP pathway in mouse lacrimal cells. *Neuron* 1:227–35

70. Leidenheimer NJ, Browning MD, Harris RA. 1991. GABA$_A$ receptor phosphorylation: multiple sites, actions and artifacts. *Trends Pharmacol. Sci.* 12: 84–87

71. Levitan IB. 1985. Phosphorylation of ion channels. *J. Membr. Biol.* 87:177–90

72. Levitan IB. 1988. Modulation of ion channels in neurons and other cells. *Annu. Rev. Neurosci.* 11:119–36

73. Li M, West JW, Lai Y, Scheuer T, Catterall WA. 1992. Functional modulation of brain sodium channels by cAMP-dependent phosphorylation. *Neuron* 8:1151–59

74. Liman ER, Knapp AG, Dowling JE. 1989. Enhancement of kainate-gated currents in retinal horizontal cells by cyclic AMP-dependent protein kinase. *Brain Res.* 481:399–402

75. Lindstrom J, Schoepfer R, Whiting P. 1987. Molecular studies of the neuronal nicotinic acetylcholine receptor family. *Mol. Neurobiol.* 1:281–337

76. Machu TK, Firestone JA, Browning MD. 1993. Ca^{2+}/calmodulin-dependent protein kinase II and protein kinase C phosphorylate a synthetic peptide corresponding to a sequence that is specific for the γ2L subunit of the GABA$_A$ receptor. *J. Neurochem.* 61:375–77

77. Madison DV, Malenka RC, Nicoll RA. 1991. Mechanisms underlying long-term potentiation of synaptic transmission. *Annu. Rev. Neurosci.* 14:379–97

78. Margiotta JF, Berg DK, Dionne VE. 1987. Cyclic AMP regulates the proportion of functional acetylcholine receptors on chicken ciliary ganglion neurons. *Proc. Natl. Acad. Sci. USA* 84:8155–59

79. Masu M, Tanabe Y, Tsuchida K, Shigemoto R, Nakanishi S. 1991. Sequence and expression of a metabotropic glutamate receptor. *Nature* 349:760–65

80. Mayer ML, Westbrook GL, Guthrie PB. 1984. Voltage-dependent block by Mg^{2+} of NMDA responses in spinal cord neurones. *Nature* 309:261–63

81. McGlade-McCulloh E, Yamamoto H, Tan SE, Brickey DA, Soderling TR. 1993. Phosphorylation and regulation of glutamate receptors by calcium/calmodulin-dependent protein kinase II. *Nature* 362:640–42

82. McMahan UJ, Wallace BG. 1989. Molecules in basal lamina that direct for-

mation of synaptic specializations at neuromuscular junctions. *Dev. Neurosci.* 11:227–47

83. Middleton P, Rubin LL, Scheutze SM. 1988. Desensitization of acetylcholine receptors in rat myotubes is enhanced by agents that elevate intracellular cAMP. *J. Neurosci.* 8:3405–12

84. Miller C. 1983. Integral membrane channels: studies in model membranes. *Physiol. Rev.* 63:1209–42

85. Miller C. 1986. *Ion Channel Reconstitution*, New York: Plenum

86. Miller C. 1988. *Shaker* shakes out potassium channels. *Trends Neuro. Sci.* 11:185–86

87. Moczydlowski E, Latorre R. 1983. Gating kinetics of Ca^{2+}-activated K^+ channels from rat muscle incorporated into planar lipid bilayers. Evidence for two voltage-dependent Ca^{2+} binding reactions. *J. Gen. Physiol.* 82:511–42

88. Moriyoshi K, Masu M, Ishii T, Shigemoto R, Mizuno N, Nakanishi S. 1991. Molecular cloning and characterization of the rat NMDA receptor. *Nature* 354:31–37

89. Moss SJ, Doherty CA, Huganir RL. 1992. Identification of the cAMP-dependent protein kinase and protein kinase C phosphorylation sites within the major intracellular domains of the β1, γ2S and γ2L subunits of the GABA A receptor. *J. Biol. Chem.* 267: 14470–76

90. Moss SJ, Smart TG, Blackstone CD, Huganir RL. 1992. Functional modulation of GABA$_A$ receptors by cAMP-dependent protein phosphorylation. *Science* 257:661–65

91. Mulle C, Benoit P, Pinset C, Roa M, Changeux JP. 1988. Calcitonin gene-related peptide enhances the rate of desensitization of the nicotinic acetylcholine receptor in cultured mouse muscle cells. *Proc. Natl. Acad. Sci. USA* 85:5728–32

92. Murphy BJ, Catterall WA. 1992. Phosphorylation of purified rat brain Na^+ channel reconstituted into phospholipid vesicles by protein kinase C. *J. Biol. Chem.* 267:16129–34

93. Nakanishi N, Shneider NA, Axel R. 1990. A family of glutamate receptor genes: Evidence for the formation of heteromultimeric receptors with distinct properties. *Neuron* 5:569–81

94. Nakanishi S. 1992. Molecular diversity of glutamate receptors and implications for brain function. *Science* 258:597–603

95. Noda M, Shimizu S, Tanabe T, et al. 1984. Primary structure of *Electroph-*

orus electricus sodium channel deduced from cDNA sequence. *Nature* 312:121–27

96. Nowak L, Bregestovski P, Ascher P, Herbet A, Prochiantz A. 1984. Magnesium gates glutamate-activated channels in mouse central neurones. *Nature* 307:462–65

97. Numann R, Catterall WA, Scheuer T. 1991. Functional modulation of brain sodium channels by protein kinase C phosphorylation. *Science* 254:115–18

98. Nunoki K, Florio V, Catterall WA. 1989. Activation of purified calcium channels by stoichiometric protein phosphorylation. *Proc. Natl. Acad. Sci. USA* 86:6816–20

99. Olsen RW, Towbin AJ. 1990. Molecular biology of GABA$_A$ receptors. *FASEB J.* 4:1469–80

100. Payet MD, Dupuis G. 1992. Dual regulation of the *n* type K$^+$ channel in jurkat T lymphocytes by protein kinases A and C. *J. Biol. Chem.* 267:18270–73

101. Pennefather P, Lancaster B, Adams PR, Nicoll RA. 1985. Two distinct Ca-dependent K currents in bullfrog sympathetic ganglion cells. *Proc. Natl. Acad. Sci. USA* 82:3040–44

102. Perozo E, Bezanilla F. 1990. Phosphorylation affects voltage gating of the delayed rectifier K$^+$ channel by electrostatic interactions. *Neuron* 5:685–90

103. Perozo E, Jong DS, Bezanilla F. 1991. Single channel studies of the phosphorylation of K$^+$ channels in the squid giant axon. *J. Gen. Physiol.* 98:19–34

104. Perozo E, Vandenberg CA, Jong DS, Bezanilla F. 1991. Single channel studies of the phosphorylation of K$^+$ channels in the squid giant axon. *J. Gen. Physiol.* 98:1–17

105. Porter NM, Twyman RE, Uhler MD, Macdonald RL. 1990. Cyclic AMP-dependent protein kinase decreases GABA$_A$ receptor current in mouse spinal neurons. *Neuron* 5:789–96

106. Qu J, Moritz E, Huganir RL. 1990. Regulation of tyrosine phosphorylation of the nicotinic acetylcholine receptor at the rat neuromuscular junction. *Neuron* 2:367–78

107. Raymond LA, Blackstone CD, Huganir RL. 1993. Phosphorylation of amino acid neurotransmitter receptors in synaptic plasticity. *Trends Neurosci.* 16:147–53

108. Raymond LA, Blackstone CD, Huganir RL. 1993. Phosphorylation and modulation of recombinant GluR6 glutamate

receptors by cAMP-dependent protein kinase. *Nature* 361:637–41

109. Rehm H, Pelzer S, Cochet C, Chambaz E, Tempel BL, et al. 1989. Dendrotoxin-binding brain membrane protein displays a K$^+$ channel activity that is stimulated by both cAMP-dependent and endogenous phosphorylations. *Biochemistry* 28:6455–60

110. Reinhart PH, Chung S, Levitan IB. 1989. A family of calcium-dependent potassium channels from rat brain. *Neuron* 2:1031–41

111. Reinhart PH, Chung SK, Levitan IB. 1993. Phosphoprotein phosphatase activity intimately associated with a reconstituted calcium-dependent potassium channel. Submitted

112. Reinhart PH, Chung SK, Martin BL, Brautigan DL, Levitan IB. 1991. Modulation of calcium-activated potassium channels from rat brain by protein kinase A and phosphatase 2A. *J. Neurosci.* 11:1627–35

113. Romey G, Lazdunski M. 1984. The coexistence in rat muscle cells of two distinct classes of Ca^{2+}-dependent K$^+$-channels with different pharmacological properties and different physiological functions. *Biochem. Biophys. Res. Commun.* 118:669–74

114. Ross AF, Green WN, Hartman DS, Claudio T. 1991. Efficiency of acetylcholine receptor subunit assembly and its regulation by cAMP. *J. Cell Biol.* 113:623–26

115. Ross AF, Rapuano M, Schmidt JH, Prives JM. 1987. Phosphorylation and assembly of nicotinic acetylcholine receptor subunits in cultured chick muscle cells. *J. Biol. Chem.* 262:14640–47

116. Rossie S, Catterall WA. 1987. Cyclic AMP-dependent phosphorylation of voltage-sensitive sodium channels in primary cultures of rat brain neurons. *J. Biol. Chem.* 262:12735–44

117. Rossie S, Catterall WA. 1989. Phosphorylation of the α subunit of rat brain sodium channels by cAMP-dependent protein kinase at a new site containing Ser[686] and Ser[687] *J. Biol. Chem.* 264:14220–24

118. Rossie S, Gordon D, Catterall WA. 1987. Identification of an intracellular domain of the sodium channel having multiple cAMP-dependent phosphorylation sites. *J. Biol. Chem.* 262:17530–35

119. Ruppersberg JP, Stocker M, Pongs O, Heinemann SH, Frank R, Koenen M. 1991. Regulation of fast inactivation of cloned mammalian I$_K$(A) channels

by cysteine oxidation. *Nature* 352:711–14

120. Sadoshima J, Akaike N, Kanaide H, Nakamura M. 1988. Cyclic AMP modulates Ca-activated K channel in cultured smooth muscle cells of rat aortas. *Am. J. Physiol.* 255:H754–59

121. Safran A, Sagi-Eisenberg R, Neumann D, Fuchs S. 1987. Phosphorylation of the acetylcholine receptor by protein kinase C and identification of the phosphorylation site within the receptor δ subunit. *J. Biol. Chem.* 262:10506–10

122. Shearman MS, Sekiguchi K, Nishizuka Y. 1989. Modulation of ion channel activity: A key function of the protein kinase C enzyme family. *Pharmacol. Rev.* 41:211–37

123. Sikdar SK, McIntosh RP, Mason WT. 1989. Differential modulation of Ca^{2+}-activated K^+-channels in ovine pituitary gonadotrophs by GnRH, Ca^{2+} and cyclic AMP. *Brain Res.* 496:113–23

124. Solaro CR, Lingle CJ. 1992. Trypsin-sensitive, rapid inactivation of a calcium-activated potassium channel. *Science* 257:1694–98

125. Stelzer A, Kay AR, Wong RKS. 1988. $GABA_A$-receptor function in hippocampal cells is maintained by phosphorylation factors. *Science* 241:339–41

126. Stühmer W, Conti F, Suzuki H, et al. 1989. Structural parts involved in activation and inactivation of the sodium channel. *Nature* 339:597–603

127. Stühmer W, Methfessel C, Sakmann B, Noda M, Numa S. 1987. Patch clamp characterization of sodium channels expressed from brain cDNA. *Eur. Biophys. J.* 14:131–38

128. Swain JE, Robitaille R, Dass GR, Charlton MP. 1991. Phosphatases modulate transmission and serotonin facilitation at synapses: Studies with the inhibitor okadaic acid. *J. Neurobiol.* 22:855–64

129. Sweetnam PM, Lloyd J, Gallombardo P, Madison RT, Gallager DW, et al. 1988. Phosphorylation of the $GABA_A$/benzodiazepine receptor α subunit by a receptor-associated protein kinase. *J. Neurochem.* 51:1274–84

130. Swope SL, Moss SJ, Blackstone CD, Huganir RL. 1992. Phosphorylation of ligand-gated ion channels: a possible mode of synaptic plasticity. *FASEB J.* 6:2514–23

131. Tabcharani JA, Chang XB, Riordan JR, Hanrahan JW. 1991. Phosphorylation-regulated Cl^- channel in CHO cells stably expressing the cystic fibrosis gene. *Nature* 352:628–31

132. Takumi T, Ohkubo H, Nakanishi S.

1988. Cloning of a membrane protein that induces a slow voltage-gated potassium current. *Science* 242:1042–45

133. Tingley WG, Roche KW, Thompson AK, Huganir RL. 1993. Regulation of NMDA receptor phosphorylation by alternative splicing of the C-terminal domain. *Nature* 364:70–73

134. Toro L, Stefani E, Latorre R. 1992. Internal blockade of a Ca^{2+}-activated K^+ channel by *Shaker* B inactivating "ball" peptide. *Neuron* 9:237–45

135. Traynelis SF, Cull-Candy SG. 1990. Proton inhibition of N-methyl-D-aspartate receptors in cerebellar neurons. *Nature* 345:347–50

136. Vassilev PM, Scheuer T, Catterall WA. 1988. Identification of an intracellular peptide segment involved in sodium channel inactivation. *Science* 241:1658–61

137. Vijayaraghavan S, Schmid HA, Halvorsen SW, Berg DK. 1990. Cyclic AMP-dependent phosphorylation of a neuronal acetylcholine receptor α-type subunit. *J. Neurosci.* 10:3255–62

138. Wafford KA, Burnett DM, Leidenheimer NJ, Burt DR, Wang JB, et al. 1991. Ethanol sensitivity of the $GABA_A$ receptor expressed in *Xenopus* oocytes requires 8 amino acids contained in the $γ_2$ subunit. *Neuron* 7:27–33

139. Wafford KA, Whiting PJ. 1992. Ethanol potentiation of $GABA_A$ receptors requires phosphorylation of the alternatively spliced variant of the $γ_2$ subunit. *FEBS Lett.* 313:113–17

140. Wallace BG, Qu Z, Huganir RL. 1991. Agrin induces phosphorylation of the nicotinic acetylcholine receptor. *Neuron* 6:869–78

141. Wang LY, Salter MW, MacDonald JF. 1991. Regulation of kainate receptors by cAMP-dependent protein kinase and phosphatases. *Science* 253:1132–35

142. Wang LY, Taverna FA, Huang XP, MacDonald JF, Hampson DR. 1993. Phosphorylation and modulation of a kainate receptor (GluR6) by cAMP-dependent protein kinase. *Science* 259:1173–75

143. Welsh MJ, Anderson MP, Rich DP, Berger HA, Denning GM, et al. 1992. Cystic fibrosis transmembrane conductance regulator: A chloride channel with novel regulation. *Neuron* 8:821–29

144. West JW, Numann R, Murphy BJ, Scheuer T, Catterall WA. 1991. A phosphorylation site in the Na^+ channel required for modulation by protein kinase C. *Science* 254:866–68

145. White RE, Lee AB, Shcherbatko AD,

Lincoln TM, Schonbrunn A, Armstrong DL. 1993. Potassium channel stimulation by natriuretic peptides through cGMP-dependent dephosphorylation. *Nature* 361:263–66

146. White RE, Schonbrunn A, Armstrong DL. 1991. Somatostatin stimulates Ca^{2+}-activated K^+ channels through protein dephosphorylation. *Nature* 351:570–73

147. Whiting P, McKelran RM, Iversen LL. 1990. Another mechanism for creating diversity in γ-aminobutyrate type A receptors: RNA splicing directs expression of two forms of γ_2 subunit, one of which contains a protein kinase C phosphorylation site. *Proc. Natl. Acad. Sci. USA* 87:9966–70

148. Zagotta WN, Hoshi T, Aldrich RW. 1990. Restoration of inactivation in mutants of *Shaker* potassium channels by a peptide derived from ShB. *Science* 250:568–71

Annu. Rev. Physiol. 1994. 56:213–36
Copyright © 1994 by Annual Reviews Inc. All rights reserved

Ca^{2+}-BINDING AND STRUCTURAL DYNAMICS IN THE FUNCTIONS OF CALMODULIN

Harel Weinstein and Ernest L. Mehler

Department of Physiology and Biophysics, Mount Sinai School of Medicine, City University of New York, New York, NY 10029–6574

KEY WORDS: cellular Ca^{2+}, calcium-binding proteins, cooperativity, protein structure, EF-hand motifs, hydrophobic patches, molecular modeling, molecular dynamics simulations

INTRODUCTION

The large number of recent reviews and evaluations devoted to the actions of calmodulin (CAM) as a mediator of Ca^{2+} signaling reflects the great interest in the key role of Ca^{2+} in a variety of processes in the cell (6, 19, 20, 26, 82), as well as the rapid increase in understanding the role of CAM in the mechanisms underlying these essential physiological functions (10, 21, 28, 33, 36, 56, 57, 59, 66, 83, 99, 100, 110, 117, 139). The examples discussed in these compendia characterize in detail some of the regulatory actions of calmodulin in the cell, but the list of such actions is growing with the continuing identification of specific targets for activation by CAM (e.g. see 6, 18, 29, 43, 53, 140). Recent explorations of CAM-regulated processes have taken advantage of the special physiological properties of a variety of organisms in which the direct requirements for Ca^{2+}-activated CAM can be revealed by genetic manipulation (25, 75). Such approaches exploit strain-specific variants of CAM (e.g. see 41, 66, 69, 76, 106), as well as differences in the properties of its targets [e.g. the CAM-regulated kinases (99) and the phosphatases that have been described earlier in vertebrates (8)]. The functional insights emerging from these studies, focused on the actions of Ca^{2+}-activated CAM, are gaining mechanistic value from

213

0066–4278/94/0315–0213$05.00

the inferences provided by rapidly accumulating data about the three-dimensional structural characteristics of the CAM molecule (e.g. see 5, 7, 15, 31, 46, 60, 85, 92, 97, 120) and its complexes with ligands (e.g. see 45, 47, 52, 61, 62, 77, 81). The literature summarizing the structural characteristics of CAM emphasizes those shared with other calcium-binding proteins (especially the EF-hand class; 80, 109), as well as those structural elements that appear to set CAM apart from other members of this family of proteins, and determine the specificity of its interaction with the various targets in the cell (7, 14, 31, 32, 47, 52, 53, 60–62, 77, 81, 85, 92, 94–96, 120, 128). Based on such structural data, hypotheses regarding the mechanisms of action of CAM in a variety of physiological processes can be formulated at a detailed molecular level (e.g. see 30, 87, 90–92, 94, 98, 99, 108, 126). Such hypotheses can serve to identify and discriminate the differences in the structural properties that underlie the diverse actions of CAM in the various physiological mechanisms it subserves in the cell. A practical consequence of the mechanistic insights at the molecular level is the opportunity they may offer to achieve specific control over the many processes that depend on Ca^{2+} concentration gradients and their decoding by CAM (e.g. see 9, 17, 96, 135). One promising avenue for achieving such control through structural manipulation is the application of protein engineering approaches to CAM based on a structurally-defined design strategy (138).

However, it is becoming increasingly clear that the CAM molecule has special dynamic properties that characterize its structure (7, 46, 47, 63, 85, 92, 128), determine the effects of Ca^{2+} binding on the biological properties of the molecule (e.g. see 31, 35, 55, 110, 119), and affect the interactions of CAM with its cellular targets (30, 32, 47, 52, 62, 77, 81, 100). These dynamic structural characteristics are major determinants of the capacity of CAM to carry out its actions in the cell with the significant functional selectivity and high fidelity required of an ubiquitous modulatory agent (e.g. see 56, 58, 66). Consequently, an essential requirement for understanding how CAM performs its diverse functions is information that reaches beyond the structural details, to the time- and Ca^{2+}-dependent properties of its molecular structure. Accordingly, we focus here on the new elements of a mechanistic understanding of CAM function that emerge from this information and on computational simulation approaches that are well suited for the analysis and interpretation of such data. We review some key aspects of the recent progress made in the elucidation of the structural and dynamic properties of CAM and their putative relations to the functional role of CAM in physiological processes. Special attention is given to the emergence of a structure-based hypothesis for selective binding of CAM to the large variety of proteins it modulates and to the role that Ca^{2+}-binding and the dynamic properties of the protein have in determining CAM selectivity for protein targets.

Ca^{2+}-BINDING AND THE STRUCTURAL PROPERTIES OF CALMODULIN

Structural Dependence of Ca^{2+} Affinities

Detailed information on the three-dimensional structure of CAM at atomic resolution is relatively recent (5, 15) and reveals an architecture that is similar to that described earlier for troponin C (TNC) (38, 39) in the positioning of two Ca^{2+}-binding globular domains linked by a long, sol-vent-exposed straight helix (see Figure 1). The two calcium-binding motifs in each globular domain are composed of pairs of helix-loop-helix elements known as EF-hands (80, 109), which define a class of calcium-binding proteins comprising an ever growing number of members being identified in a large variety of species (33, 34). The quest for understanding the relationships between Ca^{2+} binding and the physiological functions of the EF-hand proteins led to explorations of the structural properties of these Ca^{2+}-binding motifs (37) and their sequence similarities in a variety of proteins (e.g. see 89, 127). The properties of EF-hand motifs were compared

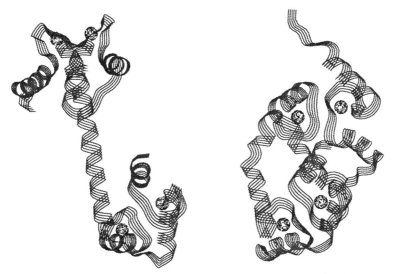

Figure 1   Ribbon tracing of the three-dimensional structure of calmodulin. (*Left: a*) The structure from X-ray crystallography (5). (*Right: b*) The structure computed from molecular dynamics simulation (see CAM2 in Reference 85). To obtain equivalent representations, the Cα carbons of the C-domains (residues 83–148) were superimposed, and the structures were then separated as shown. The Ca^{2+} ions are represented by their van der Waals surfaces.

(80, 109), and the responses of proteins incorporating such specialized motifs to the binding of ions have received special attention (2, 3, 16, 40, 42, 44, 56, 70, 73, 74, 85, 106, 110, 118, 119). Since the activation of CAM is a direct consequence of Ca^{2+}-binding, much attention was also devoted to measuring the kinetics of binding and the affinities of Ca^{2+} for calmodulins from many sources (recent reviews; 16, 22). A number of methods have been used to determine the macroscopic binding constants of CAM (e.g. see 16, 22, 72 and references therein). The results of direct binding studies suggest either four noninteracting sites with identical (or different) Ca^{2+} affinities, or cooperativity between the Ca^{2+} binding sites in at least one of the domains.

Kinetic studies of calcium binding, using $^{43}Ca^{2+}$ NMR and stopped-flow fast kinetics (see 16), led to a model in which Ca^{2+} binds first to the C-terminal domain and subsequently to EF hands I and II in the N-terminal domain when the concentration of Ca^{2+} is increased. Wang et al (131) proposed a model to resolve the discrepancies between the various inferences from the direct binding and the kinetic studies, which assumed two pairs of binding sites with high and low affinity and relatively strong cooperativity in the pair of sites within each domain.

Most of the equilibrium binding studies have suggested varying degrees of positive cooperativity in the binding of Ca^{2+} to the loops of EF-hands III and IV, which have the higher affinity, and some have indicated that cooperativity also is found between the lower affinity sites I and II in the EF-hands of the N-terminal domain (e.g. see 55, 72, 107). The products of the macroscopic binding constants (K_1K_2 of sites III,IV and K_3K_4 of sites I,II in CAM) obtained by Linse et al (72) were considered to be more precisely defined experimentally than the values of the individual binding constants because experimental errors in the latter tended to cancel each other. Comparing the values of these products from various sources (16) does in fact show them to be much closer, at a given ionic strength, than the values of the individual binding constants. The discrepancies in the values of the individual binding constants emphasized in earlier comparisons (e.g. see discussion in 16) could thus be due to greater uncertainties inherent in the experimental procedures, or to the different ways in which binding constants were obtained from the experimental data (16, 72).

To clarify the role of cooperativity between Ca-binding sites in determining the measured affinities, similar studies of Ca^{2+} binding were carried out with tryptic fragments of CAM molecules from various sources (including vertebrate- and yeast-CAM) (58, 72, 106, 113). These fragments (termed TR_1C for residues 1–77, and TR_2C for residues 78–148) are obtained by trypsin digestion that cleaves the central tether helix at Lys77 and separates the pair of EF-hands in the N-terminal domain from those in the C-terminus

(4). A least-squares fitting procedure devised recently to extract the binding constants directly from the experimental data obtained by titration, using ^{1}H-NMR spectroscopy, was applied to CAM and its two tryptic fragments (72). In these studies, the binding constants of Ca^{2+} in each of the fragments were not appreciably different from the values obtained for the corresponding sites in the complete CAM, which indicates no measurable interaction between the N- and C-terminal domains in the Ca-binding process (72). However, some authors have emphasized the experimental difficulties in the interpretation of the measurements yielding the information, e.g. from NMR data (102, 107), of the extent to which the cooperative interaction between the two calcium-binding domains of CAM affects the affinity for Ca^{2+} in the respective binding loops. In yeast-CAM an interaction between the domains seems to affect the Ca^{2+}-binding properties (106), but the amino acid sequence of this CAM form is sufficiently different from vertebrate CAM—especially in the binding loops of the EF-hands—to account for this special behavior. The relation between the Ca^{2+}-binding behavior and the differences observed in the physiological functions of yeast-CAM compared to the vertebrate forms remain unresolved.

Cooperativity and the Time-Dependent Properties of Ca^{2+}-binding Structures

Interest in the determination of the binding constants and the elucidation of inter- and intradomain cooperativity is motivated in part by the expectation that once the binding has been characterized, it may be possible to alter, through selective mutation, both the affinity for Ca^{2+} and the cooperativity, so as to affect the calcium dependence of physiological and pharmacological processes. However, results from the binding studies carried out so far on CAM (see above), as well as on other members of the EF-hand family of Ca-binding proteins (e.g. see 23, 48, 71, 73, 74, 88, 112), have indicated that simply measuring the binding constants is not sufficient for identifying amino acid residues that would be good candidates for effecting a desired change in the calcium-binding properties. Rather, the experimental approaches applied to study the structural consequences of Ca^{2+} binding have disclosed a complex array of structural changes and dynamic responses to the sequential occupation of the calcium-binding sites (e.g. see 3, 11, 24, 25, 27, 41, 65, 74, 84, 104, 105, 125). In some cases, specific mutations in the EF-hands, designed to produce significant effects on Ca^{2+} binding, yielded unexpected results (107, 130). To achieve control of CAM's functions through specifically designed structural modifications will require detailed knowledge of how the binding of Ca^{2+} is controlled by the other parts of the protein's structure that affect the Ca^{2+}-binding elements, and how this structural control is affected by individual amino acid residues.

Recent examples show that such insight at atomic detail can be obtained for the calcium-binding proteins from computational investigations of their structural and dynamic properties (e.g. see 1, 84–86, 92, 111, 118, 137, 138), using molecular simulation techniques that are based on the theoretical methods of classical physics and statistical mechanics. The significant potential of these approaches in the exploration of insights obtained from experimental measurements has been reviewed and evaluated critically (e.g. see 13, 49, 51, 79, 121, 123, 124, 134, 136). To illustrate the nature of the detailed structural and mechanistic information that is attainable from such methods, we briefly review results obtained recently for the small Ca^{2+}-binding protein, calbindin$_{D9k}$, which consists almost entirely of two EF-hand motifs (114).

The effects of Ca^{2+}-binding to calbindin$_{D9k}$ were explored experimentally and computationally to help identify the type of changes in the properties of EF-hand proteins that may determine their function. Calbindin$_{D9k}$ (CAB), the smallest EF-hand protein to be characterized structurally both in the crystal (114) and in solution (2, 105), is a calcium storage protein that binds the two Ca^{2+} ions into EF-hands I and II with a cooperativity of around 1.4 Kcal/mol (70, 73). A recent series of articles (2, 3, 64, 104, 105) report on the structure and internal dynamics of apo-, singly, and doubly occupied CAB, studied using ^{1}H-NMR spectroscopy. A major conclusion from these studies is that the structure of CAB is quite insensitive to the extent of Ca^{2+} occupancy, in contrast to the expectations for Ca-binding regulatory proteins such as CAM. However, these studies found significant effects of Ca^{2+}-binding in the form of a substantially greater degree of flexibility in the apo-form than in either the singly occupied or the holo-form of the protein, and in the modification of the local dynamic properties of the protein (3). The significant reduction in the flexibility of the protein observed with the binding of the first Ca^{2+} led Akke et al (3) to suggest a model in which the main source of cooperativity in the binding of Ca^{2+} to the EF-hands in CAB is the entropic effects arising from changes in the dynamics of the protein with different levels of Ca occupancy.

To explore the detailed effects of Ca^{2+} binding in the EF-hands of CAB on the dynamics of the protein, computational simulations with the methods of molecular dynamics (MD) (12, 13, 51, 124) were carried out (84) on doubly occupied CAB (CAB$_2$), singly occupied CAB (CAB$_1$ with Ca^{2+} only in EF-hand II), and apo-CAB (CAB$_0$). Comparisons of the structures obtained from the MD simulations to the results from NMR and hydrogen exchange measurements of Akke et al (3) showed very good agreement. First, the RMS differences among the three structures obtained from the simulations for the three CAB forms were less than 1.2Å, which indicated the same insensitivity of the structure to changes in Ca^{2+} occupancy as was observed from the NMR measurements (3). Further agreement between the properties revealed from experimental (3) and computational results (84) was established from comparisons of the observed changes in the local dynamic properties, such as the description of the local unfolding that determines the surface accessibilities of main chain amide groups and is measured by hydrogen exchange rates (see 3 and references therein).

In agreement with Akke et al (3), who concluded that the flexibility of CAB increases in the order $CAB_0 > CAB_1 \gtrsim CAB_2$, the calculated RMS fluctuations of all the protein atoms show the same rank order (84). In addition, both NMR measurements and the simulations indicate that the largest reduction in molecular flexibility takes place with the binding of the first Ca^{2+}, while binding the second Ca^{2+} causes at most a small additional reduction. This agreement between the results from MD simulations and NMR measurements made it attractive to estimate the magnitude of the entropic contribution to the cooperative effect in Ca^{2+}-binding to the EF-hands of CAB. The calculations were based on an approximation of the method proposed by Karplus & Kushick (50), which involved a truncation of the matrix of the covariances of the fluctuations of the atomic coordinates (84). The diagonal elements of the covariance matrix are the mean square fluctuations that increase the configurational entropy, while the off diagonal elements are a measure of the correlations between atomic fluctuations and therefore decrease the entropy. A first approximation of the configurational entropy can be formulated as

$$\Delta S(A \rightarrow B) = Rln(RMS_B/RMS_A),$$

where the covariance matrix has been condensed to just the average RMS fluctuation of the entire molecule given above. Thus for the binding of the first Ca^{2+}, the entropic contribution becomes (84)

$$\Delta G(CAB_0 \rightarrow CAB_1) = -RTln [RMS(CAB_1)/RMS(CAB_0)].$$

A similar expression is obtained for binding the second Ca^{2+}, i.e. the process $CAB_1 \rightarrow CAB_2$. However, because the binding of the second Ca^{2+} induces only a small change in flexibility, the latter contribution is negligible. The main entropic component of the free energy of Ca^{2+} binding to CAB obtains from the process $CAB_0 \rightarrow CAB_1$ because the major loss of flexibility is due to binding the first Ca^{2+}. The entropic contribution to the cooperativity is negative because the protein becomes rigid upon Ca^{2+} binding. The calculated values (84) are in reasonably good agreement with the experimental trends, which lends further support to the proposal (3) that cooperativity in CAB is due to the larger change in the dynamic behavior of the protein that occurs on binding the first calcium, compared to binding the second one.

Such effects of Ca^{2+}-binding on protein dynamics can be expected to occur within the N- and C-terminal domains of CAM, each of which contains a pair of EF-hands. However, the changes induced by Ca^{2+}-binding in the structural properties of CAM that are more directly relevant to its functional properties are also likely to involve the tether helix that determines the mutual orientation and the distance between the two domains (cf the two conformations of CAM in Figure 1). The functional significance of these changes in the mutual orientation of the Ca-binding domains stems from the presence of characteristic hydrophobic regions in these domains. The properties of these regions are modified, as discussed below, in the Ca^{2+}-loaded form of CAM, which prepares the molecule for specific interactions with target proteins.

STRUCTURAL VARIABILITY OF CALMODULIN IN SOLUTION

Comparison of the crystal structure of isolated CAM (5, 15) with the structure obtained from NMR spectroscopy for CAM complexed with M13, a 26-residue peptide representing the CAM-binding region in the enzyme myosin light chain kinase (45, 47), shows two types of structural changes that occur upon complex formation: (a) a reorientation of the two globular domains, and (b) a compaction of the structure that brings the two domains closer together to envelop and interact with the CAM-binding region of the target protein. Using the four Ca^{2+} ions to define a virtual dihedral angle (as outlined in Reference 92), the reorientation of the domains can be quantified as a change in the angle values from $-134°$ in the crystal structure to $109°$ in the complex. The compaction is quantifiable through the radius of gyration (e.g. see 31, 85), which decreases from 22 to 17Å.

Experimental approaches have been used to characterize the flexibility of the tether (e.g. see 7, 90) and the departure of the solution structure of uncomplexed CAM from the extended form observed in the crystal (e.g. see 31, 128). The results from small angle X-ray scattering (SAXS) experiments, which suggest some compaction of CAM in solution relative to the crystal structure, were somewhat inconclusive since different authors did not agree in their interpretation of the SAXS results (31, 101). We showed, however, that the observed solution pair distribution function of CAM obtained from SAXS experiments (e.g. see 31, 77) could be rationalized by assuming an equilibrium between structures in various states of reorientation and compaction (85) (the compacted structure shown in Figure 1 *right* illustrates one of the conformations visited by CAM). This observation agrees with results from NMR spectroscopy (7) and with inferences from energy transfer studies on CAM and troponin-C, which indicate that the two lobes move closer together when the pH is raised from 5.5 to 7.4 (e.g. see 128,129).

The agreement between observations from experiment and from computational simulation, which suggests that the structure of CAM in solution can access various configurations and the potential importance of this dynamic variability in structure for the function of CAM, made it worthwhile to inquire how this flexibility is controlled. The exploration of the mechanism by which the structural elements of CAM and their interactions determine the time-dependent behavior of the molecule was carried out by analyzing the dynamic structural details provided by the MD simulations (92).

A Mechanism of Compaction

Careful analysis of the time evolution of interactions between individual amino acid residues comprising the peptide chain from several MD trajectories (92) revealed a pattern of H-bonds that form and are severed during the simulations. A structural analysis of these time-dependent H-bonding patterns was carried out (92) to determine whether any could be directly involved in facilitating the compaction process. The formation of H-bonds, which connected groups in different elements of secondary structure and persisted for a long simulation period, were deemed the most likely candidates for key interactions in the compaction mechanism because these would be the most likely to stabilize structural changes.

The analysis identified three arginine residues (Arg74, Arg 86, and Arg90), which appeared to be involved in H-bonding patterns that met the criteria defined above. Typical in this context was the behavior of Arg74, which was found to form a new H-bond to the carbonyl group of Val55 (see hydrogen-bonding patterns in Figure 2) after only 18.5 psec of simulation and to maintain other interactions, all in a manner suggestive of a reversible compaction trigger (see below). The bond to Val55 forms at a time when the orientation of the globular domains begins to change from the *trans*-like orientation observed in the X-ray structure to one that is more *cis*-like. Figure 2 shows that the H-bond to Glu67 persists throughout the early part of the trajectory, but breaks sometime between 29 and 85 psec into the trajectory. Also in that time period, an additional H-bond forms with Glu54. The H-bonding pattern of Arg74 shares a characteristic of all three arginines, namely, an H-bond anchoring the residue to a nearby residue (Thr70 for Arg74). The pattern of first latching onto Glu67, then Val55, with the bond to Glu67 subsequently being broken and replaced by an attachment to Glu54, is suggestive of a ratcheting process where one end of the chain remains firmly anchored (to Thr70) and the other end of the

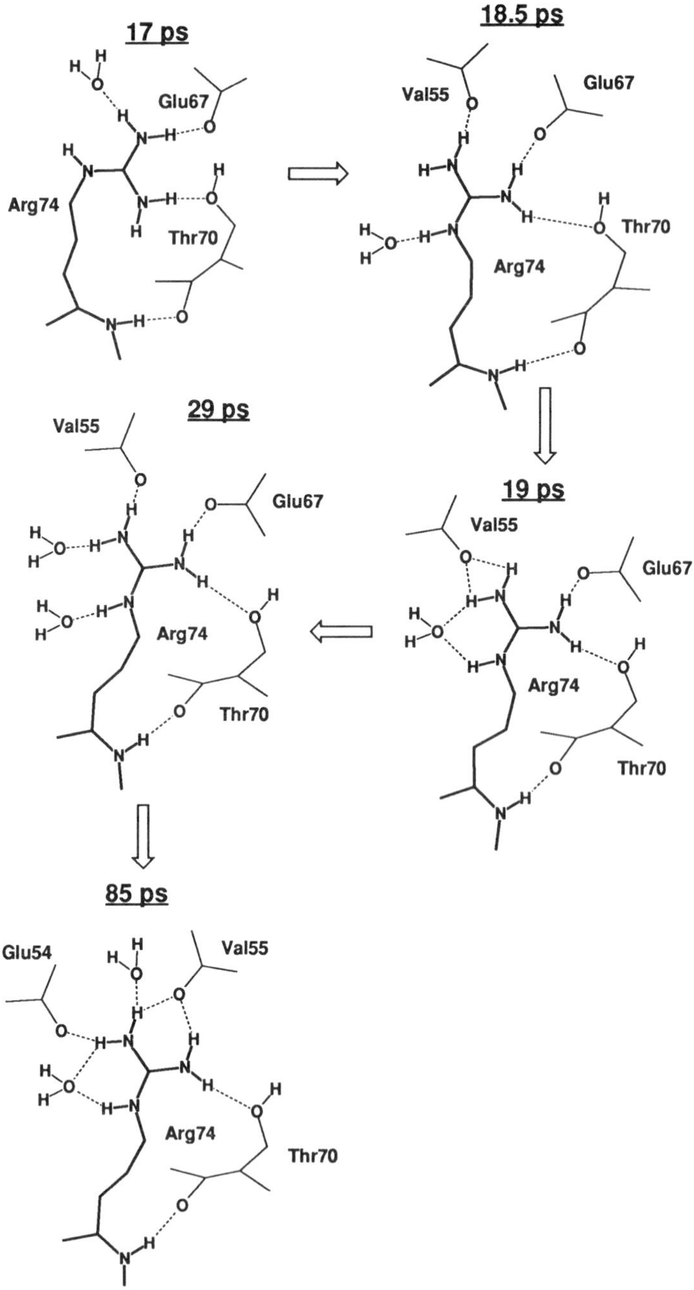

Figure 2 Schematic representation of the time-dependent evolution of the hydrogen bonding pattern involving Arg74 in molecular dynamics simulations of calmodulin. The two-dimensional structural representation is derived from snapshots of the structure taken at successive stages of the simulation. (*Top left*) at 17 psec; (*top right*) at 18.5 psec; (*middle right*) at 19 psec; (*middle left*) at 29 psec; (*lower left*) at 85 psec.

residue draws in successive attachment sites from more distant parts of the structure.

Several additional noteworthy aspects of the involvement of Arg74 in the compaction process may be seen from Figure 2. At all times there are at least two residues attached to the guanidinium moiety of Arg74, and from 19 psec onward all the guanidinium protons are involved in H-bonding. Perhaps in this way the potential for this group to stabilize intermediate structures is optimally exploited. Also of interest is the involvement of waters in the dynamics of the H-bonding patterns. Figure 2 shows that waters were involved in the H-bonding process and, in fact, continuously surrounded Arg74 (see 92).

A similar H-bonding pattern was also observed for Arg90, which was anchored to Glu87, with the residues involved in the ratcheting process including Asn97 and Gly96. At one point in the trajectory the carbonyl oxygen of Arg86 was linked to Arg90, thus forming a common H-bonding network, perhaps coordinating the movement of both. In these two latter cases, water again participated intimately in the continuously altering H-bonding networks. Finally, it is noteworthy that for both Arg74 and Arg90, residues from the Ca^{2+}-binding loops were involved in the H-bonding patterns, and that the time evolution of the interaction energies of Arg74 and Arg90 with the rest of the protein structure (see 92) also supported their involvement in the compaction process. The function of Arg74 and Arg90 in facilitating the reversible compaction appeared the clearest, but the role of Arg86 was not clear, i.e. whether it was driving or responding to structural change.

To test how essential these residues are for compaction, the simulation was repeated, but in each run, one of these residues was mutated to alanine. Thus three additional simulations were carried out (K Haydock et al, unpublished) for the three mutated forms of CAM: Arg 74 to Ala74 (R74A), Arg86 to Ala86 (R86A), and Arg90 to Ala90 (R90A), using identical simulation conditions as one of the simulations on wild-type CAM, which yielded a compacted structure (i.e. CAM10 in Reference 92). In all three mutations, the two lobes of CAM reoriented: for the wild-type CAM, the virtual dihedral angle between the four Ca^{2+} (see above) was $-72°$, and for the three mutants, the values were -77, 18, and $-43°$ for R74A, R86A, and R90A, respectively). The R74A mutant assumed nearly the same orientation as the wild-type CAM. The domains of the R86A mutant assumed quite a different disposition, but one that is close to the orientation from another simulation on the wild-type protein in which the conditions were altered (see Table 1 in Reference 85). The R90A mutant achieved an interdomain orientation intermediate between R74A and R86A. However, only R86A compacted, whereas both R74A and R90A became somewhat more extended than the starting (X-ray) structure. The simulations therefore indicate that Arg74 and Arg90 (perhaps in concert with Arg86), but not Arg86 alone, are essential for compaction. The H-bonding patterns around the residues that were not mutated still underwent the characteristic changes described above for the simulation on the wild type, but when one of the two essential residues (Arg74 or Arg90) was absent, compaction did not occur.

It is also noteworthy that both Arg74 and Arg90 seemed to contribute in important ways to the stability of the structure. Thus the CAM mutants R74A and R90A exhibited large and persistent fluctuations in their radii of gyration and in their interdomain orientations over relatively long periods of time. In contrast, the structural changes in the simulations of the wild-type CAM and the R86A mutant always took place in the first part of the run (although these changes took longer in some cases than in others), and subsequently the overall structures remained quite stable in the compacted form. These observations help support the main conclusion of these computer mutation experiments, namely that Arg74 and Arg90 play crucial roles in controlling the molecular flexibility that CAM requires for its functional viability.

THE TIME-DEPENDENT STRUCTURE OF HYDROPHOBIC PATCHES IN CALMODULIN

An early observation from experimental studies of structure-function relationships in CAM was the exposure to the solvent environment of clusters of hydrophobic residues following the binding of Ca^{2+} (e.g. see 67, 115). The steric adjacency of these hydrophobic residues caused these regions to be viewed as hydrophobic patches. Biochemical experiments, as well as structure determinations, have implicated these hydrophobic patches in the mode of action of CAM in the cell (90, 91, 115, 116). The recent structure of CAM complexed to a peptide (M13) representing the binding domain of skeletal muscle myosin light chain kinase (MLCK), obtained from NMR spectroscopy (45) and from X-ray crystallography (81), confirms the importance of interactions between specific hydrophobic residues in CAM and its target protein. As it becomes clear that degrees of Ca^{2+} occupancy determine both structural and dynamic properties of EF-hand proteins (see section above), the nature of the relationship between Ca-binding and the induced, specific structural changes in the hydrophobic patches becomes a tantalizing question. Significant insight into this question can be gained by examining the structural details of these patches, which are so intimately related to CAM/target binding, and by comparing their disposition in the CAM structures from X-ray crystallography, from NMR spectroscopy, and from computational simulations. An important consideration here is that both X-ray crystallography and NMR spectroscopy provide a time-averaged picture of the disposition of the hydrophobic patches, whereas the simulations provide the additional insight of the time evolution of the structural changes. As discussed below, it is the availability of this information on structural dynamics that allows the formulation of a mechanism for target selectivity in the actions of CAM.

Selectivity in CAM Binding to Target Proteins

Figure 3a-d displays space-filling CPK representations of the molecular structure of CAM for a comparison of the hydrophobic patches in the molecular structures obtained from crystallography (5), NMR spectroscopy (45), and computational simulations (85, 92), respectively. Only the N-ter-

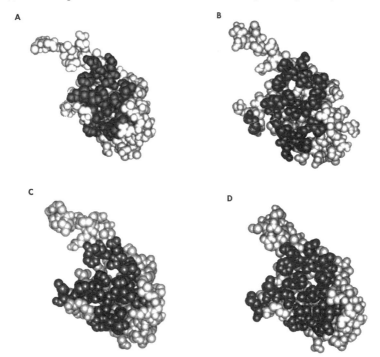

Figure 3   Space filling representations of the target-binding face of the N-terminal domain in various conformations of calmodulin. (*a*) The crystallographic structure (as in Figure 1 left). (*b*) The structure from NMR spectroscopy (45). (*c*) The structure from molecular dynamics simulation (as in Figure 1 right). (*d*) The structure obtained from an alternative molecular dynamics simulation (92). Atoms involved in interactions with the M13 peptide from the CAM-binding domain of skeletal muscle myosin light chain kinase (residues 577–602) are darkly shaded; the other atoms are lightly shaded. Residues 12–76 in all the CAM structures shown were superimposed on the N-terminal segment of the structure from NMR spectroscopy to obtain the equivalent views shown.

minal segment (residues 1–76) is shown, in a perspective that is "looking into" the domain head-on (the tether, residues 77–83, is included in the Kendrew representation). To secure the same orientation in the display of each structure, residues 12–76 of the structures from the crystal and from the computational simulations were superimposed on the corresponding segment of the N-terminal domain of the NMR structure. Charged and polar residues, as well as hydrophobic residues (dark area in Figure 3) have been identified from the NMR studies (45) as being involved in binding to M13. The exposed surfaces of these polar and hydrophobic residues provide regions of interaction with the target peptide and constitute a surface area relevant to binding (SARB). The SARB is defined quantitatively for the interaction of CAM with M13 by taking the difference in solvent accessible surface area between the CAM/M13 holo- and apo- structures (i.e. the NMR structure with and without the M13 peptide).

The overall configuration of the residues in the SARB, with the hydrophilic residues framing several hydrophobic regions on the outside, is similar in all the cases shown. Nevertheless, there are several key differences: comparison of the structures from X-ray crystallography and NMR spectroscopy reveals that in the latter structure the entire domain appears to span a larger space, albeit with several holes; importantly, the disposition of the hydrophobic patches differs in the crystal and in solution. In the NMR structure in solution, the patches have spread out and form several distinct islands. The conformations of the hydrophilic residues have also changed, and in the particular view shown, the Ca^{2+} ion is accessible to the solvent in the NMR structure, but not in the crystal structure.

The SARB construct defined for the particular M13 target makes it possible to track the time-dependent developments in the target-binding potential of CAM by following its behavior in a computational simulation of CAM dynamics. The working hypothesis is that the accessibility of this surface area, which is relevant to the binding of a particular target, will change with time, as it changes with the binding of Ca^{2+} and of various peptides (e.g. see 46, 52-54, 67, 115, 119). The mechanistic implication is that the dynamic changes in the SARB will determine the time-dependence of the binding probability for certain targets. As different targets are likely to require different SARB, these changes are likely to constitute a time-dependent (and Ca^{2+} occupancy-dependent) scheme for achieving selectivity in the physiological actions of CAM.

It is clear from Figure 3 that the three-dimensional configuration of the SARB for M13 defined from the NMR structure is different from the surface outlined by the same residues in the crystal structure of CAM. Examination of the same area in the results from the MD simulations performed on isolated CAM (with various solvent models, but no binding peptides or inhibitors) provides SARB shapes that are time-dependent. An average structure (obtained from the last part of the simulation trajectory) could mimic the properties of a relevant SARB conformation. However, in the absence of a target protein, the hydrophobic patches would evolve further to what could become a nonbinding configuration. The results of the computational simulation can be explored for the time-dependent appearance of the appropriate SARB configuration. For example, such a search for potentially significant structures was performed on the trajectory of the computational simulations by comparing the developments in the SARB, starting from the crystal structure (5) (which is the starting point for the dynamics simulations) (85, 92) and going towards the structure of CAM in the complex with M13 from the NMR measurement (45). To quantify the changes, a numerical value was calculated for the solvent-accessible-surface area (SASA) using the GEPOL algorithm (93, 103). The SASA of the 39 interacting residues in the SARB was calculated for the NMR and crystal structures of CAM, and it was found that the SASAs of 28 residues were larger in the NMR than in the crystal structure, while in the remaining 11 residues the SASAs of the NMR structure were smaller. The SASAs for a series of snapshots from several dynamics trajectories were calculated for each of the 39 interacting residues, and the value was compared to the SASAs obtained for these residues in the X-ray structure and checked for qualitative agreement with the trend found for the change in SASAs between the NMR and crystal structures. The agreement in the preparation of the SARB for binding (i.e. the transition from the crystal structure to the NMR structure) tended to improve early in the trajectory, persisted briefly, and then became less good. For example, for CAM10 (defined in Reference 92), the change in SASA was correctly predicted for 20 residues from the snapshot at 20 psec, 27 residues were correctly predicted at 40 psec, but for the average structure obtained from the last part of the simulation (286–326 psec), the agreement was reduced to 24 residues. This trend was observed for all the trajectories examined, independently of how well the changes in accessible surface area agreed with the observed changes between the NMR and crystal structures. However, it is important to emphasize that even the final average structures resulting from the computational simulations maintain a SARB that is closer to that defined by the NMR structure than the crystal structure. Thus in both CAM2 and CAM10 structures (see 85, 92, respectively), the patches have spread out relative to the X-ray structure, with the tendency to form islands similar to those seen in the NMR structure. This further illustrates the agreement between the computed and observed structures and lends support to the analysis of the time-dependent features in the SARB defined for CAM from computational studies.

The Role of the Central Tether Helix in the Interactions of CAM with Its Targets

Residues 73–82 constitute the tether connecting the two Ca^{2+}-binding domains on which the SARB for a specific target can be identified. This tether region is helical in the crystal structure of CAM, but dissolves into a flexible loop in the complex with M13 (45, 47, 81). In both the CAM2 and CAM10 structures obtained from the computational simulations (85, 92), this is also an important region of flexible structural rearrangement that contributes to the reorientation of the domains and to subsequent compaction (e.g. see Figure 1 *right*). The special dynamic properties of this region were also identified in the NMR structure of the uncomplexed CAM (7). It is of interest that between residues 73 to 82, only Met76 and Ser81 interact with M13 and, in fact, their interaction is marginal because binding of M13 decreases the SASA of these two residues by less than 4% even though about 80% of the maximum SASA is exposed in the apo-NMR structure. This lack of interaction between M13 and the tether suggests that the structural change observed between the crystal and NMR structures of the CAM/M13 complex is not the result of interactions of M13 with the tether. This conclusion is supported by two further observations: first, structures obtained from various trajectories suggest that CAM's flexibility may result from distortions in different parts of the linker (92). Moreover, as mentioned above, the pair distribution functions observed from SAXS experiments in solution (31, 77) can be rationalized as we described (85) by assuming an equilibrium between structures in various states of compaction and reorientation. Second, the Ca-binding studies by Forsen et al (e.g. see 72, 73) discussed above failed to detect interdomain cooperativity in the binding. Certainly, a very flexible tether, which assumes a continuously variable range of conformations in solution (7), is unlikely to be involved in transmitting information between the two lobes. Rather, the early observations of the importance of such flexibility (e.g. see 90, 91, 94, 95) are likely to reflect the role of the flexible tether in placing the SARBs (evolving in the two separate domains) into positions appropriate for interaction with the target (for some recent discussions, see 30, 87, 99). Early mutation studies designed to determine the functional significance of the central helix of CAM (96) reached similar conclusions with regard to the role of this structure in the appropriate positioning of the sites required for specific interaction with the target protein.

Since the exposure of hydrophobic residues in the crystal and NMR structures was similar, the prediction from model building of the residues that interact with such peptides as M13 (e.g. see 91, 94) or with CAM inhibitors (108) was quite successful. In the specific case of M13, it was necessary to assume some deformation of CAM in order to bring the domains closer together, and here the modeling was less successful (assuming a single kink in Ser81), since both the NMR and the crystal data for the complex (45, 81) ultimately showed that the domains came closer together because the tether was deformed into an extended loop with complete loss of helicity. The structures generated by the dynamics calculations predicted (85, 92) that compaction resulted from tether distortion over its entire length (residues 73–84), a development that is much closer to the dissolution exhibited by the NMR structures (7, 45) than the models that assumed a localized kink resulting from an alteration in the ϕ and ψ angles of a single residue. This difference in results obtained from model building compared to computational simulation clearly illustrates the advantage of the latter (see also 137), in which the time evolution of the structure is obtained through a straightforward application of Newton's laws of motion, and the inherent approximations and errors are, in principle, correctable (e.g. see 13, 51, 68, 78, 79, 121–124, 132–134).

CONCLUDING REMARKS

The mechanistic insight provided by the analysis of structure and dynamics of the CAM molecule outlined in this review suggests several novel possibilities for modulating the physiological functions of CAM. First, of course, is alteration of Ca^{2+} binding. An obvious approach is to alter one or more residues in the Ca-binding regions but, as discussed here, attempted changes through mutations suggested by the average structure of the molecule have not always led to the expected results. An alternative, more subtle type of structural manipulation, suggested from the results of the computational simulations would be to change the dynamic behavior of the apo-structure relative to the fully Ca^{2+}-loaded CAM. The specific modifications can be probed with computational simulations, and the results can be directly tested experimentally. However, the mechanisms of the measured effects on activity may still be difficult to interpret because at present it is not clear which of the two components of the structural dynamics, i.e. compaction in solution, or flexibility (or both), is the controlling factor in CAM's activity. The most complex, but perhaps the most effective, mutations would be aimed at altering the structures of the hydrophobic patches. Here, the simulation techniques might be an extremely powerful tool in searching for effective mutations, since the experimental or modeling approaches would essentially have to proceed by trial and error.

From this review it should be clear that the study of the structural and dynamic properties of calmodulin and related Ca-binding proteins provides a potentially rich source for gaining the type of mechanistic insights that will be required to implement structurally defined design strategies (138) in developing engineered proteins with desirable properties. At the same time, it is evident that the application of computer simulation techniques to this class of proteins has only just begun and that considerable work will be required to provide a generally useful body of mechanistic information. The main motivation for continuing this effort is that these techniques reveal time-dependent structural properties that appear to be crucial to the behavior of the system and are more difficult to evaluate with other methods.

ACKNOWLEDGMENTS

Critical reading of the manuscript by Dr. JN Kushick is gratefully acknowledged. The authors' work was supported in part by National Institutes of Health grants GM-41373, and DA-00060. Computations were performed on the supercomputer systems at the Pittsburgh Supercomputer Center (sponsored by the National Science Foundation), the Cornell National Supercomputer Facility (sponsored by the National Science Foundation and IBM), the Advanced Scientific Computing Laboratory at the Frederick Cancer Research Facility of the National Cancer Institute (Laboratory for Mathematical Biology), and the University Computer Center of the City University of New York.

Literature Cited

1. Ahlstrom P, Teleman O, Kordell J, Forsen S, Jonsson B. 1989. A molecular dynamics simulation of bovine calbindinD9k. Molecular structure and dynamics. *Biochemistry* 28:3205–11
2. Akke M, Drakenberg T, Chazin WJ. 1992. Three-dimensional solution structure of Ca^{2+}-loaded porcine calbindinD9k determined by NMR spectroscopy. *Biochemistry* 31:1011–20
3. Akke M, Forsen S, Chazin WJ. 1991. Molecular basis for co-operativity in Ca^{2+} binding to calbindinD9k. *J. Mol. Biol.* 229:173–89
4. Andersson A, Forsen S, Thulin E, Vogel HJ. 1983. Cadmium-113 nuclear magnetic resonance studies of proteolytic fragments of calmodulin: Assignment of strong and weak binding sites. *Biochemistry* 22:2309–13
5. Babu YS, Bugg CE, Cook WJ. 1988. Structure of calmodulin refined at 2.2 Å resolution. *J. Mol. Biol.* 204:191–204
6. Bading H, Ginty DD, Greenberg ME. 1993. Regulation of gene expression in hippocampal neurons by distinct calcium signalling pathways. *Science* 260:181–86
7. Barbato G, Ikura M, Kay LE, Pastor RW, Bax A. 1992. Backbone dynamics of calmodulin studied by ^{15}N relaxation using inverse detected two-dimensional NMR spectroscopy: The central helix is flexible. *Biochemistry* 31:5269–78
8. Bartelt DC, Fidel S, Farber LH, Wolff DJ, Hammell RL. 1988. Calmodulin-dependent protein kinase in *Aspergillus nidulans*. *Proc. Natl. Acad. Sci. USA* 85:3279–83
9. Beckingham K. 1991. Use of site-directed mutations in the individual Ca^{2+}-binding sites of calmodulin to examine Ca^{2+}-induced conformational changes. *J. Biol. Chem.* 266:6027–30
10. Bowman BR, Peterson JA, Stull JT. 1992. Pre-steady-state kinetics of the activation of rabbit skeletal muscle myosin light chain kinase by $Ca^{2+}/$ calmodulin. *J. Biol. Chem.* 267: 5346–54
11. Brito RMM, Putkey JA, Strynadka

NCJ, James MNG, Rosevear PR. 1991. Comparative NMR studies on cardiac troponin C and a mutant incapable of binding calcium at site II. *Biochemistry* 30:10236–45

12. Brooks BR, Bruccoleri RE, Olafson BD, States DJ, Swaminathan S, et al. 1983. CHARMM: A program for macromolecular energy, minimization and dynamics calculations. *J. Comput. Chem.* 4:187–217

13. Brooks CL, Karplus M, Pettitt BM. 1988. *Proteins: A Theoretical Perspective of Dynamics, Structure, and their Thermodynamics*, New York: Wiley & Sons. 259 pp.

14. Chapman ER, Alexander K, Vorherr T, Carafoli E, Storm DR. 1992. Fluorescence energy transfer analysis of calmodulin-peptide complexes. *Biochemistry* 31:12819–25

15. Chattopadhyaya R, Meador WE, Means AR, Quiocho FA. 1992. Calmodulin structure refined at 1.7A resolution. *J. Mol. Biol.* 228:1177–92

16. Cox JA, Comte M, Mamar-Bachi A, Milos M, Schaer J-J. 1988. Cation binding to calmodulin and relation to function. In *Calcium and Calcium Binding Proteins*, ed. C Gerday, L Bolis, R Gilles, pp. 141–62. New York: Springer Verlag

17. Craig TA, Watterson DM, Prendergast FG, Haiech J, Roberts DM. 1987. Site-specific mutagenesis of the alpha-helices of calmodulin. *J. Biol. Chem.* 262:3278–84

18. Davis JRE, Hoggard N, Wilson EM, Vidal ME, Sheppard MC. 1991. Calcium/calmodulin regulation of the rat prolactin gene is conferred by the proximal enhancer region. *Mol. Endocrinol.* 5:8–12

19. Davis TN. 1992. What's new with calcium? *Cell* 71:557–64

20. Evered D, Whelan J, eds. 1986. *Calcium and the Cell*. New York: Wiley & Sons

21. Fitzsimons DP, Herring BP, Stull T, Gallagher PJ. 1992. Identification of basic residues involved in activation and calmodulin binding of rabbit smooth myosin light chain kinase. *J. Biol. Chem.* 267:23903–9

22. Forsen S, Linse S, Drakenberg T, Kordel J, Akke M, et al. 1991. Ca^{2+} binding in proteins of the calmodulin superfamily: cooperativity, electrostatic contributions and molecular mechanisms. In *Protein Conformation*, ed. DJ Chadwick, K Widdows, pp. 222–36. Chichester: Wiley & Sons

23. Forsen S, Linse S, Thulin E, Lindegard

B, Martin SR, et al. 1988. Kinetics of calcium binding to calbindin mutants. *Eur. J. Biochem.* 177:47–52

24. Fujimori K, Sorenson M, Herzberg O, Moult J, Reinach FC. 1990. Probing the calcium-induced conformational transition of troponin C with site-directed mutants. *Nature* 345:182–84

25. Geiser JR, van Tuinen D, Brockerhoff SE, Neff MM, Davis TN. 1991. Can calmodulin function without binding calcium? *Cell* 65:949–59

26. Gerday C, Bolis L, Gilles R, eds. 1988. *Calcium and Calcium Binding Proteins*. Berlin: Springer

27. Grabarek Z, Leavis PC, Gergely J. 1986. Calcium binding to the low affinity sites in troponin C induces conformational changes in the high affinity domain. A possible route of information transfer in activation of muscle contraction. *J. Biol. Chem.* 261:608–13

28. Hahn K, DeBiasio R, Taylor DL. 1992. Patterns of elevated free calcium and calmodulin activation in living cells. *Nature* 359:736–38

29. Hanson PI, Schulman H. 1992. Neuronal Ca^{2+}/calmodulin-dependent protein kinases. *Annu. Rev. Biochem.* 61:559–601

30. Head JF. 1992. A better grip on calmodulin: Two atomic resolution structures show just how calmodulin binds to a peptide that represents the natural binding of a calmodulin-activated enzyme. *Curr. Biol.* 2:609–11

31. Heidorn DB, Trewhella J. 1988. Comparison of the crystal and solution structures of calmodulin and troponin C. *Biochemistry* 27:909–15

32. Heidorn DB, Seeger PA, Rokop SE, Blumenthal DK, Means, AR, et al. 1989. Changes in the structure of calmodulin induced by a peptide based on the calmodulin-binding domain of myosin light chain kinase. *Biochemistry* 28:6757–64

33. Heizmann CW, ed. 1991. *Novel Calcium-Binding Proteins*. New York: Springer-Verlag. 624 pp.

34. Heizmann CW, Hunziker W. 1991. Intracellular calcium-binding proteins: more sites than insights. *Trends Biochem. Sci.* 16:98–103

35. Hennessey JP, Manavalan P, Johnson WC, Malencik DA, Anderson SR, et al. 1987. Conformational transitions of calmodulin as studied by vacuum-UV CD. *Biopolymers* 26:561–71

36. Herring BP, Gallagher PJ, Stull JT. 1992. Substrate specificity of myosin

light chain kinases. *J. Biol. Chem.* 267:25945–50

37. Herzberg O, James MNG. 1985. Common structural framework of the two Ca^{2+}/Mg^{2+} binding loops of troponin C and other Ca^{2+} binding proteins. *Biochemistry* 24:5298–302

38. Herzberg O, James MNG. 1985. Structure of the calcium regulatory muscle protein troponin C at 2.8A resolution. *Nature* 313:653–59

39. Herzberg O, James MNG. 1988. Refined crystal structure of troponin C from turkey skeletal muscle at 2.0A resolution. *J. Mol. Biol.* 203:761–79

40. Herzberg O, Moult J, James MNG. 1986. A model for the Ca^{2+}-induced conformational transition of troponin C. A trigger for muscle contraction. *J. Biol. Chem.* 261:2638–44

41. Hinrichsen R, Wilson E, Lukas T, Craig T, Schultz J, et al. 1990. Analysis of the molecular basis of calmodulin defects that affect channel-mediated cellular responses: site-specific mutagenesis and microinjection. *J. Cell Biol.* 111:2537–42

42. Hori K, Kushick JN, Weinstein H. 1988. Structural and energetic parameters of Ca^{2+} binding to peptides and proteins. *Biopolymers* 27:1865–86

43. Hsu Y-T, Molday RS. 1993. Modulation of the cGMP-gated channel of rod photoreceptor cells by calmodulin. *Nature* 361:76–79

44. Iida S, Potter JD. 1986. Calcium binding to calmodulin. Cooperativity of the calcium-binding sites. *J. Biochem. (Tokyo)* 99:1765–72

45. Ikura M, Clore GM, Gronenborn AM, Zhu G, Klee CB, Bax A. 1992. Solution structure of a calmodulin-target peptide complex by multidimensional NMR. *Science* 256:632–38

46. Ikura M, Hiraoki T, Hikichi K, Mikuni T, Yazawa M, et al. 1983. Nuclear magnetic resonance studies on calmodulin: Calcium-induced conformational change. *Biochemistry* 22:2573–79

47. Ikura M, Kay LE, Krinks M, Bax A. 1991. Triple-resonance multidimensional NMR study of calmodulin complexed with the binding domain of skeletal muscle myosin light-chain kinase: Indication of a conformational change in the central helix. *Biochemistry* 30:5498–504

48. Imaizumi M, Tanokura M, Yamada K. 1987. A calorimetric study on calcium binding by troponin C from bullfrog skeletal muscle. *J. Biol. Chem.* 262:7963–66

49. Jonsson B, ed. 1989. *Structure and Dynamics in Biological Systems.* Cambridge/New York: Cambridge Univ. Press

50. Karplus M, Kushick JN. 1981. Methods for estimating the configurational entropy of macromolecules. *Macromolecules* 14:325–32

51. Karplus M, Petsko GA. 1990. Molecular dynamics simulations in biology. *Nature* 347:631–39

52. Kataoka M, Head JF, Seaton BA, Engelman DM. 1989. Melittin binding causes a large calcium-dependent conformational change in calmodulin. *Proc. Natl. Acad. Sci. USA* 86:6944–48

53. Kataoka M, Head JF, Vorherr T, Krebs J, Carafoli E. 1991. Small-angle X-ray scattering study of calmodulin bound to two peptides corresponding to parts of the calmodulin-binding domain of the plasma membrane Ca^{2+} pump. *Biochemistry* 30:6247–51

54. Kawasaki Y, Van Eerd JP. 1972. The effect of Mg^{2+} on the conformation of the Ca^{2+}-binding component of troponin. *Biochem. Biophys. Res. Commun.* 49:898–905

55. Kilhoffer M-C, Kubina M, Travers F, Haiech J. 1992. Use of engineered proteins with internal tryptophan reporter groups and perturbation techniques to probe the mechanism of ligand-protein interactions: Investigation of the mechanism of calcium binding to calmodulin. *Biochemistry* 31:8098–106

56. Klee CB. 1988. Interaction of calmodulin with Ca^{2+} and target proteins. In *Calmodulin,* ed. P Cohen, CB Klee, pp. 35–56. Amsterdam: Elsevier

57. Klee CB, Crouch TH, Richman PG. 1980. Calmodulin. *Annu. Rev. Biochem.* 49:489–515

58. Klee CB, Newton DL, Ni W-C, Haiech J. 1986. Regulation of the calcium signal by calmodulin. See Ref. 20, pp. 162–82

59. Klee CB, Vanaman TC. 1982. Calmodulin. *Adv. Protein Chem.* 35:213–303

60. Klevit RE. 1981. *A study of calmodulin in solution using high resolution ^{1}H NMR.* PhD thesis. Oxford Univ., Oxford. 173 pp.

61. Klevit RE. 1987. Study of calmodulin—peptide interactions by NMR spectroscopy. *Methods Enzymol.* 139:197–206

62. Klevit RE, Blumenthal DK, Wemmer DE, Krebs EG. 1985. Interaction of calmodulin and a calmodulin-binding peptide from myosin light chain kinase:

Major spectral changes in both occur as the result of complex formation. *Biochemistry* 24:8152–57

63. Klevit RE, Dalgarno DC, Levine BA, Williams RJP. 1984. H-NMR studies of calmodulin—the nature of the Ca^{2+}-dependent conformational change. *Eur. J. Biochem.* 139:109–14

64. Kordel J, Forsen S, Drakenberg T, Chazin WJ. 1990. The rate and structural consequences of proline cis-trans isomerization in calbindin$_{D9k}$: NMR studies of the minor (cis-Pro43) isoform and the Pro43Gly mutant. *Biochemistry* 29:4400–409

65. Krudy GA, Brito RMM, Putkey JA, Rosevear PR. 1992. Conformational changes in the metal-binding sites of cardiac troponin C induced by calcium binding. *Biochemistry* 31:1595–602

66. Kung C, Preston RR, Maley ME, Ling K-Y, Kanabrocki JA, et al. 1992. In vivo *Paramecium* mutants show that calmodulin orchestrates membrane responses to stimuli. *Cell Calcium* 13:413–25

67. LaPorte DC, Wierman BM, Storm DR. 1980. Calcium-induced exposure of a hydrophobic surface on calmodulin. *Biochemistry* 19:3814–19

68. Levitt M, Sharon R. 1988. Accurate simulation of protein dynamics in solution. *Proc. Natl. Acad. Sci. USA* 85:7557–61

69. Ling K-Y, Preston RR, Burns R, Kink JA, Saimi Y, et al. 1992. Primary mutations in calmodulin prevent activation of the Ca^{2+}-dependent Na^+ channel in *Paramecium*. *Proteins: Struct. Funct. Gen.* 12:365–71

70. Linse S, Brodin P, Drakenberg T, Thulin E, Sellers P, et al. 1987. Structure-function relationships in EF-hand Ca^{2+}-binding proteins. Protein engineering and biophysical studies of calbindin$_{D9k}$. *Biochemistry* 26:6723–35

71. Linse S, Brodin P, Johansson C, Thulin E, Grundstrom T, et al. 1988. The role of protein surface charges in ion binding. *Nature* 335:651–52

72. Linse S, Helmersson A, Forsen S. 1991. Calcium binding to calmodulin and its globular domains. *J. Biol. Chem.* 266:8050–54

73. Linse S, Johansson C, Brodin P, Grundstrom T, Drakenberg, T, et al. 1991. Electrostatic contributions to the binding of Ca^{2+} in calbindin$_{D9k}$. *Biochemistry* 30:154–62

74. Linse S, Teleman O, Drakenberg T. 1990. Ca^{2+} binding to calbindin D9k strongly affects backbone dynamics:

Measurements of exchange rates of individual amide protons using ^1H NMR. *Biochemistry* 29:5925–34

75. Lu KP, Rasmussen CD, May GS, Means AR. 1992. Cooperative regulation of cell proliferation by calcium and calmodulin in *Aspergillus nidulans*. *Mol. Endocrinol.* 6:365–74

76. Lukas TJ, Wallen-Friedman M, Kung C, Watterson DM. 1989. In vivo mutations of calmodulin: A mutant *Paramecium* with altered ion current regulation has an isoleucine-to-threonine change at residue 136 and an altered methylation state at lysine residue 115. *Proc. Natl. Acad. Sci. USA* 86:7331–35

77. Matsushima N, Izumi Y, Matsuo T, Yoshino H, Ueki, T, et al. 1989. Binding of both Ca^{2+} and mastoparan to calmodulin induces a large change in tertiary structure. *J. Biochem.* 105:883–87

78. McCammon JA. 1987. Computer-aided molecular design. *Science* 238:486–91

79. McCammon JA, Harvey SC. 1987. *Dynamics of Proteins and Nucleic Acids*, New York: Cambridge Univ. Press. 234 pp.

80. McPhalen CA, Strynadka NCJ, James MNG. 1991. Calcium binding sites in proteins: A structural perspective. *Adv. Protein Chem.* 42:77–144

81. Meador WE, Means AR, Quiocho FA. 1992. Target enzyme recognition by calmodulin: 2.4Å structure of a calmodulin-peptide complex. *Science* 257:1251–55

82. Means AR, Conn PM, eds. 1987. *Cellular Regulators. Part A. Calcium-and Calmodulin-Binding Proteins*. New York: Academic. 917 pp.

83. Means AR, VanBerkum MFA, Bagchi IC, Lu KP, Rasmussen, CD. 1991. Regulatory functions of calmodulin. *Pharmacol. Ther.* 50:255–70

84. Mehler EL, Kushick JN, Weinstein H. 1993. Consequences of sequential Ca^{2+} occupancy for the structure and dynamics of calbindinD9k: Computational simulations and comparison to experimental determinations in solution. *Mol. Simulation.* 10:309–34

85. Mehler EL, Pascual-Ahuir JL, Weinstein H. 1991. Structural dynamics of calmodulin and troponin C. *Protein Eng.* 4:625–37

86. Mehler EL, Solmajer T. 1991. Electrostatic effects in proteins: Comparison of dielectric and charge models. *Protein Eng.* 4:903–10

87. Meyer T, Hanson PI, Stryer L, Schulman H. 1992. Calmodulin trapping by

calcium-calmodulin-dependent protein kinase. *Science* 256:1199–2202

88. Monera OD, Shaw GS, Zhu B-Y, Sykes BD, Kay CM, et al. 1992. Role of interchain alpha-helical hydrophobic interactions in Ca^{2+} affinity, formation, and stability of a two-site domain in troponin C. *Protein Sci.* 1:945–55

89. Nakayama S, Moncrief ND, Kretsinger RH. 1992. Evolution of EF-hand calcium-modulated proteins. II. Domains of several subfamilies have diverse evolutionary histories. *J. Mol. Evol.* 34:416–48

90. O'Neil KT, DeGrado WF. 1989. The interaction of calmodulin with fluorescent and photoactive model peptides: Evidence of a short interdomain separation. *Proteins: Struct. Funct. Gen.* 6:284–93

91. O'Neil KT, DeGrado WF. 1990. How calmodulin binds its targets: sequence independent recognition of amphiphilic alpha-helices. *Trends Biochem. Sci.* 15:59–64

92. Pascual-Ahuir J-L, Mehler EL, Weinstein H. 1991. Calmodulin structure and function: Implication of arginine residues in the compaction related to ligand binding. *Mol. Eng.* 1:231–47

93. Pascual-Ahuir JL, Silla E. 1990. GEPOL: An improved description of molecular surfaces. I. Building the spherical surface set. *J. Comput. Chem.* 11:1047–60

94. Persechini A, Kretsinger RH. 1988. Towards a model of the calmodulin-myosin light chain kinase complex: Implications for calmodulin function. *J. Cardiovasc. Pharmacol.* 12 (Suppl.5): S1–12

95. Persechini A, Kretsinger RH. 1988. The central helix of calmodulin functions as a flexible tether. *J. Biol. Chem.* 263:12175–78

96. Putkey JA, Ono T, VanBerkum MFA, Means AR. 1988. Functional significance of the central helix in calmodulin. *J. Biol. Chem.* 263:11242–49

97. Rao ST, Wu S, Satyshur KA, Ling K-Y, Kung C, et al. 1993. Structure of *Paramecium tetraurelia* calmodulin at 1.8Å resolution. *Protein Sci.* 2:436–47

98. Rao U, Teeter MM, Erickson-Viitanen S, DeGrado WF. 1992. Calmodulin binding to alpha₁-purothionin: Solution binding and modeling of the complex. *Proteins: Struct. Funct. Gen.* 14:127–38

99. Schulman H. 1993. The multifunctional Ca^{2+}/calmodulin-dependent protein kinase. *Curr. Opin. Cell Biol.* 5:247–53

100. Schulman H, Hanson PI, Meyer T. 1992. Decoding calcium signals by multifunctional CaM kinase. *Cell Calcium* 13:401–11

101. Seaton BA, Head JF, Engelman DM, Richards FM. 1985. Calcium-induced increase in the radius of gyration and maximum dimension of calmodulin measured by small-angle x-ray scattering. *Biochemistry* 24:6740–43

102. Shelling JG, Sykes BD. 1985. ^{1}H Nuclear magnetic resonance study of the two calcium-binding sites of porcine intestinal calcium-binding protein. *J. Biol. Chem.* 260:8342–47

103. Silla E, Tunon I, Pascual-Ahuir JL. 1991. GEPOL: An improved description of molecular surfaces. II. Computing the molecular area and volume. *J. Comput. Chem.* 12:1077–88

104. Skelton NJ, Kordel J, Forsen S, Chazin WJ. 1990. Comparative structural analysis of the calcium free and bound states of the calcium regulatory protein calbindin D9k. *J. Mol. Biol.* 213:593–98

105. Skelton NJ, Kordel J, Akke M, Chazin WJ. 1992. Nuclear magnetic resonance studies of the internal dynamics in apo, $(Cd^{2+})1$ and $(Ca^{2+})2$ calbindin D9k. *J. Mol. Biol.* 227:1100–17

106. Starovasnik MA, Davis TN, Klevit RE. 1993. Similarities and differences between yeast and vertebrate calmodulin: An examination of the calcium-binding and structural properties of calmodulin from the yeast *Saccharomyces cerevisiae*. *Biochemistry* 32:3261–70

107. Starovasnik MA, Su D-R, Beckingham K, Klevit RE. 1992. A series of point mutations reveal interactions between the calcium-binding sites of calmodulin. *Protein Sci.* 1:245–53

108. Strynadka NCJ, James MNG. 1988. Two trifluoperazine-binding sites on calmodulin predicted from comparative molecular modeling with troponin-C. *Proteins: Struct. Funct. Gen.* 3:1–17

109. Strynadka NCJ, James MNG. 1989. Crystal structures of the helix-loop-helix calcium-binding proteins. *Annu. Rev. Biochem.* 58:951–98

110. Strynadka NCJ, James MNG. 1991. Towards an understanding of the effect of calcium on protein structure and function. *Curr. Opin. Struct. Biol.* 1:905–14

111. Sussman F, Weinstein H. 1989. On the ion selectivity in Ca-binding proteins: The cyclo(-L-Pro-Gly)3 peptide as a model. *Proc. Natl. Acad. Sci. USA* 86:7880–84

112. Svensson B, Jonsson B, Woodward C. 1990. Electrostatic contribution to the binding of Ca^{2+} in calbindin mutants. *Biophys. Chem.* 38:179–83

113. Svensson B, Jonsson B, Thulin E. 1993. Binding of Ca^{2+} to calmodulin and its tryptic fragments: Theory and experiment. *Biochemistry* 32:2828–34

114. Szebenyi DME, Moffat K. 1986. The refined structure of vitamin D-dependent calcium-binding protein from bovine intestine. *J. Biol. Chem.* 261:8761–77

115. Tanaka T, Hidaka H. 1980. Hydrophobic regions function in calmodulin-enzyme(s) interaction. *J. Biol. Chem.* 255:11078–80

116. Tanaka T, Hidaka H. 1981. Interaction of local anesthetics with calmodulin. *Biochem. Biophys. Res. Commun.* 101:447–53

117. Tansey MG, Word RA, Hidaka H, Singer HA, Schworer CM, et al. 1992. Phosphorylation of myosin light chain kinase by the multifunctional calmodulin-dependent protein kinase II in smooth muscle cells. *J. Biol. Chem.* 267:12511–16

118. Teleman A, Drakenberg T, Forsen S. 1986. Kinetics of Ca^{2+} binding to calmodulin and its tryptic fragments studied by ^{43}Ca-NMR. *Biochim. Biophys. Acta* 873:204–13

119. Torok K, Lane AN, Martin SR, Janot J-M, Bayley PM. 1992. Effects of calcium binding on the internal dynamic properties of bovine brain calmodulin, studied by NMR and optical spectroscopy. *Biochemistry* 31:3452–62

120. Trewhella J, Liddle WK, Heidorn DB, Strynadka N. 1989. Calmodulin and troponin C structures studied by Fourier transform infrared spectroscopy: effects of Ca^{2+} and Mg^{2+} binding. *Biochemistry* 28:1294–301

121. van Gunsteren WF. 1988. The role of computer simulation techniques in protein engineering. *Protein Eng.* 1:5–13

122. van Gunsteren WF, Berendsen HJC, Hermans J, Hol WGJ, Postma JPM. 1983. Computer simulation of the dynamics of hydrated protein crystals and its comparison with x-ray data. *Proc. Natl. Acad. Sci. USA* 80:4315–19

123. van Gunsteren WF, Brunne RM, Mark AE, van Helden SP. 1992. Computer simulation of biomolecules: Comparison with experimental data. In *Molecular Aspects of Biotechnology: Computational Models and Theories*, ed. J Bertran, pp. 105–22. Dordrecht, The Netherlands: Kluwer

124. van Gunsteren WF, Weiner PK, eds. 1989. *Computer Simulation of Biomolecular Systems.* Leiden, The Netherlands: ESCOM. 224 pp.

125. Verhoeven AS, Shea MA. 1993. Ca^{2+}-induced domain interactions of calmodulin. *Biophys. J.* 64:A169 (Abstr.)

126. Vorherr T, Kessler O, Mark A, Carafoli E. 1992. Construction and molecular dynamics simulation of calmodulin in the extended and in a bent conformation. *Eur. J. Biochem.* 204:931–37

127. Vyas NK, Meenakshi NV, Quiocho FA. 1987. A novel calcium binding site in the galactose-binding protein of bacterial transport and chemotaxis. *Nature* 327:635–38

128. Wang C-LA. 1989. pH-dependent conformational changes of wheat germ calmodulin. *Biochemistry* 28:4816–20

129. Wang CA, Zhan Q, Tao T, Gergely J. 1987. pH-dependent structural transition in rabbit skeletal troponin C. *J. Biol. Chem.* 262:9636–40

130. Wang CK, Cheung HC. 1985. Energetics of the binding of calcium and troponin I to troponin C from rabbit skeletal muscle. *Biophys. J.* 48:727–39

131. Wang JH, Pallen C, Sharma RK, Adachi AM, Adachi K. 1985. The calmodulin regulatory system. *Curr. Topics Cell Regul.* 27:419–36

132. Warshel A, Chu ZT, Parson WW. 1989. Dispersed polaron simulation of electron transfer in photosynthetic reaction center. *Science* 246:112–16

133. Warshel A, Hwang JK, Aqvist J. 1992. Computer simulations of enzymatic reactions: Examination of linear free-energy relationships and quantum-mechanical corrections in the initial proton-transfer step of carbonic anhydrase. *Faraday Disc.* 93: In press

134. Warshel A, Sussman F, King G. 1986. Free-energy of charges in solvated proteins: Microscopic calculations using a reversible charging process. *Biochemistry* 25:8368–72

135. Weber PC, Lukas TJ, Craig TA, Wilson E, King MM, et al. 1989. Computational and site-specific mutagenesis analyses of the asymmetric charge distribution on calmodulin. *Proteins: Struct. Funct. Genet.* 6:70–85

136. Weinstein H, ed. 1986. *Computational Approaches to Enzyme Structure and Function.* Basel: Karger. 164 pp.

137. Weinstein H. 1992. Computational simulations of molecular structure, dynamics and signal transduction in biological systems: Mechanistic implications for ecological physical chemistry. In *Ecological Physical Chemistry*, ed. L

Bonati, U Cosentino, M Lasagni, G Moro, D Pitea, A Schiraldi, pp. 1–16. Amsterdam: Elsevier

138. Weinstein H, Mehler EL. 1992. Structural specificity in the engineering of biological function: Insights from the dynamics of calmodulin. See Ref. 123, pp. 153–73

139. Yazawa M, Vorherr T, James P, Carafoli E, Yagi K. 1992. Binding of calcium by calmodulin: influence of the calmodulin binding domain of the plasma membrane calcium pump. *Am. Chem. Soc.* 31:3171–76

140. Yoo SH. 1992. Identification of the Ca^{2+}-dependent calmodulin-binding region of chromogranin A. *Biochemistry* 31:6134–40

Annu. Rev. Physiol. 1994. 56:237–72
Copyright © 1994 by Annual Reviews Inc. All rights reserved

STRUCTURE AND FUNCTION OF CYCLIC NUCLEOTIDE-DEPENDENT PROTEIN KINASES

Sharron H. Francis and Jackie D. Corbin

Department of Molecular Physiology and Biophysics, Vanderbilt University, School of Medicine, Nashville, Tennessee 37232–0615

KEY WORDS: cAMP, cGMP, second messenger, signal transduction, phosphorylation, intracellular receptors

INTRODUCTION

Cyclic AMP-dependent protein kinase (cAK) was first described in 1963–1964 (43, 132) as a cAMP-dependent glycogen synthase kinase that, in the presence of Mg/ATP, transferred the γ-phosphate of ATP to serines or threonines on many cellular enzymes. It was found to phosphorylate a number of proteins and was permanently named in 1968 (168). Ensuing years produced vast numbers of reports regarding properties of cAK and the signal mechanisms that elicit its activation. Many of these have been reviewed recently (8, 33, 47, 85, 141, 155, 181). In 1970 cyclic GMP-dependent protein kinase (cGK) was discovered (86). cGK is homologous in structure and function to cAK (24, 49, 59, 66, 93, 141, 154). The role of cGMP in physiological processes is increasingly appreciated (15, 39, 92, 94, 113, 170), but cGK is only one of several intracellular receptors for cGMP. Studies of the heterogeneity, function, and regulation of cAK and cGK have provided insight into the enzymology of diverse protein kinases and into the roles of these kinases in cellular processes.

0066–4278/94/0315–0237$05.00

cAMP-DEPENDENT PROTEIN KINASE

Holoenzyme Structure, Isozymic Forms, and Subcellular Location

cAK is present in all mammalian tissues examined. Although its concentration varies, the typical cellular level is 0.2–2 μM (146). cAK was purified to homogeneity in 1968 (168), and the complete amino acid sequences were first obtained using the purified regulatory and catalytic subunits (147, 153, 159). In the absence of cAMP, mammalian cAK is an inactive tetramer composed of two regulatory subunits (R) and two catalytic subunits (C) (Figure 1), but in vitro it can function as a dimer of one R and one C

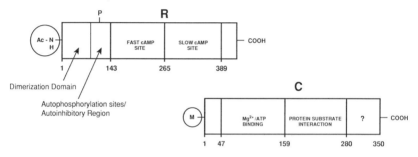

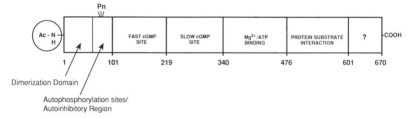

Figure 1   Linear arrangement of functional domains of cAK and cGK. Amino acid numbers are from the literature (147, 153, 154). The amino-terminal domain is subdivided to emphasize the multiplicity of function in this part of the kinases. The most amino-terminal segment is important in dimerization and, in some instances, subcellular localization. The region adjoining the dimerization domain includes the autoinhibitory domain and the autophosphorylation domain. The autophosphorylation region is phosphorylated either singly (P) in cAK or multiply (Pn) in cGK, and its boundaries overlap the inhibitory domain, i.e. the minimal amino acid sequence required for maintaining full dependency on cAMP or cGMP for activation. Fast and slow cAMP or cGMP-binding sites are also known as sites A and B, sites 2 and 1, and as low affinity and high affinity binding sites, respectively. The role of the carboxyl-terminal segment (indicated as ?) is unknown although recent studies suggest interactions with protein/peptide substrate. Amino termini labels indicate acetylation (Ac) for RII and cGK and myristoylation (M) for C subunit.

(127, 130). In the holoenzyme, the catalytic activity of the C subunit is latent because of the inhibition conferred by the inhibitory domain of R (Figure 1). When two cAMP molecules bind per R (26), the affinity of R for C decreases 10,000–100,000-fold (30a), tetrameric cAK dissociates into dimeric R and two monomers of C (35, 47, 168), and inhibition of C by R is concomitantly released (35, 68).

REGULATORY SUBUNIT ISOZYMES   Two major mammalian R subunit iso-forms (RI and RII with M_r of 43 and 45 K, respectively) have been identified, and within these isoforms there are still further distinctions (RIα, RIβ, RIIα, and RIIβ). These R subunits are apparently products of different genes (8, 47, 72, 85, 106, 107). Expression of RI and RII varies with the species and tissue in question. RIα is expressed in many tissues, and RIIβ is more selectively expressed [central nervous system, neuroendocrine tissues, Sertoli cells, ovarian granulosa cells (72), and lung (131)]. The physiological importance of these variations is unclear (30a). Studies with cyclic nucleotide analogues selective for either RI or RII suggest that activation of either can elicit a given physiological response (8, 9, 104, 164). RI and RII complex with the same C subunit isoforms, thus release and activation of C from either holoenzyme would target the same substrates, assuming equal distri-bution of all components within the cell (30a). The R subunits are apparently homodimerized through interactions of monomers mainly near the amino termini. Highly divergent amino acid sequences at the amino termini of the R isoforms may provide for selective interaction between homologous R subunits (72), although heterodimers may also occur.

CATALYTIC SUBUNIT ISOZYMES   Three forms of mammalian C subunit (M_r= 40 K) are known (Cα, Cβ$_{1,2}$, and Cγ) (10, 106, 163); Cβ$_1$ and Cβ$_2$ are thought to be products of alternative mRNA splicing. Yeast has three C isoforms that are products of separate genes (160). The human Cγ appears to be specific to testis and is the product of a single gene localized to chromosome 9 (38). In the absence of cAMP, the R homodimer is believed to combine with any of the C isoforms with an affinity ~0.2 nM. Physical features of the R component of cAK account for the major chromatographic and functional differences (35).

With four R isoforms that can form homodimers, and three isoforms of C, it is possible that 24 different holoenzymes are present in mammalian tissues. Under certain in vitro conditions, differences in K_a of cAMP for types I and II can be observed (16, 35), and complexes of RCγ may dissociate less readily (10). Under cellular conditions, however, the isozymes are activated approximately equally (8, 9, 47, 164), perhaps because MgATP stabilizes type I, while autophosphorylation and MgADP stabilize type II (35). Active C in the presence of Mg^{2+}/ATP catalytically transfers the γ-phosphate of ATP to a myriad of protein and peptide substrates containing the -RRXSX- substrate consensus amino acid sequence (53, 80, 81, 82, 183, 186). The protein-bound phosphoserine ($\Delta G^\circ = -6.5$ kcal/mole) retains a portion of the high free energy of hydrolysis of ATP ($\Delta G^\circ = -8.4$ kcal/mole) as compared to free serine phosphate ($\Delta G^\circ = -2.9$ kcal/mole) (35). cAK can be partially saturated with cAMP (20), but both cAMP binding sites on native R must be filled for C to dissociate and thereby activate catalysis. Possible mechanisms of regulation of cAK activity other than by cAMP elevation that are discussed here are autophosphorylation, cellular location, cross-activation by cGMP, and phosphodiesterase activation.

DOMAIN STRUCTURE OF R   Isoforms of R are comparable in size and have homologous amino acid sequences that contain similar functional domains (Figure 1). Sequences of the R isoforms are most divergent at their amino termini, which provide for dimerization and, in some instances, also specify subcellular localization of R (102, 141, 143). Carboxyl terminal to the dimerization domain is the autoinhibitory/autophosphorylation domain that provides a major portion of the inhibitory interaction of R with C subunit. In each R, two homologous cAMP binding sites ($\sim$35% identity) are positioned in tandem in the primary structure (153, 159). The sites are also homologous to an evolutionarily related bacterial cAMP-binding protein, catabolite gene-activating protein (CAP), whose molecular structure is known (173). The cAMP-binding sites in R are proposed to be products of a gene duplication that occurred prior to divergence of RI and RII, as well as to cGK divergence (146). Differences in structures confer different cAMP dissociation rates and cyclic nucleotide analogue specificities on the sites in both RI and RII (26, 31, 111, 117, 119, 120).

AUTOPHOSPHORYLATION/AUTOINHIBITION OF C AND R   Purified mammalian C subunit contains covalently linked phosphates at Thr-197 and Ser-338, and another phosphate can be incorporated in vitro at Ser-10 (148, 152, 162). Phosphates at Thr-197 and Ser-338 are introduced either posttranslationally or co-translationally, perhaps autocatalytically, and are inaccessible to phosphatases (148, 152, 162). Phosphorylation of Thr-197 is associated with a mobility shift of C on SDS-PAGE, concomitant with C subunit activation (152), although phosphorylation at serine(s) may also be involved. Phosphorylation lowers K_ms for both ATP and peptide substrate (152, 162). In the crystal structure of C (83, 84), the phosphate on Thr-197 is sequestered among side chains of Thr-195, His-87, Arg-165, and Lys-189 near the catalytic center and close to the P+2 position of a co-crystallized substrate analogue, protein kinase inhibitor peptide (PKIP). It may structurally stabilize the catalytic site and foster optimal alignment of peptide substrate within the site for phosphotransfer (83, 84). Phosphorylated Thr-197 is also implicated in the interaction of C with R; mutation of the homologous threonine in yeast C (90) reduces its affinity for substrates and for R (also a substrate analogue). The phosphorylation site at Ser-338 is outside the conserved kinase core and is absent in cGK (59, 147, 154). In C, this phosphate is not exposed to solvent and interacts with Lys-342 and with the protein backbone amide at Ile-339 (83, 84). Phosphorylation at serine in C may precede that at threonine (152), but the order of phosphorylation, whether it is autocatalytic, and the functional relationship between sites are not known.

Upon holoenzyme formation, C rapidly phosphorylates RII in a substrate sequence, -RRXSX-, in the autoinhibitory domain, whereas RI has a pseudosubstrate sequence in which either alanine or glycine replaces the serine (35, 81, 82, 153, 159). Phosphorylated RII has ~tenfold lower affinity for C and is shifted in electrophoretic mobility to a more slowly migrating form (35, 126). Inhibition of C by R involves both the substrate-like sequence in R (-RRXSX-) as well as other undefined elements (36), perhaps including the cAMP-binding sites. Modification of the RR component by site-directed mutagenesis or by limited proteolysis renders R unable to inhibit C (26, 171, C Poteet, unpublished results). Heat denaturation of RII does not alter its phosphorylation by C, but abrogates its inhibition of catalysis (36). Thus R inhibition of C may involve a high affinity interaction of C with a substrate-like sequence in R as well as additional contacts that provide for inhibition of catalysis. Following dissociation and activation, it would seem pivotal for R and C to maintain a high affinity interaction point to provide for rapid reassociation. It is possible that the progenitor of R was a substrate that evolved into a kinase regulatory element (131).

Deleting an entire cAMP binding domain, i.e. the slow site (Figure 1), produces a truncated R that recombines with C and suppresses catalytic activity in a cAMP-dependent fashion (138, 180). Truncation of R just amino-terminal to the two arginines in the RII substrate site (-RRXSX-), or the pseudosubstrate site of RI (-RRXGX-), also produces an R that retains full inhibitory activity toward C (127, 130, C Poteet, unpublished results). Thus the R sequence encoding the pseudosubstrate site through the first cAMP-binding site (fast site), Arg-94 through Lys-259 in RI, provides for high affinity inhibition of C by R as well as for binding one cAMP. An invariant glutamate at the P+4 position in the substrate-like sequence in the inhibitory domains of all R subunits and cGKs can be changed to glutamine or alanine in RI with minimal effect on holoenzyme formation, or on its inhibitory potency (123). This and other invariant residues, including those in the cAMP-binding sites, may play roles in C inhibition that have not yet been elucidated.

ANCHORING PROTEINS   In many tissues a significant proportion of cAK, primarily the type II isoform, is associated with particulate fractions, including, among others, elements of the cytoskeleton, the Golgi complex, and microtubule organizing centers (12, 13, 79, 97, 115, 133, 134, 141, 157). In neurons, greater than 70% of cAK (predominantly type IIβ) is localized to the post-synaptic densities and dendritic cytoskeletal elements (18, 50). Proteins that interact with RII to anchor either holoenzyme (RIIαC or RIIβC) or the respective R dimers to these subcellular compartments have been dubbed A Kinase Anchoring Proteins (AKAPs) (64). They vary in size, amino acid sequence (12, 13, 17, 50, 141), and in some instances, the relative affinities for either RIIα or RIIβ (89).

Amino acids 1–79 in dimeric RIIβ contain the structure required to complex with AKAPs (102, 141, 143); monomeric RII does not interact with AKAPs. AKAPs apparently have conserved sequences that retain in their secondary structures an acidic amphipathic helix necessary for inter-actions with basic residues in the amino terminus of RIIβ (17, 134). Overexpression of a neuronally associated AKAP (AKAP75) is associated with redistribution of >90% of RII from the cytoplasm to the particulate fraction of the cell (114). AKAPs may specifically localize cAK to re-gions/substrates for which rapid regulatory control is important. Some AKAPs are cAK substrates, so co-localization of holoenzyme could provide immediate responsiveness to hormonal stimuli (79, 108, 141). The proportion of cAK anchored in most tissues remains to be determined, and post-ho-mogenization artifacts in R binding to particulate fractions should be closely scrutinized (79).

Catalytic Subunit

STRUCTURE   C subunit, one of the smallest known protein kinases (59, 147), is a globular protein of 350 amino acids that is myristoylated at its amino terminus. The role of the myristate is not known (106, 107). The X-ray crystallographic structure of C subunit (Figure 2) has recently been determined (83, 84, 187); it will be invaluable as a structural prototype for the many members of the protein kinase family (59, 155, 156). Structural analysis reveals C to be an asymmetric bilobate molecule (Figure 2) with the catalytic site located in a deep cleft bisecting the lobes. The smaller, more amino-terminal lobe is involved in binding Mg^{2+}/ATP and is char-acterized by five strands of anti-parallel β-sheets. The larger, more car-boxyl-terminal lobe provides recognition sites for protein/peptide substrate

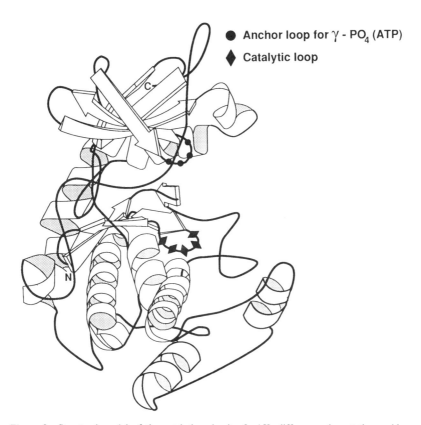

Figure 2 Structural model of the catalytic subunit of cAK: differences in putative residues contacting substrate in cAK and cGK. (*solid circle*) indicates the glycine-rich loop (residues 50–55) involved in anchoring ATP and (*diamonds*) indicates the catalytic loop (residues 165–171) (model adapted from 83, 84).

binding and catalysis and is richer in α-helical content. C binds Mg^{2+}/ATP through a glycine-rich segment at residues 50–55 (Gly-X-Gly-X-X-Gly) that fixes the nontransferable α- and β-phosphates. The γ-phosphate is coordinated with Mg^{2+} and sites in the large lobe. The nucleotide-binding fold in C differs from those of other known nucleotide-binding proteins (83, 84). Eight of the amino acids considered nearly invariant in protein kinases are involved in binding the adenine nucleotide. The adenine portion of ATP is buried in a hydrophobic pocket and forms hydrogen bonds at the C-6 amino and N-7 positions (187). Energy for ATP binding comes largely from interactions of C with the adenine and ribose rings and is minimally affected by residues involved in appropriately aligning the γ-phosphate for transfer to protein/peptide substrate (35, 83, 84, 187).

The catalytic site in the depression bisecting the bilobate structure is characterized by the apposition of three conserved loops that extend into the cleft (Figure 2); one is the glycine-rich loop, and two are catalytically important. These include the catalytic loop (residues 165–171), which contains three residues (Asp-166, Lys-168, and Asn-171) that are invariant in Ser/Thr protein kinases; Asp-166 is positioned suitably to serve as the catalytic base in transferring the phosphate to the substrate peptide, but its role in catalysis is unclear (1, 187). The γ-phosphate of ATP interacts with Lys-168, and Asn-171 serves two functions by (a) complexing with one of the Mg^{2+} at the ATP-binding site, and (b) stabilizing the catalytic loop by forming a hydrogen bond with the backbone carbonyl of Asp-166. Glu-170 coordinates with the P-2 arginine in the PKIP pseudosubstrate sequence. Arginine-165, which just precedes this in the sequence, is coordinated with the phosphorylated Thr-197. The second loop is a short sequence that extends from Asp-184 through Phe-186. Asp-184 coordinates with the major Mg^{2+} that is complexed with the α- and β-phosphates of ATP; this arrangement thus precisely orients the γ-phosphate for transfer to the serine/threonine in the protein substrate (83, 84).

The more carboxyl-terminal lobe of C provides most of the interaction with the -RRXSX- substrate consensus sequence to position it in the catalytic cleft. P-3 arginine interacts with Glu-127 and perhaps also with Glu-331, which is located in a cluster of six acidic residues near the carboxyl terminus (83, 84). Glu-170 and Glu-230 ion pair with the P-2 arginine. Other conserved elements within the core kinase structure may stabilize the structure. Chemical modifications and site-directed mutagenesis of C have aided in assignation of function in the structure (35, 48, 155, 156, 161). The role of segments of C located at the extreme amino terminus and the extreme carboxyl terminus is not known. Deletion of twenty three residues at the amino terminus of C has no effect on catalytic rate, substrate binding, or the ability to interact with R (122). Alterations at the carboxyl terminus of C adversely affect catalysis; mutations at Glu-332, -333, and -334 destroy catalytic activity due to impaired interaction with peptide substrate (48, 84). Removal of forty nine residues at the carboxyl terminus produces an inactive C (122), and removal of shorter segments causes progressive activity losses that may relate to defects in either catalytic efficiency or substrate binding.

In addition to interactions of the catalytic center of C with substrate-like sequences on R, other contacts that bind R are known to exist, but they are poorly defined. Heat-denatured RII is rapidly phosphorylated by C subunit, but it is unable to bind cAMP and does not inhibit catalysis (36). In the absence of the two arginines in the R substrate consensus site, C and R still form holoenzyme by a cAMP-dependent mechanism, but catalytic activity is not inhibited (171). Phosphorylated Thr-197 in C may play a role in interaction with R (90). Based on site-directed mutagenesis, C is proposed to contain a high affinity R binding domain involving Trp-196, Leu-198, and the surrounding His-87 and Lys-189, -213, -217 (122); conversion of His-87 to Gln and Trp-196 to Arg has little effect on catalysis or inhibition of C by PKI, but interaction with R is lost (48, 122), as also happens when Lys-189, -213, and -217 are altered (48). It is expected that many structural elements of C that interact with R and PKI will be shared, but other contacts will differ significantly.

INTERACTIONS WITH MgATP AND PEPTIDE/PROTEIN SUBSTRATES   The MgATP and protein substrate specificities of cAK have been studied extensively (21, 24, 33, 35, 53, 80, 81, 82, 183, 186). ATP binds to a high affinity site in the anti-conformation (K_m= 3–15 μM), and two Mg^{2+} neutralize the negative charges of the ATP phosphates. Binding the second Mg^{2+} lowers the K_m for ATP tenfold (22, 57). In type I holoenzyme, Mg^{2+}/ATP binding stabilizes RC association and increases the rate of cAMP dissociation from RI. Mg^{2+}/ATP binding to free C precedes binding of protein substrate. This is supported by kinetic studies (22, 57, 176, 184) and by the observation that all mutant C subunits with altered k_{cat}/K_m for Mg^{2+}/ATP also have defective kinetics for peptide substrate (156). Peptide substrates containing the consensus -RRXSX- motif assume an extended coil conformation (11, 56) when bound to C and induce structural changes in C (121, 156), perhaps narrowing the catalytic cleft by contraction of the two lobes around a conserved "glycine hinge", Gly-125 in C (121).

Following formation of the enzyme-Mg^{2+}/ATP ternary complex, the γ-phosphate of ATP is rapidly transferred to the substrate (1, 22, 57, 65, 176, 184), and configuration at the transferred phosphate is inverted (65). A general base catalyst at the active site may mediate phosphotransfer, but direct nucleophilic attack by the acceptor serine of the substrate peptide has also been suggested (57, 184, 187). Following transfer of the phosphate to peptide substrate, the phospho-peptide quickly dissociates from C, followed by the rate limiting dissociation of Mg^{2+}/ADP (1, 22). The affinity of C for Mg^{2+}/ADP is relatively high (~40 μM), and high concentrations of Mg^{2+}/ADP can be used to reverse protein phosphorylations (35). In the absence of protein substrate, C has an intrinsic ATPase activity that transfers the γ-phosphate of ATP to water. In most instances, the primary sequence of a protein phosphorylation site contains the information required for high affinity interaction with the catalytic center. Negative determinants in substrate sequences for cAK catalysis include threonine instead of serine at the phosphotransfer site, an acidic residue in the P-1 site, lysine in the P+2 position, and phenylalanine in the P+4 site (21, 35, 53, 81, 82).

INTERACTION WITH PROTEIN KINASE INHIBITOR AND PROTEIN KINASE INHIBITOR PEPTIDES   The heat stable inhibitor protein of cAK is a highly selective and potent (K_i <1 nM) competitive inhibitor of Cα and Cβ catalytic function (19, 142, 166, 167), but not of Cγ (10), yeast C (188), or cGK (52). Significant inhibitory potency (K_i= 1–2 nM) is retained in a heptadecapeptide (TYADFIASGRTGRRNAI) PKIP (6–22) amide. PKIP has a pseudosubstrate site (-RRNAI) at the carboxyl terminus, and an amino-terminal amphipathic α-helix (19, 142, 166). In the binary complex (C subunit/PKIP), C forms contacts with Phe-10, Arg-18, Arg-19, and Ile-22 in PKIP (83, 84). Arg-15 also contributes to the interaction, but to a lesser degree. Phe-10 (PKIP) binds in a hydrophobic pocket on C that is formed by Tyr-235, Pro-236, and Phe-239. Replacing Phe-10 of PKIP with alanine greatly reduces its inhibitory potency. In type I cGK, positions homologous to Tyr-235 and Phe-239 are replaced by serines, but proline is conserved in the position homologous to Pro-236 (154). In yeast C_1, this same proline is replaced by threonine (160). Decreased hydrophobicity in this area of the yeast C and of cGK may account, in part, for the weak inhibition by PKIP (52).

In the Cα-PKIP complex, contacts between C and PKIP also occur in the PKIP pseudosubstrate region, but all of these are not conserved in yeast C, mammalian Cγ, or cGK (10, 154, 160). Studies of substrate specificities document the importance of arginine in the P-3 and P-2 positions for both cAK and cGK (51, 53, 54, 80, 82, 183). Arg-18 of PKIP is the P-3 basic residue in the pseudosubstrate consensus sequence and interacts with Glu-127, Asp-329, and Glu-331 in Cα (83, 84). The glutamate homologous to Glu-127 is present in both yeast C and cGK, but residues homologous to Asp-329 and Glu-331 are not conserved in either; proline replaces Glu-331 in both yeast C and cGK, and Asp-329 is replaced by lysine, glutamine, or arginine in yeast C, and by serine in cGK. Thus under catalytic conditions, ionic interaction between the substrate P-3 arginine and the conserved glutamate [Glu-127 (Cα), Glu-444 (cGKIα)] is predicted to suffice for substrate positioning at P-3.

Arg-19 (PKIP), representing the P-2 basic residue in the pseudosubstrate motif, interacts electrostatically with Glu-170 and Glu-230 in C. These contact residues are conserved in the sequences of both the cGK and the yeast C isoforms. Alteration of Glu-170 by site-directed mutagenesis significantly disrupts catalytic efficiency towards peptide substrates (161). Amino acid sequence differences between mammalian C, cGK, and yeast C at sites where mammalian C contacts PKIP are likely to account for differences in substrate specificities and the interaction of cGK with its autoinhibitory domain.

TRANSLOCATION   Since the early 1970's, it has been suggested that after cAMP elevation elicits dissociation of cAK into its component R and C subunits, these subunits translocate into different cellular compartments (5, 61, 108, 114, 157). It was hypothesized that anchoring the RC complex to cellular membranes or organelles via R could emplace cAK near either adenylate cyclase, phosphodiesterase, substrate(s) for C, or combinations of these proteins. Several lines of evidence including biochemical and immunocytochemical approaches and results of tagged R and C microinjection (5, 76, 79, 108, 115) suggest that prolonged cAMP elevation causes gradual translocation of C to the nucleus while holoenzyme remains excluded. Overexpression of C induces cAMP-dependent genes, an effect that is blocked by coexpression of R subunit (107, 109). Whether C translocates via indiscriminate diffusion through nuclear membrane pores or by a more active process is not known. A sequence that is identical to the nuclear translocation signal in human c-myc has been identified in C at Ala-188 (-AKRVK-) (106). Upon relocation of C to the nucleus, phosphorylation of nuclear proteins, e.g. transcription factors such as CREB, could alter gene expression (55, 106, 109). Increases in nuclear C are reversible (5, 108), but it is unclear whether in the face of decreased cAMP, C non-specifically diffuses back into the cytoplasm to rejoin R, or whether a specific mechanism provides for returning C to the cytoplasm. It is also possible that the decrease in cytoplasmic C is replenished by synthesis of new C and that C, which translocates to the nucleus, does not return to the cytoplasm in the active form. Given the lability of C in the absence of R, the latter would seem possible. The case for nuclear translocation of C as a means for cAMP effects in the nucleus is improving, but it is also possible that the smaller cAMP molecule rapidly diffuses into the nucleus and activates a low level of nuclear holoenzyme to cause nuclear cAK effects. This might generate sufficient free C to catalyze phosphorylation of the trace levels of transcription factors present in the nucleus. It is not known if the nucleus contains anchoring proteins for R. Thus far, there is only scattered evidence for R subunit translocation into the nucleus.

Regulatory Subunit

STRUCTURE AND CHARACTERISTICS OF cAMP-BINDING SITES   The two cAMP binding sites in R (Figure 1) have been termed the fast and slow sites (dissociation rate constants, $k_2 = 0.15$ min^{-1} and $k_1 = \sim0.04$ min^{-1}, respectively) due to the relative rates of the biphasic cAMP dissociation kinetics (8, 26, 31, 117). cAMP binding to one site stimulates binding at the other site, and this positive cooperativity (Hill coefficient = 1.6) is mainly due to interaction of binding sites within a single subunit (8, 47, 180, 181). The apparent activation constant of cAMP (120 nM) for cAK holoenzyme is more consistent with the average affinity constants of the two cAMP sites than it is with the affinity constant of either independent site, as would be expected if both sites were involved in activating C (20, 119, 120, 131). However, inhibition of C by a mutated R containing only one cAMP-binding site is at least partially relieved by cAMP binding (180). Each site is approximately 110 amino acids in length (153, 159), and the structural information contained therein appears sufficient to provide for a relatively high affinity binding of cAMP (35, 127, J Shabb, unpublished results). Using coordinates derived from X-ray crystallographic analysis of CAP, the cAMP-binding sites of mammalian R subunit have been modeled (173). The sites are characterized by three α-helices and an eight-stranded, anti-parallel β-barrel (Figure 3A) that combine to form a cyclic nucleotide-binding pocket. Critical elements of the binding site have been identified by chemical modification techniques and site-directed mutagenesis (29, 118, 145, 146, 180). Six amino acids are invariant in this family of CAP-related nucleotide-binding sites and include three glycines thought to have structural importance: an alanine of unknown function, an arginine that contacts an exocyclic phosphate oxygen, and a glutamate that forms a hydrogen bond with the 2'OH of the ribose (Figure 3B). One of the glycines may also form hydrogen bonds with cAMP. cAMP apparently binds in the *syn* conformation (111, 145, 146, 173), and analogue studies emphasize the importance of the negative charge in the cyclized phosphate and the ribose 2'OH. Binding site elements that provide preference for adenine vs guanine are not known; the C-6 amino group is important, but not critical for interaction, and may function indirectly by changing the electron distribution in the purine.

ANALOGUE SPECIFICITIES   The cAMP-binding sites (slow and fast sites) differ in primary structure and in kinetics, and the slow site cyclic nucleotide analogue specificities vary between RI and RII (8, 24, 111, 117, 119, 120, 131). Analogue selectivity between sites is relative, and at sufficiently high concentrations, an analogue will interact with both sites in R. Thus use of single analogues to target one isozyme in intact tissues is difficult. Analogues derivatized at C-8 generally bind preferentially to the slow site, whereas analogues modified at C-6 or N^6 show fast site selectivity. 8-piperidino-cAMP differs in its interaction with the two R isoforms; this analogue shows fast-site selectivity in RI, but preferentially binds to the slow site in RII (120). When combinations of subsaturating concentrations of slow site-selective and fast site-selective analogues for each isoform are used, the respective cAK is synergistically activated with such isozyme-directed pairs

(8, 9, 119, 120, 131). These differences have been exploited in vivo by using pairs of site-selective cAMP analogues to address the role of each isoform in physiological processes (8, 9, 104, 164). By appropriate manipulation of the concentrations of analogue pairs selective for the respective sites of the R subunits, predictions can be made regarding the role of cAK isoform(s) in physiological events. Using such an approach, a role for type I cAK has recently been suggested for the effects of cAMP on DNA replication in T lymphocytes (149).

Other Possibilities for Regulation of cAK Activity and cAMP Action

Since the 1960's there has been speculation that cAMP could act through mechanisms other than C subunit activation. One possibility is that R subunit containing bound cAMP has functions independent of its interaction with C subunit. Secondly, by analogy with CAP, an unidentified cAMP-binding protein could mediate cAMP effects. CAP, which is homologous to R, does not interact with a kinase domain (173). It has both a cAMP-binding domain and a DNA-binding domain; the latter regulates gene transcription when cAMP is bound. A CAP-like protein in mammals has not been demonstrated. A third possibility is that cAMP could act by binding to the cGMP-binding sites of cGK or of ion channels, a process referred to as cross-activation (73, 78, 101).

CROSS-ACTIVATION   Elevation of either cAMP or cGMP causes vascular smooth muscle relaxation (60, 70, 92, 113), and cGK can mediate both effects (73). cGK is relatively specific (50–100-fold) for cGMP over cAMP, but basal cAMP concentration in smooth muscle is five to sixfold higher than that of cGMP, which allows cross-activation when cAMP is moderately elevated. Conversely, in some instances, cAK may be cross-activated by cGMP. In the T84 intestinal epithelial cell line, cGMP accumulation by the heat stable enterotoxin increases chloride conductance across the membranes of those cells (37). cAMP analogues that potently activate cAK also increase conductance, in contrast to the ineffectiveness of cGMP analogues. cAK is present in these cells, whereas there is no measurable cGK (37). Thus a pathological process that causes large increases in cGMP may exploit the degeneracy of the cAK cyclic nucleotide-binding sites to effect the response. This type of cross-activation may also occur under physiological circumstances. ANP-induced increases of cGMP in Leydig cells is also proposed to increase testosterone production by activating cAK (140).

Finally, an olfactory cation channel is believed to bind cAMP to mediate the effects of certain odorants (78, 101), but it is relatively specific for cGMP over cAMP in vitro. Thus cAMP could be considered to act by

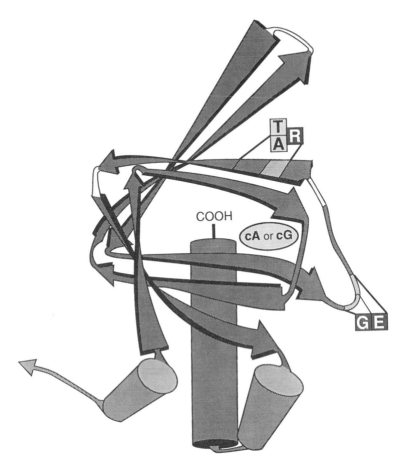

Figure 3   (A) Tertiary structural features of a single cyclic nucleotide-binding site in either cAK or cGK as predicted from the CAP crystal structure. Boxed white letters denote amino acids predicted to directly contact cAMP or cGMP in the binding pockets of all CAP-related cyclic nucleotide binding sites such as those in the cAK or cGK. Boxed black letters indicate the alanine/threonine that provides for cAMP/cGMP binding specificity in these sites. White portions indicate segments where insertions or deletions occur in a variety of these domains. The helix at the carboxyl terminus is shortened in this cartoon to more aptly depict its length in cAK and cGK binding sites. (B) Predicted contacts for cAMP and cGMP within the cyclic nucleotide binding sites of cAK and cGK. Depicted models apply for the fast or slow site on either cAK or cGK. Except for the alanine/threonine variance, the residues shown are invariant. Cyclic GMP is shown bound in the *syn* conformation; positions that are likely to form hydrogen bonds within the site are indicated by dotted lines. The purported hydrogen bond involving the C-2 amino of cGMP and a specific threonine in cGMP-specific binding sites are shaded.

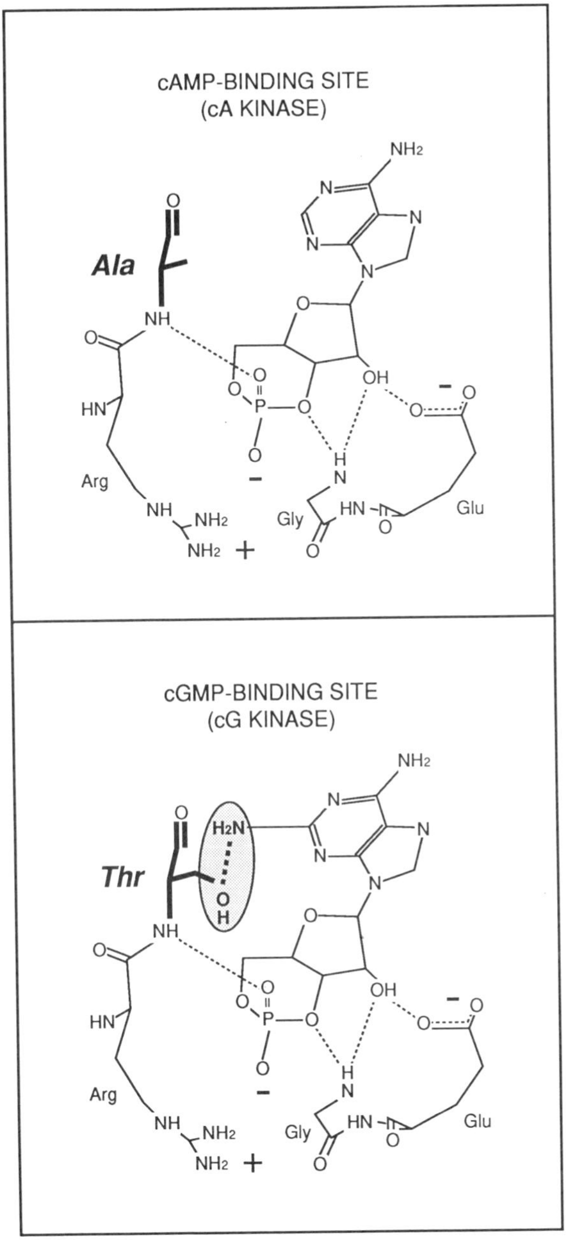
cAMP-BINDING SITE
(cA KINASE)
Ala
NH
Arg
Gly
Glu
cGMP-BINDING SITE
(cG KINASE)
Thr
NH
Arg
Gly
Glu

cross-activation for this process also. Such a channel protein could also be present in other tissues. It should be emphasized that there is strong evidence that most cAMP effects in mammals are mediated by cAK through protein phosphorylation. Still, it would not be surprising if some of the putative receptors mentioned above, or perhaps undiscovered receptors, play important roles in cAMP action.

NEGATIVE FEEDBACK   Regulation of most cellular processes by cAK probably occurs over a narrow range of activity changes, since two to threefold increases in cAMP produce maximum physiological responses in most tissues (79, 151). Nature has doubtless evolved regulatory mechanisms for maintaining cAMP levels and the resulting cAK activity within a narrow range for optimal modulation of cellular function. This same general principle is likely to apply to other signal transduction cascades. One mechanism for limiting cAMP elevation is through negative feedback control. In the cAMP cascade, the activated cAK phosphorylates and activates a phosphodiesterase, which accelerates the rate of cAMP degradation (23, 46, 47, 100). The phosphodiesterase that is a likely target for this effect in adipose tissue, liver, platelets, and other tissues is a so-called low K_m phosphodiesterase, also denoted as cGMP-inhibited or type III phosphodiesterase (7, 103). By this negative feedback control, cAK could regulate its own steady-state activity, and the same process would accelerate termination of the cAMP signal when extracellular stimuli decline. The cGMP-inhibited phosphodiesterase is also a target for insulin action (100, 103), which causes phosphorylation of this enzyme by activation of a different uncharacterized protein kinase (103). This effect could explain the insulin antagonism of several cAMP-elevating hormones, including antagonism of gene transcription effects mediated by CREB phosphorylation.

cGMP-DEPENDENT PROTEIN KINASES

Holoenzyme Structure and Isozymic Forms

cGK is less widely distributed than cAK and is highest in concentration in lung, cerebellum, smooth muscle, smooth muscle related tissues (pericytes, contractile mesangial cells of kidney glomeruli), and platelets (75, 99, 169). In most other tissues, cGK is approximately one tenth to one hundreth the cAK concentration (24). cGK is found in both cytoplasmic and membranous fractions, and the relative distribution is tissue-dependent. In lung and smooth muscle, cGK is predominantly in the soluble fraction (24, 71, 93), whereas intestinal or platelet cGK is almost entirely membrane-bound (30, 169, 170). cGK is negligible in liver, adipocytes, cardiac and skeletal muscle, fibroblasts, and macrophages (24, 169). cGK is also low in neutrophils, but chemotactic stimuli elicit a time-dependent cGK relocation within the cell that correlates with increased phosphorylation of endogenous substrates such as vimentin and phospholamban (28, 124, 182). Absolute cGK concentration may not predict the importance of cGK in a tissue since low cGK levels may still catalyze critical phosphorylations. Subcellular cGK redistribution in response to stimuli suggests that cGK-anchoring proteins may localize cGK to specific compartment(s).

Two forms of cGK (types I and II) occur in mammalian tissues. Type I is usually cytoplasmic, although a type I cGK may be associated with membranes in some cells (24, 93, 169, 170). Type I cGK more closely resembles RI than RII of cAK based on comparisons of primary sequence and interaction with MgATP (32, 146, 153, 154, 159). Type II is tightly associated with the membrane in intestinal epithelial cells (30) and can be solubilized by limited proteolysis. Two closely related isoforms of type I cGK (types Iα and Iβ) have been purified (96, 177, 178) and differ in amino acid sequence only in the amino-terminal ~100 amino acids (42, 137, 174, 177). In their divergent amino termini, which include the dimerization domain, the autoinhibitory domain, and the autophosphorylation sites, the two isoforms are only 36% identical. Type Iα predominates in bovine lung (90%), bovine trachealis smooth muscle (70% type Iα vs 30% type Iβ), cerebellum, and uterine smooth muscle (177). Types Iα and Iβ are present in approximately equal proportions in vascular smooth muscle (pig coronary arteries, bovine and human aortas) (144, 177).

Both type I isoforms are homodimers with blocked amino termini (type Iα is acetylated) (154), both bind two moles of cGMP per mole of cGK monomer (25, 177), and both undergo multiple autophosphorylations albeit at distinct sites in their differing amino-terminal domains (2, 41, 67, 88, 150, 177). Selectivity for cGMP vs cAMP is approximately 100-fold for both type I isoforms (Table 1), and the K_as for cGMP activation of catalysis for the two isoforms are similar (120 nM for type Iα, and 250 nM for type Iβ, respectively, using typical assay conditions at 20°) (40, 144, 177). No differences in substrate specificities and catalytic rates are evident for types Iα and Iβ (177). However, despite identical amino acid sequences in the cGMP-binding domains, the two isoforms have very different cGMP analogue specificities (Table 1) (144, 177). These differences must be conferred by influences of the respective amino termini on the binding domains (42, 66, 135, 177).

Type II cGK is an 86-K monomeric kinase (30) that is similar to type I isoforms in catalytic rate and relative specificity for cGMP vs cAMP, and it undergoes slow autophosphorylation. It differs in being monomeric and less electronegative, and binding only 1 mole of cGMP per monomer. The

Table 1

Cyclic nucleotide	K_a (nM)		Relative affinity $I\alpha/I\beta$
	Type $I\alpha$	Type $I\beta$	
cGMP	110	250	2.3
8-Br-cGMP	26	210	8.1
1,N^2-PET-cGMP	26	20	0.8
8-Br-1,N^2-PET-cGMP	13	9	0.7
8-(4-OH-Ph-S)-1,N^2-PET-cGMP	17	23	1.4
8-(4-OH-Ph-S)-cGMP	50	440	8.8
8-(2,4-Di-OH-Ph-S)-cGMP	5	360	72.0
8-(2-NH_2-Ph-S)-cGMP	7	1370	196.0
8-Br-1,N^2-β-NET-cGMP	54	3000	56.0

amino acid sequence of type II cGK has recently been deduced from the cDNA (162a) and predicts an 87-K protein that contains a carboxyl-terminal kinase domain and two cGMP-binding domains. The calculated isoelectric point of the predicted cGK (pH 8.2) is similar to that determined for intestinal epithelium cGK (pH 7.5) (30). It has ~53% overall homology with type I cGK isoforms (137, 154, 174). The highest degree of homology with the other cGKs is in the catalytic domain (~65%), as compared to 45% homology in the cGMP-binding domain and virtually no homology in the amino-terminal 110 amino acids (162a). In contrast to the intestinal enzyme, the type II cGK expressed in COS cells is soluble.

Chromosomal Location and Alternative Splicing

In humans, the type $I\beta$ gene is located on chromosome 10 in the p11.2-q11.2 region (136). It contains at least eight exons and exceeds 100 kb in length. Seven exons encode sequences shared by types $I\alpha$ and $I\beta$, and the eighth is specific for the amino-terminal portion of type $I\beta$. The location of the type II cGK gene is not known. In *Drosophila,* two genes have been isolated whose predicted products would contain both cGMP-binding domains and a protein kinase catalytic domain (77). Predicted amino acid sequences derived from these genes are homologous with those of mammalian type I and type II cGKs, 55 and 48%, respectively (137, 154, 162a, 174). The predicted proteins are most divergent in their amino termini, which would contain the dimerization and autoinhibitory/autophosphorylation domains. The human cGK gene and the *Drosophila* cGK genes (DG1 and DG2) share at least four of seven splice junctions (77, 136), but in two regions where the *Drosophila* gene contains one exon, the human gene has multiple exons.

No similarities are apparent between the exon organization of the cGK gene and that of the RIα and RIβ of cAK (136).

The marked variation in amino terminal sequences of the types Iα and Iβ, as compared to identical sequences for the remainder of the proteins (42, 137, 174), suggests that these isoforms derive from alternative mRNA splicing (42). mRNA sequences encoding the unique amino termini would be spliced to shared segments starting at Ser-89 (type Iα) and Ser-104 (type Iβ). This is supported by analysis of the mRNA sequences surrounding these areas (136), and by an exon/intron junction in the corresponding sequence in the *Drosophila* genes (77). mRNAs for both types Iα and Iβ are present in a number of tissues (137) with sizes ranging from 6.2 to 7.5 kb. This significantly exceeds the coding length required for expression of the final protein products. cGK mRNA levels increase in rat cerebellum and cerebrum between 5 to 30 days following birth, while cGK mRNA levels decline in heart. Expressed cGK is detected in all of these tissues by Western immunoblots. Three mRNA products of the *Drosophila* DG2 gene have been identified, but the expressed cGK has not been detected (77).

Domain Structure

cGK is an asymmetric molecule whose overall structure reveals both α-helices and β-pleated sheets; cGMP binding increases the content of β-pleated sheet and decreases the random coil content (87). The functional domains of cGK are closely related to those in the R and C subunits of cAK (Figure 1), and studies of cGK and cAK regulation complement each other. Unlike cAK, the regulatory and catalytic components of cGK are linked in one polypeptide chain, thus providing for continual interaction between various regions. Many of the most thorough biochemical studies of cAK are performed on purified R and C subunits in the absence of the other component. Similar studies in cGK are influenced by interactions between the various domains in the protein. For instance, interaction of C subunit with R subunit of cAK affects the dissociation kinetics of cAMP from R, and phosphorylation of the RII inhibitory domain by C subunit alters cAMP binding. These interactions are always present in cGK, thus complicating studies of some domain functions; however, they provide insight into domain interaction that may be difficult to study in cAK since it readily dissociates into the free subunits.

DIMERIZATION DOMAIN   Type I cGKs homodimerize through interactions at the amino terminus of each monomer. Partial proteolysis to remove the amino termini of types Iα or Iβ monomerizes the enzymes (39, 62, 66, 112, 178). A disulfide bridge at Cys-42 links type Iα subunits, but type Iβ

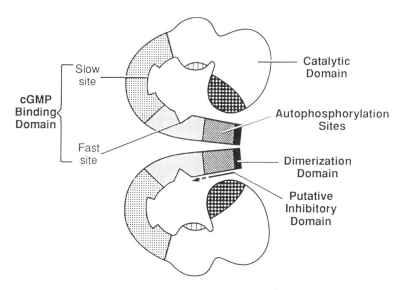

Figure 4   Current structural model for type I cGK. Revision of the model for type I cGK derives from new information demonstrating that autoinhibition of catalytic function involves interaction between the catalytic domain and inhibitory domain in a single cGK polypeptide chain (178). Parallel alignment of the amino-termini within the dimerization domain is in agreement with a head-to-head arrangement of sequences containing leucine/isoleucine zippers (4). The dashed arrow indicates that contacts between the inhibitory and the catalytic domains are likely to involve multiple sites and include a substrate-like sequence in this region.

lacks a cysteine in this region (112, 137, 174). Despite limited sequence homology in this region ($\sim 36\%$), both type I isoforms possess a leucine/iso-leucine zipper motif (6 heptad repeats in type Iα and 7–8 repeats in type Iβ) (4). A synthetic peptide based on the type Iα amino acid sequence (1–39) has strong α-helical content (70–80%) (4) and is dimerized in solution. The modeled α-helix formed by this sequence suggests strong hydrophobic interactions generated along a leucine/isoleucine face.

In accordance with the structure determined for leucine zippers, the monomers are predicted to be aligned in parallel in the dimer. Juxtaposition of Cys-42 in the respective monomers of type Iα would allow formation of the disulfide bridge previously identified in this isoform (112). No heterodimers of types Iα and Iβ have been identified, although it seems feasible for such forms to occur. Isolation of the cGMP-dependent monomer of type Iβ (178) and recognition of a leucine zipper motif in the dimerization domains (4) have prompted adoption of a new working model for cGK (Figure 4). In this model, autoinhibition arises from interaction between inhibitory and catalytic domains within one monomer, and monomers are aligned in parallel within the dimer (4, 15, 39, 66). The parallel alignment for cGK monomers differs from that predicted for cAK (14) and could account, in part, for differences in enzyme function.

AUTOPHOSPHORYLATION/AUTOINHIBITORY DOMAIN   Components involved in autoinhibition and autophosphorylation of cGK coexist in a short amino acid sequence that is carboxyl terminal to the dimerization domain. cGK substrate specificities are similar to those of cAK (51, 53, 54, 80, 81, 82, 183, 186) but, unlike cAK, the autoinhibitory domains of types Iα and Iβ cGK lack typical substrate (RRXSX) or pseudosubstrate sequences (RRXGX). Both isoforms autophosphorylate this region at multiple sites [type Iα at Ser-50, Ser 72, Thr-58, and Thr-84 (2), and type Iβ at Ser-63 and at least one unidentified site (41, 150)]. This suggests less rigid interaction than that which occurs with R and C, in which C rapidly phosphorylates a single serine in the autoinhibitory domain of RII. Autophosphorylation of types Iα or Iβ cGK (67, 88, 150) in the presence of cAMP increases basal activity and affinity for cAMP. In the presence of cGMP, Thr-84 in type Iα and Ser-63 in type Iβ are the major autophosphorylation sites (41, 150). The rate of autophosphorylation of type Iβ is increased more than fourfold by cGMP or cAMP and occurs at physiological concentrations of cGK and cyclic nucleotide. High concentrations of heptapeptide substrate do not diminish the rate or extent of phosphorylation, which suggests that autophosphorylation is a preferential process as compared to phosphorylation of exogenous substrates (41, 150). In the presence of protein substrates, the rate of cGK autophosphorylation is comparable to or greater than that of protein substrate phosphorylation (S Francis, unpublished results).

The mechanism of partial activation of cGK by autophosphorylation may be similar to the activation mechanism upon cGMP binding, since negatively-charged phosphates are added in each case. The increased negativity could repel elements within the catalytic domain such as those that interact with the positively charged amino acids of the autoinhibitory domain. Presumably, a surface location of either the cyclic nucleotide phosphate or the phosphate introduced by autophosphorylation would be required for this effect. The fact that phosphates introduced into cGK by either route cause an electronegative charge-shift on DEAE columns is consistent with such a requirement (179). Alternatively, enzyme activation could be by a more indirect mechanism, in which the bound cyclic nucleotides, and phosphate in the autoinhibitory domain, coincidentally produce a similar conformational change to activate the enzyme.

The physiological importance of cGK autophosphorylation is not known. Stimulation of autophosphorylation by cGMP or cAMP would tend to prolong the duration of the activated state following cessation of a hormonal stimulus, not only because of increased affinity for (hence slowed release of) cyclic nucleotides, but also because of increased basal cGK catalytic activity even after release of the activator. The demise of this elevated activity would be determined by the rate of removal of the phosphates from cGK by phosphatase action. The phosphorylated cGK remaining would be more responsive to small changes in cGMP or cAMP because of a higher affinity for these ligands. It is likely that intact tissues contain cGK in both phosphorylated and dephosphorylated forms.

Structural features comprising the autoinhibitory domain of cGK are not known. A synthetic undecapeptide based on the sequence of the major autophosphorylation site in type Iα (Thr-58) is a poor substrate for cGK (51), and peptides duplicating pseudosubstrate sequences from cAK or cGK are relatively poor inhibitors of cGK catalysis (39, 51). Evolutionary pressure to conserve a high affinity substrate site in the inhibitory domain of cGK is diminished since interacting elements are localized on one polypeptide and are less dependent on such a site for initiating reassociation. Partial proteolysis of type Iα generates a cGMP-independent monomer (minus 77 residues at the amino terminus) (62), and removal of 74 residues from the amino terminus of Iβ produces a monomer with complete cGMP dependency (39). Partial cGMP-dependence (40% stimulation by cGMP) is retained in type Iβ even with removal of 85 residues at the amino terminus (39, 178), which is well past the putative pseudosubstrate site for cGK at Lys-75 (-KRQAISAE-) (81). Thus as for cAK, autoinhibition of cGK is likely to involve regions other than substrate-like sites.

cGMP-BINDING DOMAINS: CHARACTERISTICS AND ANALOGUE SPECIFICITIES
Two homologous cyclic nucleotide-binding sites ($\sim$110 amino acids each) are arranged in tandem in the amino-terminal half of cGK (154). Like those in cAK, the binding sites in cGK are related evolutionarily to the CAP family of cyclic nucleotide-binding proteins (146, 173). cGK and cAK are distinct in this family since both contain two cyclic nucleotide-binding domains. The mechanistic import of two cyclic nucleotide-binding sites is unclear. The two sites differ kinetically, one being a high affinity slow site ($k_1 = 0.04$ min^{-1} for type Iα and $k_1 = 0.057$ min^{-1} in type Iβ at 30°) and the other being the lower affinity fast site ($k_2 = 3$–5 sec^{-1} at 0°). cGMP binding affinity at 0° is $\sim$100-fold greater than that at 30° (25, 32, 40).

Cyclic GMP analogue specificities of the two binding sites differ in type Iα (25, 32), perhaps because of different hydrophobicities in the binding pockets (154, 173). The fast site contains more hydrophobic amino acids than the slow site. Despite identical amino acid sequences in the binding sites of types Iα and Iβ, their cyclic nucleotide analogue specificities differ

(Table 1) (144, 177); whether different analogue selectivities for the two isoforms will persist under all conditions is not known. Activation of type Iα cGK by cGMP is positively cooperative (Hill constant = 1.5–1.8) (105). Occupation of the fast site slows dissociation from the slow site, but whether cooperativity involves interaction of binding domains in the same monomer or through site interactions between monomers is not known. As for type I cAK, MgATP promotes dissociation of cGMP from the enzyme. cGMP binding to both sites is required to fully activate cGK, but unlike cAK, cGMP binding to the slow site partially activates type Iα (25, 179).

$$E_2 + 2\ cGMP \rightarrow E_2\text{-}cGMP_2 + 2\ cGMP \rightarrow E_2\text{-}cGMP_4$$
(inactive)   (~50% active)   (fully active)

Since monomer alignment within the cGK and cAK dimers may differ, the partial activation of cGK could relate to differences in the interaction of domains in the tertiary structures. Alternatively, it could due to differences in the potency of interaction between the respective inhibitory and catalytic domains in cAK vs cGK. Partial activation of cGK by low cGMP levels expands the responsiveness in cGK catalytic activity over a broader range of cGMP concentrations. The K_a of cGMP or site-specific analogues for full activation of cGK most closely relates to the average affinity constants of the nucleotides for both binding sites. This points to a role for both sites in the activation process (25, 32). Partially activated type Iβ cGK has not been observed, which could suggest that activation in this isoform requires cGMP binding to both sites.

The predicted structures of the cGMP-binding domains are similar to those for cAK (Figure 3A,B) and CAP and include the six invariant amino acids conserved in all these sites (146, 172, 173). Analogue studies suggest that cGMP is bound in the *syn* conformation and confirm the importance of the 2′-OH and the cyclic phosphate for high affinity binding (25, 32, 111). In all eukaryotic cGMP-binding sites belonging to the CAP family, an invariant threonine or serine appears to be critical for providing cGMP vs cAMP selectivity, as well as for increasing binding affinity for cGMP (78, 101, 145, 146, 162a). In those binding sites with a preference for cAMP vs cGMP, alanine replaces the threonine; in type Iα cGK, these are Thr-177 (fast site) and Thr-301 (slow site) (154). In the cGMP-binding sites modeled after the CAP protein, the hydroxyl of the unique threonine lies proximal to the C-2 amino group of the guanine and could form a hydrogen bond (145, 172). Cyclic nucleotide analogues lacking the amino group at C-2 bind weakly to these sites (cIMP has a 200-fold lower affinity than cGMP), whereas analogues with increased hydrogen bonding potential at this position bind with higher affinity than does cGMP (25, 144, 177). The import of the threonine in binding site specificity is supported by the results of site-directed mutagenesis of RI of cAK and of the cGMP-gated cation channel (78, 145, 146). Replacing the homologous alanines in RI cAMP-binding sites with threonines increases cGMP-binding affinity ~200-fold with minimal effects on cAMP binding; the resultant sites were equally good for cAMP or cGMP (145). Conversely, in the cation channel, altering the conserved threonine to alanine greatly decreases cGMP-binding affinity with little effect on cAMP binding (78). Thus a conserved threonine in the cGMP-binding sites, in conjunction with the conserved arginine and glutamate, interact with different portions of cGMP to provide for its high affinity binding.

The two homologous cGMP-binding sites in cGK vary in amino acid sequences, thus providing for structural differences reflected in cyclic nucleotide analogue specificities. Most cGMP analogues interact to some extent with both the fast and slow binding sites, but close scrutiny reveals site selectivity. In general, analogues with alterations at N-7 or C-8 of guanine preferentially bind to the slow site, but changes in substituents at N-1 increase selectivity toward the fast site. Addition of subsaturating concentrations of two analogues, each being selective for the opposite site, synergistically activates cGK (25, 32).

Types Iα and Iβ have quite similar K_as for cGMP, but exhibit different analogue specificities (Table 1) (144, 177). Some analogues such as $1,N^2$-phenyletheno-cGMP activate both isoforms equally well, whereas others, most notably those with changes at C-8, potently interact with type Iα, but are weak activators of type Iβ. The marked discrimination between the types Iα and Iβ due to C-8 modifications in analogues is ablated by substitutions at N-1/C-2 (Table 1). This suggests few structural constraints in regions of the binding sites that adjoin the C-8 position and the N-1/C-2 positions of the cyclic nucleotide. The divergent amino termini of the isoforms must impart different biochemical properties to these cGMP-binding sites (135, 144, 177) that are identical in amino acid sequence (137, 154, 174). This should caution against extrapolations regarding enzyme function based on similarities in primary sequence only.

CATALYTIC DOMAIN: SUBSTRATE SPECIFICITY   The catalytic domain of type I cGK resides in the carboxyl-terminal half of the polypeptide chain (Figure 1) (154) and is predicted to have a structure similiar to that of cAK (Figure 2) (93). Modeling of the catalytic domain of cGK using the coordinates for the C subunit supports this prediction (66). Asp-483 in cGK (the corollary of Asp-166 in C subunit) is proposed as the catalytic base crucial to the transfer of the ATP γ-phosphate to serine/threonine in a peptide or protein structure, although a phospho-enzyme intermediate has not been observed (65). However, as mentioned for cAK, the transfer may involve direct nucleophilic attack of the substrate hydroxyl on ATP (1, 187).

Despite many similarities, comparisons between cGK and cAK structure should be approached with caution since the cGK catalytic domain is continually complexed with its regulatory elements (Figure 1). Furthermore, the structure determined for C subunit is that of a complex with PKIP (5–24) (83, 84, 187), which does not inhibit cGK. Differences in interaction with PKIP and in substrate specificities between the C subunit and cGK are probably because of distinguishing features in the larger lobe of the catalytic domain of cGK. Like cAK, cGK preferentially phosphorylates serines in substrates having the consensus sequence RRXSX, but there are exceptions (51, 53, 54). Most notable are the autophosphorylation sites in both types Iα and Iβ cGK that lack the dibasic motif (2, 41). Further, in type Iα the main autophosphorylation site is a threonine (2), which appears less frequently as the phospho-acceptor amino acid in cGK substrates (51, 53, 54). Two serines in close proximity in histone H2b (Ser-32 and Ser-36) are selectively phosphorylated by cAK and cGK, with cGK showing preference towards Ser-32 in the basic sequence -DGKKRKSRKE- (51, 53, 54). Using a synthetic peptide based on this sequence, cGK has a lower K_m and a higher V_{max} than does cAK. Furthermore, the arginine that is carboxyl-terminal to the serine is a positive determinant for cGK as compared to cAK (51). A heptapeptide based on this sequence in histone H2b (RKRSRAE) is commercially available for use in assaying cGK.

A stronger selectivity for cGK vs cAK is present in a phosphorylation site in the cGMP-binding, cGMP-specific phosphodiesterase (BPDE). cGMP binding to BPDE is required for phosphorylation of this protein, which suggests that it is a physiological substrate for cGK (158). In the intact protein, cGK phosphorylates BPDE at a rate at least ten times that of cAK. The phosphorylation-site peptide (RKISASEFDRPLR) retains the same selectivity for cGK over cAK (21) with cGK having a four to fivefold lower K_m and a threefold higher V_{max} as compared to cAK. A truncated octapeptide (RKISASEF) retains the same selectivity between the kinases, but a heptapeptide (RKISASE) does not, which suggests that the phenylalanine is critical for the selectivity for cGK over cAK (21). Such distinctions in substrate preferences are likely to reveal differences in the fine structure of the catalytic domain of cGK as compared to the C subunit.

Other substrates with selectivity for cGK over cAK are known, but the structural features providing for this selectivity are unclear. Purified bovine skeletal muscle RI is phosphorylated at Ser-99 by cGK, but not by cAK (44) and is the only known substrate to be absolutely selective between these kinases. The α-subunit of skeletal muscle phosphorylase b kinase is phosphorylated by cGK at a rate three times that of cAK (183). A 23-K protein (G-substrate) isolated from mammalian cerebellum is phosphorylated at two threonines (3, 139), and the K_m of cGK for this peptide is ~0.2

μM, 30 times lower than that for cAK (3, 51). Histone H1 also contains a site reported to be very selective towards cGK.

Function

SMOOTH MUSCLE RELAXATION Activation of guanylate cyclase in vascular smooth muscle by ANP, EDRF, and nitrovasodilators increases cGMP levels and concomitantly decreases muscle tone (34, 60, 70, 92, 113, 128, 170). Cyclic nucleotide analogue effects on tracheal and vascular smooth muscle show a strong correlation between the potencies with which analogues activate purified type Iα cGK and the concentrations required to induce relaxation of tension in these tissues (39, 40, 144). Whether type Iβ cGK is also involved in smooth muscle relaxation is not known since cGMP analogues specific for this isoform have not been found. Analogues specific and potent for activating cAK do not relax smooth muscle, and cAMP analogues that decrease tension do so at concentrations that would cross-activate cGK. It has long been known that cAMP elevation in smooth muscle is associated with decreased muscle tension (60), but it now seems likely that cAMP effects are mediated through cGK in this tissue (40, 73, 94, 95). This possibility is further strengthened by the fact that the affinity of cGK for cAMP is increased ~tenfold by autophosphorylation (88, 150). Thus it is possible that cAMP will cross-activate cGK under a variety of conditions.

PLATELET AGGREGATION Elevation of cGMP or cAMP in platelets inhibits aggregation, and protein phosphorylation patterns are distinct in each instance (116, 165, 170). VASP, the vasodilator-stimulated protein (46–50 K) in platelets, is phosphorylated quantitatively by elevation of either cyclic nucleotide. Phosphorylation is temporally and quantitatively related to cGMP elevation and inhibition of platelet aggregation (45, 58, 170), but the role of VASP in platelet function is not known.

LOWERING INTRACELLULAR CALCIUM One of the main mechanisms of action of cGMP and cGK in many tissues, including smooth muscle and platelets, may be to lower intracellular calcium, but the mechanism for this effect is unknown (27, 63, 70, 74, 92, 94, 98, 110, 129). ANP or cyclic nucleotides lower intracellular calcium in cultured smooth muscle cells in early passage, but fail to do so in cells in later passage, which have greatly diminished levels of cGK, though normal cAK levels. Reintroduction of cGK via osmotic permeabilization of the cell restores the ability of either cGMP or cAMP to lower calcium (27, 94, 95). This supports a central role for a cGK-catalyzed phosphorylation in the decrease in intracellular calcium and also supports the interpretation that cGK mediates the calcium lowering effects of both cGMP and cAMP in smooth muscle cells. Despite the presence of a number of preferential substrates for cGK in smooth muscle (6, 71), the mechanism for lowering calcium is unknown. Regulation of cGK activity is likely to be pivotal in calcium homeostasis, but cGK effects on other pathways may be equally important in cGMP regulation of smooth muscle tone.

Proteins associated with calcium mobilization are potential targets for cGK phosphorylation. These include phospholamban (28, 69, 125), Ca^{2+}/ ATPases from the sarcoplasmic reticulum and the plasma membrane (27, 28, 92, 95, 129, 185), and a G protein involved in the regulation of phospholipase C (63). Other substrate targets of cGK such as VASP in platelets, or the cerebellar G-substrate proteins, could also be involved in calcium metabolism or independent processes (3, 45, 58, 170). Regulation of ion channel function by cGMP and cGK continues to be a major focus. cGMP or constitutively activated cGK inhibit L-type Ca^{2+} currents in ventricular cells (98, 110). Direct effects of cGMP binding as well as cGK phosphorylation to inhibit conductance through an amiloride-sensitive cation channel in kidney have been reported (91). Increased conductance through calcium- and voltage-activated potassium channels in response to ANP may involve a cGK-mediated activation of protein phosphatase 2A by a cGK phosphorylation event (175). There may be other schemes for cGMP and cGK action, but our understanding of the cGMP cascade as mediated through cGK is in its infancy as compared to the many examples for cAK action.

OTHER cGMP RECEPTORS   cGK and cAK may both be receptors for cGMP in cells, but other cGMP receptors must also be considered. These include the cGMP-binding phosphodiesterases that modulate cellular cGMP and cAMP levels (7, 103, 158), cGMP-binding cation channels (78, 101), and perhaps others.

CONCLUDING REMARKS

It is assumed that alteration of either intracellular cAMP or cGMP modulates the activity of the corresponding protein kinase. Cross-activation by the other cyclic nucleotide may also exist in some cells or in pathological conditions. Kinase activities may also be modulated by changes wrought by autophosphorylation, translocation, or by subcellular location depending on the isoform present. Slower modulation occurs by changes in total enzyme level. It is now clear that there are literally hundreds of protein substrates for cAK, and the same is likely to be true for cGK. Since these substrates regulate most cellular processes, this subject is beyond the scope of our review. Consensus sequences that identify potential phosphorylation sites are enticingly common in protein sequences. To have physiological relevance, phosphorylation of a protein in intact cells must be demonstrated, and phosphorylation should be related to changes in function. Substrates for cAK and cGK seem to bear little resemblance to each other in functional or structural features except for the presence of simple consensus amino acid sequences. Perhaps cAK and cGK recognize subtle differences in these sequences. As with any protein kinase substrate, it appears that there are at least two general mechanisms by which the phosphate incorporated into a protein by cAK or cGK can alter its activity: (*a*) by direct effects of the phosphate on the ligand- or substrate-binding site of the protein, and (*b*) by a phosphate-induced conformational change produced at a more distal site on the protein.

Literature Cited

1. Adams JA, Taylor SS. 1993. Phosphorylation of peptide substrates for catalytic subunit of cAMP-dependent protein kinase. *J. Biol. Chem.* 268:7747–52

2. Aitken A, Hemmings B, Hofmann F. 1984. Identification of residues on cGMP-dependent protein kinase that are autophosphorylated in the presence of cAMP and cGMP. *Biochim. Biophys. Acta* 790:219–25

3. Aswad DW, Greengard P. 1981. A specific substrate from rabbit cerebellum for guanosine 3′:5′-monophosphate-dependent protein kinase: purification and characterization. *J. Biol. Chem.* 256:3487–93

4. Atkinson RA, Saudek V, Huggins JP, Pelton JT. 1991. ^{1}H NMR and circular dichroism studies of the N-terminal domain of cGMP-dependent protein kinase: a leucine/isoleucine zipper. *Biochemistry.* 30:9387–95

5. Bacskai BJ, Hochner B, Mahaut-Smith M, Adams, SR, Kaang B, et al. 1993. Spatially resolved dynamics of cAMP and protein kinase A subunits in *Aplysia* sensory neurons. *Science* 260:222–26

6. Baltensperger K, Chiesi M, Carafoli E. 1990. Substrates of cGMP kinase in vascular smooth muscle and their role in the relaxation process. *Biochemistry* 29:9753–60

7. Beavo JA. 1988. Multiple isoenzymes of cyclic nucleotide phosphodiesterase. *Adv. Second Messenger Phosphoprotein Res.* 11:1–38

8. Beebe SJ, Corbin JD. 1986. Cyclic nucleotide-dependent protein kinases. In *The Enzymes,* ed P Boyer, E Krebs, 17A:43–111. Orlando; Academic

9. Beebe SJ, Holloway R, Rannels SR, Corbin JD. 1984. Two classes of cAMP analogs which are selective for the two different cAMP-binding sites of Type II protein kinase demonstrate synergism when added together to intact adipocytes. *J. Biol. Chem.* 259: 3539–47

10. Beebe SJ, Salomonsky P, Jahnsen T, Li Y. 1992. The Cγ subunit is a unique isozyme of the cAMP-dependent protein kinase. *J. Biol. Chem.* 267: 25505–12

11. Bramson HN, Thomas NE, Miller WT, Fry DC, Mildvan AS, Kaiser ET. 1987. Conformation of Leu-Arg-Arg-Ser-Leu-Gly bound in the active site of adenosine cyclic 3′,5′-phosphate-dependent protein kinase. *Biochemistry* 26:4466–70

12. Bregman DB, Bhattacharyya N, Rubin CS. 1989. High affinity binding protein for the regulatory subunit of cAMP-dependent protein kinase II-B. *J. Biol. Chem.* 264:4648–56

13. Bregman DB, Hirsch AH, Rubin CS. 1991. Molecular characterization of bovine brain P75, a high affinity binding protein for the regulatory subunit of cAMP-dependent protein kinase IIβ. *J. Biol. Chem.* 266:7207–13

14. Bubis J, Vedvick TS, Taylor SS. 1987. Anti-parallel alignment of the two protomers of the regulatory subunit dimer

of cAMP-dependent protein kinase I. *J. Biol. Chem.* 262:14961–66

15. Butt E, Geiger J, Jarchau T, Lohmann SM, Walter U. 1993. The cGMP-dependent protein kinase-gene, protein and function. *Neurochem. Res.* 18:27–42

16. Cadd GG, Uhler MD, McKnight GS. 1990. Holoenzymes of cAMP-dependent protein kinase containing the neural form of type I regulatory subunit have an increased sensitivity to cyclic nucleotides. *J. Biol. Chem.* 265:19502–6

17. Carr DW, Stofko-Hahn RE, Fraser IDC, Bishop SM, Acot TS, Brennan RG, et al. 1991. Interaction of the regulatory subunit (RII) of cAMP-dependent protein kinase with RII-anchoring proteins occurs through an amphipathic helix binding motif. *J. Biol. Chem.* 266:14188–89

18. Carr DW, Stofko-Hahn RE, Fraser IDC, Cone RD, Scott JD. 1992. Localization of the cAMP-dependent protein kinase to the postsynaptic densities by A Kinase Anchoring Proteins. *J. Biol. Chem.* 267:16816–23

19. Cheng HC, Kemp BE, Pearson RB, Smith AJ, Misconi L, Van Patten SM, et al. 1986. A potent synthetic peptide inhibitor of the cAMP-dependent protein kinase. *J. Biol. Chem.* 261:989–92

20. Cobb CE, Beth AH, Corbin JD. 1987. Purification and characterization of an inactive form of cAMP-dependent protein kinase containing bound cAMP. *J. Biol. Chem.* 262:16566–74

21. Colbran JL, Francis SH, Leach AB, Thomas MK, Jiang H, McAllister LM, et al. 1992. A phenylalanine in peptide substrates provides for selectivity between cGMP- and cAMP-dependent protein kinases. *J. Biol. Chem.* 267:9589–94

22. Cook PF, Neville ME Jr, Vrana KE, Hart FT, Roskoski R Jr. 1982. Adenosine cyclic 3′,5′-monophosphate-dependent protein kinase: kinetic mechanism for the bovine skeletal muscle catalytic subunit. *Biochemistry* 21:5794–99

23. Corbin JD, Beebe SJ, Blackmore PF. 1985. cAMP-dependent protein kinase activation lowers hepatocyte cAMP. *J. Biol. Chem.* 260:8731–35

24. Corbin JD, Lincoln TM. 1978. Comparison of cAMP- and cGMP-dependent protein kinases. *Adv. Cyclic Nucleotide Res.* 9:159–70

25. Corbin JD, Ogreid D, Miller JP, Suva RH, Jastorff B, Doskeland SO. 1986. Studies of cGMP analog specificity

and function of the two intrasubunit binding sites of cGMP-dependent protein kinase. *J. Biol. Chem.* 261:1208–14

26. Corbin JD, Sugden PH, West L, Flockhart DA, Lincoln TM, McCarthy D. 1978. Studies on properties and mode of action of the purified regulatory subunit of bovine heart cAMP-dependent protein kinase. *J. Biol. Chem.* 253:3997–4003

27. Cornwell TL, Lincoln TM. 1989. Regulation of intracellular Ca^{2+} levels in cultured vascular smooth muscle cells. *J. Biol. Chem.* 264:1146–55

28. Cornwell TL, Pryzwansky KB, Wyatt TA, Lincoln TM. 1991. Regulation of sarcoplasmic reticulum protein phosphorylation by localized cGMP-dependent protein kinase in vascular smooth muscles. *Mol. Pharmacol.* 40:923–31

29. Correll LA, Woodford TA, Corbin JD, Mellon PL, McKnight GS. 1989. Functional characterization of cAMP-binding mutations in type I protein kinase. *J. Biol. Chem.* 264:16672–78

30. DeJonge HR. 1981. Cyclic GMP-dependent protein kinase in intestinal brush borders. *Adv. Cyclic Nucleotide Res.* 14:315–33

30a. Doskeland SO, Maronde E, Gjertsen BT. 1993. The genetic subtypes of cAMP-dependent protein kinase—functionally different or redundant? *Biochim. Biophys. Acta.* 1178:249–58

31. Doskeland SO, Ogreid D. 1984. Characterization of the interchain and intrachain interactions between the binding sites of the free regulatory moiety of protein kinase 1. *J. Biol. Chem.* 259:2291–301

32. Doskeland SO, Vintermyr OK, Corbin JD, Ogreid D. 1987. Studies on the interactions between the cyclic nucleotide-binding sites of cGMP-dependent protein kinase. *J. Biol. Chem.* 262:3534–40

33. Edelman AM, Blumenthal DK, Krebs EG. 1987. Protein serine/threonine kinases. *Annu. Rev. Biochem.* 56:567–613

34. Fiscus RP, Rapoport RM, Murad F. 1984. Atriopeptin II elevates cGMP, activates cGMP-dependent protein kinase and causes relaxation in rat thorax aorta. *Biochim. Biophys. Acta* 846:179–84

35. Flockhart DA, Corbin JD. 1982. Regulatory mechanisms in the control of protein kinases. *Crit. Rev. Biochem.* 12:133–86

36. Flockhart DA, Watterson DM, Corbin JD. 1980. Studies on func-

tional domains of the regulatory subunit of bovine heart cAMP-dependent protein kinase. *J. Biol. Chem.* 255: 4435–40

37. Forte L, Thorne PK, Eber SL, Krause WJ, Freeman RH, et al. 1992. Stimulation of intestinal Cl⁻ transport by heat-stable enterotoxin: activation of cAMP-dependent protein kinase by cGMP. *Am. J. Physiol.* 263:C607–15

38. Foss K, Simard J, Berube D, Beebe SJ, Sandberg M, et al. 1992. Localization of the catalytic subunit Cγ of the cAMP-dependent protein kinase gene (PRKACG) to human chromosome region 9q13. *Cytogenet. Cell Genet.* 60:22–25

39. Francis SH, Corbin JD. 1993. Progress in understanding the mechanism and function of cGMP-dependent protein kinase. In *Advance in Pharmacology, Cyclic GMP: Synthesis, Metabolism and Function,* ed. F Murad. Vol. 26. Orlando: Academic. In press

40. Francis SH, Noblett BD, Todd BW, Wells JN, Corbin JD. 1988. Relaxation of vascular and tracheal smooth muscle by cyclic nucleotide analogs that preferentially activate purified cGMP-dependent protein kinase. *Mol. Pharmacol.* 34:506–17

41. Francis SH, Smith J, Walsh K, Kumar S, Colbran J, Corbin J. 1993. Autophosphorylation of bovine aorta type Iβ cGMP-dependent protein kinase occurs at serine-63 in the inhibitory domain of the enzyme. *FASEB J.* 7:A1123

42. Francis SH, Woodford TA, Wolfe L, Corbin JD. 1988–89. Types Iα and Iβ isozymes of cGMP-dependent protein kinase: alternative mRNA splicing may produce different inhibitory domains. *Second Messengers Phosphoproteins* 12:301–10

43. Friedman DL, Larner J. 1963. Studies on UDPG-α-glucan transglucosylase III. Interconversion of two forms of muscle UDPG-α-glucan transglucosylase by a phosphorylation-dephosphorylation reaction sequence. *Biochemistry* 4:669–75

44. Geahlen RL, Krebs EG. 1980. Regulatory subunit of the type I cAMP-dependent protein kinase as an inhibitor and substrate of the cGMP-dependent protein kinase. *J. Biol. Chem.* 255: 1164–69

45. Geiger J, Nolte C, Butt E, Sage SO, Walter U. 1992. Role of cGMP and cGMP-dependent protein kinase in nitrovasodilator inhibition of agonist-evoked calcium elevation in human platelets. *Proc. Natl. Acad. Sci. USA* 89:1031–35

46. Gettys TW, Blackmore PF, Redmon JB, Beebe SJ, Corbin JD. 1987. Short term feedback regulation of cAMP by accelerated degradation in rat tissues. *J. Biol. Chem.* 262:333–39

47. Gettys TW, Corbin JD. 1989. The protein kinase family of enzymes. In *Receptor Phosphorylation,* ed. VK Moudgil, pp. 40–88. Boca Raton: CRC Press

48. Gibbs CS, Knighton DR, Sowadski JM, Taylor SS, Zoller MJ. 1988. Systematic mutational analysis of cAMP-dependent protein kinase identifies unregulated catalytic subunits and defines regions important for the recognition of the regulatory subunit. *J. Biol. Chem.* 267:4806–14

49. Gill GN, Holdy KE, Walton GM, Kanstein CB. 1976. Purification and characterization of cGMP-dependent protein kinase. *Proc. Natl. Acad. Sci. USA* 73:3918–22

50. Glantz SB, Amat JA, Rubin CS. 1992. cAMP signaling in neurons: patterns of neuronal expression and intracellular localization for a novel protein, AKAP 150, that anchors the regulatory subunit of cAMP-dependent protein kinase II beta. *Mol. Biol. Cell* 3:1215–28

51. Glass DB. 1990. Substrate specificity of the cGMP-dependent protein kinase. In *Peptides and Protein Phosphorylation,* ed. BE Kemp, pp. 210–38. Boca Raton: CRC Press

52. Glass DB, Feller MJ, Levin LR, Walsh DA. 1992. Structural basis for the low affinities of yeast cAMP-dependent and mammalian cGMP-dependent protein kinases for protein kinase inhibitor peptides. *Biochemistry* 31:1728–34

53. Glass DB, Krebs EG. 1979. Comparison of the substrate specificity of cAMP- and cGMP-dependent protein kinases. *J. Biol. Chem.* 254:9728–38

54. Glass DB, Krebs EG. 1982. Phosphorylation by cGMP-dependent protein kinase of synthetic peptide analogs of a site phosphorylated in histone H2B. *J. Biol. Chem.* 257:1196–200

55. Gonzalez GA, Montminy MR. 1989. Cyclic AMP stimulates somatostatin gene transcription by phosphorylation of CREB at serine 133. *Cell* 59:675–80

56. Granot J, Mildvan AS, Bramson HN, Kaiser ET. 1981. Nuclear magnetic resonance studies of the conformation and kinetics of the peptide-substrate at the active site of bovine heart protein kinase. *Biochemistry* 20:602–10

57. Granot J, Mildvan AS, Kaiser ET.

1980. Studies of the mechanism of action and regulation of cAMP-dependent protein kinase. *Arch. Biochem. Biophys.* 205:1–17

58. Halbrugge M, Friedrich C, Eigenthaler M, Schanzenbacher P, Walter U. 1990. Stoichiometric and reversible phosphorylation of a 46 kDa protein in human platelets in response to cGMP- and cAMP-elevating vasodilators. *J. Biol. Chem.* 265:3088–93

59. Hanks SK, Quinn AM, Hunter T. 1988. The protein kinase family: conserved features and deduced phylogeny of the catalytic domains. *Science* 241:42–52

60. Hardman JG. 1984. Cyclic nucleotides and regulation of vascular smooth muscle. *J. Cardiovasc. Pharmacol.* 6:5639–45

61. Hayes JS, Brunton LL. 1982. Functional compartments in cyclic nucleotide action. *J. Cyclic Nucleotide Res.* 8:1–16

62. Heil WG, Landgraf W, Hofmann F. 1987. A catalytically active fragment of cGMP-dependent protein kinase: occupation of its cGMP-binding sites does not affect its phosphotransferase activity. *Eur. J. Biochem.* 168:117–21

63. Hirata M, Kohse KP, Chang C, Ikebe T, Murad F. 1990. Mechanism of cGMP inhibition of inositol phosphate formation in rat aorta segments and cultured bovine aortic smooth muscle cells. *J. Biol. Chem.* 265:1268–73

64. Hirsch AH, Glantz SB, Li Y, You Y, Rubin CS. 1992. Cloning and expression of an intron-less gene for AKAP 75, an anchor protein for the regulatory subunit of cAMP-dependent protein kinase IIβ. *J. Biol. Chem.* 267:2131–34

65. Ho M-f, Bramson HN, Hansen DE, Knowles JR, Kaiser ET. 1988. Stereochemical course of the phospho group transfer catalyzed by cAMP-dependent protein kinase. *J. Am. Chem. Soc.* 110:2680–81

66. Hofmann F, Dostmann W, Keilbach A, Landgraf W, Ruth P. 1992. Structure and physiological role of cGMP-dependent protein kinase. *Biochim. Biophys. Acta* 1135:51–60

67. Hofmann F, Gensheimer H, Gobel C. 1985. cGMP-dependent protein kinase: autophosphorylation changes the characteristics of binding site 1. *Eur. J. Biochem.* 147:361–65

68. Houge G, Steinberg RA, Ogreid D, Doskeland SO. 1990. The rate of recombination of the subunits (RI and C) of cAMP-dependent protein kinase depends on whether one or two cAMP

molecules are bound per RI monomer. *J. Biol. Chem.* 265:19507–16

69. Huggins JP, Cook EA, Piggott JR, Mattinsley TJ, England PJ. 1989. Phospholamban is a good substrate for cGMP-dependent protein kinase in vitro, but not in intact cardiac or smooth muscle. *Biochem. J.* 260:829–35

70. Ignarro LJ, Kadowitz PJ. 1985. The pharmacological and physiological role of cGMP in vascular smooth muscle relaxation. *Annu. Rev. Pharmacol. Toxicol.* 25:171–91

71. Ives HE, Casnellie JE, Greengard P, Jamieson JD. 1980. Subcellular localization of cGMP-dependent protein kinase and its substrates in vascular smooth muscle. *J. Biol. Chem.* 255:3777–85

72. Jahnsen T, Hedin L, Kidd VJ, Beattie WG, Lohmann SM, Walter U, et al. 1986. Molecular cloning, cDNA structure, and regulation of the regulatory subunit of type II cAMP-dependent protein kinase from rat ovarian granulosa cells. *J. Biol. Chem.* 261: 12352–61

73. Jiang H, Colbran JL, Francis SH, Corbin JD. 1992. Direct evidence for cross-activation of cGMP-dependent protein kinase by cAMP in pig coronary arteries. *J. Biol. Chem.* 267:1015–19

74. Johansson JS, Haynes DH. 1992. Cyclic GMP increases the rate of the calcium extrusion pump in intact human platelets but has no direct effect on the dense tubular calcium accumulation system. *Biochim. Biophys. Acta.* 1105: 40–50

75. Joyce NC, DeCamilli P, Lohmann SM, Walter U. 1986. cGMP-dependent protein kinase is present in high concentrations in contractile cells of the kidney vasculature. *J. Cyclic Nucleotide Protein Phosphorylation Res.* 11:191–98

76. Jungmann RA, Hiestand PC, Schweppe JS. 1974. Mechanism of action of gonadotropin. Cyclic adenosine monophosphate-dependent translocation of ovarian cytoplasmic cyclic adenosine monophosphate-binding protein and protein kinase to nuclear acceptor sites. *Endocrinology* 94:168–83

77. Kalderon D, Rubin GM. 1989. cGMP-dependent protein kinase genes in *Drosophila*. *J. Biol. Chem.* 264:10738–48

78. Kaupp UB. 1992. Role of cGMP and Ca^{2+} in vertebrate photoreceptor excitation and adaptation. *Annu. Rev. Physiol.* 54:153–75

79. Keely SL, Corbin JD, Park CR. 1975. Regulation of adenosine 3',5' mono-

phosphate-dependent protein kinase. Regulation of the heart enzyme by epinephrine, glucagon, insulin and 1-methyl-3-isobutylxanthine. *J. Biol. Chem.* 250:4832–40

80. Kemp BE, Graves DJ, Benjamini E, Krebs EG. 1977. Role of multiple basic residues in determining the substrate specificity of cAMP-dependent protein kinase. *J. Biol. Chem.* 252: 4888–94

81. Kemp BE, Pearson RB. 1990. Protein kinase recognition sequence motifs. *Trends Biochem. Sci* 15:342–46

82. Kennelly PJ, Krebs EG. 1991. Consensus sequences as substrate specificity determinants for protein kinases and protein phosphatases. *J. Biol. Chem.* 266:15555–58

83. Knighton DR, Zheng J, Ten Eyck LF, Ashford VA, Xuong N-h, et al. 1991. Crystal structure of the catalytic subunit of cAMP-dependent protein kinase. *Science* 253:407–13

84. Knighton DR, Zheng J, Ten Eyck LF, Xuong N-h, Taylor SS, Sowadski JM. 1991. Structure of a peptide inhibitor bound to the catalytic subunit of cAMP-dependent protein kinase. *Science* 253: 414–20

85. Krebs EG. 1986. The enzymology of control by phosphorylation. In *The Enzymes*, ed. PD Boyer, EG Krebs, 58:3–20. New York: Academic

86. Kuo JF, Greengard P. 1970. Isolation and partial purification of a protein kinase activated by cGMP. *J. Biol. Chem.* 245:2493–98

87. Landgraf W, Hofmann F, Pelton JT, Huggins JP. 1990. Effects of cGMP on the secondary structure of cGMP-dependent protein kinase and analysis of the enzyme's amino-terminal domain by far-ultraviolet circular dichroism. *Biochemistry* 29:9921–28

88. Landgraf W, Hullin R, Gobel C, Hofmann F. 1986. Phosphorylation of cGMP-dependent protein kinase increases the affinity for cAMP. *Eur. J. Biochem.* 154:113–17

89. Leiser M, Rubin CS, Erlichman J. 1986. Differential binding of the regulatory subunits (RII) of cAMP-dependent protein kinase II from bovine brain and muscle to RII-binding proteins. *J. Biol. Chem.* 261:1904–8

90. Levin LR, Kuret J, Johnson KE, Powers S, Cameron S, Michaeli T, Wigler M, Zoller MJ. 1988. A mutation in the catalytic subunit of cAMP-dependent protein kinase that disrupts regulation. *Science* 240:68–70

91. Light DB, Corbin JD, Stanton BA.

1990. Dual ion-channel regulation by cGMP and cGMP-dependent protein kinase. *Nature* 344:336–39

92. Lincoln TM. 1989. Cyclic GMP and mechanisms of vasodilation. *Pharmacol. Ther.* 41:479–502

93. Lincoln TM, Corbin JD. 1983. Characterization and biological role of the cGMP-dependent protein kinase. *Adv. Cyclic Nucleotide Res.* 15:139–92

94. Lincoln TM, Cornwell, TL. 1993. Intracellular cGMP receptor proteins. *FASEB J.* 7:328–38

95. Lincoln TM, Cornwell TL, Taylor AE. 1990. cGMP-dependent protein kinase mediates the reduction of Ca^{2+} by cAMP in vascular smooth muscle cells. *Am. J. Physiol.* 258:C399–497

96. Lincoln TM, Thompson M, Cornwell TL. 1988. Purification and characterization of two forms of cGMP-dependent protein kinase from bovine aorta. *J. Biol. Chem.* 263:17632–37

97. Lohmann SM, DeCamilli P, Einig I, Walter U. 1984. High-affinity binding of the regulatory subunit (RII) of cAMP-dependent protein kinase to microtubule-associated and other cellular proteins. *Proc. Natl. Acad. Sci. USA* 81:6723–27

98. Lohmann SM, Fischmeister R, Walter U. 1991. Signal transduction by cGMP in heart. *Basic Res. Cardiol.* 86:503–14

99. Lohmann SM, Walter U, Miller PE, Greengard P, DeCamilli P. 1981. Immunohistochemical localization of cGMP-dependent protein kinase in mammalian brain. *Proc. Natl. Acad. Sci. USA* 78:653–57

100. Loten EG, Sneyd JG. 1970. An effect of insulin on adipose tissue adenosine-3′, 5′-monophosphate phosphodiesterase. *Biochem. J.* 120:187–93

101. Ludwig J, Margalit T, Eismann E, Lancet D, Kaupp UB. 1990. Primary structure of cAMP-gated channel from bovine olfactory epithelium. *FEBS Lett.* 270:24–29

102. Luo A, Shafit-Zagardo B, Erlichman J. 1990. Identification of the MAP2- and P75-binding domain in the regulatory subunit (RIIβ) of type II cAMP-dependent protein kinase. *J. Biol. Chem.* 265:21804–10

103. Manganiello VC, Smith CJ, Degerman E, Belfrage P. 1990. Cyclic GMP-inhibited cyclic nucleotide phosphodiesterases. In *Cyclic Nucleotide Phosphodiesterases: Structure, Regulation and Drug Action*, ed. J Beavo, M Houslay, pp. 87–109. New York: Wiley

104. Mauer RA. 1989. Both isoforms of

the cAMP-dependent protein kinase catalytic subunit can activate transcription of the prolactin gene. *J. Biol. Chem.* 264:6870–73

105. McCune RW, Gill GN. 1979. Positive cooperativity in guanosine 3′,5′-monophosphate binding to guanosine 3′,5′-monophosphate-dependent protein kinase. *J. Biol. Chem.* 254:5083–91

106. McKnight GS. 1991. Cyclic AMP second messenger systems. *Curr. Opin. Cell Biol.* 3:213–17

107. McKnight GS, Cadd GG, Clegg CH, Otten AD, Correll LA. 1988. Expression of wild-type and mutant subunits of the cAMP-dependent protein kinase. *Cold Spring Harbor Symp. Quant. Biol.* 53:111–19

108. Meinkoth JL, Ji Y, Taylor SS, Feramisco JR. 1990. Dynamics of the distribution of cyclic AMP-dependent protein kinase in living cells. *Proc. Natl. Acad. Sci. USA* 87:9565–99

109. Mellon PL, Clegg CH, Correll LA, McKnight GS. 1989. Regulation of transcription by cyclic AMP-dependent protein kinase. *Proc. Natl. Acad. Sci USA* 86:4887–91

110. Mery PF, Lohmann SM, Walter U, Fischmeister R. 1991. Ca^{2+} current is regulated by cGMP-dependent protein kinase in mammalian cardiac myocytes. *Proc. Natl. Acad. Sci. USA* 88:1197–201

111. Miller JP, Uno H, Christensen LJ, Robins RK, Meyer RB Jr. 1981. Effect of modification of the 1-, 2-, and 6-positions of 9-β-D-ribofuranosyl-purine cyclic 3′,5′-phosphate on the cyclic nucleotide specificity of adenosine 3′,5′-phosphate and guanosine cyclic 3′,5′-phosphate dependent protein kinases. *Biochem. Pharmacol.* 30:509–15

112. Monken CE, Gill GN. 1980. Structural analysis of cGMP-dependent protein kinase using limited proteolysis. *J. Biol. Chem.* 255:7067–70

113. Murad F. 1986. Cyclic guanosine monophosphate as a mediator of vasodilation. *J. Clin. Invest.* 78:1–5

114. Ndubuka C, Li Y, Rubin CS. 1993. Expression of A Kinase Anchor Protein 75 depletes type II cAMP-dependent protein kinases from the cytoplasm and sequesters the kinases in a particulate pool. *J. Biol. Chem.* 268:7621–24

115. Nigg EA, Hilz H, Eppenberger HM, Dutly F. 1985. Rapid and reversible translocation of the catalytic subunit of cAMP-dependent protein kinase type II from the Golgi complex to the nucleus. *EMBO J.* 4:2801–6

116. Nolte C, Eigenthaler M, Schanzenbacher P, Walter U. 1991. Endothelial cell-dependent phosphorylation of a platelet protein mediated by cAMP- and cGMP-elevating factors. *J. Biol. Chem.* 266:14808–12

117. Ogreid D, Doskeland SO. 1981. The kinetics of association of cyclic AMP to the two types of binding sites associated with protein kinase II from bovine myocardium. *FEBS Lett.* 129:287–92

118. Ogreid D, Doskeland SO, Gorman KG, Steinberg RA. 1988. Mutations that prevent cyclic nucleotide binding to binding sites A or B of type I cAMP-dependent protein kinase. *J. Biol. Chem.* 263:17397–404

119. Ogreid D, Doskeland SO, Miller JP. 1983. Evidence that cyclic nucleotides activating rabbit muscle protein kinase I interact with both types of cAMP binding sites associated with the enzyme. *J. Biol. Chem.* 258:1041–49

120. Ogreid D, Ekanger RH, Suva JP, Miller JP, Sturm P, et al. 1985. Activation of protein kinase isozymes by cyclic nucleotide analogs used singly or in combination. *Eur. J. Biochem.* 150:219–27

121. Olah GA, Mitchell RD, Sosnick TR, Walsh DA, Trewhella J. 1993. Solution structure of the cAMP-dependent protein kinase catalytic subunit and its contraction upon binding the protein kinase inhibitor peptide. *Biochemistry* 32:3649–57

122. Orellana SA, Amieux PS, Zhao X, McKnight GS. 1993. Mutations in the catalytic subunit of the cAMP-dependent protein kinase interfere with holoenzyme formation without disrupting inhibition by protein kinase inhibitor. *J. Biol. Chem.* 268:6843–46

123. Poteet CE, Shabb JB, Woodford-Thomas T, Corbin JD. 1993. The conserved glu in the putative autoinhibitory domain of mammalian cyclic nucleotide dependent protein kinase is not essential for inhibition. *FASEB J.* 7:A1123

124. Pryzwansky KB, Wyatt TA, Nichols H, Lincoln TM. 1990. Compartmentalization of cGMP-dependent protein kinase in formyl-peptide stimulated neutrophils. *Blood* 76:612–18

125. Raeymaekers L, Hofmann F, Casteels R. 1988. Cyclic GMP-dependent protein kinase phosphorylates phospholamban in isolated sarcoplasmic reticulum from cardiac and smooth muscle. *Biochem. J.* 252:269–73

126. Rangel-Aldao R, Kupiec JW, Rosen OM. 1979. Resolution of the phos-

phorylated and dephosphorylated cAMP-binding proteins of bovine cardiac muscle by affinity labeling and two dimensional electrophoresis. *J. Biol. Chem.* 254:2499–508

127. Rannels SR, Cobb CE, Landiss LR, Corbin JD. 1985. The regulatory subunit monomer of cAMP-dependent protein kinase retains the salient kinetic properties of the native dimeric subunit. *J. Biol. Chem.* 260:3423–30

128. Rapoport RM, Dragnin MB, Murad F. 1983. Endothelium-dependent relaxation in rat aorta may be mediated through cGMP-dependent protein phosphorylation. *Nature* 306:174–76

129. Rashatwar SS, Cornwell T, Lincoln TM. 1987. Effects of 8-bromo-cGMP on Ca^{2+} levels in vascular smooth muscle cells: possible regulation of Ca^{2+} ATPase by cGMP-dependent protein kinase. *Proc. Natl. Acad. Sci. USA* 84:5685–89

130. Reimann EM. 1986. Conversion of bovine cardiac adenosine cyclic 3′,5′-phosphate dependent protein kinase to a heterodimer by removal of 45 residues at the N-terminus of the regulatory subunit. *Biochemistry* 25:119–25

131. Robinson-Steiner AM, Corbin JD. 1983. Probable involvement of both intrachain cAMP binding sites in activation of protein kinase. *J. Biol. Chem.* 258:1032–40

132. Rosell-Perez M, Larner J. 1964. Studies on UDPG-α-glucan transglucosylase V. Two forms of the enzyme in dog skeletal muscle and their interconversion. *Biochemistry* 3:81–88

133. Rubin CS, Rangel-Aldao R, Sarkar D, Erlichmann J, Fleischer N. 1979. Characterization and comparison of membrane-associated and cytosolic cAMP-dependent protein kinases. *J. Biol. Chem.* 254:3797–805

134. Rubino HM, Dammerman M, Shafit-Zagardo B, Erlichman J. 1989. Localization and characterization of the binding site for the regulatory subunit of type II cAMP-dependent protein kinase on MAP2. *Neuron* 3:631–38

135. Ruth P, Landgraf W, Keilbach A, May B, Egleme C, Hofmann F. 1991. The activation of expressed cGMP-dependent protein kinase isozymes Iα and Iβ is determined by the different aminotermini. *Eur. J. Biochem.* 202:1339–44

136. Sandberg M, Natarajan V, Orstavik S, Lohmann SM, Jahnsen T. 1991. The human type I cGMP-dependent protein kinase gene. *NATO ASI Ser. Biol. Signal Transd.* H-52:301–8

137. Sandberg M, Natarajan V, Ronander I, Kalderon D, Walter U, et al. 1989. Molecular cloning and predicted full-length amino acid sequence of the type Iβ isozyme of cGMP-dependent protein kinase from human placenta. *FEBS Lett.* 255:321–29

138. Saraswat LD, Ringheim GE, Bubis J, Taylor SS. 1988. Deletion mutants as probes for localizing regions of subunit interaction in cAMP dependent protein kinase. *J. Biol. Chem.* 263:18241–46

139. Schlichter DJ, Casnellie JE, Greengard P. 1978. An endogenous substrate for cGMP-dependent protein kinase in mammalian cerebellum. *Nature* 273:61–62

140. Schumacher H, Muller D, Muk-hopadhyay AK. 1992. Stimulation of testosterone production by atrial natriuretic peptide in isolated mouse Leydig cells results from a promiscuous activation of cyclic AMP-dependent protein kinase by cyclic GMP. *Mol. Cell. Endocrinol.* 90:47–52

141. Scott JD. 1991. Cyclic nucleotide-dependent protein kinases. *Pharmacol. Ther.* 50:123–45

142. Scott JD, Glaccum MB, Fischer EH, Krebs EG. 1986. Primary-structure requirements for inhibition by the heat-stable inhibitor of the cAMP-dependent protein kinase. *Proc. Natl. Acad. Sci. USA* 83:1613–16

143. Scott JD, Stofko RE, McDonald JR, Comer JD, Vitalis EA, Mangili JA. 1990. Type II regulatory subunit dimerization determines the subcellular localization of the cAMP-dependent protein kinase. *J. Biol. Chem.* 265:21561–66

144. Sekhar KR, Hatchett RJ, Shabb JB, Wolfe L, Francis SH, et al. 1992. Relaxation of pig coronary arteries by new and potent cGMP analogs that selectively activate type Iα, compared with type Iβ, cGMP-dependent protein kinase. *Mol. Pharm.* 42:103–8

145. Shabb JB, Buzzeo BD, Ng L, Corbin JD. 1991. Mutating protein kinase cAMP-binding sites into cGMP-binding sites. *J. Biol. Chem.* 266:24320–26

146. Shabb JB, Corbin JD. 1992. Cyclic nucleotide-binding domains in proteins having diverse functions. *J. Biol. Chem.* 267:5723–26

147. Shoji S, Ericsson LH, Walsh KA, Fischer EH, Titani K. 1983. Amino acid sequence of the catalytic subunit of bovine type II adenosine cyclic 3′,5′-phosphate dependent protein kinase. *Biochemistry* 22:3702–9

148. Shoji S, Titani K, Demaille JG, Fischer

EH. 1979. Sequence of two phosphorylated sites in the catalytic subunit of bovine cardiac muscle adenosine 3':5'-monophosphate-dependent protein kinase. *J. Biol. Chem.* 254:6211–14

149. Skalhegg BS, Landmark B, Doskeland SO, Hansen V, Lea T, Jahnsen T. 1992. Cyclic AMP-dependent protein kinase type I mediates the inhibitory effects of 3',5'-cyclic adenosine monophosphate on cell replication in T lymphocytes. *J. Biol. Chem.* 267: 15707–14

150. Smith JA, Francis SH, Corbin JD. 1992. Activation of type Iβ of cGMP-dependent protein kinase by preincubation with MgATP and cAMP. *FASEB J.* 6:A315

151. Soderling TR, Corbin JD, Park CR. 1973. Regulation of the adenosine 3',5'-monophosphate-dependent protein kinase II. Hormonal regulation of the adipose tissue enzyme. *J. Biol. Chem.* 248:1822–29

152. Steinberg RA, Cauthron RD, Symcox MM, Shuntoh H. 1993. Autoactivation of catalytic (Cα) subunit of cyclic AMP-dependent protein kinase by phosphorylation of threonine 197. *Mol. Cell. Biol.* 13:2332–41

153. Takio K, Smith SB, Krebs EG, Walsh KA, Titani K. 1984. Amino acid sequence of the regulatory subunit of bovine type II adenosine 3',5'-phosphate dependent protein kinase. *Biochemistry* 23:4200–6

154. Takio K, Wade RD, Smith SB, Krebs EG, Walsh KA, Titani K. 1984. Guanosine cyclic 3',5'-phosphate dependent protein kinase, a chimeric protein homologous with two separate protein families. *Biochemistry* 23: 4207–18

155. Taylor SS, Buechler JA, Yonemoto Y. 1990. cAMP-dependent protein kinase: framework for diverse family of regulatory enzymes. *Annu. Rev. Biochem.* 59:971–1005

156. Taylor SS, Knighton DR, Zheng J, Sowadski JM, Gibbs CS, Zoller MJ. 1993. A template for the protein kinase family. *Trends Biochem. Sci.* 18:84–89

157. Terasaki WL, Brooker G. 1977. Cardiac adenosine 3':5'-monophosphate. Free and bound forms in the isolated rat atrium. *J. Biol. Chem.* 252:1041–50

158. Thomas MK, Francis SH, Corbin JD. 1990. Substrate- and kinase-directed regulation of phosphorylation of a cGMP-binding phosphodiesterase by cGMP. *J. Biol. Chem.* 265:14971–78

159. Titani K, Sasagawa T, Ericsson LH, Kumar S, Smith SB, et al. 1984.

Protein sequence of the rabbit Type I regulatory subunit of the cAMP-dependent kinase. *Biochemistry* 23:4193–99

160. Toda T, Cameron S, Sass P, Zoller MN, Wigler M. 1987. Three different genes in *S. cerevisiae* encode the catalytic subunits of the cAMP-dependent protein kinase. *Cell* 50:277–87

161. Tomoda T, Murata T, Arai K, Muramatsu M. 1993. Mutations on 170Glu, a substrate recognition residue in mouse cAMP-dependent protein kinase, generate enzymes with altered substrate affinity and biological functions. *Biochim. Biophys. Acta* 1175: 333–42

162. Toner-Webb J, van Patten SM, Walsh DA, Taylor SS. 1992. Autophosphorylation of the catalytic subunit of cAMP-dependent protein kinase. *J. Biol. Chem.* 267:25174–80

162a. Uhler MD. 1993. Cloning and expression of a novel cyclic GMP-dependent protein kinase from mouse brain. *J. Biol. Chem.* 268:13586–91

163. Uhler MD, Chrivia JC, McKnight GS. 1986. Evidence for a second isoform of the catalytic subunit of cAMP-dependent protein kinase. *J. Biol. Chem.* 261:15360–63

164. Van Sande J, Lefort A, Beebe S, Roger P, Perret J, et al. 1989. Pairs of cAMP analogs, that are specifically synergistic for type I and type II cAMP-dependent protein kinases, mimic thyrotropin effects on function, differentiation expression and mitogenesis of dog thyroid cells. *Eur. J. Biochem.* 183:699–708

165. Waldmann R, Nieberding M, Walter U. 1987. Vasodilator-stimulated protein phosphorylation in platelets is mediated by cAMP- and cGMP-dependent protein kinases. *Eur. J. Biochem.* 167:-441–48

166. Walsh DA, Angelos KL, Van Patten SM, Glass DB, Garetto LP. 1990. The inhibitor protein of the cAMP-dependent protein kinase. See Ref. 51, pp. 43–84

167. Walsh DA, Ashby CD, Gonzalez C, Calkins D, Fischer EH, Krebs EG. 1971. Purification and characterization of a protein inhibitor of adenosine 3',5'-monophosphate-dependent protein kinases. *J. Biol. Chem.* 246:1977–85

168. Walsh DA, Perkins JP, Krebs EG. 1968. An adenosine 3',5'-monophosphate-dependent protein kinase from rabbit skeletal muscle. *J. Biol. Chem.* 243:3763–65

169. Walter U. 1981. Distribution of cGMP-dependent protein kinase in various rat

tissues and cell lines determined by a sensitive and specific radioimmunoassay. *Eur. J. Biochem.* 118:339–46

170. Walter U. 1989. Physiological role of cGMP and cGMP-dependent protein kinase in the cardiovascular system. *Rev. Physiol. Biochem. Pharmacol.* 113:42–88

171. Wang Y, Scott JD, McKnight GS, Krebs EG. 1991. A constitutively active holoenzyme form of the cAMP-dependent protein kinase. *Proc. Natl. Acad. Sci. USA* 88:2446–50

172. Weber IT, Shabb JB, Corbin JD. 1989. Predicted structure of the cGMP binding domains of the cGMP-dependent protein kinase: a key alanine/threonine difference in evolutionary divergence of cAMP and cGMP binding sites. *Biochemistry* 28:6122–27

173. Weber IT, Steitz TA, Bubis J, Taylor SS. 1987. Predicted structures of cAMP binding domains of type I and II regulatory subunits of cAMP- dependent protein kinases. *Biochemistry* 26:343–51

174. Wernet W, Flockerzi V, Hofmann F. 1989. The cDNA of the two isoforms of bovine cGMP-dependent protein kinase. *FEBS Lett.* 251:191–96

175. White RE, Lee AB, Shcherbatko AD, Lincoln TM, Schonbrunn A, Armstrong DL. 1993. Potassium channel stimulation by natriuretic peptides through cGMP-dependent dephosphorylation. *Nature* 361:263–65

176. Whitehouse S, Feramisco JR, Casnellie JE, Krebs EG, Walsh DA. 1983. Studies on the kinetic mechanism of the catalytic subunit of the cAMP-dependent protein kinase. *J. Biol. Chem.* 258:3693–701

177. Wolfe L, Corbin JD, Francis SH. 1989. Characterization of a novel isozyme of cGMP-dependent protein kinase from bovine aorta. *J. Biol. Chem.* 264:7734–41

178. Wolfe L, Francis SH, Corbin JD. 1989. Properties of a cGMP-dependent monomeric protein kinase from bovine aorta. *J. Biol. Chem.* 264:4157–62

179. Wolfe L, Francis SH, Landiss LR, Corbin JD. 1987. Interconvertible cGMP-free and cGMP-bound forms of cGMP-dependent protein kinase in

mammalian tissues. *J. Biol. Chem.* 262:16906–13

180. Woodford TA, Correll LA, McKnight GS, Corbin JD. 1989. Expression and characterization of mutant forms of the type I regulatory subunit of cAMP-dependent protein kinase. *J. Biol. Chem.* 264:13321–28

181. Woodford TA, Taylor SJ, Corbin JD. 1992. The biological functions of protein phosphorylation-dephosphorylation. In *Fundamentals of Medical Cell Biology,* ed. EE Bittar, 3B:453–507. London: JAI Press

182. Wyatt TA, Lincoln TM, Pryzwansky KB. 1991. Vimentin is transiently colocalized with and phosphorylated by cGMP-dependent protein kinase in formyl-peptide-stimulated neutrophils. *J. Biol. Chem.* 266:21274–80

183. Yeaman SJ, Cohen P, Watson DC, Dixon GH. 1977. The substrate specificity of adenosine 3′,5′-cyclic monophosphate-dependent protein kinase. *Biochem. J.* 162:411–21

184. Yoon M-Y, Cook PF. 1987. Chemical mechanism of the adenosine cyclic 3′,5′-monophosphate dependent protein kinase from pH studies. *Biochemistry* 26:4118–25

185. Yoshida Y, Sun H-T, Cai J-Q, Imai S. 1991. cGMP-dependent protein kinase stimulates the plasma membrane Ca^{2+} pump ATPase of vascular smooth muscle via phosphorylation of a 240-kDa protein. *J. Biol. Chem.* 266: 19819–25

186. Zetterqvist O, Ragnarsson U, Engstrom L. 1990. Substrate specificity of cyclic AMP-dependent protein kinase. See Ref. 51, pp. 171–88

187. Zheng JH, Knighton DR, Ten Eyck LF, Karlsson R, Xuong NH, et al. 1993. Crystal structure of the catalytic subunit of cAMP-dependent protein kinase complexed with MgATP and peptide inhibitor. *Biochemistry* 32: 2154–61

188. Zoller MJ, Kuret J, Cameron S, Levin L, Johnson KE. 1988. Purification and characterization of C_1, the catalytic subunit of *Saccharomyces cerevisiae* cAMP-dependent protein kinase encoded by TPK 1. *J. Biol. Chem.* 263:9142–48

Annu. Rev. Physiol. 1994. 56:273–295

ROLES OF ATP IN INSULIN ACTIONS[1]

Hideichi Makino
Chiba University School of Medicine, Chiba 280, Japan

Vincent C. Manganiello
NHLBI, National Institutes of Health, Bethesda, Maryland 20892

Tetsuro Kono
Vanderbilt University School of Medicine, Nashville, Tennessee 37232

KEY WORDS: ATP, insulin, protein kinase, glucose transport, cAMP, phosphodiesterase

INTRODUCTION

Insulin exerts profound effects on human physiology by controlling the activities of many enzymes, especially those involved in energy metabolism. Since the actions of insulin are highly complex, we conveniently divided them into six groups in this review (Table 1). Group 1 represents the initial phase of insulin actions, whereas Group 2 through Group 6 represent the hormonal actions that are involved: Group 2, the phosphorylation of certain protein kinases, most of which are also phosphorylated by growth-promoting factors; Group 3, the phosphorylation of phosphatases and metabolic enzymes; Group 4, the dephosphorylation of several enzymes; Group 5, the translocation of membrane proteins; and Group 6, the regulation of gene expression. The results of our present review are summarized in Figure 1.

In this work, we attempt to cover all the known functions of ATP in every aspect of insulin action. Thus each subject is succinctly described,

[1]The US Government has the right to retain a nonexclusive, royalty-free license in and to any copyright covering this paper

Table 1   Grouping of insulin actions[a]

Group 1: initial phase of insulin actions,[b] including
   1–1 phosphorylation of IRS-1 and PI 3-kinase
   1–2 activation of PI 3-kinase and Ras

Group 2: phosphorylation of protein kinases most of which are also phosphorylated by growth-promoting factors:[b] MAPKK, MAP kinases, ribosomal S6 kinases, casein kinase II, and Mn^{2+}-dependent protein kinase

Group 3: phosphorylation of phosphatases and metabolic enzymes:[b,c] PP1G, PDE, and ACC

Group 4: dephosphorylation of metabolic enzymes:[b,c] glycogen synthase, phosphorylase, phosphorylase kinase, PDH, pyruvate kinase, triglyceride lipase, and ACC

Group 5: translocation of membrane proteins:[c] glucose transporters, IGF-IIR, transferrin receptor, α_2-macroglobulin receptor[d], Na/K-ATPase[e], and insulin receptor

Group 6: regulation of gene expressions[b]
   6–1 stimulation of gene transcription: glucokinase, 6-phosphofructo-1-kinase, and kinase/Pase
   6–2 inhibition of gene transcription: PEPCK and fructose 1,6-bisphosphatase
   6–3 growth promoting actions: cell proliferation and differentiation

---

[a] Abbreviations used are IRS-1, insulin receptor substrate-1; PI 3-kinase, phosphatidylinositol 3-kinase; MAP, microtubule associated protein; MAPKK, MAP kinase kinase; PP1G, protein phosphatase-1G; PDH, pyruvate dehydrogenase; PDE, cAMP phosphodiesterase; ACC, acetyl-CoA carboxylase; IGF-IIR, insulin-like growth factor II receptor; kinase/Pase, 6-phosphofructo-2-kinase/fructose-2,6-bisphosphatase; and PEPCK, phosphoenolpyruvate carboxykinase. [b] See text for references. [c] See reviews (57, 58) for references. [d] Corvera et al (24). [e] Omatsu-Kanbe & Kitasato (83).

with a limited number of references. Excellent and more comprehensive reviews for individual subjects are cited throughout this review. Recently, Lawrence (66) reviewed the role of phosphorylation in the transduction of the insulin signal.

HISTORICAL DEVELOPMENT

In 1961, Kono & Colowick (61) reported that the action of insulin on glucose transport in rat diaphragm was completely blocked by 1 mM 2,4-dinitrophenol. Yu & Gould (133), observing similar effects of dinitrophenol and anoxia, suggested that ATP might have a permissive effect on the hormones. Zinman & Hollenberg (135) and Kono et al (63) found that several agents known to reduce the cellular concentration of ATP blocked the action of insulin on PDE (see Table 1 for a partial list of abbreviations) in adipocytes. The inhibitory effects of dinitrophenol, KCN, etc were reversible, which indicated that the cells were not destroyed under the low ATP conditions (63). In spite of several similarities, the roles of ATP in the actions of insulin on glucose transport and PDE appeared to be different.

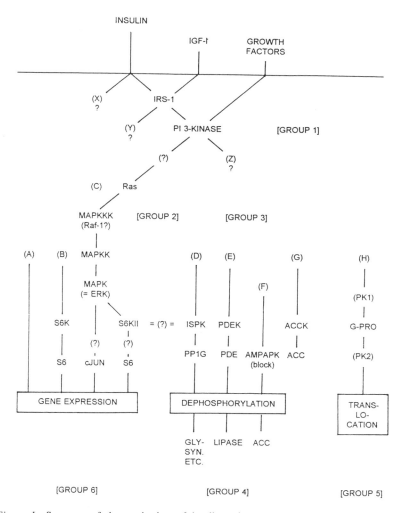

Figure 1 Summary of the mechanism of insulin actions. Abbreviations used are IGF-I, insulin-like growth factor I; K, kinase; PK, protein kinase; G-PRO, GTP-binding protein; AMPAPK (AMP-APK in the text), AMP-activated protein kinase; and GLY-SYN, glycogen synthase. See Table 1 for other abbreviations.

Whereas the hormonal effect on PDE was reversed upon reducing the ATP concentration in cells that had been exposed to insulin (124), the effect on glucose transport was not (124; see 57 for review).

Benjamin & Singer (11, 12) found that insulin had dual effects on the incorporation of ^{32}P into adipocyte proteins. The hormone promoted the labeling of some proteins with ^{32}P, while reducing the incorporation of the label into other proteins in the same cell preparation. Alexander et al (2) and Ramakrishna & Benjamin (89) identified ATP-citrate lyase as one of the proteins phosphorylated by the action of insulin. It appears, however, that this phosphorylation is physiologically irrelevant since the reaction does not alter the enzyme activity (5). Smith et al (109) found that insulin stimulated phosphorylation of S6, a major protein in the 40S subunit of ribosomes. These initial studies were followed by numerous investigations on the insulin-dependent phosphorylation of intracellular proteins (reviewed by Avruch et al 4, 5; Denton 32).

Kasuga et al (54) discovered that insulin stimulated phosphorylation of its own receptor. Several studies subsequently established that (a) the insulin receptor is an insulin-sensitive tyrosine kinase with its domain located in the β-subunit of the receptor, and (b) the kinase is stimulated as a result of hormonal binding to the α-subunit of the receptor followed by autophosphorylation of at least three specific tyrosine residues in the β-subunit. The characteristics of the insulin receptor and its tyrosine kinase have been extensively reviewed by Kahn et al (52), Rothenberg et al (96), and Roth (95). In addition, Taylor et al (120) and Makino et al (74) reviewed the physiological and clinical effects of receptor mutations. Note that two different amino-acid numbering systems are used in the above review articles since Ullrich et al (123) and Ebina et al (34) allocated different numbers of amino acids to the α-subunit of the receptor.

In the following sections, the function of ATP in each of the six groups of insulin actions (listed in Table 1) is discussed.

INITIAL PHASE OF INSULIN ACTION (GROUP 1)

Most of the intracellular proteins that are phosphorylated by the action of insulin are modified at their serine or threonine residues (4, 5, 32). However, the insulin receptor itself is a tyrosine-specific protein kinase (52, 96), and it phosphorylates several intracellular proteins, such as those collectively known as pp185, on tyrosine residues (126).

Sun et al (115) cloned the cDNA for a major protein in the band of pp185 (see above) and designated the protein IRS-1. Six of the insulin-phosphorylated tyrosine residues in IRS-1 had a common neighboring amino-acid sequence, Y(P)MXM, in which X represented an unspecified amino acid (115). Two similar sequences, Y(P)MDM and Y(P)VPM, were previously found in the platelet-derived growth factor β-receptor (PDGFβr), and identified as the site to which the receptor binds to the regulatory subunit of PI 3-kinase and stimulates the latter. See Carpenter & Cantley (19) and Pazin & Williams (86) for reviews.

It was conceivable, therefore, that IRS-1 might work as an intracellular second messenger of insulin. In support of this view, Backer et al (7) immunoprecipitated a complex of phosphorylated IRS-1 and activated PI 3-kinase from the extract of modified Chinese hamster ovary (CHO) cells that had been exposed to insulin. Kadowaki et al (51) found that pp185 was phosphorylated not only by insulin, but also by IGF-I (insulin-like growth factor-I), but not by EGF (epidermal growth factor). Hayashi et al (44, 46) discovered that PI 3-kinase itself was phosphorylated at its tyrosine residues by the action of insulin and appeared to be stimulated as a consequence (45).

White et al (125) showed that when tyrosine 960 in the insulin receptor was replaced with phenylalanine, the modified receptor failed to transmit the hormonal signal(s) that would stimulate the phosphorylation of pp185 and regulate various metabolic activities such as glycogen synthesis, amino acid transport, and thymidine-incorporation into DNA. These data suggest that both IRS-1 and tyrosine 960 are essential for the transduction of the hormonal signals. It is yet to be established, however, that the actions of insulin on metabolic activities are secondary to the phosphorylation of IRS-1.

The role of PI 3-kinase in the action of insulin is still obscure. However, it has been suggested that the enzyme might be involved in the growth factor-dependent stimulation of Ras, p21*ras*, as reviewed by Pazin & Williams (86). Ras is a GTP-binding protein that may be involved in the activation of the MAP-kinase cascade (described below). PI 3-kinase is not a member of the classical phosphatidylinositol cycle that yields diacylglycerol. Instead, the kinase is thought to generate a new type of messenger (considered by Carpenter & Cantley 19).

STIMULATION OF PROTEIN KINASES THAT ARE ALSO ACTIVATED BY GROWTH-PROMOTING FACTORS (GROUP 2)

Most of the protein kinases in Group 2 (see Table 1) are phosphorylated and activated not only by insulin, but also by a variety of growth-promoting agents such as polypeptide growth factors and the tumor-promoting phorbol ester, PMA (phorbol 12-myristate 13-acetate). These protein kinases appear to be phosphorylated (and dephosphorylated) in succession as described below and schematically illustrated in Figure 1.

Family of Ribosomal S6 Kinases

Johns et al (50) cloned cDNAs for two species of 92-kd protein kinases (S6 kinase IIα and S6 kinase IIβ) from mitogen-stimulated unfertilized *Xenopus* oocytes. These kinases had a region of amino acid sequence that was similar to that of protein kinase C (50). Banerjee et al (10) cloned the cDNA for a 70-kd protein kinase (S6 kinase) that had been purified by Price et al (88) from cycloheximide-treated rat liver; this enzyme was highly active in liver that was regenerating after surgery (88). All of these kinases were phosphorylated at their serine residues and exhibited strong activities to several oligopeptides that corresponded to the C-terminal portions of ribosomal S6. Nonetheless, Lavoinne et al (65) reported that 92-kd S6 kinase II was very weak toward the ribosomal S6 protein, although 70-kd S6 kinase was equally active toward both ribosomal S6 protein and its C-terminal fragments.

The 92-kd S6 kinase II, which had been deactivated with protein phosphatase 2A, was rephosphorylated and reactivated, at least in part (30–60%), by MAP-2 kinase (114). The immediate activator (or kinase) of 70-kd S6 kinase is unknown; the enzyme was not a substrate of MAP-2 kinase (9).

Lavoinne et al (65) reported that ISPK, a 91-kd protein kinase from rabbit skeletal muscle, was similar to the 92-kd S6 kinase II from *Xenopus* oocytes.

Family of MAP-2 Kinases

Ray & Sturgill (91) purified a MAP-2 kinase from insulin-stimulated 3T3-L1 cells and found that the enzyme was phosphorylated at both tyrosine and threonine residues. Gotoh et al (39) cloned a 42-kd MAP-2 kinase from *Xenopus* oocytes in the M phase. Boulton et al (14) cloned several species of cDNAs for MAP-2 kinases and proposed to rename the family of MAP-2 kinases ERKs (extracellular signal-regulated kinases). The protein kinases in this group are stimulated by a large variety of extracellular stimuli, as reviewed by Pelech & Sanghera (87).

Sturgill et al (114) found that MAP-2 kinase phosphorylated and activated 92-kd S6 kinase II. MAP-2 kinases (ERKs) also used myelin basic protein, MBP, as a substrate (87). Karin & Smeal (53) suggested that ERKs might be involved in the growth hormone-dependent regulation of cJun, a potent modulator of gene transcription.

Family of MAP-2 Kinase Kinase

Matsuda et al (78) purified and characterized a 45-kd MAP-2 kinase activator (or kinase kinase) from *Xenopus* oocytes. Ashworth et al (3) cloned a 43-kd MAP-2 kinase kinase, which had been purified by Nakielny et al (81) from rabbit skeletal muscle. Wu et al (130) cloned the cDNA for a MAP kinase kinase from rat kidney. These kinase kinases phosphorylated the family of MAP-2 kinases at both tyrosine and threonine residues and activated the enzymes. The kinase kinases themselves could be phosphorylated at their serine or threonine residues and deactivated by treatment with protein phosphatase 2A (78). Ahn et al (1) purified a MAP-2 kinase kinase from cultured Swiss 3T3 cells treated with EGF.

MAP Kinase Kinase Kinase and Related Factors

Izumi et al (48) found that insulin and platelet-derived growth factor (PDGF) phosphorylated c-Raf at its serine and threonine residues and concomitantly activated the enzyme. Kyriakis et al (64) reported that Raf-1 appeared to be a MAP kinase kinase kinase that could phosphorylate MAP-2 kinase kinase. However, Lee et al (68) suggested that Raf-1 was the substrate of MAP-2 kinase. Recently, de Vries-Smits et al (33) reported that Ras might be involved in the stimulation of MAP-2 kinase (ERK2), and Kyriakis et al (64) suggested that Ras functioned upstream of Raf-1. As mentioned above, Ras is a GTP-binding protein thought to be activated (possibly indirectly) by PI 3-kinase; see Pazin & Williams (86) for review. Upon injection of insulin into the rat portal vein, Tobe et al (121) observed a sequential increase in the hepatic activities of MAP kinase kinase, MAP kinase, and S6 peptide kinase.

STIMULATION OF PROTEIN KINASES WHOSE PHYSIOLOGICAL FUNCTIONS ARE UNKNOWN (IN GROUP 2)

Insulin and epidermal growth factor were found to stimulate casein kinase II in 3T3-L1 adipocytes (112). The same enzyme in a cell-free system was stimulated by spermine and inhibited by heparin. Insulin was also found to stimulate Mn^{2+}-dependent protein kinase in adipocytes (134) and Kemptide kinase in the liver (55). The physiological roles of these enzymes are currently obscure.

STIMULATION OF ACETYL-CoA CARBOXYLASE (ACC) (GROUPS 3 AND 4)

ACC catalyzes the first step of fatty acid synthesis: namely, the formation of malonyl CoA from acetyl-CoA and CO_2. Insulin stimulates this enzyme in rat adipocytes two to threefold (reviewed by Brownsey & Denton 17; Witters 127). The hormonal action on ACC is classified into both Groups 3 and 4 (see Table 1) since two distinct mechanisms have been proposed.

  Brownsey & Denton (16) found that insulin phosphorylated ACC (in rat epididymal adipocytes) primarily at a serine residue designated as I-site. Brownsey et al (15) further observed that a plasma membrane fraction from rat adipocytes prompted a cell-free phosphorylation of ACC at the I-site and concomitantly stimulated the enzyme. The kinase in the plasma membrane fraction was not insulin-sensitive, however.

More recently, Borthwick et al (13) partially purified ACC kinase from insulin-stimulated adipocytes. The kinase incorporated ^{32}P from Mg-[γ-^{32}P]ATP into the I-site of ACC and stimulated the enzyme, provided that a large quantity of the kinase preparation was used. By investigating this phenomenon, Borthwick et al (13) found that the enzyme preparation enriched with the kinase was also enriched with an inhibitor. The latter was a heat-stable, low-molecular weight compound (<10,000), separable from the kinase by Centricon filtration. However, the purified kinase, devoid of the inhibitor, had only a mild stimulatory effect on ACC, which suggested that the mechanism of ACC stimulation was highly complex.

In apparent disagreement with this phosphorylation theory, Witters et al (129) reported that in cultured Fao hepatocytes, insulin reduced the overall phosphorylation level of ACC. Witters & Kemp (128) then suggested that insulin might stimulate ACC by inhibiting AMP-APK (AMP-activated protein kinase) that would phosphorylate ACC and deactivate the enzyme (see below). This suggestion was based on their observations that in Fao cells (a) the insulin-dependent stimulation of ACC was preceded by the hormone-dependent deactivation of AMP-APK, and (b) the dose-response effects of insulin on ACC and AMP-APK were almost identical: the apparent K_m value (for insulin) was approximately 0.3 nM in both cases (128).

Earlier, Carling et al (18) and Davies et al (27) reported that ACC was greatly inhibited as a result of phosphorylation at its serine residues 79, 200, and 1215 (27) by a newly purified kinase, AMP-APK. As reviewed by Hardie (42), this kinase from rat liver was half-maximally stimulated with 14 μM AMP (18) in the presence of a physiological concentration of ATP (2 mM), provided that the kinase itself was phosphorylated by another kinase.

Thus it is yet to be determined whether insulin stimulates ACC through the activation of ACC kinase, or through the inhibition of AMP-APK. Alternatively, the two proposed mechanisms might be operational in two different cell types.

PHOSPHORYLATION AND STIMULATION OF cAMP PHOSPHODIESTERASE (PDE) (GROUP 3)

The insulin-stimulated PDE is mainly localized in the liver and adipose tissue and hydrolyzes cAMP into AMP. As a result, the PDE induces (a) an insulin-dependent inactivation of cAMP-dependent protein kinase (protein kinase A) and, consequently, (b) a reduction in the phosphorylation level of enzymes that are phosphorylated by the kinase. One such enzyme is the hormone-sensitive lipase that catalyzes the first step of lipolysis, namely the hydrolysis of triglycerides. Based on studies with inhibitors, Elks & Manganiello (35) and Makino et al (73) concluded that the PDE-mediated dephosphorylation and concomitant deactivation of the lipase is the major mechanism by which insulin inhibits lipolysis.

The insulin-sensitive PDE in rat adipocytes is a membrane-bound enzyme (76) that is associated mostly with the endoplasmic reticulum and, to some extent, with the plasma membrane (72). The enzyme is stimulated by insulin two and one half to threefold (62, 72) and specifically inhibited by cilostamide (35). Degerman et al (28) purified the enzyme using a derivative of cilostamide as an affinity ligand, and Taira et al (119) recently cloned the cDNA for the enzyme. The action of the PDE to hydrolyze 0.1 μM cAMP is almost completely inhibited in the presence of 10 μM cGMP (28, 30, 93). Nevertheless, the intrinsic activity of the enzyme is considerably stimulated by the same concentration of cGMP (93) (see 36, 59, 75 for general review).

Recently, Degerman et al (30) reported that insulin prompted the incorporation of ^{32}P into PDE in rat adipocytes. Independently, Shibata et al (106) discovered that reversal of the insulin effect on PDE was blocked by okadaic acid, a potent inhibitor of protein phosphatases 1 and 2A. Shibata & Kono further found that the cytosol fraction from the insulin-treated rat liver (104) or adipocytes (103) stimulated, in a cell-free system, the membrane-bound, insulin-sensitive PDE from adipocyte in the presence of ATP plus Mg^{2+} (103, 104). Subsequently, the two groups of investigators collaborated, and Smith et al (110) found that PDE was labeled with ^{32}P when the cell-free experiment was carried out in the presence of [γ-^{32}P]ATP. Taken together, the above results (30, 103, 104, 106, 110) indicate that the membrane-bound PDE is phosphorylated and concomitantly stimulated by an insulin-stimulated cytosolic kinase (putative PDE kinase).

The putative PDE kinase from insulin-treated rat liver was partially purified by chromatography on DE53 in the presence of 0.25 M sucrose and various phosphatase inhibitors (H Shibata et al personal communication). For preparation of the kinase in its active form, it was essential to add a cocktail of phosphatase inhibitors to the buffers used for tissue homogenization and enzyme purification (103, 104). This suggested that the putative PDE kinase itself was stimulated as a result of phosphorylation by another insulin-stimulated protein kinase (putative PDE kinase kinase).

In the above cellular experiments with ^{32}P (30), adipocytes were incubated first with ^{32}P$_i$ (0.6–1.4 mCi/ml) for 105 min in the absence of any hormones, and then with 1 nM insulin for 12 min without ^{32}P$_i$. The labeled PDE, still associated with the membrane, was solubilized with a non-ionic detergent in the presence of 50 mM NaF and a cocktail of protease inhibitors. After partial purification with *Staphylococcus aureus,* the solubilized ^{32}P-PDE was immunoprecipitated by treatment with anti-PDE IgG (raised against purified PDE and partially purified; 29) plus *Staphylococcus aureus.* Subsequently, the immunoprecipitate was subjected to SDS-PAGE (polyacrylamide gel electrophoresis), and the ^{32}P activity in the PDE-band determined. In cell-free experiments with ^{32}P (110), the membrane-bound PDE from the basal state of adipocytes was incubated for 10 min with a preparation of putative PDE-kinase in the presence of 0.5 mM [γ-^{32}P]ATP (1000-3000 cpm/pmol), 5 μM PKI, and a mixture of protease inhibitors. The ^{32}P-labeled PDE (still associated with the membrane) was then processed as in the whole cell experiments mentioned above.

Unlike most other insulin-sensitive enzymes, PDE is stimulated not only by insulin but also by β-adrenergic agonists (72, 85, 135) or cAMP (37); therefore, it is critically important to note that the above effects of insulin and okadaic acid were observed under conditions in which protein kinase A was completely inhibited with either PKI (103, 110) or H-7 (106). The tests with several inhibitors revealed that the putative PDE kinase was distinct from various other protein kinases such as ribosomal S6 kinase, Mn^{2+}-specific protein kinase, protease-stimulated protein kinase, casein kinase II, protein kinase A, or Ca^{2+}/phospholipid protein kinase, i.e. protein kinase C (103).

It is highly unlikely that protein kinase C is involved in the insulin-dependent stimulation of PDE since a phorbol ester, PMA, that activates protein kinase C did not stimulate PDE (T Kono, unpublished observation), and the hormonal effect on PDE was not significantly affected by a concentration of H-7, which completely blocked the kinase activity in adipocytes (105). It is also unclear how the so-called insulin-mediator substance (84, 102) could be involved in the insulin-dependent stimulation of PDE since the mediator substance stimulates the enzyme in the absence of ATP (84, 102), whereas the hormone apparently phosphorylates PDE (see above).

REGULATION OF GLYCOGEN SYNTHASE ETC (GROUP 4)

As is well documented, insulin causes dephosphorylation of glycogen synthase (which is thereby stimulated), glycogen phosphorylase (which is then inhibited), and phosphorylase kinase (which is inhibited). As considered previously (22, 66), the cause of these hormonal effects may be ascribed, at least in part, to the PDE-dependent deactivation of a protein-phosphatase inhibitor (inhibitor-1), provided that the tissue contains insulin-sensitive PDE. Recently, Dent et al (31) reported that insulin dephosphorylated the above-mentioned enzymes in the skeletal muscle primarily by stimulating a form of protein phosphatase-1, PP1G, which was associated with glycogen particles. The phosphatase activity of PP1G was elevated when the enzyme was phosphorylated at a specific serine residue designated as Site 1. The selective phosphorylation of PP1G at Site 1 was catalyzed (in a cell-free system) by a particular insulin-stimulated protein kinase (see below). The level of phosphorylation at Site 1 was also increased in vivo (approximately twofold) upon treatment of rabbits with insulin (31).

The serine residue designated as Site-1 was located in the regulatory subunit (G-subunit) of PP1G; the same subunit also contained another serine residue referred to as Site 2. The incubation of PP1G with protein kinase A (in a cell-free system) prompted phosphorylation of PP1G at both Site 1 and Site 2, which caused a reduction in the enzyme activity (31).

Dent et al (31) partially purified an insulin-stimulated protein kinase (ISPK, initially referred to as Site-1 kinase) from the extract of insulin-treated rabbit skeletal muscle that had been homogenized in the presence of sodium fluoride (a phosphatase inhibitor). The partially purified enzyme phosphorylated PP1G at Site 1, but not at Site 2. Nevertheless, the specificity of the enzyme was not absolute; it also phosphorylated some other proteins including the substrates of ribosomal S6 kinase. The subsequent characterization of ISPK by Dent et al (31) and Lavoinne et al (65) revealed that the enzyme had certain similarities to the 92-kd S6 kinase II from *Xenopus* oocytes. Both kinases were recognized by the same antibody, commonly deactivated by treatment with protein phosphatase 2A, and partially reactivated by MAP-2 kinase. One can speculate, therefore, that insulin might exert its effect on glycogen synthase and some other enzymes in Group 4 via the cascade involving MAP-2 kinase and ISPK.

TRANSLOCATION OF GLUCOSE TRANSPORTERS (GROUP 5)

Insulin stimulates cellular glucose transport activity primarily, if not entirely, by causing translocation of glucose transporters from the slowly-sedimenting intracellular-fraction (107) to the plasma membrane, as originally reported by Cushman & Wardzala (26) and Suzuki & Kono (117); see (57, 58, 108) for review.

Standaert et al (113) reported that the effect of insulin on glucose transport was blocked by staurosporine, sangivamycine, or H-7, all protein kinase inhibitors. Yano et al (132) confirmed the effect of staurosporine, but found that H-7 inhibited the intrinsic glucose transport activity both in the cellular- and reconstituted-systems. Staurosporine is a potent, but not specific, inhibitor of protein kinase C; the involvement of the latter in the hormonal action on glucose transport has been controversial (reviewed by Klip & Douen 56; and Kono 58). Although a phorbol ester, PMA, which activates protein kinase C, significantly stimulates glucose transport in several cell types, the maximum effect of the agent is considerably less than that of insulin, at least in rat epididymal adipocytes (56, 58). Recently, Cooper et al (23) reported that protein kinase C added to the electroporated rat adipocytes exhibited a permissive effect on the action of insulin.

Baldini et al (8) reported that GTPγS, which stimulates exocytotic secretion of various neurotransmitters, induced translocation of glucose transporters in adipocytes that had been partially permeabilized with α-toxin. This suggested that GTP-binding protein (G protein) might be involved in the action of insulin on glucose transport. Using adipocytes that had been partially permeabilized by electroporation, Yano et al (132) confirmed this observation and further found that staurosporine had a stronger inhibitory effect on the action of insulin than that of GTPγS. If it is assumed that insulin and GTPγS stimulate the cellular glucose transport activity by modulating a common G protein, the data by Yano et al (132) indicate that the action of insulin on glucose transport is mediated by two protein kinases and that the kinase (PK1) localized prior to the G protein step is more sensitive to staurosporine than the one (PK2) located in the subsequent steps (see Figure 1). Using electroporated adipocytes, Suzuki et al (118) found that the cellular glucose transport activity was stimulated not only by insulin or GTPγS, but also by mastoparan or NaF. Mastoparan, a wasp venom, stimulates a certain type of G protein, while NaF is known to activate trimeric G proteins without affecting small G proteins such as Ras in Group 1 (118).

Although the above experiments with staurosporine (113, 132), plus the data obtained earlier (61, 63, 133), strongly suggest that ATP-dependent phosphorylation is involved in the action of insulin on glucose transport, an excessive phosphorylation of cells with catecholamines (111) or okadaic acid (25, 67, 106) is injurious. Years ago, Randle & Smith (90) suggested that under basal conditions the glucose transport activity might be inhibited by phosphorylation. Their suggestion was based on their observation that the transport activity in rat diaphragm muscle was considerably increased by treatment of the tissue with anoxia or a low concentration of 2,4-dinitrophenol (0.1 mM). Their observation was confirmed in experiments with rat diaphragm (61) and perfused rat hearts (80), but not with rat adipocytes. It is yet to be determined why the transport systems in muscle and fat cells show different responses to a low-ATP condition. Recently, Reusch et al (91a) and Begum et al (10a) reported that the glucose transporter (GLUT4) in rat adipocytes appeared to be deactivated by Ca^{2+}-dependent phosphorylation and activated by insulin-dependent dephosphorylation.

Experiments with partially-permeabilized cells (8, 118, 132) indicate that neither the membrane potential nor ion-channel activities in the plasma membrane may have any serious effect on the insulin-dependent stimulation of glucose transport. Other insulin actions that have been demonstrated in partially permeabilized cells include those on PDE (105), PDH (98), lipogenesis (97), and lipolysis (97).

INTERNALIZATION AND RECYCLING OF THE INSULIN RECEPTOR (GROUP 5)

While insulin externalizes glucose transporters and certain other membrane-bound proteins (Table 1), it internalizes its own receptor (47). The internalized receptor labeled with ^{125}I-insulin was first detected as a peak of radioactivity in the fractions of adipocyte-membranes that were separated by sucrose density gradient centrifugation (62, 63). The newly found peak was distinct from the peak of the surface-bound ^{125}I-insulin, and apparently formed from the latter in a time- and ATP-dependent manner (63). The level of internalization of ^{125}I-insulin was maximal in approximately 5 min (63) when as much as 30% of the cell-bound insulin is associated with certain vesicles in the cell (57, 63). Most of the internalized insulin was then dissociated from the receptor and decomposed in the cell (116). On the other hand, the internalized receptor, now free from the hormone, was recycled back onto the cell surface (77). A small fraction of internalized insulin was recycled back onto the cell surface without being decomposed (116).

Ueda et al (122) discovered that monensin-treated adipocytes failed to decompose internalized insulin, and allowed intracellular PDE to remain activated even after the surface-bound insulin had been removed. Monensin is an ionophore for monovalent cations and blocks the dissociation of internalized ligands from their receptors; see (122) for review. More recently, Backer et al (6) found that the internalized receptor was tyrosine phosphorylated, but the insulin-free receptor that had been recycled back to the cell surface was not. Taken together, the above data suggest that the internalized receptor, which is still phosphorylated, may continue to generate the hormonal signal in the cell until the receptor is freed from the hormone and subsequently dephosphorylated. Hashimoto et al (43) identified several tyrosine-specific phosphatases that dephosphorylated the insulin receptor. Taylor et al (120) reviewed the effects of receptor-mutation on its internalization.

REGULATION OF GENE EXPRESSION (GROUP 6)

Insulin regulates several metabolic activities by changing intracellular concentrations of relevant enzymes. This type of insulin action has been studied most extensively in the liver, where insulin and glucagon exhibit antagonistic effects on the de novo syntheses of several key enzymes for carbohydrate metabolism; see Granner & Pilkis (41) for review. As might be expected from the hepatic effects of insulin, the hormone stimulates the synthesis of key glycolytic enzymes such as glucokinase (71), pyruvate kinase (21), 6-phosphofructo-1-kinase (41), and kinase/Pase (20). Concomitantly, the hormone inhibits the synthesis of key gluconeogenic enzymes such as PEPCK (40, 69) and fructose-1,6-bisphosphatase (41). Insulin also controls the synthesis of other hepatic and non-hepatic proteins such as α-amylase, casein, ovalbumin, serum albumin etc (reviewed by Messina 79; O'Brien & Granner 82).

Insulin can regulate protein synthesis at various steps; however, it often does so by controlling gene transcription, namely, the formation of mRNA (41, 79, 82). The mechanism of this insulin action is still unclear; however, it is of interest that the action of glucagon, which is generally antagonistic to insulin, is mediated by protein kinase A (92) and a transcription factor. The latter (a protein) binds to the DNA at either a specific site referred to as CRE (cAMP response element), or another site designated as AP-2 (activator protein-2 binding site) (see Roesler et al 94; Lucas & Granner 70, for review). The transcription factor that binds to CRE was purified by Yamamoto et al (131), cloned by Gonzalez et al (38), and found to contain amino acid sequences that could be phosphorylated by protein kinase A, protein kinase C, and casein kinase II (38).

The regions of DNA that are thought to be involved in the insulin-dependent regulation of gene transcription have been identified for several proteins including PEPCK, glucokinase, and α-amylase (reviewed by O'Brien & Granner 82). Therefore, it would not be surprising if insulin were found to modulate transcription of certain genes by activating a hypothetical transcription factor, possibly by promoting its phosphorylation or dephosphorylation.

Although insulin is known to stimulate cell growth and differentiation, little is known about the mechanism. Sadler (99, 100) reported that Type III PDE might be involved in the insulin- and growth factor-dependent maturation of *Xenopus* oocytes.

DISCUSSION

Figure 1 summarizes the major actions of insulin. In the reactions labeled as Group 1, insulin binds to the cellular receptor and stimulates its tyrosine kinase, which subsequently phosphorylates IRS-1 (115, 126). The phosphorylated IRS-1 then binds to PI 3-kinase and stimulates the latter (7), which is thought to be involved in the activation of Ras (86). Note that these reactions are not insulin-specific; IRS-1 is phosphorylated by the IGF-I receptor as well (51), while PI 3-kinase can be stimulated by a direct interaction with the growth factor receptors (19, 86). Although not shown in the figure, PI 3-kinase may also be stimulated by insulin-dependent phosphorylation (44–46). Other types of hormonal signals, X, Y, and Z, could also be generated in theory by the insulin receptor, IRS-1, and PI 3-kinase, respectively. Among these hypothetical signals, only X is insulin-specific; Y and Z are not.

Group 2 includes two cascades of protein kinases (Cascades B and C) that are activated by insulin as well as by other growth-promoting factors. The upstream region of S6 kinase in Cascade B is currently unknown (9). MAP kinase (= ERK) in Cascade C (when stimulated by a growth factor) is thought to activate cJun, which is a potent modulator of gene transcription (53). MAP kinase may also phosphorylate and stimulate S6 kinase II (114), which is weakly active toward ribosomal S6 protein (65) and has similarities to ISPK in Cascade D (31, 65).

Group 3 includes several cascades that are involved in the phosphorylation and stimulation of (a) phosphatases such as PP1G (in Cascade D; 31, 65) and PDE (in Cascade E; 30, 103, 104, 106, 110), and (b) metabolic enzymes such as ACC (in Cascade G; 13). The stimulation of phosphatases (PP1G and PDE) in Cascades D and E is responsible for the dephosphorylation of glycogen synthase, phosphorylase, phosphorylase kinase, lipase, etc (labeled as Group 4) at the lower parts of the respective cascades. Among the Group 4 reactions, however, the dephosphorylation of ACC (in Cascade F) is distinct in that the reaction is secondary to the insulin-dependent deactivation of AMP-APK (AMPAPK in Figure 1; 128). It is yet to be determined whether insulin stimulates ACC by phosphorylation (Cascade G; 13) or dephosphorylation (Cascade F; 128).

The signal of insulin to regulate gene expressions (in Group 6) may be transmitted, at least in part, via the cascade involving MAP-kinase (Cascade C), which is activated by insulin and various growth-promoting factors. However, it is still possible that insulin might have its own, exclusive, cascade that is yet to be described (Cascade A).

Group 5 includes a largely hidden cascade (Cascade H) of hormonal action that facilitates translocation of glucose transporters. This cascade appears to include a G protein (8, 118, 132) that is distinct from Ras (118) and two protein kinases that are located before and after the G protein in the putative cascade (132).

Considerable progress has been made in recent years on the mechanisms of insulin actions, especially on (a) the structure and function of the insulin receptor, (b) the last few steps of the hormonal actions toward its various targets, and (c) the MAP-kinase cascade that is activated by both insulin and growth-promoting factors. Nevertheless, it is still a big challenge to envision the entire mechanism(s) of insulin actions from the data now available. The difficulty is compounded by the fact that the effects of insulin on its targets are highly diverse, the initial phase of insulin actions so far uncovered is shared by various growth promoting factors, and little is known about the upper regions of many of the cascades shown in Figure 1.

Although insulin has certain growth-promoting activities, many of its activities are necessarily specific. Theoretically, insulin could express its specific activities if (a) different cell types were equipped with different sets of hormone receptors and intracellular enzymes, (b) cells were provided with a certain switchboard mechanism by which different hormonal signals could be sorted out, or (c) insulin had an exclusive mechanism for the transmission of its own signals. An example of (a) can be found in the cAMP system; as is well documented, cAMP in different cell types can duly mediate the signals of different hormones since the individual cell types are equipped with specific receptors and enzymes. The second mechanism (b) assumes that the signals of different hormones that have been transmitted through a common cascade may be sorted out in the cell, possibly because certain enzymes are either activated or deactivated by (hypothetical) secondary signals generated by different hormone receptors. The third mechanism (c) may be most straightforward if the insulin-specific cascade does exist. Although no such cascade has been described, it should be pointed out that IRS-1 is not the only protein that is tyrosine phosphorylated by the insulin receptor; see 4, 5, 32 for review.

Since ISPK (in Cascade D) is stimulated by MAP kinase (in Cascade C) in a cell-free system (65), it may be of interest to determine if other cascades shown in Figure 1 might also be activated by either MAP kinase or other elements in Cascade C. Sadler & Maller (101) reported that PDE in *Xenopus* oocytes was stimulated by insulin and insulin-like growth factor I. Alternatively, new pathways or conduits for the transmission of the insulin-specific signals might be discovered by exploring the upper parts of the cascades for the stimulation of PDE (Cascade E) or glucose transport (Cascade H). Note that PDE and glucose transport in rat adipocytes are hardly or only slightly stimulated by the tumor-promoting phorbol ester, PMA, which activates MAP kinase.

Insulin at high concentrations is known to promote the proliferation of certain cell types in culture and the differentiation of 3T3-L1 fibroblasts into adipocytes. The hormone at high concentrations may interact with the insulin-like growth factor receptors (49), but the apparent binding constant of the insulin receptor itself is approximately 10 nM (60). Therefore, it is not (mechanistically) surprising to observe that insulin at 10–15 nM induces a half-maximal stimulation of, for example, the receptor tyrosine kinase

(51), phosphorylation of pp185 (51), and incorporation of thymidine into DNA (125). It should be noted, however, that the maximum physiological concentration of insulin is approximately 1 nM in the peripheral blood vessels, and only up to 4–6 nM even in the portal vein. In harmony with these figures, (a) the effect of insulin for the hepatic synthesis of kinase/Pase mRNA is half-maximum when the hormone concentration is 1 nM (20), and (b) the hormone at 1 nM stimulates either maximally or almost maximally various metabolic activities such as glucose transport (60), amino acid transport (125), glycogen synthase (125), PEPCK (2a, 40a), and PDE (62).

It is of interest that insulin and its receptor are programmed to carry out distinct biological tasks in response to the hormone at unphysiologically high concentrations. When the insulin concentration is at physiologically acceptable 1 nM, the hormone occupies only approximately 5% of its receptors on the surface of rat epididymal adipocytes (60). Nevertheless, this is apparently sufficient for the hormone to express its maximum physiological activities (57, 60). The significance of the so-called spare receptors, which are not bound by insulin under normal conditions, has been discussed (57, 60).

In conclusion, the search for the mechanism(s) of insulin actions is far from over. It now appears that several series of ATP-dependent phosphorylation and a few GTP-dependent reactions may be the major mechanism by which the hormonal messages are transmitted from the cellular receptor to the insulin-sensitive metabolic activities.

ACKNOWLEDGMENTS

We thank many investigators who sent us their publications. The original work of H.M. was supported by a Grant for Diabetic Research from Otsuka Pharmaceutical Co., Ltd., Tokushima, Japan, that of V.C.M. by National Institutes of Health, and that of T.K. by the National Institutes of Health Grants DK 06725 and 19925 from the United States Public Service. T.K. is grateful to Dr. Daryl K. Granner of Vanderbilt University and to Dr. Hiromichi Kasahara of Teikyo University for their encouragement.

Literature Cited

1. Ahn NG, Seger R, Bratlien RL, Diltz CD, Tonks NK, Krebs EG. 1991. Multiple components in an epidermal growth factor- stimulated protein kinase cascade. *J. Biol. Chem.* 266:4220–27

2. Alexander MC, Kowaloff EM, Witters LA, Dennihy DT, Avruch J. 1979. Purification of a hepatic 123,000-dalton hormone-stimulated [32]2P-peptide and its identification as ATP-citrate lyase. *J. Biol. Chem.* 254:8052–56

2a. Andreone TL, Beale EG, Bar RS, Granner DK. 1982. Insulin decreases phosphoenolpyruvate carboxykinase mRNA activity by a receptor-mediated process. *J. Biol. Chem.* 257:35–38

3. Ashworth A, Nakielny S, Cohen P, Marshall C. 1992. The amino acid sequence of a mammalian MAP kinase kinase. *Oncogene* 7:2555–56

4. Avruch J, Nemenoff RA, Pierce M, Kwok YC, Blackshear PJ. 1985. Protein phosphorylations as a mode of insulin action. In *Molecular Basis of Insulin Action*, ed. MP Czech, pp. 263–96. New York: Plenum

5. Avruch J, Tornqvist HE, Gunsalus JR, Yurkow EJ, Kyriakis JM, Price DJ. 1990. Insulin regulation of protein phosphorylation. *Handb. Exp. Pharmacol.* 92:313–66

6. Backer JM, Kahn CR, White MF. 1989. Tyrosine phosphorylation of the insulin receptor during insulin-stimulated internalization in rat hepatoma cells. *J. Biol. Chem.* 264: 1694–701

7. Backer JM, Myers MG Jr, Shoelson SE, Chin DJ, Sun X-J, et al. 1992. Phosphatidylinositol 3'-kinase is activated by association with IRS-1 during insulin stimulation. *EMBO J.* 11:3469–79

8. Baldini G, Hohman R, Charron MJ, Lodish HF. 1991. Insulin and non-hydrolyzable GTP analogs induce translocation of GLUT4 to the plasma membrane in α-toxin-permeabilized rat adipcose cells. *J. Biol. Chem.* 266: 4037–40

9. Ballou LM, Luther H, Thomas G. 1991. MAP2 kinase and 70k S6 kinase lie on distinct signalling pathways. *Nature* 349:348–50

10. Banerjee P, Ahmad MF, Grove JR, Kozlosky C, Price DJ, Avruch J. 1990. Molecular structure of a major insulin/mitogen-activated 70-kDa S6 protein kinase. *Proc. Natl. Acad. Sci. USA* 87:8550–54

10a. Begum N, Leitner W, Reusch JE-B, Sussman KE, Draznin B. 1993. GLUT-4 phosphorylation and its intrinsic activity: mechanism of Ca^{2+}-induced inhibition of insulin-stimulated glucose transport. *J. Biol. Chem.* 268:3352–56

11. Benjamin WB, Singer I. 1974. Effect of insulin on the phosphorylation of adipose tissue protein. *Biochim. Biophys. Acta* 351:28–41

12. Benjamin WB, Singer I. 1975. Action of insulin, epinephrine, and dibutyryl cyclic adenosine 5'-monophosphate on fat cell protein phosphorylations: cyclic adenosine 5'-monophosphate dependent and independent mechanisms. *Biochemistry* 14: 3301–9

13. Borthwick AC, Edgell NJ, Denton RN. 1990. Protein-serine kinase from rat epididymal adipose tissue which phosphorylates and activates acetyl-CoA carboxylase. *Biochem. J.* 270:795–801

14. Boulton TG, Nye SH, Robbins DJ, Ip NY, Radziejewska E, et al. 1991. ERKs: a family of protein-serine/threonine kinases that are activated and tyrosine phosphorylated in response to insulin and NGF. *Cell* 65:663–75

15. Brownsey RW, Belsham GJ, Denton RM. 1981. Evidence for phosphorylation and activation of acetyl-CoA carboxylase by a membrane-associated cyclic AMP-independent protein kinase. *FEBS Lett.* 124:145–50

16. Brownsey RW, Denton RM. 1982. Evidence that insulin activates fat-cell acetyl-CoA carboxylase by increased phosphorylation at a specific site. *Biochem. J.* 202:77–86

17. Brownsey RW, Denton RM. 1985. Role of phosphorylation in the regulation of acetyl-CoA carboxylase activity. See Ref. 4, pp. 297–314

18. Carling D, Clarke PR, Zammit VA, Hardie DG. 1989. Purification and characterization of the AMP-activated protein kinase. *Eur. J. Biochem.* 186: 129–36

19. Carpenter CL, Cantley LC. 1990. Phosphoinositide kinases. *Biochemistry* 29: 11147–56

20. Cifuentes ME, Espinet C, Lange AJ, Pilkis SJ, Hod Y. 1991. Hormonal control of 6-phosphofructo-2-kinase/fructose-2,6-bisphosphatase gene expression in rat hepatoma cells. *J. Biol. Chem.* 266:1557–63

21. Cimbala MA, Lau D, Daigneault JF. 1885. Regulation of pyruvate kinase gene expression by hormones and developmental factors. See Ref. 4, pp. 385–95

22. Cohen P, Cohen PTW. 1989. Protein phosphatases come of age. *J. Biol. Chem.* 264:21435–38

23. Cooper DR, Watson JE, Hernandez H, Yu B, Standaert ML, et al. 1992. Direct evidence for protein kinase C involvement in insulin-stimulated hexose uptake. *Biochim. Biophys. Acta* 188:142–48

24. Corvera S, Graver DF, Smith RM. 1989. Insulin increases the cell surface concentration of α2-macroglobulin receptor in 3T3-L1 adipocytes. *J. Biol. Chem.* 264:10133–38

25. Corvera S, Jaspers S, Pasceri M. 1991. Acute inhibition of insulin-stimulated glucose transport by the phosphatase inhibitor, okadaic acid. *J. Biol. Chem.* 266:9271–75

26. Cushman SW, Wardzala LJ. 1980.

Potential mechanism of insulin action on glucose transport in the isolated rat adipose cell: apparent translocation of intracellular transport systems to the plasma membrane. *J. Biol. Chem.* 255: 4758–62

27. Davies SP, Sim ATR, Hardie DG. 1990. Location and function of three sites phosphorylated on rat acetyl-CoA carboxylase by the AMP-activated protein kinase. *Eur. J. Biochem.* 187:183–90

28. Degerman E, Belfrage P, Newman AH, Rice KC, Manganiello VC. 1987. Purification of the putative hormone-sensitive cyclic AMP phosphodiesterase from rat adipose tissue using a derviative of cilostamide as a novel affinity ligand. *J. Biol. Chem.* 262: 5797–807

29. Degerman E, Manganiello VC, Newman AH, Rice KC, Belfrage P. 1988. Purification, properties, and polyclonal antibodies for the particulate, low-K_m cAMP phosphodiesterase from bovine adipose tissue. *Second Messenger Phosphoproteins* 12:171–82

30. Degerman E, Smith CJ, Tornqvist H, Vasta V, Belfrage P, Manganiello VC. 1990. Evidence that insulin and isoprenaline activate the cGMP-inhibited low-K_m cAMP phosphodiesterase in rat fat cells by phosphorylation. *Proc. Natl. Acad. Sci. USA* 87:533–37

31. Dent P, Lavoinne A, Nakielny S, Caudwell FB, Watt P, Cohen P. 1990. The molecular mechanism by which insulin stimulates glycogen synthesis in mammalian skeletal muscle. *Nature* 348:302–8

32. Denton, R.M. 1986. Early events in insulin actions. *Adv. Cyclic Nucleotide Protein Phosphorylation Res.* 20:293–341

33. de Vries-Smits AMM, Burgering BMTh, Leevers SJ, Marshall CJ, Bos JL. 1992. Involvement of p21^{ras} in activation of extracellular signal-regulated kinase 2. *Nature* 357:602–4

34. Ebina Y, Ellis L, Jarnagin K, Edery M, Graf L, et al. 1985. The human insulin receptor cDNA: the structural basis for hormone-activated transmembrane signalling. *Cell* 40:747–58

35. Elks ML, Manganiello VC. 1984. Selective effects of phosphodiesterase inhibitors on different phosphodiesterases, adenosine 3′,5′-monophosphate metabolism, and lipolysis in 3T3-L1 adipocytes. *Endocrinology* 115:1262–68

36. Francis SH, Kono T. 1982. Hormone-sensitive cAMP phosphodiesterase in liver and fat cells. *Mol. Cell. Biochem.* 42:109–16

37. Gettys TW, Vine AJ, Simonds MF, Corbin JD. 1988. Activation of the particulate low K_m phosphodiesterase of adipocytes by addition of cAMP-dependent protein kinase. *J. Biol. Chem.* 263:10359–63

38. Gonzalez GA, Yamamoto KK, Fischer WH, Karr D, Menzel P, et al. 1989. A cluster of phosphorylation sites on the cyclic AMP-regulated nuclear factor CREB predicted by its sequence. *Nature* 337:749–52

39. Gotoh Y, Moriyama K, Matsuda S, Okumura E, Kishimoto T, et al. 1991. *Xenopus* M phase MAP kinase: isolation of its cDNA and activation by MPF. *EMBO J.* 10:2661–68

40. Granner DK, Andreone TL. 1985. Insulin modulation of gene expression. *Diabetes Metab. Rev.* 1:139–70

40a. Granner DK, Andreone TL, Sasaki K, Beale E. 1983. Inhibition of transcription of the phosphoenolpyruvate carboxykinase gene by insulin. *Nature* 305:545–49

41. Granner DK, Pilkis S. 1990. The genes of hepatic glucose metabolism. *J. Biol. Chem.* 265:10173–76

42. Hardie DG. 1992. Regulation of fatty acid and cholesterol metabolism by the AMP-activated protein kinase. *Biochim. Biophys. Acta* 1123:231–38

43. Hashimoto N, Feener EP, Zhang W-R, Goldstein BJ. 1992. Insulin receptor protein-tyrosine phosphatases. *J. Biol. Chem.* 267:13811–14

44. Hayashi H, Kamohara S, Nishioka Y, Kanai F, Miyake N, et al. 1992. Insulin treatment stimulates the tyrosine phosphorylation of the α-type 85-kDa subunit of phosphatidylinositol 3-kinase in vivo. *J. Biol. Chem.* 267:22575–80

45. Hayashi H, Miyake N, Kanai F, Shibasaki F, Takenawa T, Ebina Y. 1991. Phosphorylation in vitro of the 85 kDa subunit of phosphatidylinositol 3-kinase and its possible activation by insulin receptor tyrosine kinase. *Biochem. J.* 280:769–75

46. Hayashi H, Nishioka Y, Kamohara S, Kanai F, Ishii K, et al. 1993. The α-type 85-kDa subunit of phosphatidylinositol 3-kinase is phosphorylated at tyrosines 368, 580, and 607 by the insulin receptor. *J. Biol. Chem.* 268:7107–17

47. Hedo JA, Simpson IA. 1984. Internalization of insulin receptors in the isolated rat adipose cell: demonstration of the vectorial disposition of receptor subunits. *J. Biol. Chem.* 259:11083–89

48. Izumi T, Tamemoto H, Nagao M, Kadowaki T, Takaku F, Kasuga M. 1991. Insulin and platelet-derived growth factor stimulate phosphorylation of the c-*raf* product at serine and threonine residues in intact cells. *J. Biol. Chem.* 266:7933–39

49. Janicot M, Flores-Riveros JR, Lane MD. 1991. The insulin-like growth factor 1 (IGF-1) receptor is responsible for mediating the effects of insulin, IGF-1, and IGF-2 in *Xenopus laevis* oocytes. *J. Biol. Chem.* 266:9382–91

50. Jones SW, Erikson E, Blenis J, Maller JL, Erikson RL. 1988. A *Xenopus* ribosomal protein S6 kinase has two apparent kinase domains that are each similar to distinct protein kinases. *Proc. Natl. Acad. Sci. USA* 85:3377–81

51. Kadowaki T, Koyasu S, Nishida E, Tobe K, Izumi T, et al. 1987. Tyrosine phosphorylation of common and specific sets of cellular proteins rapidly induced by insulin, insulin-like growth factor I, and epidermal growth factor in an intact cell. *J. Biol. Chem.* 262: 7342–50

52. Kahn CR, White MF, Crigorescu F, Takayama S, Häring HU, Crettaz M. 1985. The insulin receptor protein kinase. See Ref. 4, pp. 67–93

53. Karin M, Smeal T. 1992. Control of transcription factors by signal transduction pathways: the beginning of the end. *Trends Biochem. Sci.* 17:418–22

54. Kasuga M, Karlsson FA, Kahn CR. 1982. Insulin stimulates the phosphorylation of the 95,000-dalton subunit of its own receptor. *Science* 215:185–87

55. Klarlund JK, Bradford AP, Milla MG, Czech MP. 1990. Purification of a novel insulin-stimulated protein kinase from rat liver. *J. Biol. Chem.* 265:227–34

56. Klip A, Douen AG. 1989. Role of kinases in insulin stimulation of glucose transport. *J. Membr. Biol.* 111:1–23

57. Kono T. 1983. Action of insulin on glucose transport and cAMP phosphodiesterase in fat cells: involvement of two distinct molecular mechanisms. *Recent Progr. Hormone Res.* 39:519–57

58. Kono T. 1988. Insulin-sensitive glucose transport. *Vitamins Hormones* 44:103–54

59. Kono T. 1990. Insulin-sensitive cAMP phosphodiesterase. *Handb. Exp. Pharmacol.* 92:385–98

60. Kono T, Barham FW. 1971. The relationship between the insulin-binding capacity of fat cells and the cellular response to insulin: studies with intact and trypsin-treated fat cells. *J. Biol. Chem.* 246:6210–16

61. Kono T, Colowick SP. 1961. Stereospecific sugar transport caused by uncouplers and SH-inhibitors in rat diaphragm. *Arch. Biochem. Biophys.* 93:514–19

62. Kono T, Robinson FW, Sarver JA. 1975. Insulin-sensitive phosphodiesterase: its localization hormonal stimulation and oxidative stabilization. *J. Biol. Chem.* 250:7826–35

63. Kono T, Robinson FW, Sarver JA, Vega FV, Pointer RH. 1977. Action of insulin in fat cells: effects of low temperature, uncouplers of oxidative phosphorylation, and respiratory inhibitors. *J. Biol. Chem.* 252:2226–33

64. Kyriakis JM, App H, Zhang X-F, Banerjee P, Brautigan DL, et al. 1992. Raf-1 activates MAP kinase kinase. *Nature* 358:417–21

65. Lavoinne A, Erikson E, Maller JL, Price DJ, Avruch J, Cohen P. 1991. Purification and characterization of the insulin-stimulated protein kinase from rabbit skeletal muscle: close similarity to S6 kinase II. *Eur. J. Biochem.* 199:723–28

66. Lawrence JC Jr. 1992. Signal transduction and protein phosphorylation in the regulation of cellular metabolism by insulin. *Annu. Rev. Physiol.* 54: 177–93

67. Lawrence JC Jr, Hiken JF, James DE. 1990. Stimulation of glucose transport and glucose transporter phosphorylation by okadaic acid in rat adipocytes. *J. Biol. Chem.* 265:19768–76

68. Lee R-M, Cobb MH, Blackshear PJ. 1992. Evidence that extracellular signal-regulated kinases are the insulin activated raf-1 kinase kinases. *J. Biol. Chem.* 267:1088–92

69. Loose DS, Wynshaw-Boris A, Meisner HM, Hod Y, Hanson RW. 1985. Hormonal regulation of phosphoenolpyruvate carboxykinase gene expression. See Ref. 4, pp. 347–68

70. Lucas PC, Granner DK. 1992. Hormone response domains in gene transcription. *Annu. Rev. Biochem.* 61: 1131–73

71. Lynedjian PB, Gjinovci A, Renold AE. 1988. Stimulation by insulin of glucokinase gene transcription in liver of diabetic rats. *J. Biol. Chem.* 263: 740–44

72. Makino H, Kono T. 1980. Characterization of insulin-sensitive phosphodiesterase in fat cells. *J. Biol. Chem.* 255:7850–54

73. Makino H, Suzuki T, Kajinuma H,

Yamazaki M, Ito H, Yoshida S. 1992. The role of insulin-sensitive phosphodiesterase in insulin action. *Adv. Second Messenger Phosphoprotein Res.* 25:185–99

74. Makino H, Taira M, Shimada F, Hashimoto N, Suzuki Y, et al. 1992. Insulin receptor gene mutation: a molecular genetical and functional analysis. *Cell. Signal.* 4:351–63

75. Manganiello VC, Smith CJ, Newman AH, Rice K, Degerman E, Belfrage P. 1987. Hormonal regulation of adipocyte particulate "low K_m" cAMP phosphodiesterase. *Adv. Cyclic Nucleotide Protein Phosphorylation Res.* 11:497–511

76. Manganiello VC, Vaughan M. 1973. An effect of insulin on cyclic adenosine 3':5'-monophosphate phosphodiesterase activity in fat cells. *J. Biol. Chem.* 248:7164–70

77. Marshall S, Green A, Olefsky JM. 1981. Evidence for recycling of insulin receptors in isolated rat adipocytes. *J. Biol. Chem.* 256:11464–70

78. Matsuda S, Kosako H, Takenaka K, Moriyama K, Sakai H, et al. 1992. *Xenopus* MAP kinase activator: identification and function as a key intermediate in the phosphorylation cascade. *EMBO J.* 11:973–82

79. Messina JL. 1990. Regulation of gene expression by insulin. *Handb. Exp. Pharmacol.* 92:399–419

80. Morgan HE, Henderson MJ, Regen DM, Park CR. 1961. Regulation of glucose uptake in muscle: effects of insulin and anoxia on glucose transport and phosphorylation in the isolated, perfused heart of normal rats. *J. Biol. Chem.* 236:253–61

81. Nakielny S, Campbell DG, Cohen P. 1992. MAP kinase kinase from rabbit skeletal muscle. *FEBS Lett.* 308:183–89

82. O'Brien RM, Granner DK. 1991. Regulation of gene expression by insulin. *Biochem. J.* 278:609–19

83. Omatsu-Kanbe M, Kitasato H. 1990. Insulin stimulates the translocation of Na^+/K^+-dependent ATPase molecules from intracellular stores to the plasma membrane in frog skeletal muscle. *Biochem. J.* 272:727–33

84. Parker JC, Kiechle FL, Jarett L. 1982. Partial purification from hepatoma cells of an intracellular substance which mediates the effects of insulin on pyruvate dehydrogenase and low K_m cyclic AMP phosphodiesterase. *Arch. Biochem. Biophys.* 215:339–44

85. Pawlson LG, Lovell-Smith CJ,

Manganiello VC, Vaughan M. 1974. Effects of epinephrine, adrenocorticotrophic hormone, and theophylline on adenosine 3',5'-monophosphate phosphodiesterase activity in fat cells. *Proc. Natl. Acad. Sci. USA* 71:1639–42

86. Pazin MJ, Williams LT. 1992. Triggering signaling cascades by receptor tyrosine kinases. *Trends Biochem. Sci.* 17:374–78

87. Pelech SL, Sanghera JS. 1992. Mitogen-activated protein kinases: versatile transducers for cell signaling. *Trends Biochem. Sci.* 17:233–38

88. Price DJ, Nemenoff RA, Avruch J. 1989. Purification of a hepatic S6 kinase from cycloheximide-treated rats. *J. Biol. Chem.* 264:13825–33

89. Ramakrishna S, Benjamin WB. 1979. Fat cell protein phosphorylation: identification of phosphoprotein-2 as ATP-citrate lyase. *J. Biol. Chem.* 254:9232–36

90. Randle PJ, Smith GH. 1958. Regulation of glucose uptake by muscle. Parts I and II. *Biochem. J.* 70:490–500; 501–8

91. Ray LB, Sturgill TW. 1988. Insulin-stimulated microtubule-associated protein kinase is phosphorylated on tyrosine and threonine in vivo. *Proc. Natl. Acad. Sci. USA* 85:3753–57

91a. Reusch JE-B, Sussman KE, Draznin B. 1993. Inverse relationship between GLUT-4 phosphorylation and its intrinsic activity. *J. Biol. Chem.* 268:3348–51

92. Riabowol KT, Fink JS, Gilman MZ, Walsh DA, Goodman RH, Feramisco JR. 1988. The catalytic subunit of cAMP-dependent protein kinase induces expression of genes containing cAMP-responsive enhancer elements. *Nature* 336:83–86

93. Robinson FW, Smith CJ, Flanagan JE, Shibata H, Kono T. 1989. Cyclic GMP-dependent stimulation of the membrane-bound insulin-sensitive cAMP phosphodiesterase from rat adipocytes. *J. Biol. Chem.* 264:16458–64

94. Roesler WJ, Vandenbark GR, Hanson RW. 1988. Cyclic AMP and the induction of eukaryotic gene transcription. *J. Biol. Chem.* 263:9063–66

95. Roth RA. 1990. Insulin receptor structure. *Handb. Exp. Pharmacol.* 92:169–81

96. Rothenberg P, White MF, Kahn CR. 1990. The insulin receptor tyrosine kinase. *Handb. Exp. Pharmacol.* 92:209–36

97. Rutter GA, Denton RM. 1992. Effects of insulin and guanosine 5'-[γ-thio]-

triphosphate on fatty acid synthesis and lipolysis within electropermeabilized fat-cells. *Biochem. J.* 281:431–35

98. Rutter GA, Diggle TA, Denton RM. 1992. Regulation of pyruvate dehydrogenase by insulin and polyamines within electropermeabilized fat-cells and isolated mitochondria. *Biochem. J.* 285:435–39

99. Sadler SE. 1991. Type III phosphodiesterase plays a necessary role in the growth promoting actions of insulin, insulin-like growth factor-1, and Ha 21*ras* in *Xenopus laevis* oocytes. *Mol. Endocrinol.* 5:1939–46

100. Sadler SE. 1991 Inhibitors of phosphodiesterase III block stimulation of *Xenopus laevis* oocyte ribosomal S6 kinase activity by insulin-like growth factor-1. *Mol. Endocrinol.* 5: 1947–54

101. Sadler SE, Maller JL. 1987. In vivo regulation of cyclic AMP phosphodiesterase in *Xenopus* oocytes: stimulation by insulin and insulin-like growth factor 1. *J. Biol. Chem.* 262:10644–50

102. Saltiel AR, Fox JA, Sherline P, Cautrecasas P. 1986. Insulin-stimulated hydrolysis of a novel glycolipid generates modulators of cAMP phosphodiesterase. *Science* 233:967–72

103. Shibata H, Kono T. 1990. Stimulation of the insulin-sensitive cAMP phosphodiesterase by an ATP-dependent soluble factor from insulin-treated rat adipocytes. *Biochem. Biophys. Res. Commun.* 167:614–20

104. Shibata, H., Kono, T. 1990. Cell-free stimulation of the insulin-sensitive cAMP phosphodiesterase by the joint actions of ATP and the soluble fraction from insulin-treated rat liver. *Biochem. Biophys. Res. Commun.* 170:533–39

105. Shibata H, Robinson FW, Benzing CF, Kono T. 1991. Evidence that protein kinase C may not be involved in the insulin action on cAMP phosphodiesterase: studies with electroporated rat adipocytes that were highly responsive to insulin. *Arch. Biochem. Biophy.* 285:97–104

106. Shibata H, Robinson FW, Soderling TR, Kono T. 1991. Effects of okadaic acid on insulin-sensitive cAMP phosphodiesterase in rat adipocytes: evidence that insulin may stimulate the enzyme by phosphorylation. *J. Biol. Chem.* 266:17948–53

107. Shibata Y, Flanagan JE, Smith MM, Robinson FW, Kono T. 1987. Sedimentation characteristics of vesicles associated with insulin-sensitive intracellular glucose transporter from rat

adipocytes. *Biochim. Biophys. Acta* 902:154–58

108. Simpson IA, Cushman SW. 1986. Hormonal regulation of mammalian glucose transport. *Annu. Rev. Biochem.* 55: 1059–89

109. Smith CJ, Rubin CS, Rosen OM. 1980. Insulin-treated 3T3-L1 adipocytes and cell-free extracts derived from them incorporate 32P into ribosomal protein S6. *Proc. Natl. Acad. Sci. USA* 77: 2641–45

110. Smith CJ, Shibata H, Manganiello V, Belfrage P, Kono, T. 1992. Phosphorylation and activation of hormone-sensitive cAMP phosphodiesterase by cytosolic extracts of insulin-treated rat adipocytes. *FEBS Lett.* 6(1):A340 (Abstr.)

111. Smith U, Kuroda M, Simpson IA. 1984. Counter-regulation of insulin-stimulated glucose transport by catecholamines in the isolated rat adipose cell. *J. Biol. Chem.* 259:8758–63

112. Sommercorn J, Mulligan JA, Lozeman FJ, Krebs EG. 1987. Activation of casein kinase II in response to insulin and to epidermal growth factor. *Proc. Natl. Acad. Sci. USA* 84:8834–39

113. Standaert ML, Buckley DJ, Ishizuka T, Hoffman JM, Cooper DR, et al. 1990. Protein kinase C inhibitors block insulin- and PMA-stimulated hexose transport in isolated rat adipocytes and BC3H-1 myocytes. *Metabolism* 39: 1170–79

114. Sturgill TW, Ray LB, Erikson E, Maller JL. 1988. Insulin-stimulated MAP-2 kinase phosphorylates and activates ribosomal protein S6 kinase II. *Nature* 334:715–18

115. Sun XJ, Rothenberg P, Kahn CR, Backer JM, Araki E, et al. 1991. Structure of the insulin receptor substrate IRS-1 defines a unique signal transduction protein. *Nature* 352:73–77

116. Suzuki K, Kono T. 1979. Internalization and degradation of fat cell-bound insulin: separation and partial characterization of subcellular vesicles associated with iodoinsulin. *J. Biol. Chem.* 254:9786–94

117. Suzuki K, Kono T. 1980. Evidence that insulin causes translocation of glucose transport activity to the plasma membrane from an intracellular storage site. *Proc. Natl. Acad. Sci. USA* 77: 2542–45

118. Suzuki Y, Shibata H, Inoue S, Kojima I. 1992. Stimulation of glucose transport by guanine nucleotides in permeabilized rat adipocytes. *Biochem. Biophys. Res. Commun.* 189:572–80

119. Taira M, Hockman S, Calvo J, Taira M, Belfrage P, Manganiello VC. 1993. Molecular cloning of the rat adipocyte hormone-sensitive, cyclic GMP-inhibited, cyclic nucleotide phosphodiesterase. *J. Biol. Chem.* 268:18573–79
120. Taylor SI, Cama A, Accili D, Barbetti F, Quon MJ, et al. 1992. Mutations in the insulin receptor gene. *Endocrinol. Rev.* 13:566–95
121. Tobe K, Kadowaki T, Hara K, Gotoh Y, Kosako H, et al. 1992. Sequential activation of MAP kinase activator, MAP kinase, and S6 peptide kinase in intact rat liver following insulin injection. *J. Biol. Chem.* 267:21089–93
122. Ueda M, Robinson FW, Smith MM, Kono T. 1985. Effects of monensin on insulin processing in adipocytes: evidence that the internalized insulin-receptor complex has some physiological activities. *J. Biol. Chem.* 260: 3941–46
123. Ullrich A, Bell JR, Chen EY, Herrera R, Petruzzelli LM, et al. 1985. Human insulin receptor and its relationship to the tyrosine kinase family of oncogenes. *Nature* 313:756–61
124. Vega FV, Key RJ, Jordan JE, Kono T. 1980. Reversal of insulin effects in fat cells may require energy for deactivation of glucose transport, but not for deactivation of phosphodiesterase. *Arch. Biochem. Biophys.* 203:167–73
125. White MF, Livingston JN, Backer JM, Lauris V, Dull TJ, et al. 1988. Mutation of the insulin receptor at tyrosine 960 inhibits signal transmission but does not affect its tyrosine kinase activity. *Cell* 54:641–49
126. White MF, Maron R, Kahn CR. 1985. Insulin rapidly stimulates tyrosine phosphorylation of a M_r-185,000 protein in intact cells. *Nature* 318:183–86
127. Witters LA. 1985. Regulation of acetyl-CoA carboxylase by insulin and other hormones. See Ref. 4, pp. 315–26
128. Witters LA, Kemp BE. 1992. Insulin activation of acetyl-CoA carboxylase accompanied by inhibition of the 5′-AMP-activated protein kinase. *J. Biol. Chem.* 267:2864–67
129. Witters LA, Watts TD, Daniels DL, Evans, JL. 1988. Insulin stimulates the dephosphorylation and activation of acetyl-CoA carboxylase. *Proc. Natl. Acad. Sci. USA* 85:5473–77
130. Wu J, Harrison JK, Vincent LA, Haystead C, Haystead TAJ, et al. 1993. Molecular structure of a protein-tyrosine/threonine kinase activating p42 mitogen-activated protein kinase: MAP kinase kinase. *Proc. Natl. Acad. Sci. USA* 90:173–77
131. Yamamoto KK, Gonzalez GA, Biggs WH III, Montminy MR. 1988. Phosphorylation-induced binding and transcriptional efficacy of nuclear factor CREB. *Nature* 334:494–98
132. Yano Y, Sumida Y, Benzing CF, Robinson FW, Kono T. 1993. Primary sites of actions of staurosporine and H-7 in the cascade of insulin action to glucose transport. *Biochim. Biophys. Acta* 1176:327–32
133. Yu K-T, Gould MK. 1978. Permissive effect of ATP on insulin-stimulated sugar transport by rat soleus muscle. *J. Am. Physiol.* 234:E407–16
134. Yu K-T, Khalaf N, Czech MP. 1987. Insulin stimulates a novel Mn^{2+}-dependent cytosolic serine kinase in rat adipocytes. *J. Biol. Chem.* 262:16677–85
135. Zinman B, Hollenberg CH. 1974. Effect of insulin and lipolytic agents on rat adipocyte low K_m cyclic adenosine 3′:5′-monophosphate phosphodiesterase. *J. Biol. Chem.* 249:2182–87

Annu. Rev. Physiol. 1994. 56:297–319
Copyright © 1994 by Annual Reviews Inc. All rights reserved

CALCIUM AND HORMONE ACTION

Ole H. Petersen

MRC Secretory Control Research Group, The Physiological Laboratory,
University of Liverpool, Post Office Box 147, Liverpool, L69 3BX, England

Carl C. H. Petersen

AFRC Laboratory of Molecular Signalling, Department of Zoology, University
of Cambridge, Cambridge, CB2 3EJ, England

Haruo Kasai

Department of Physiology, Faculty of Medicine, University of Tokyo, Hongo,
Bunkyo-ku, Tokyo 113, Japan

KEY WORDS: cytosolic Ca^{2+} oscillations, inositol trisphosphate, Ca^{2+} release channels, Ca^{2+} stores, Ca^{2+} pumps, Ca^{2+}-induced Ca^{2+} release, secretion

INTRODUCTION

It has been known for more than 20 years that hormones and neurotransmitters can evoke release of Ca^{2+} from intracellular stores followed by Ca^{2+} entry from the extracellular fluid (62). Ten years ago, the discovery that inositol (1,4,5) trisphosphate (InsP$_3$) was the messenger linking hormone-receptor interaction to intracellular Ca^{2+} release marked an important turning point in the development of this subject (85). With the development of methods for high resolution intracellular calcium measurement (100), considerable insights have been obtained into the complex spatiotemporal patterns of hormone-evoked changes in the cytosolic Ca^{2+} concentration ($[Ca^{2+}]_i$). Astonishingly subtle spatial and temporal regulations of $[Ca^{2+}]_i$ can induce ordered sequences of events (dynamic decoding) (38, 39) and agonist-specific $[Ca^{2+}]_i$ signatures (63, 68, 69, 77, 96, 108).

Hormones and neurotransmitters often act via the same mechanisms. In pancreatic acinar cells both the neurotransmitter acetylcholine (ACh) and

0066–4278/94/0315–0297$05.00

the peptide hormone cholecystokinin (CCK) evoke cytosolic Ca^{2+} signals mediated via Ca^{2+} release through $InsP_3$ receptors ($InsP_3R$) (84). The gastrointestinal hormone CCK is also a neurotransmitter (20). It is therefore not useful to make a sharp distinction between hormone and neurotransmitter actions. This review concentrates on the events following the formation of $InsP_3$ that led to cytosolic Ca^{2+} signal generation. See J Exton (this volume) for an article on the production and metabolism of $InsP_3$. As a basis for understanding cytosolic Ca^{2+} signal generation, we first briefly describe the various types of Ca^{2+} transporters known, then discuss the spatial and temporal aspects of Ca^{2+} signaling, including various oscillator models, and attempt to explain dose-dependent regulation as well as hormone-specific signal patterns. Lastly, we describe some of the molecular targets for Ca^{2+} action as well as the dynamic decoding of the signals.

CELLULAR CALCIUM HOMEOSTASIS

$[Ca^{2+}]_i$ is controlled by the interaction of cytosolic calcium buffers and three categories of transport proteins (channels, carriers, and pumps) expressed differentially on the plasma membrane and on the membranes of calcium stores. The resting $[Ca^{2+}]_i$ is maintained low at 0.1 μM, but under hormone stimulation it may rise to 1 μM and in small domains to even higher levels. In the following, the most important functional characteristics of the components involved in cellular Ca^{2+} control are described.

Calcium Pumps

Work on muscle relaxing factor led to the discovery of ATP-linked concentration of Ca^{2+} in a particulate fraction (sarcoplasmic reticulum) (21). It was only later that the role of the endoplasmic reticulum (ER) in controlling $[Ca^{2+}]_i$ became clear (8). The Ca^{2+} pump in the cell membrane was discovered by Schatzmann in 1966 (81). The molecular properties of the purified enzyme have been described in some detail (12). The electrogenic Ca^{2+} pump in the ER, sarcoplasmic reticulum, and cell membrane belong to the P-type of ATPases that are inhibited by orthovanadate (8, 12). From a practical experimental point of view, it is important that the tumor promoter, thapsigargin, inhibits the Ca^{2+}-ATPase in the ER but not in the plasma membrane (93).

Until recently there has been little precise information about the acute regulation of Ca^{2+} pumps in intact cells. The relationship between $[Ca^{2+}]_i$ and the velocity of Ca^{2+}-pump-mediated Ca^{2+} extrusion has been assessed with the double-fluorescence microdroplet method, which allows simultaneous measurements of Ca^{2+} extrusion and $[Ca^{2+}]_i$ in single cells (90).

During agonist stimulation, the velocity of Ca^{2+} extrusion is directly and acutely regulated by changes in $[Ca^{2+}]_i$ within the range 0.1 to 1 μM (89, 90, 91). When agonist stimulation evokes repetitive cytosolic Ca^{2+} spikes, each spike is associated with a synchronous increase in Ca^{2+} extrusion velocity (91). A large amount of Ca^{2+} is transported since the whole of the mobilizable cellular Ca^{2+} pool can be pumped out within a few minutes (90). The Ca^{2+} uptake and the Ca^{2+}-ATPase in the ER are half-maximally inhibited when the intravesicular Ca^{2+} concentration is about 300 μM (8). It is therefore likely that the ER Ca^{2+}-ATPase is regulated by $[Ca^{2+}]_i$ (an increase activating the pump) and the free Ca^{2+} concentration in the ER lumen (an increase inhibiting the pump). There may also be receptor-mediated control of Ca^{2+} pumps (111).

In several electrically excitable cell types there is also Na^+-Ca^{2+} exchange. This is an electrogenic process with a stoichiometry of 3 Na^+ per Ca^{2+} (8). Na^+-Ca^{2+} exchange is not linked to ATP consumption, but does depend on the establishment of an adequate transmembrane Na^+ gradient by the Na^+-K^+-ATPase. In some epithelial cells, Na^+-Ca^{2+} exchange is insignificant (58).

Ca^{2+} Channels

There are two types of Ca^{2+} release channels in the ER, namely the ryanodine receptor (RYR) and the $InsP_3$ receptor ($InsP_3R$). The RYR has been characterized at the single channel level and its amino acid sequence determined. It is now recognized that there is a family of RYRs (2). The RYR is activated by a rise in $[Ca^{2+}]_i$, which explains the Ca^{2+}-induced Ca^{2+} release process (23). The curve relating channel open state probability (P_o) to $[Ca^{2+}]_i$ shows that P_o increases when $[Ca^{2+}]_i$ increases from 0.1 to 1 μM, but decreases when $[Ca^{2+}]_i$ increases from 10 μM to 1 mM (3). The rapid kinetics of the RYR have been investigated at the single channel level. The channel shows a novel adaptation phenomenon by which it rapidly closes following activation by a rise in Ca^{2+}, but is still able to respond to subsequent Ca^{2+} elevations (32a).

Caffeine potentiates Ca^{2+}-induced Ca^{2+} release via the RYR, and at high enough concentrations, the RYR becomes sensitive to the resting $[Ca^{2+}]_i$ (22). Caffeine is a convenient tool because it is extremely membrane-permeant (99), but unfortunately caffeine inhibits $InsP_3$-evoked Ca^{2+} release (105) and also inhibits agonist-induced $InsP_3$ production (99) so that the interpretation of caffeine-evoked effects in intact cells can be difficult. Recent evidence suggests that the NAD^+ metabolite cyclic ADP-ribose can enhance Ca^{2+}-induced Ca^{2+} release by sensitizing the RYR to Ca^{2+} (29, 87).

The InsP$_3$ R has been studied at the single channel level (3) and its amino acid sequence determined (28). There is a family of InsP$_3$Rs derived from three or four distinct genes (78) with different sensitivities to InsP$_3$ (41). Although the RYR is about twice as large as the InsP$_3$R, there are regions of homology particularly in their C-terminal domains that have membrane-spanning regions (2). Binding of InsP$_3$ to its receptor causes channel opening (3), but cytosolic Ca^{2+} also acts as a co-agonist together with InsP$_3$ (3, 27, 34, 35). In the presence of submaximal InsP$_3$ concentrations, a rise in [Ca^{2+}]$_i$ from 0.1 to 0.3 μM evokes a sharp increase in P$_o$, whereas a further increase in [Ca^{2+}]$_i$ to 1 μM markedly decreases P$_o$. The Ca^{2+} dose-response curve for the InsP$_3$ receptor is thus bell-shaped with a maximum P$_o$ at a [Ca^{2+}]$_i$ of 0.2 − 0.3 μM (3). We have no single-channel data about the dynamic response to acute changes in [Ca^{2+}]$_i$ and InsP$_3$ concentration. InsP$_3$R sensitivity to InsP$_3$ can be enhanced by thiol reagents (7, 95).

Heparin competes with InsP$_3$ for binding to the InsP$_3$R, but does not induce channel opening and is therefore a good competitive antagonist (26). A monoclonal antibody to the InsP$_3$R microinjected into oocytes has been shown to block Ca^{2+} oscillations and Ca^{2+} waves (57), but such a large molecule cannot easily be applied to small cells via patch-clamp pipettes.

The Ca^{2+} entry channels in the plasma membrane, other than the well characterized voltage-gated Ca^{2+} channels, are manifold and are not yet fully characterized. Kuno & Gardner (42) reported direct InsP$_3$-induced opening of Ca^{2+} permeable channels in excised inside-out patches from Jurkat T cells, and a recent study shows InsP$_3$ activation of a Ca^{2+} current in human T cells that is inhibited when [Ca^{2+}]$_i$ is elevated (53). These channels are not activated by inositol (1,3,4,5) tetrakisphosphate (InsP$_4$) (53), but Luckhoff & Clapham (46) have found an InsP$_4$-activated Mn^{2+} permeable Ca^{2+} channel in excised patches from endothelial cells. The InsP$_4$-sensitive channels were not activated by InsP$_3$, and InsP$_4$ only opened pathways when [Ca^{2+}]$_i$ was elevated (46). There is indirect evidence for Ca^{2+} entry evoked by a combination of InsP$_3$ and InsP$_4$ in lacrimal gland cells (71).

Possibly the most important Ca^{2+} influx pathway is activated by depletion of intracellular Ca^{2+} stores (73), and recently patch-clamp studies have revealed a Ca^{2+}-selective current [Ca^{2+}release-activated Ca^{2+} current (I$_{CRAC}$)] through a Mn^{2+}-permeable pathway. The ionophore, ionomycin, and the Ca^{2+} chelator, EGTA, can activate I$_{CRAC}$ in the presence of heparin, which indicates that InsP$_3$ does not directly control these channels (33, 67a). A recent study of noradrenaline-mediated Ca^{2+} entry in smooth muscle cells suggests that Ca^{2+} store depletion, InsP$_3$, and InsP$_4$ all contribute to the control of Ca^{2+} entry (64).

Ca^{2+} Stores

The non-mitochondrial Ca^{2+} stores in the ER or modified portions of the ER contain Ca^{2+} pumps, Ca^{2+} release channels and, in the lumen, Ca^{2+}-binding proteins such as calsequestrin and calreticulin (55). The distribution of InsP$_3$Rs and RYRs can vary considerably between different cell types with InsP$_3$Rs and RYRs segregated in separate stores or colocalized (2, 10, 102). Primary $[Ca^{2+}]_i$ rises have been detected near the nucleus (106), Golgi apparatus (103), rough ER (40), and secretory granules (40). With the ion microscope (14), a rapid exchange of Ca^{2+} can be demonstrated not only in the ER, but also in the Golgi apparatus and the nucleus. There is evidence for InsP$_3$Rs in the nucleus (48), although it may be the nuclear envelope or an organelle closely associated with it that is responsible for the InsP$_3$ effects observed with isolated nuclei (31).

In the 1970's, mitochondria were thought to play a key role in intracellular Ca^{2+} homeostasis, but in the 1980's the view was modified and a significant involvement of mitochondria in Ca^{2+} homeostasis was proposed only when $[Ca^{2+}]_i$ had risen to pathological levels (55). It is now clear that agonist stimulation primarily releases Ca^{2+} from the ER and/or ER-derived organelles (2), and it is generally accepted that in the resting unstimulated state, the mitochondria contain little Ca^{2+} (31, 55). However, the role of mitochondria in cellular Ca^{2+} homeostasis is now being re-assessed. In intact cells, mitochondria accumulate Ca^{2+} after agonist stimulation (31, 75), and in permeabilized cells there is a very marked increase in mitochondrial Ca^{2+} content when $[Ca^{2+}]_i$ increases above 0.5 μM (97). Ca^{2+} uptake into mitochondria is mediated by a carrier, namely a uniporter. The large electrical potential difference created by the respiratory chain H^+ extrusion mechanism provides the driving force (8). The Ca^{2+} exit pathway from mitochondria is mainly via Na^+-Ca^{2+} exchange (8).

Cytosolic Calcium Buffers

The cytosol contains slowly diffusible Ca^{2+}-binding proteins that are capable of rapidly buffering Ca^{2+} (60). The effect of these buffers is likely to be highly significant near the Ca^{2+} release channels, and the saturation of such buffers may be essential for both Ca^{2+} spike initiation and Ca^{2+} wave propagation (68a).

SPATIAL ORGANIZATION OF Ca^{2+} SIGNALS

Calcium Micro-gradients

Agonists can induce steep spatial gradients of $[Ca^{2+}]_i$ because Ca^{2+} is buffered and sequestered efficiently. Ca^{2+} gradients formed by this mechanism are referred to as Ca^{2+} micro-gradients, since the gradients occur within a spatial dimension of 1–10 μm. The Ca^{2+} micro-gradients can be visualized with currently available methods of Ca^{2+} imaging. Three distinct aspects of the Ca^{2+} micro-gradients are discussed separately below: the primary site of the $[Ca^{2+}]_i$ rise, the Ca^{2+} spikes, and the spread of the $[Ca^{2+}]_i$ rise.

Several distinct mechanisms for the primary $[Ca^{2+}]_i$ rise seem to exist. Firstly and most simply, the primary $[Ca^{2+}]_i$ rise can be triggered at the site of the primary stimulus, for example, sperm triggering the initial $[Ca^{2+}]_i$ rise at the point of entry in the egg (37, 57). This mechanism could also account for synapse-specific control of $[Ca^{2+}]_i$ rises at postsynaptic dendrites (4). Secondly, if agonist receptors are localized, even homogeneous stimuli

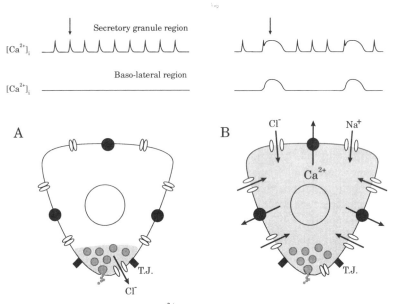

Figure 1   Local and global cytosolic Ca^{2+} spikes illustrated diagrammatically on the basis of data obtained on pancreatic acinar cells (39, 40, 63, 68, 69, 70, 96). The cartoons A and B show single acinar cells in which tight junctions (T.J.) separate a small luminal from a much larger basolateral plasma membrane area. Secretory (zymogen) granules are shown in the area close to the luminal membrane (secretory granule region). Ca^{2+}-activated Cl^- and non-selective cation (at physiological membrane potentials mainly allowing Na^+ influx) channels are shown together with Ca^{2+} pumps. The nucleus is also indicated. The shaded areas represent regions in which $[Ca^{2+}]_i$ is elevated at the times corresponding to the arrows above the $[Ca^{2+}]_i$ traces shown in the top part of the figure. In A the Ca^{2+} signal (for example generated by a low concentration of ACh or intracellular InsP3 infusion) consists of repetitive Ca^{2+} spikes exclusively in the secretory granule region, whereas in B a more complex signal pattern is shown composed of short-lasting spikes in the secretory granule region followed, in some cases, by larger global transients [generated for example by stimulation with the hormone cholecystokinin (CCK)].

could give rise to inhomogeneous $[Ca^{2+}]_i$ rises. Thirdly, the primary Ca^{2+} release site will depend on the spatial distribution and heterogeneity of the Ca^{2+} release channels. In *Limulus* photoreceptors, only the light-sensitive R-lobe is sensitive to $InsP_3$ (67). In *Xenopus* oocytes, flash photolysis of caged $InsP_3$ revealed primary $[Ca^{2+}]_i$ rises at certain hot spots or foci (43, 65). More recently, we proposed such a mechanism to account for the agonist-induced primary $[Ca^{2+}]_i$ rises in a small trigger zone within the secretory granule area of pancreatic acinar cells (40, 96) (Figure 1). $InsP_3$ injected from the opposite side (basal area) of the cells evoked a primary $[Ca^{2+}]_i$ rise in the trigger zone. This observation indicates that, during agonist stimulation, $InsP_3$ produced at the basolateral membrane could diffuse and primarily act on $InsP_3$ receptors in the trigger zone. In fact, $InsP_3$ could act as a global messenger in small cells (1). The higher $InsP_3$ sensitivity in the trigger zone is probably due to the localized presence of $InsP_3$ receptors with higher affinity than those in the basal area. Alternatively, the density of $InsP_3$ receptors in the trigger zone may be very high.

Local and Global Ca^{2+} Spikes

Rises in $[Ca^{2+}]_i$ induced via Ca^{2+} release channels often occur in the form of repetitive spiking; the spikes exhibit a sharp upstroke from a threshold $[Ca^{2+}]_i$ level and recover to the resting level during sustained stimulation (56). The mechanisms for spike generation are discussed below. As typified in the case of pancreatic acinar cells, these Ca^{2+} spikes can occur locally at a specific subcellular domain and form Ca^{2+} micro-gradients (Figure 1). With a sufficiently high $InsP_3$ level and $InsP_3R$ sensitivity, the local Ca^{2+} spike subsequently can spread as a wave towards other cellular areas (2, 37, 72, 89, 101). The global rises in $[Ca^{2+}]_i$ can also be induced transiently and are referred to as global Ca^{2+} spikes (Figure 1). The cell is thus able to control the spatial extent of the Ca^{2+} signal, which is functionally and energetically important (Figure 1).

Ca^{2+} Waves

The coordinated Ca^{2+} activation of many cellular processes is the result of Ca^{2+} waves propagating through the cytosol at velocities of 5–100 μm/s (37, 39, 59, 98). Since the amplitude of a Ca^{2+} wave is non-decremental, active release processes must be triggered by a diffusible factor. Ca^{2+} itself is likely to be the diffusible factor, since positive feedback effects of Ca^{2+} on Ca^{2+} release channels, $InsP_3Rs$ and $RYRs$, have been discovered.

$InsP_3Rs$ seem to be responsible for the regenerative Ca^{2+} waves in some oocytes since they do not have RYRs (43, 57). Injection of antibodies against the $InsP_3R$ blocks the $InsP_3$-induced as well as sperm-induced Ca^{2+} waves in hamster eggs (57). Many other cells, however, express both

InsP$_3$Rs and RYRs. For example, smooth muscle cells appear to utilize primarily InsP$_3$Rs for the agonist-induced Ca^{2+} waves despite the fact that they have sufficient RYRs (36). In sea urchin eggs, on the other hand, RYRs are localized in the cortex, and sperm induces Ca^{2+} waves in the cortical area (54). In pancreatic acinar cells, InsP$_3$Rs and RYR-like channels appear to be distributed in different subcellular areas; InsP$_3$Rs appear in the trigger zone and basolateral region (40, 96), whereas RYR-like channels are in the secretory granule region (40). The Ca^{2+} wave in the secretory granule region is always induced by the primary [Ca^{2+}]$_i$ rise in the trigger zone, while at high agonist concentrations, the Ca^{2+} wave in the basolateral region is triggered by the [Ca^{2+}]$_i$ rise in the secretory granule region. The Ca^{2+} wave speed may depend on agonist concentration (59). Finally, a positive feedback effect of Ca^{2+} on PLC may be important for intercellular Ca^{2+} wave generation in epithelial (5) and glial cells (15, 18).

Calcium Nano-gradients

A distinct type of Ca^{2+} gradient may be formed by the efficient mobilization of Ca^{2+} through Ca^{2+} channels; if Ca^{2+} mobilization is more rapid than the diffusion of Ca^{2+} in the cytosol, then steep gradients of Ca^{2+} appear close to the inner mouth of open Ca^{2+} channels. This form of Ca^{2+} gradient will be referred to as a Ca^{2+} nano-gradient since theoretical analysis indicates that it decays with a space constant of several tens of nanometers (13, 82). The nano-gradients have two further characteristics; the maximum [Ca^{2+}]$_i$ near these nano-gradients (Ca^{2+} domain) may be as high as 100 µM (76), and these gradients may appear and disappear within a fraction of a millisecond depending on the state of the Ca^{2+} channels. On the other hand, in the case of Ca^{2+} micro-gradients, [Ca^{2+}]$_i$ rarely exceeds 1 µM and recovery of the [Ca^{2+}]$_i$ rise normally takes at least several seconds because of abundant Ca^{2+} buffering and the slow uptake by pumps. The Ca^{2+} nano-gradients may be too small and rapid to be captured with the current state of Ca^{2+} imaging methods (45, 101).

CALCIUM OSCILLATIONS

Agonist-evoked cytosolic Ca^{2+} oscillations were first demonstrated in blowfly salivary glands where it was also shown that the frequency of Ca^{2+} spikes increased with increasing agonist concentration (74). It is now clear that the InsP$_3$R is intimately involved in the mechanism of agonist-evoked cytosolic Ca^{2+} spike generation in numerous cell types (2). Many different oscillation patterns have been observed depending on cell type and stimulus (89). In an individual cell, the oscillation pattern depends on receptor type, agonist concentration, intracellular Ca^{2+} buffering, and Ca^{2+} influx (30, 69).

How Much Stored Ca^{2+} is Released per Spike?

There is evidence from many systems that agonists can evoke Ca^{2+} spikes in the absence of external Ca^{2+} (56, 72), and the primary event must therefore be release of stored Ca^{2+}. The number of Ca^{2+} spikes that can be evoked by a constant hormone level, in the absence of external Ca^{2+}, varies between cell types and also depends on the type and strength of stimulation. In pancreatic acinar cells, many shortlasting local Ca^{2+} spikes in the secretory granule region can be evoked by $InsP_3$ or a low ACh concentration when the external Ca^{2+} concentration is very low (104). So far it has not been possible to estimate the amount of intracellular Ca^{2+} released during these short lasting spikes. In the same cells, CCK additionally evokes broader global Ca^{2+} transients (Figure 1), and in experiments with low external Ca^{2+} concentration, only a few (2–8) such events occur (91). The amount of Ca^{2+} extruded during a CCK-evoked spike, measured with the droplet method (90), corresponded to about 40% of the total mobilizable intracellular Ca^{2+} pool (91). The amount of stored Ca^{2+} released during a spike must be at least equal to the amount extruded, and therefore at least 40% of the Ca^{2+} stores are emptied. The ER Ca^{2+} pumps are likely to take up a considerable proportion of the primarily released Ca^{2+}. A large proportion of the stored Ca^{2+}, perhaps all, is released during each spike, and in at least the pancreatic acinar cells, about 40% of the Ca^{2+} released may be extruded, whereas the remaining 60% is likely to be taken back into the ER. The large Ca^{2+} extrusion (91) highlights the need for compensatory Ca^{2+} entry and explains why only a few global spikes can be fired in the absence of external Ca^{2+}.

What Determines Latency and Interspike Periods?

In hepatocytes there is a linear correlation between the time required to observe the first spike after start of hormonal stimulation (latency) and the period of Ca^{2+} oscillation (77). It is not clear what exactly happens during the latent period, but results obtained with confocal microfluorimetry of Ca^{2+} signals evoked by photoreleased $InsP_3$ in oocytes show that there is a substantial dose-dependent latency (about 50–100 ms) from $InsP_3$ release to a measurable rise in $[Ca^{2+}]_i$ (66). This is not due to a diffusion delay for $InsP_3$ to reach the $InsP_3R$ as $[Ca^{2+}]_i$ in the localized region investigated is initially flat after the photorelease of $InsP_3$ until a sudden and sharp rise in $[Ca^{2+}]_i$ occurs. It seems unlikely that there should be a long delay in $InsP_3$-induced opening of $InsP_3R$ channels since ligand-gated channels usually respond within a few milliseconds (79), but since Ca^{2+} is a co-agonist, there could be a delay in the build-up of $[Ca^{2+}]_i$ to reach a critical threshold. Intracellular infusion of the Ca^{2+} buffer citrate has been shown to increase both the latency and the period between ACh- and $InsP_3$-evoked Ca^{2+} spikes in pancreatic acinar cells (69, 70). The buffering of the primary $InsP_3$-evoked Ca^{2+} release may therefore be an important point to consider. The relevant buffering undoubtedly has many components including a variety of Ca^{2+}-binding proteins in the cytosol and on the surface of organelles, as well as active uptake into ER or ER-derived vesicular structures and possibly also into mitochondria (60). It is characteristic for solutions that buffer H^+ or Ca^{2+} to find little change in pH or pCa upon addition of the relevant ion until a sharp transition point is reached. The active Ca^{2+} buffers may behave in a similar fashion. The lumen of the Ca^{2+} stores contain Ca^{2+}-binding proteins, and progressive Ca^{2+} accumulation could saturate these buffers and cause a sharp rise in the luminal-free Ca^{2+} concentration. This would inhibit the Ca^{2+} pump, thus inducing a sharp rise in $[Ca^{2+}]_i$. An important reason for the latency as well as the quiet period between Ca^{2+} spikes may therefore be charging of passive Ca^{2+} buffers and Ca^{2+} stores (11, 68a).

Oscillation Models

Models based on pulsatile $InsP_3$ formation have attracted attention since they could provide a straightforward explanation for pulsatile Ca^{2+} liberation (56). The $InsP_3$-Ca^{2+} cross-coupling (ICC) model (56) is based on the idea that Ca^{2+} exerts a positive feedback effect on the phospholipase C (PLC) and thus stimulates $InsP_3$ formation. The following sequence is envisaged: Agonist stimulation generates $InsP_3$, which in turn initiates Ca^{2+} release via the $InsP_3R$. The rise in $[Ca^{2+}]_i$ stimulates further $InsP_3$ formation, thus leading to acceleration of Ca^{2+} release. Ca^{2+} activation of PLC can occur (17), but this process may only operate when the PLC is activated via its G protein (83). At a high level of $[Ca^{2+}]_i$, the $InsP_3R$ is inhibited and Ca^{2+} release stops, which allows Ca^{2+} reuptake into the ER and/or Ca^{2+} extrusion. The resulting fall in $[Ca^{2+}]_i$ terminates PLC activation and $InsP_3$ formation is reduced to the prespike level. The whole process can now repeat itself (56).

Spiking can be evoked by direct infusion of $InsP_3$ or the non-metabolizable $InsP_3$ analogue inositol (1,4,5) trisphosphorothioate $(InsPS_3)$ (104). Digital imaging experiments on pancreatic cells have shown directly that a low concentration of $InsPS_3$ can evoke repetitive cytosolic Ca^{2+} spikes in the secretory granule region just as in the case of stimulation with low agonist concentrations (96). Since a constant $InsP_3$ level evokes Ca^{2+} spiking (70, 96, 104), it is necessary to consider how a steady messenger level can induce pulsatile Ca^{2+} release. Before 1990 it was not known that $InsP_3R$ was Ca^{2+}-sensitive, and it was natural to consider a two-pool model in which a small primary $InsP_3$-induced Ca^{2+} release would be amplified by Ca^{2+}-induced Ca^{2+} release from RYRs in a separate Ca^{2+} store (32). Following the discovery that an increase in $[Ca^{2+}]_i$ markedly enhances $InsP_3$-induced release through $InsP_3Rs$ (3, 27, 34), one-pool models became attractive (19, 40, 68a).

In a simple one-pool model, $InsP_3$-evoked Ca^{2+} release evokes a modest slow rise in $[Ca^{2+}]_i$ and, at a threshold level, Ca^{2+} markedly enhances the open state probability of the $InsP_3$-activated Ca^{2+} release channels, thereby leading to a dramatic rise in $[Ca^{2+}]_i$. At a higher level of $[Ca^{2+}]_i$, the negative feedback effect of Ca^{2+} on the $InsP_3R$ becomes important and the channels close. At this point, the Ca^{2+} pumps cause reuptake of Ca^{2+} into the ER and extrusion into the extracellular solution. In such a model, the negative feedback initiated by a high $[Ca^{2+}]_i$ should continue for a period after $[Ca^{2+}]_i$ has been reduced below the level necessary to induce the effect in the first place. Since the sensitivity to $InsP_3$ recovers as $[Ca^{2+}]_i$ recovers (44, 66), it is doubtful whether the direct Ca^{2+} inhibition of the $InsP_3R$ is sufficient. An additional effect that may be more long-lasting could be mediated by arachidonic acid, which inhibits both ACh and $InsP_3$-evoked Ca^{2+} release. The phospholipase A_2 inhibitor, 4-bromophenacyl bromide, prolongs and potentiates $InsP_3$-evoked Ca^{2+} transients (49, 50). The following negative feedback may therefore occur: the Ca^{2+} spike activates phospholipase A_2, which induces arachidonic acid formation. This in turn inhibits the $InsP_3R$, and Ca^{2+} release is terminated. However, it is not yet clear whether arachidonic acid formation actually plays any role in the Ca^{2+} oscillation mechanism, and for that reason it is useful to consider two-pool models in which the problem concerning long interspike intervals can more easily be overcome.

Figure 2 illustrates a new form of a two-pool model and takes into account that the $InsP_3$-sensitive Ca^{2+} pool may be compartmentalized into stores that differ in their sensitivity to $InsP_3$ (6,25, 65). This suggests that at a submaximal $InsP_3$ concentration not all $InsP_3Rs$ will be open. A subthreshold $InsP_3$ level therefore does not primarily activate Ca^{2+} release from all parts of the $InsP_3$-sensitive pool. The small steady Ca^{2+} release is buffered both by cytosolic buffers and active uptake into stores (68a) not all of which are initially participating in the Ca^{2+} release process (Figure 2, i-ii). This causes a gradual increase in the Ca^{2+} content of these stores and, when the intrastore buffers are saturated, gives rise to a sharp increase in the intravesicular free Ca^{2+} concentration that in turn inhibits the Ca^{2+} pump in the membrane of the vesicles (Figure 2, iii). Now $[Ca^{2+}]_i$ rises and the channels already participating in the Ca^{2+} release open more frequently and channels hitherto not responding to $InsP_3$ also open (Figure 2, iv). This initiates the explosive Ca^{2+} release that causes the steep rise in $[Ca^{2+}]_i$. Because of the high Ca^{2+}

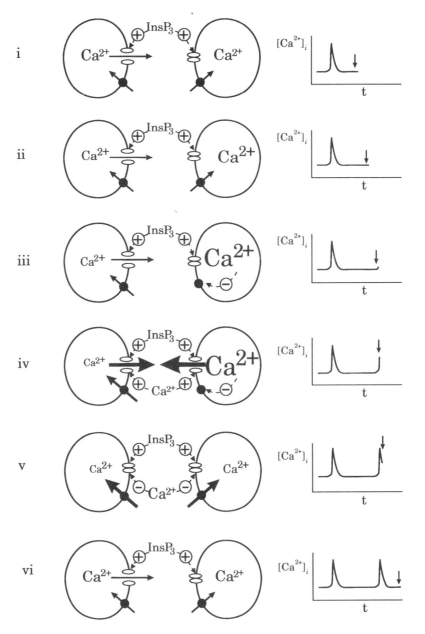

Figure 2   Two-pool model explaining repetitive cytosolic Ca^{2+} spike generation. For explanation see text.

concentration in the lumen of the vesicles, there is a substantial driving force for Ca^{2+} release. Soon $[Ca^{2+}]_i$ has risen to a point where the negative feedback on the $InsP_3R$ dominates and the channels close (Figure 2, v). The intravesicular Ca^{2+} concentration is now low because of the marked release that has taken place, and the Ca^{2+} pumps will be fully activated, which explains the falling phase of the Ca^{2+} spike. When $[Ca^{2+}]_i$ is back to the resting level, the whole cycle can repeat itself (Figure 2, vi). The two components shown in Figure 2 do not correspond to the two regions of $InsP_3$ sensitivity illustrated in Figure 1, but could represent individual Ca^{2+} stores in, for example, secretory granule areas.

The model in Figure 2 can be reduced to a single-pool model if all pools are equally sensitive to $InsP_3$. In this case, the Ca^{2+} released (difference between Ca^{2+} release and Ca^{2+} uptake in the same pools) during the interspike period is sequestered exclusively by cytosolic Ca^{2+} buffers. If the $InsP_3Rs$ from the less $InsP_3$-sensitive pools are replaced by RYRs, then Figure 2 is transformed into the classical two-pool model (32). It is possible, of course, that the "second" pool contains both $InsP_3Rs$ and RYRs. It cannot be excluded that some agonists may induce fluctuating $InsP_3$ levels that could modulate the basic pattern produced by the mechanism shown in Figure 2 (combination of ICC and two-pool model). Several other elements play a role. Substantial amounts of Ca^{2+} are extruded from the cell during each spike (91), and Ca^{2+} entry is needed to compensate for this loss because otherwise the stores will be unable to reload fully after a spike (30). The relative importance of passive cytosolic buffering and active buffering by ER Ca^{2+} uptake may vary considerably according to the time course of the oscillating events (11, 68a).

DOSE-DEPENDENT REGULATION

A physiologically important intracellular messenger such as Ca^{2+} must be regulated in such a way that small changes in the plasma level of the relevant hormone evoke appropriate changes in messenger concentration. In blowfly salivary gland cells, the frequency of Ca^{2+} oscillations increases with increasing 5-hydroxytryptamine concentration in the dose range over which fluid secretion is stimulated. The rate of secretion, therefore, may be a function of second messenger frequency rather than amplitude (74). In hepatocytes, the frequency, but not the amplitude or shape of global cytosolic Ca^{2+} spikes, increases with increasing vasopressin or phenylephrine concentration (94, 107). The simplest explanation is that the cellular $InsP_3$ level is controlled by the intensity of hormone stimulation. An increased level of $InsP_3$ causes a larger primary Ca^{2+} release which, all other factors being unchanged, more rapidly saturates passive and/or active Ca^{2+} buffers.

This allows the positive feedback on the $InsP_3Rs$ to start earlier in the cycle (Figure 2) and explains the increase in spike frequency. Indeed, the shape and frequency of Ca^{2+} spiking evoked by $InsPS_3$ or $InsP_3$ is concentration-dependent (70).

In cells capable of generating both local and global Ca^{2+} spikes, the situation is more complex. Pancreatic acinar cells can be stimulated to secrete by the hormone CCK, and the physiological concentration range in plasma after a meal is about 5–20 pM (20). A threshold concentration of CCK (about 5 pM) evokes short-lasting Ca^{2+} spikes at a low frequency and only a few of these local spikes in the secretory granule region trigger global Ca^{2+} spikes (Figure 1). At a slightly higher concentration (10–20 pM), the frequency of local spikes is increased and Ca^{2+} waves are more often triggered. At an unphysiologically high CCK concentration (for example 50 pM), every local Ca^{2+} spike triggers a spreading Ca^{2+} wave (69). The frequency modulation of the local spikes could be explained, as already discussed, by changing $InsP_3$ levels, since an increased $InsP_3$ concentration tends to be associated with a higher spike frequency (70, 104). A higher $InsP_3$ level may also explain the tendency towards spreading of the Ca^{2+} signal. The local spikes are generated in the secretory granule region either by $InsP_3Rs$ with a particularly high affinity for $InsP_3$, or because of a very high density of $InsP_3Rs$ in this part of the cell (40, 96). When the $InsP_3$ concentration is increased by a higher hormone level, the low-affinity or low-density $InsP_3Rs$ in the rest of the cell can also be activated and participate in the Ca^{2+}-induced Ca^{2+} release process, which allows formation of Ca^{2+} waves. In experiments with the non-metabolizable $InsP_3$ analogue, $InsPS_3$, an increase in $InsPS_3$ concentration was associated with a tendency towards generation of broader Ca^{2+} spikes of the global type (70).

In the case of stimulating pancreatic acinar cells with CCK in the physiological concentration range, there is no evidence for regulation of $InsP_3$ production because it is impossible to detect $InsP_3$ generation in response to CCK concentrations below 100 pM (a toxic level) (52). In this context, it is interesting that the sulfhydryl reagent, thimerosal, can evoke Ca^{2+} spike generation in several cell types, which are dependent on functional $InsP_3$ receptors; however, thimerosal does not increase the $InsP_3$ concentration (7, 95). The sensitivity of the $InsP_3R$ to $InsP_3$ may therefore be regulated, and it is possible that a hormone, via a mechanism still unknown, can regulate frequency and spreading of Ca^{2+} spikes not only by varying $InsP_3$ levels, but also by varying the sensitivity of the $InsP_3Rs$.

There are other mechanisms by which dose-dependent regulation of Ca^{2+} signaling could occur. Hormones may control the Ca^{2+} pumps in the ER and/or the cell membrane. A theoretical model calculation by Goldbeter et al (32) shows that a reduction of the velocity of Ca^{2+} extrusion accelerates Ca^{2+} spiking. There may be messengers that simultaneously control both Ca^{2+} release channel sensitivity and the operation of Ca^{2+} pumps. Arachidonic acid reduces the responsiveness to applied $InsP_3$ and $InsP_4$ (50). This could be explained by the effects on Ca^{2+} pumps and/or Ca^{2+} release channels.

HORMONE-SPECIFIC CALCIUM SIGNAL PATTERNS

Two hormones interacting with separate membrane receptors on the same cell may both use Ca^{2+} as an intracellular messenger, but nevertheless evoke distinct signal patterns so that the information input to the cell is different. In hepatocytes, it has been shown that phenylephrine and vasopressin evoke cytosolic Ca^{2+} spikes, but the shape of the spikes is receptor-specific (94, 108). The initial phase of the Ca^{2+} spikes (upstroke) is identical, but each vasopressin-induced spike lasts longer due to a slower rate of recovery than in the case of phenylephrine stimulation (94). Such a relatively simple difference in Ca^{2+} signal pattern could be explained by different receptor-controlled Ca^{2+}-pump transport rates.

In pancreatic acinar cells, the two main agonists, ACh and CCK, applied at just suprathreshold concentrations evoke repetitive local Ca^{2+} spikes in the secretory granule region, but whereas some of the CCK-evoked local spikes trigger global Ca^{2+} transients (Figure 1), this is rare for ACh (69). When the agonist concentration is increased, the Ca^{2+} signal pattern in the case of ACh stimulation switches to a global sinusoidal oscillation (regular fluctuations about a mean elevated $[Ca^{2+}]_i$), whereas in the case of CCK, the local Ca^{2+} spike frequency increases and global transients are triggered more often (69). CCK and ACh therefore evoke very different patterns. The ACh-evoked sinusoidal oscillations cannot be mimicked by any level of CCK and are probably caused by specific stimulation of Ca^{2+} entry since the sinusoidal oscillations can only be maintained in the presence of external Ca^{2+}, whereas the transient spikes can continue for many minutes after removal of external Ca^{2+} (109, 110). Why low CCK stimuli more easily evoke global Ca^{2+} transients than the equivalent ACh stimuli (dose evoking same local spike frequency) (69) is not clear, but CCK may produce a yet unknown spreading factor (69). One function of such a spreading factor may be to increase the sensitivity of $InsP_3Rs$ and/or RYRs.

MOLECULAR TARGETS FOR CALCIUM ACTION

Ca^{2+} is different from other second messengers because it has so many target molecules, namely the Ca^{2+}-binding proteins (CaBPs) and because diffusion in the cytosol is restricted (1). CaBPs differentially control various cellular processes such as phosphorylation and dephosphorylation. Coordinated activation of different CaBPs is essential for integrated cellular function.

The coordination is achieved by the spatio-temporal organization of the Ca^{2+} signal and the heterogeneous distribution, affinity, kinetics, and function of CaBPs. Affinities of CaBPs to Ca^{2+} range widely betwen 10 nM and 1 mM, and time courses of activation and deactivation of CaBPs by Ca^{2+} are also different (38). Although hundreds of CaBPs have been discovered, much work is still required to find further CaBPs and to obtain kinetic data to formulate concrete models for cellular functions. There appears to be a correlation between the affinity and the distribution of CaBPs such that low-affinity CaBPs are closely associated with membranes. This can be seen by comparing three major families of CaBPs: EF-hand proteins, the annexin family, and a class of proteins that share the same Ca^{2+}-dependent translocation domain, including cytosolic phospholipase A_2, protein kinase C γ, phospholipase C γ, synaptotagmine, and GTPase-activating protein (16). Many of the EF-hand proteins show high affinity to Ca^{2+} and are distributed in the cytosol. On the other hand, the latter two families of CaBPs display a rather low affinity to Ca^{2+} and are likely to play their roles closely associated with membranes. This may be physiologically relevant (see below).

CELLULAR FUNCTIONS AND DYNAMICS OF Ca^{2+} SIGNALS

Ca^{2+} spikes and oscillations have three advantages over a graded amplitude regulation of $[Ca^{2+}]_i$ (2, 56). (a) Ca^{2+} spikes are more resistant to noise than graded rises in $[Ca^{2+}]_i$; (b) a certain frequency of Ca^{2+} spikes could selectively activate CaBPs with particular association and dissociation rate constants for Ca^{2+} (56); (c) local short-lasting Ca^{2+} spikes may have advantages over a global rise. A rise in $[Ca^{2+}]_i$ rapidly activates the Ca^{2+} pump in the plasma membrane (90, 91), but when the Ca^{2+} rise is confined to a small region, only a minor proportion of the plasma membrane will be exposed to an elevated $[Ca^{2+}]_i$, and the amount of Ca^{2+} pumped out of the cell during a spike would be relatively small (Figure 1). Apart from this energetic advantage, local spikes may also prevent undesirable Ca^{2+}-dependent activation processes elsewhere in the cell. Ca^{2+} can activate proteases and endonucleases that lead to cell death (61).

Ca^{2+} micro-gradients may have considerable physiological significance. For example, a rise in $[Ca^{2+}]_i$ at the postsynaptic membrane is assumed to trigger a synapse-specific modification of synaptic transmission (4). A polarized rise in $[Ca^{2+}]_i$ of blood cells can modify the direction of migration of these cells (9). The case of exocrine acinar cells exemplifies the necessity of organized activation of CaBPs in cellular functions (39, 88). At low agonist concentrations, Ca^{2+}-dependent Cl^- channels are selectively activated by Ca^{2+} spikes in the secretory granule region and Cl^- ions are pushed into the lumen ("push-phase," Figure 1). Outward movement of Cl^- could be driven either by the resting K^+ permeability (39) or by Ca^{2+}-dependent K^+ channels (88). Pulsatile fluid secretion expected from the local Ca^{2+} oscillations in the secretory granule region could be optically monitored by digital differential interference microscopy in salivary glands (92). Exocytotic secretion also appears to be directly triggered by local Ca^{2+} spikes in the granular region (51) (Figure 1). Thus primary $[Ca^{2+}]_i$ spikes within the granular area are necessary and sufficient for triggering both fluid and protein secretion. Spread of Ca^{2+} waves to the basal area at higher agonist concentrations further induces a "pull-phase," where cation and Cl^- channels in the basolateral membrane are activated (39) (Figure 1) and, hence, Cl^- is taken up from blood to cytosol (72). Thus the Ca^{2+} micro-gradients serve as selective switches for the functions of certain areas of the cells in a concentration-dependent manner. In general, temporal sequences of cellular processes activated by Ca^{2+} waves could have a physiological role. Alternatively, spread of Ca^{2+} waves could just be utilized to activate the functions of cells synchronously, as may be the case with smooth muscle cells (36).

The Ca^{2+} nano-gradients beneath Ca^{2+} channels in the plasma membrane could play a role in triggering neurotransmitter release (82). In this case, CaBPs in the plasma membrane with low affinity to Ca^{2+} may be essential. The functions of many low affinity CaBPs may be influenced by high $[Ca^{2+}]_i$ within the Ca^{2+} nano-gradients, and in this context the preferential localization of low affinity CaBPs close to the membrane is physiologically relevant. Ca^{2+} release channels may also be responsible for Ca^{2+} nano-gradients around the mouth facing the cytosolic space. One possible example is the transient activation of Ca^{2+}-activated Cl^- channels in *Xenopus* oocytes (65) and in pancreatic acinar cells (39), where Cl^- currents decay when bulk $[Ca^{2+}]_i$ measured with Ca^{2+} imaging reaches its plateau level. This may indicate that the $[Ca^{2+}]_i$ rise and fall that governs the gating of the Cl^- channels is too localized to be captured with Ca^{2+} imaging techniques.

The two distinct forms of Ca^{2+} gradients may offer a way to differentially stimulate distinct CaBPs (dynamic decoding; 38). For dynamic decoding, a lower affinity CaBP must be located close to the Ca^{2+} channels, and another high affinity CaBP distributed in the bulk cytosol. The Ca^{2+} nano-gradient is selectively induced at the beginning of a $[Ca^{2+}]_i$ rise or by a weak stimulus. Thus weaker stimuli could selectively activate lower affinity CaBPs by high $[Ca^{2+}]_i$ within the Ca^{2+} nano-gradients. On the other hand, longer or stronger stimuli cause a Ca^{2+} micro-gradient, and activate high-affinity CaBPs present in the bulk cytosol. Importantly, after the Ca^{2+} channels close, the Ca^{2+} nano-gradients dissipate quickly, while the Ca^{2+} micro-gradients persist for several seconds, or propagate to other cellular areas as Ca^{2+} waves. Thus stronger stimuli could rather selectively activate higher affinity CaBPs because the micro-gradients influence a larger cellular space and for a longer period than the nano-gradients, and their effects thereby dominate the cellular response. One example of dynamic decoding is frequency coding of synaptic efficacy; a single presynaptic spike induces a Ca^{2+} nano-gradient and triggers low affinity CaBPs responsible for neurotransmitter release, while tetanic stimulation evokes a Ca^{2+} micro-gradient and activates high affinity CaBPs, which induce post-tetanic potentiation (86). The dynamic decoding could account for alternate openings of luminal and basolateral Cl^- channels in pancreatic acinar cells if luminal Cl^- channels have lower affinity to Ca^{2+} than basolateral Cl^- channels (Figure 1). The notion of dynamic decoding might also apply to other cellular processes where Ca^{2+} mobilizing stimuli induce distinct or opposing cellular functions depending on intensity.

Ca^{2+} release from an organelle may serve to regulate that particular organelle. Two intriguing possibilities could be considered. Firstly, the $[Ca^{2+}]_i$ in the lumen of the stores may have a direct regulatory role. Transport of protein in the ER to the Golgi apparatus may be regulated by emptying of Ca^{2+} from the ER (80). The mitochondrial matrix has a relatively low $[Ca^{2+}]_i$, and agonist stimuli can induce a transient rise (75). There are many matrix proteins that are regulated by Ca^{2+} (47). Secondly, the functions of organelles could be regulated by Ca^{2+} nano-domains formed just outside the organelles. If secretory granules were provided with Ca^{2+} release channels (40), the nano-gradient could trigger their exocytotic secretion (51). Hormones may regulate the functions of these organelles in a dose-dependent and hormone-specific manner.

FUTURE PERSPECTIVE

Recent progress in the Ca^{2+} signaling field has been spectacular, but there are nevertheless many crucial questions that have not been answered. The subcellular distribution of the different kinds of Ca^{2+} stores is still obscure in most cell types, and we have hardly any precise information about total and free Ca^{2+} concentrations in the various stores in the resting or stimulated states. We also have very little useful information about the control of ER Ca^{2+} pumps and the mechanisms employed in such a regulation that may be important for a full understanding of the spatio-temporal Ca^{2+} signal patterns. Finally, the nature and regulation of Ca^{2+} entry pathways in electrically non-excitable cells are still uncertain. The next few years should see substantial progress in these areas.

Literature Cited

1. Allbritton NL, Meyer T, Stryer L. 1992. Range of messenger action of calcium ion and inositol 1,4,5-trisphosphate. *Science* 258:1812–15
2. Berridge MJ. 1993. Inositol trisphosphate and calcium signalling. *Nature* 361: 315–25
3. Bezprozvanny I, Watras J, Ehrlich BE. 1991. Bell-shaped calcium-response curves of Ins(1,4,5)P₃ and calcium-gated channels from endoplasmic reticulum of cerebellum. *Nature* 351: 751–54
4. Bliss TVP, Collingridge GL. 1993. Synaptic model memory: long-term potentiation in the hippocampus. *Nature* 361:31–39
5. Boitano S, Dirksen ER, Sanderson MJ. 1992. Intercellular propagation of calcium waves mediated by inositol trisphosphate. *Science* 258:292–95
6. Bootman MD, Berridge MJ, Taylor CW. 1992. All-or-nothing Ca²⁺ mobilization from the intracellular stores of single histamine-stimulated HeLa cells. *J. Physiol.* 450:163–78
7. Bootman MD, Taylor CW, Berridge MJ. 1992. The thiol reagent, thimerosal evokes Ca²⁺ spikes in HeLa cells by sensitizing the inositol 1,4,5-trisphosphate receptor. *J. Biol. Chem.* 267: 25113–19
8. Bronner F. 1990. *Intracellular Calcium Regulation.* New York: Wiley-Liss, 480 pp.
9. Brundage RA, Fogarty KE, Tuft RA, Fay FS. 1991. Calcium gradients underlying polarization and chemotaxis of eosinophils. *Science* 254:703–6
10. Burgoyne RD, Cheek TR, Morgan A, O'Sullivan AJ, Moreton RB, et al. 1989. Distribution of two distinct Ca²⁺-ATPase-like proteins and their relationships to the agonist-sensitive calcium store in adrenal chromaffin cells. *Nature* 342:72–74
11. Camacho P, Lechleiter JD. 1993. Increased frequency of calcium waves in *Xenopus laevis* oocytes that express a calcium-ATPase. *Science* 260:226–29
12. Carafoli E. 1992. The Ca²⁺ pump of the plasma membrane. *J. Biol. Chem.* 267:2115–18
13. Chad JE, Eckert R. 1984. Calcium domains associated with individual channels can account for anomalous voltage relations of Ca-dependent responses. *Biophys. J.* 45:993–99
14. Chandra S, Ausserer WA, Morrison GH. 1992. Subcellular imaging of calcium exchange in cultured cells with ion microscopy. *J. Cell Sci.* 102:417–25
15. Charles AC, Merril JE, Dirksen ER, Sanderson MJ. 1991. Intercellular signalling in glial cells: Calcium waves and oscillations in response to mechanical stimulation and glutamate. *Neuron* 6:983–92
16. Clark JD, Lin L, Kriz RW, Ramesha CS, Sultzman, LA, et al. 1991. A novel arachidonic acid-selective cytosolic PLA₂ contains a Ca-dependent translocation domain with homology to PKC and GAP. *Cell* 65:1043–51
17. Cockroft S, Thomas GMH. 1992. Inositol-lipid-specific phospholipase C isoenzymes and their differential regulation by receptors. *Biochem. J.* 288: 1–14
18. Dani JW, Chernjavsky A, Smith SJ. 1992. Neuronal activity triggers calcium waves in hippocampal astrocyte network. *Neuron* 8:429–40
19. De Young GW, Keizer J. 1992. A single-pool inositol 1,4,5-trisphosphate-receptor-based model for agonist-stimulated oscillations in Ca²⁺ concentration. *Proc. Natl. Acad. Sci. USA* 89: 9895–99
20. Dockray GJ. 1982. The physiology of cholecystokinin in brain and gut. *Brit. Med. Bull.* 38:253–58
21. Ebashi S, Lipmann F. 1962. Adenosine triphosphate-linked concentration of calcium ions in a particulate fraction of rabbit muscle. *J. Cell Biol.* 14:389–400
22. Endo M. 1977. Calcium release from the sarcoplasmic reticulum. *Physiol. Rev.* 57:71–108
23. Endo M, Tanaka M, Ogawa Y. 1970. Calcium-induced release of calcium from the sarcoplasmic reticulum of skinned muscle fibres. *Nature* 228:34–36
24. Deleted in proof
25. Ferris CD, Cameron AM, Huganir RL, Snyder SH. 1992. Quantal calcium release by purified reconstituted inositol 1,4,5-trisphosphate receptors. *Nature* 356:350–52
26. Ferris CD, Snyder SH. 1992. Inositol 1,4,5-trisphosphate-activated calcium channels. *Annu. Rev. Physiol.* 54:469–88
27. Finch EA, Turner TJ, Goldin SM. 1991. Calcium as a coagonist of inositol 1,4,5-trisphosphate-induced calcium release. *Science* 252:443–46

28. Furuichi T, Yoshikawa S, Miyawaki A, Wada K, Maeda N, Mikoshiba K. 1989. Primary structure and functional expression of the inositol 1,4,5-trisphosphate-binding protein P400. *Nature* 342:32–38

29. Galione A. 1992. Ca^{2+}-induced Ca^{2+} release and its modulation by cyclic ADP-ribose. *Trends Pharmacol. Sci.* 13:304–6

30. Girard S, Clapham D. 1993. Acceleration of intracellular calcium waves in *Xenopus* oocytes by calcium influx. *Science* 260:229–32

31. Glennon MC, Bird G St, Takemura H, Thastrup O, Leslie BA, Putney JW Jr. 1992. In situ imaging of agonist-sensitive calcium pools in AR4-2J pancreatoma cells. *J. Biol. Chem.* 267: 25568–75

32. Goldbeter A, Dupont G, Berridge MJ. 1990. Minimal model for signal-induced Ca^{2+} oscillations and for their frequency encoding through protein phosphorylation. *Proc. Natl. Acad. Sci. USA* 87:1461–65

32a. Györke S, Fill M. 1993. Ryanodine receptor adaptation: control mechanism of Ca^{2+}-induced Ca^{2+} release in heart. *Science* 260:807–9

33. Hoth M, Penner R. 1992. Depletion of intracellular calcium stores activates a calcium current in mast cells. *Nature* 355:353–56

34. Iino M. 1990. Biphasic Ca^{2+} dependence of inositol 1,4,5-trisphosphate-induced Ca^{2+} release in smooth muscle cells of the guinea pig Taenia Caeci. *J. Gen. Physiol.* 95: 1103–22

35. Iino M, Endo M. 1992. Calcium-dependent immediate feedback control of inositol 1,4,5-trisphosphate induced Ca^{2+} release. *Nature* 360:76–78

36. Iino M, Yamazawa T, Miyashita Y, Endo M, Kasai H. 1993. Critical intracellular Ca^{2+} concentration for all-or-none Ca^{2+} spiking in single smooth muscle cells. *EMBO J.* In press

37. Jaffe LF. 1991. The path of calcium in cytosolic calcium oscillations: A unifying hypothesis. *Proc. Natl. Acad. Sci. USA* 88:9883–87

38. Kasai H. 1993. Cytosolic Ca^{2+} gradients, Ca^{2+} binding proteins and synaptic plasticity. *Neurosci. Res.* 16:1–7

39. Kasai H, Augustine GJ. 1990. Cytosolic Ca^{2+} gradients triggering unidirectional fluid secretion from exocrine pancreas. *Nature* 348:735–38

40. Kasai H, Li Y, Miyashita Y. 1993. Subcellular distribution of Ca^{2+} release channels underlying Ca^{2+} waves and oscillations in exocrine pancreas. *Cell* 74:669–77

41. Khan AA, Steiner JP, Snyder SH. 1992. Plasma membrane inositol 1,4,5-trisphosphate receptor of lymphocytes: selective enrichment in sialic acid and unique binding specificity. *Proc. Natl. Acad. Sci. USA* 89:2849–53

42. Kuno M, Gardner P. 1987. Ion channels activated by inositol 1,4,5-trisphosphate in plasma membrane of human T-lymphocytes. *Nature* 326: 301–4

43. Lechleiter JD, Clapham DE. 1992. Molecular mechanisms of intracellular calcium excitability in X. laevis oocytes. *Cell* 69:283–94

44. Levy S, Payne R. 1993. A lingering elevation of Ca_i accompanies inhibition of inositol 1,4,5 trisphosphate-induced Ca release in *Limulus* ventral photoreceptors. *J. Gen. Physiol.* 101:67–84

45. Llinas R, Sugimori M, Silver RB. 1992. Microdomains of high calcium concentration in a presynaptic terminal. *Science* 256:677–79

46. Luckhoff A, Clapham DE. 1992. Inositol 1,3,4,5-tetrakisphosphate activates an endothelial Ca^{2+}-permeable channel. *Nature* 355:356–58

47. MacCormack JG, Halestrap AP, Denton RM. 1990. Role of calcium ions in regulation of mammalian intramitochondrial metabolism. *Physiol. Rev.* 70:391–425

48. Malviya A, Rogue P, Vincendon G. 1990. Stereospecific inositol 1,4,5-[^{32}P] trisphosphate binding to isolated rat liver nuclei: Evidence for inositol trisphosphate receptor-mediated calcium release from the nucleus. *Proc. Natl. Acad. Sci. USA* 87:9270–74

49. Maruyama Y. 1990. Inhibitory effects of arachidonic acid on muscarinic current response in single pancreatic acinar cells of rat. *J. Physiol.* 430:471–82

50. Maruyama Y. 1993. Control of inositol polyphosphate-mediated calcium mobilization by arachidonic acid in pancreatic acinar cells of rats. *J. Physiol.* 463:729–46

51. Maruyama Y, Inooka G, Li Y, Miyashita Y, Kasai H. 1993. Agonist-induced localized Ca^{2+} spikes directly triggering exocytotic secretion in exocrine pancreas. *EMBO J.* 12:3017–22

52. Matozaki T, Goke B, Tsunoda Y, Rodriguez M, Martinez J, Williams JA. 1990. Two functionally distinct cholecystokinin receptors show different modes of actions on Ca^{2+} mobilization and phospholipid hydrolysis in

isolated rat pancreatic acini. *J. Biol. Chem.* 265:6247–54

53. McDonald TV, Premack BA, Gardner P. 1993. Flash photolysis of caged inositol 1,4,5-trisphosphate activates plasma membrane calcium current in human T-cells. *J. Biol. Chem.* 268: 3889–96

54. McPherson SM, McPherson PS, Matthews L, Campbell KP, Longo FJ. 1992. Cortical localization of a calcium release channel in sea urchin eggs. *J. Cell Biol.* 116:1111–21

55. Meldolesi J, Maddedu L, Pozzan T. 1990. Intracellular Ca^{2+} organelles in non muscle cells: heterogeneity and functional assignment. *Biochim. Biophys. Acta* 1055:130–40

56. Meyer T, Stryer L. 1991. Calcium spiking. *Annu. Rev. Biophys. Chem.* 20:153–74

57. Miyazaki S, Yuzaki M, Nakada K, Shirakawa H, Nakanishi S, et al. 1992. Block of Ca^{2+} wave and Ca^{2+} oscillation by antibody to the inositol 1,4,5-trisphosphate receptor in fertilized hamster egg. *Science* 257:251–55

58. Muallem S. 1989. Calcium transport pathways of pancreatic acinar cells. *Annu. Rev. Physiol.* 51:83–105

59. Nathanson MH, Padfield PJ, O'Sullivan AJ, Burghstahler AD, Jamieson JD. 1992. Mechanism of Ca^{2+} wave propagation in pancreatic acinar cells. *J. Biol. Chem.* 267:18118–21

60. Neher E, Augustine GJ. 1992. Calcium gradients and buffers in bovine chromaffin cells. *J. Physiol.* 450:273–301

61. Nicotera P, Bellomo G, Orrenius S. 1992. Calcium-mediated mechanisms in chemically induced cell death. *Annu. Rev. Pharmacol. Toxicol.* 32:449–70

62. Nielsen SP, Petersen OH. 1972. Transport of calcium in the perfused submandibular gland of the cat. *J. Physiol.* 223:685–97

63. Osipchuk YV, Wakui M, Yule DI, Gallacher DV, Petersen OH, 1990. Cytoplasmic Ca^{2+} oscillations evoked by receptor stimulation, G-protein activation, internal application of inositol trisphosphate or Ca^{2+}: simultaneous microfluorimetry and Ca^{2+}-dependent Cl^- current recording in single pancreatic acinar cells. *EMBO J.* 9:697–704

64. Pacaud P, Loirand G, Gregoire G, Mironneau C, Mironneau J. 1993. Noradrenaline-activated heparin-sensitive Ca^{2+} entry after depletion of intracellular Ca^{2+} store in portal vein smooth muscle cells. *J. Biol. Chem.* 268:3866–72

65. Parker I, Ivorra I. 1990. Localized all-or-none calcium liberation by inositol trisphosphate. *Science* 250:977–79

66. Parker I, Ivorra I. 1993. Confocal microfluorimetry of Ca^{2+} signals evoked in *Xenopus* oocytes by photoreleased inositol trisphosphate. *J. Physiol.* 461:133–65

67. Payne R, Fein A. 1987. Inositol 1,4,5-trisphosphate releases calcium from specialized sites within *Limulus* photoreceptors. *J. Cell Biol.* 104:933–37

67a. Penner R, Fasolato C, Hoth M. 1993. Calcium influx and its control by calcium release. *Curr. Opin. Neurobiol.* 3:368–74

68. Petersen CCH, Petersen OH. 1991. Receptor-activated cytoplasmic Ca^{2+} spikes in communicating clusters of pancreatic acinar cells. *FEBS Lett.* 284:113–16

68a. Petersen CCH, Petersen OH, Berridge MJ. 1993. The role of endoplasmic reticulum calcium pumps during cytosolic calcium spiking in pancreatic acinar cells. *J. Biol. Chem.* 268:22262–64

69. Petersen CCH, Toescu EC, Petersen OH. 1991. Different patterns of receptor-activated cytoplasmic oscillations in single pancreatic acinar cells: dependence on receptor type, agonist concentration and intracellular Ca^{2+} buffering. *EMBO J.* 10:527–33

70. Petersen CCH, Toescu EC, Potter BVL, Petersen OH. 1991. Inositol trisphosphate produces different patterns of cytoplasmic Ca^{2+} spiking depending on its concentration. *FEBS Lett.* 293: 179–82

71. Petersen OH. 1989. Does inositol tetrakisphosphate play a role in the receptor-mediated control of calcium mobilization? *Cell Calcium* 10:375–83

72. Petersen OH. 1992. Stimulus-secretion coupling: cytoplasmic calcium signals and control of ion channels in exocrine acinar cells. *J. Physiol.* 448:1–51

73. Putney JW. 1986. A model for receptor-regulated calcium entry. *Cell Calcium* 7:1–12

74. Rapp PE, Berridge MJ. 1981. The control of transepithelial potential oscillations in the salivary gland of *Calliphora erythrocephala*. *J. Exp. Biol.* 93:119–32

75. Rizzuto R, Simpson AWM, Brini M, Pozzan T. 1992. Changes of mitochondrial Ca^{2+} revealed by specifically targeted recombinant aequorin. *Nature* 358:325–27

76. Roberts WM, Jacobs RA, Hudspeth AJ. 1990. Colocalization of ion chan-

nels involved in frequency selectivity and synaptic transmission at presynaptic active zones of hair cells. *J. Neurosci.* 10:3664–84

77. Rooney TA, Sass EJ, Thomas AP. 1989. Characterization of cytosolic calcium oscillations induced by phenylephrine and vasopressin in single fura-2-loaded hepatocytes. *J. Biol. Chem.* 264:17131–41

78. Ross CA, Danoff SK, Schell MJ, Snyder SH, Ullrich A. 1992. Three additional inositol 1,4,5-trisphosphate receptors: Molecular cloning and differential localization in brain and peripheral tissues. *Proc. Natl. Acad. Sci. USA* 89:4265–69

79. Sakmann B. 1992. Elementary steps in synaptic transmission revealed by currents through single ion channels. *EMBO J.* 11:2003–16

80. Sambrook JF. 1990. The involvement of calcium in transport of secretory proteins from endoplasmic reticulum. *Cell* 61:197–99

81. Schatzmann HJ. 1966. ATP-dependent Ca^{2+} extrusion from human red cells. *Experientia* 22:364–68

82. Smith SJ, Augustine GJ. 1988 Calcium ions, active zones and synaptic transmitter release. *Trends Neurosci.* 11: 458–64

83. Smrcka AV, Hepler JR, Brown KD, Sternweiss PC. 1991. Regulation of phosphoinositide specific phospholipase C activity by purified G_q. *Science* 251:804–7

84. Streb H, Heslop JP, Irvine RF, Schulz I, Berridge MJ. 1985. Relationship between secretagogue-induced Ca^{2+} release and inositol polyphosphate production in permeabilized pancreatic acinar cells. *J. Biol. Chem.* 260:7309–15

85. Streb H, Irvine RF, Berridge MJ, Schulz I. 1983. Release of Ca^{2+} from a nonmitochondrial intracellular store in pancreatic acinar cells by inositol 1,4,5-trisphosphate. *Nature* 306:67–69

86. Swandulla D, Han M, Zipser K, Augustine GJ. 1991. Role of residual calcium in synaptic depression and posttetanic potentiation: fast and slow calcium signaling in nerve terminals. *Neuron* 7:915–26

87. Takasawa S, Nata K, Yonekura H, Okamoto H. 1993. Cyclic ADP-ribose in insulin secretion from pancreatic β-cells. *Science* 259:370–73

88. Tan YP, Marty A, Trautmann A. 1992. High density of Ca^{2+}-dependent K^+ and Cl^- channels on the luminal membrane of lacrimal acinar cells. *Proc. Natl. Acad. Sci. USA* 89:11229–33

89. Tepikin AV, Petersen OH. 1992. Mechanisms of cellular calcium oscillations in secretory cells. *Biochim. Biophys. Acta* 1137:197–207

90. Tepikin AV, Voronina SG, Gallacher DV, Petersen, OH. 1992. Acetylcholine-evoked increase in the cytoplasmic Ca^{2+} concentration and Ca^{2+} extrusion measured simultaneously in single mouse pancreatic acinar cells. *J. Biol. Chem.* 267:3569–72

91. Tepikin AV, Voronina SG, Gallacher DV, Petersen OH. 1992. Pulsatile Ca^{2+} extrusion from single pancreatic acinar cells during receptor-activated cytosolic Ca^{2+} spiking. *J. Biol. Chem.* 267: 14073–76

92. Terakawa S, Murakami M, Xu K. 1992. Exocytosis and water secretion in the Tupai sublingual gland. In *Salivary Secretion: Control and Mechanisms,* ed. M Murakami, Y Seo, T Ishikawa, pp. 49–51. Okazaki, Japan: Int. Workshop Salivary Secretion

93. Thastrup O, Cullen PJ, Drobak BK, Hanley MR, Dawson AP. 1990. Thapsigargin, a tumor promoter, discharges intracellular Ca^{2+} stores by specific inhibition of the endoplasmic reticulum Ca^{2+}-ATPase. *Proc. Natl. Acad. Sci. USA* 87:2466–70

94. Thomas AP, Renard DC, Rooney TA. 1991. Spatial and temporal organization of calcium signalling in hepatocytes. *Cell Calcium* 12:111–26

95. Thorn P, Brady P, Llopis J, Gallacher DV, Petersen OH. 1992. Cytosolic Ca^{2+} spikes evoked by the thiol reagent thimerosal in both intact and internally perfused single pancreatic acinar cells. *Pflügers Arch.* 422:173–78

96. Thorn P, Lawrie AM, Smith P, Gallacher DV, Petersen OH. 1993. Local and global cytosolic Ca^{2+} oscillations in exocrine cells evoked by agonists and inositol trisphosphate. *Cell* 74:661–68

97. Toescu EC, Gardner JM, Petersen OH. 1993. Mitochondrial Ca^{2+} uptake at submicromolar $[Ca^{2+}]_i$ in permeabilized pancreatic acinar cells. *Biochem. Biophys. Res. Comm.* 192: 854–59

98. Toescu EC, Lawrie AM, Petersen OH, Gallacher DV. 1992. Spatial and temporal distribution of agonist-evoked cytoplasmic Ca^{2+} signals in exocrine acinar cells analysed by digital image microscopy. *EMBO J.* 11:1623–29

99. Toescu EC, O'Neill SC, Petersen OH, Eisner DA. 1992. Caffeine inhibits the

agonist-evoked cytosolic Ca^{2+} signal in mouse pancreatic acinar cells by blocking inositol trisphosphate production. *J. Biol. Chem.* 267:23467–70

100. Tsien RY, Poenie M. 1986. Fluorescence ratio imaging: a new window into intracellular ionic signalling. *Trends Biochem. Sci.* 11:450–55

101. Tsien RW, Tsien RY. 1990. Calcium channels, stores and oscillation. *Annu. Rev. Cell. Biol.* 6:715–60

102. Volpe P, Villa A, Damiani E, Sharp AH, Podini P, et al. 1991. Heterogeneity of microsomal Ca^{2+} stores in chicken Purkinje neurons. *EMBO J.* 10:3183–89

103. Wahl M, Sleight RG, Gruenstein E. 1992. Association of cytoplasmic free Ca^{2+} gradients with subcellular organelles. *J. Cell. Physiol.* 150:593–609

104. Wakui M, Potter BVL, Petersen OH. 1989. Pulsatile intracellular calcium release does not depend on fluctuations in inositol trisphosphate concentration. *Nature* 339:317–20

105. Wakui M, Osipchuk YV, Petersen OH. 1990. Receptor activated cytoplasmic Ca^{2+} spiking mediated by inositol trisphosphate is due to Ca^{2+}-induced Ca^{2+} release. *Cell* 63:1025–32

106. Waybill MM, Yelamarty RV, Ahang Y, Scaduto RC, Lanoue KF, et al. 1991. Nuclear calcium gradients in cultured rat hepatocytes. *Am. J. Physiol.* 261:E49–57

107. Woods NM, Cuthbertson KSR, Cobbold PH. 1986. Repetitive transient rises in cytoplasmic free calcium in hormone-stimulated hepatocytes. *Nature* 319:600–2

108. Woods NM, Cuthbertson KSR, Cobbold PH. 1987. Agonist-induced oscillations in cytoplasmic free calcium concentration in single rat hepatocytes. *Cell Calcium* 8:79–100

109. Yule DI, Gallacher DV. 1988. Oscillations of cytosolic calcium in single pancreatic acinar cells stimulated by acetylcholine. *FEBS Lett.* 239:358–62

110. Yule DI, Lawrie AM, Gallacher DV. 1991. Acetylcholine and cholecystokinin induce different patterns of oscillating calcium signals in pancreatic acinar cells. *Cell Calcium* 12:145–51

111. Zhang B-X, Zhao H, Loessberg P, Muallem S. 1992. Activation of the plasma membrane Ca^{2+} pump during agonist stimulation of pancreatic acini. *J. Biol. Chem.* 267:15419–25

Annu. Rev. Physiol. 1994. 56:321–348
Copyright © 1994 by Annual Reviews Inc. All rights reserved

REGULATION OF PROTEIN SYNTHESIS BY INSULIN

Scot R. Kimball, Thomas C. Vary, and Leonard S. Jefferson

Department of Cellular and Molecular Physiology, The Pennsylvania State University College of Medicine, P.O. Box 850, Hershey, Pennsylvania 17033

KEY WORDS: insulin signal transduction, protein phosphorylation, protein synthesis, gene transcription, mRNA, peptide-chain initiation, peptide-chain elongation, ribosome biogenesis

---

INTRODUCTION

It has been recognized for many years that one consequence of insulin-deficient states such as diabetes mellitus and starvation is a net loss of body protein. Net gain or loss of protein is ultimately determined by a balance between two opposing processes, protein synthesis and its degradation. To examine the actions of insulin, investigators have developed both in vivo and in vitro techniques for assessing rates of synthesis and breakdown of protein. These techniques have evolved over the years as both the complexity of the process under investigation and the limitations of the earlier investigative methods have come to be more thoroughly appreciated. In recent years, investigative approaches have relied more and more on the use of various cell culture systems that lend themselves to the techniques of molecular biology. These recent studies have identified numerous effects of insulin on the overall pathway of protein synthesis. In general, the effects of insulin usually involve a change in the state of phosphorylation of a protein involved in one of the multiple steps in the pathway. In many instances, the physiological relevance of the observed change as well as the questions of whether the change is a consequence of a direct or indirect action of insulin and whether the change causes a modification of the rate of protein synthesis have yet to be established.

Recently, rapid advances have also occurred in our understanding of the signal transduction pathway involved in mediating the actions of insulin on target cells. Again, these findings have been largely derived from studies

321

0066–4278/94/0315–0321$05.00

using various cell culture systems and the same limitations mentioned above apply. However, it is abundantly clear that modification of the state of phosphorylation of various proteins constitutes key steps in the signal transduction pathway, as well as often representing the end-point action of the hormone. In the case of the regulation of protein synthesis by insulin, there are many gaps in our knowledge of the steps involved between the signal transduction pathway and the ultimate protein that exhibits a change in the state of phosphorylation in response to the hormone.

The aim of this review is to briefly discuss the evidence leading to our present understanding of the actions of insulin on protein synthesis. We focus on actions involving changes in the state of phosphorylation of various proteins involved in the pathway of protein synthesis. For this reason, kinases and phosphatases that catalyze phosphorylation/dephosphorylation of these proteins are sometimes discussed even when there is currently no evidence to link them directly to the insulin signal transduction pathway.

SIGNAL TRANSDUCTION PATHWAY FOR INSULIN ACTION

Although the intracellular events that mediate the actions of insulin are incompletely understood, it is generally accepted that regulation of protein phosphorylation plays an important role. The insulin receptor itself is a ligand-activated, tyrosine-specific protein kinase that undergoes autophosphorylation upon insulin binding (reviewed in 139), which results in the increased tyrosine phosphorylation of several intracellular proteins (reviewed in 138). One of these proteins is the recently discovered insulin receptor substrate designated IRS-1, a tyrosyl-phosphorylated cytosolic protein that is highly serine phosphorylated and is rapidly tyrosine phosphorylated in response to insulin and IGF-1 (reviewed in 98). IRS-1 contains numerous potential tyrosine phosphorylation sites that are thought to associate with high affinity to cellular proteins that contain *src* homology-2 (SH2) domains. One such protein, phosphatidylinositol 3-kinase, is activated when the SH2 domains in its regulatory subunit bind to phosphorylated IRS-1. Other cellular proteins such as SHPTP2, a novel SH2 domain containing tyrosine phosphatase, and growth factor receptor-bound protein 2 (GRB2), a protein that is implicated in activation of the protooncogene Ras, have also been found to interact with phosphorylated IRS-1. Subsequent events following activation of phosphatidylinositol 3-kinase or of binding SHPTP2 to IRS-1 are presently unknown. However, recent studies have identified a complex consisting of tyrosine phosphorylated IRS-1, GRB2, and the guanine nucleotide-releasing factor sos (the product of the mammalian homologue of *son of sevenless* gene) (6, 147). Since sos is thought to activate Ras by increasing the exchange of GTP for GDP, these findings provide a possible linkage of the insulin receptor to Ras signaling pathways. The observation of Ras activation by insulin through enhanced exchange of guanine nucleotides on p21*ras* is consistent with this scheme (89).

Activation of Ras by the insulin receptor as well as other receptor tyrosine kinases is thought to be a critical link between ligand binding and signal transduction involving a cascade of serine/threonine protein kinases that lead ultimately to target regulatory sites in the cytoplasm as well as in the nucleus (reviewed in 12, 13). The cascade is viewed as a linear linkage between Ras, Raf-1, MEK (MAP kinase/ERK-activating kinase), MAP [mitogen-activated protein kinase/ERK (extracellular signal-regulated kinase)], RSK or pp90^{rsk} (originally identified as an ~90,000 M_r cell cycle-regulated S6 protein kinase), and ultimately ribosomal protein S6 phosphorylation. Phosphorylation of nuclear transcription factors by MAP/ERK and RSK links the cascade to gene expression. Furthermore, identification of a MEK kinase, which is activated by a G protein-mediated mechanism independent of Ras, provides evidence of a point of divergence in the cascade and allows for differential regulation (73). Thus this intracellular signal transduction pathway may participate in the regulation of protein synthesis as well as a variety of other cellular processes by insulin and other modulators acting on receptors at the cell surface.

Although the protein phosphorylation pathway described above may participate in mediating many of the actions of insulin, particularly those involving gene expression, recent evidence suggests that some of the actions of the hormone may occur through other mechanisms. For example, insulin activation of the pp70-S6 kinase (pp70^{S6k}) has been shown to be dissociated from activation of MAP/ERK and RSK (40). Furthermore, a PC-12 pheochromocytoma cell line has been described that is responsive to insulin, exhibiting increases in glycogen, lipid, and protein synthesis in response to the hormone, but in which insulin does not cause activation of Ras, Raf-1, MEK, or MAP/ERK (110). Finally, a considerable amount of evidence supports the view of insulin receptor signaling through non-tyrosine kinase pathways (reviewed in 155). For example, a role for protein kinase C has been implicated in many actions of insulin (reviewed in 33), including the stimulation of protein synthesis by the hormone (174). However, other workers have questioned whether protein kinase C is a mediator or inhibitor of insulin action (18).

PATHWAY OF PROTEIN SYNTHESIS

Synthesis of new protein in eukaryotic cells is achieved via a complex series of discrete reactions that occur in the nucleus, cytosol, and various subcellular locations. In the nucleus, transcription of specific genes by three classes of RNA polymerases results in the production of mRNA, tRNA, 5S RNA, and 45S preribosomal RNA (reviewed in 119, 149, 178). The RNA products are processed and, in the case of mRNA and tRNA, are transported to the cytoplasm. The 45S preribosomal RNA is processed to yield the mature 18S, 5.8S, and 28S RNA constituents of the ribosome. These three products along with the 5S RNA and approximately 85 ribosomal proteins move to the nucleolus where they assemble into the 40S and 60S pre-ribosomal particles that are then transported to the cytoplasm. In the cytoplasm, the ribosomal particles bind to mRNA to form polysomes, which can exist free or bound to the endoplasmic reticulum, cytoskeleton, and perhaps other subcellular structures. Protein synthesis in the cytoplasm begins with the aminoacylation of tRNA and ends with the release of a completed peptide chain from a polysome. Translation of mRNA into protein by ribosomes is usually divided into three phases: (*a*) initiation, in which the initiator methionyl-tRNA is bound to mRNA, which in turn binds first to a 40S ribosomal subunit and subsequently to a 60S subunit, thus forming a translationally competent ribosome; (*b*) elongation, during which tRNA-bound amino acids are incorporated into a growing peptide chain in the order specified by the mRNA to which the ribosome is bound; and (*c*) termination, the phase when the completed peptide chain is released from the ribosome. Each of these steps requires the intervention of protein factors known collectively as eukaryotic initiation factors (eIF), elongation factors (eEF), and releasing factor (RF).

ACTIONS OF INSULIN ON NUCLEAR EVENTS IN THE PATHWAY OF PROTEIN SYNTHESIS

Gene Transcription

Multiple examples of both positive and negative effects of insulin on the rate of RNA polymerase II directed gene transcription have been described in the past few years (reviewed in 81, 90, 106). The common goal of most of these studies has been to identify and characterize *cis*-acting DNA sequences required to mediate insulin-induced modifications in gene transcription. Insulin-responsive elements (IREs) have been delineated in the 5′ flanking region of a number of genes including those for phosphoenolpyruvate carboxykinase (PEPCK), c-fos, amylase, liver pyruvate kinase, glyceraldehyde-3-phosphate dehydrogenase (GAPDH), glucagon, and insulin-like growth factor binding protein-1 (IGFBP-1) (59, 64, 102, 107, 125, 153, 157). The IRE of the PEPCK gene, which mediates negative regulation by insulin, has been mapped to a 15 bp sequence from -416 to -402 of the proximal promoter region (107) and subsequently to a 10 bp sequence from -416 to -407 (105). The IRE of the IGFBP-1 gene, which also mediates negative regulation by insulin, has been mapped to a 37 bp sequence of the proximal promoter region from -140 to -103 (157). This region contains two AT-rich, 8 bp elements, both of which must be present for maximal responsiveness to insulin and each of which shares sequence similarity with the IREs for PEPCK, amylase, and glucagon (157). The IRE of the amylase gene, which mediates positive regulation by insulin, has been mapped to a 30 bp sequence of the proximal promoter region, from positions -167 to -138 (59). Within the amylase IRE is a sequence from -150 to -139 that has 8 of 12 nucleotides identical to the PEPCK element. However, mutation of two of the eight identical nucleotides in the amylase IRE does not affect the insulin response (59). The IREs of GAPDH and glucagon genes have been mapped to positions -488 to $+21$ and -274 to -234, respectively, of the proximal promoter regions (102, 125). These IREs share some sequence similarity to the IRE of the PEPCK gene, as do the promoter regions of several other insulin-regulated genes that have not yet been analyzed by functional tests (106). In contrast, the IRE of the liver pyruvate kinase gene, which has been mapped to positions -168 to -144 of the proximal promoter region, appears to contain no sequence homology with the PEPCK IRE (9, 160). Thus the possibility exists for different DNA sequences to confer insulin responsiveness.

Although most studies thus far have focused on regulation of initiation of transcription, at least one report has provided evidence of an effect of insulin on the rate of transcript elongation (141a). In this study, the dominant inhibitory effect of insulin on PEPCK gene transcription in cAMP-treated H4IIE cells appears to be partially the result of a reduction in elongation of PEPCK mRNA transcripts. However, the decreased rate of elongation is insufficient to account for the entire effect of insulin on PEPCK gene transcription. Instead, the major effect of insulin to reduce the rate of PEPCK gene transcription in H4IIE cells appears to involve an inhibition of transcript initiation.

Gel mobility shift assays suggest that a single DNA-binding protein may confer the effect of insulin on the amylase and IGFBP-1 promoters (59, 157), whereas the IREs for PEPCK and glucagon appear to bind two or more proteins (107, 125). None of the proteins responsible for the different bands formed during gel mobility shift assays with each of these IREs has been characterized. A high mobility group box protein that binds the IRE of the GAPDH gene has been cloned from a liver cDNA library (101). This protein also binds the amylase IRE (59). Studies of mutations of transgene expression in diabetic mice suggest the presence of an amylase IRE-binding protein that acts in a competitive manner with pancreatic nuclear protein PTF1, a protein containing one DNA-binding subunit and one subunit required for nuclear translocation (59). These studies indicate that the IRE is functionally distinct from the PTF1-binding site, although the two overlap physically (59).

The mechanism by which insulin alters the amount or activity of a transcription factor to change the rate of transcription of any gene is unknown. In general, gel mobility shift assays have not detected effects of insulin on the amount of protein binding activity (59, 107, 125, 157). Assuming that insulin does not alter expression of these proteins, then the hormone must modify them in a way that alters their effect on the rate of transcription without altering their IRE binding affinity. A similar scheme has been observed for the cAMP-responsive element-binding protein (CREB), in which a cAMP-mediated increase in phosphorylation of CREB results in a stimulation of transcription without a change in either CREB expression or the binding affinity of CREB for its cAMP-response element (93). In contrast to this scheme, insulin has been found to increase the amount of protein that binds to the IREs for growth hormone and GAPDH, apparently by a phosphorylation event that increases the affinity of the protein for its IRE (1, 102, 127). Thus phosphorylation/dephosphorylation of transcription factors may be a common mechanism by which insulin regulates the rate of transcription of different genes (11).

Ribosome Biogenesis

Ribosomes are complex intracellular structures comprised of approximately 85 ribosomal proteins and four ribosomal RNAs (reviewed in 149, 150). As discussed below, insulin regulates the translation of ribosomal protein mRNAs in a number of systems. Insulin also stimulates the synthesis of rRNA in such diverse systems as chick embryo fibroblasts (26), mouse myoblasts (53), rat hepatocytes (5), and an oligodendroglial-derived cell line (152). In addition, rRNA transcription is enhanced in mouse liver during recovery from a period of starvation (17). The mechanism involved in the regulation of rRNA synthesis by insulin is unknown. In mammals, ribosomal RNA genes are transcribed by RNA polymerase I to yield a 45S pre-rRNA product (reviewed in 149, 150). The rRNA genes are present in approximately 150–200 copies per haploid genome. Generally, this rDNA is arranged in tandem head-to-tail arrays, with regions coding for the primary transcript separated by nontranscribed spacer or intergenic spacer regions. Transcription from a mammalian rDNA promoter in vivo requires cooperative DNA-protein interactions over a region of the DNA extending from approximately $+6$ to -147 ($+1$ being the transcription start site) (149). Functionally, the promoter consists of two domains, the core promoter domain, which extends from approximately $+6$ to -30, and an upstream promoter domain, which extends from approximately -31 to -147. Requirements for efficient transcription from mammalian rDNA promoters include RNA polymerase I and at least two transcription factors that are generally referred to as SL-1 and upstream binding factor (UBF) (reviewed in 149). Thus regulation of transcription of rDNA by insulin and other agents could occur through modulation of the amount or activity of either RNA polymerase I or the transcription factors that interact with the *cis*-elements of the rDNA promoter. An example of regulation involving RNA polymerase I is the reported effect of glucocorticoids to depress transcription of rDNA in murine lymphosarcoma P1798 cells in culture (83). The inhibition caused by glucocorticoids has been attributed to a decrease in the amount or activity of a component of RNA polymerase I, which is termed transcription factor IC (TFIC). No evidence exists for the regulation of rDNA transcription through modulation of the activity or quantity of SL1. However, recent studies have suggested alterations in the amount as well as differential phosphorylation of the transcription factor UBF as mechanisms for regulating rDNA transcription (reviewed in 179). Changes in the amount of UBF appear to be responsible for the decrease in rDNA transcription in differentiated L6 myotubes compared to nondifferentiated L6 myoblasts, as well as for the increase in rDNA transcription in contracting neonatal cardiomyocytes compared to noncontracting, KCl-arrested cells (reviewed in 179). In one recent study (109), the two isoforms of UBF, UBF1 and UBF2, have been shown to be phosphoproteins, and the phosphorylation state of UBF is reduced approximately 80% in serum-starved CHO cells compared to logarithmically growing cells. Furthermore, following serum-deprivation, the subcellular distribution of UBF is shifted from a predominantly nucleolar localization to a dispersed distribution throughout the nucleolus, nucleus, and cytoplasm. Finally, treatment of purified UBF with alkaline phosphatase results in a reduction in the activity of UBF as assessed in an in vitro transcription assay, which suggests that phosphorylation of UBF is necessary for transactivation of RNA polymerase I. Although the mechanism involved in the modulation of UBF phosphorylation state by serum is unknown, it is noteworthy that UBF can be phosphorylated in vitro by casein kinase II (108) and that casein kinase II activity is stimulated by insulin in a variety of cell types (62, 70, 82, 151). Thus it is possible that insulin could stimulate UBF activity and thereby enhance rDNA transcription through activation of casein kinase II and a resultant increase in phosphorylation of UBF.

RNA Processing and Transport

In addition to altering the RNA polymerase II and RNA polymerase I directed rates of gene transcription, insulin also modifies other nuclear events related to the pathway of protein synthesis. For example, the hormone has been shown to induce the release of mRNA from the nucleus, an effect that appears to be mediated by the dephosphorylation and activation of the nuclear envelope nucleoside triphosphatase-mRNA carrier complex (131, 132, 143). Furthermore, an insulin-induced efflux of protein and RNA from the nucleus has been observed by several laboratories (20, 131, 144). A recent report shows a close correlation of the dose-response curves of insulin-induced nuclear RNA efflux and serine phosphorylation of the nucleolar protein nucleolin (20). This observation suggests that insulin may regulate nuclear RNA efflux by changing the extent of phosphorylation of nucleolin, a protein that is thought to participate in packaging and transport of rRNA (20). The insulin-stimulated phosphorylation of nucleolin is prevented by a cell-permeable inhibitor of casein kinase II, which suggests that casein kinase II may mediate this effect of the hormone (20).

Insulin has been found to induce the phosphorylation of a number of dsDNA-binding nuclear proteins including lamins A and C (19, 44) and numatrin (38). Lamins are a family of nuclear skeletal proteins that play a critical role in the structure of the nucleus and that are phosphorylated during interphase and hyperphosphorylated during mitosis (46, 114). They also appear to be associated with nuclear pores and chromatin (45), which presents the possibility that phosphorylation modulates nuclear transport and/or chromatin structure. Numatrin is a nuclear matrix protein that has been implicated in mitogenesis of normal and malignant cells (37) and that has been shown to be identical to the nuclear phosphoprotein B23 (39). Although a suggestion has been made for the involvement of protein kinase C and nuclear S6 kinase (20), the exact identification of the protein kinases and phosphatases that participate in the insulin-induced phosphorylation of lamins A and C and numatrin has yet to be established.

Studies using isolated nuclei suggest that insulin might exert a direct action on nuclear events, thus bypassing a plasma membrane receptor-mediated signal transduction pathway. These studies have shown stimulation of nucleoside triphosphatase activity (132) and nuclear-pore mediated transport of macromolecules (142, 148) following addition of insulin to nuclear preparations. Stimulation of RNA and protein synthesis following microinjection of insulin into the cytoplasm of frog oocytes (92), as well as increased transcription of immediate-early genes by intranuclear insulin in cells in which the plasma membrane insulin receptors had been abolished (80), support the direct action of insulin on the nucleus.

ACTIONS OF INSULIN ON CYTOPLASMIC EVENTS IN THE PATHWAY OF PROTEIN SYNTHESIS

The Cytoskeleton and Protein Synthesis

The cytoskeleton, i.e. the structure-forming component of the cell, consists of cytoplasmic networks of microfilaments, intermediate filaments, microtubules and their associated proteins, together with the postulated microtrabecular lattice. The role of the cytoskeleton in the cytoplasmic localization of mRNA and ribosomes as well as in the translational regulation of protein synthesis has been discussed in numerous recent reviews (3, 57, 69, 145, 156). A number of reports suggest that insulin affects cytoskeletal proteins, which in turn causes changes in the cytoskeletal organization and thus the structural features and adhesion properties of cells. Insulin has been reported to have effects on actin polymerization (2, 3, 56, 168), microfilament organization (130), and membrane ruffling, as well as the association of actin with such ruffles (50). Morphological changes induced by insulin have been associated with differences in protein composition and altered amounts of free, cytoskeletal-bound, and membrane-bound polysomes (68). Furthermore, increased association of polysomes with the cytoskeleton has been observed under conditions of increased protein synthesis in response to insulin (56, 167). Finally, insulin has been found to rapidly, but transiently, increase transcription of the cytoskeletal β-actin and α-tubulin genes (91).

Amino Acid Transport

In part, the amino acids used as substrates for protein synthesis are provided by transport of extracellular amino acids into the cell. A number of amino acid transport systems exist in mammalian cells, but insulin is thought to regulate primarily the activity of the system A amino acid transporter (reviewed in 24). System A is a sodium-dependent transporter that exhibits a preference for uncharged amino acids with small or unbranched sidechains (reviewed in 65). The insulin-induced increase in system A-mediated amino acid transport activity is slow in onset and is blocked by co-treatment with either cycloheximide or actinomycin D (65). These results suggest that insulin stimulates amino acid transport in hormone-sensitive cells by an increase in the transcription of either the system A transporter gene or the gene coding for a protein that is involved in the regulation of the activity of the transporter. Hyperinsulinemia is associated with an overall reduction in intracellular amino acid concentrations (24), which suggests that the rate-limiting step in protein synthesis that is stimulated by insulin is distal to amino acid transport.

Aminoacyl-tRNA Synthetases

Aminoacyl-tRNA synthetases play an integral role in providing the immediate precursors for protein synthesis, i.e. aminoacyl-tRNAs. In addition, these enzymes play a potentially important role in the regulation of the synthetic process. Inhibition of individual tRNA synthetases, either by treating cells with an amino acid analogue such as histidinol (67), or by incubation of cells containing a temperature-sensitive mutation in leucyl-tRNA synthetase at the nonpermissive temperature (16, 126) results in an inhibition of charging of the corresponding tRNA and a reduction in the rate of protein synthesis due to increased phosphorylation of the α-subunit of eIF-2.

Many, if not most, of the aminoacyl-tRNA synthetases are subject to phosphorylation in vivo (8, 47, 48, 122, 164, 171). In addition, a number of them can be phosphorylated in vitro (43, 121, 169, 171). Furthermore, the activity of a number of the aminoacyl-tRNA synthetases is known to be modulated by phosphorylation. Phosphorylation of glutamyl-, isoleucyl-, methionyl-, and lysyl-tRNA synthetases in a complex of seven different synthetases by casein kinase I lowers the affinity of the complex for tRNA (121). Phosphorylation of these synthetases also results in a decrease in aminoacylation activity to 15–32% of control values. The activity of the remaining synthetases in the complex that are not phosphorylated is unchanged. In contrast, phosphorylation of lysyl-tRNA synthetase by casein kinase II causes an increase in synthetase activity with a concomitant increase in misincorporation of amino acids into tRNA, i.e. incorporation of amino acids other than lysine (43). Furthermore, phosphorylation of either glutamyl- (171) or valyl-tRNA synthetase (169) by protein kinase C has no effect on the activity of the enzymes. However, treatment of rabbit reticulocytes with phorbol esters to activate protein kinase C results in a 38% reduction in aminoacylation activity of partially purified glutamyl-tRNA synthetase (171) and a 1.7-fold stimulation of the activity of valyl-tRNA synthetase (169). These results suggest that the change in enzyme activity in phorbol ester-treated cells might be due to phosphorylation of a protein, distinct from the synthetases themselves, that can modulate the activity of the synthetases. Overall, phosphorylation of aminoacyl-tRNA synthetases could play a role in the regulation of protein synthesis by insulin; however, to date few studies have investigated this action of the hormone.

Translation of mRNA

Insulin appears to regulate both the initiation and elongation phases of translation, probably by modulating the state of phosphorylation of initiation and elongation factors (reviewed in 61). In eukaryotic cells, 6 of the 11 known initiation factors are phosphoproteins (reviewed in 54). Insulin has been shown to alter the phosphorylation state of four of these initiation factors, i.e. eIF-2, eIF-2B, eIF-3, and eIF-4. The following discussion focuses on these four factors.

The activity of eIF-2 is regulated by phosphorylation of the α-subunit of the factor in a variety of systems (reviewed in 54, 55, 136). Phosphorylation of eIF-2α does not appear to alter the activity of the factor directly (163), but instead impedes the guanine nucleotide exchange reaction catalyzed by eIF-2B by sequestration of eIF-2B into an inactive eIF-2B•eIF-2α(P) complex. The α-subunit of eIF-2 can be phosphorylated in eukaryotic cells by at least three different protein kinases termed HCR, PKR, and GCN2 (reviewed in 55, 129). All three kinases phosphorylate the same amino acid, i.e. Ser^{51}, in eIF-2α.

One report indicates that insulin treatment of calf chondrocytes results in a stimulation of protein synthesis accompanied by a decrease in the incorporation of ^{32}P$_i$ into the α-subunit of eIF-2 (161). A limitation of this study is that a change in incorporation of ^{32}P$_i$ into a protein could reflect a change in the rate of turnover of P$_i$ in the protein, i.e. an alteration in both protein kinase and protein phosphatase activity rather than a change in the steady-state level of phosphorylation of the protein. In contrast, another laboratory reports no effect of insulin on the state of phosphorylation of eIF-2α in Swiss 3T3 fibroblasts, although the rate of protein synthesis is significantly elevated in response to the hormone (173). Furthermore, the phosphorylation state of eIF-2α is unchanged in fast-twitch skeletal muscle from diabetic and insulin-treated diabetic rats compared to controls (61). In both latter studies, phosphorylated eIF-2α was separated from the unphosphorylated subunit by isoelectric focusing and the relative amount of eIF-2α in each form was quantitated by protein immunoblot analysis (61, 173). Thus the proportion of eIF-2α in the phosphorylated form was unchanged by insulin in either Swiss 3T3 fibroblasts or rat skeletal muscle.

Although insulin treatment of diabetic rats or of cultures of Swiss 3T3 fibroblasts has no effect on the phosphorylation state of eIF-2α, the hormone does cause an increase in the activity of eIF-2B (62, 66, 173). The mechanism involved in the modulation of eIF-2B activity by insulin is unknown, but may involve phosphorylation of the ϵ-subunit of the factor. The ϵ-subunit of eIF-2B is phosphorylated in vitro by casein kinase I (112) and casein kinase II (28, 112). Phosphorylation of eIF-2Bϵ by casein kinase II reportedly stimulates the activity of the factor in in vitro assays (28). Since casein kinase II activity can be modulated by insulin (62, 70, 82, 151), it is speculated that the hormone might regulate protein synthesis through a mechanism involving a stimulation of casein kinase II activity, which in turn would phosphorylate, and thus activate, eIF-2B. In contrast to this speculation, a recent study (112) has failed to identify any change in eIF-2B activity in vitro following phosphorylation of eIF-2Bε by casein kinase I or II. However, in that study, eIF-2B was not dephosphorylated prior to phosphorylation by casein kinase I or II, and, therefore, the apparent lack of effect of phosphorylation on eIF-2B activity might be attributed to the original substrate being partially phosphorylated. Finally, an eIF-2Bε kinase that is modulated by insulin has been identified in skeletal muscle (SR Kimball & LS Jefferson, unpublished observations) as well as in CHO cells stably over-expressing the human insulin receptor (113). Based on its chromatographic properties, this eIF-2Bε kinase appears to be distinct from casein kinase I and II. Whether phosphorylation of eIF-2Bε by the insulin-stimulated kinase results in modulation of eIF-2B activity is presently unknown.

At least three of the eight subunits of eIF-3 are phosphoproteins (reviewed in 54). The η- and θ-subunits of eIF-3 can be phosphorylated in vitro by several different protein kinases (165). In serum-starved 3T3-L1 cells, insulin promotes increased incorporation of $^{32}P_i$ into the η-subunit of eIF-3 (96). Down-regulation of protein kinase C by prolonged exposure to phorbol esters prevents the insulin-stimulated phosphorylation of eIF-3η, which suggests that the phosphorylation is mediated by protein kinase C. However, there is no evidence to suggest that phosphorylation of eIF-3 has any effect on the activity of the factor.

As many as eight phosphorylation sites are present on eIF-4B as estimated by isoelectric focusing (29), and the factor can be phosphorylated in vitro by a variety of protein kinases (88, 165). An increase in the proportion of eIF-4B present in highly phosphorylated forms is associated with the increase in protein synthesis that is observed under conditions such as addition of epidermal growth factor (EGF) (177) to serum-deprived cells and activation of protein kinase C in response to phorbol esters (95, 177). Insulin treatment of serum-starved 3T3-L1 cells causes an increase in $^{32}P_i$ incorporation into a protein that co-migrates with eIF-4B during SDS-polyacrylamide gel electrophoresis (96). Prolonged exposure of the cells to phorbol esters reduces, but does not prevent, the insulin-induced increase in $^{32}P_i$ incorporation into this protein, thus suggesting that the increased phosphorylation occurs through protein kinase C-dependent and -independent pathways. Two limitations to this study are that the protein has not been positively identified as eIF-4B and that incorporation of $^{32}P_i$ into proteins can reflect a change in $^{32}P_i$ turnover rather than an absolute change in the proportion of the protein in the phosphorylated form. In another study, incorporation of $^{32}P_i$ into eIF-4B has been found to be stimulated by insulin treatment of serum-starved HIR 3.5 cells, which stably overexpress the human insulin receptor (86). It is important to note that, although phosphorylation of eIF-4B is associated with increased rates of translation in various cell types, it is not known whether phosphorylation of the factor modulates its activity.

The α-subunit of eIF-4F can exist either as a complex with the β- and γ-subunits of the factor or as the free protein; both the free subunit and the subunit in the eIF-4F complex are present as a phosphoprotein (72). In vitro, eIF-4Fα is phosphorylated by protein kinase C (165), casein kinase I (52), and cGMP-dependent protein kinase (88). The phosphorylation of eIF-4α is increased in vivo in response to various conditions that are associated with an increase in the rate of protein synthesis (63, 86, 96). The mechanism by which phosphorylation of eIF-4Fα stimulates protein synthesis appears to involve an enhanced binding of the factor to mRNA because mutation of the major phosphorylation site in eIF-4Fα, i.e. Ser[53] to Ala, abolishes association of the factor with 48S preinitiation complexes in rabbit reticulocyte lysates (60). Phosphorylation of eIF-4Fα is increased upon insulin stimulation of serum-starved 3T3 cells (96). The kinase involved in the insulin-stimulated increase in eIF-4Fα phosphorylation is unknown. However, the insulin-stimulated phosphorylation of eIF-4Fα in 3T3 cells can be blocked by pretreatment of the cells with phorbol esters to down-regulate protein kinase C (96), which implicates protein kinase C in the increased phosphorylation of eIF-4Fα. Furthermore, an insulin-stimulated protamine kinase has been shown to phosphorylate eIF-4Fα (4). Other studies suggest that the intracellular signaling pathway by which insulin stimulates the phosphorylation of eIF-4Fα, and thus the translation of specific mRNAs, probably involves the oncogene Ras (137). Transformation of cloned rat embryo fibroblasts with the Harvey Ras oncogene results in an increase in the rate of protein synthesis, as well as an increase in the rate of phosphate incorporation into eIF-4Fα. Interestingly, overexpression of eIF-4Fα causes an activation of Ras, i.e. an increase in the proportion of Ras in the Ras•GTP binary complex, and results in malignant transformation (74). Overexpression of the dominant negative regulator of Ras, GTPase-activating protein, or intracellular injection of anti-Ras antibodies reverses the transformation caused by overexpression of eIF-4Fα.

The γ-subunit of eIF-4F is also a phosphoprotein. The protein is phosphorylated in vitro by protein kinase C, multifunctional S6 kinase, and protease-activated protein kinase I (165). Insulin increases the phosphorylation of eIF-4Fγ in serum-deprived 3T3-L1 cells (96). The insulin-induced phosphorylation of eIF-4Fγ is independent of protein kinase C because down-regulation of protein kinase C by pretreatment with phorbol esters does not prevent phosphorylation of the factor, and peptide maps of eIF-4Fγ from cells stimulated by either insulin or phorbol esters are distinct. However, little information about the possible regulatory significance of phosphorylation of eIF-4Fγ is available although phosphorylation of eIF-4Fγ by the multifunctional S6 protein kinase results in increased binding of eIF-4F to the cap structure (94).

Although the majority of the available evidence suggests that the primary effect of insulin on translation occurs through control of peptide-chain initiation, the hormone has also been shown to regulate peptide-chain elongation (41, 176). The mechanism involved in the regulation of elongation by insulin is unknown, but could potentially involve phosphorylation of eEF-1. All three subunits of eEF-1 purified from rabbit reticulocytes are phosphorylated in vitro by protein kinase C (169). However, phosphorylation of the α-subunit is dependent upon whether eEF-1 is associated with valyl-tRNA synthetase. As much as 50% of the total eEF-1 activity in rabbit reticulocytes is present in a high M_r complex with valyl-tRNA synthetase (170). When eEF-1 is present in the valyl-tRNA synthetase•eEF-1 complex, eEF-1α is phosphorylated to a significantly lesser extent by protein kinase C than when eEF-1 is not associated with the synthetase. In contrast, phosphorylation of the β- and γ-subunits of eEF-1 by protein kinase C is unaffected by association with valyl-tRNA synthetase. All three subunits of eEF-1 are also phosphorylated in rabbit reticulocytes treated with phorbol esters to induce protein kinase C (170). Phosphopeptide mapping of the α-subunit suggests that the same sites are phosphorylated in vitro by protein kinase C as are phosphorylated in vivo in response to phorbol esters. Both the β- and γ-subunits of eEF-1 are also phosphorylated in vitro by casein kinase II (7, 58, 116). However, phosphorylation of eEF-1 by casein kinase II reportedly only occurs in the presence of polylysine (116) and therefore may not be physiologically relevant.

The effect of phosphorylation on the activity of eEF-1 is unclear and may depend upon which subunits of the factor are phosphorylated. Phosphorylation of the α-subunit of the factor is reported to decrease the binding of the protein to ribosomal subunits (22). In contrast, in another study, phosphorylation of eEF-1α reportedly enhances poly(U)-directed binding of phenylalanyl-tRNA to 80S ribosomes (166). However, in neither of these studies has the kinase responsible for the phosphorylation been identified. In addition, phosphorylation of eEF-1 by protein kinase C results in an increase in eEF-1 activity as measured by poly(U)-directed polyphenylalanine synthesis in vitro (169, 170). It is noteworthy that phosphorylation of isolated eEF-1α by protein kinase C has no effect on activity, which suggests that eEF-1 activity is regulated by phosphorylation of the β- and/or γ-subunits. It is also interesting that eEF-1 is phosphorylated by casein kinase II (116) and that casein kinase II is stimulated by insulin (70, 82, 151). However, the functional consequences of phosphorylation of eEF-1 by casein kinase II are unknown.

eEF-2 is specifically phosphorylated by a protein kinase termed calcium/calmodulin-dependent protein kinase III (CaM-PK III) (99). Three adjacent threonine residues, Thr^{53}, Thr^{56}, and Thr^{58} are phosphorylated in vitro (115, 128); only the latter two sites are phosphorylated in rabbit reticulocytes in vivo with phosphorylation of Thr^{56} preceding that of Thr^{58} (133). CaM-PK III is apparently regulated in vivo by elevation of the cytoplasmic calcium concentration, since phosphorylation of eEF-2 correlates temporally with the calcium transient (118). The activity of CaM-PK III is also regulated by phosphorylation by cAMP-dependent protein kinase (104). A physiological role for cAMP-dependent protein kinase in regulating translational elongation is suggested by the finding that addition of cAMP to rabbit reticulocyte lysate decreases the amount of eEF-2 present in the phosphorylated form and increases the rate of protein synthesis (146).

Phosphorylation of eEF-2 by CaM-PK III results in an inhibition of the activity of the factor as determined by poly(U)-directed synthesis of polyphenylalanine (100, 141) and synthesis of globin in reticulocyte lysate (15, 134). Both the monophosphorylated and bisphosphorylated forms of the factor are inactive in poly(U)-directed in vitro translation assays (129). The mechanism by which phosphorylation of eEF-2 inhibits the ability of the factor to mediate the translocation step of translation (140) is unknown. Studies by two different groups suggest that phosphorylation reduces the affinity of the factor for ribosomes (15, 135). However, in reticulocyte lysate, the rate of protein synthesis is still 50% of the control rate when greater than 97% of eEF-2 is present in the phosphorylated state (133), which suggests that either eEF-2 is not absolutely required for translation or that the phosphorylated factor must be able to bind to ribosomes.

The phosphorylation state of eEF-2 is altered in vivo in response to a variety of stimuli including treatment of cells in culture with insulin (reviewed in 129). However, relatively little is known about the role of insulin in modulating the activity of eEF-2. Insulin reportedly stimulates the rate of protein synthesis and the synthesis of eEF-2 in HIR 3.5 cells stably expressing the human insulin receptor (78). In contrast, insulin also rapidly stimulates the incorporation of $^{32}P_i$ into eEF-2 in HIR 3.5 cells (77). These results are paradoxical because phosphorylation of eEF-2 inhibits the activity of the factor in vitro, whereas an increase in eEF-2 content would be expected to stimulate protein synthesis.

Preferential Translation of Specific mRNAs

In addition to enhancing the synthesis of total cellular protein in responsive tissues and cells, insulin also stimulates the synthesis of certain individual proteins to a greater extent than overall protein synthesis. An enhanced rate of synthesis of an individual protein can be the result of either an increase in expression of the mRNA coding for the particular protein, or an increase in the efficiency of translation of existing message. In a number of instances, insulin has been shown to increase the synthesis of a particular protein without a corresponding change in mRNA expression. In chick embryo fibroblasts, insulin elevates the synthesis of ribosomal proteins fourfold, whereas the synthesis of total cellular protein is increased only one and one-half-fold (27). The stimulation of ribosomal protein synthesis by insulin is unaffected by concentrations of actinomycin D that inhibit the synthesis of mRNA by 95%, which suggests that the hormone acts at a post-transcriptional level to stimulate ribosomal protein synthesis. Insulin also preferentially stimulates the translation of ribosomal protein mRNAs in mouse myoblasts (53). In these cells, less than 50% of the mRNA for ribosomal proteins S16, L18, and L32 is associated with polysomes in insulin-deprived myoblasts. Addition of insulin to the medium results in a one and one-half-fold increase in the fraction of these mRNAs associated with polysomes. In comparison, there is little or no effect of insulin on the translational efficiency of nonribosomal proteins since greater than 95% of the mRNAs for p31, β-actin, and c-myc are associated with polysomes in both insulin-deprived and insulin-treated cells.

The selective nature of the translational control by insulin suggests that mRNAs have a distinctive property that is recognized by the translational apparatus or by proteins involved in messenger ribonucleoprotein particle formation. One common feature of all sequenced vertebrate ribosomal protein mRNAs is an oligopyrimidine tract at the 5′-terminus consisting of a cytidine residue at the cap site followed by an uninterrupted stretch of 7–13 pyrimidine residues (124). Two recent studies have shown that the 5′-untranslated region (UTR) from ribosomal protein mRNAs can confer to a heterologous mRNA the translational behavior typical of ribosomal proteins (79, 87). These results indicate that the 5′-pyrimidine tract plays a critical role in the translational control of ribosomal protein synthesis.

The synthesis of ornithine decarboxylase (ODC) is also specifically induced by insulin. In HIR 3.5 cells, insulin causes a 50-fold increase in ODC activity within 3 hr of addition of the hormone to serum-deprived cells, whereas ODC mRNA increases only threefold (86). Actinomycin D reduces the magnitude of, but does not prevent, the increase in ODC activity caused by insulin, which suggests that the hormone regulates ODC synthesis through a post-transcriptional mechanism. In a study similar to those described above for ribosomal proteins, insulin stimulation of serum-deprived cells causes a two to fourfold increase in human growth hormone (hGH) synthesis in cells expressing a chimeric mRNA consisting of the 5′-UTR of ODC and the coding region of hGH (86). Furthermore, insulin stimulates the synthesis of hGH from a plasmid containing just the 5′-most 115 nucleotides corresponding to a G/C-rich region that is predicted to form a stable stem-loop structure (85). Thus insulin appears to play a critical role in the translational control of ODC and ribosomal protein synthesis. However, because of the great disparity in 5'-UTR sequences and the predicted structures between ODC and the ribosomal protein mRNAs, it is likely that insulin is acting through separate, but parallel, mechanisms in regulating the synthesis of these proteins.

One mechanism by which insulin might stimulate the translation of specific mRNAs would be through phosphorylation of eIF-4B and eIF-4Fα, whereby phosphorylation of eIF-4Fα would result in preferential selection of particular mRNA molecules such as ODC mRNA, and phosphorylation of eIF-4B would stimulate unwinding of the secondary structure in the 5'-untranslated region of the mRNA. Thus the in vivo translation of a series of mRNA constructs containing 5'-untranslated regions with increasing amounts of secondary structure is inversely proportional to the predicted stability of the secondary structure (71). Overexpression of eIF-4Fα in these cells enhances translation of these mRNAs and obviates the difference in translation. This effect requires phosphorylation of Ser^{53} since over-expression of mutant eIF-4Fα where Ser^{53} is converted to Ala does not affect translation of the series of mRNAs.

Regulation of the translation of specific mRNAs could also involve an interaction of a *trans*-acting factor with the *cis*-acting element in the 5'-UTR of the messages. One possibility is that binding of such a factor to the *cis*-acting element could prevent the mRNA from interacting with ribosomes or peptide-chain initiation factors. An example of this type of regulation is the protein that represses the translation of ferritin mRNA by binding to a stem loop structure (the iron responsive element) (IRE) in the 5'-UTR of ferritin mRNA (76, 97, 172). Moving the IRE in the 5'-UTR to a position 67 nt or more downstream of the 5'-terminus abolishes iron-dependent translational regulation (49). Based on these results, it has been proposed that the IRE binding protein/IRE complex regulates translation of ferritin mRNA by a position-dependent interference with one of the initial steps in peptide-chain initiation (49).

Stability of Specific mRNAs

One mechanism that could account for a change in the expression of a specific mRNA would be an alteration in the stability of the mRNA. In a number of studies, an increase in the stability of an individual mRNA has been inferred from the observation that the expression of the particular mRNA is elevated without a corresponding change in the rate of transcription of the gene (21, 34, 35, 162). In other studies, the rates of degradation of particular mRNAs have been measured as the decrease in the amount of radiolabel associated with mRNA that had been radiolabeled prior to the start of the experiment. In such experiments, insulin causes a twofold increase in the half-life of GLUT 1 glucose transporter mRNA in L6 cells (84) and of GAPDH mRNA in 3T3-L1 cells (10). Furthermore, the combination of insulin and glucose increases the half-life of pyruvate kinase mRNA 24-fold in hepatocytes isolated from adult fasted rats (23). In contrast, insulin treatment of 3T3-L1 cells results in a decrease in the expression and half-life of GLUT 4 glucose transporter mRNA (42). Insulin treatment of insulin-deprived H4 cells also causes a reduction in expression of glycogen synthase mRNA because of a decrease in the half-life of the message to 25% of the control value, with no change in the rate of transcription of the glycogen synthase gene (111). One caveat to the studies measuring changes in mRNA half-life is that the experiments are usually performed in the presence of an inhibitor of RNA synthesis to prevent the reincorporation of radiolabel released from existing RNA into new RNA molecules. Most of the RNA synthesis inhibitors used are cytotoxic and therefore might alter the apparent half-life of the mRNA being studied.

The mechanism responsible for alterations of mRNA stability in response to insulin is unknown but may resemble the scheme described for regulation of the half-life of transferrin receptor mRNA by iron. The 3'-untranslated region of the transferrin receptor mRNA contains multiple copies of a regulatory sequence (iron-responsive element) (IRE) that are involved in regulation of the rate of degradation of the message (reviewed in 75, 158). In cells deprived of iron, a *trans*-acting factor, termed the IRE-binding protein (IRE-BP), binds to the IREs in the transferrin receptor mRNA. How binding of the IRE-BP to the IRE prevents degradation of the mRNA is unknown, but it has been proposed that binding of the protein to the IRE might force the mRNA to adopt a conformation that makes it less susceptible to degradation by ribonucleases or that the factor might protect a ribonuclease cleavage site in the mRNA.

Ribosomal Protein S6 Phosphorylation

An increase in phosphorylation of ribosomal protein S6 is observed in vivo in response to a variety of stimuli including treatment of cells in culture with insulin (reviewed in 32, 129, 154). Phosphorylation of S6 in response to these stimuli results in the incorporation of up to 5 mol of phosphate/mol S6 into serine residues clustered in the C-terminal region of the protein. Phosphorylation of S6 by cAMP-dependent protein kinase, cGMP-dependent protein kinase, protein kinase C, casein kinase I, or multifunctional calcium/calmodulin-dependent protein kinase individually does not result in phosphorylation of all five sites that are phosphorylated in cells stimulated with mitogens (14, 25, 120, 175). However, phosphorylation by a combination of protein kinase C, which alone incorporates up to 3 mol of phosphate into S6, and cAMP-dependent protein kinase, which incorporates up to 2 mol of phosphate, results in incorporation of 5 mol of phosphate into the protein (i.e. the same stoichiometry as is observed in vivo) (120). In contrast, multifunctional S6 kinase (123), $pp70^{S6k}$ (36), and $pp90^{rsk}$ (31) can individually phosphorylate the same five sites on S6 that are phosphorylated in vivo. Of the numerous protein kinases that can phosphorylate S6 in vitro, only the $pp70^{S6k}$ and $pp90^{rsk}$ families of enzymes are currently thought to be potentially important in regulating translation in vivo (32, 129, 154).

Phosphorylation of S6 in vivo generally correlates with increased protein synthesis in a variety of cells (reviewed in 129). Furthermore, S6 phosphorylation is associated with an increase in the aggregation of ribosomal particles into polysomes, which suggests that S6 phosphorylation is involved in an increase in the rate of initiation relative to elongation. The mechanism involved in the increase in translation associated with S6 phosphorylation is still undefined. Several studies have suggested that 40S subunits containing highly phosphorylated S6 are preferentially incorporated into polysomes compared with 40S subunits in which S6 has less incorporated phosphate (30, 103, 159). In addition, phosphorylation of S6 in 40S ribosomal subunits does not change the amount of poly(U) bound to the subunits, but does increase the rate at which the subunits dissociate from poly(U) (51). Finally, phosphorylation of S6 by multifunctional S6 protein kinase results in an increase in the binding of both globin mRNA and poly(A,U,G) to 40S ribosomal subunits and an increase in translation from those templates in a reconstituted translation system (14, 117).

In contrast, phosphorylation of S6 is not always associated with a stimulation of translation (see 129 and references therein). For instance, phosphorylation of S6 by cAMP-dependent protein kinase causes a decrease in the binding of poly(A,U,G) to 40S ribosomal subunits and a decline in translation of poly(A,U,G) (14). The differential effects of phosphorylation of S6 by the multifunctional S6 protein kinase (14, 117) compared with cAMP-dependent protein kinase on binding and translation of poly(A,U,G) may reflect the difference in stoichiometry of phosphorylation, or the sites that are phosphorylated by these kinases. Furthermore, the insulin-stimulated increase in protein synthesis in 3T3 cells can be blocked by pre-treatment of the cells with phorbol esters (173), whereas the insulin-stimulated increase in S6 phosphorylation is only partially reduced by such treatment (96). More importantly, the sites on S6 that are phosphorylated in phorbol ester pre-treated 3T3 cells appear to be identical to those phosphorylated by multifunctional S6 protein kinase (96), which suggests that phosphorylation of those sites in vivo is not, by itself, sufficient for stimulation of protein synthesis.

CONCLUDING REMARKS

Whereas much has been learned in recent years regarding the identity of signaling molecules and pathways that are involved in mediating the actions of insulin and of specific end-point changes that occur in the pathway of protein synthesis in response to the hormone, many questions remain unanswered. A few of the more important questions are: Is more than one signal transduction pathway involved in mediating the effects of insulin on protein synthesis and what is the identity and mechanism of action of each component in the signaling pathway(s)? What is the identity and mechanism of action of all components in the pathway of protein synthesis that are modified in response to insulin? Are all the actions of insulin on protein synthesis mediated by phosphorylation/dephosphorylation of specific proteins? If so, what is the identity of the protein kinases and phosphatases involved in mediating these changes? Which of the observed changes in the pathway of protein synthesis result from a direct action of insulin as opposed to those changes that occur indirectly as a result of an action of the hormone on another cellular process? Which of the modifications that occur in response to insulin result in a change in a rate-limiting reaction in the pathway of protein synthesis? Which of the effects of insulin are tissue-specific and how are these mediated? Future studies will be required to answer these and other questions about the action of insulin on protein synthesis.

Literature Cited

1. Alexander-Bridges M, Buggs C, Giere L, Denaro M, Kahn B, et al. 1992. Models of insulin action on metabolic and growth response genes. *Mol. Cell. Biochem.* 109:99–105
2. Almas B, Pryme IF, Vedeler A. 1992. The effects of insulin, cycloheximide, and phalloidin on the content of actin and p35 in extracts prepared from the nuclear fraction of Krebs II ascites cells. *Mol. Cell. Biochem.* 115:187–94
3. Almas B, Pryme IF, Vedeler A, Hesketh JE. 1992. Insulin: signal transmission and short term effects on the cytoskeleton and protein synthesis. *Int. J. Biochem.* 24:183–91
4. Amick GD, Damuni Z. 1992. Protamine kinase phosphorylates eukaryotic protein synthesis initiation factor 4E. *Biochem. Biophys. Res. Commun.* 183: 431–37
5. Antonetti DA, Kimball SR, Horetsky RL, Jefferson LS. 1993. Regulation of rDNA transcription by insulin in primary cultures of rat hepatocytes. *J. Biol. Chem.* In press
6. Baltensperger K, Kozma LM, Cherniack AD, Klarlund JK, Chawla A, et al. 1993. Binding of the *ras* activator *son of sevenless* to insulin receptor substrate-1 signaling complexes. *Science* 260:1950–52
7. Belle R, Derancourt J, Poule R, Capony J-P, Ozon R, Mulner-Lorillon O. 1989. A purified complex from *Xenopus* oocytes contains a p47 protein, an in vivo substrate of MDF, and a p30 protein respectively homologous to elongation factors EF-1γ and EF-1β. *FEBS Lett.* 255:101–4
8. Berg BH. 1990. Chromatofocussing of aminoacyl-tRNA synthetases extracted from NMRI mouse liver. *Biochem. Biophys. Acta* 1038:391–94
9. Bergot MO, Diaz-Guerra MJ, Puzenat N, Raymondjean M, Kahn A. 1992.

Cis-regulation of the L-type pyruvate kinase gene promoter by glucose, insulin and cyclic AMP. *Nucleic Acids Res.* 20:1871–78

10. Bhandari B, Saini KS, Miller RE. 1991. Glycerol 3-phosphate dehydrogenase gene expression in cultured 3T3-L1 adipocytes: regulation by insulin, dexamethasone and dibutyryl cAMP at the level of mRNA abundance, transcription and mRNA stability. *Mol. Cell. Endocrinol.* 76: 71–77

11. Blackshear PJ. 1992. Early protein kinase and biosynthetic responses to insulin. *Biochem. Soc. Trans.* 20:682–85

12. Blenis J. 1993. Signal transduction via the MAP kinases: proceed at your own RSK. *Proc. Natl. Acad. Sci. USA* 90:5889–92

13. Bokoch GM, Der CJ. 1993. Emerging concepts in the *Ras* superfamily of GTP-binding proteins. *FASEB J.* 7: 750–59

14. Burkhard SJ, Traugh JA. 1983. Changes in ribosome function by cAMP-dependent and cAMP-independent phosphorylation of ribosomal protein S6. *J. Biol. Chem.* 258:14003–8

15. Carlberg U, Nilsson A, Nygard O. 1990. Functional properties of phosphorylated elongation factor 2. *Eur. J. Biochem.* 191:639–45

16. Clemens MJ, Galpine A, Austin SA, Panniers R, Henshaw EC, et al. 1987. Regulation of polypeptide chain initiation in Chinese hamster ovary cells with a temperature-sensitive leucyl-tRNA synthetase. Changes in phosphorylation of initiation factor eIF-2 and in the activity of the guanine nucleotide exchange factor GEF. *J. Biol. Chem.* 262:767–71

17. Conde RD, Franze-Fernando MT. 1980. Increased transcription and decreased degradation control and recovery of liver ribosomes after a period of protein starvation. *Biochem. J.* 192: 935–40

18. Considine RV, Caro JF. 1993. Protein kinase C: mediator or inhibitor of insulin action. *J. Cell. Biochem.* 52:8–13

19. Csermely P, Kahn CR. 1992. Insulin induces the phosphorylation of DNA-binding nuclear proteins including lamins in 3T3-F442A. *Biochemistry* 31:9940–46

20. Csermely P, Schnaider T, Cheatham B, Olson MOJ, Kahn CR. 1993. Insulin induces the phosphorylation of nucleolin. A possible mechanism of insulin-induced RNA efflux from nuclei. *J. Biol. Chem.* 268:9747–52

21. Davis BB, Magge S, Mucenski CG, Drake RL. 1988. Insulin-mediated post-transcriptional regulation of hepatic malic enzyme and albumin mRNAs. *Biochem. Biophys. Res. Commun.* 154: 1081–87

22. Davydova EK, Sitikov AS, Ovchinnikov LP. 1984. Phosphorylation of elongation factor 1 in polyribosome fraction of rabbit reticulocytes. *FEBS Lett.* 176:401–5

23. Decaux J-F, Antoine B, Kahn A. 1989. Regulation of the expression of the L-type pyruvate kinase gene in adult rat hepatocytes in primary culture. *J. Biol. Chem.* 264:11584–90

24. DeFronzo RA, Ferrannini E. 1992. Insulin actions in vivo: protein metabolism. In *International Textbook of Diabetes Mellitus*, ed. KGMM Alberti, RA DeFronzo, H Keen, P Zimmet, P, pp. 467–510. New York: Wiley & Sons

25. Del Grande RW, Traugh JA. 1982. Phosphorylation of 40S ribosomal subunits by cAMP-dependent, cGMP-dependent, and protease-activated kinases. *Eur. J. Biochem.* 123:421–28

26. DePhilip RM, Chadwick DE, Ignotz RA, Lynch WE, Lieberman I. 1979. Rapid stimulation by insulin of ribosome synthesis in cultured chick embryo fibroblasts. *Biochemistry* 18: 4812–17

27. DePhilip RM, Rudert WA, Lieberman I. 1980. Preferential stimulation of ribosomal protein synthesis by insulin and in the absence of ribosomal and messenger ribonucleic acid formation. *Biochemistry* 19:1662–69

28. Dholakia JN, Wahba AJ. 1988. Phosphorylation of the guanine nucleotide exchange factor from rabbit reticulocytes regulates its activity in polypeptide chain initiation. *Proc. Natl. Acad. Sci. USA* 85:51–54

29. Duncan R, Hershey JWB. 1984. Heat shock-induced translational alterations in HeLa cells. Initiation factor modifications and the inhibition of translation. *J. Biol. Chem.* 259:11882–89

30. Duncan R, McConkey EH. 1982. Preferential utilization of phosphorylated 40S ribosomal subunits during initiation complex formation. *Eur. J. Biochem.* 123:535–38

31. Erikson E, Maller JL. 1985. A protein kinase from *Xenopus* specific for ribosomal protein S6. *Proc. Natl. Acad. Sci. USA* 82:742–46

32. Erikson RL. 1991. Structure, expres-

sion, and regulation of protein kinases involved in the phosphorylation of ribosomal protein S6. *J. Biol. Chem.* 266:6007–10

33. Farese RV, Standaert ML, Arnold T, Yu B, Ishizuka T, et al. 1992. The role of protein kinase C in insulin action. *Cell. Signalling* 4:133–43

34. Fattal PG, Schneider DJ, Sobel BE, Billadello JJ. 1992. Post-transcriptional regulation of expression of plasminogen activator inhibitor type 1 mRNA by insulin and insulin-like growth factor 1. *J. Biol. Chem.* 267:12412–15

35. Fernyhough P, Mill JF, Roberts JL, Ishii DN. 1989. Stabilization of tubulin mRNAs by insulin and insulin-like growth factor I during neurite formation. *Brain Res. Mol. Brain Res.* 6: 109–20

36. Ferrari S, Bandi HR, Hofsteenge J, Bussian BM, Thomas G. 1991. Mitogen activated 70K S6 kinase. Identification of in vitro 40S ribosomal S6 phosphorylation sites. *J. Biol. Chem.* 266:22770–75

37. Feuerstein N, Mond JJ. 1987. "Numatrin," a nuclear matrix protein associated with induction of proliferation in B lymphocytes. *J. Biol. Chem.* 262:11389–97

38. Feuerstein N, Randazzo PA. 1991. In vivo and in vitro phosphorylation studies of numatrin, a cell cycle regulated nuclear protein, in insulin-stimulated NIH 3T3 HIR cells. *Exp. Cell Res.* 194:289–96

39. Feuerstein N, Spiegel S, Mond JJ. 1988. The nuclear matrix protein, numatrin (B23), is associated with growth factor-induced mitogenesis in Swiss 3T3 fibroblasts and with T lymphocyte proliferation stimulated by lectins and anti-T cell antigen receptor antibody. *J. Cell Biol.* 107:1629–42

40. Fingar DC, Hausdorff SF, Blenis J, Birnbaum MJ. 1993. Dissociation of pp70 ribosomal protein S6 kinase from insulin-stimulated glucose transport in 3T3-L1 adipocytes. *J. Biol. Chem.* 268:3005–8

41. Flaim KE, Copenhaver ME, Jefferson LS. 1980. Effects of diabetes on protein synthesis in fast- and slow-twitch rat skeletal muscle. *Am. J. Physiol.* 239: E88–95

42. Flores-Riveros JR, McLenithan JC, Ezaki O, Lane MD. 1993. Insulin down-regulates expression of the insulin-responsive glucose transporter (GLUT4) gene: Effects on transcription and mRNA turnover. *Proc. Natl. Acad. Sci. USA* 90:512–16

43. Freist W, Sternbach H, Cramer F. 1992. Lysyl-tRNA synthetase from yeast. Discrimination of amino acids by native and phosphorylated species. *Eur. J. Biochem.* 204:1015–23

44. Friedman DL, Ken R. 1988. Insulin stimulates incorporation of $^{32}P_i$ into nuclear lamins A and C in quiescent BHK-21 cells. *J. Biol. Chem.* 263:1 103–6

45. Gerace L. 1986. Nuclear lamina and organization of nuclear architecture. *Trends Biochem. Sci.* 11:443–46

46. Gerace L, Blobel G. 1980. The nuclear envelope lamina is reversibly depolymerized during mitosis. *Cell* 19:277–87

47. Gerken SC, Andrulis IL, Arfin SM. 1986. Histidyl-tRNA synthetase of Chinese hamster ovary cells contains phosphoserine. *Biochem. Biophys. Acta* 869:215–17

48. Gerkin SC, Arfin SM. 1989. Threonyl-tRNA synthetase from Chinese hampster ovary cells is phosphorylated on serine. *J. Biol. Chem.* 259:11160–61

49. Goossen B, Caughman SW, Harford JB, Klausner RD, Hentze MW. 1990. Translational repression by a complex between the iron-responsive element of ferritin mRNA and its specific cytoplasmic binding protein is position-dependent in vivo. *EMBO J.* 9:4127–33

50. Goshima K, Masuda A, Owaribe K. 1984. Insulin-induced formation of ruffling membranes of KB cells and its correlation with enhancement of amino acid transport. *J. Cell Biol.* 98:801–9

51. Gressner AM, van der Leur E. 1980. Interaction of synthetic polynucleotides with small rat liver ribosomal subunits possessing low and highly phosphorylated protein S6. *Biochem. Biophys. Acta* 608:459–68

52. Haas DW, Hagedorn CH. 1991. Casein kinase I phosphorylates the 25-kDa mRNA cap binding protein. *Arch. Biochem. Biophys.* 284:84–89

53. Hammond ML, Bowman LH. 1988. Insulin stimulates the translation of ribosomal proteins and the transcription of rDNA in mouse myoblasts. *J. Biol. Chem.* 263:17785–91

54. Hershey JWB. 1989. Protein phosphorylation controls translation rates. *J. Biol. Chem.* 264:20823–26

55. Hershey JWB. 1991. Translational control in mammalian cells. *Annu. Rev. Biochem.* 60:717–55

56. Hesketh JE, Pryme IF. 1988. Evidence that insulin increases the proportion of polysomes that are bound to the cytoskeleton in 3T3 fibroblasts. *FEBS Lett.* 231:62–66

57. Hesketh JE, Pryme IF. 1991. Interaction between mRNA, ribosomes and the cytoskeleton. *Biochem. J.* 277:1–10
58. Jassen GMC, Maessen GDF, Amons R, Moller W. 1988. Phosphorylation of elongation factor 1β by an endogenous kinase affects its catalytic nucleotide exchange activity. *J. Biol. Chem.* 263:11063–66
59. Johnson TM, Rosenberg MP, Meisler MH. 1993. An insulin-responsive element in the pancreatic enhancer of the amylase gene. *J. Biol. Chem.* 268:464–68
60. Joshi-Barve S, Rycklik W, Rhoads RE. 1990. Alteration of the major phosphorylation site of eukaryotic protein synthesis initiation factor 4E prevents its association with the 48S initiation complex. *J. Biol. Chem.* 265:2979–83
61. Karinch AM, Kimball SR, Jefferson LS. 1993. Alterations in protein metabolism in diabetes mellitus. In *Joslin's Diabetes Mellitus*, ed. CR Kahn, pp. 116–38. Philadelphia: Lea & Febiger
62. Karinch AM, Kimball SR, Vary TC, Jefferson LS. 1993. Regulation of eukaryotic initiation factor 2B activity in muscle of diabetic rats. *Am. J. Physiol.* 264:E101–8
63. Kaspar RL, Rychlik W, White MW, Rhoads RE, Morris DR. 1990. Simultaneous cytoplasmic redistribution of ribosomal protein L32 mRNA, phosphorylation of eukaryotic initiation factor 4E after mitogenic stimulation of Swiss 3T3 cells. *J. Biol. Chem.* 265:3619–22
64. Keller SA, Rosenberg MP, Johnson TM, Howard G, Meisler MH. 1990. Regulation of amylase gene expression in diabetic mice is mediated by a *cis*-acting upstream element close to the pancreas-specific enhancer. *Genes Dev.* 4:1316–21
65. Kilberg MS, Barber EF, Handlogten ME. 1985. Characteristics and hormonal regulation of amino acid transport system A in isolated rat hepatocytes. *Curr. Topics Cell. Reg.* 25:133–63
66. Kimball SR, Jefferson LS. 1988. Effect of diabetes on guanine nucleotide exchange factor activity in skeletal muscle and heart. *Biochem. Biophys. Res. Commun.* 156:706–11
67. Kimball SR, Jefferson LS. 1991. Mechanism of inhibition of peptide chain initiation by amino acid deprivation in perfused rat liver. Regulation involving inhibition of eukaryotic initiation factor 2α phosphatase activity. *J. Biol. Chem.* 266:1969–76

68. Kirkeeide E-K, Pryme IF, Vedeler A. 1992. Morphological changes in Krebs II ascites tumour cells induced by insulin are associated with differences in protein composition and altered amounts of free, cytoskeletal-bound and membrane-bound polysomes. *Mol. Cell. Biochem.* 118:131–40
69. Kirkeeide E-K, Pryme IF, Vedeler A. 1993. Microfilaments and protein synthesis; Effects of insulin. *Int. J. Biochem.* 25:853–64
70. Klarlund JK, Czech MP. 1988. Insulin-like growth factor I and insulin rapidly increase casein kinase II activity in BALB/c 3T3 fibroblasts. *J. Biol. Chem.* 263:15872–75
71. Koromilas AE, Lazaris-Karatzas A, Sonenberg N. 1992. mRNAs containing extensive secondary structure in their 5′ non-coding region translate efficiently in cells over-expressing initiation factor eIF-4E. *EMBO J.* 11:4153–58
72. Lamphear BJ, Panniers R. 1990. Cap binding protein complex that restores protein synthesis in heat-shocked Ehrlich cell lysates contains highly phosphorylated eIF-4E. *J. Biol. Chem.* 265:5333–36
73. Lange-Carter CA, Pleiman CM, Gardner AM, Blumer KJ, Johnson GL. 1993. A divergence in the MAP kinase regulatory network defined by MEK kinase and raf. *Science* 260:315–19
74. Lazaris-Karatzas A, Smith MR, Frederickson RM, Jaramillo ML Liu Y-I, et al. 1992. Ras mediates translational initiation factor 4E-induced malignant transformation. *Genes Dev.* 6:1631–42
75. Leibold EA, Guo B. 1992. Iron-dependent regulation of ferritin and transferrin receptor expression by the iron-responsive element binding protein. *Annu. Rev. Nutri.* 12:345–68
76. Leibold EA, Munro HN. 1988. Cytoplasmic protein binds in vitro to a highly conserved sequence in the 5′ untranslated region of ferritin heavy- and light-subunit mRNAs. *Proc. Natl. Acad. Sci. USA* 85:2171–75
77. Levenson RM, Blackshear PJ. 1989. Insulin-stimulated protein tyrosine phosphorylation in intact cells evaluated by giant two-dimensional gel electrophoresis. *J. Biol. Chem.* 264:19984–93
78. Levenson RM, Nairn AC, Blackshear PJ. 1989. Insulin rapidly induces the biosynthesis of elongation factor 2. *J. Biol. Chem.* 264:11904–11
79. Levy S, Avni D, Hariharan N, Perry RP, Meyuhas O. 1991. Oligopyrimid-

ine tract at the 5' end of mammalian ribosomal protein mRNAs is required for their translational control. *Proc. Natl. Acad. Sci. USA* 88:3319–23

80. Lin YJ, Harada S, Loten EG, Smith RM, Jarett L. 1992. Direct stimulation of immediate-early genes by intranuclear insulin in trypsin-treated H35 hepatoma cells. *Proc. Natl. Acad. Sci. USA* 89:9691–94

81. Lucas PC, Granner DK. 1992. Hormone response domains in gene transcription. *Annu. Rev. Biochem.* 61: 1131–73

82. Maeda R, Ras I, Zurlo F, Sommercorn J. 1991. Activation of skeletal muscle casein kinase II by insulin is not diminished in subjects with insulin resistance. *J. Clin. Invest.* 87:1017–22

83. Mahajan PB, Thompson EA Jr. 1990. Hormonal regulation of transcription of rDNA. Purification and characterization of the hormone-regulated transcription factor IC. *J. Biol. Chem.* 265:16225–33

84. Maher F, Harrison LC. 1990. Stabilization of glucose transporter mRNA by insulin/IGF-1 and glucose deprivation. *Biochem. Biophys. Res. Commun.* 171:210–15

85. Manzella JM, Blackshear PJ. 1990. Regulation of rat ornithine decarboxylase mRNA translation by its 5'-untranslated region. *J. Biol. Chem.* 265: 11817–22

86. Manzella JM, Rychlik W, Rhoads RE, Hershey JWB, Blackshear PJ. 1991. Insulin induction of ornithine decarboxylase. Importance of mRNA secondary structure and phosphorylation of eucaryotic initiation factors eIF-4B and eIF-4E. *J. Biol. Chem.* 266:2382–89

87. Mariotinni P, Amaldi F. 1990. The 5' untranslated region of mRNA for ribosomal protein S19 is involved in its translational regulation during *Xenopus* development. *Mol. Cell. Biol.* 10:816–22

88. McMullin EL, Hogancamp WE, Abramson RD, Thach RE, Merrick WC, Hagedorn CA. 1988. Phosphorylation of the p220 subunit of eIF-4F by cAMP dependent protein kinase and protein kinase C in vitro. *Biochem. Biophys. Res. Commun.* 153: 925–32

89. Medema RH, de Vries-Smits AMM, van der Zon GCM, Maassen JA, Bos JL. 1993. Ras activation by insulin and epidermal growth factor through enhanced exchange of guanine nucleotides on p21*ras*. *Mol. Cell. Biol.* 13:155–62

90. Meisler MH, Howard G. 1989. Effects of insulin on gene transcription. *Annu. Rev. Physiol.* 51:701–14

91. Messina JL. 1992. Induction of cytoskeletal gene expression by insulin. *Mol. Endocrinol.* 6:112–19

92. Miller DS. 1988. Stimulation of RNA and protein synthesis by intracellular insulin. *Science* 240:506–9

93. Montminy MR, Gonzalez GA, Yamamoto KK. 1990. Characteristics of the cAMP response unit. *Recent Prog. Horm. Res.* 46:219–30

94. Morley SJ, Dever TE, Etchison D, Traugh JA. 1991. Phosphorylation of eIF-4F by protein kinase C or multipotential S6 kinase stimulates protein synthesis at initiation. *J. Biol. Chem.* 266:4669–72

95. Morley SJ, Traugh JA. 1989. Phorbol esters stimulate phosphorylation of eukaryotic initiation factors 3, 4B, and 4F. *J. Biol. Chem.* 264:2401–4

96. Morley SJ, Traugh JA. 1990. Differential stimulation of phosphorylation of initiation factors eIF-4F, eIF-4B, eIF-3, and ribosomal protein S6 by insulin and phorbol esters. *J. Biol. Chem.* 265:10611–16

97. Mullner EW, Neupert B, Kuhn LC. 1989. A specific mRNA binding factor regulates the iron-dependent stability of cytoplasmic transferrin receptor mRNA. *Cell* 58:373–82

98. Myers MG Jr, White MF. 1993. The new elements of insulin signaling. Insulin receptor substrate-1 and proteins with SH2 domains. *Diabetes* 42:643–50

99. Nairn AC, Bhagat B, Palfrey HC. 1985. Identification of calmodulin-dependent protein kinase III, its major M_r 100,000 substrate in mammalian tissue. *Proc. Natl. Acad. Sci. USA* 82:7939–43

100. Nairn AC, Palfrey HC. 1987. Identification of the major M_r 100,000 substrate for calmodulin-dependent protein kinase III in mammalian cells as elongation factor-2. *J. Biol. Chem.* 262: 17299–303

101. Nasrin N, Buggs C, Kong XF, Carnazza J, Goebl M, Alexander-Bridges M. 1991. DNA-binding properties of the product of the testis-determining gene and a related protein. *Nature* 354:317–20

102. Nasrin N, Ercolani L, Demaro M, Kong XF, Khang I, Alexander M. 1990. An insulin response element in the glyceraldehyde-3-phosphate dehydrogenase gene binds a nuclear protein induced by insulin in cultured cells

and by nutritional manipulations in vivo. *Proc. Natl. Acad. Sci. USA* 87:5273–77

103. Nielsen PJ, Duncan R, McConkey EH. 1981. Phosphorylation of ribosomal protein S6. Relationship to protein synthesis in HeLa cells. *Eur. J. Biochem.* 120:523–27

104. Nygard O, Nilsson A, Carlberg U, Nilsson L, Amons R. 1991. Phosphorylation regulates the activity of the eEF-2-specific Ca^{2+}- and calmodulin-dependent protein kinase III. *J. Biol. Chem.* 266:16425–30

105. O'Brien RM, Bonovich MT, Forest CD, Granner DK 1991. Signal transduction convergence: Phorbol esters and insulin inhibit phosphoenolpyruvate carboxykinase gene transcription through the same 10-base-pair sequence. *Proc. Natl. Acad. Sci. USA* 88:6580–84

106. O'Brien RM, Granner DK. 1991. Regulation of gene expression by insulin. *Biochem. J.* 278:609–19

107. O'Brien RM, Lucas PC, Forest CD, Magnuson MA, Granner DK. 1990. Identification of a sequence in the PEPCK gene that mediates a negative effect of insulin on transcription. *Science* 249:533–37

108. O'Mahony DJ, Smith SD, Xie W, Rothblum LI. 1992. Analysis of the phosphorylation, DNA-binding and dimerization properties of and of the nucleolar fibrillar localization of the RNA polymerase I transcription factors UBF1 and UBF2. *Nucleic Acids Res.* 20:1301–8

109. O'Mahony DJ, Xie W, Smith SD, Singer HA, Rothblum LI. 1992. Differential phosphorylation and localization of the transcription factor UBF in vivo in response to serum deprivation. In vitro dephosphorylation of UBF reduces its transactivation properties. *J. Biol. Chem.* 267:35–38

110. Ohmichi M, Pang L, Ribon V, Saltiel AR. 1993. Divergence of signaling pathways for insulin in PC-12 pheochromocytoma cells. *Endocrinology* 133:46–56

111. Okubo M, Villar-Palasi C, Nagasaka Y, Larner J, Larner AC, et al. 1991. Long-term effects of insulin on the enzyme activity and messenger mRNA of glycogen synthase in rat hepatoma cells: An effect of insulin on glycogen synthase mRNA stability. *Arch. Biochem. Biophys.* 288:126–30

112. Oldfield S, Proud CG. 1992. Purification, phosphorylation and control of the guanine-nucleotide-exchange factor from rabbit reticulocyte lysates. *Eur. J. Biochem.* 208:73–81

113. Oldfield S, Welsh GI, Proud CG. 1992. Phosphorylation of the guanine nucleotide exchange factor eIF-2B and its activation by insulin and epidermal growth factor. In *Translational Control*, ed. MB Mathews, AG Hinnebusch, pp. 111. Cold Spring Harbor: Cold Spring Harbor Lab.

114. Ottaviano Y, Gerace L. 1985. Phosphorylation of the nuclear lamins during interphase and mitosis. *J. Biol. Chem.* 260:624–32

115. Ovchinnikov LP, Motuz LP, Natapov PG, Averbuch LJ, Wettenhall REH, et al. 1990. Three phosphorylation sites in elongation factor 2. *FEBS Lett.* 275:209–12

116. Palen E, Huang TT, Traugh JA. 1990. Comparison of phosphorylation of elongation factor 1 from different species by casein kinase II. *FEBS Lett.* 274:12–14

117. Palen E, Traugh JA. 1987. Phosphorylation of ribosomal protein S6 by cAMP-dependent protein kinase and mitogen-stimulated S6 kinase differentially alters translation of globin mRNA. *J. Biol. Chem.* 262:3518–23

118. Palfrey HC, Nairn AC, Muldoon LL, Villereal ML. 1987. Rapid activation of calmodulin-dependent protein kinase III in mitogen-stimulated human fibroblasts. Correlation with intracellular Ca^{2+} transients. *J. Biol. Chem.* 262:9785–92

119. Palmer JM, Folk WR. 1990. Unraveling the complexities of transcription by RNA polymerase III. *Trends Biochem. Sci.* 15:300–4

120. Parker PJ, Katan M, Waterfield MD, Leader DP. 1985. The phosphorylation of eukaryotic ribosomal protein S6 by protein kinase C. *Eur. J. Biochem.* 148:579–86

121. Pendergast AM, Traugh JA. 1985. Alteration of aminoacyl-tRNA synthetase activities by phosphorylation with casein kinase I. *J. Biol. Chem.* 260:11769–74

122. Pendergast AM, Venema RC, Traugh JA. 1987. Regulation of the aminoacyl-tRNA synthetase complex of rat liver by phosphorylation/dephosphorylation in vitro and in vivo. *J. Biol. Chem.* 262:5939–42

123. Perisic O, Traugh JA. 1983. Protease-activated kinase II mediates multiple phosphorylation of ribosomal protein S6 in reticulocytes. *J. Biol. Chem.* 258:13998–4002

124. Perry RP, Meyuhas O. 1991. Trans-

lational control of ribosomal protein production in mammalian cells. In *Translationally Regulated Genes in Higher Eukaryotes*, ed. RE Thach, pp. 83–92. Basel: Karger

125. Philippe J. 1991. Insulin regulation of the glucagon gene is mediated by an insulin-responsive DNA element. *Proc. Natl. Acad. Sci. USA* 88:7224–27

126. Pollard JW, Galpine AR, Clemens MJ. 1989. A novel role for aminoacyl-tRNA synthetases in the regulation of polypeptide chain initiation. *Eur. J. Biochem.* 182:1–9

127. Prager D, Gebremedhin S, Melmed S. 1990. An insulin-induced DNA-binding protein for the human growth hormone gene. *J. Clin. Invest.* 85:1680–85

128. Price NT, Redpath NT, Severinov KV, Campbell DG, Russell JM, Proud CG. 1991. Identification of the phosphorylation sites in elongation factor-2 from rabbit reticulocytes. *FEBS Lett.* 282: 253–58

129. Proud CG. 1992. Protein phosphorylation in translational control. *Curr. Topics Cell. Reg.* 32:243–369

130. Pryme IF, Hesketh JE. 1990. Insulin induces cell adhesion and normal flattened morphology in Krebs II ascites cells. *Cell. Biol. Int. Rep.* 14:447–55

131. Purello F, Burnham DB, Goldfine ID. 1983. Insulin regulation of protein phosphorylation in isolated rat liver nuclear envelopes: Potential relationship to mRNA metabolism. *Proc. Natl. Acad. Sci. USA* 80:1189–93

132. Purello F, Vigneri R, Clawson GA, Goldfine ID. 1982. Insulin stimulation of nucleoside triphosphatase activity in isolated nuclear envelopes. *Science* 216:1005–7

133. Redpath NT, Price NT, Severinov KV, Proud CG. 1993. Regulation of elongation factor-2 by multisite phosphorylation. *Eur. J. Biochem.* 211:689–99

134. Redpath NT, Proud CG. 1989. The tumour promoter okadaic acid inhibits reticulocyte-lysate protein synthesis by increasing the net phosphorylation of elongation factor 2. *Biochem. J.* 262: 69–75

135. Redpath NT, Proud CG. 1990. Activity of protein phosphatases against initiation factor-2 and elongation factor 2. *Biochem. J.* 272:175–80

136. Rhoads RE. 1993. Regulation of eukaryotic protein synthesis by initiation factors. *J. Biol. Chem.* 268:3017–20

137. Rinker-Schaeffer CW, Austin V, Zimmer S, Rhoads RE 1992. *ras* transformation of cloned rat embryo fibroblasts results in increased rates of protein synthesis and phosphorylation of eukaryotic initiation factor 4E. *J. Biol. Chem.* 267:10659–64

138. Roth RA, Zhang B, Chin JE, Kovacina K. 1992. Substrates and signalling complexes; The tortured path to insulin action. *J. Cell. Biochem.* 48:12–18

139. Rothenberg P, White MF, Kahn CR. 1990. The insulin receptor tyrosine kinase. In *The Handbook of Experimental Pharmacology, Insulin*, ed. P Cuatrecasas, S Jacob, pp. 169–81. New York: Springer-Verlag

140. Ryazanov AG, Davydova EK. 1989. Mechanism of elongation factor 2 (EF-2) inactivation upon phosphorylation. Phosphorylated EF-2 is unable to catalyze translocation. *FEBS Lett.* 251: 187–90

141. Ryazanov AG, Shestakova EA, Natapov PG. 1988. Phosphorylation of elongation factor 2 by EF-2 kinase affects rate of translation. *Nature* 334: 170–73

141a. Sasaki K, Granner DK. 1988. Regulation of phosphoenolpyruvate carboxykinase gene transcription by insulin and cAMP: Reciprocal actions on initiation and elongation. *Proc. Natl. Acad. Sci. USA* 85:2954–58

142. Schindler M, Jiang L-W. 1987. Epidermal growth factor and insulin stimulate nuclear pore-mediated macromolecular transport in isolated rat liver nuclei. *J. Cell Biol.* 104:849–53

143. Schroder HC, Wenger R, Ugarkovic D, Friese K, Bachmann M, Muller WEG. 1990. Differential effects of insulin and epidermal growth factor on the mRNA translocation system and transport of specific poly(A^+) mRNA and poly(A^-) mRNA in isolated nuclei. *Biochemistry* 29:2368–78

144. Schumm DE, Webb TE. 1983. Effect of physiological concentrations of insulin and antidiabetic drugs on RNA release from isolated liver nuclei. *J. Cell. Biochem.* 23:223–29

145. Singer RH. 1993. Spatial organization of mRNA within cells. *J. Cell. Biochem.* 52:125–26

146. Sitikov AS, Simonenko PN, Shestakova EA, Ryazanov AG, Ovchinnikov LP. 1988. cAMP-dependent activation of protein synthesis correlates with dephosphorylation of elongation factor 2. *FEBS Lett.* 228:327–31

147. Skolnik EY, Batzer A, Li N, Lee C-H, Lowenstein E, et al. 1993. The function of GRB2 in linking the insulin receptor to Ras signaling pathways. *Science* 260:1953–55

148. Soler AP, Smith RM, Jarett L. 1992.

Insulin stimulates accumulation and efflux of macromolecules in isolated nuclei from H35 hepatoma cells. *Diabetes* 41:194–201

149. Sollner-Webb B, Mougey EB. 1991. News from the nucleolus: rRNA gene expression. *Trends Biochem. Sci.* 16: 58–62

150. Sollner-Webb B, Tower J. 1986. Transcription of cloned eukaryotic ribosomal RNA genes. *Annu. Rev. Biochem.* 55:801–30

151. Sommercorn J, Mulligan JA, Lozeman FJ, Krebs EG. 1987. Activation of casein kinase II in response to insulin and to epidermal growth factor. *Proc. Natl. Acad. Sci. USA* 84:8834–38

152. Stanley FM. 1990. Insulin stimulated ribosomal DNA transcription. *Diabetes (Suppl.)* 39:129A

53. Stumpo DJ, Stewart TN, Gilman MZ, Blackshear PJ. 1988. Identification of c-fos sequences involved in induction by insulin and phorbol esters. *J. Biol. Chem.* 263:1611–14

154. Sturgill TW, Wu J. 1991. Recent progress in characterization of protein kinase cascades for phosphorylation of ribosomal protein S6. *Biochem. Biophys. Acta* 1092:350–57

155. Sung CK. 1992. Insulin receptor signaling through non-tyrosine kinase pathways: evidence from anti-receptor antibodies and insulin receptor mutants. *J. Cell. Biochem.* 48:26–32

156. Suprenant KA. 1993. Microtubules, ribosomes, and RNA: Evidence for cytoplasmic localization and translational regulation. *Cell Motil. Cytoskeleton* 25:1–9

157. Suwanickul A, Morris SL, Powell DR. 1993. Identification of an insulin-responsive element in the promoter of the human gene for insulin-like growth factor binding protein-1. *J. Biol. Chem.* 268:17063–68

158. Theil EC. 1990. Regulation of ferritin and transferrin receptor mRNAs. *J. Biol. Chem.* 265:4771–74

159. Thomas GT, Martin-Perez J, Siegman MS, Otto AM. 1982. The effect of serum, EGF, $PGF_{2\alpha}$, and insulin on S6 phosphorylation and the initiation of protein and DNA synthesis. *Cell* 30:235–42

160. Thompson KS, Towle HC. 1991. Localization of the carbohydrate response element of the rat L-type pyruvate kinase gene. *J. Biol. Chem.* 266:8679–82

161. Towle CA, Mankin HJ, Avruch J, Treadwell BV. 1984. Insulin promoted decrease in the phosphorylation of pro-tein synthesis initiation factor eIF-2. *Biochem. Biophys. Res. Commun.* 121: 134–40

162. Tozzo E, Desbuquois B. 1992. Effects of STZ-induced diabetes and fasting on insulin receptor mRNA expression and insulin receptor gene transcription in rat liver. *Diabetes* 41:1609–16

163. Trachsel H, Staehelin T. 1978. Binding and release of eukaryotic initiation factor eIF-2 and GTP during protein synthesis initiation. *Proc. Natl. Acad. Sci. USA* 75:204–8

164. Traugh JA, Pendergast AM. 1986. Regulation of protein synthesis by phosphorylation of ribosomal protein S6 and aminoacyl-tRNA synthetases. *Prog. Nucleic Acid Res. Mol. Biol.* 33:195–230

165. Tuazon PT, Merrick WC, Traugh JA. 1989. Comparative analysis of phosphorylation of translational initiation and elongation factors by seven protein kinases. *J. Biol. Chem.* 264:2773–77

166. Tuhackova Z, Ullrichova J, Hradec J. 1985. Regulation of the activity of eukaryotic peptide elongation factor 1 by autocatalytic phosphorylation. *Eur. J. Biochem.* 146:161–66

167. Vedeler A, Pryme IF, Hesketh JE. 1990. Insulin and step-up conditions cause a redistribution of polysomes among free, cytoskeletal-bound and membrane-bound fractions in Krebs II ascites cells. *Cell Biol. Int. Rep.* 14: 211–18

168. Vedeler A, Pryme IF, Hesketh JE. 1991. Insulin induces changes in the subcellular distribution of actin and 5′-nucleotidase. *Mol. Cell. Biochem.* 108:67–74

169. Venema RC, Peters HI, Traugh JA. 1991. Phosphorylation of elongation factor 1 (EF-1) and valyl-tRNA synthetase by protein kinase C, stimulation of EF-1 activity. *J. Biol. Chem.* 266: 12574–80

170. Venema RC, Peters HI, Traugh JA. 1991. Phosphorylation of valyl-tRNA synthetase and elongation factor 1 in response to phorbol esters is associated with stimulation of both activities. *J. Biol. Chem.* 266:11993–98

171. Venema RC, Traugh JA. 1991. Protein kinase C phosphorylates glutamyl-tRNA synthetase in rabbit reticulocytes stimulated by tumor promoting phorbol esters. *J. Biol. Chem.* 266:5298–302

172. Walden WE, Patino MM, Gaffield L. 1989. Purification of a specific repressor of ferritin mRNA translation from rabbit liver. *J. Biol. Chem.* 264:13765–69

173. Welsh GI, Proud CG. 1992. Regulation of protein synthesis in Swiss 3T3 fibroblasts. Rapid activation of the guanine nucleotide exchange factor by insulin and growth factors. *Biochem. J.* 284:19–23

174. Welsh GI, Proud CG. 1993. Evidence for a role for protein kinase C in the stimulation of protein synthesis by insulin in Swiss 3T3 fibroblasts. *FEBS Lett.* 316:241–46

175. Wettenhall REH, Cohen P. 1982. Isolation and characterisation of cyclic AMP-dependent phosphorylation sites from rat liver ribosomal protein S6. *FEBS Lett.* 140:263–69

176. Williams IH, Chua BHL, Sahms RH, Siehl D, Morgan HE. 1980. Effects of diabetes on protein turnover in cardiac muscle. *Am. J. Physiol.* 239: E178–85

177. Wolthuis RMF, Cremers AFM, Kasperaitis MAM, van der Mast C, Voorma HO, Boonstra J. 1993. Epidermal growth factor stimulates phosphorylation of eukaryotic initiation factor 4B, independently of protein kinase C. *Biochem. Biophys. Acta* 1177:160–66

178. Woychik NA, Young RA. 1990. RNA polymerase II: subunit structure and function. *Trends Biochem. Sci.* 15:347–51

179. Xie W, Rothblum LI. 1993. rDNA transcription and cardiac hypertrophy. *Trends Cardiovasc. Med.* 3:7–11

Annu. Rev. Physiol. 1994 56:349–69
Copyright © 1994 by Annual Reviews Inc. All rights reserved

PHOSPHOINOSITIDE PHOSPHOLIPASES AND G PROTEINS IN HORMONE ACTION

J. H. Exton

Howard Hughes Medical Institute and Department of Molecular Physiology and Biophysics, Vanderbilt University School of Medicine, Nashville, Tennessee 37232

KEY WORDS: phosphoinositides, phospholipase, G proteins, receptors, calcium

INTRODUCTION

Many hormones, neurotransmitters, and growth factors exert their physiological effects by activating isozymes of phosphoinositide-specific phospholipase C (PI-PLC). This results in the hydrolysis of phosphatidylinositol 4,5-bisphosphate (PtdInsP$_2$), a minor plasma membrane phospholipid, producing myoinositol 1,4,5-trisphosphate (InsP$_3$), which releases Ca^{2+} from intracellular stores, and 1,2-diacylglycerol (DAG), which activates protein kinase C. InsP$_3$ acts by binding to specific receptors located on Ca^{2+}-storing organelles that are specialized components of the endoplasmic reticulum (6). It is now known that the InsP$_3$ receptors represent a family of proteins with membrane-spanning domains in the C-terminal region and a large N-terminal domain ending in the InsP$_3$-binding site (27). Four of the monomers combine to form an InsP$_3$-sensitive Ca^{2+} channel. The InsP$_3$ receptors show considerable structural and functional similarity to the ryanodine receptors (27), which also form intracellular Ca^{2+} channels in many cell types (6). In skeletal muscle, ryanodine receptors are located in the sarcoplasmic reticulum as components of the T-tubule foot structures, together with the voltage-sensing dihydropyridine receptors.

Binding of InsP$_3$ to its receptors causes quantal release of Ca^{2+} (6). At

349

the cellular level, this release occurs at certain focal points, which implies a differential sensitivity of the receptors to InsP₃. As the local cytosolic Ca^{2+} concentration rises, the release of Ca^{2+} in response to $InsP_3$ is enhanced until inhibitory levels of Ca^{2+} are reached (6). In many cells, the Ca^{2+} increase spreads as a wave from the initiating focal point (6). These waves can be observed in cells at the spatial level using fluorescent Ca^{2+} indicators and fluorescence imaging techniques, or at the temporal level as repetitive Ca^{2+} spikes. Propagation of the Ca^{2+} waves is dependent upon Ca^{2+} influx and involves the regenerative release of Ca^{2+} from stores regulated by either $InsP_3$ receptors or ryanodine receptors (6). The phenomenon of wave propagation appears to involve calcium-induced calcium release, but the specific mechanisms are unclear.

In agonist-stimulated cells, the mobilization of intracellular Ca^{2+} is invariably accompanied by an influx of extracellular Ca^{2+}. In cells of neural origin, the entry of Ca^{2+} is attributed to the opening of voltage-dependent Ca^{2+} channels by the activation of receptors for neurotransmitters that are linked directly to the channels or regulate them through GTP-binding regulatory proteins (G proteins) (4). The control by G proteins may be positive or negative and may be exerted directly or via the generation of second messengers (4, 25). In non-excitable cells, the nature of the Ca^{2+} entry process and the mechanism(s) by which it is activated are poorly understood. It may be that Ca^{2+} entry is controlled by $InsP_3$ acting at the plasma membrane, sometimes in conjunction with myoinositol 1,3,4,5-tetraksphosphate ($InsP_4$), a metabolite of $InsP_3$ (6, 37). Alternatively, Ca^{2+} influx may be controlled by the Ca^{2+} content of the endoplasmic reticulum stores adjacent to the plasma membrane (6, 68). However, the details of these mechanisms remain unclear and appear to differ among cell types.

There are two basic mechanisms by which agonists activate $PtdInsP_2$ hydrolysis. In the case of growth factors, activation of their receptors results in enhanced tyrosine kinase activity (70). This leads to phosphorylation of specific tyrosine residues in the cytoplasmic domains of the receptors, to which γ isozymes of PI-PLC become associated. In the case of hormones, neurotransmitters and certain other agonists, the signal is transduced by G proteins from receptors with seven membrane-spanning segments to β-isozymes of PI-PLC (70).

IDENTIFICATION OF THE G PROTEIN α-SUBUNITS REGULATING PtdInsP₂ PHOSPHOLIPASE C

G proteins were first implicated in the regulation of PI-PLC about ten years ago by experiments demonstrating the effects of GTP analogues in permeabilized cells and isolated plasma membranes (for references, see 26).

However, identification of the specific G proteins involved remained elusive until 1990–91. Taylor et al (88) demonstrated that a 42-kd protein purified from GTPγS-treated liver plasma membranes activated partially purified PI-PLC. Western blotting identified the protein as a G protein α-subunit that was different from any known at that time. Later, Smrcka et al (79) showed that a 42-kd α-subunit prepared from rat brain by affinity chromatography on G protein $\beta\gamma$-subunits linked to agarose (57) also activated PI-PLC in the presence of AlF_4^-. It had been shown earlier by Pang & Sternweis (57) that tryptic peptides from the 42-kd α-subunit had sequences identical to those deduced from two novel α-subunit cDNAs that were cloned from a mouse brain cDNA library by Strathmann & Simon (81), using polymerase chain reaction, and designated α_q and α_{11}. These α-subunits are now known to be members of a new family of G proteins designated the G_q family. The α-subunits of these G proteins show less than 50% sequence identity with other α-subunits (78, 81). The α-subunits of G_q and G_{11} show close (88%) sequence identity (81), but those of other members of the family (G_{14-16}) are less closely related (78).

Sternweis and associates (57, 79) developed polyclonal antibodies to peptide sequences in α_q and α_{11}. One of the antisera (WO82) recognized α_q uniquely, whereas two others (WO83 and X384) recognized both α_q and α_{11}. Using these antisera and another (E976) raised to a peptide sequence unique to α_{11}, Taylor and associates (86, 87) showed that their α-subunit preparations from liver contained a 42-kd protein that was α_q, and a 43-kd protein that was α_{11}. These designations have been confirmed by sequencing peptides derived from both proteins. Taylor & Exton (87) subsequently separated α_q and α_{11} in the GTPγS-liganded form and showed that they were approximately equal in their ability to activate PI-PLC. Harden and co-workers purified a 43-kd protein from turkey erythrocyte membranes and showed that it activated PI-PLC in the presence of AlF_4^- (91). This protein was later shown to be α_{11} by amino acid sequencing and Western blotting with antisera specific for α_q and α_{11} (50a). As found for the 42-kd protein from brain (79), GTPγS induced little activation of PI-PLC in comparison to AlF_4^- (91).

α_q and α_{11} are widely present in mammalian tissues as demonstrated at the mRNA (81) and protein (57) levels. α_{14} is also widely distributed, but α_{15} and α_{16} are confined to hematopoietic tissues (1a, 94). A homologue of α_q ($DG_{\alpha q}$) is present in the photoreceptors of *Drosophila* where it couples rhodopsin to norp A (PI-PLC) (48). A cDNA for an α-subunit that is 98% identical to α_{11} and another that is a homologue of α_{14} have been identified in bovine liver (54).

Blank et al (10) purified G_q and G_{11} in the heterotrimeric ($\alpha\beta\gamma$) form from bovine liver. These G proteins elicit marked activation of partially purified bovine brain PI-PLC or purified bovine brain PI-PLCβ1 in the presence of AlF$_4^-$ or poorly hydrolyzable analogues of GTP. The G proteins were shown to consist of 42- and 43-kd proteins that cross-reacted with antisera raised to peptide sequences in α_q and α_{11}, respectively. They also contained 35- and 36-kd proteins that were recognized by an antiserum specific for transducin β-subunits, and a 8-kd protein(s) presumed to be a γ-subunit(s) (10). The stoichiometry between the α-subunits and β-subunits was approximately 1:1 (10) consistent with the heterotrimeric form of the G proteins.

The activation of hepatic $G_{q/11}$ by GTPγS required high concentrations of the nucleotide (> 1 μM) (10). Activation was blocked by high concentrations of GDPβS and by excess βγ-subunits from brain or liver (10). Significant activation of PI-PLC was achieved with sub-stoichiometric amounts of the G proteins, and equimolar amounts stimulated the activity of the enzyme sixfold. As expected from previous studies of the effects of pertussis toxin in liver cells, neither the 42- nor 43-kd protein was ADP-ribosylated or inactivated by this toxin (10). This is further proof that they are members of the G_q family whose α-subunits lack the cys residue in the C-terminus that is the toxin substrate (78).

As alluded to above, pertussis toxin inhibits the effects of certain Ca^{2+}-mobilizing agonists on PIP_2 hydrolysis in some cell types (e.g. neutrophils, HL60 cells, cardiac myocytes, smooth muscle cells, platelets, mesangial cells) (26, 51) and in cells transfected with certain receptors (3, 24). This implies that pertussis toxin-sensitive G proteins are also involved in signal transduction to PI-PLC. Studies in whole cells (*Xenopus* oocytes, neutrophils, HL60 cells) suggests that these may be G_i and G_o subtypes. In HL60 cells, the chemotactic peptide f-met-leu-phe (FMLP) stimulates the cholera toxin-dependent ADP-ribosylation of two pertussis toxin substrates of 40 and 42 kd that co-migrate on polyacrylamide gels with α_{i2} and α_{i3} (29, 35). The 42-kd protein can also be labeled with the photoreactive GTP analogue [α-^{32}P]GTP azidoanilide in HL60 membranes incubated with FMLP (73). A complex between the FMLP receptor and a 40-kd pertussis toxin substrate has been partially purified from HL60 membranes (65), and binding of FMLP to the complex is inhibited by GTPγS, which suggests the presence of a G protein.

There was an early report that G_i and G_o restored FMLP-stimulated formation of $InsP_3$ in pertussis toxin-treated HL60 membranes (41). G_o has also been implicated in the regulation of PI-PLC by experiments in which its injection into *Xenopus* oocytes enhanced the muscarinic receptor-stimulated Cl^- current (52). This current, resulting from $InsP_3$-mediated Ca^{2+} mobilization, was also stimulated by injection of GTPγS-activated α_o (52). Later work has shown that muscarinic stimulation of the Cl^- current is enhanced by the two forms of G_o isolated from bovine brain and also by recombinant α_o (56). Since the specificity of the effect was not determined by testing the potency of G_o against other G proteins, e.g. G_q, the significance of these observations remains unclear, particularly in view of recent evidence that the $\beta\gamma$-complex may mediate G_i or G_o regulation of PI-PLC (see below). Irrespective of the mechanism by which G_o activates PI-PLC, its limited tissue distribution (53, 66, 82) means that it cannot be the pertussis-sensitive G protein that controls PI-PLC in most cells.

COUPLING OF G PROTEINS OF THE G_q FAMILY TO Ca^{2+}-MOBILIZING RECEPTORS

Wange et al (92) showed that vasopressin and other Ca^{2+}-mobilizing agonists induced the labeling of 42- and 43-kd proteins with [^{32}P] GTP-azidoanilide in liver plasma membranes, whereas glucagon promoted the labeling of two proteins that were recognized by antisera to the two forms of α_s. The proteins labeled in response to vasopressin were recognized by antisera to α_q and α_{11}, respectively (92). They were also selectively immunoprecipitated by an antiserum raised against the C-terminal dodecapeptide common to α_q and α_{11}. These data indicate that the Ca^{2+}-mobilizing receptors of liver plasma membranes interact with the same G proteins (G_q and G_{11}) that regulate PI-PLC. In a separate study, Shenker et al (77) found that another antiserum raised to a C-terminal peptide common to α_q and α_{11} inhibited the stimulation of GTPase by thromboxane A_2 in human platelets, and also recognized a 42-kd protein, presumably α_q.

In more recent studies, a mixture of G_q and G_{11} ($G_{q/11}$), purified from liver, has been reconstituted with the M_1-muscarinic cholinergic receptor, purified from a Baculovirus/Sf9 expression system, in phospholipid vesicles (8). In this system, GTPase activity and [^{35}S]GTPγS binding were strongly stimulated by the muscarinic agonist carbachol, but only weakly by the antagonist atropine. When the M_1 receptor was replaced by the M_2 receptor, stimulation by carbachol was greatly reduced (8). Furthermore, negligible stimulation of GTPγS-binding was observed when other G proteins (G_s, G_i, G_o, and G_z were used in place of $G_{q/11}$). These observations are consistent with previous findings that the M_1 muscarinic receptor subtype preferentially mediates cholinergic effects on PtdInsP$_2$ hydrolysis, whereas the M_2 subtype is linked to inhibition of adenylate cyclase (64).

Activation of $G_{q/11}$ by carbachol in phospholipid vesicles containing M_1 muscarinic receptors has also been demonstrated by measuring the activation of purified PI-PLCβ1 in a two-step assay (8). The time course of binding of [[^{35}S] GTPγS closely followed the activation of the phospholipase as measured by the hydrolysis of [^{3}H] PtdInsP$_2$ to [^{3}H]InsP$_3$. The half-maximal concentrations of carbachol for stimulation of GTPγS binding and of PI-PLC activity were also similar. Co-reconstitution of M_1 receptor, $G_{q/11}$ and PI-PLCβ1 allowed the demonstration of GTPγS-dependent, carbachol-stimulated hydrolysis of PtdInsP$_2$ (8). These data show that the three components are sufficient to allow in vitro reconstitution of agonist-stimulated InsP$_3$ formation without the need for additional proteins.

Although GTPγS could support agonist-stimulated PtdInsP$_2$ hydrolysis in the co-reconstituted system described above, little or no coupling was observed when the GTP analogue was replaced by GTP (8). A reason for this emerged when it was discovered that PI-PLCβ1 greatly stimulated the GTPase activity of $G_{q/11}$ (7). The ability of the phospholipase to act as a GTPase-activating protein (GAP) was specific in that it was not exerted against G_o or G_s. It was also blocked by monoclonal antibodies against PI-PLCβ1. The physiological function of the GAP activity of PI-PLCβ1 is presumed to relate to the rapid turnoff of activation of the enzyme that is observed when an agonist is removed or an antagonist is introduced.

There is other, more recent, evidence that G_q and G_{11} are the transducing G proteins for receptors linked to PtdInsP$_2$ hydrolysis. Gutowski et al (32) showed that antiserum X384 raised to the C-terminal dodecapeptide common to α_q and α_{11} abrogated the stimulation of PtdInsP$_2$ hydrolysis by bradykinin, angiotensin II, and histamine in membranes derived from NG108–15, rat liver, and 1321N1 cells, respectively. Activation of the enzyme by GTPγS alone was also blocked by the antiserum, and the inhibition was reversed or attenuated by addition of the C-terminal peptide (32).

Wu et al (97) have shown that transfection of cDNAs coding for α_q and α_{11} into COS-7 cells prelabeled with [3H] inositol results in marked increases in [3H] InsP$_3$ formation upon stimulation with AlF$_4^-$. Co-transfection of the cells with a cDNA for PI-PLCβ1 resulted in higher production of [3H] InsP$_3$. On the other hand, transfection with cDNA for α_o, α_t, α_z, or α_{12}, or with PI-PLCδ3 in place of PI-PLCβ1, did not result in enhanced formation of InsP$_3$. Transfection with cDNAs to mutant forms of α_{11} or α_q, in which gln 209 was changed to leu (Q209L), or arg 183 to cys (R183C), resulted in the production of high levels of InsP$_3$ in the absence of AlF$_4^-$, consistent with these mutations rendering the α-subunits constitutively active (97). When membranes isolated from COS-7 cells transfected with α_q or α_{11} were incubated with PI-PLCβ1, GTPγS stimulation of PtdInsP$_2$ hydrolysis was enhanced compared with that in membranes from non-transfected cells. The enhancement in the α_{11}-transfected membranes was blocked by an antibody specific for α_{11} (97).

Conklin et al (22) also examined the effects of mutations in α_q on agonist-stimulated $InsP_3$ production in different cell types. In agreement with Wu et al (97), they found that transient expression of R183C-mutated α_q in COS-7 or HEK-293 cells resulted in constitutive activation of PI-PLC. It had been previously found that mutation of the corresponding arg residues in α_s and α_{i2} resulted in constitutive activation of these α-subunits (12). To examine the coupling of α_q to receptors, Conklin et al (22) co-transfected cDNAs for α_q and the α_2-adrenergic receptor into COS-7 or HEK-293 cells. In these cells, the α_2-adrenergic agonist UK-14304 enhanced $InsP_3$ formation, whereas in cells expressing the receptor alone, the response was absent or reduced.

Using chimeric constructs in which there was replacement of amino acids in the extreme C-terminus of α_q by the corresponding residues in α_{i2}, Conklin et al (23) showed that a minimum of three amino acids in this region was a major determinant of the specificity of receptor interaction. This was because these chimeras were able to mediate the activation of PI-PLC by two receptors (D_2 dopamine and A_1 adenosine) that normally couple exclusively to G_i.

Wu et al (96) also looked at the activation of PI-PLC isozymes in COS-7 cells transfected with cDNAs for different G protein α-subunits and for α_1-adrenergic receptor subtypes. Activation of PI-PLCβ1 was only observed with α-subunits of the G_q family, and PI-PLCγ and PI-PLCδ isozymes were not affected. All the α_1-adrenergic receptor subtypes ($\alpha_1 A$, $\alpha_1 B$, $\alpha_1 C$) were shown to activate PI-PLCβ1 in the presence of α_q or α_{11}, but some differences were noted with α_{14} and α_{16} (96).

Roles for α_q and/or α_{11} in the stimulation of PI-PLC by thyrotropin-releasing hormone (TRH) were demonstrated by the observation that antibodies raised to the C-terminal decapeptide common to α_q and α_{11} inhibited this response in membranes from GH_3 anterior pituitary cells (2). An antibody to the highly homologous C-terminal decapeptide of α_{14} was also inhibitory, but α_{14} was found to be absent from the membranes. In contrast, antibodies to α_{oA}, α_{oB} and $\alpha_{15/16}$ had no effect. Overexpression of the TRH receptor and α_q or α_{11} in HEK-293 human embryonic kidney cells resulted in synergistic activation of $PtdInsP_2$ hydrolysis in membranes incubated with TRH and GTPγS (2).

Recent studies by Amatruda et al (1) indicate an interesting selectivity of a receptor for different members of the G_q family. In COS-7 cells co-transfected with cDNA for the receptor for the active cleavage product of the complement component C5A and with cDNAs for α_q, α_{11} and α_{16}, activation of PI-PLC by C5A was only observed in cells containing α_{16} and not α_q or α_{11}. Thus the chemoattractant ligand selectively interacted with the G_q α-subunit that is specific for hematopoietic cells. Another study (96) also shows α_1-adrenergic receptor selectivity between α_{16} and α_q or α_{11}. On the other hand, no selectivity between α_q and α_{11} has been observed for any receptor (8, 92, 96, 97), presumably because of their very high amino acid identity (78).

Conklin & Bourne (21) recently discussed the various functions of G protein α-subunits in terms of their presumed three-dimensional structure. The face of the α-subunit encompassing the guanine nucleotide binding pocket was proposed to be on the opposite side of the molecule to the face that is oriented towards the membrane and has the structural features for interaction with $\beta\gamma$-subunits, effectors, and receptors. Evidence was cited in support of the idea that the $\beta\gamma$-subunits interact at the N-terminal end of the α-subunit. This included the fact that N-terminal myristoylation increases the affinity of α_o for $\beta\gamma$-subunits and that a myristoylated N-terminal peptide competitively inhibits binding of α_t to $\beta\gamma$.

G protein-coupled receptors have seven transmembrane helical segments with three intracellular loops and a C-terminal cytoplasmic tail (46, 55, 72). Chimeric constructions, deletions, and point mutations have identified four regions that are thought to determine the specificity of the interaction with G protein α-subunits. These are the C-terminal portion of the second intracellular loop, the N- and C-terminal portions of the third loop and part of the C-terminal tail. The structural elements of the α-subunits that determine their interaction with the receptor reside principally in the C-terminal end, but there is some evidence for the involvement of the N-terminus and another domain (apparently loops 9 and 10 and β-sheet 6) that is adjacent to the C-terminus (21). As described above, Conklin et al (23) have employed α_q/α_i chimeras to show that the extreme C-terminus is a major determinant of the specificity of interaction with the receptor. Several pieces of evidence are also cited by Conklin & Bourne (21) to support the hypothesis that receptor activation of α-subunits involves relief of a restraining effect of the C-terminus on the release of GDP.

The structural determinants of G protein α-subunit interactions with effectors have only been reported for α_s and α_t. Berlot & Bourne (5) found by mutagenesis of α_s that three regions were involved in stimulation of adenylate cyclase. If two of these regions were substituted in α_{i2}, activation of adenylate cyclase by the chimeric protein could be observed. The three regions reside in the distal half of the α-subunit (apparently in the distal half of α-helix 2 and insert 2/loop 7 and insert 4/loop 9 regions) (21). A peptide corresponding to one of these regions in α_t (insert 4/loop 9) was also found by Rarick et al (69) to activate cGMP phosphodiesterase. Conklin & Bourne (21) have pointed out that the regions that interact with the effector are all on the membrane-facing surface of the α-subunit and that one of them, in α-helix 2, is known to undergo a GTP-induced conformational change.

SPECIFICITY OF PHOSPHOINOSITIDE PHOSPHOLIPASES ACTIVATED BY G_q AND G_{11}

There are at least 16 isozymes of PI-PLC that can be divided into three types (β, γ, δ) (51, 70). The reported sequence for an α isozyme differs markedly from those of the other isozymes and probably represents another enzyme—thiol:protein disulfide oxidoreductase (80). The β, γ and δ isozymes have two domains of high (40–60%) sequence identity that are designated X and Y regions, and the γ isozymes contain regions (SH_2 and SH_3) that are homologous to conserved regions in the regulatory domains of *src* and other non-receptor tyrosine kinases (51, 70).

The γ-isozyme exists in two forms of high sequence identity that have wide tissue and cell distribution. Both forms have been shown to be coupled to growth factor receptor tyrosine kinases (70). Binding of growth factors to their receptors in many cell lines leads to dimerization of the receptor and activation of its tyrosine kinase activity (18, 33), which leads to phosphorylation of several tyrosine residues in its C-terminus (cytoplasmic tail). This results in the association of several cytoplasmic proteins with specific sites of autophosphorylation (18, 51). These proteins include PI-PLCγ1, the 85-kd regulatory subunit of phosphatidylinositol 3-kinase, and the GTPase-activating protein of p21*ras* (GAP) (18, 63, 70). The proteins bind with high affinity to different autophosphorylated sites through their SH_2 domains. Tyrosine phosphorylation of these proteins may then occur. In the case of PI-PLCγ1, the major sites of tyrosine phosphorylation induced by growth factors are residues 771, 783, and 1254 (70). Studies of the replacement of tyr by phe at these sites and expression of the mutant enzymes in NIH 3T3 cells have indicated that phosphorylation of tyr 783 is essential for activation of the enzyme (42). However, activity changes resulting from phosphorylation of PI-PLCγ1 have only been demonstrated in vitro under special conditions, e.g. in the presence of Triton X-100 (90), or of the actin-binding protein profilin (30). It is possible that phosphorylation results in a conformational change that allows the SH_3 domain of the enzyme to associate with the membrane, thus bringing the enzyme into apposition to its substrate.

Epidermal growth factor (EGF) activates PI-PLC in rat hepatocytes as indicated by the increase in $InsP_3$ and cytosolic Ca^{2+}, and the tyrosine phosphorylation of a PI-PLCγ isozyme (39, 49, 98). However, unlike what is seen in other cell types, the activation of the PLC is abolished by pertussis toxin treatment. This implies the involvement of a toxin-sensitive G protein. Since the toxin does not alter the tyrosine phosphorylation of PI-PLCγ induced by EGF (49, 98, 99), the putative G protein must be required for the expression of increased activity. Yang et al (99) have provided evidence that the G protein may be a species of G_i, but its function remains unknown.

Non-receptor tyrosine kinases can also phosphorylate and activate PI-PLCγ1. The T cell antigen receptor consists of at least seven polypeptides, none of which is a tyrosine kinase (71). Nevertheless, activation of the T cell receptor leads to activation of two non-receptor tyrosine kinases of the *src* family, p56*lck* and p60*fyn* (71) and tyrosine phosphorylation and activation of PI-PLCγ1 (31, 62a, 75, 93). Recent evidence based on transfections in COS-1 cells indicates that the ζ chain of the receptor and p59[fynT] are responsible for the tyrosine phosphorylation of the phospholipase and consequent Ca^{2+} mobilization (32a). Ligation of the membrane immunoglobulin complex on B lymphocytes activates a non-receptor tyrosine kinase(s), which results in tyrosine phosphorylation and activation of PI-PLCγ1 (19). Similar changes are observed when the high affinity IgE receptor ($Fc_\epsilon RI$) is activated in basophilic cells and the IgG receptors ($Fc_\gamma RI$ and $Fc_\gamma RII$) are activated in monocytic cells (50, 61). Activation of a non-receptor tyrosine kinase(s) as a result of stimulation of the above receptors also results in the phosphorylation of PI-PLCγ2, although the degree of phosphorylation of PI-PLCγ2 compared with PI-PLCγ1 may differ markedly in different cell types (20, 70).

In contrast to growth factors, agonists acting through G proteins activate the β-isozymes of PI-PLC. The evidence came initially from reconstitution studies with GTPγS-activated α_q and α_{11} and various PI-PLC isozymes (86), which showed unequivocally that the β1 isozyme was stimulated, but not the γ1 or δ1 isozyme. Further evidence that the β1 isozyme was a target of G_q and G_{11} came from the observation that monoclonal and polyclonal antibodies to this isozyme blocked the stimulation of PI-PLC in liver plasma membranes by GTPγS-activated α_q and α_{11} and by GTPγS itself, whereas antibodies to the γ1 and δ1 isozymes were without effect (86).

Support for the concept that PI-PLCβ1 responds to α_q and α_{11} comes from some of the cell transfection studies described above (96, 97). In these, co-expression of these α-subunits and PI-PLCβ1 in COS-7 cells led to enhanced accumulation of $InsP_3$ in response to AlF_4^- or to norepinephrine in cells also transfected with α_1-adrenergic receptors (96, 97). Furthermore, incubation of membranes from cells transfected with α_q or α_{11}, but not α_o, with PI-PLCβ1 led to enhanced hydrolysis of $PtdInsP_2$ in response to GTPγS (96, 97). When α_{14} or α_{16} was transfected, stimulation of PI-PLCβ1 was also observed, and α_{16} was found to activate PI-PLCβ2 (47). However, in cells transfected with α_q and the $\gamma 1$, $\gamma 2$, and $\delta 3$ isozymes of PI-PLC, AlF_4^- did not stimulate PtdInsP$_2$ hydrolysis (47).

The PI-PLC that is the target of GTPγS-activated α_q and α_{11} has been partially purified from bovine liver and identified by purification and Western blotting as the $\beta 1$ isozyme (76). This PI-PLC isozyme was found to be largely plasma membrane-bound, whereas the $\gamma 1$ isozyme was mainly in the cytosol, and the $\delta 1$ form was found in both fractions. The final preparation contained a 150-kd protein (PI-PLC$\beta 1$) that responded strongly to $\alpha_{q/11}$, and a much less responsive 140-kd protein that is probably a proteolyzed form of the phospholipase.

Recent findings have indicated that other PI-PLCβ isozymes are responsive to G proteins of the G$_q$ family. As indicated above, Lee et al (47) reported that in membranes from COS-7 cells transfected with α_{16}, GTPγS produced a larger stimulation of PI-PLC$\beta 2$ than of PI-PLC$\beta 1$. In contrast, Park et al (58) incubated PI-PLC$\beta 1$ and PI-PLC$\beta 2$, prepared from HeLa cells transfected with vaccinia virus containing the respective cDNAs, with α_q and AlF_4^- in phospholipid vesicles, and found stimulation of the $\beta 1$ isozyme, as expected, but negligible effect on the $\beta 2$ isozyme. In further work, Jhon et al (38) purified PI-PLC$\beta 3$ from 1000 rat brains and demonstrated that this 152-kd enzyme was activated by α_q, α_{11} and α_{16} in the presence of GTPγS to a much greater extent than PI-PLC$\beta 2$ and nearly as well as PI-PLC$\beta 1$. Using PI-PLCβ isozymes purified from rat brain membranes or HL60 cells, Smrcka & Sternweis (79a) also found that PI-PLC$\beta 1$ and PI-PLC$\beta 3$ responded about equally to $\alpha_{q/11}$, whereas PI-PLC$\beta 2$ was less responsive.

There has been some research to define the domains in PI-PLC$\beta 1$ that are involved in interaction with α_q. Wu et al (95) co-expressed various mutant forms of the phospholipase with α_q in COS-7 cells and found that the region required for membrane association and α_q activation was localized to residues 903–1142. This domain could be further subdivided into a sequence 1030–1142 required for interaction with α_q (95). These results were supported by the observation that two peptides from the G protein interaction region inhibited activation of the enzyme by α_q plus GTPγS (95). The conclusion that sequences in the C-terminal portion of PI-PLC$\beta 1$ are involved in its interaction with α_q was reinforced by the work of Park et al (60), who examined the ability of proteolyzed forms of the phospholipase to interact with the α-subunits. Their data indicate that the activation site is located between residues 880 and 1130.

The regulation of PI-PLC$\delta 1$ remains unclear. It is not phosphorylated on tyrosine in response to growth factor receptor activation and is not regulated by members of the G$_q$ family, as described above. This isozyme is also not stimulated by G protein $\beta\gamma$ subunits (see below). Taylor et al (85) have provided evidence that the PI-PLC isozyme previously designated α is probably a proteolytic product of PI-PLCδ1. The regulation of PI-PLCδ1 may be mainly through changes in cytosolic Ca^{2+}.

ACTIVATION OF PHOSPHOINOSITIDE PHOSPHOLIPASES BY G PROTEIN $\beta\gamma$ SUBUNITS

It is well known that PI-PLC can also be regulated by pertussis toxin-sensitive G proteins, and there is much evidence that these are subtypes of G_i and G_o. However, efforts to demonstrate stimulation of PI-PLC isozymes by the α-subunits of these G proteins have met with little or no success. Recent evidence suggests that the $\beta\gamma$ subunits of these proteins may be responsible for PI-PLC activation. Camps et al (16) first reported that $\beta\gamma$-subunits purified from transducin (G_t) or bovine brain activated soluble PI-PLC from HL-60 human promyeolocytes and neutrophils. Critical evidence that the stimulation was due to the $\beta\gamma$-subunits, and not to possible contaminating α-subunits, was provided by the finding that the stimulation was reversed in a dose-dependent manner by GDP-liganded α-subunits of G_t. Blank et al (9) and Boyer et al (13) independently reported similar stimulatory effects of $\beta\gamma$-subunits on PI-PLC. Blank et al (9) identified an apparently novel PI-PLC in cytosol from bovine liver and brain that was strongly activated by GTPγS-activated G proteins from liver. Purification of the activating factor led to the surprising discovery that it was the G protein $\beta\gamma$-complex and not an α-subunit. The stimulatory effect of the $\beta\gamma$-subunits was half-maximal at 33 nM and was reversed by GDP-liganded α_i or α_o. Stimulation was minimal or absent with the β1, γ1 or δ1 isozymes of PI-PLC. Subsequent work (11) has shown that the $\beta\gamma$-sensitive phospholipase has a M_r of 110,000, i.e. it is different from the various β, γ, and δ isozymes of PI-PLC (70). Western blotting with antisera raised to peptide sequences in PI-PLCβ3 indicates that it is a C-terminally truncated, possibly proteolyzed, form of this isozyme. The 110-kd enzyme is completely unresponsive to GTPγ-activated α_q (11), which supports the conclusion that the C-terminus contains the domain for interaction with this G-protein subunit (60, 95) and that the site for interaction with $\beta\gamma$ subunits is toward the N-terminus.

In studies of the turkey erythrocyte PI-PLC, Boyer et al (13) noted that low concentrations of G protein $\beta\gamma$-subunits (from the erythrocytes or bovine brain) were able to reverse the stimulatory effect of α_{11} plus AlF_4^- as expected, whereas higher concentrations of the subunits were stimulatory. When the phospholipase (1–2 nM) was incubated with $\beta\gamma$-subunits alone, stimulation of activity was observed with $\beta\gamma$ concentrations as low as 6 nM, and the addition of α_o inhibited the response (13).

As noted by Blank et al (9) and Boyer et al (13), the concentrations of $\beta\gamma$ subunits required to half-maximally stimulate their enzymes were much greater than the concentration of α_q or α_{11} (0.5 nM) needed to stimulate PI-PLCβ1 or the turkey enzyme. This suggests a priori that the G proteins that are the source of the $\beta\gamma$-subunits are more abundant than G_q or G_{11} i.e. they may be G_i or G_o subtypes.

Further work has indicated that the β2 and β3 isozymes of PI-PLC are targets for stimulation by $\beta\gamma$-subunits. Camps et al (15) expressed PI-PLCβ1 and PI-PLCβ2 in COS-1 cells and demonstrated that the β2 isozyme was more responsive to $\beta\gamma$-subunits from G_t. Katz et al (40) co-expressed the β1 and β2 PI-PLC isozymes together with different β-, γ- and α-subunits of G proteins in COS-7 cells and examined the inositol phosphate responses to carbachol. Transfection of β_1- and γ_1- or γ_2-subunits together with PI-PLCβ2, but not PI-PLCβ1, resulted in a marked carbachol response. The response was abrogated by co-transfection with α_{i2} and was not observed if mutant γ-subunits, which cannot be prenylated, were used. Most interestingly, the release of inositol phosphates induced by carbachol in cells transfected with M_2 muscarinic receptors and PI-PLCβ2 could be ablated by pertussis toxin, which indicates that the endogenous G protein from which $\beta\gamma$-subunits were released by receptor activation was a substrate for the toxin, e.g. G_i. Complete reconstitution of muscarinic-stimulated PtdInsP$_2$ hydrolysis was attempted by co-transfecting cDNAs for the M_2 receptor, PI-PLCβ2 and the G protein subunits α_{i2}, α_{i3}, β_1, γ_1, or γ_2 (40). In the full system with either γ_1- or γ_2-subunits, or either α_{i2}- or α_{i3}-subunits, carbachol produced a marked stimulation of inositol phosphate formation, which was abolished by pertussis toxin. However, if PI-PLCβ2 was replaced by the β1 isozyme, the response was less and was minimally affected by the toxin.

In more recent studies, Park et al (59) have examined the effects of $\beta\gamma$-subunits from bovine brain on the β1, β2, and β3 isozymes of PI-PLC in lipid vesicles. Their results showed that the β3 isozyme was much more responsive to the subunits than was either the β1 or β2 isozyme. In agreement with Blank et al (9), the γ1 and δ1 isozymes were essentially unaffected, and the concentration of $\beta\gamma$-subunits required for half-maximal activation of PI-PLCβ3 or PI-PLCβ2 (25 nM) was much higher than that for α_q on PI-PLCβ1 (0.6 nM). Carozzi et al (17) and Smrcka & Sternweis (79a) have also found that PI-PLCβ3 is activated by $\beta\gamma$-subunits to a greater extent than is PI-PLCβ1 or PI-PLCβ2.

The recent findings described above clearly establish that $\beta\gamma$-subunits of certain G proteins can stimulate the β isozymes of PI-PLC, with the β3 isozyme being the most responsive. Although the G proteins that release the βγ-subunits as a result of receptor activation are not absolutely identified, there is indirect evidence that they are subtypes of G_i and G_o. Cloning studies have indicated that there are at least four different subtypes of β-subunit and seven different subtypes of γ-subunit. These subunits show distinct specificity in their interactions (36, 67, 74) and in their tissue distribution (34, 78). Thus using subunits prepared by in vitro transcription and translation, Schmidt et al (74) found that $β_1$ formed dimers with $γ_1$ or $γ_2$, $β_2$ bound $γ_2$, but not $γ_1$, and $β_3$ did not bind to either $γ_1$ or $γ_2$. Using a transfected cell assay system, similar specific associations between β- and γ-subtypes were found by Pronin & Gautum (67). Likewise, although individual β- and γ-subtypes were all expressed in Sf9 insect cells, only certain combinations produced functional complexes as shown by their ability to support ADP-ribosylation of the $α_{i1}$ subunit (36). The functional combinations were $β_1γ_1$, $β_1γ_2$, $β_1γ_3$, $β_2γ_2$, and $β_2γ_3$. The failure to form an active $β_2γ_1$ complex is consistent with the binding data described above.

Although the prenylation and/or carboxymethylation of the γ-subunits was found not to be required for association with the β-subunits, it was essential for interaction with $α_{i1}$ and with adenylate cyclase (see below). The tissue distribution of β- and γ-subunits has been explored at both the RNA and protein levels (34, 78). The $β_1$-, $β_2$-, and $β_3$-subunits are ubiquitously expressed, while $β_4$, although widespread, shows more tissue variation (34, 78, 89). The $γ_1$-subunit is expressed only in photoreceptors, whereas $γ_2$ is found at different levels in all tissues, being highest in brain (14, 34, 78). The $γ_3$-subunit is found mainly in brain and testis, but $γ_5$ and $γ_7$ are much more widely distributed (14).

As noted above (40), both the $β_1γ_1$ and $β_1γ_2$ complexes appear to be effective in activating PI-PLCβ2, but other complexes have not been tested. The view that βγ-subunits as well as α-subunits play a major role in signal transduction by G proteins has received added impetus from the findings that βγ-subunits are also stimulatory for certain adenylate cyclase isozymes (Types II and IV) (28, 36, 83, 84). However, in this situation, the stimulation is dependent upon the presence of activated α-subunits of G_s (83, 84). The abilities of various combinations of β- and γ-subunits to activate Type II adenylate cyclase have been explored by Gilman and associates (36). The results show that $β_1γ_1$ and βγ from transducin (mainly $β_1γ_1$) are significantly less potent than $β_1γ_2$, $β_1γ_3$, $β_2γ_2$, $β_2γ_3$, and βγ from bovine brain. Similar findings were obtained when different βγ combinations were tested on a 110-kd form of PI-PLC (JL Blank et al, unpublished observations).

Roles for βγ-subunits in the regulation of other effectors have been proposed (for references, see 9 and 34). These include activation of phospholipase A_2 in rod outer segments, stimulation of cardiac muscarinic-gated K^+ channels, and targeting of the β-adrenergic receptor kinase to the plasma membrane, where it phosphorylates receptors. In addition, genetic evidence indicates that the mating response to pheromones in *Saccharomyces cerevisiae* is mediated by the βγ-complex.

A key point to be considered in the mediation of G protein effects via βγ-subunits is whether different G proteins have different complements of β- and γ-subunits. Kleuss et al (44) have microinjected antisense oligonucleotides to suppress the synthesis of specific β-subunits in GH_3 cells and have examined the effects on the inhibition of the L-type voltage-dependent Ca^{2+} channel by somatostatin or carbachol. Their data indicate that the $β_3$-subunit is involved in inhibition by the somatostatin receptor, whereas the $β_1$-subunit couples to the muscarinic receptor. No evidence was obtained for the involvement of $β_2$- or $β_4$-subunits. These interesting findings build on the previous work of this group (43), which showed that the inhibition of the Ca^{2+} channel exerted by carbachol involved $α_{o1}$-subunits, whereas that exerted by somatostatin involved $α_{o2}$-subunits. Kleuss et al (45) have also used microinjection of antisense oligonucleotides to examine the involvement of γ-subunits in agonist regulation of the channel. The results show the specific involvement of the $γ_3$-subunit in the inhibition by somatostatin and of the $γ_4$-subunit in the action of carbachol.

The above findings raise the possibility that the specificity of interaction of different G proteins with their effectors is determined not only by the nature of their α-subunits, but also by their β- and γ-subunit composition. Furthermore, the striking observations of Kleuss et al (43–45) indicate that the β- and γ-subunits can also influence the specificity of receptor coupling. In comparison to the detailed information concerning the specificity of the interactions of different α-subunits with receptors and effectors, there is little knowledge of the specificity of these interactions for different β- and γ-subunits.

CONCLUDING REMARKS

Present findings indicate that the regulation of phosphoinositide breakdown by G protein-coupled receptors involves an unexpected degree of complexity in that the phospholipases involved can be stimulated not only by the α-subunits of certain G proteins, but also by βγ complexes. There is common agreement that the α-subunits of the G_q family of G proteins stimulate β-isozymes of PI-PLC, although with varying efficacy and potency, and that those receptors that elicit phosphoinositide breakdown in a pertussis toxin-insensitive manner couple to G_q-type G proteins. However, efforts to identify pertussis toxin-sensitive α-subunits that activate PI-PLC isozymes have generally been unsuccessful, and it is now thought that activation of PI-PLC by pertussis-toxin-sensitive G proteins involves their $\beta\gamma$-complexes. The PI-PLC isozymes involved are also of the β-type, but the specific subtypes differ in their relative responses to α_q and $\beta\gamma$-subunits.

An issue that needs to be resolved before a physiological role of $\beta\gamma$-complexes in the regulation of PI-PLC can be accepted is the finding that the concentrations of $\beta\gamma$ required for activation are two to three orders of magnitude higher than those of α_q. Although this could be due to a loss of activity of the $\beta\gamma$-complexes during their preparation or because the most effective combinations of β- and γ-subunits have not been tried, a more likely explanation is that α_q has always been tested in its GTPγS-liganded form, and its potency has been overestimated (83a). This is because this form of α_q is not susceptible to inactivation by GTPase. This point becomes even more significant in view of the ability of PI-PLCβ1 to activate the GTPase of α_q (7). Another contributing factor to the apparent requirement for higher concentrations of $\beta\gamma$-complexes is that they are generated from more abundant G proteins, e.g. subtypes of G_i or G_o. Irrespective of these issues, there is a need to demonstrate in intact cells, that $\beta\gamma$-complexes can control PI-PLC and are generated in sufficient concentration and with the appropriate subtype composition from either G_i or G_o.

An important point to be investigated further is to determine if different G proteins have different complements of β- and γ-subunit subtypes, and if these subtypes, along with the α-subunits, are determinants of the specificity of interaction with receptor subtypes as well as with different effectors. The fact that $\beta\gamma$-subunits can be either stimulatory or inhibitory, depending on the effector, also raises the possibility of complex effects on target enzymes or ion channels when two or more G proteins are activated in a single cell.

The PI-PLC domain that interacts with α_q is the C-terminal, whereas that which interacts with $\beta\gamma$ subunits is towards the N-terminus, but the molecular details of either interaction are incomplete. The domains on α_q that interact with PI-PLC are also presently unknown, and the molecular details of the interaction of the $\beta\gamma$-complex with the enzyme are unexplored. Likewise, the structural determinants in the α-subunits of the G_i and G_o and the G_q family that determine the specificity of their interactions with agonist receptors are undefined, apart from an indication that the extreme C-terminal region of the α-subunit is important.

In addition to these issues of defining domains of interaction, there is the more important question of how, in molecular terms, the interactions result in structural changes, and how these in turn cause activity changes. Although insights into some of these questions have been obtained from models of G protein α-subunits based on the crystal structure of other GTPases, i.e. the p21*ras* oncoprotein and the elongation factor EFTu, the solution to these questions and those described above offers a formidable, but enticing, prospect.

Literature Cited

1. Amatruda TT, Gerard NP, Gerard C, Simon MI. 1993. Specific interactions of chemoattractant factor receptors with G-proteins. *J. Biol. Chem.* 268:10139–44

1a. Amatruda TT, Steele DA, Zlepak VZ, Simon MI. 1991. Gα16, a G protein α subunit specifically expressed in hematopoietic cells. *Proc. Natl. Acad. Sci. USA* 88:5587–91

2. Aragay AM, Katz A, Simon MI. 1992. The Gα$_q$ and Gα$_{11}$ proteins couple the thyrotropin-releasing hormone receptor to phospholipase C in GH3 rat pituitary cells. *J. Biol. Chem.* 267:24983–88

3. Ashkenazi A, Peralta EG, Winslow JW, Ramachandran J, Capon DJ. 1989. Functionally distinct G proteins selectively couple different receptors to PI hydrolysis in the same cell. *Cell* 56: 487–93

4. Barnard EA. 1992. Receptor classes and the transmitter-gated ion channels. *Trends Biochem. Sci.* 17:368–74

5. Berlot CH, Bourne HR. 1992. Identification of effector-activating residues of G$_{sα}$. *Cell* 68:911–22

6. Berridge MJ. 1993. Inositol trisphosphate and calcium signalling. *Nature* 361: 315–25

7. Berstein G, Blank JL, Jhon D-Y, Exton JH, Rhee SG, Ross EM. 1992. Phospholipase C-β1 is a GTPase-activating protein for G$_{q/11}$, its physiologic regulator. *Cell* 70:411–18

8. Berstein G, Blank JL, Srmcka AV, Higashijima T, Sternweis PC. 1992. Reconstitution of agonist-stimulated phosphatidylinositol 4,5-bisphosphate hydrolysis using purified m1 muscarinic receptor, Gq/11_, and phospholipase C-b1. *J. Biol. Chem.* 267:8081–88

9. Blank JL, Brattain KA, Exton JH. 1992. Activation of cytosolic phosphoinositide phospholipase C by G-protein βγ subunits. *J. Biol. Chem.* 267:23069–75

10. Blank JL, Ross AH, Exton JH. 1991. Purification and characterization of two G-proteins which activate the β1 isozyme of phosphoinositide-specific phospholipase C. Identification as members of the G$_q$ class. *J. Biol. Chem.* 266:18206–16

11. Blank, JL, Shaw K, Ross AH, Exton JH. 1993. Purification of a 110 kDa phospholipase C from bovine brain cytosol that is activated by G-protein βγ-subunits. *J. Biol. Chem.* In press

12. Bourne HR, Sanders DA, McCormick F. 1991. The GTPase superfamily: conserved structure and molecular mechanism. *Nature* 349:117–27

13. Boyer JL, Waldo GL, Harden TK. 1992. βγ-subunit activation of G-protein-regulated phospholipase C. *J. Biol. Chem.* 267:25451–56

14. Cali JJ, Balcueva EA, Rybalkin I, Robishaw JD. 1992. Selective tissue distribution of G protein γ subunits including a new form of the γ subunits identified by cDNA cloning. *J. Biol. Chem.* 267:24023–27

15. Camps M, Carozzi A, Schnabel P, Scheer P, Parker PJ, Gierschik P. 1992. Isozyme-selective stimulation of phospholipase C-β2 by G protein βγ subunits. *Nature* 360:684–86

16. Camps M, Hou C, Sidiropoulos D, Stock JB, Jakobs KH, Gierschik P. 1992. Stimulation of phospholipase C by guanine-nucleotide-binding protein βγ subunits. *Eur. J. Biochem.* 206: 821–31

17. Carozzi A, Camps M, Gierschik P, Parker PJ. 1993. Activation of phosphatidylinositol lipid-specific phospholipase C-β3 by G-protein βγ subunits. *FEBS Lett.* 315:340–42

18. Carpenter, G. 1992. Receptor tyrosine kinase substrates; *src* homology domains and signal transduction. *FASEB J.* 6:3283–89

19. Carter RH, Park DJ, Rhee SG, Fearon DT. 1991. Tyrosine phosphorylation of phospholipase C induced by membrane immunoglobulin in B lymphocytes. *Proc. Natl. Acad. Sci. USA* 88:2745–49

20. Coggeshall KM, McHugh JC, Altman A. 1992. Predominant expression and activation-induced tyrosine phosphory-

lation of phospholipase C-γ2 in B lymphocytes. *Proc Natl. Acad. Sci. USA* 89:5660–64

21. Conklin BR, Bourne HR. 1993. Structural elements of G_α subunits that interact with $G_{\beta\gamma}$, receptors and effectors. *Cell* 73:631–41

22. Conklin BR, Chabre O, Wong YH, Federman AD, Bourne HR. 1992. Recombinant $G_{q\alpha}$: mutational activation and coupling to receptors and phospholipase C. *J. Biol. Chem.* 267:31–34

23. Conklin BR, Farfel Z, Lustig KD, Julius D, Bourne HR. 1993. Substitution of three amino acids switches receptor specificity of $G_{\alpha q}$ to that of $G_{i\alpha}$. *Nature* 363:274–76

24. Cotecchia S, Kobilka BK, Daniel KW, Nolan RD, Lapetina EY. 1990. Multiple second messenger pathways of α-adrenergic receptor subtypes expressed in eukaryotic cells. *J. Biol. Chem.* 265:63–69

25. Dolphin AC. 1991. Regulation of calcium channel activity by GTP binding proteins and second messengers. *Biochim. Biophys. Acta* 1091:68–80

26. Exton JH. 1988. The roles of calcium and phosphoinositides in the mechanisms of α_1-adrenergic and other agonists. *Rev. Physiol. Biochem. Pharmacol.* 111:118–224

27. Ferris CD, Snyder SH. 1992. Inositol 1,4,5-trisphosphate-activated calcium channels. *Annu. Rev. Physiol.* 54:469–88

28. Gao B, Gilman AG. 1991. Cloning and expression of a widely distributed (type IV) adenylyl cyclase. *Proc. Natl. Acad. Sci. USA* 88:10178–82

29. Gierschik P, Sidiropoulos D, Jakobs KH. 1989. Two distinct G_i-proteins mediate formyl peptide receptor signal transduction in human leukemia (HL-60) cells. *J. Biol. Chem.* 264:21470–73

30. Goldschmidt-Clermont PJ, Kim JW, Machesky LM, et al. 1991. Regulation of phospholipase Cγ by profilin and tyrosine phosphorylation. *Science* 251:1231–33

31. Granja C, Lin L-L, Yunis EJ, Relilas V. Dasgupta JD. 1991. PLCγ1, a possible mediator of T cell receptor function. *J. Biol. Chem.* 266:16277–80

32. Gutowski S, Smrcka A, Nowak L, Wu D, Simon M, Sternweis PC. 1991. Antibodies to the α_q subfamily of guanine nucleotide-binding regulatory protein α subunits attenuate activation of phosphatidylinositol 4,5-bisphosphate hydrolysis by hormones. *J. Biol. Chem.* 266:20519–24

32a. Hall CG, Sancho J, Terhost C. 1993.

Reconstitution of T cell receptor ζ-mediated calcium mobilization in nonlymphoid cells. *Science* 26:915–18

33. Heldin C-H. 1992. Structural and functional studies on platelet-derived growth factor. *EMBO J.* 11:4251–59

34. Hepler JR, Gilman AG. 1992. G proteins. *Trends Biochem. Sci.* 17:383–87

35. Iiri T, Tohkin M, Morishima N, Ohoka Y, Ui M. 1989. Chemotactic peptide receptor-supported ADP-ribosylation of a pertussis toxin substrate GTP-binding protein by cholera toxin in neutrophil-type HL-60 cells. *J. Biol. Chem.* 264: 21394–400

36. Iniguez-Lluhi JA, Simon MI, Robishaw JD, Gilman AG. 1992. G protein βγ βsubunits synthesized in Sf9 cells. Functional characterization and the significance of prenylation of γ. *J. Biol. Chem.* 267:23409–17

37. Irvine RF. 1992. Inositol phosphates and Ca^{2+} entry: toward a proliferation or a simplification? *FASEB J.* 6:3085–91

38. Jhon D-Y, Lee H-H, Park D, Lee C-W, Lee K-H, et al. 1993. Cloning, sequencing, purification and G_q-dependent activation of phospholipase C-β3. *J. Biol. Chem.* 268:6654–61

39. Johnson RM, Garrison JC. 1987. Epidermal growth factor and angiotensin sII stimulate formation of inositol 1,4,5- and inositol 1,3,4- trisphosate in hepatocytes. Differential inhibition by pertussis toxin and phorbol 12-myristate 13-acetate. *J. Biol. Chem.* 262: 17285–93

40. Katz A, Wu D, Simon MI. 1992. Subunits βγ of heterotrimeric G protein activate β2 isoform of phospholipase C. *Nature* 360:686–89

41. Kikuchi A, Kawaoa O, Kaibuchi K, Katada T, Ui M. 1986. Direct evidence for involvement of a guanine nucleotide-binding protein in chemotactic peptide-stimulated formation of inositol bisphosphate and trisphosphate in differentiated human leukemic (HL-60) cells. *J. Biol. Chem.* 261:11558–62

42. Kim HK, Kim JW, Zilberstein A, Margolis B, Kim JG. 1991. PDGF stimulation of inositol phospholipid hydrolysis requires PLC-γ1 phosphorylation on tyrosine residues 783 and 1254. *Cell* 65:435–41

43. Kleuss C, Hescheler J, Ewel C, Rosenthal W, Schultz G, Wittig B. 1991. Assignment of G-protein subtypes to specific receptors inducing inhibition of calcium currents. *Nature* 353:43–48

44. Kleuss C, Scherubl H, Hescheler J, Schultz G, Wittig B. 1992. Different β-subunits determine G-protein interaction with transmembrane receptors. *Nature* 358:424–26

45. Kleuss C, Scherubl H, Hescheler J, Schultz G, Wittig B. 1993. Selectivity of signal transduction determined by γ subunits of heterotrimeric G proteins. *Science* 259:832–34

46. Kobilka B. 1992. Adrenergic receptors as models for G protein-coupled receptors. *Annu. Rev. Neurosci.* 15:87–114

47. Lee CH, Park D, Wu D, Rhee SG, Simon MI. 1992. Members of the G_q α subunit gene family activate phospholipase C β isozymes. *J. Biol. Chem.* 267:16044–47

48. Lee Y-J, Dobbs MB, Verardi ML, Hyde DR. 1990. dgq: A *Drosophila* gene encoding a visual system-specific Gα molecule. *Nature* 5:889–98

49. Liang M, Garrison JC. 1992. Epidermal growth factor activates phospholipase C in rat hepatocytes via a different mechanism from that in A431 or Rat1hER cells. *Mol. Pharmacol.* 42:743–52

50. Liao F, Shin HS, Rhee SG. 1992. Tyrosine phosphorylation of phospholipase C-γ1 induced by cross-linking of the high-affinity or low-affinity Fc receptor for IgG in U937 cells. *Proc. Natl. Acad. Sci. USA* 89:3659–63

50a. Maurice DH, Waldo GL, Morris AJ, Nicholas RA, Harden TK. 1993. Identification of Gα11 as the phospholipase C-activating G-protein in turkey erythrocytes. *Biochem. J.* 290:765–70

51. Meldrum E, Parker PJ, Carozzi A. 1991. The PtdIns-PLC superfamily and signal transduction. *Biochim. Biophys. Acta* 1092:49–71

52. Moriarty TM, Padrell E, Carty DJ, Omri G, Landau M. 1990. G_o protein as a signal transducer in the pertussis toxin-sensitive phosphatidylinositol pathway. *Nature* 343:79–82

53. Mumby S, Pang I-H, Gilman AG, Sternweis PC. 1988. Chromatographic resolution and immunologic identification of the α40 and α41 subunits of guanine nucleotide-binding regulatory proteins from bovine brain. *J. Biol. Chem.* 263:2020–26

54. Nakamura F, Ogata K, Shiozaki K, Kameyama K, Ohara K, et al. 1991. Identification of two novel GTP-binding protein α-subunits that lack apparent ADP-ribosylation sites for pertussis toxin. *J. Biol. Chem.* 266:12676–81

55. Ostrowski J, Kjelsberg MA, Caron MG, Lefkowitz RJ. 1992. Mutagenesis of the β 2-adrenergic receptor: How structure elucidates function. *Annu. Rev. Pharmacol. Toxicol.* 32:167–83

56. Padrell E, Carty DJ, Moriarty TM, Hildebrand JD, Landau EM. 1991. Two forms of the bovine brain G_o that stimulate the inositol trisphosphate-mediated Cl⁻ currents in *Xenopus* oocytes. Distinct guanine nucleotide binding properties. *J. Biol. Chem.* 266:9771–77

57. Pang I-H, Sternweis PC. 1990. Purification of unique α subunits of GTP-binding regulatory proteins (G proteins) by affinity chromatography with immobilized βγ subunits. *J. Biol. Chem.* 265:18717–12

58. Park D, Jhon D-Y, Kriz R, Knopf J, Rhee SG. 1992. Cloning, sequencing, expression, and G q-independent activation of phospholipase C-β2. *J. Biol. Chem.* 267:16048–55

59. Park D, Jhon D-Y, Lee C-W, Lee C-H, Rhee SG. 1993. Activation of phospholipase C isozymes by G protein βγ subunits. *J. Biol. Chem.* 268:4573–76

60. Park D, Jhon D-Y, Lee C-W, Ryu S-H, Rhee SG. 1993. Removal of the carboxyl-terminal region of phospholipase C-β1 by calpain abolishes activation by Gαq. *J. Biol. Chem.* 268:3710–14

61. Park DJ, Min HK, Rhee SG. 1991. IgE-induced tyrosine phosphorylation of phospholipase C-γ1 in rat basophilic leukemia cells. *J. Biol. Chem.* 266:24237–40

62. Park DJ, Min HK, Rhee SG. 1992. Inhibition of CD3-linked phospholipase C by phorbol ester and by cAMP is associated with decreased phosphotyrosine and increased phosphoserine contents of PLC-γ1. *J. Biol. Chem.* 267:1496–01

62a. Park DJ, Rho HW, Rhee SG. 1991. CD3 stimulation causes phosphorylation of phospholipase C-γ1 on serine and tyrosine residues in a human T-cell line. *Proc. Natl. Acad. Sci. USA* 88:5453–56

63. Pawson T, Gish GD. 1992. SH2 and SH3 domains: from structure to function. *Cell* 71:359–62

64. Peralta EG, Ashkenazi A, Winslow JW, Ramachandran J. 1988. Differential regulation of PI hydrolysis and adenylate cyclase by muscarinic receptor subtypes. *Nature* 334:434–37

65. Polakis PG, Uhing RJ, Snyderman R. 1988. The formylpeptide chemoattractant receptor copurifies with a GTP-binding protein containing a distinct

40-kDa pertussis toxin substrate. *J. Biol. Chem.* 263:4969–76

66. Price SR, Tsai S-C, Adamik R, Angus W, Serventi IM. 1989. Expression of $G_{o\alpha}$ mRNA and protein in bovine tissues. *Biochemistry* 28:3803–7

67. Pronin AN, Gautam N. 1992. Interaction between G-protein β and γ subunit types is selective. *Proc. Natl. Acad. Sci. USA* 89:6220–24

68. Putney JW Jr. 1990. Capacitative calcium entry revisited. *Cell Calcium* 11:611–24

69. Rarick HM, Artemyev NO, Hamm HE. 1992. A site on rod G protein α subunit that mediates effector activation. *Science* 256:1031–33

70. Rhee SG, Choi KD. 1992. Regulation of inositol phospholipid-specific phospholipase C isozymes. *J. Biol. Chem.* 267:12393–96

71. Samelson LE, Klausner RD. 1992. Tyrosine kinases and tyrosine-based activation motifs. *J. Biol. Chem.* 267:24913–16

72. Savarese TM, Fraser CM. 1992. In vitro mutagenesis and the search for structure-function relationships among G protein-coupled receptors. *Biochem. J.* 283:1–19

73. Schäfer SO, Hoffman B, Bombien E, Spicher K. 1990. Agonist-sensitive binding of a photoreactive GTP analog to a G-protein α-subunit in membranes of HL-60 cells. *FEBS Lett.* 260:14–18

74. Schmidt CJ, Thomas TC, Levine MA, Neer EJ. 1992. Specificity of G protein β and γ subunit interactions. *J. Biol. Chem.* 267:13807–10

75. Secrist JP, Karnitz L, Abraham RT. 1991. T-cell antigen receptor ligations induces tyrosine phosphorylation of phospholipase C-γ1. *J. Biol. Chem.* 266:12135–39

76. Shaw K, Exton JH. 1992. Identification in bovine liver plasma membrane of a G_q-activatable phosphoinositide phospholipase C. *Biochemistry* 31:6347–54

77. Shenker A, Goldsmith P, Unson CG, Spiegel AM. 1991. The G protein coupled to the thromboxane A_2 receptor in human platelets is a member of the novel G_q family. *J. Biol. Chem.* 266:9309–13

78. Simon MI, Strathmann MP, Gautam N. 1991. Diversity of G proteins in signal transduction. *Science* 252:802–8

79. Smrcka AV, Hepler JR, Brown KO, Sternweis PC. 1991. Regulation of polyphosphoinositide-specific phospholipase C activity by purified G_q. *Science* 251:804–7

79a. Smrcka AV, Sternweis PC. 1993. Reg-

ulation of purified subtypes of phosphatidylinositol-specific phospholipase Cβ by G protein α and βγ subunits. *J. Biol. Chem.* 268:9667–74

80. Srivastava SP, Chen NQ, Liu YX, Holtzman JL. 1991. Purification and characterization of a new isozyme of thiol-protein-disulfide oxidoreductase from rat hepatic microsomes. Relationship of this isozyme to cytosolic phosphatidylinositol-specific phospholipase C form 1A. *J. Biol. Chem.* 266:20337–44

81. Strathmann M, Simon MI. 1990. G protein diversity: a distinct class of α subunits is present in vertebrates and invertebrates. *Proc. Natl. Acad. Sci. USA* 87:9113–17

82. Strathmann M, Wilkie TM, Simon MI. 1990. Alternative splicing produces transcripts encoding two forms of the α subunit of GTP-binding protein G_o. *Proc. Natl. Acad. Sci. USA* 87:6477–81

83. Tang W-J, Gilman AG. 1991. Type-specific regulation of adenylyl cyclase by G protein βγ subunits. *Science* 254:1500–3

83a. Taussig R, Iñiguez-Lluhi JA, Gilman AG. 1993. Inhibition of adenylyl cyclase by $G_{i\alpha}$. *Science* 261:218–21

84. Taussig R, Quarmby LM, Gilman AG. 1993. Regulation of purified type I and type II adenylylcyclases by G protein βγ subunits. *J. Biol. Chem.* 268:9–12

85. Taylor GD, Fee JA, Silbert DF, Hofmann SL. 1992. PI-specific phospholipase C "α" from sheep seminal vesicles is a proteolytic fragment of PI-PLCδ. *Biochem. Biophys. Res. Commun.* 188:1176–83

86. Taylor SJ, Chae HZ, Rhee SG, Exton JH. 1991. Activation of phospholipase C by α subunits of the G_q class of G proteins. *Nature* 350:516–18

87. Taylor SJ, Exton JH. 1991. Two α subunits of the G_q class of G proteins stimulate phosphoinositide phospholipase C-β1 activity. *FEBS Lett.* 286:214–16

88. Taylor SJ, Smith JA, Exton JH. 1990. Purification from bovine liver membranes of a guanine nucleotide-dependent activator of phosphoinositide-specific phospholipase C. Immunologic identification as a novel G-protein α subunit. *J. Biol. Chem.* 265:17150–56

89. von Weizsacker E, Strathmann MP, Simon MI. 1992. Diversity among the beta subunits of heterotrimer GTP-binding proteins: characterization of a novel

beta-subunit cDNA. *Biochem. Biophys. Res. Commun.* 183:350–56
90. Wahl MI, Jones GA, Nishibe S, Rhee SG, Carpenter G. 1992. Growth factor stimulation of phospholipase C-β1 activity. Comparative properties of control and activated enzymes. *J. Biol. Chem.* 267:10447–56
91. Waldo GL, Boyer JL, Morris AJ, Harden TK. 1991. Purification of an AlF4⁻ and G-protein βγ-subunit-regulated phospholipase C-activating protein. *J. Biol. Chem.* 266: 14217–25
92. Wange RL, Smrcka AV, Sternweis PC, Exton JH. 1991. Photoaffinity labeling of two rat liver plasma membrane proteins with [³²P]γ-azidoanilide GTP in response to vasopressin. *J. Biol. Chem.* 266:11409–12
93. Weiss A, Koretzky G, Schatzman RC, Kadlecek T. 1991. Functional activation of the T-cell antigen receptor induces tyrosine phosphorylation of phospholipase C-γ1. *Proc. Natl. Acad. Sci. USA* 88:5484–88
94. Wilkie TM, Scherle PA, Strathmann MP, Slepax VZ, Simon MI. 1991. Characterization of G-protein α subunits in the Gq class: expression in murine tissues and in stromal and

hematopoietic cell lines. *Proc. Natl. Acad. Sci. USA* 88:10049–53
95. Wu D, Jiang H, Katz A, Simon MI. 1993. Identification of critical regions on phospholipase C-β1 required for activation by G-proteins. *J. Biol. Chem.* 268:3704–9
96. Wu D, Katz A, Lee C-H, Simon MI. 1992. Activation of phospholipase C by α1-adrenergic receptors is mediated by the α subunits of Gq family. *J. Biol. Chem.* 267:25798–802
97. Wu D, Lee CH, Rhee SG, Simon MI. 1992. Activation of phospholipase C by the α subunits of the Gq and G11 proteins in transfected COS-7 cells. *J. Biol. Chem.* 267:1811–17
98. Yang L, Baffy G, Rhee SG, Manning D, Hansen CA, Williamson JR. 1991. Pertussis toxin-sensitive Gi protein involvement in epidermal growth factor-induced activation of phospholipase C-γ in rat hepatocytes. *J. Biol. Chem.* 266:22451–58
99. Yang L, Camoratto AM, Baffy G, Raj S, Manning DR, Williamson, JR. 1993. Epidermal growth factor-mediated signaling of Gi-protein to activation of phospholipases in rat-cultured hepatocytes. *J. Biol. Chem.* 268:3739–36

Annu. Rev. Physiol. 1994. 56:371–97
Copyright © 1994 by Annual Reviews Inc. All rights reserved

VESICLE TARGETING AND ION SECRETION IN EPITHELIAL CELLS:
Implications for Cystic Fibrosis

Andrew P. Morris

Department of Physiology and Cell Biology, and Gastroenterology, The University of Texas at Houston, Health Science Center, Medical School, 6431 Fannin St., Houston, Texas 77030

Raymond A. Frizzell

Department of Physiology and Biophysics, The University of Alabama at Birmingham, 1918 University Blvd., Birmingham, Alabama 35294

KEY WORDS: constitutive secretion, CFTR expression, transport, polarization, and targeting

INTRODUCTION

The asymmetric distribution of plasma membrane components is a fundamental characteristic of epithelial cells. The elucidation of the cellular mechanisms that establish and maintain spatial asymmetry (cellular polarization) continues to be the major quest of modern epithelial cell biology. The level of research activity and depth of our knowledge in this area is evident from the many detailed reviews published in recent years (17, 60, 87, 103, 130, 142, 143).

The ability of an epithelium to secrete or absorb fluid is intimately linked to the asymmetric distribution of ion transport processes within its membranes. The last ten years has seen the wide-spread application of high resolution electrophysiologic recording techniques to epithelial cells, which has led to detailed biophysical descriptions of many of the ion transport proteins involved in the conductive movements of ions across apical and basolateral membranes (31, 47, 145). As a result, epithelial cells have

371

0066–4278/94/0315–0371$05.00

become ideal subjects for studies that integrate our emerging knowledge of cellular biochemistry, molecular biology, and transport physiology.

A good example of the convergence of these different disciplines to provide a unique level of understanding of epithelial cell physiology is the progress made in our understanding of the disease cystic fibrosis (CF) and the cellular mechanisms that produce the CF phenotype. Modern molecular biological techniques have been used to elucidate the genetic basis of this disease, and the methods of epithelial transport and cell biology have provided the physiologist with the means to identify the underlying cellular defects produced by these genetic lesions. Normal and mutant versions of the translated gene product, the cystic fibrosis transmembrane conductance regulator (CFTR) (126, 131), when heterologously expressed in host cells, have been used to show that mutations in this protein are responsible for defective cAMP-mediated Cl^- secretion (40, 124). Moreover, some mutant forms of CFTR appear to be trapped early in the protein targeting pathway of host cells (21). This is true of the most common CFTR mutation, deletion of the phenylalanine residue at position 508 (ΔF508) of the protein. The frequency of this CFTR mutant (present on at least one allele in ~90% of CF patients) suggests that significant therapeutic potential lies in a better understanding of this targeting anomaly. Moreover, recent data suggest that CFTR itself is involved in the acute control of membrane traffic in epithelial cells (11). Because of these developments, we use CFTR as a model for interactions between epithelial ion transport and cell biology.

The purpose of this review is to integrate emerging concepts in the fields of cell biology and transport physiology in an attempt to provide an overview of the mechanisms whereby integral membrane ion transport proteins target to the appropriate membrane domains in epithelial cells. To accomplish this goal, we first identify the proteins that target to the specific apical or basolateral membrane domains and then summarize the current state of our understanding of the intracellular trafficking processes that lead to epithelial cell polarization.

Polarization of the Ion Transport Components

The polarized epithelial cell contains apical and basolateral membrane domains with unique protein and lipid compositions (142). In simple epithelia and in clonal, polarized epithelial cell lines, this composition is repeated in neighboring cells to form a contiguous, single cell layer that establishes the barrier and transport functions of the monolayer. The apical membrane of epithelial cells is generally endowed with microvilli that form a brush border. Restricted in location to this domain are various hydrolytic enzymes and carriers designed for oligo-peptide and oligo-saccharide digestion, and pro-teins responsible for solute and water transport. The asymmetric steady-state distribution of the hydrolytic enzymes of the kidney and intestine have historically provided the model system for studies of the sorting and trafficking mechanisms associated with the polarized phenotype (see earlier references; 17, 103, 129, 142). Of the proteins involved in ion transport, the amiloride-sensitive Na^+ channel and the H^+/K^+ ATPase are apically targeted (145–147). Recently, CFTR has been localized at the apical membranes of salt-secreting epithelial cells using both functional (98) and immunocytochemical methods (34, 100, 121).

The lateral and basal membranes of epithelial cells contact adjacent cells and the substratum, respectively, and contain a different complement of ion transport proteins. For example, in Cl^--secreting epithelial cells, the basolaterally located Na^+/K^+ ATPase provides the driving force required for the secondary active transport of chloride into the cell across the basolateral membrane and therefore maintains the cell-to-lumen electrochemical gradient required for Cl^- exit across the apical membrane by diffusion (46). Other examples of ion transport proteins that have been functionally localized to the basolateral membrane are the $Na^+/K^+/2Cl^-$ co-transporter and the Ca^{2+}-sensitive K^+ channel of salt-secreting epithelia (31).

At the morphological and functional levels, the segregation of membrane transport components is maintained by the presence of specific junctional complexes and cytoskeletal proteins that are also polarized within the cell. Central to the polarized epithelial phenotype is the formation of the tight junction, a circumferential ring found in the apical pole that acts as both a fence to the lateral diffusion of protein and lipids within the extracellular membrane leaflet (38) and as a gate between neighboring cells that controls the diffusional flow of ions through the paracellular pathway (85). The importance of the tight junction in the maintenance of cell polarity is highlighted by the effects of junctional disruption, which compromises the restricted distribution of membrane glycoproteins, and by the subsequent re-accumulation of these proteins in their correct sites upon the reinstatement of junctional integrity (for example, see 26).

The Role of the Cytoskeleton in the Control of Ion Secretion

The structural polarization of the surface membrane components is also reflected in the internal organization of epithelial cells. Microtubules are aligned in the apical-to-basal axis of the cell and provide a framework for the spatial organization of organelles and actin microfilaments (59). While it appears that microtubules play a role in the biogenesis of the apical membrane domain (1, 8), the extent to which they participate in the steady-state maintenance of the polarization of individual apical membrane proteins varies. Gilbert and colleagues (48) determined the effect of microtubule disruption by colchicine on the steady-state polarity index (PI, ratio of apical-to-basolateral membrane protein distribution) in Caco-2 cells. These authors found that colchicine had only a modest effect on the steady-state distribution of aminopeptidase N, a protein with a high PI value near 100. In contrast, colchicine had more severe effects on the PI values of proteins that were inherently more evenly distributed (e.g. dipeptidyl peptidase IV, PI ~10). In the case of both high and low PI proteins, colchicine delays the trafficking of proteins that reach the apical membrane directly as well as those that target indirectly via the basolateral membrane and transcytosis (see below). Nocodazole, another microtubule depolymerizing drug, perturbs both the direct and indirect trafficking of modestly polarized apical membrane hydrolases and was found to have much less effect on their long term steady-state distribution in these cells (89). Therefore, the extent to which microtubule disruption affects ion transport may depend upon the steady-state distribution of transport proteins, their mechanism of apical membrane targeting, and on the type of microtubule disruption conditions employed.

Actin microfilaments maintain the structural integrity of the cell wall and are associated with a diverse group of binding proteins, some of which physically anchor membrane proteins in place (e.g. the Na^+ channel or Na^+/K^+ ATPase; see 105). Within the apical pole of the cell, the actin microfilaments extend from the tips of the microvilli into a terminal web, which lies just below the membrane surface where the microtubules terminate (135). A mechanism for the movement of vesicles containing membrane proteins between the microtubule assembly and the brush border actin cytoskeleton has recently been proposed (44). Vesicles containing apically targeted glycoproteins isolated from the brush borders of epithelial cells were found to bind actin in an ATP-dependent manner and contain on their outer membranes the mechano-enzyme myosin I. The myosin I motor may, therefore, mediate vesicular trafficking within this sub-cellular compartment. This filamentous actin-protein network terminates laterally at the zonula adherens (intermediate junction) of the epithelial cell border. Lying apical to this network is the zonula occludens (tight junction), and basal to it are the maculae adherens (desmosomes) and gap junctions (59).

In contrast to the microtubules, the actin cytoskeleton appears to play a central role in the control of electrolyte secretion. However, its role in this process does not appear to involve the targeting and functional expression of the apical membrane cAMP-dependent CFTR Cl^- channel. Although depolymerization of the actin web appears to occur during Ca^{2+}- or cAMP-mediated exocytosis in exocrine cells (115), actin found within the apical terminal web of salt-secreting colonic epithelial cells is insensitive to Ca^{2+} and cAMP, second messengers for Cl^- secretion in epithelial cells. Stabilization of cellular actin by (NBD)-phallicidin treatment prevents cAMP-dependent, but not Ca^{2+}-dependent, Cl^- secretion. Yet this effect appears to be localized to the reorganization of actin within the basal pole of the cell (141). These findings suggest that the cytoskeleton interacts with Cl^- secretory mechanisms through the localized movement of a basolateral transport component of the Cl^- secretory pathway, probably the $Na^+/K^+/2Cl^-$ co-transporter (107).

Receptor and fluid phase endocytosis at the apical, but not the basolateral, membranes of MDCK cells is blocked selectively by cytochalasin D, a drug that induces actin depolymerization (52). The site of cytochalasin D interaction is at the level of the surface membrane clathrin-coated pit. The movement of endocytosed proteins associated with clathrin coats along the microvilli and from the apical membrane into the endocytotic pathway was inhibited by this drug. This suggests that the different membrane domains of polarized epithelial cells contain separate, actin-mediated motors for vesicle transport and recycling. Actin found near the basolateral membrane is primarily associated with the ankyrin/fodrin cytoskeleton, which serves to maintain the steady-state distribution of ion transport proteins such as the Na^+/K^+ ATPase (105). In contrast, apical actin appears to play a cytoarchitectural role in the biogenesis of the apical membrane through a myosin I-associated apical vesicular targeting pathway. Gottlieb and colleagues (52) have suggested that cytochalasin D may act at the actin/myosin I pool to limit the availability of membrane components needed for endocytosis. Forskolin-stimulated Cl^- secretion is not affected by short term incubation with this drug (A Morris & R Frizzell, unpublished observations). In light of the hypothesis of Gottlieb and colleagues, the effects of cytochalasin D on cAMP-dependent fluid secretion may be limited to a reduction in the rate of turnover of CFTR already present in the surface membrane. Modulation of the residency time of CFTR in the apical plasma membrane might have important consequences for the treatment of CF (see below).

Polarized Intracellular Movements of Glycoproteins in Epithelial Cells

DEFINITION OF TERMS   Plasma membrane proteins synthesized within the endoplasmic reticulum (ER) pass through a series of membranous intracellular compartments before arriving at their appropriate destinations (15). The mechanisms by which proteins move through these targeting pathways have been the focus of recent intense interest in cell biology. Evidence supporting the original notion (112) that proteins move though the cell in discrete vesicular packages has been confirmed repeatedly over the last two decades, and today many of the individual compartments of the protein secretory pathway are well characterized.

The intracellular trafficking (movement) of glycoproteins (65, 166) and glycophospholipids (170) from their sites of synthesis within the ER through the Golgi and into the plasma membrane occurs at rates that can be accounted for by bulk flow. Unlike proteins that are secreted by the cell, membrane proteins do not undergo condensation and storage for release by the regulated secretory pathway. Instead, they are inserted into their correct cellular membranes at densities that are unchanged during their passage through the cell. By definition, they are constitutively trafficked (18). When direction-ality is established for the trafficking of a membrane protein, then targeting has occurred. The information necessary to confer trafficking directionality, and hence the selective targeting of a protein to a specific vesicular membrane domain, is believed to be encoded in the protein structure. This information exists in the form of sorting signals that reside in the protein's primary amino acid sequence. The bulk of vesicular protein sorting (see below) appears to occur at the level of the *trans*-Golgi network (TGN), since it is from this structure that carrier vesicles containing basolaterally and apically destined proteins bifurcate (6, 55, 94). Existing evidence also suggests that a second site for glycoprotein sorting resides in epithelial cells at the level of the basolateral endosome vesicle pool (129).

The following three sections summarize developments in the area of protein targeting and sorting that are relevant to the polarized movement of constitutively secreted (membrane targeted) glycoproteins such as CFTR in epithelial cells.

PROTEIN TARGETING MECHANISMS CAN BE CELL-SPECIFIC   As originally hy-pothesized (43), epithelial cells appear to traffic proteins to the apical membrane either directly from the Golgi or indirectly through a transcytotic compartment via another membrane domain. However, the importance of these routes in the targeting of individual proteins appears to be both tissue- and cell-specific. For example, the apical membrane hydrolases dipeptidyl peptidase IV (DPPIV) and amino-peptidase N (ApN) are targeted directly from Golgi to apical membrane in canine kidney (MDCK) epithelial cells (84, 164), but both direct and indirect (via basolateral membrane transcytosis) mechanisms are utilized to target these proteins in porcine (LLC-PK1) kidney epithelial cells (83). MDCK cells may use both of these routes for the targeting of exogenously (104) and endogenously (12) expressed membrane proteins. The colonic epithelial cell line, Caco-2, targets DPPIV and ApN by both direct and indirect routes. Other apical membrane hydrolases, for instance sucrase isomaltase (SI) and alkaline phosphatase (AP), target directly from the Golgi to the apical membrane (73, 88).

It has been shown that a prokaryotic protein, when expressed heterolo-gously in MDCK and Caco-2 cell lines, achieves a different apical to basolateral membrane distribution in each of these cell types. Since this evolutionarily rudimentary molecule should not possess the sorting signals found in eukaryotic proteins, this difference in membrane distribution may reflect an inherent dominance of certain pathways for targeting membrane proteins that is cell-type-specific (149). Similarly, the human LDL receptor, when expressed in transgenic mice, is found in the apical membranes of kidney tubule cells, but in the basolateral membranes of hepatocytes and enterocytes (113). Sorting sequences, presumed to be present in these proteins so that they selectively target to apical or basolateral membranes, may be either used or ignored depending upon the cell type in which these proteins are expressed. This may be explained by cell-specific differences in the intracellular location of the targeting pathways (see section on sorting).

CFTR TARGETING DEPENDS ON EPITHELIAL CELL POLARIZATION   Electrophys-iological assays localize the CFTR Cl channel to the apical membrane domain of polarized colonocytes (e.g. the Cl.19A subclone of the HT-29 human colonic adenocarcinoma cell line), but in the same cell line, a cAMP-activated Cl conductance cannot be detected in the plasma membranes of unpolarized cells (98). This difference in cAMP-stimulated Cl^- conductance could not be accounted for by differences in either the efficacy of agonists in elevating cellular cAMP levels or in the level of CFTR mRNA or protein expression. In contrast, Ca^{2+}-mobilizing agonists were at least as effective at stimulating the Ca^{2+}-sensitive anion conductance in un-polarized cells as in their polarized counterparts. The biophysical charac-teristics of the cAMP-stimulated Cl^- channels found within the apical membranes of these cells matched those attributed to CFTR in heterologous expression systems (66, 124) and after reconstitution into planar lipid bilayers (4, 158). The Ca^{2+}-sensitive Cl^- channel recorded from both the polarized and unpolarized HT-29 cells has biophysical properties that clearly distin-guish it from CFTR (102).

The localization of CFTR to the apical membranes of these (101) and other polarized epithelial cells has been confirmed at the light and electron microscopic level (34, 121). In the same cells grown at sub-confluent densities, under conditions where contact with neighboring cells was absent or just forming (101), the location of CFTR was perinuclear. Thus the acquisition of cAMP-dependent Cl^- secretion, which requires the apical membrane targeting of CFTR in HT-29 colonocytes, coincides with the generation of cellular polarity. Interestingly, the extent of CFTR glycosyla-tion in the polarized and unpolarized cells was similar. This indicates that CFTR passes through Golgi glycoprocessing sites in both cell lines, but is retained, probably at the level of the TGN, in the unpolarized cells until tight junctions form.

SORTING MECHANISMS   The signals that ensure the polarized apical membrane targeting of constitutively trafficked proteins in epithelial cells are for the most part unknown. However, attempts have been made to describe sorting signals in viral glycoproteins that are trafficked to the apical membrane of virus-infected epithelial cells. The expression of apically-directed viral protein chimeras suggests that targeting information resides within the protein extracellular domains (25, 132, 150), but the targeting sequence(s) has not been identified. The lack of structural homology between amino acid sequences within this region has been taken to support the hypothesis that tertiary structure, rather than the primary amino acid sequence, may provide the sorting signal (130).

A study that exemplifies the complexity of the sorting mechanism at this level focused on the expression of chimeric integral membrane proteins in polarized LLC-PK1 epithelial cells. cDNA sequences from both the apical membrane gastric H^+/K^+ ATPase and the basolateral membrane Na^+/K^+ ATPase were fused to generate chimeras (51). These proteins are highly homologous, but they are normally maintained with high efficiency at their correct apical (H^+/K^+) and basolateral (Na^+/K^+) membrane locations. These authors found that both subunits of the H^+/K^+ ATPase encode signals for apical membrane localization, one of which appears to be an amino acid sequence located near the amino terminus of the α-subunit. It is shared with the colonic isoform of this protein, which is also apically polarized. However, this sequence is not shared with the nearly identical α-subunit of the Na^+/K^+ ATPase. The β-subunit of the H^+/K^+ ATPase was localized to the basolateral membrane of MDCK cells, but was expressed at the apical membranes in LLC-PK1 cells. In this proximal tubule-derived cell line, apical rather than basolateral membrane endocytosis predominates, presumably due to the cellular specialization required for protein and fluid absorption. Thus the authors argue that the sorting of the β-subunit corresponds to the functional background of these cell types, which are derived from different renal tubule segments. In support of this hypothesis, Gottardi & Caplan (51) suggest that this explains the differences in the cellular location of chimeric LDL receptors expressed in the kidney and intestine of mice (113, see above). Other cell-specific differences in plasma membrane protein expression may also be subject to this interpretation. However, the cellular mechanism responsible for the generation of differences in the surface expression of an heterologously expressed prokaryotic protein without any recognizable sorting signals (149) (see above) remains unknown.

The converse of the apical sorting hypothesis holds that proteins that do not contain specific apical sorting sequences in their extracellular domains are, by default, targeted to the basolateral membranes of polarized epithelial cells (125, 143). However, recent findings suggest that this idea requires modification. Basolateral as well as apical membrane glycoproteins contain sorting signals (13, 16, 61, 74). These signals appear to be located within the cytoplasmic domains of basolaterally-targeted proteins and, without them, such proteins are constitutively delivered to the apical membrane (for review see Matlin, 87). Basolateral sorting signals are related structurally to the tyrosine-containing motif of the coated pit localization signal, which suggests that these regions interact with the clathrin coats of the TGN. Recent evidence suggests that the basolateral membrane targeting signal is different from and independent of the endocytotic sorting signal (30, 90), although both are dependent on tyrosine residues for their activity.

The only direct evidence for a specific apical membrane targeting signal has come from studies of a small group of glycosyl-phosphatidylinositol (GPI) anchored proteins (79), whose apical membrane location coincides with the polarized distribution of glycolipids in the outer leaflet of the apical membrane (60). Recently, it was suggested that the sorting of these components occurs at the level of the TGN where both GPI-linked proteins and glycosphingolipids are targeted together to the apical plasma membrane (14). Based on the limited detergent solubility of these complexes compared to basolaterally destined vesicular compartments, a protein, VIP21, was isolated from apically-destined vesicles (72). VIP21 was shown recently to be homologous to caveolin (133), a major protein component of non-clathrin coated pits. VIP21 is postulated to recycle between the TGN and the apical membrane as a component of glycolipid-based apical membrane carrier vesicles. However, since VIP21/caveolin is not limited to the apical membrane, but is found also on the basolateral cell surface, the authors note that other protein interactions must be responsible for conferring targeting information (42). The slow kinetics of clathrin-independent endocytosis and the apparently long residency time for caveolae in the plasma membrane suggest that proteins carried by this pathway would not be subject to rapid membrane turnover (162). However, the fact that only a small fraction of apical membrane proteins appears to be GPI-linked argues that this does not serve as a general mechanism for apical targeting. Other pathways must be responsible for sorting the majority of apically-targeted transmembrane proteins, like CFTR.

Models now exist showing the presence of protein-specific sorting signals in both apical and basolateral membrane proteins. It remains to be determined whether these models can account for the asymmetric distribution of the majority of plasma membrane proteins in epithelial cells. The demonstration of cellular specificity of targeting pathways and the use or neglect of sorting signals by different cell types serve to highlight the gaps in our understanding of the role of specific sorting signals in the generation of cell polarity. This lack of uniformity also begs the question of whether there are other, as yet unrecognized, determinants of membrane protein asymmetry. It has been proposed that polarized epithelial cells use a combination of both targeting and selective retention mechanisms to generate membrane asymmetry. This hypothesis has centered around the finding that the basolateral membrane distribution of the Na^+/K^+ ATPase appears to be maintained by cytoskeletal elements (57, 105, 129).

PROTEINS INVOLVED IN VESICULAR TRANSPORT IN EPITHELIAL CELLS

The development of genetic, molecular, and biochemical approaches to identify the mechanisms of vesicular transport in yeast and mammalian cells has highlighted two types of protein interactions with intracellular transport vesicles. They are (*a*) proteins associated with the vesicle that are integral to their function as carriers, and (*b*) proteins that are implicated in the control of vesicle formation, movement, and fusion. Together, they form the membrane transport compartments (packages) in which constitutively trafficked plasma membrane proteins are carried through the cell. The former group consists of a broad range of proteins that form, or are associated with, vesicular coats. Thus far, they are identified in the ER and Golgi, are associated with transcytotic vesicles, or are part of the vesicular coats of the regulated secretory pathway. The second group of proteins represent candidates for the regulation of vesicular transport in both the constitutive and regulated secretory pathways. The best characterized of these are the low molecular weight G proteins of the *ras* superfamily, some of the subunits of the heterotrimeric G proteins, and proteins associated with the N-ethylmaleamide-sensitive vesicle fusion protein (NSF). Since the CFTR Cl^- channel is an integral membrane glycoprotein that does not appear to participate in the regulated macromolecular secretory pathway of epithelial cells (95), we focus on protein interactions found within the constitutive secretory pathway.

Vesicle-Associated Proteins of the Constitutive Trafficking Pathway

GOLGI TRANSPORT   The trafficking of proteins between the endoplasmic reticulum (ER) and Golgi appears to be mediated by non-clathrin coated vesicles. Cell-free intra-Golgi stacks have been assayed biochemically to define the identity of the protein·components of these non-clathrin coated vesicles (86, 140). Four major coat proteins were discovered: α-, β-, γ-, and δ-COP. These are found together with some less well characterized, lower molecular weight proteins, one of which is the GTP-binding protein

ADP-ribosylation factor, ARF (139). In particular, one coat protein, β-COP, has proven to be pivotal in enhancing our understanding of the cellular mechanisms of constitutive vesicle movements and the generation of models for vesicle trafficking within the endoplasmic reticulum and Golgi.

β-COP is reversibly dissociated from the Golgi stacks by the fungal metabolite, brefeldin A (BFA; 36). BFA prevents vesicle formation in vitro (111), blocks intra-Golgi vesicle transport (77), and therefore blocks constitutive protein targeting in many cell types including epithelial cells (82, 96, 156). The effects of BFA on intra-Golgi transport appear to involve G protein interactions since pretreatment with GTPγS or AlF^{4-} prevents the BFA-induced dissociation of β-COP from Golgi membranes (37). Lastly, the N-terminal amino acid sequence of β-COP has been shown to be structurally related to the N-terminal regions of clathrin adaptin (41, 140), which are known to auto-phosphorylate and promote clathrin-coated vesicle assembly in vitro (67). The COPs, however, do not appear to be able to self-assemble non-clathrin coated vesicles. β-COP binding, and hence intra-Golgi transport, is dependent upon cellular ATP levels (23). The cellular location of β-COP has recently been investigated in exocrine pancreatic cells, and the protein was found to be associated predominantly with the cis-Golgi cisternae (109). This supports the conclusions drawn from earlier biochemical studies, which indicate that this protein is involved in vesicle transport between the ER and the early Golgi compartments within cells.

TGN/ENDOSOMAL AND PLASMA MEMBRANE VESICLE TRANSPORT   In some cell lines, e.g. kangaroo rat kidney (PtK1) and canine kidney (MDCK) epithelial cells, BFA has little effect on β-COP binding and ER-to-Golgi vesicle transport. However, in these systems BFA affects more peripheral organelle transport events (62, 70). This finding led to the identification of a second site of BFA action in cells. However, our current understanding of this mechanism is complicated by what appear to be cell-specific effects of the drug.

In normal rat kidney (NRK) cells, BFA collapsed the TGN into a tubulo-vesicular structure lying near the microtubule organizing center (MTOC). In these cells, BFA did not redistribute TGN markers into earlier compartments of the protein secretory pathway (122). A similar phenomenon has been reported in MDCK cells, human skin fibroblasts, and baby hamster kidney (BHK) cells. In these cells, markers that usually recycle in clathrin-coated vesicles between the TGN and lysosomes appeared at higher than normal levels at the plasma membrane after BFA treatment (29, 169). Markers associated with the plasma membrane and early endosome pool were largely unaffected by BFA (168).

Recently, the membrane binding of a second vesicle-associated protein was shown to be altered by BFA, and this finding could explain its more distal targeting effects. In vivo, BFA has been shown to disrupt the membrane association of γ-adaptin in both intact and permeabilized NRK and African rat kidney (Vero) cells (128). γ-adaptin is part of the HA1 adapter complex of Golgi-associated clathrin-coated vesicles (114). The HA1 adapter complex is a heterotrimer consisting of γ and β adaptin subunits of molecular weight (M_r) 100–110 K, plus two other proteins of M_r 20 and 50 K. Similarly, the dissociation of clathrin from the *trans*-Golgi network has been reported in Madin-Darby bovine kidney (MDBK) and PtK1 epithelial cells, both of which have BFA-resistant Golgi (167). These studies showed that BFA did not alter the cellular distribution of α-adaptin, part of the plasma membrane HA2 adapter complex (composed of 100–110 K α and β-adaptins plus 17 and 50 K proteins). The mannose-6-phosphate receptor (M6PR) (see 169) binds to both the Golgi (HA1) and plasma membrane (HA2) adapter complexes (68). After BFA treatment, the M6PR appears at higher than normal levels in the plasma membranes. This can be explained by coalescence of the TGN and loss of its HA1-associated clathrin coats, which result in a spill-over of M6P receptors from the TGN-lysosomal pool into the sub-plasmalemma recycling HA2-associated clathrin vesicle pool. The sub-plasmalemma pool is still functional in the presence of BFA because it does not interact with the plasma membrane HA2 adapter complex.

For many plasma membrane recycling molecules, the picture in polarized epithelial cells is not as clear cut. BFA's inhibiting effect on epithelial transcytosis, in particular, is presently obscure. Damke and colleagues (29) found little effect of BFA on transferrin receptor (TfR) recycling at the basolateral membranes of polarized MDCK cells. In contrast, Wan et al (163) found that BFA caused a mis-sorting of TfRs that led to their transcytosis to the apical membrane. However, BFA did not affect trans-cytosis of the fluid phase endocytotic marker, horse radish peroxidase (HRP). In other studies, BFA was reported to stimulate basolateral-to-apical trans-cytosis of HRP in polarized MDCK cells and to stimulate apical endocytosis without affecting basolateral endocytosis (119). Further complicating this picture is the observation that BFA has been shown also to inhibit the apical-to-basolateral transcytosis of the heterologously expressed polymeric immunoglobulin receptor (pIgR) in polarized MDCK cells. This effect is independent of basolateral internalization, recycling, or degradation of pIgR (62). The following two paragraphs attempt to explain these discordant findings.

Endocytotic tracers that enter across both surfaces of a polarized epithelial cell usually mix in a common late endosome pool (9). For the case of pIgR transcytosis, Hunzinger and colleagues showed that an early transfer step in the transcytotic pathway is responsible for the BFA-induced inhibition of pIgR transcytosis. This step appeared to be proximal to the TfR-accessible basolateral early endosome, since the recycling of TfR and pIgR out of the basolateral early endosome was not affected by BFA. This suggests that BFA inhibits pIgR transfer into a later endosome pool where it is sorted for transcytosis to the apical membrane. On the other hand, the stimulation of TfR transcytosis by BFA (119) suggests the existence of extensive connections between the apical and basolateral membrane early endosome pools. In this context, Tooze & Hollinshead (159) recently demonstrated that, in the presence of BFA, transferrin and HRP rapidly and extensively load all of the tubulated early endosomes of cervix epithelioid (HeLa) and pituitary (AtT-20) cells. Thus it appears that early endosomes throughout the cell become functionally linked in the presence of BFA. The early endosome pool that becomes accessible to transcytosed TfR appears to be inaccessible to constitutively secreted proteins arising from the TGN (96, 152). Thus both the BFA induced mis-sorting of transferrin receptor and HRP into the same pool, and the connection of this pool with the apical membrane endosome pool, would account for the apparent stimulation of transcytosis of the early endosomal markers TfR and HRP and the apparent decrease in basolateral TfR recycling (by mass action), as reported by Wan, Prydz, and colleagues (119, 163). The inhibition of pIgR transcytosis by BFA can be explained by a block of late-to-early endosomal transport. pIgR enters a late endosomal pool and cannot progress either into the apical secretory pathway or recycle to basolateral early endosomes. On the other hand, stimulation of transcytosis of basolateral early endosomal markers by BFA probably reflects a functional connection between the early endosomal pools of the apical and basolateral membrane domains.

Functionally, the BFA-induced connection of the TGN with the early endosome pool appears to proceed in a fashion similar to that described for BFA-induced condensation of the ER/Golgi network. Both are energy-dependent and are facilitated by microtubule interactions (76, 122). BFA has since been shown to cause the collapse or condensation of lysosomal compartments in cells, while at the same time either inhibiting (78) or not altering (152, 168) TGN-to-lysosome and plasma membrane-to-lysosome vesicle transport. Condensation of the lysosomal vesicles is likewise energy- and microtubule-dependent and varies in extent between different cell lines. It is possible that many of the more peripheral effects of BFA on vesicle transport can be explained by the dissociation of γ-adaptin from the TGN clathrin-coated vesicle.

VESICULAR COATS OF THE TRANSCYTOTIC PATHWAY   The vesicular coats of the transcytotic pathway have not been identified. It is clear that proteins can be carried into this pathway at the basolateral membrane through receptor-mediated or fluid phase endocytosis, and this indicates that both clathrin and non-clathrin pathways are involved in the initial endocytic process. However, very few markers for transcytosing vesicles have been identified. An exception is the transcytotic vesicle-associated protein, TAP (153, 154). TAP appears to participate in the fusion of vesicles with the apical plasma membrane (see below), but is not involved in endosome/endosome or intra-Golgi fusion events. This protein is not recognized by antisera against β-COP and is not dissociated from membranes by BFA.

The Control of DPPIV and CFTR Targeting to Apical Membrane

The formation of large apical vesicular compartments in the region of the TGN after BFA treatment has been demonstrated in a variety of polarized epithelial cells (58, 99, 119). This site has been traditionally thought to be responsible for glycoprotein sorting in epithelia (55). Furthermore, BFA has been shown to inhibit the constitutive targeting, to the apical membrane, of a heterologously expressed apical hydrolase, dipeptidyl peptidase IV (DPPIV), in polarized MDCK epithelial cells (82). In this study, BFA did not affect the targeting of basolateral membrane resident proteins. Where apical targeting of DPPIV was inhibited by BFA, some of the hydrolase was mis-sorted to the basolateral membrane. Low and colleagues (82) found that the subsequent transcytosis of mis-sorted DPPIV from the basolateral to the apical membrane was also inhibited by BFA. Interestingly, following BFA removal only the constitutively secreted apical membrane DPPIV was hypersialated, while transcytosed DPPIV was not. Hypersialation has been reported also for the TGN-resident mannose-6-phosphate receptor (M6PR) during BFA treatment (22). The phenomenon of hypersialation arises within the collapsed TGN of BFA-treated cells (134). Therefore, these results predict that membrane glycoproteins inserted directly into the apical membrane are hypersialated in the presence of BFA through a longer residence time in the TGN. Glycoproteins that follow the indirect route (involving basolateral-to-apical transcytosis) apparently are not hypersialated in the presence of BFA because they do not re-enter the TGN. As discussed above, the effects of BFA on transcytosis could be related to the entry of these proteins into or out of the basolateral endosome compartment prior to their trafficking across the cell. It is not certain whether the effect of BFA on this compartment involves an interaction with γ-adaptin in clathrin-coated vesicles.

A peripherally located constitutive glycoprotein targeting pathway that is sensitive to BFA has been described in polarized epithelial cells (99). BFA reversibly inhibited the apical membrane cAMP-activated Cl⁻ conductance of Cl⁻secreting epithelial cells with a time-course similar to that predicted for the half-life of CFTR protein turnover (21). Further, CFTR was relocated from the apical membrane domain into large, subapical intracellular vesicles, which corresponded in location to the cell's microtubule organizing centers (MTOCs), a cellular marker for the TGN (122). The effects of drug treatment were specific for the apical membrane cAMP-stimulated Cl^- conductance; the Ca^{2+}-stimulated Cl^- conductance was unaltered.

These two examples raise the question whether TGN clathrin coats, specifically γ-adaptin binding, is utilized by epithelial cells for the presentation of constitutively targeted glycoproteins to the apical membrane surface or, whether another BFA-sensitive, non-clathrin pathway is also present at the cell periphery. There is currently no evidence for involvement of a third BFA-sensitive pathway, distinct from β-COP and γ-adaptin. It is likewise unclear whether the pathway responsible for apical membrane glycoprotein insertion overlaps with the BFA-sensitive basolateral-to-apical transcytotic pathway. In addition, there is no direct evidence for TGN clathrin mediation of the direct trafficking of glycoproteins that constitutively target to apical membrane. The apical membrane CFTR Cl channel has been localized to clathrin-coated vesicles in cAMP-responsive epithelial cells (10); however, it is not clear at present whether this is endocytosed CFTR, nascent CFTR of TGN origin, or both. Determination of whether adaptin is associated with clathrin-coated vesicles containing CFTR would settle this issue.

Constitutive-like Macromolecular Secretion

Clathrin-coated vesicles have been implicated in the control of constitutive-like macromolecular secretion from exocrine epithelial cells and a variety of other cell types (109). Constitutive-like secretion refers to the exocytosis of partially condensed secretory proteins that would normally be stored and released by agonists, but instead are continuously lost from the cell at a rate approximating the rate of bulk flow between the Golgi and the plasma membrane. Canavanine, a fungal amino acid that substitutes for arginine in translated proteins, blocks the constitutive-like secretion of the contents of immature secretory granules from pancreatic islet β cells. Regulated insulin secretion from mature secretory granules is not affected by canavanine (71). The block of constitutive-like secretion appears to occur at the level of the immature secretory granule, where the arginine substituted pro-insulin remains uncleaved by processing enzymes. As a result, the granules fail to mature (106). These immature secretory granules have been shown to retain their clathrin coats (110), which suggests that the transport blockade is linked to the retention, within the TGN, of the HA1-adaptin/clathrin complex. Recently, BFA was shown to block the constitutive-like secretion of sulfated secretogranin from immature secretory granules of adrenal pheochromocytoma (PC12) cells, but it did not affect the regulated secretion of preformed mature secretory granules (96). Thus in the case of constitutive-like immature granule secretion, it is likely that the cellular target for BFA is the TGN-associated γ-adaptin of the HA1-adaptin/clathrin complex. However, it is not likely that the HA1 adapter complex itself contains the signals for the specific sorting of immature secretory proteins at the level of the TGN. γ-adaptin has a widespread cellular distribution; it will also bind proteins targeted to the basolateral membrane and those subject to endocytosis (see above) (49).

Recent studies have shown that the plasma membrane expression and recycling of the insulin regulated glucose transporter (GLUT-4) in insulin secreting β-cells is unaffected by BFA (19). This confirms the lack of effect of BFA on regulated secretory phenomena, since GLUT-4 is an integral membrane protein that is concentrated in regulated secretory vesicles. The exocytotic membrane targeting and endocytotic recycling of this transporter is critically regulated by hormonal stimulation at the level of the plasma membrane/clathrin-coated endosome pool in neurons and adipocytes. When transfected into non-neuronal cells, GLUT-4 localizes to the constitutively recycling early endosomes, but does not enter a functionally distinct, regulated endosomal compartment like that seen in neurons or adipocytes (117, 127, 144).

PROTEINS INVOLVED IN THE CONTROL OF CONSTITUTIVE VESICULAR TRANSPORT

Cell-free (160) and permeabilized cell (54, 97) assays have demonstrated that both immature secretory granule secretion and constitutive protein transfer between the TGN and the plasma membrane is inhibited by GTPβS and requires ATP and other cytoplasmic factors. Similarly, it is known that GTPγS blocks transport between the ER and Golgi (5), within Golgi compartments (93), and within endosomal compartments (91, 92). G proteins have therefore been implicated at all stages of the vesicular targeting pathway.

Monomeric G proteins

The proteins that are best characterized for their regulation of vesicular trafficking between discrete cellular compartments are the *ras* superfamily of monomeric G proteins. These proteins were identified by their homology to the YPT1 and SEC genes, in which mutations produce defects in protein transport and sorting in yeast. Many detailed reviews have documented the genetic and biochemical approaches that have identified the GTPases involved in vesicle traffic (56, 120, 155). Rab GTPases are thought to be involved in vesicle targeting and/or vesicle fusion. There is a considerable amount of morphological evidence localizing specific rab proteins to different intracellular compartments (2, 20, 53, 56). Recent studies have employed cell-free assays to identify a requirement for rab proteins in vesicle fusion within the ER (118, 123, 138), in vesicle transit between the early endosome and plasma membrane (rab 5; 50), in synaptic vesicle exocytosis (rab3A; 45), in the recycling of early endosomes (rab 4; 161), and in vesicle transfer between the late endosomes and the TGN (rab9; 80). Nevertheless, to date an epithelial cell-specific role for rab proteins in apical vesicle targeting has not been demonstrated. This suggests that while rabs play an essential role in the regulation of intra-vesicular transport in all cell types, the asymmetric distribution of ion transporting components in epithelial cells may depend upon other mechanisms.

In addition to the monomeric rab-like G proteins, another group of small molecular weight G proteins, originally isolated from genetic analysis of the yeast SAR1 gene, appears to be involved in the control of vesicle formation from donor membranes (32, 33, 108, 114). The mammalian homologue of SAR1 is a member of the ADP-ribosylation factor (ARF) family of small GTPases (64). These proteins are structural components of the non-clathrin coated, Golgi-derived vesicles (see above). GTP-dependent ARF binding to these vesicles is independent of vesicle budding and is thought to occur through interaction with an unidentified vesicle-associated nucleotide exchange protein. Based on its role as a cofactor in the cholera toxin-induced ADP-ribosylation of the heterotrimeric G protein α-subunit of Gs, ARF has been postulated to be a site of heterotrimeric G protein involvement in vesicle transport (139). BFA, which inhibits the effects of GTPγS in cell-free Golgi assays (111), has been shown to dissociate β-COP and ARF from Golgi-membranes (35). More recently, two ARF-like proteins have been identified as the site of GTPγS sensitivity in cell-free intra-Golgi transport assays (157). Since BFA does not affect fusion, but inhibits both ARF and β-COP binding, these studies predict that ARF's role in the control of vesicle transport is at the level of vesicle formation.

Heterotrimeric G proteins

In addition to monomeric G proteins, recent studies have demonstrated that heterotrimeric G proteins are involved in the control of constitutive vesicle movement. The heterotrimeric G protein activator, AlF^{4-} (63), appears to mimic the GTPγS inhibitory effect on intra-Golgi transport (93) and on endosome fusion (92, 165). More recent studies have shown that AlF^{4-} inhibits the formation of constitutive and immature secretory vesicles by the isolated TGN. Large amounts of purified heterotrimeric G protein $\beta\gamma$-subunits have been found to promote vesicle formation, which directly implicates a heterotrimeric G protein α-subunit in the control of vesicle formation (3). Further, Barr and colleagues have since shown that the addition of activated pertussis toxin results in the accumulation of metabolically labeled Gαi3 and stimulates constitutive and immature secretory granule secretion. The bee venom toxin, mastoparan, mimics receptor-activated nucleotide exchange by the Gαi/o subunits and holds them in their active (GTP bound) conformation. Mastoparan inhibits vesicular secretion. Conversely, activated cholera toxin stimulates both constitutive and immature secretory granule formation from the TGN preparation (75). The ADP-ribosylation of the Gαi/o subunit by pertussis toxin inhibits their interaction with effector proteins, while cholera toxin-induced ADP-ribosylation of the Gαs subunit results in the constitutive activation of their substrate effectors of Gαs (e.g. adenylate cyclase). Thus these authors have demonstrated that both inhibitory and stimulatory heterotrimeric α-subunits participate in TGN vesicle formation. By extension of these findings to other vesicular compartments, βγ-subunits have been shown to reverse the stimulatory effects of GTPγS on endosome fusion (24) and to interfere with ARF and β-COP binding to Golgi membranes (35). Mastoparan, which inhibits endosome fusion (see Colombo, 24), antagonizes the effects of BFA in permeabilized cells and promotes β-COP binding in vitro (69). Morphological evidence has linked these findings to vectorial glycoprotein trafficking in polarized epithelial cells by localizing the Gαi3 subunit to the Golgi membranes of LLC-PK1 cells. Further, the over-expression of Gαi3 inhibits basolateral secretion of heparin sulfate proteoglycan, an effect that can be reversed by pertussis toxin (151).

Further, heterotrimeric G proteins have been shown to affect the direction of vesicular targeting in epithelial cells. The direct targeting of apical glycoprotein in MDCK cells was facilitated by cholera toxin (CTX), while basolaterally directed vesicular transport was unchanged. Antibodies against Gs specifically inhibited TGN-to-apical membrane vesicular trafficking, while earlier stages in the secretory pathway were found to function normally. In contrast, treatment with pertussis toxin resulted in increased basolateral protein secretion without a corresponding effect on apical membrane glycoprotein transport (116). Thus the control of apical membrane glycoprotein targeting in epithelial cells appears to be governed not by monomeric G proteins, but by heterotrimeric Gαs. Since ARF-like proteins also appear to be involved in controlling vesicle coat formation (139, 157), it will be interesting to see whether the effects of Gαs are mediated by interaction with one of these monomeric G proteins.

In the context of CFTR-mediated Cl⁻ secretion, Schwiebert and colleagues recently demonstrated that pertussis toxin can activate Cl⁻ currents and restore cAMP-dependent Cl⁻channel activity in CF nasal epithelial cells. In normal airway cells, GTPγS and AlF^{4-} inhibited cAMP activation of Cl$^-$ currents (137). These studies were carried out using the whole-cell patch-clamp technique, which requires that individual cells are electrically isolated from each other, thus the degree of polarization present in these cells would be minimal. As described above, heterologously expressed mutant CFTR may become trapped early in the protein secretory pathway of host cells (22). Accordingly, modification of protein trafficking mechanisms might be expected to relieve the block in mutant CFTR progression through the targeting pathway. Schwiebert (137) demonstrated that pretreatment of CF cell lines with pertussis toxin (PTX) evoked cAMP-stimulated Cl conductance where none was present before PTX treatment. The stimulation of constitutive intracellular vesicle transport by PTX-induced ADP-ribosylation of a Gαi/o protein, in a manner consistent with the observations of Leyte and colleagues (75) and Pimplikar & Simons (116), is likely to explain these findings. In some expression systems (28, 39), this restriction on targeting of mutant protein is presumably not as strict, since mutant CFTR function is observed without PTX treatment. Some biochemical studies (136, 171) have also detected mutant CFTR in the same plasma membrane fractions as in cells that express wild-type CFTR. Nevertheless, there appears to be a class of CFTR mutations that are not trafficked optimally. It will be interesting and potentially important to identify the rate-limiting steps in the protein secretory pathway that are responsible for this apparent heterotrimeric G protein-mediated restriction on CFTR targeting.

Other Proteins

A number of proteins required for vesicle fusion have been identified using in vitro assays measuring exchange of markers between Golgi compartments (7). They include the N-ethylmaleamide-sensitive fusion protein (NSF) and soluble accessory proteins (SNAPs) of the NSF-proteinaceous complex. NSF binding to vesicle membranes is mediated by these accessory proteins, which have been identified, from salt-washed brain membranes, as members of the syntaxin and synaptobrevin protein families (148). Rothman and colleagues have postulated that specificity for membrane fusion could be generated by differences in vesicle (donor) and target (acceptor) receptors within the SNAP/NSF complex. This hypothesis is supported by the localization of synaptobrevin to (donor) vesicles and of syntaxin on the plasma membrane (acceptor) of neuronal terminals. This arrangement was proposed by these investigators to reflect a universal mechanism for regulating the fusion process. This hypothesis is supported by ER and Golgi exchange assays in which the NSF complex is required for vesicle fusion. In addition, transcytotic-associated vesicle (TAP) fusion has likewise been shown to require a N-ethylmaleamide-sensitive factor (153). With this in mind, and in light of TAP's donor role in mediating the fusion of transcytotic vesicles with the apical membrane, TAP could conceivably act as a vesicle receptor for the SNAP/NSF complex in epithelial cells.

Other examples of a common mechanistic basis for vesicular fusion also exist. Recently, synaptobrevin was shown to be associated with the plasma membrane recycling endosomal vesicles that contain the insulin-regulated glucose transporter (GLUT-4) in pancreatic islet cells (27). Thus synaptobrevin may facilitate the regulated fusion of GLUT-4 containing vesicles to the plasma membrane. As discussed by Rothman and colleagues (148), this concept could provide, at the level of donor membrane fusion, a physical means of generating specificity for the routing of glycoproteins between the intracellular compartments of the cell. Hence, in an epithelial cell, the polarized distribution of apical and basolateral glycoproteins may reflect both the presence of specialized, protein-specific sorting/retention signals and a unique complement of vesicle/organelle-specific receptor and acceptor signals for targeted fusion.

SUMMARY

The cellular mechanisms that lead to the asymmetric distribution of ion transport proteins and the capacity for cAMP-stimulated Cl^- secretion at the cell and organelle level are beginning to emerge. Testable models exist for many of the steps involved in the generation and maintenance of epithelial plasma membrane protein asymmetry. The challenge today for the cellular physiologist is to integrate these findings into an understanding of epithelial targeting phenomena and the manner in which these mechanisms are altered by disease states.

ACKNOWLEDGMENTS

The authors thank Jan Tidwell for preparation of the manuscript. APM and RAF were supported by grants from the National Institutes of Health (DK31091, DK38518, DK41330) and the Cystic Fibrosis Foundation.

Literature Cited

1. Achler C, Filmer D, Merte C, Drenckhahn D. 1989. Role of microtubules in polarized delivery of apical membrane proteins to the brush border of the intestinal epithelium. *J. Cell Biol.* 109:179–89

2. Balch WE. 1990. Small GTP-binding proteins in vesicular transport. *Trends Biochem. Sci.* 15(12):473–77

3. Barr FA, Leyte A, Mollner S, Pfeuffer T, Tooze SA, Huttner WB. 1991. Trimeric G-proteins of the *trans*-Golgi network are involved in the formation of constitutive secretory vesicles and immature secretory granules. *FEBS Lett.* 294(3):239–43

4. Bear CE, Li CH, Kartner N, Bridges RJ, Jensen TJ, et al. 1992. Purification

and functional reconstitution of the cystic fibrosis transmembrane conductance regulator (CFTR). *Cell* 68:809–18

5. Beckers CJ, Balch WE. 1989. Calcium and GTP: essential components in vesicular trafficking between the endoplasmic reticulum and Golgi apparatus. *J. Cell Biol.* 108:1245–56

6. Bennett MK, Wandinger-Ness A, Simons K. 1988. Release of putative exocytic transport vesicles from perforated MDCK cells. *EMBO J.* 7:4075–85

7. Block MR, Glick BS, Wilcox CA, Wieland FT, Rothman JE. 1988. Purification of an N-ethylmaleimide-sensitive protein catalyzing vesicular transport. *Proc. Natl. Acad. Sci. USA* 85:7852–56

8. Bloom GS. 1992. Motor proteins for cytoplasmic microtubules [published erratum, appears in *Curr. Opin. Cell Biol.* 4(3):502, 1992]. *Curr. Opin. Cell Biol.* 4:66–73

9. Bomsel M, Prydz K, Parton RG, Gruenberg J, Simons K. 1989. Endocytosis in filter-grown Madin-Darby canine kidney cells. *J. Cell Biol.* 109: 3243–58

10. Bradbury NA, Cohn JA, Venglarik CJ, Bridges RJ. 1992. CFTR is in clathrin coated vesicles. *Ped. Pulm. Suppl.* 2A (Abstr)

11. Bradbury NA, Jilling T, Berta G, Sorscher EJ, Bridges RJ, Kirk KL. 1992. Regulation of plasma membrane recycling by CFTR. *Science* 256:530–32

12. Brandli AW, Parton RG, Simons K. 1990. Transcytosis in MDCK cells: identification of glycoproteins transported bidirectionally between both plasma membrane domains. *J. Cell Biol.* 111:2909–21

13. Brewer CB, Roth MG. 1991. A single amino acid change in the cytoplasmic domain alters the polarized delivery of influenza virus hemagglutinin. *J. Cell Biol.* 24 114:413–21

14. Brown DA, Rose JK. 1992. Sorting of GPI-anchored proteins to glycolipid-enriched membrane subdomains during transport to the apical cell surface. *Cell* 68:533–44

15. Burgess TL, Kelly RB. 1987. Constitutive and regulated secretion of proteins. *Annu. Rev. Cell Biol.* 3:243–93

16. Casanova JE, Apodaca G, Mostov KE. 1991. An autonomous signal for basolateral sorting in the cytoplasmic domain of the polymeric immunoglobulin receptor. *Cell* 66:65–75

17. Cereijido M, Contreras RG, Gonzalez-

Mariscal L. 1989. Development and alteration of polarity. *Annu. Rev. Physiol.* 51:785–95

18. Chanat E, Huttner WB. 1991. Milieu-induced, selective aggregation of regulated secretory proteins in the *trans*-Golgi network. *J. Cell Biol.* 115(6): 1505–19

19. Chakrabarti AR, Buxton J, Czech M, Corvera S. 1992. Insulin-sensitive association of Glut-4 with endocytotic clathrin-coated vesicles evidenced by the actions of brefeldin A. *Mol. Biol. Cell* 3:330A (Abstr.)

20. Chavrier P, Parton RG, Hauri HP, Simons K, Zerial M. 1990. Localization of low molecular weight GTP binding proteins to exocytic and endocytic compartments. *Cell* 62(2):317–29

21. Cheng SH, Gregory RJ, Marshall J, Paul S, Souza DW, et al. 1990. Defective intracellular transport and processing of CFTR is the molecular basis of most cystic fibrosis. *Cell* 63:827–34

22. Chenge NW, Pfeffer SR. 1990. Compartmentalization of the Golgi complex: brefeldin A distinguishes *trans*-Golgi cisternae from the *trans*-Golgi network. *J. Cell Biol.* 111:893–99

23. Cluett EB, Wood SA, Banta M, Brown WJ. 1993. Tubulation of Golgi membranes in vivo and in vitro in the absence of brefeldin A. *J. Cell Biol.* 120:15–24

24. Colombo MI, Mayorga LS, Casey PJ, Stahl PD. 1992. Evidence of a role for heterotrimeric GTP-binding proteins in endosome fusion. *Science* 255:1695–97

25. Compton T, Ivanov IE, Gottlieb T, Rindler M, Adesnik M, Sabatini DD. 1989. A sorting signal for the basolateral delivery of the vesicular stomatis virus (VSV) G protein lies in its luminal domain: analysis of the targeting of VSVg G-influenza hemagglutinin chimeras. *Proc. Natl. Acad. Sci. USA* 86:4112–16

26. Contreras RG, Gonzalez-Mariscal L, Balda MS, Garcia-Villegas MR, Cereijido M. 1992. The role of calcium in the making of a transporting epithelium. *News Physiol. Sci.* 7:105–8

27. Corley-Cain C, Trimble WS, Liendard GE. 1992. Members of the VAMP family of synaptic vesicle proteins are components of glucose transport-containing vesicles from rat adipocytes. *J. Biol. Chem.* 267:11681–84

28. Dalemans W, Barby P, Champigny G, Jallat S, Dott K, et al. 1991. Altered chloride ion channel kinetics associated

with the delta F508 cystic fibrosis mutation. *Nature* 354(6354):526–8

29. Damke H, Klumperman J, von Figura K, Braulke T. 1991. Effects of brefeldin A on the endocytic route. Redistribution of mannose 6-phosphate/insulin-like growth factor II receptors to the cell surface. *J. Biol. Chem.* 266(36):24829–33

30. Dargemont C, le Bivic A, Rothenberger S, Lacopetta B, Kuhn LC. 1993. The internalization signal and the phosphorylation site of transferrin receptor are distinct from the main basolateral sorting information. *EMBO J.* 12(4):1713–21

31. Dawson DC. 1991. Ion channels and colonic salt transport. *Annu. Rev. Physiol.* 53:321–39

32. d'Enfert C, Gensse M, Gaillardin C. 1992. Fission yeast and a plant have functional homologues of the Sar1 and Sec12 proteins involved in ER to Golgi traffic in budding yeast. *EMBO J.* 11(11):4205–11

33. d'Enfert C, Wuestehube LJ, Lila T, Schekman R. 1991. Sec12p-dependent membrane binding of the small GTP-binding protein Sar1p promotes formation of transport vesicles from the ER. *J. Cell Biol.* 114(4):663–70

34. Denning G, Ostedgaard LS, Cheng SH, Smith AE, Welsh MJ. 1992. Localization of cystic fibrosis transmembrane conductance regulator in chloride secretory epithelia. *J. Clin. Invest.* 89:339–49

35. Donaldson JG, Kahn RA, Lippincott-Schwartz J, Klausner RD. 1991. Binding of ARF and beta-COP to Golgi membranes: possible regulation by a trimeric G protein. *Science* 254:1197–99

36. Donaldson JG, Lippincott-Schwartz J, Bloom GS, Kreis TE, Klausner RD. 1990. Dissociation of a 110-kD peripheral membrane protein from the Golgi apparatus is an early event in brefeldin A action. *J. Cell Biol.* 111:2295–306

37. Donaldson JG, Lippincott-Schwartz J, Klausner RD. 1991. Guanine nucleotides modulate the effects of brefeldin A in semipermeable cells: regulation of the association of a 110-kD peripheral membrane protein with the Golgi apparatus. *J. Cell Biol.* 112:579–88

38. Dragsten PR, Blumenthal R, Handler JS. 1981. Membrane asymmetry in epithelia: is the tight junction a barrier to diffusion in plasma membrane. *Nature* 294:718–22

39. Drumm ML, Pope HA, Cliff WH,

Rommens JM, Marvin SA, et al. 1990. Correction of the cystic fibrosis defect in vitro by retrovirus-mediated gene transfer. *Cell* 62(6):1227–33

40. Drumm ML, Wilkinson DS, Smit LS, Worrell RT, Strong TV, et al. 1991. Chloride conductance expressed by delta F508 and other mutant CFTRs in *Xenopus* oocytes. *Science* 254(5039):1797–99

41. Duden R, Griffiths G, Frank R, Argos P, Kreis TE. 1991. β-COP a 110 kd protein associated with non-clathrin coated vesicles and the Golgi complex shows homology to β-adaptin. *Cell* 64:649–65

42. Dupree P, Parton RG, Raposo G, Kurchalia TV, Simons K. 1993. Caveolae and sorting in the trans-Golgi network of epithelial cells. *EMBO J.* 12(4):1597–605

43. Evans WH. 1980. A biochemical dissection of the functional polarity of the plasma membrane of the hepatocyte. *Biochim. Biophys. Acta* 604:27–64

44. Fath KR, Burgess DR. 1993. Golgi-derived vesicles from developing epithelial cells bind actin filaments and possess myosin-I as a cytoplasmically oriented peripheral membrane protein. *J. Cell Biol.* 120:117–27

45. Fischer von Mollard G, Sudhof TC, Jahn R. 1991. A small GTP-binding protein dissociates from synaptic vesicles during exocytosis. *Nature* 349(6304):79–81

46. Frizzell RA, Field M, Schultz SG. 1979. Sodium coupled chloride transport by epithelial tissues. *Am. J. Physiol.* 236(5):F1–8

47. Frizzell RA, Halm DR. 1990. Chloride channels in epithelial cells. In *Current Topics in Membrane Transport: Channels, Noise and Impedance in Epithelia*, ed. SI Helman, W Van Driessche, 8:247–82. New York: Academic

48. Gilbert T, LeBivic A, Quaroni A, Rodriguez-Boulan E. 1991. Microtubular organization and its involvement in the biogenetic pathways of plasma membrane proteins in Caco-2 intestinal epithelial cells. *J. Cell Biol.* 113(2):275–88

49. Glickman JN, Conibear E, Pearse BM. 1989. Specificity of binding of clathrin adaptors to signals on the mannose-6-phosphate/insulin-like growth factor II receptor. *EMBO J.* 8:1041–47

50. Gorvel JP, Chavrier P, Zerial M, Gruenberg J. 1991. Rab5 controls early endosome fusion in vitro. *Cell* 64:915–25

51. Gottardi CJ, Caplan MJ. 1993. An ion-transporting ATPase encodes multiple apical localization signals. *J. Cell Biol.* 121(2):283–93

52. Gottlieb TA, Ivanov IE, Adesnik M, Sabatini DD. 1993. Actin microfilaments play a critical role in endocytosis at the apical but not the basolateral surface of polarized epithelial cells. *J. Cell Biol.* 120:695–710

53. Gould B, McCaffrey M. 1991. Small GTP-binding proteins and their role in transport. *Curr. Opin. Cell Biol.* 3: 626–33

54. Gravotta D, Adesnik M, Sabatini DD. 1990. Transport of influenza HA from the *trans*-Golgi network to the apical surface of MDCK cells permeabilized in their basolateral plasma membranes: energy dependence and involvement of GTP-binding proteins. *J. Cell Biol.* 111(6 Pt2):2893–90

55. Griffiths G, Simons K. 1986. The *trans* Golgi network: sorting at the exit site of the Golgi complex. *Science* 234(4775):438–43

56. Gruenberg J, Clague MJ. 1992. Regulation of intracellular membrane transport. *Curr. Opin. Cell Biol.* 4:593–99

57. Gundersen D, Orlowski J, Rodriguez-Boulan E. 1991. Apical polarity of Na,K-ATPase in retinal pigment epithelium is linked to a reversal of the ankyrin-fodrin submembrane cytoskeleton. *J. Cell Biol.* 112:863–72

58. Hendricks LC, McCaffery M, Palade GE, Farquhar MG. 1992. Dissociated β-COP accumulates in large sedimentable aggregates in BFA or N2-treated pancreatic exocrine cells (PEC). *Mol. Biol. Cell* 3:A1279

59. Ho SB. 1992. Cytoskeleton and other differentiation markers in the colon. *J. Cell. Biochem. Suppl.* 16G:119–28

60. Hopkins CR. 1991. Polarity signals. *Cell* 66:827–29

61. Hunziker W, Harter C, Matter K, Mellman I. 1991. Basolateral sorting in MDCK cells requires a distinct cytoplasmic domain determinant. *Cell* 66:907–20

62. Hunziker W, Whitney JA, Mellman I. 1991. Selective inhibition of transcytosis by brefeldin A in MDCK cells. *Cell* 67:617–27

63. Kahn RA. 1991. Fluoride is not an activator of the smaller (20–25 kDa) GTP-binding proteins. *J. Biol. Chem.* 266(24):15595–97

64. Kahn RA, Kern FG, Clark J, Gelmann EP, Rulka C. 1991. Human ADP-ribosylation factors. A functionally conserved family of GTP-binding proteins. *J. Biol. Chem.* 266(4):2606–14

65. Karrenbauer A, Jeckel D, Just W, Birk R, Schmidt RR, et al. 1990. The rate of bulk flow from the Golgi to the plasma membrane. *Cell* 63:259–67

66. Kartner N, Hanrahan JW, Jensen TJ, Naismith AL, Sun SZ, et al. 1991. Expression of the cystic fibrosis gene in non-epithelial invertebrate cells produces a regulated anion conductance. *Cell* 64(4):681–91

67. Keen JH, Chestnut MH, Beck KA. 1987. The clathrin coat assembly polypeptide complex: autophosphorylation and assembly activities. *J. Biol. Chem.* 262:3864–71

68. Kornfield S, Mellman I. 1989. The biogenesis of lysosomes. *Annu. Rev. Cell Biol.* 5:483–525

69. Ktistakis NT, Linder ME, Roth MG. 1992. Action of brefeldin A blocked by activation of a pertussis-toxin-sensitive G protein. *Nature* 356(6367): 344–46

70. Ktistakis NT, Roth MG, Bloom GS. 1991. PtK1 cells contain a nondiffusible, dominant factor that makes the Golgi apparatus resistant to brefeldin A. *J. Cell Biol.* 113(5):1009–23

71. Kuliawat R, Arvan P. 1992. Protein targeting via the "constitutive-like" secretory pathway in isolated pancreatic islets: passive sorting in the immature granule compartment. *J. Cell Biol.* 118(3):521–29

72. Kurzchalia TV, Dupree P, Parton RG, Kellner R, Virta H, et al. 1992. VIP21, a 21-kD membrane protein is an integral component of *trans*-Golgi-network-derived transport vesicles. *J. Cell Biol.* 118(5):1003–14

73. Le Bivic A, Quaroni A, Nichols B, Rodriguez-Boulan E. 1990. Biogenetic pathways of plasma membrane proteins in Caco-2, a human intestinal epithelial cell line. *J. Cell Biol.* 111:1351–61

74. Le Bivic A, Sambuy Y, Patzak A, Patil N, Chao M, Rodriguez-Boulan E. 1991. An internal deletion in the cytoplasmic tail reverses the apical localization of human NGF receptor in transfected MDCK cells. *J. Cell Biol.* 115:607–18

75. Leyte A, Barr FA, Kehlenbach RH, Huttner WB. 1992. Multiple trimeric G-proteins on the *trans*-Golgi network exert stimulatory and inhibitory effects on secretory vesicle formation. *EMBO J.* 11:4795–804

76. Lippincott-Schwartz J, Donaldson JG, Schweizer A, Berger EG, Hauri HP, et al. 1990. Microtubule-dependent ret-

rograde transport of proteins into the ER in the presence of brefeldin A suggests an ER recycling pathway. *Cell* 60:821–36

77. Lippincott-Schwartz J, Yuan LC, Bonifacino JS, Klausner RD. 1989. Rapid redistribution of Golgi proteins into the ER in cells treated with brefeldin A: evidence for membrane cycling from Golgi to ER. *Cell* 56:801–13

78. Lippincott-Schwartz J, Yuan L, Tipper C, Amherdt M, Orci L, et al. 1991. Brefeldin A's effects on endosomes, lysosomes, and the TGN suggest a general mechanism for regulating organelle structure and membrane traffic. *Cell* 67:601–16

79. Lisanti MP, Caras IW, Davitz MA, Rodriguez-Boulan E. 1989. A glyco-phospholipid membrane anchor acts as an apical targeting signal in polarized epithelial cells. *J. Cell Biol.* 109:2145–56

80. Lombardi D, Soldati T, Riederer MA, Goda Y, Zerial M, et al. 1993. Rab9 functions in transport between the late endosomes and the *trans* Golgi network. *EMBO J.* 12(2):677–82

81. Deleted in proof

82. Low SH, Tang BL, Wong SH, Hong W. 1992. Selective inhibition of protein targeting to the apical domain of MDCK cells by brefeldin A. *J. Cell Biol.* 118:51–62

83. Low SH, Wong SH, Tang BL, Hong WJ. 1991. Involvement of both vectorial and transcytotic pathways in the preferential apical cell surface localization of rat dipeptidyl peptidase IV in transfected LLC-PK1 cells. *J. Biol. Chem.* 266:19710–16

84. Low SH, Wong SH, Tang BL, Subramaniam VN, Hong WJ. 1991. Apical cell surface expression of rat dipeptidyl peptidase IV in transfected Madin-Darby canine kidney cells. *J. Biol. Chem.* 266:13391–96

85. Madara JL. 1990. Contributions of the paracellular pathway to secretion, absorption, and barrier function in the epithelium of the small intestine. In *Textbook of Secretory Diarrhea*, ed. E Lebenthal, M Duffey, 11:125–38. New York: Raven

86. Malhotra V, Serafini T, Orci L, Shepherd JC, Rothman JE. 1989. Purification of a novel class of coated vesicles mediating biosynthetic protein transport through the Golgi stack. *Cell* 58:329–36

87. Matlin KS. 1992. W(h)ither default? Sorting and polarization in epithelial cells. *Curr. Opin. Cell Biol.* 4(4):623–28

88. Matter K, Brauchbar M, Bucher K, Hauri HP. 1990. Sorting of endogenous plasma membrane proteins occurs from two sites in cultured human intestinal epithelial cells (Caco-2). *Cell* 60(3):429–37

89. Matter K, Bucher K, Hauri HP. 1990. Microtubule perturbation retards both the direct and indirect apical pathway but does not effect sorting of plasma membrane proteins in intestinal epithelial cells (Caco-2). *EMBO J.* 9(10):3163–70

90. Matter K, Hunziker W, Mellman I. 1992. Basolateral sorting of LDL receptor in MDCK cells: the cytoplasmic domain contains two tyrosine-dependent targeting determinants. *Cell* 71:741–53

91. Mayorga LS, Diaz R, Colombo MI, Stahl PD. 1989. GTP gamma S stimulation of endosome fusion suggests a role for a GTP-binding protein in the priming of vesicles before fusion. *Cell Regul.* 1:113–24

92. Mayorga LS, Diaz R, Stahl PD. 1989. Regulatory role for GTP-binding proteins in endocytosis. *Science* 244:1475–77

93. Melancon P, Glick BS, Malhotra V, Weidman PJ, Serafini T, et al. 1987. Involvement of GTP-binding "G" proteins in transport through the Golgi stack. *Cell* 51(6):1053–62

94. Mellman I, Simons K. 1992. The Golgi complex: in vitro veritas? *Cell* 68:829–40

95. Merlin D, Augeron C, Laboisse CL, Hopfer U. 1992. cAMP-dependent Cl secretion is probably not associated with mucin granules in HT-29 CL16E. *Ped. Pulm. Suppl.* 8:A144 (Abstr.)

96. Miller SG, Carnell L, Morre H-PH. 1992. Post-Golgi membrane traffic: brefeldin A inhibits export from distal Golgi compartments to the cell surface but not recycling. *J. Cell Biol.* 118(2):267–83

97. Miller SG, Moore HP. 1991. Reconstitution of constitutive secretion using semi-intact cells: regulation by GTP but not calcium. *J. Cell Biol.* 112(1):39–54

98. Morris AP, Cunningham SA, Benos DJ, Frizzell, RA. 1992. Cellular differentiation is required for cAMP but not Ca^{2+}-dependent Cl^- secretion in colonic epithelial cells expressing high levels of cystic fibrosis transmembrane conductance regulator. *J. Biol. Chem.* 267:5575–83

99. Morris AP, Cunningham SA, Benos DJ, Frizzell RA. 1993. Polarization-dependent apical membrane CFTR targeting underlies cAMP-stimulated Cl⁻ secretion in epithelial cells. *Am. J. Physiol.* In press

100. Morris AP, Cunningham SA, Benos DJ, Frizzell RA. 1993. The glycosylation status of endogenously expressed CFTR does not affect cAMP-stimulated Cl- secretion in epithelial cells. *Am. J. Physiol.* 265:C688–94

101. Morris AP, Cunningham SA, Frizzell RA. 1993. CFTR targeting in epithelial cells. *J. Bioenerg. Biomembr.* 25(1):21–26

102. Morris AP, Frizzell RA. 1993. Ca^{2+}-dependent Cl⁻ channels in undifferentiated human colonic cells (HT-29). I. Single-channel properties. *Am. J. Physiol.* 33:C968–76

103. Mostov K, Apodaca G, Aroeti B, Okamoto C. 1992. Plasma membrane protein sorting in polarized epithelial cells. *J. Cell Biol.* 116(3):577–83

104. Mostov K, Deitcher DL. 1986. Polymeric immunglobulin receptor expressed in MDCK cells transcytosis IgA. *Cell* 46:429–37

105. Nelson WJ. 1992. Regulation of cell surface polarity from bacteria to mammals. *Science* 258:948–55

106. Noe BD. 1981. Inhibition of islet prohormone conversion by incorporation of arginine and lysine analogs. *J. Biol. Chem.* 256:4940–46

107. O'Grady SM, Palfrey HC, Field M. 1987. Characteristics and functions of Na:K:Cl cotransport in epithelial tissues. *Am. J. Physiol.* 253:C177–92

108. Oka T, Nishikawa S, Nakano A. 1991. Reconstitution of GTP-binding Sar1 protein function in ER to Golgi transport. *J. Cell Biol.* 114:671–79

109. Oprins A, Duden R, Kreis TE, Geuze HJ, Slot JW. 1993. β-COP localizes mainly to the *cis*-Golgi side in exocrine pancreas. *J. Cell Biol.* 121(1):49–59

110. Orci L, Halban P, Amherdt M, Ravazzola M, Vassalli J-D, et al. 1984. Nonconverted, amino acid analog-modified proinsulin stays in a Golgi-derived clathrin-coated membrane compartment. *J. Cell Biol.* 99:2187–92

111. Orci L, Tagaya M, Amherst M, Perrelet A, Donaldson JG, et al. 1991. Brefeldin A, a drug that blocks secretion, prevents the assembly of non-clathrin-coated buds on Golgi cisternae. *Cell* 64(6):1183–95

112. Palade G. 1975. Intracellular aspects of the process of protein synthesis. *Science* 189:347–58

113. Pathak RK, Yokode M, Hammer RE, Hofmann SL, Brown MS, et al. 1990. Tissue-specific sorting of the human LDL receptor in polarized epithelia of transgenic mice. *J. Cell Biol.* 111:347–59

114. Pearse BMF, Robinson NS. 1990. Clathrin, adaptor, and sorting. *Annu. Rev. Cell Biol.* 6:151–71

115. Perrin D, Moller K, Hankę K, Soling HD. 1992. cAMP and Ca^{2+}-mediated secretion in parotid acinar cells is associated with reversible changes in the organization of the cytoskeleton. *J. Cell Biol.* 116:127–34

116. Pimplikar SW, Simons K. 1993. Regulation of apical transport in epithelial cells by a Gs class of heterotrimeric G protein. *Nature* 362:256–58

117. Piper RC, Tai C, Slot JW, Hahn CS, Rice CM, et al. 1992. The efficient intracellular sequestration of the insulin-regulatable glucose transporter (GLUT-4) is conferred by the NH2 terminus. *J. Cell Biol.* 117:729–43

118. Plutner H, Cox AD, Pind S, Khosravi-Far R, Bourne JR, et al. 1991. Rab1b regulates vesicular transport between the endoplasmic reticulum and successive Golgi compartments. *J. Cell Biol.* 115:31–43

119. Prydz K, Hansen SH, Sandvig K, Van Deurs B. 1992. Effects of brefeldin A on endocytosis, transcytosis and transport to the Golgi complex in polarized MDCK cells. *J. Cell Biol.* 119:259–72

120. Pryer NK, Wuestehube LJ, Schekman R. 1992. Vesicle-mediated protein sorting. *Annu. Rev. Biochem.* 61:471–516

121. Puchelle E, Gaillard D, Ploton D, Hinnrasky J, Fuchey C, et al. 1992. Differential localization of the cystic fibrosis transmembrane conductance regulator in normal and cystic fibrosis airway epithelium. *Am. J. Respir. Cell Molec. Biol.* 7:485–91

122. Reaves B, Banting G. 1992. Perturbation of the morphology of the *trans*-Golgi network following Brefeldin A treatment: redistribution of a TGN-specific integral membrane protein, TGN38. *J. Cell Biol.* 116:85–94

123. Rexach MF, Schekman RW. 1991. Distinct biochemical requirements for the budding, targeting, and fusion of ER-derived transport vesicles. *J. Cell Biol.* 114(2):219–29

124. Rich DP, Anderson MP, Gregory RJ, Cheng SH, Paul S, et al. 1990. Expression of cystic fibrosis transmembrane conductance regulator corrects defective chloride channel regulation

in cystic fibrosis airway epithelial cells. *Nature* 347(6291):358–63

125. Rindler MJ, Traber MG. 1988. A specific sorting signal is not required for the polarized secretion of newly synthesized proteins from cultured intestinal cells. *J. Cell Biol.* 107:471–79

126. Riordan JR, Rommens JM, Kerem B, Alon N, Rozmahel R, et al. 1989. Identification of the cystic fibrosis gene: cloning and characterization of complementary DNA. *Science* 245: 1066–73

127. Robinson LJ, Pang S, Harris DS, Heuser J, James DE. 1992. Translocation of the glucose transporter (GLUT4) to the cell surface in permeabilized 3T3-L1 adipocytes: effects of ATP insulin, and GTP gamma S and localization of GLUT4 to clathrin lattices. *J. Cell Biol.* 117(6):1181–96

128. Robinson MS, Kreis TE. 1992. Recruitment of coat proteins onto Golgi membranes in intact and permeabilized cells: effects of brefeldin A and G protein activators. *Cell* 69(1):129–38

129. Rodriguez-Boulan E, Nelson WJ. 1989. Morphogenesis of the polarized epithelial cell phenotype. *Science* 245:718–25

130. Rodriguez-Boulan E, Powell SK. 1992. Polarity of epithelial and neuronal cells. *Annu. Rev. Cell Biol.* 8:395–427

131. Rommens JM, Iannuzzi MC, Kerem B, Drumm ML, Melmer G, et al. 1989. Identification of the cystic fibrosis gene: chromosome walking and jumping. *Science* 245:1059–65

132. Roth MG, Gundersen D, Patil N, Rodriguez-Boulan E. 1987. The large external domain is sufficient for the correct sorting of secreted or chimeric influenza virus hemagglutinins in polarized monkey kidney cells. *J. Cell Biol.* 104:769–82

133. Rothberg KG, Heuser JE, Donzell WC, Ying YS, Glenney JR, et al. 1992. Caveolin, a protein component of caveolae membrane coats. *Cell* 68:673–82

134. Sampath D, Varki A, Freeze HH. 1992. The spectrum of incomplete N-linked oligosaccharides synthesized by endothelial cells in the presence of brefeldin A. *J. Biol. Chem.* 267:4440–55

135. Sandoz D, Laine MC, Nicolas G. 1985. Distribution of microtubules within the intestinal terminal web as revealed by quick-freezing and cryo-substitution. *Eur. J. Cell Biol.* 39:481–84

136. Sarkadi B, Bauzon D, Huckle WR, Earp HS, Berry A, et al. 1992. Bio-

chemical characterization of the cystic fibrosis transmembrane conductance regulator in normal and cystic fibrosis epithelial cells. *J. Biol. Chem.* 267(3): 2087–95

137. Schwiebert EM, Kizer N, Gruenert DC, Stanton BA. 1992. GTP-binding proteins inhibit cAMP activation of chloride channels in cystic fibrosis airway epithelial cells. *Proc. Natl. Acad. Sci USA* 89(22):10623–27

138. Segev N. 1991. Mediation of the attachment or fusion step in vesicular transport by the GTP binding YPT1 protein. *Science* 252:1553–55

139. Serafini T, Orci L, Amherdt M, Brunner M, Kahn RA, et al. 1991. ADP-ribosylation factor is a subunit of the coat of Golgi-derived COP-coated vesicles: a novel role for a GTP-binding protein. *Cell* 67(2):239–53

140. Serafini T, Stenbeck G, Brecht A, Lottspeich F, Orci L, et al. 1991. A coat subunit of Golgi-derived nonclathrin-coated vesicles with homology to the clathrin-coated vesicle coat protein beta-adaptin. *Nature* 349(6306): 215–20

141. Shapiro M, Matthews J, Hecht G, Delp C, Madara JL. 1991. Stabilization of F-actin prevents cAMP-elicited Cl⁻ secretion in T84 cells. *J. Clin. Invest.* 87(6):1903–9

142. Simons K, Fuller SD. 1985. Cell surface polarity in epithelia. *Annu. Rev. Cell Biol.* 1:243–88

143. Simons K, Wandinger-Ness A. 1990. Polarized sorting in epithelia. *Cell* 62: 207–10

144. Slot JW, Geuze HJ, Gigengack S, Lienhard GE, James DE. 1991. Immuno-localization of the insulin regulatable glucose transporter in brown adipose tissue of the rat. *J. Cell Biol.* 113:123–35

145. Smith PR, Benos DJ. 1990. Epithelial Na⁺ channels. *Annu. Rev. Physiol.* 53:509–30

146. Smith PR, Bradford AL, Joe EH, Angelides KJ, Benos DJ, et al. 1993. Gastric parietal cell H(⁺)-K(⁺)-ATPase microsomes are associated with isoforms of ankyrin and spectrin. *Am. J. Physiol.* 264(1):C63–70

147. Smith PR, Saccomani G, Joe EH, Angelides KJ, Benos DJ. 1991. Amiloride-sensitive sodium channel is linked to the cytoskeleton in renal epithelial cells. *Proc. Natl. Acad. Sci. USA* 88(16):6971–75

148. Sollner T, Whiteheart SW, Brunner M, Erdjument-Bromage H, Geromanos S, et al. 1993. SNAP receptors im-

plicated in vesicle targeting and fusion. *Nature* 362:318–24

149. Soole KL, Hall J, Jepson MA, Hazlewood GP, Gilbert HJ, et al. 1992. Constitutive secretion of a bacterial enzyme by polarized epithelial cells. *J. Cell Sci.* 102:495–504

150. Stephens EB, Compans RW. 1988. Assembly of animal viruses at cellular membranes. *Annu. Rev. Microbiol.* 42: 489–516

151. Stow JL, De Almeida JB, Narula N, Holtzman EJ, Ercolani L, et al. 1991. A heterotrimeric G protein, G alpha i-3, on Golgi membranes regulates the secretion of a heparan sulfate proteoglycan in LLC-PK1 epithelial cells. *J. Cell Biol.* 114:1113–24

152. Strous GJ, Van Kerkhof P, Van Meer G, Rijnboutt S, Stoorvogel W. 1993. Differential effects of brefeldin A on transport of secretory and lysosomal proteins. *J. Biol. Chem.* 268:2341–47

153. Sztul E, Colombo M, Stahl P, Samanta R. 1993. Control of protein traffic between distinct plasma membrane domains. *J. Biol. Chem.* 268:1876–85

154. Sztul E, Kaplin A, Saucan L, Palade G. 1991. Protein traffic between distinct plasma membrane domains: isolation and characterization of vesicular carriers involved in transcytosis. *Cell* 64:81–89

155. Takai Y, Kaibuchi K, Kikuchi A, Kawata M. 1992. Small GTP-binding proteins. *Intl. Rev. Cytol.* 133:187–30

156. Takami N, Oda K, Fujiwara T, Ikehara Y. 1990. Intracellular accumulation and oligosaccharide processing of alkaline phosphatase under disassembly of the Golgi complex caused by brefeldin A. *Eur. J. Biochem.* 194:805–10

157. Taylor TC, Kahn RA, Melancon P. 1992. Two distinct members of the ADP-ribosylation factor family of GTP-binding proteins regulate cell-free intra-Golgi transport. *Cell* 70(1):69–79

158. Tilly BC, Winter MC, Ostedgaard LS, O'Riordan C, Smith AE, et al. 1992. Cyclic AMP-dependent protein kinase activation of cystic fibrosis transmembrane conductance regulator chloride channels in planar lipid bilayers. *J. Biol. Chem.* 267(14):9470–73

159. Tooze J, Hollinshead M. 1992. In AtT20 and HeLa cells brefeldin A induces the fusion of tubular endosomes and changes their distribution and some of their endocytic properties. *J. Cell Biol.* 118(4):813–30

160. Tooze SA, Weiss U, Huttner WB. 1990. Requirement for GTP hydrolysis in the formation of secretory vesicles. *Nature* 347(6289):207–8

161. Van Der Sluijs P, Hull M, Zahraoui A, Tavitian A, Goud B, et al. 1991. The small GTP-binding protein rab4 is associated with early endosomes. *Proc. Natl. Acad. Sci. USA* 88:6313–17

162. Van Deurs B, Petersen OW, Olsnes S, Sandvig K. 1989. The ways of endocytosis. *Intl. Rev. Cytol.* 117:131–77

163. Wan J, Taub ME, Shah D, Shen WC. 1992. Brefeldin A enhances receptor-mediated transcytosis of transferrin in filter-grown Madin-Darby canine kidney cells. *J. Biol. Chem.* 267(19): 13446–50

164. Wessels HP, Hansen GH, Fuhrer C, Look AT, Sjosfrom HG, et al. 1990. Aminopeptidase N is directly sorted to the apical domain in MDCK cells. *J. Cell Biol.* 111:2932–40

165. Wessling-Resnick M, Braell WA. 1990. Characterization of the mechanism of endocytic vesicle fusion in vitro. *J. Biol. Chem.* 265:16751–59

166. Wieland FT, Gleason ML, Serafini TA, Rothman RA. 1987. The rate of bulk flow from the endoplasmic reticulum to the cell surface. *Cell* 50:289–300

167. Wong DH, Brodsky FM. 1992. 100-kD proteins of the Golgi- and *trans*-Golgi network-associated coated vesicles have related but distinct membrane binding properties. *J. Cell Biol.* 117:1171–79

168. Wood SA, Brown WJ. 1992. The morphology but not the function of endosomes and lysosomes is altered by Brefeldin A. *J. Cell Biol.* 119(2):273–85

169. Wood SA, Park JE, Brown WJ. 1991. Brefeldin A causes a microtubule-mediated fusion of the *trans*-Golgi network and early endosomes. *Cell* 67: 591–600

170. Young WW, Mallory SL, Blackburn WA. 1992. Endogenous glycosphingolipids move to cell surface at a rate consistent with bulk flow estimates. *J. Biol. Chem.* 267(17): 12011–15

171. Zeitlin PL, Crawford I, Lu L, Woel S, Cohen ME, et al. 1992. CFTR protein expression in primary and cultured epithelial. *Proc. Natl. Acad. Sci. USA* 89:344–47

Annu. Rev. Physiol. 1994. 56:399–417
Copyright © 1994 by Annual Reviews Inc. All rights reserved

PRIMARY CULTURES FOR STUDIES OF CELL REGULATION AND PHYSIOLOGY IN INTESTINAL EPITHELIUM

G. S. Evans, N. Flint, and C. S. Potten

CRC Department of Epithelial Biology, Paterson Institute for Cancer Research, Christie Hospital NHS Trust, Manchester M20 9BX, England

KEY WORDS: in vitro, stem cells, differentiation, stroma, epithelial-mesenchymal interactions

INTRODUCTION

The transport functions of intestinal epithelium are critical to health, and defects in these functions underlie clinical conditions such as diarrhea, mucoviscidosis, and malabsorption of sugars, iron, lipids, and bile acids. Many of these conditions can be reversed by direct intervention using pharmacological agents, but inherited genetic defects such as cystic fibrosis (71) and glucose-galactose malabsorption (91) represent a different challenge for therapy. The development of new pharmacological agents depends upon physiological studies to identify, characterize, and understand the regulation of these cellular processes.

Traditional techniques for studying transport processes, such as patch clamping and Ussing chambers, depend on ex vivo manipulation of mucosa. This has been achieved by physically dissecting sheets of mucosa (15) and by isolating intact crypt and villus epithelium with divalent ion chelating solutions (17). These methods provide important insights into transport function, but the short-term viability of the isolated cells is an important limiting factor. Organ culture was initially used as a method to maintain cells ex vivo for longer periods, but tissue cultured in this way was also

399

0066–4278/94/0315–0399$05.00

limited in viability (24–72 hr; 40). Advances in cell culture techniques have made it possible to keep many different cell types in vitro for prolonged periods. However, normal intestinal epithelium has proven to be difficult to isolate and grow in culture.

A few continuously growing lines have successfully been derived from developing rat and mouse intestinal epithelium (6, 20, 60, 68, 90). These nontransformed cells are easy to maintain, but they have immature characteristics and express only limited enterocyte-like features when induced to differentiate in response to glucocorticoids (68) or the cytostatic factor TGFβ (45). These lines are now generally regarded as poor models of intestinal epithelial differentiation (40, 61). In contrast, the development of tumor-derived epithelial cell lines that differentiate in culture (61, 95) has been a significant stimulus to physiological studies. The differentiated characteristics of some of these lines has prompted their widespread use as models of gut epithelium. However, these models must be utilized with some caution. The function of normal epithelial cells is regulated by the extra-cellular and peri-cellular environment, but cancer cells, by definition, are not expected to respond to their environment in a normal fashion.

The epithelium lining the intestine renews itself within a few days so that adaptative changes in this tissue are relevant to questions of physiology. The epithelial stem cells located in the crypts of Lieberkühn are essential for this continuous renewal and are implicated in some adaptational changes of function. Stem cells are self-maintaining, multi-potent cells producing at least four specialized lineages, e.g. Paneth, goblet, entero-endocrine cells, and enterocytes (66). The proportion of these stem cells is very small (<0.1% of the crypt and villus cells), but as progenitor cells they are targets for signals that redirect programs of differentiation in the epithelium.

Our aim has been to understand the environmental role of stromal factors that regulate these stem cells, using in vitro models. In particular, we are interested in factors released by non-parenchymal stromal cells within the connective tissue surrounding the gut epithelium. To address this problem, a reproducible primary culture technique has been developed to grow epithelial cells from developing rat small intestine (21). Although, predominantly epithelial, these cultures are heterogenous and as such reflect epithelial-stromal interactions that are not present in the continuously growing cell line models. In this article, the applications and limitations of primary cultures for the study of normal gut epithelium are discussed.

PRIMARY CULTURES

All culture models are at best caricatures of the tissue from which they were derived. One criterion by which to judge their relevance is the extent to which their properties reflect cellular interactions present in intact tissue. In this respect, homogeneous lines that can be continuously propagated on plastic surfaces are very different from primary cultures.

Primary cultures usually refer to the propagation of freshly isolated cells prior to their first subculture (28). Many studies of normal gut epithelium have reported the difficulties in maintaining cultures of these cells for more than a few days (8, 29, 31, 43, 48, 64, 88), others have observed limited proliferation (1, 30, 33, 34, 37, 41, 49, 69, 74, 93, 94), but in a few studies, more extensive passaging has been claimed (5, 11, 57, 86). These problems probably reflect the difficulty of providing an environment appropriate for these cells in vitro, and the use of inappropriate methodology, such as the type of cell isolation procedure.

Isolation of Cells for Primary Culture

Intestinal epithelial cells seem to be susceptible to damage during isolation, in comparison to other epithelial cells such as keratinocytes that are routinely grown in primary cultures. Consequently the best separation methods are those that are quick and cause the least damage to the integrity and function of the cells. Finding such a method has been one limitation to the successful development of gut epithelial primary cultures.

Early work was based on organ cultures where the mucosa was dissected into small 1 mm^3 segments and maintained in culture medium at the air/fluid interface on sterile rafts. The major disadvantage of this method was anoxia at the center of the tissue, which led to rapid degeneration in structure and function within 24–72 hr (40). The establishment of cell lines has been based on a related technique, termed spill culture (68). Segments of developing rat intestine were maintained floating in culture in the continuous presence of collagenase. Cells released from the tissue by this enzyme attached to the dish and formed heterogenous cultures of epithelial and mesenchymal cells. After prolonged culture (up to six weeks), colonies of epithelial cells were selected, using cloning cylinders for further sub-culture. While this method has proved satisfactory for establishing cell lines, it has been impractical for routine isolation.

There has been considerable interest in methods for the isolation of populations of epithelial cells for physiological and culture studies. These methods include physical isolation (1, 34, 43, 57, 60, 67), divalent ion-chelating solutions at 37°C (20, 86, 88) and 4°C (26), trypsin (11, 54, 33), hyaluronidase (8, 21, 30, 64), collagenase (8, 21, 30, 64), dispase (21), neuramidase (64), and combinations of these procedures (5, 21, 31). Combinations of collagenase and dispase are now favored (21) because the isolation is quick (within 30–60 min digestion), gentle (very low concentrations of both enzymes are required), and preserves cellular integrity.

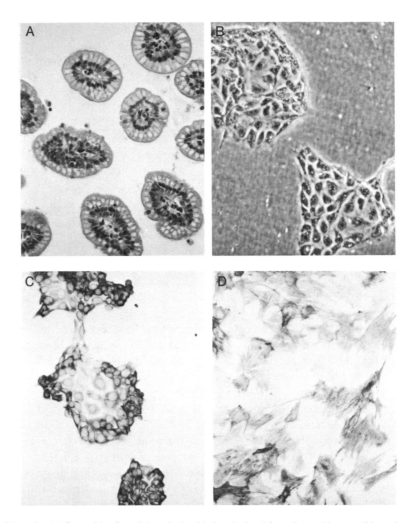

Figure 1 (*a*) Organoids of small intestinal epithelium isolated from 6 day old rat small intestine by collagenase/dispase digestion (×175 magnification); (*b*) Attaching colonies of the above organoids after 24 hr in culture; photographed in phase contrast (×200 magnification); (*c*) Colonies derived from attached organoids in culture stained by immunoperoxidase with monoclonal antibodies to cytokeratins 8, 18, and 19; diaminobenzidine/nickel chloride substrate: (×200 magnification); (*d*) Smooth muscle-like stromal cells in primary cultures of developing rat small intestine stained by immunoperoxidase with monoclonal antibody 1A-4 to smooth muscle α actin; diaminobenzidine/nickel chloride substrate (×200 magnification).

When collagenase/dispase enzymes are used, the epithelium is released as intact units (termed organoids; see Figure 1a) with some closely associated stromal cells. The presence of these stromal cells might be viewed as an apparent disadvantage; however, the retention of an organized structure has proved necessary for attachment and culture of the epithelium. After 24 hr in culture, these epithelial cells spread to form monolayer colonies (Figure 1b,c) with some smooth muscle-like fibroblasts, endothelial, and neural cells (originating from the attached stroma) at the periphery. The epithelial cells will proliferate up to one month, but the smooth muscle-like cells (Figure 1d) overgrow the cultures if serum concentrations greater than 2.5% are used (21).

Proliferation of Cells in Primary Culture

Another limiting factor in many studies has been the difficulty of getting normal gut epithelium to proliferate in primary culture in a reproducible way. For physiological studies this may be a problem if, for example, intact monolayers of cells are needed to completely cover micro-porous filters (82). Factors that influence whether cells proliferate in vitro include the donor age of the tissue, the culture medium, effects of supplements and growth factors, and the role of heterologous interactions with mesenchyme.

A progressive, age-dependent loss in the capacity for proliferation in vitro has been reported for rat intestinal epithelium (43), so it is, perhaps, not surprising that there are so few reports of primary culture of these cells from the adult stage. Whether this problem is due to intrinsic differences in proliferative potential between fetal and adult tissues remains to be established. Indeed, it may be too simple an explanation, since fetal epithelium proliferates well in vitro, but only for periods of a few days (41). It is also a paradox that adult mucosa renews (and regenerates) so rapidly, but apparently fails to grow well in vitro. Changes in the extracellular environment of the epithelial cells may be an important developmental factor (76). Reproducing the appropriate environment ex vivo may therefore be essential for primary culture of adult gut epithelium.

When freshly isolated cells fail to proliferate in vitro, this may be a consequence of the stress to which they have been subjected. Poor culture conditions can contribute to this stress. Consequently, the growth medium and supplements should be of high purity since primary cultures are very sensitive to deficiencies in nutrients and the presence of chemical toxins (21). For example, medium prepared from concentrated stocks is inferior in its growth-supporting capacity compared to the use of single strength medium (21). It is also beneficial to replace medium stocks at regular (monthly) intervals. When epithelial cells can be maintained but fail to proliferate in culture, it is difficult to select the best medium additives. In these circumstances, measuring cell survival may help to identify better cell culture conditions. It is appealing to imagine that these problems can be answered by swapping one type of medium for another. Unfortunately many different formulations have been used for gut primary cultures without obvious benefits for any type.

However, dramatic improvements in proliferation have been seen with some medium additives. For example, large differences between batches of fetal calf serum (FCS) have been noted (64). Low concentrations of FCS have been found more suitable for the epithelium, as concentrations greater than 2% promote growth of contaminating stromal cells and can inhibit epithelial proliferation (11, 21). Serum factors, such as fibronectin (9) and vitronectin (85), are also critical during attachment and spread of epithelial cells.

The development of serum-free media for the growth of intestinal cells would remove some of the variability due to batches of FCS (30). Some practical steps include the use of attachment factors (see below) and the addition of growth factors, lipids, hormones, and iron-saturated transferrin (30). Many established cell lines have been grown in medium where all of the constituents are chemically defined. However, it is unlikely that chemically defined conditions will be achieved for primary cultures because the epithelial cells require biological substratum and as yet uncharacterized stromal factors derived from stromal cells.

Polypeptide growth factors are now considered essential additives for culture media particularly for serum-free conditions. The pleiotrophic nature of many growth factors is such that a single factor may promote proliferation, cell survival, differentiation, and motility (59). With advances in biotechnology, many recombinant growth factors can be used as supplements in culture medium. For normal gut epithelium, however, the effects of numerous growth factors have yet to be properly investigated in vitro. An exception is the recent study by Fukamachi (30) on the effects of growth factors in fetal gut epithelium grown in serum-free conditions.

Most published data on the growth factor requirements of gut epithelium have been based on studies of either continuously growing nontumorigenic lines or colon cancer lines. These results suggest that insulin and insulin-like growth factors I and II (IGFs; 13, 14, 65), epidermal growth factor (EGF), and transforming growth factor alpha (TGFα; 2, 12, 13, 14), fibroblast growth factors (FGFs; 89) and gastrin (12, 62, 56) stimulate epithelial proliferation. EGF/TGFα also stimulates migration of epithelial cells (7). Other agents like TGFβ (4, 45) and somatostatin (56, 62, 81) inhibit the growth of epithelial cells and sometimes promote differentiation in a manner similar to the glucocorticoids (68).

The impact of exogenous growth factors in primary culture has been more difficult to evaluate because many stimulate proliferation of epithelial and

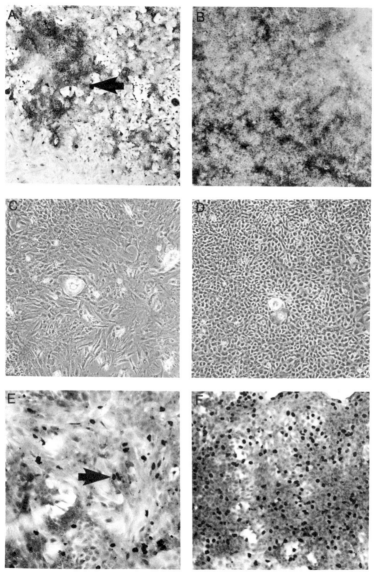

Figure 2   (*a*) Primary cultures of developing rat small intestinal epithelium grown for 11 days in DMEM medium with 2.5% FCS, 20 ng/ml EGF, and 0.25 IU/ml insulin: arrow marks a colony of epithelium surrounded by stromal cells (×40 magnification); (*b*) As above but with 50 μg/ml of heparin added, showing an expansive colony of epithelial cells (×40 magnification); (*c*) Higher power phase contrast picture of (*a*) (×150 magnification); (*d*) Higher power phase contrast picture of (*b*) (×150 magnification); (*e*) Autoradiograph showing localization (*arrow*) of proliferating stromal cells in a control culture labeled with tritiated thymidine (×150 magnification); (*f*) Autoradiograph showing localization of many proliferating epithelial cells in a culture treated with heparin and labeled with tritiated thymidine (×150 magnification).

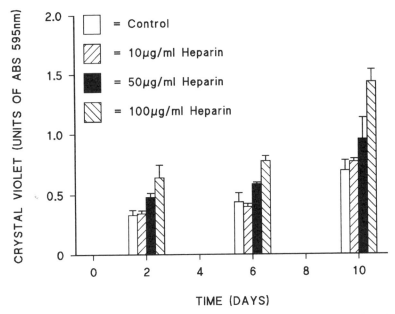

Figure 3 Dose response to heparin in primary cultures of developing rat small intestinal epithelium. The basal medium consisted of DMEM with 2.5% FCS, 20 ng/ml EGF, and 0.25 IU/ml insulin. The cellularity of the epithelial cells was measured by changes in bound crystal violet dye (at low pH 2.5; 27) measured at OD 595 nm; the data represent means ± S.E.

stromal cells in a nonselective way (27). These nonselective effects are also observed in response to holo-transferrin and essential lipids (Albumax; a lipid/albumin complex; Gibco Ltd). These preliminary findings seem disappointing; however, factors that are selective in supporting growth of other types of epithelial cell have been identified. These originate as paracrine signals produced by adjacent stromal fibroblasts (25, 58). Whether a growth factor acts on a certain cell type may also depend on other constituents of the peri-cellular and extra-cellular matrix (ECM). ECM molecules specifically bind to many growth factors, which provides the appropriate context (59) for the growth factor to elicit a cellular response. Heparan sulfate proteoglycans (HSPGs) are one type of ECM constituents in which there has been much interest. HSPGs and the structurally related molecule heparin bind specifically to many growth factors (59, 72). For fibroblast growth factors there is clear evidence that binding to heparin-like molecules is necessary to activate high affinity cell surface receptors (92).

The importance of glycosaminoglycans (GAGs) has been underlined by the finding that heparin selectively stimulates proliferation of epithelial cells, but inhibits stromal cell growth, in primary gut culture (27). The stimulation of epithelial growth by heparin (Figure 2a-f) is dose-dependent (Figure 3) and is a novel effect. In comparison, inhibitory effects of heparin on smooth muscle-like cells have been recognized for some time (38).

One interpretation of these results is that heparin mimics an endogenous cell surface or ECM heparan-sulfate. However, heparan sulfate and other matrix GAGS such as chondroitins A, B, C, and hyaluronic acid were unable to stimulate epithelial proliferation in these primary cultures. In contrast, heparin, dextran sulfate, and pentosan polysulfate, molecules with a high negative sulfation charge, were able to stimulate epithelial proliferation (27). Experimental evidence suggests the effect of heparin on epithelial growth is in part the result of interaction of heparin with paracrine growth factors derived from the stromal cells in these cultures. From a practical perspective, the addition of heparin results in rapidly growing large monolayer colonies of epithelium, while minimizing the contamination by stromal cells. A comparison of heparin-treated and control cultures is shown in Figure 2a-d, and the significant increase in epithelial proliferation compared to control conditions shown in Figure 2e-f. Another useful feature is that heparin has proved most effective in low concentrations of serum (<2.5%) and serum-free conditions.

Cellular Interactions in Primary Cultures

The general importance of mesenchymal interactions for morphogenesis and differentiation of epithelial cells has been demonstrated in vivo (16) and in vitro (44, 53) and specifically for fetal gut development (32). These interactions are likely to be equally important in developing and adult tissues. The widespread use of stromal cells in co-culture with, for example, keratinocytes (70), breast (80), bronchial epithelium (47), and colonic adenoma (63) has confirmed the importance of these interactions. This technique usually involves fibroblast cells (e.g. Swiss 3T3 fibroblasts) that are lethally irradiated to stop their proliferation. These sterilized cells are then plated into dishes to settle prior to the addition of the epithelial cells. These stromal cells have been termed feeders and have been used to support prolonged maintenance and differentiation of fetal gut epithelium in culture (41).

Morphological and culture studies suggest that intimate contact between epithelial and stromal cells may be required at certain times for appropriate differentiation (51). Direct cell-cell contact between heterologous cells also may be important for the effects of some feeder cells (19). Synthesis of a normal basement membrane is dependent upon close association of epithelial and stromal cells (34, 77); different constituents of this membrane are also contributed by the two tissues (77, 78). However, it is less clear if soluble paracrine influences exist between gut epithelium and stromal cells. Examples of stromal-derived growth factors with selective effects on epithelial cells include keratinocyte growth factor (25) and hepatocyte growth factor (58). In some circumstances, paracrine factors may be involved in maintaining tissue stem cells. For example, some feeder layers express a molecule termed differentiating inhibitory activity (DIA; 23, 79) that blocks differentiation of embryonic stem cells.

Two different types of irradiated feeder layer (3T3 fibroblast and bovine corneal endothelium; BCE) have now been found to support proliferation of developing rat intestinal epithelium (Figure 4a). This effect was not dependent upon direct contact, but was an example of paracrine stimulation. Conditioned medium collected from these two feeder lines supported proliferation of normal epithelial cells. This effect does not require the direct presence of feeder cells (22; GS Evans & N Flint, manuscript in preparation), and resulted in large coalescing colonies of epithelium (Figure 4b). In addition, the conditioned medium was inhibitory to proliferation of stromal cells in these cultures.

To demonstrate that gut stromal cells also produce paracrine factors, smooth muscle-like lines have been derived from the lamina propria stroma

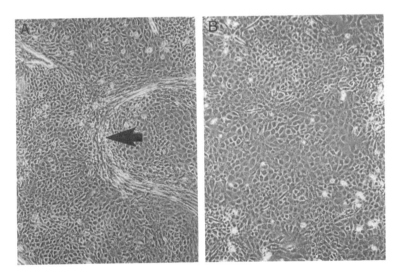

Figure 4   (*a*) Primary cultures of developing rat small intestinal epithelium grown on an irradiated feeder layer of BCE cells for 7 days, showing expanded epithelial colonies and compression of feeder cells into ridges (*arrow*); photographed in phase contrast ($\times 150$ magnification); (*b*) The same cells on collagen-coated plastic and grown for 7 days in medium conditioned (DMEM with 2.5% FCS, 20 ng/ml EGF, and 0.25 IU/ml insulin) for 18 hours by irradiated BCE cells; photographed in phase contrast ($\times 150$ magnification).

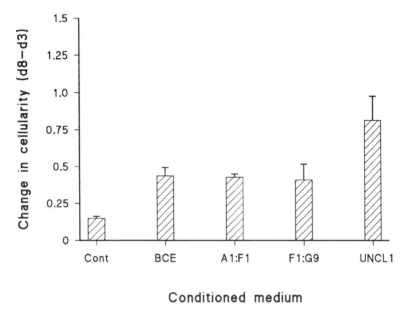

Conditioned medium

Figure 5   A comparison of the growth-promoting effects of conditioned medium on primary cultures of developing rat small intestinal epithelium. The medium was DMEM with 2.5% FCS, 20 ng/ml EGF, and 0.25 IU/ml insulin conditioned for 18 hr by BCE cells, or three different smooth muscle-like lines (A1:F1; F1:G9, and UNCL1) derived from rat intestine. The cellularity of the cultures was measured by changes in bound crystal violet dye (at low pH 2.5; 27) measured at OD 595 nm and expressed as differences over a five day period; the data represent means differences ± S.E.

of developing rat small intestine. These cells, in particular one line, UNCL1, also produce conditioning factors (for a comparison, see Figure 5) that selectively stimulate proliferation in the epithelium. A preliminary study suggests these are heparin-binding growth factors (22; GS Evans & N Flint, manuscript in preparation). The identification of stromal cell-derived mitogens could lead to improved methods for feeder-free culture of normal gut epithelium. This has certainly proved to be possible for the feeder-free maintenance of embryonic stem cells using recombinant DIA (79).

The Basement Membrane and Differentiation of Epithelial Cells

Stromal elements or feeder layers might be regarded as contaminants in some physiological techniques. For example, homogenous lines such as T84 and HT29 can form tight monolayers over micro-porous filters so that a "pure" cell population can be used for transport studies. Nevertheless, the influence of stromal cells on differentiation and function in normal gut epithelial cells cannot be ignored. Differentiation and polarity in epithelial cells is dependent upon a basement membrane formed during interactions with mesenchymal cells (34, 78).

Coating culture dishes with biological substratum may help to promote maturation processes in epithelial cells (3). Basement membrane constituents such as laminin promote the expression of digestive enzymes by cultured enterocytes, particularly those rich in laminin and nidogen, e.g. the Engelbreth-Holm-Swarm tumor (EHS) matrix (39). In contrast, spread and proliferation of epithelial cells in primary culture is observed on stromal collagens (I and III) substratum (21). The structure of the basement membrane is also complex, e.g. the way that laminin is laid down by fibroblasts depends upon epithelial-stromal interactions and the presence of glucocorticoids (75). Consequently, the difficulty of reproducing native basement membranes in vitro may limit the differentiation of epithelial cells in primary culture.

Cell Shape and Differentiation of Epithelial Cells

The monolayer culture of epithelial cells is a standard and convenient technique. However, such two-dimensional cultures may limit the capacity of epithelial cell differentiation in vitro. There is increasing recognition that differentiation in epithelium is dependent upon cell shape (52, 87) and the presence of a basement membrane (3). Appropriate in vitro differentiation of some glandular epithelial cells has only been observed in suspension (1, 42, 67, 73), in gels of collagen (1, or on EHS matrix (10). A recent exciting discovery has been the tubular morphogenesis of the MDCK (Madin-Darby canine kidney) epithelial line, when grown in collagen cels in the presence of fibroblasts (53).

Topographical signals are also important to the maintenance of a differentiated polarized phenotype of normal gut epithelium in vitro. When intact clumps of epithelium from developing rat intestine were cultured in suspension, they quickly formed sealed spheres that retained a structural polarity not observed in monolayers of these cells. In these spheroids, epithelial cells retained high transmembrane electro-potential gradients compared to epithelial cells grown in monolayers (84). Another interesting feature of these spheroids was an increase in their volume over several days, which suggested that fluid transport was occurring.

CONCLUSIONS

The choice of colorectal lines as models of gut epithelium reflects the requirement for cells that differentiate in vitro and can be used with techniques that measure physiological function, e.g. Ussing chambers. A reproducible and homogenous culture model is therefore critical, and by definition, epithelial primary cultures do not satisfy these requirements. Covering large (e.g. 9 mm diameter) macroporous filters with a monolayer of a cell line such as T84 is now a routine procedure in some laboratories. However, this is not a trivial exercise with primary cultures. If these techniques are to be applied to primary cultures, then changes to the existing methods may be required, for example, the use of smaller diameter filters. Epithelial dome formation (Figure 6a) and expression of enterocyte markers, e.g. alkaline phosphatase (Figure 6b), have been observed in such primary cultures (27), and studies of transport and differentiation may nevertheless be worth pursuing.

Although the question of proliferation in epithelial primary cultures has been discussed in depth, this may not necessarily be the only, or best, strategy for studying these cells in vitro. For example a progressive loss of differentiation with time has been observed in established gut epithelial lines (40). However, the differentiated cells are of most interest to the physiologist. Intact villi, for example, have been isolated from adult human (and rat small intestine) using collagenase and dispase, and this epithelium readily

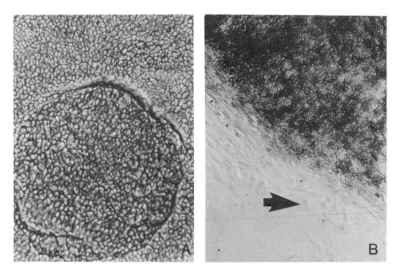

Figure 6   (*a*) The development of an epithelial dome in a primary culture of developing rat small intestine after 10 days in culture: photographed in phase contrast (×150 magnification); (*b*) Expression of alkaline phosphatase by epithelial cells in primary culture of developing rat small intestine after 10 days in culture. The enzyme activity was demonstrated by incubating the cultures in Vector Red (Vector Laboratories). An arrow marks the position of nonexpressing fibroblast cells; photographed in oblique contrast (×150 magnification).

attached to form coalescing nonproliferating monolayers when plated at high density. These cells retained differentiated features not seen in proliferating cultures (GS Evans, unpublished observations). Similar results have been reported for intact crypts of human colorectal epithelium (31).

Recent technological innovations could lead to new ways of studying gut epithelium in culture. Improvements in microscopes and imaging systems now mean that physiological studies on single or small groups of cells are a practical reality (46, 55). There are also many fluorescent probes that can be used for microscopic measurements of cellular changes, for example, ions, pH, membrane fluidity, macro-molecular transport, and ligand-receptor binding (35, 46). These techniques are suitable for studying epithelial cells even in heterogenous cultures. Similar advances in sensitive immuno-histochemical, in situ-hybridization, and PCR technology have also made it easier to study gene and protein expression in small numbers of cells.

There is growing interest in the way that different factors regulate the function of gut epithelial cells. In vivo studies have shown altered expression of some digestive enzymes such as sucrase/isomaltase in response to glucocorticoids (36). The expression of glucose transporters is modified in response to dietary factors (24). The expression of these changes in the villus enterocytes is typically delayed by at least 24 hr. This implicates the undifferentiated crypt (stem) cells as the target for dietary or hormonal signals. A similar sequence of enzyme expression has been observed in primary cultures of fetal gut epithelium treated with glucocorticoids (41), but this required the support of stromal cells.

It is likely that primary cultures will be of most value in studies of factors that regulate differentiation in normal gut epithelium. Interactions with stroma are now recognized to be important in this respect (39, 41), but the challenge for future work is to identify the molecular basis of these interactions. A significant advance would be to maintain the tissue stem cells in primary culture, which would enable studies into the role of these cells in replacement and differentiation of the epithelium. This is a plausible aim, given the evidence that fetal (32, 83) and neonatal epithelium (33), co-cultured with mesenchyme for several days, retains the ability to regenerate into mucosa when grafted under the kidney capsule. In this grafted mucosa, goblet cells, Paneth cells, enteroendocrine cells, and enterocytes were formed, which supports the idea that progenitor cells were retained during the period of culture. There are other examples where stromal support is necessary to maintain in vitro hematopoiesis (18) and embryo stem cells (50).

The development of reproducible primary culture techniques for gut epithelium has progressed slowly. Consequently, researchers have often avoided using primary cultures of gut epithelium because of their inherent difficulties. However, dependency on colorectal cancer lines alone as models of gut epithelium raises questions about the overall relevance of some findings. Whereas, reproducible methods for growing normal gut epithelium would provide a significant stimulus to clinical studies and would be useful for testing pharmacological agents.

Heterologous cellular interactions are the unique feature of these primary cultures, and further advances in this methodology are going to depend upon a better understanding of these processes. This is illustrated by the development of methods to differentiate epithelial cells by growing them in three-dimensional gels of collagen (or ECM) in the presence of fibroblasts. The innovative use of new technology should enable cell biologists and physiologists to take advantage of these developments.

ACKNOWLEDGMENTS

The authors would like to thank Drs. Helen Cox and Alistair Watson for their advice and help during the preparation of this manuscript. We also would like to acknowledge Drs. M Kédinger, R Pérez-Tömas, S Shirhazi-Beechey, and G Warhurst for their interest and support. This work has been funded by the Cancer Research Campaign. NF is also a joint research student with the Department of Biochemistry, Aberystwyth, University of Wales.

Literature Cited

1. Altmann GG, Quaroni A. 1990. Behaviour of fetal intestinal organ culture explanted onto a collagen substratum. *Development* 110:353–70

2. Baliga BS, Borowitz SM, Barnard JA. 1989. Effects of EGF and PMA on the growth and proliferation of the IEC-6 cells. *Biochem. Int.* 19:1045–56

3. Barcellos-Hoff MH, Bissell MJ. 1989. Mammary epithelial cells as a model for studies of the regulation of gene expression. In *Functional Epithelial Cells in Culture*, ed. KS Matlin, JD Valentich, pp. 399–433. New York: Liss

4. Barnard JA, Beauchamp RD, Coffey RJ, Moses HL. 1989. Regulation of intestinal cell growth by transforming growth factor typeβ. *Proc. Natl. Acad. Sci. USA* 86:1578–82

5. Baten A, Sakamoto K, Shamsuddin AM. 1992. Long term culture of normal human colonic epithelial cells in vitro. *FASEB. J.* 6:2726–34

6. Blay J, Brown KD. 1984. Characterisation of an epithelioid cell line derived from rat small intestine: Demonstration of cytokeratin filaments. *Cell Biol. Int. Rep.* 8:551–60

7. Blay J, Brown KD. 1985. Epidermal growth factor promotes the chemotactic migration of cultured rat intestinal epithelial cells. *J. Cell. Physiol.* 124:107–12

8. Brubaker PL, Vranic M. 1987. Fetal rat intestinal cells in monolayer culture: A new in vitro system to study the glucagon-like immunoreactive peptides. *Endocrinology* 120:1976–85

9. Burrill PH, Bernardini I, Kleinman HK, Kretchner N. 1981. Effect of serum fibronectin and laminin on adhesion of rabbit intestinal epithelial cells in culture. *J. Supramol. Struct. Cell. Biochem.* 16:385–92

10. Carroll KM, Wong TT, Drabik DL, Cheng EB. 1988. Differentiation of rat small intestinal epithelial cells by extracellular matrix. *Am. J. Physiol.* (17)254:G355–60

11. Chopra DP, Yeh K-Y. 1981. Long term culture of epithelial cells from

the normal rat. colon. *In Vitro* 17:441–49

12. Conteas CN, Adhip P, Majumdar N. 1987. The effects of gastrin, epidermal growth factor and somatostatin on DNA synthesis in a small intestinal cell line (IEC-6). *Proc. Soc. Exp. Biol. Med.* 184:307–11

13. Conteas CN, McMorrow B, Luk GD. 1989. Modulation of epidermal growth factor induced cell proliferation and receptor binding by insulin in cultured intestinal epithelial cells. *Biochem. Biophys. Res. Comm.* 161:414–19

14. Corps AN, Brown KD. 1986. Stimulation of intestinal epithelial cell proliferation in culture by growth factors in human and ruminant mammary secretions. *J. Endocrinol.* 113:285–90

15. Cox HM, Cuthbert AW. 1988. Neuropeptide Y antagonises secretagogue evoked chloride transport in rat jejunal epithelium. *Pflügers Arch.* 413:38–42

16. Cunha GR, Bigsby RM, Cooke PS, Sugimura Y. 1985. Stromal-epithelial interactions in adult organs. *Cell Diff.* 17:137–48

17. Del Castillo JR. 1987. The use of hyperosmolar intracellular like solutions for the isolation of epithelial cells from guinea-pig small intestine. *Biochim. Biophys. Acta* 901:201–8

18. Dexter TM. 1982. Stromal cell associated haemopoiesis. *J. Cell Physiol. Proc Symp. Cell. Mol. Biol. Hematopoietic Stem Cell Diff. Suppl. 1.* 87–94

19. Ehmann UK. 1992. Feeder cells impart a growth stimulus to recipient epithelial cells by direct contact. *Exp. Cell Res.* 199:314–22

20. Emami S, Mir L, Gespach C, Rosselin G. 1989. Transfection of fetal rat intestinal epithelial cells by viral oncogenes: Establishment and characterisation of the E1A-immortalized SLC-11 cell line. *Proc. Natl. Acad. Sci. USA* 86:3194–98

21. Evans GS, Flint N, Somers AS, Eyden B, Potten CS. 1992. The development of a method for the preparation of rat intestinal epithelial cell primary cultures. *J. Cell Sci.* 101:219–231

22. Evans GS, Flint N, Tait I, Campbell FC. 1993. Epithelial mesenchymal interactions in intestinal epithelial proliferation in vitro. *Gut Suppl.* 34:W25

23. Evans GS, Potten CS. 1991. Stem cells and the elixir of life. *BioEssays* 13:135–38

24. Ferraris RP, Diamond J. 1992. Crypt villus site of glucose transport induction by dietary carbohydrate in mouse intestine. *Am. J. Physiol.* 262:G1069–73

25. Finch PW, Rubin JS, Miki T, Ron D, Aaronson SA. 1989. Human KGF is FGF related with properties of a paracrine effector of epithelial cell growth. *Science* 245:752–55

26. Flint N, Cove FL, Evans GS. 1991. A low temperature method for the isolation of small intestinal epithelium along the crypt-villus axis. *Biochem. J.* 280:331–34

27. Flint N, Cove FL, Evans GS. 1993. Heparin stimulates the proliferation of intestinal epithelial cell in primary culture. *J. Cell Sci.* In press

28. Freshney RI. 1986. Introduction. Principles of sterile technique and cell propagation. In *Animal Cell Culture: A Practical Approach.* ed. RI Freshney, 1:4–5. Oxford: IRL

29. Friedman EA, Higgins PJ, Lipkin M, Shinya H, Gelb AM. 1981. Tissue culture of human epithelial cells from benign colonic tumours. *In Vitro* 17: 632–44

30. Fukamachi H. 1992. Proliferation and differentiation of fetal rat intestinal epithelial cells in primary serum free culture. *J. Cell Sci.* 103:511–19

31. Gibson PR, Van de Pol E, Maxwell LE, Gabriel A, Doe WF. 1989. Isolation of colonic crypts that maintain structural and metabolic viability in vitro. *Gastroenterology* 96:283–91

32. Haffen K, Kedinger M, Simon-Assmann P. 1987. Mesenchyme dependent differentiation of epithelial progenitor cells in the gut. *J. Ped. Gastroenterol. Nutr.* 6:14–23

33. Haffen K, Kedinger M, Simon PM, Raul F. 1981. Organogenetic potentialities of rat intestinal epithelial cell cultures. *Differentiation* 18:97–103

34. Hahn U, Schuppan D, Hahn EG, Merker H-J, Riecken E-O. 1987. Intestinal cells produce basement membrane proteins in vitro. *Gut* 28:143–51 (Suppl. 1)

35. Haugland RP. 1992. *Molecular Probes: Handbook of Fluorescent Probes and Research Chemicals 1992–1994,* ed. KD Larison, Eugene, OR: Molecular Probes. 5th Ed.

36. Henning SJ. 1985. Ontogeny of enzymes in the small intestine. *Annu. Rev. Physiol.* 47:231–45

37. Hoffman AGD, Kuksis A. 1980. Culture of presumptive epithelial cells from jejunal mucosa of axenic rats. *Experientia* 36:202–4

38. Karnovsky MJ, Wright TC Jr, Castellot JJ, Choay J, Lormeau JC, Petitou M.

1989. Heparin, heparan-sulphate, smooth muscle cells and atherosclerosis. *Ann. NY Acad. Sci.* 556:268–81

39. Kedinger M, Bouziges F, Simon-Assmann, P, Haffen K. 1989. Influence of cell interactions on intestinal brush border enzyme expression. *Highlights Mod. Biochem.* 2:1103–12

40. Kedinger M, Haffen K, Simon-Assmann P. 1987. Intestinal tissue and cell cultures. *Differentiation* 36:71–85

41. Kedinger M, Simon-Assmann P, Alexandre E, Haffen K. 1987. Importance of a fibroblastic support for in vitro differentiation of intestinal endodermal cells and for their response to glucocorticoids. *Cell Diff.* 20:171–82

42. Koide N, Sakaguchi K, Koide Y, Asano K, Kawaguchi M, et al. 1990. Formation of multi-cellular spheroids composed of adult rat hepatocytes in dishes with positively charged surfaces and under other non-adherent environments. *Exp. Cell Res.* 186:227–35

43. Kondo Y, Young GP, Rose I, Whitehead RH. 1985. Organ specificity of epithelial cells grown in tissue culture from explants obtained from various levels of rat gut. *Exp. Cell Res.* 159: 158–70

44. Kuri-Harcuch W, Mendoza-Figueroa T. 1989. Cultivation of adult rat hepatocytes on 3T3 cells: Expression of various liver differentiated functions. *Differentiation* 41:148–57

45. Kurokawa M, Lynch K, Podolsky DK. 1987. Effects of growth factors on an intestinal epithelial cell line: Transforming growth factorβ inhibits proliferation and stimulates differentiation. *Biochem. Biophys. Res. Commun.* 142: 775–82

46. Lansing Taylor D, Wang YL, eds. 1989. *Fluorescence Microscopy of Living Cells in Culture, Parts A and B: Methods in Cell Biology.* Vols. 29, 30. San Diego: Academic

47. Lechner JF, Haugen A, Autrup H, McClendon IA, Trump BF, Harris CC. 1981. Clonal growth of epithelial cells from normal adult human bronchus. *Cancer Res.* 41:2294–304

48. Lichtenberger LM, Lechago JM, Miller TA. 1979. Cell culture of human intestinal mucosae. *Gastroenterology* 77:1291–300

49. Lichtenberger L, Miller TA, Erwin DN, Johnson LR. 1973. Effects of pentagastrin on adult rat duodenal cells in culture. *Gastroenterology* 65:242–51

50. Martin GR, Evans MJ. 1975. Differentiation of clonal teratocarcinoma cells: Formation of embryoid bodies

in vitro. *Proc. Natl. Acad. Sci. USA* 72:1441–45

51. Mathan M, Hermos JA, Trier JS. 1972. Structural features of the epithelio-mesenchymal interface of rat duodenal mucosa during development. *J. Cell Biol.* 52:577–88

52. Mauchamp J, Chambard M, Verrier B, Gabrian J, Chabaud O, et al. 1987. Epithelial cell polarization in culture: orientation of cell polarity and expression of specific functions, studied with cultured thyroid cells. In *Cell Behaviour: Shape, Adhesion and Motility.* ed. JEM Heaysman, CA Middleton, FM Watt, 8:345–58. Cambridge: Company of Biologists

53. Montesano R, Schaller G, Orci L. 1991. Induction of epithelial tubular morphogenesis in vitro by fibroblast derived soluble factors. *Cell* 66:697–711

54. Montgomery RK. 1986. Morphogenesis in vitro of dissociated fetal rat small intestinal cells upon an open surface and subsequent to collagen gel overlay. *Dev. Biol.* 117:64–70

55. Moore EDW, Becker PL, Fogarty KE, Williams DA, Fay FS. 1990. Ca^{2+} imaging in single living cells: theoretical and practical issues. *Cell Calcium* 11:157–79

56. Moyer PM, Armstrong A, Bradley-Aust J, Levine BA, Sirinek KR. 1986. Effects of gastrin, glutamine and somatostatin on the in vitro growth of normal and malignant human gastric mucosal cells. *Arch. Surg.* 121:285–88

57. Moyer PM, Dixon PS, Culpepper A-L, Bradley-Aust J. 1990. In vitro propagation and characterisation of normal, pre-neoplastic, and neoplastic colonic epithelial cells. In *Colon Cancer Cell,* ed. MP Moyer, GH Poste, 5:85–136. San Diego: Academic

58. Nakamura T. 1991. Structure and function of hepatocyte growth factor. *Prog. Growth Factor Res.* 3:67–85

59. Nathan C, Sporn M. 1991. Cytokines in context. *J. Cell Biol.* 113:981–86

60. Négrel R, Rampal P, Nano J-L, Cavenal C, Ailhaud G. 1983. Establishment and characterisation of an epithelial intestinal cell line from rat fetus. *Exp. Cell. Res.* 143:427–37

61. Neutra M, Louvard D. 1989. Differentiation of intestinal cells in vitro. See Ref. 3, pp.363–98

62. Palmer Smith J, Solomon TE. 1988. Effects of gastrin, proglumide and somatostatin on growth of human colon cancer. *Gastroenterology* 95:1541–48

63. Paraskeva C, Buckle BG, Sheer D,

Wigley CB. 1984. The isolation and characterisation of colorectal epithelial cell lines at different stages in malignant transformation from familial polyposis coli patients. *Int. J. Cancer* 34:49–56

64. Paraskeva C, Williams AC. 1992. The Colon. In *Culture of Specialized Cells: Culture of Epithelial Cells,* ed. RI Freshney, 4:81–105. New York: Wiley/Liss

65. Park JHY, McCusker RH, VanDerhoof JA, Mohammadpour H, Harty RF, MacDonald RG. 1992. Secretion of insulin-like growth factor II (IGF II) and IGF binding protein-2 by intestinal epithelial (IEC-6) cells: Implications for autocrine growth regulation. *Endocrinology* 131:1359–68

66. Potten CS, Loeffler M. 1990. Stem cells: attributes, cycles, spirals, pitfalls and uncertainties. Lessons for and from the crypt. *Development* 110:1001–20

67. Quaroni A. 1985. Development of fetal rat intestine in organ and monolayer culture. *J. Cell Biol.* 100:1611–22

68. Quaroni A, May RJ. 1980. Establishment and characterisation of intestinal epithelial cell cultures. In *Methods in Cell Biology,* ed. GC Harris, BF Trump, GD Stoner. 21B:403–27. New York: Academic

69. Raul F, Kedinger M, Simon P, Greier JF, Haffen K. 1978. Behaviour of isolated rat intestinal cells maintained in suspension or monolayer cultures. *Biol. Cell* 33:163–68

70. Rheinwald JG, Green H. 1975. Serial cultivation of strains of human epidermal keratinocytes: the formation of keratinizing colonies from single cells. *Cell* 6:331–43

71. Riordan JR, Rommens JM, Kerem B, Alan N, Rozmahel R, et al. 1989. Identification of the cystic fibrosis gene: cloning and characterization of complementary DNA. *Science* 245:1066–73

72. Ruoslahti E, Yamaguchi Y. 1991. Proteoglycans as modulators of growth factor activities. *Cell* 64:867–869

73. Sambuy Y, DeAngelis I. 1986. Formation of organoid structures and extracellular matrix production in an intestinal epithelial cell line during long term in vitro culture. *Cell Diff.* 19:139–47

74. Siddiqui KM, Chopra DP. 1984. Primary and long term epithelial cell cultures from human fetal colonic mucosa. *In Vitro* 20:859–68

75. Simo P, Simon-Assmann P, Arnold C, Kedinger M. 1992. Mesenchyme me-

diated effects of dexamethasone on laminin in cocultures of embryonic gut epithelial cells and mesenchyme derived cells. *J. Cell Sci.* 101:161–71

76. Simo P, Simon-Assmann P, Bouziges F, Leberquier C, Kedinger M, et al. 1991. Changes in the expression of laminin during intestinal development. *Development* 112:477–87

77. Simon-Assmann P, Bouziges F, Arnold C, Haffen K, Kedinger M. 1988. Epithelial-mesenchymal interactions in the production of basement membrane components in the gut. *Development* 102:339–47

78. Simon-Assmann P, Bouziges F, Vigny M, Kedinger M. 1989. Origin and deposition of basement membrane heparan sulphate proteoglycan in the developing intestine. *J. Cell Biol.* 109: 1837–48

79. Smith AG, Heath JK, Donaldson, DD, Wong GG, Moreau J, Stahl M, et al. 1988. Inhibition of pluripotent embryonic stem cell differentiation by purified polypeptides. *Nature* 336:688–90

80. Smith HS, Lan S, Ceriani R, Hackett AJ, Stampfer MR. 1981. Clonal proliferation of cultured nonmalignant and malignant human breast epithelia. *Cancer Res.* 41:4637–43

81. Stange EF, Schneider A, Schusdziarra V, Ditschuneit H. 1984. Inhibitory effects of somatostatin on growth and differentiation in cultured intestinal mucosa. *Horm. Metabol. Res.* 16:74–78

82. Steel RE, Preston AS, Johnson JP, Handler JS. 1986. Porous bottomed dishes for culture of polarized cell. *Am. J. Physiol.* 251:C136–39

83. Tait IS, Flint N, Evans GS, Potten CS, Kedinger M, Campbell FC. 1993. Progressive morphogenesis in vivo after transplantation of cultured small bowel epithelium. *Cell Trans.* In press

84. Tsuchiya W, Okada Y. 1982. Membrane potential changes associated with differentiation of enterocytes in the rat intestinal villi in culture. *Dev. Biol.* 94:284–90

85. Underwood PA, Bennett FA. 1989. A comparison of the biological activities of the cell adhesive proteins vitronectin and fibronectin. *J. Cell Sci.* 93:641–49

86. Vidrich A, Ravidranath R, Farsi K, Targan S. 1988. A method for the rapid establishment of normal adult mammalian colonic epithelial cell cultures. *In Vitro Cell. Dev. Biol.* 24:188–94

87. Watt FM. 1986. The extracellular matrix and cell shape. *Trends Biochem. Sci.* 11:482–485

88. Whitehead RH, Brown A, Bhathal PS. 1987. A method for the isolation and culture of human colonic crypts in collagen gels. *In Vitro Cell. Dev. Biol.* 23:436–42

89. Whitehead RH, Nice EC, Lloyd CJ, James R, Burgess AW. 1990. Detection of colonic growth factors using a human colonic carcinoma line (LIM 1215). *Int. J. Cancer* 46:858–863

90. Whitehead RH, VanEeden PE, Noble MD, Ataliotis P, Jat PS. 1993. Establishment of conditionally immortalized epithelial cell lines from both colon and small intestine of adult H-2KBtsA58 transgenic mice. *Proc. Natl. Acad. Sci. USA* 90:587–91

91. Wright EM, Turk E, Zabel B, Mundios S, Dyer J. 1991. Molecular genetics of intestinal glucose transport. *J. Clin. Invest.* 88:1435–40

92. Yahon A, Klagsbrun M, Esko JD, Leder P, Ornitz DM. 1991. Cell surface heparin-like molecules are required for binding of basic fibroblast growth factor to its high affinity receptor. *Cell* 64:841–48

93. Yeh KY, Chopra DP. 1980. Epithelial cell cultures from the colon of suckling rat. *In Vitro* 16:976–86

94. Yeh KY, Yeh M, Holt PR. 1989. Induction of rat jejunal epithelial cells expression of sucrase isomaltase by glucocorticoids in primary culture and in vivo. *Biol. Cell* 65:139–50

95. Zweibaum A, Laburthe M, Grasset E, Louvard D. 1991. The use of cultured cell lines in studies of intestinal cell differentiation and function. In *Handbook of Physiology: Intestinal Absorption and Secretion*, ed. M Feild, RA Frizzell, Vol. 4 Sec. 6:233–55. Bethesda: Am. Physiol. Soc.

Annu. Rev. Physiol. 1994. 56:419–43
Copyright © by Annual Reviews Inc. All rights reserved

PANCREATIC DUCT CELL CULTURES

Sherwood Githens

Department of Biological Sciences, University of New Orleans, New Orleans,
Louisiana 70148

KEY WORDS: primary cultures, cell lines, pancreatic cancer, cellular markers

CHARACTERISTICS OF DUCT CELLS IN VIVO

The duct cell is a minor cell type of the pancreas, which comprises 10%
of the cells and 4% of the volume of the pancreas (39). The predominant
acinar cells are much denser than the other cell types because of their large
content of zymogen granules (145), thus the duct cells contain less than
4% of the pancreatic protein. The duct cells comprise a tubular epithelium
through which the secretions of the acinar cells (digestive enzymes in a
small volume of chloride-rich fluid) reach the duodenum. The duct system
adds a large volume of a bicarbonate-rich fluid that aids the movement of
the digestive enzymes through the duct system and neutralizes stomach acid
in the duodenum, although there is considerable species variation in the
details of duct cell function (21, 22).

The smallest of the pancreatic ducts, the intralobular ducts (ductules),
are in direct epithelial continuity with the acinar cells and tend to project
into the acinus as centroacinar cells. Ductular cells comprise about 80% of
the cells of the duct system (75). Ductules drain into interlobular ducts and
these drain into one or more main ducts. As duct size (luminal diameter
and number of cells in circumference) increases, the height of the epithelium
and the thickness of surrounding connective tissue increases (39). Duct cells
generally exhibit an unspecialized cytoplasm containing a few mucin secretory granules in interlobular and main ducts, apical microvilli, a single
apical cilium, and extensive interdigitations of lateral plasma membrane.
Small numbers of goblet, brush, and endocrine cells are scattered among
the principal cells of interlobular and main ducts (39, 96, 119).

419

0066–4278/94/0315–0419$05.00

Table 1 Pancreatic duct cell markers

Marker	Species	Reference	Marker	Species	Reference
Enzymes					
DPP IV[a]	Rat	(47, 61)[b]	CA II	Guinea pig, human	(79, 83, 150, 151)
APA	Rat	(47, 93)	CA III	Monkey	(110)
APN[d]	Rat	(47)	Na^+, K^+-ATPase	Various[c]	(18, 19, 67, 95, 149, 154)
Growth factors					
Insulin-like growth factor I	Rat	(55)	EGF	Pig	(160)
TGFα	Human	(9)			
Cytoskeletal proteins					
Cytokeratin 4	Human	(141)	Cytokeratin 19	Human, mouse	(7, 77, 106, 141)
Cytokeratin 5	Human	(105)	Cytokeratin 20	Rat	(11, 107)
Cytokeratin 7	Human	(77, 106, 141)			
Lectins					
Assorted[e]	Dog, cat	(147)	GSII	Human	(25)
DBA	Mouse	(140)			
Mucins					
Deglycosylated mucin	Human	(65)	Mucins[f]	Human	(39, 143, 166)
Proteoglycans and extracellular matrix molecules					
Syndecan	Mouse	(62)	Osteopontin	Human	(17)
Proteoglycan	Human	(132, 134)			
Blood group antigens					
Le[a]	Human	(71, 121, 139, 142)	Le[x]	Human	(71)

Histocompatibility antigens					
HLA-ABC	Human	(15)	MHC-I	Rat	(60)
HLA-DR	Human	(15)			
Pancreatic duct adenocarcinoma antigens[g]					
CA50	Human	(52, 136, 142)	Anti-GER cell line	Human	(48)
CA54-0	Human	(137)	YPAN-1	Human	(169, 170)
CA19-9	Human	(6, 52, 136, 142)	S3-23	Human	(76)
DU-PAN-2	Human	(103, 136, 143)	SLX, SLEX	Human	(136)
CEA	Human	(39)	SPAN-1	Human	(79)
CA242	Human	(51)	KMO1	Human	(113)
LDB1	Human	(54)			
Miscellaneous					
Anti-main pancreatic duct	Human	(39)	SC	Human	(79, 131)
Anti-duct cell	Human	(39)	Cell CAM 105	Rat	(112)
Anti-duct cell	Pig	(115)	Vit B$_{12}$ R binder	Human	(82)
Duct-1	Mouse	(28)	ADCP	Human	(30)
CFTR	Human, rat	(27, 35, 101, 157)	P-glycoprotein[h]	Human	(26, 111, 155)
Anti-N-terminal GRP	Human, pig	(143, 159)			

[a] Abbreviations used: APA = aminopeptidase A; CA = carbonic anhydrase; CEA = carcinoembryonic antigen; CFTR = cystic fibrosis transmembrane conductance regulator; DPP IV = dipeptidyl peptidase IV; EGF = epidermal growth factor; GRP = gastrin releasing peptide; SC = secretory component; TGF = transforming growth factor. [b] DPP IV is mainly in islet A cells of the pig, with weaker stain in both acinar and duct cells (123). [c] Rat, pig, guinea pig, dog, cat, human. [d] Another report suggests that aminopeptidase N is present in both acinar and duct cells (20). [e] BS-1, DBA, SBA, S-WGA, UEA-1. [f] Detected often by stains such as alcian blue, which may also stain proteoglycans. [g] Many of these antibodies, such as DU-PAN-2 and CA19-9, are directed against the glycosyl portion of the antigen. [h] Other monoclonal antibodies stain islet (8) or acinar (122) cells selectively.

Duct cells are characterized by the presence of a variety of biochemical and antigenic markers that are either found exclusively or in much greater concentrations in duct cells, as compared with acinar and endocrine cells of the pancreas. A list of some of these markers is presented in Table 1. These markers are generally found throughout the duct system. In some cases, only certain duct cells exhibit the marker. It is important to recognize that these markers may be present in other cells of the pancreas, such as capillary endothelium, and may also be present in other organs, especially in duct cells of those organs. In fact, only two antigenic markers apparently unique to pancreatic duct cells have been identified thus far (39).

These markers are important because they represent the principal means of showing that epithelial cultures prepared from the pancreas have a ductal phenotype. The concentrations of the markers are a measure of the extent to which the cells remain differentiated. However, the presence of duct cell markers does not necessarily mean that the cultures originated from duct cells because there is increasing evidence that the phenotype of pancreatic cells can change in vivo when the pancreas is damaged (98, 126) and also in culture (28, 43, 46, 53).

PRIMARY CULTURES

The establishment of primary duct cell cultures requires methods for duct cell isolation and purification from the other cell types of the pancreas, as well as for their propagation in culture under conditions that preserve their in vivo characteristics. This review deals mainly with cultures established from isolated epithelial cells. It also deals to a lesser extent with cultures of pancreatic duct fragments, which contain connective tissue cells as well as duct epithelium, and with cultures established from pancreatic explants (fetal, neonatal, and adult), which are potentially even more complex. Reviews of such cultures have been published previously (4, 22, 39, 56, 91).

Duct cell cultures have been established from all parts of the duct system (Table 2). Main duct cell cultures have been established from human (74, 156), bovine (135, 152), and rat (32) pancreas. Interlobular duct cell cultures have been established from rat (44, 64), mouse (45, 46), guinea pig (69), and hamster (70) pancreas. Probable intralobular duct cell cultures have been established from mouse (46), Rhesus monkey (43), and human (53) pancreas. Duct cell cultures from unknown parts of the duct system have been established from rat pancreas (14, 158).

Isolation of Duct Cells

The strategy for duct cell isolation is largely a function of duct diameter. The main pancreatic ducts of most mammals are large enough to permit them to be isolated by dissection and cut open longitudinally so that the duct epithelial cells may be harvested by scraping (32, 152) or by enzyme dissociation after the bulk of the stroma is dissected away (156). Alternatively, the main duct may simply be cannulated at both ends and perfused with enzymes that release the duct epithelium into the perfusate (74, 135).

While the larger interlobular ducts of large mammals may be handled like main ducts, the smaller interlobular ducts of large mammals and all of the interlobular ducts of small mammals must be approached differently because they cannot be readily obtained in large numbers by dissection, and they are too small to be perfused. Interlobular ducts are obtained by digestion of the minced pancreas with collagenase, sometimes supplemented with other proteases or with hyaluronidase, often in the presence of soybean trypsin inhibitor (44–46, 64, 69, 70). Interlobular ducts, as well as main ducts from small mammals and larger blood vessels, perhaps because of their connective tissue sheaths, are relatively resistant to this treatment as compared with the rest of the pancreas. Thus while the larger ducts and vessels remain intact, the rest of the pancreas is broken up into much smaller fragments consisting of acinar tissue, islets of Langerhans, intralobular ducts, and small vessels. If the interlobular duct fragments are large enough, they may be removed manually (69). Alternatively, they may be separated from the smaller fragments by trapping on a sieve (64, 70), although larger blood vessels are also trapped and the duct fragments must still be selected manually under a microscope. If the pancreas is digested further, small clusters of cells with ductal properties, but from an unknown part of the duct system, may be obtained (158).

Interlobular duct fragments obtained in this way consist of both duct epithelium and connective tissue. The connective tissue can be removed from freshly isolated ducts by dissection (161). Alternatively, all of the fragments trapped on the sieve may be cultured for a few days in a collagen gel so as to make the duct fragments in the mixture more easily recognizable because of their ability to form elongate cysts and distend, probably through their ability to secrete fluid (44–46, 64, 70). The distended duct fragments may then be harvested manually after dissolution of the collagen gel and further dissociated by divalent cation chelation and collagenase digestion, followed by separation of the epithelial fragments from the connective tissue by centrifugation through 4% bovine serum albumin (44–46, 64, 70).

The isolation and purification of intralobular ducts (ductules) is a bigger problem because their small size makes manual selection under a dissecting microscope much more difficult, and methods for bulk purification have not been described. Ductules may be more sensitive to the digestion process because of their lack of a connective tissue sheath. Alternatively, they may remain attached to larger ducts (42, 69) or to acini.

Table 2 Summary of duct epithelial cultures: morphological features and specific markers

	Duct class	Species	Age	Sex	Cilia	Apical MV[a]	Lateral MV	SG[a]	BL	Duct markers	Acinar/islet markers	Reference
In vivo	Main	Various	Adult	M and F	+[b]	+	+	+	+	Table 1	Islet cells	Table 1
In culture	Main	Bovine	Adult	M	−	+	−	+/ND	−	—	Islet A and B cells[c]	(152)
In culture	Main	Bovine	Adult	?	−	−	−	−	−	—	—	(135)
In culture	Main	Human	Adult	?	−	−	−	−	−	—	—	(74)
In culture	Main	Human	Adult	?	−	−	−	−	−	CK19[d], CAII, DU-PAN-2, CA19-9	Amylase$^-$, lipase$^-$, trypsin$^-$, islet cells$^-$	(156)
In vivo	Inter[e]	Various	Adult	M and F	+	+	+	+	+	Table 1	Islet cells	Table 1
In culture	Inter	Rat	Adult	M and F	+	+	+	−	ND	Mucins	—	(44)
In culture	Inter	Guinea pig	Adult	M	−	+	+	−	ND	—	—	(69)
In culture	Inter	Hamster	Adult	M	−	+	+	−	−	Ca, Sn-stimulated adenylate cyclase	—	(70)
In culture	Inter	Rat	Adult	M and F	−	−	−	−	−	CA	—	(64)
In culture	Inter	Mouse	Adult	M	−	+	+	ND	ND	Ca, CFTR, GGT, Sn-stimulated I_{sc}	Amylase$^-$, CA[f]	(45, 46)

									Markers present	Markers absent	Reference
In vivo	Intra[e]	Various	Adult	M and F	+	+	ND	+	Table 1	ND	Table 1
In culture	Intra	Human	Adult	?	—	—	—	—	CK19, mucins	—	(53)
In culture	Intra	Rhesus	Adult	M and F	—	—	—	—	CA	—	(43)
In culture	Intra	Mouse	Adult	M	+	+	ND	ND	CA, CFTR, GGT, Sn-stimulated I_{sc}	Amylase$^-$ CA[f]	(46)
In culture	?	Rat	Adult	M and F	+	—	ND/+	—	CA, GGT	insulin$^-$, glucagon$^-$	(144, 158)
In culture	?	Rat	Adult	M	—	—	—	—	CK7	amylase$^-$, elastase$^-$	(14)
In culture	?	Rat	Neonatal	M and F	+	+	—	—	—	—	(23)
In culture	?	Human	Fetal	?	+	+	+	+	CK19, CAII, mucin, CFTR, CA19-9, DU-PAN-2, Cl$^-$ channels	—	(50, 56, 57, 58, 59)

[a] Abbreviations: BL = basal lamina; CA = carbonic anhydrase; CFTR = cystic fibrosis transmembrane conductance regulator; CK = cytokeratin; GGT = γ-glutamyl transferase; I_{sc} = short-circuit current; MV = microvilli; SG = secretory granules; Sn = secretin. [b] + = present; ND = not detectable; — = no information given. [c] A superscript − indicates that the marker was not detectable. [e] Inter = interlobular; intra = intralobular. [f] The CA specific activity was 0.25% of the activity in freshly isolated acinar/ductular tissue.

If they survive the digestion process, isolated ductules and ductules attached to acinar tissue should be present among the small fragments resulting from the enzymatic digestion of the pancreas and should, therefore, be present in the tissue fragments that pass through the sieve that is used to trap interlobular duct fragments. When this filtrate is resuspended in 27% Ficoll, overlaid with lower density layers of Ficoll and centrifuged, as done for the purification of pancreatic islets (145), the ductules should float as the denser acinar tissue sediments. When this is done, small numbers of probable ductules are found (46), but their numbers are far less than would be expected given that the ductules represent 80% or more of the duct system of the pancreas of rats (75, 129). This suggests that many of the ductules are disrupted during the isolation process or remain attached to the denser acinar tissue.

Small numbers of ductules have recently been isolated from Rhesus monkey (43) and human (S Githens, unpublished) pancreas using a dissociation procedure that differs significantly from the procedures used for rodent pancreas, probably because of the much more compact nature of the pancreas of larger mammals. The Rhesus pancreas is cut into small chunks and these are digested with collagenase and papain on a wrist-action shaker. Every 2 min the chunks are allowed to sediment under gravity, the supernatant is removed and centrifuged to collect released small tissue fragments, and these are resuspended in a protective medium. The digestion medium is returned to the chunks for another round of digestion. When the released fragments are fractionated by Ficoll density gradient centrifugation, small numbers of probable ductules are recognizable in the tissue that floats. When floating tissue is cultured as a suspension in a collagen gel, epithelial cysts appear within a few days. However, the small numbers of these apparent ductules precludes much further analysis.

Probable ductular cell cultures may be derived from acinar/ductular tissue (the acinus with its centroacinar cells and any attached intralobular ducts) and from pancreatic explants, as is described in the section entitled Culture of Acinar/Ductular Tissue and Pancreatic Explants.

Duct cells from an unknown part of the duct system have been isolated and cultured after extensive digestion of the rat pancreas (14, 158). These cells share many of the features of the other duct cell cultures. In one paper (14) it is argued that the cells are stem cells because cells with virtually identical properties may be isolated from the rat liver. Putative rat pancreatic stem cells have also been isolated from rats fed a copper-deficient diet (125). Rats treated in this fashion exhibit an extensive loss of acinar cells while the duct system remains intact (126). The isolation procedure was designed to exclude intact duct and ductular fragments. These cells exhibit many of the properties of cultured duct epithelium.

Culture Media

A variety of basal media have been used for the culture of duct cells including a 1:1 mixture of Dulbecco's modified Eagle's medium and Ham's F12 (DMEM/F12) (43, 46, 64, 70, 74), which is often used for the culture of epithelial cells, Eagle's minimal essential medium (MEM) (152), an improved version of MEM (158), CMRL-1066 (58, 135, 161), and RPMI-1640 (156). In only two studies were different basal media compared, and these showed that CMRL-1066 produced the most rapid growth of bovine main duct (135) and human fetal pancreatic (58) cells.

The basal culture media have been enriched with a wide variety of supplements, with fetal bovine serum (2.5–20%) the most common, although growth in the absence of serum is possible if a variety of other supplements are present (64, 70). The most common additives are insulin (0.17–1.5 mM), dexamethasone (1–2.5 mM), epidermal growth factor (EGF) (0.6–10 nM), and soybean trypsin inhibitor (0.1–0.2 mg/mL). Many of these supplements were chosen because they had been shown to stimulate survival and growth of primary cultures of other types of epithelial cells. In only a few cases have the additives been shown to be important in pancreatic duct cell proliferation (see below), and none has been shown to have an effect on the maintenance of duct cell differentiation.

Culture Matrix

Duct epithelial cells may be grown on plastic (58, 69, 74, 135, 152, 156, 158, 161), on plastic coated with a thin film of collagen or a basement membrane extract (32, 58, 69, 70), on thick collagen gels (46, 69, 70, 161), or on permeable filter supports coated with either collagen or Matrigel (46, 64, 69, 70). Such cultures are planar in organization and therefore mimic the structure of ducts with a relatively large diameter. Although growth on Matrigel or other types of basement membrane extracts is reported to be important for the maintenance of the differentiated properties of other cell types (80), this does not appear to be the case with duct epithelium, since mouse duct and ductular cells express the same concentrations of carbonic anhydrase (CA) activity (a duct cell marker, see Table 1) when grown on porous supports coated with either basement membrane extract or collagen (46). Duct epithelial cells may also be grown suspended in collagen or other gels where they typically form three-dimensional cystic structures, presumably because of continued fluid/electrolyte secretion (43, 44, 46). Permitting the duct epithelium to form spherical or ovoid structures may help to maintain the differentiation of duct epithelium by better mimicking their tubular structure in vivo.

Elimination of Fibroblasts

Contaminating fibroblasts can be a problem in epithelial cell cultures because of their tendency to grow faster than the epithelial cells and to overgrow the culture. Elimination of fibroblasts is also important if the cells are to be homogenized or extracted for analysis. On the other hand, fibroblasts are required for the construction of basement membrane (146) and may therefore be important if an intact basement membrane is needed for normal function, assuming that the use of a basement membrane extract is insufficient.

Fibroblasts have been reduced or eliminated from duct cell cultures by the following stratagems: centrifugation of the freshly isolated duct epithelial fragments through 4% bovine serum albumin (44, 46, 64, 70); the more rapid rate of attachment to plastic by fibroblasts, as opposed to epithelial cells, which permits purified epithelial cells to be removed selectively (158); use of cloning wells to isolate and remove purely epithelial colonies (70); manual isolation of small clusters of pure epithelial cells under a microscope (158); dissection of surrounding connective tissue from the duct epithelial cylinder (161); use of 10% horse serum in the culture medium (158); and selective scraping of fibroblasts from the culture surface (58). In spite of these efforts, most cultures are slightly contaminated with fibroblasts, although cultures can be obtained that are devoid of fibroblasts by means of cloning procedures (70, 152, 158).

Cell Proliferation

It has been repeatedly noted that cell proliferation only occurs from clusters of duct epithelial cells, as opposed to single cells, probably because of the damage caused to single cells as they are separated from one another during dissociation (23, 44, 58, 70, 100, 135, 152, 156). However, the establishment of clonal cell lines in two cases (14, 152) showed that under certain circumstances individual cells can proliferate. Cell proliferation on a planar surface occurs in the form of expanding epithelial islands that eventually merge with one another (46, 64, 69, 161). In some cases, mitotic activity is reported to be mainly at the periphery of the islands (46, 64, 100). Growth rate is rapid, with a mitotic index of 0.6% (64) and doubling times of 18–45 hr during early passages (70, 74, 135, 152, 158, 161) and 16–20 hr during later passages (70, 158), which suggests that the more rapidly growing cells are being selected. The cultures may be subcultured at least a few times (46, 58, 64, 156), or many times (70, 152, 158). Cell proliferation is greater on a thick collagen gel than on plastic (161).

Duct cell proliferation is stimulated by EGF (100, 161), which stimulates the proliferation of a wide variety of epithelial cell types, by secretin (100), the main hormonal agonist of duct epithelial cell function (22), and by the combination of insulin, transferrin, and selenium (100). Transforming growth factor-β inhibits duct cell proliferation (14).

Morphological Characteristics

The cultures in all cases have the typical cobblestone appearance of epithelial cells. The cells tend to be flatter when cultured on plastic, as opposed to thick collagen gels (161), and after extended subculture (70). Cells at the periphery of epithelial islands tended to be flatter than cells in the center (46, 58, 64, 69).

The cultured epithelia generally have the ultrastructural appearance of duct epithelium in vivo, as summarized in Table 2. Apical microvilli, lateral membrane interdigitations, a relatively small volume of unspecialized cytoplasm, and tight junctions generally characterize the cultured epithelia. No basement membrane is present (69, 135) except when main duct epithelium is cultured on fetal mesenchyme (32) and when the epithelium remains in contact with connective tissue associated with the original duct explant (69). Secretory vesicles are present only in cultures derived from the main pancreatic duct (156). An occasional cilium is seen (44, 158).

Expression of Ductal, Acinar, and Islet Markers

It is clear that the cultures are ductal in origin when the main and interlobular ducts are isolated and used as the source of the epithelial cells. When mixtures of pancreatic cells are cultured and when small fragments of probable ductal epithelium are isolated, ultrastructural features can be used to suggest that the epithelial cells are indeed ductal, but the ultrastructural features cannot be used as definitive proof because the duct cells have few if any unique features. Thus the best criterion for the identification of duct cells is the presence of duct markers. However, the presence of markers could also mean that pancreatic acinar (or islet) cells had acquired ductal characteristics in culture. If markers are absent, this could simply mean that the cells, while ductal in origin, have lost the markers as a consequence of isolation and culture.

The extent to which the cultured duct epithelia possess duct cell markers is summarized in Table 2. It is clear that in many cases little attention has been paid to this point, and thus it is unclear how well the cultured epithelia have maintained their in vivo characteristics. If cultured epithelia are to be used as models for duct epithelium in vivo, more evidence for their ductal character needs to be obtained. In addition to demonstrating that a marker is expressed, it is important to show that it is expressed at a level similar to in vivo expression to indicate that the cells are maintaining their differentiated state. It is also important to show that the cells express small or undetectable concentrations of markers for acinar and islet cells. If markers for the latter cell types are detected biochemically, it is important to determine by morphological techniques whether all of the cells express small amounts of the markers, or whether a few cells express large amounts. The former case could be interpreted as indicating that the cells are pro-todifferentiated and express small concentrations of pancreas-specific products (41). The latter case would suggest contamination with the other cell types or differentiation of some of the duct cells into acinar or islet cells, consistent with the notion that pancreatic stem cells may be present in the duct epithelium (41).

Duct cultures have been assayed for their content of γ-glutamyl transferase (GGT) even though acinar cells express substantially greater amounts in vivo, as indicated mainly by histochemical studies of GGT activity (40). The specific activities of GGT expressed by mouse and rat duct cell cultures are 7% of the value in freshly isolated mouse pancreatic acinar tissue (46), which is consistent with their being duct cells.

Culture of Duct Fragments

Main and interlobular duct fragments (epithelium plus surrounding connective tissue) have been isolated, cultured, and characterized extensively, as described in recent reviews (4, 22, 39, 91). The epithelial cells retain the morphological features of duct epithelium in vivo. While these preparations are not suitable for biochemical studies because of the presence of more than one cell type, they have been shown by morphological and physiological means to retain differentiated features of duct epithelium such as secretin-stimulated adenylate cyclase, CA, Na^+,K^+-ATPase and apical Cl^- channels. They have been most valuable in the characterization of ductal fluid/electrolyte secretion in ways not possible with the intact pancreas.

Culture of Acinar/Ductular Tissue and Pancreatic Explants

As stated above, some ductules may remain attached to acinar tissue fragments, and acinar fragments typically contain centroacinar cells, the terminal part of the intralobular duct system (3, 68, 78, 165). Therefore, purification of acinar tissue by Ficoll density gradient centrifugation should lead to the isolation of centroacinar and ductular cells from other duct classes as well as from other pancreatic tissue types, even though acinar cells will be the predominant cell type in the preparation. If the acinar cells atrophy and die during subsequent culture, the surviving cells would be ductular cells. This appears to occur. Purified mouse acinar/ductular tissue, when cultured on porous supports coated with extracellular matrix, progressively loses its acinar characteristics (amylase, chymotrypsin, and zymogen granules) while gaining (or maintaining) ductal characteristics [CA activity, CA II mRNA, the cystic fibrosis transmembrane regulator (CFTR), and secretin-stimulated Cl^- transport](46). These cultures are indistinguishable from parallel cultures established from interlobular duct epithelium by all of these criteria.

Many investigators have isolated pancreatic acinar/ductular tissue and cultured it with the intent of studying the properties of acinar cells (5, 12, 16, 28, 91, 116, 117, 130). Most of these studies have reported the rapid loss, within a few days, of acinar cell characteristics such as the level of secretory enzymes (usually amylase) and zymogen granules. Indeed, many of the studies were terminated within the first week of culture. At least some of the residual amylase reported in such cultures might be due to residual amylase in acinar cell debris, especially when the plating density was large (12, 16, 92). We have found that the level of residual amylase and chymotrypsin in mouse acinar/ductular cultures is proportional to the amount of tissue plated (46). These studies of acinar/ductular tissue have, however, produced valuable information concerning the factors that modulate the rate of loss of acinar cell characteristics and stimulate cell proliferation.

It is possible that at least some of the studies of acinar/ductular tissue may have been on cell populations that were rapidly gaining ductular characteristics as acinar cells disappeared and were replaced by proliferating ductular cells. The possible presence of ductal markers was investigated in only one of these studies (28). However, possible acinar characteristics were maintained for several weeks in some of these cultures, including the expression of an acinar cell antigen (Acinar-1), but not amylase (28), and the presence of secretory granules, but not amylase (91), in mouse cultures. Acinar-1, which is abundant in freshly isolated acinar/ductular tissue, nearly disappears as the cells proliferate and express a ductal antigen (Duct-1) (28). As proliferation slows, Acinar-1 is reexpressed and Duct-1 disappears. This was taken as evidence that acinar cells become ductal in character while they proliferate and then resume their acinar character when proliferation ceases, even though they do not synthesize amylase. An alternative hypothesis is that the cell population becomes truly ductal in character by some combination of acinar cell death and/or dedifferentiation, followed by proliferation of these and ductular cells present in the original preparation (46). The cells then reexpress Acinar-1, which is also present in fetal acinar cells, while remaining predominantly ductal in character. In support of the concept of acinar cell death and ductular cell survival and proliferation, isolated clusters of rat acinar cells die in culture under conditions where duct cells survive (158), and the disappearance of acinar cells following ductal ligation is caused by apoptosis of acinar cells (162, 163). Determination of the extent to which acinar cells either die or dedifferentiate into duct-like cells requires a more complete survey of the presence or absence of acinar and ductal markers at the various stages of culture.

The simultaneous loss of acinar cells and increase in the proportion of cells with a duct-like appearance has also been noted frequently in explant cultures of late fetal (63, 164), neonatal (88), and adult (99, 120, 127, 128) pancreas, and in cultures from dissociated neonatal pancreas (2, 118). As with the studies of acinar/ductular tissue, it is unclear whether the acinar cells die and are replaced with surviving and proliferating duct cells, or whether some or all of the acinar cells become phenotypically ductal.

Both fetal and neonatal pancreatic explants have been cultured with no effort to purify any single cell type (23, 58, 59). The epithelial cultures generated by Harris and colleagues (58, 59) clearly exhibit many properties of adult duct epithelium (Table 2) and therefore appear to be a suitable model for the study of duct cells, especially electrolyte transport (50).

CELL LINES WITH DUCTAL CHARACTERISTICS

A number of continuous cell lines with morphological characteristics of duct cells have been established from human pancreatic adenocarcinomas of putative ductal origin (37). These cell lines generally express ductal markers and do not express acinar markers, although the sensitivity of the techniques for detecting acinar cell markers was usually not stated (Table 3). Thus at least some of the lines appear to be good models for duct cells in vivo.

Duct cell markers such as mucins, carcinoembryonic antigen (CEA), cytokeratins 7 and 19, carbohydrate epitopes detected by a variety of monoclonal antibodies (DU-PAN-2, CA19–9, and S3–23), GGT, and CA II are often present. However, the percentage of the cells expressing a given marker is often variable, which suggests either phenotypic variability or the presence of more than one cell type. The use of mucins as a duct cell marker is problematic because the presence of mucins has often been demonstrated by histochemical stains or biochemical analyses of secretions that reveal the presence of acidic macromolecules, which also detect proteoglycans and thus are not mucin-specific, in contrast with the detection of the mRNA or protein of the apomucin MUC-1. However, the presence of the apomucin is only consistent with the ductal origin of the cells because both duct and acinar cells express this protein (104). Duct and acinar cells differ in how the apomucin is glycosylated, which suggests that these cell types may be distinguished by the kinds of glycosyl transferases they express (104). Cellular and secreted CEA are often present, but the quantitative radioimmunoassay used shows that the cells vary considerably in the amount of CEA secreted, thus suggesting that maintenance of differentiation varies among the cell lines. GGT is expressed in both acinar and ductal cells, with the former exhibiting a substantially greater specific activity (40), which indicates that the specific activity in the cell lines is an important parameter. Human pancreatic acinar tissue has a GGT-specific activity of 75 mU/mg protein (S Githens, unpublished observations). Thus the much lower GGT activity in the cell lines in most cases is consistent with the ductal nature of the cells. The CEA and GGT data underline the importance of obtaining quantitative estimates of the concentrations of markers as indicators of the degree to which cell lines are differentiated. Two of the cell lines, MiaPaCa-2 and Panc-1, are notable in not exhibiting several ductal markers, which suggests that they may not be good models of duct cells in vivo.

In most instances the absence of acinar markers was noted by the observation that a particular exocrine secretory enzyme was not detectable. Because of the possibility that adult duct cells may retain the features of fetal protodifferentiated cells, which are hypothesized to express low levels of exocrine enzymes, it is recommended that sensitive assays be used and that the data be expressed as the minimal specific activity that could have been detected by the assay. In addition, the absence of small concentrations of islet markers should be better documented.

CONCLUSIONS

Although the primary cultures and established cell lines exhibit many properties of duct cells in vivo, in many instances further characterization would be required to make a convincing case that they retain the properties of duct cells and do not express the properties of acinar or islet cells. If they express very small amounts of acinar and/or islet markers, this would suggest that they resemble the protodifferentiated cells of the embryonic pancreas, which are hypothesized to express small concentrations of most if not all of the proteins specific to the pancreas (41).

However, it is important to recognize that differentiated pancreatic cell types may both lose their original markers and gain markers of other cell types when the pancreas is damaged in vivo or when specific cell types of the pancreas are placed in culture. If markers can be gained and lost, the set of markers in a cell population cannot be used to conclusively identify the kind of cells from which that population arose. The markers only describe the phenotype of the cells at the time of analysis. In order to analyze the kinds of interconversions among the pancreatic cell types that are possible, pure cell populations must be prepared and changes in their phenotype followed in culture, or culture conditions must be identified where shifts in phenotype occur with mixed cell populations in the absence of cell proliferation and death.

Table 3 Duct, acinar, and islet marker substances in human pancreatic duct adenocarcinoma cell lines

Cell line	Duct markers[a]	Acinar and islet markers[a]	Reference
AsPC-1	Mucin[b], MUC-1 apomucin mRNA, CEA[c], CK19, S3-23		(24, 87, 124)
BxPC-3	Mucin, apomucin[-], CEA, CK7, CK19, CA II, S3-23		(36, 87, 124, 133, 153)
Capan-1	Mucin, MUC-1 apomucin mRNA, CEA (20 ng/10^6 cells, 30 ng secreted/10^6 cells/24 h), DU-PAN-2, DPP IV, APA[-], TGFα, anion channel	CPA-, CPB[-]	(11, 13, 33, 34, 86, 87, 89, 103)
Capan-2	Mucin, MUC-1 apomucin mRNA, CK7, CK19, CA II, DU-PAN-2, YPan1		(36, 84, 86, 103, 124, 168, 169)
CFPAC	CEA secreted, CA19-9 secreted, CFTR		(138)
COLO 357	MUC-1 apomucin mRNA, CEA (250 ng secreted/10^6 cells/7 days), DU-PAN-2, S3-23	0.5 μg trypsin, 11.7 μg CT, and 3.1 ng elastase secreted/20 hr/flask[d]	(86, 87, 102, 103, 108)
GER	CA	Trypsin[-], CT[-], CPA[-], lipase[-], elastase[-]	(49)
HPAF	MUC-1 apomucin, DU-PAN-2, HLA II DR, HLA I	Amylase[-] (<30 mU/mg protein)	(79, 86, 87, 103)
HPC-x	CEA (10 of 10 lines), CA19-9 (10/10), DU-PAN-2 (6/10), GGT (8/10), SC (8/10)	Amylase (1/10), trypsin (10/10)	(167)
HS0214	GGT (30 mU/mg protein)		(109)
HS766T	MUC-1 apomucin, CEA (39 ng/mg protein), YPan1		(87, 109, 169)
MDAPanc-3	CA II	Amylase mRNA[-], insulin mRNA[-]	(36, 38)

Cell line	Markers	(Negative markers)	References
MiaPaCa-2	Mucin, CEA⁻, CK7⁻, CK19, DU-PAN-2⁻, CA, CA II mRNA, TGFα mRNA, Na⁺, K⁺-ATPase, GGT (43 mU/mg protein), Ypan1	Trypsin⁻, CT⁻	(1, 10, 36, 94, 103, 124, 149, 169, 171)
PANC-1	Mucin, MUC-1 apomucin⁻, CEA⁻ (<10 ng/10⁶ cells, ND in medium), CK19, CA (specific activity similar to human pancreas homogenate), CA II⁻, Na⁺, K⁺-ATPase, GGT (2.9 mU/mg protein), TGFα mRNA, S3-23, YPan1	Amylase⁻, secretory enzymes⁻	(10, 33, 36, 87, 90, 97, 124, 134, 149, 169)
PK-1	CEA	Trypsin	(81)
RWP-1, RWP-2	Mucin, CEA (1090, 414 ng secreted/10⁶ cells/3 days), S3-23, YPan1	Amylase⁻, trypsin⁻, CT⁻	(29, 169)
SUIT-2	CEA (26 ng/10⁶ cells, 4.8 ng secreted/10⁶ cells/24 h), CA19-9 (162 U/10⁶ cells, 233 U secreted/10⁶ cells/24 h)		(72, 73)
Su.86.86	CEA (594 ng secreted/10⁶ cells/3 days)		(31)
SW-1990	Mucin, MUC-1 apomucin mRNA, CEA (150 ng secreted/10⁶ cells/21 days), CK7, CK19	Amylase⁻, trypsin⁻, and CT⁻ in culture medium	(66, 85, 124, 168)
T3M4	MUC-1 apomucin, CEA (305 ng secreted/10⁶ cells/48 h during exponential growth), TGFα	Amylase⁻ in culture medium	(86, 114, 148)

[a] Markers that have been demonstrated to be present are listed. If a marker was not detected, it is indicated with a superscript ⁻. Quantitative data are given when available. [b] Macromolecules with a strong negative charge detected by histochemical stains such as alcian blue. [c] Abbreviations used: APA = aminopeptidase A; CA = carbonic anhydrase; CEA = carcinoembryonic antigen; CK = cytokeratin; CPA = carboxypeptidase A; CPB = carboxypeptidase B; CT = chymotrypsin; DPP IV = dipeptidyl peptidase IV; GGT = γ-glutamyl transferase; mU = nmol of product formed/min; SC = secretory component; TGF = transforming growth factor. [d] Amount secreted by confluent cells in a T75 flask.

Literature Cited

1. Allen L, Meck R, Yunis A. 1980. The inhibition of gamma-glutamyl transpeptidase from human pancreatic carcinoma cells by (alpha, 5S)-alpha-amino-3-chloro-4,5-dihydro-5-isoxazo leacetic acid (AT-125; NSC-163501). *Res. Commun. Chem. Pathol. Pharmacol.* 27:175–82

2. Amory B, Mourmeaux J-L, Remacle C. 1988. In vitro cytodifferentiation of perinatal rat islet cells within a tridimensional matrix of collagen. *In Vitro Cell Dev. Biol.* 24:91–99

3. Amsterdam A, Jamieson JD. 1974. Studies on dispersed pancreatic exocrine cells. I. Dissociation techniques and morphological characteristics of the separated cells. *J. Cell Biol.* 63:1037–56

4. Argent BE, Gray MA. 1990. Pancreatic ducts: isolation, culture and bicarbonate transport. In *Epithelia. Advances in Cell Physiology and Cell Culture,* ed. CJ Jones, pp. 69–97. Dordrecht: Kluwer

5. Arias AE, Bendayan M. 1991. Secretagogue induction of cell differentiation in pancreatic acinar cells in vitro. *Exp. Cell Res.* 195:199–206

6. Atkinson BF, Ernst CF, Herlyn M, Steplewski Z, Sears HF, Koprowski H. 1982. Gastrointestinal cancer-associated antigens in immunoperoxidase assay. *Cancer Res.* 42:4820–23

7. Bader BL, Franke WF. 1990. Cell type-specific and efficient synthesis of human cytokeration 19 in transgenic mice. *Differentiation* 45:109–18

8. Bani D, Brandi ML, Axiotis CA, Bani-Sacchi T. 1992. Detection of P-glycoprotein on endothelial and endocrine cells of the human pancreas by C494 monoclonal antibody. *Histochemistry* 98:207–9

9. Barton CM, Hall PA, Hughes CM, Gullick WJ, Lemoine NR. 1991. TGFα and EGF in human pancreatic cancer. *J. Pathol.* 163:111–16

10. Beauchamp RD, Lyons RM, Yang EY, Coffey RJJ, Moses HL. 1990. Expression of and response to growth regulatory peptides by two human pancreatic carcinoma cell lines. *Pancreas* 5:369–80

11. Becq F, Fanjul M, Mahier I, Berger Z, Gola M, Hollande E. 1992. Anion channels in a human pancreatic cancer cell line (Capan-1) of ductal origin. *Pflügers Arch.* 420:46–53

12. Bendayan M, Duhr M-A, Gingras D. 1986. Studies on pancreatic acinar cells in tissue culture: basal lamina (basement membrane) matrix promotes three-dimensional reorganization. *Eur. J. Cell Biol.* 42:60–67

13. Bensaadi N, Clemente F, Vaysse N. 1989. Modulation of enzymatic activities during spontaneous and induced differentiation in a human pancreatic adenocarcinoma cell line CAPAN-1. *Int. J. Pancreatol.* 4:391–406

14. Bisgaard HC, Thorgeirsson SS. 1991. Evidence for a common cell of origin for primitive epithelial cells isolated from rat liver and pancreas. *J. Cell. Physiol.* 147:333–43

15. Bovo P, Mirakian R, Merigo F, Angelini G, Cavallini G, et al. 1987. HLA molecule expression on chronic pancreatitis specimens: Is there a role for autoimmunity? A preliminary study. *Pancreas* 2:350–56

16. Brannon PM, Orrison BM, Kretchmer N. 1985. Primary cultures of rat pancreatic acinar cells in serum-free medium. *In Vitro Cell Dev. Biol.* 21:6–14

17. Brown LF, Berse B, van de Water L, Papadopoulos-Sergiou A, Perruzzi CA, et al. 1992. Expression and distribution of osteopontin in human tissues: widespread association with luminal epithelial surfaces. *Mol. Biol. Cell* 3:1169–80

18. Buanes T, Grotmol T, Landsverk T, Raeder MG. 1987. Localization of K-NPPase and Li⁺ secretion in the exocrine pancreas of the pig. *Acta Physiol. Scand.* 130:457–66

19. Bundgaard M, Moller M, Poulsen JH. 1981. Localization of sodium pump sites in the cat pancreas. *J. Physiol.* 313:405–14

20. Burstone MS, Folk JE. 1956. Histochemical demonstration of aminopeptidase. *J. Histochem. Cytochem.* 4:217–26

21. Case RM, Argent BE. 1989. Pancreatic secretion of electrolytes and water. In *Handbook of Physiology,* ed. JG Forte, SG Schultz, Vol. III Sec. 6 pp. 383–417. Bethesda: Am. Physiol. Soc.

22. Case RM, Argent BE. 1993. Pancreatic duct cell secretion: control and mechanisms of transport. In *The Pancreas: Biology, Pathobiology, and Disease,* ed. VLW Go, EP DiMagno, JD Gardner, E Lebenthal, HA Reber, GA Scheele, pp. 301–50. New York: Raven. 2nd ed.

23. Chen J, Stuckey EC, Berry CL. 1985. Three-dimensional culture of rat exo-

crine pancreatic cells using collagen gels. *Br. J. Exp. Pathol.* 66:551–59

24. Chen WH, Horoszewicz JS, Leong SS, Shimano T, Penetrante R, et al. 1982. Human pancreatic adenocarcinoma: in vitro and in vivo morphology of a new tumor line established from ascites. *In Vitro* 18:24–34

25. Ching CK, Black R, Heliwell T, Savage A, Barr H, Rhodes JM. 1988. Use of lectin histochemistry in pancreatic cancer. *J. Clin. Pathol.* 41:324–28

26. Cordon-Cardo C, O'Brien JP, Boccia J, Casals D, Bertino JR, Melamed MR. 1990. Expression of the multidrug resistance gene product (P-glycoprotein) in human normal and tumor tissue. *J. Histochem. Cytochem.* 38:1277–87

27. Crawford I, Maloney PC, Zeitlin PL, Guggino WB, Hyde SC, et al. 1991. Immunocytochemical localization of the cystic fibrosis gene product CFTR. *Proc. Natl. Acad. Sci. USA* 88:9262–66

28. De Lisle RC, Logsdon CD. 1990. Pancreatic acinar cells in culture: expression of acinar and ductal antigens in a growth-related manner. *Eur. J. Cell Biol.* 51:64–75

29. Dexter DL, Matook GM, Meitner PA, Bogaars HA, Jolly GA, et al. 1982. Establishment and characterization of two human pancreatic cell lines tumorigenic in athymic mice. *Cancer Res.* 42:2705–14

30. Dinjens WN, Ten Kate J, van der Linden EP, Wijnen JT, Khan PM, Bosman FT. 1989. Distribution of adenosine deaminase complexing protein (ADCP) in human tissues. *J. Histochem. Cytochem.* 37:1869–75

31. Drucker BJ, Marincola FM, Siao DY, Donlon TA, Bangs CD, Holder WDJ. 1988. A new human pancreatic carcinoma cell line developed for adoptive immunotherapy studies with lymphokine-activated killer cells in nude mice. *In Vitro Cell Dev. Biol.* 24:1179–87

32. Dudek RW, Lawrence IEJ. 1988. Morphological evidence of interactions between adult ductal epithelium of pancreas and fetal foregut mesenchyme. *Diabetes* 37:891–900

33. El-Deriny SE, O'Brien MJ, Christensen TG, Kupchik HZ. 1987. Ultrastructural differentiation and CEA expression of butyrate-treated human pancreatic carcinoma cells. *Pancreas* 2:25–33

34. Estival A, Clerc P, Vaysse N, Tam JP, Clemente F. 1992. Decreased expression of transforming growth factor α during differentiation of human pancreatic cancer cells. *Gastroenterology* 103:1851–59

35. Foulkes AG, Harris A. 1993. Localization of expression of the cystic fibrosis gene in human pancreatic development. *Pancreas* 8:3–6

36. Frazier ML, Lilly BJ, Wu EF, Ota T, Hewett-Emmett D. 1990. Carbonic anhydrase II gene expression in cell lines from human pancreatic adenocarcinoma. *Pancreas* 5:507–14

37. Frazier ML, Longnecker DS. 1993. Cell lines of the human and rodent exocrine pancreas. See Ref. 22, pp. 565–74

38. Frazier ML, Pathak S, Wang Z-W, Cleary K, Singletary SE, et al. 1990. Establishment of a new human pancreatic adenocarcinoma cell line, MDAPanc-3. *Pancreas* 5:8–16

39. Githens S. 1988. The pancreatic duct cell: proliferative capabilities, specific characteristics, metaplasia, isolation and culture. *J. Pediatr. Gastroenterol. Nutr.* 7:486–506

40. Githens S. 1991. Glutathione metabolism in the pancreas compared with that in the liver, kidney and small intestine. *Int. J. Pancreatol.* 8:97–109

41. Githens S. 1993. Differentiation and development of the pancreas in animals. See Ref. 22, pp. 21–55

42. Githens S, Holmquist DRG, Whelan JF, Ruby JR. 1980. Characterization of ducts isolated from the pancreas of the rat. *J. Cell Biol.* 85:122–35

43. Githens S, Patke CL, Schexnayder JA. 1993. Isolation and culture of Rhesus monkey pancreatic ductules and ductular-like epithelium. *Pancreas* 8(6): In press

44. Githens S, Schexnayder JA, Desai K, Patke CL. 1989. Rat pancreatic interlobular duct epithelium: isolation and culture in collagen gel. *In Vitro Cell Dev. Biol.* 25:679–88

45. Githens S, Schexnayder JA, Frazier ML. 1992. Carbonic anhydrase II gene expression in mouse pancreatic duct cells. *Pancreas* 7:556–61

46. Githens S, Schexnayder JA, Moses RL, Denning GM, Smith JL, Frazier ML. 1994. Establishment of ductular cell cultures from mouse pancreatic acinar/ductular tissue: morphological and biochemical comparison with mouse interlobular duct cell cultures. *In Vitro Cell Dev. Biol.* Submitted

47. Gossrau R. 1981. Investigation of proteinases in the digestive tract using 4-methoxy-2-naphthylamine (MNA) substrates. *J. Histochem. Cytochem.* 29:64–480

48. Grant AG, Duke D. 1981. Production of monoclonal antibodies against circulating antigens released from pancreatic tumour xenografts. *Br. J. Cancer* 44:388–95

49. Grant AG, Duke D, Hermon-Taylor J. 1979. Establishment and characterization of primary human pancreatic carcinoma in continuous cell culture and in nude mice. *Br. J. Cancer* 39:143–51

50. Gray MA, Harris A, Coleman L, Greenwell JR, Argent BE. 1989. Two types of chloride channel on duct cells cultured from human fetal pancreas. *Am. J. Physiol.* 257:C240–51

51. Haglund C, Lindgren J, Roberts PJ, Kuusela P, Nordling S. 1989. Tissue expression of the tumour-associated antigen CA242 in benign and malignant pancreatic lesions. A comparison with CA50 and CA19–9. *Br. J. Cancer* 60:845–51

52. Haglund C, Lindgren J, Roberts PJ, Nordling S. 1986. Gastrointestinal cancer-associated antigen CA19–9 in histological specimens of pancreatic tumours and pancreatitis. *Br. J. Cancer* 53:189–95

53. Hall PA, Lemoine NR. 1992. Rapid acinar to ductal transdifferentiation in cultured human exocrine pancreas. *J. Pathol.* 166:97–103

54. Halwani F, Cheung M, Jothy S. 1990. Isolation and immunohistochemical characterization of a pancreatic carcinoma-associated monoclonal antibody. *Exp. Mol. Pathol.* 53:99–111

55. Hansson HA, Edwall D, Lowenadler B, Norstedt G, Paleus S, Skottner A. 1988. Insulin-like growth factor-I in the pancreas of normal and diabetic adult rats. *Acta Physiol. Scand.* 132:569–76

56. Harris A. 1990. Cultured epithelial cells derived from human fetal pancreatic duct. See Ref. 4, pp. 99–115

57. Harris A, Chalkley G, Goodman S, Coleman L. 1991. Expression of the cystic fibrosis gene in human development. *Development* 113:305–10

58. Harris A, Coleman L. 1987. Establishment of a tissue culture system for epithelial cells derived from human pancreas: a model for the study of cystic fibrosis. *J. Cell Sci.* 87:695–703

59. Harris A, Coleman L. 1988. Cultured epithelial cells derived from human foetal pancreas as a model for .the study of cystic fibrosis: further analyses on the origins and nature of the cell types. *J. Cell Sci.* 90:73–77

60. Hart DNJ, Newton MR, Reese-Smith H, Fabre JW, Morris PJ. 1983. Major histocompatibility complex antigens in the rat pancreas, isolated pancreatic islets, thyroid, and adrenal. *Transplantation* 36:431–35

61. Hartel S, Gossrau R, Hanski C, Reutter W. 1988. Dipeptidyl peptidase (DPP) IV in rat organs. Comparison of immunohistochemistry and activity histochemistry. *Histochemistry* 89:151–61

62. Hayashi K, Hayashi M, Jalkanen M, Firestone JH, Trelstad RL, Bernfield M. 1987. Immunocytochemistry of cell surface heparan sulphate proteoglycan in mouse tissues. A light and electron microscopic study. *J. Histochem. Cytochem.* 35:1079–88

63. Hegre OD, McEvoy RC, Bachelder V, Lazarow A. 1972. Organ culture of fetal rat pancreas: quantitative analysis by linear scanning of islet and other tissue components. *In Vitro* 7:366–76

64. Heimann TG, Githens S. 1991. Rat pancreatic duct epithelium cultured on a porous support coated with extracellular matrix. *Pancreas* 6:514–21

65. Ho JJ, Bi N, Yan PS, Yuan M, Norton KA, Kim YS. 1991. Characterization of new pancreatic cancer-reactive monoclonal antibodies directed against purified mucin. *Cancer Res.* 51:372–80

66. Ho JJL, Chung Y-S, Fujimoto Y, Bi N, Ryan W, et al. 1988. Mucin-like antigens in a human pancreatic cancer cell line identified by murine monoclonal antibodies SPan-1 and Y-Pan . *Cancer Res.* 48:3924–31

67. Hootman SR. 1986. Neuroendocrine control of secretion in pancreatic and parotid gland acini and the role of Na^+,K^+-ATPase activity. *Int. Rev. Cytol.* 105:129–81

68. Hootman SR, Ernst SA, Williams JA. 1983. Secretagogue regulation of Na^+-K^+ pump activity in pancreatic acinar cells. *Am. J. Physiol.* 245:G339–46

69. Hootman SR, Logsdon CD. 1988. Isolation and monolayer culture of guinea pig pancreatic duct epithelial cells. *In Vitro Cell. Dev. Biol.* 24:566–74

70. Hubchak S, Mangino MM, Reddy MK, Scarpelli DG. 1990. Characterization of differentiated Syrian golden hamster pancreatic duct cells maintained in extended monolayer culture. *In Vitro Cell Dev. Biol.* 26:889–97

71. Ito N, Nishi K, Nakajima M, Okamura Y, Hirota T. 1990. Histochemical localization and analysis of blood group-related antigens in human pancreas using immunostaining with monoclonal antibodies and exoglycosidase digestion. *J. Histochem. Cytochem.* 38:1331–40

72. Iwamura T, Katsuki T. 1987. Kinetics of carcinoembryonic antigen and carbohydrate antigen 19–9 production in a human pancreatic cancer cell line (SUIT-2). *Gastroenterol. Jpn.* 22:640–46

73. Iwamura T, Katsuki T, Ide K. 1987. Establishment and characterization of a human pancreatic cancer cell line (SUIT-2) producing carcinoembryonic antigen and carbohydrate antigen CA 19–9. *Jpn. J. Cancer Res.* 78:54–62

74. Jones RT, Trump BF, Stoner GD. 1980. Culture of human pancreatic ducts. *Methods Cell Biol.* 21B:429–39

75. Kachar B, Taga R, Kniebel GA, Sesso A. 1979. Morphometric evaluation of the number of exocrine pancreatic cells during early postnatal growth in the rat. *Acta Anat.* 103:11–15

76. Kajiji SM, Davceva B, Quaranta V. 1987. Six monoclonal antibodies to human pancreatic cancer antigens. *Cancer Res.* 47:1367–76

77. Kasper M, Hahn von Dorsche H, Stosiek P. 1991. Changes in the distribution of intermediate filament proteins and collagen IV in fetal and adult human pancreas. *Histochemistry* 96:271–77

78. Kempen HJM, DePont JJHHM, Bonting SL. 1977. Rat pancreas adenylate cyclase. V. Its presence in isolated rat pancreatic acinar cells. *Biochim. Biophys. Acta* 496:521–31

79. Kim J-H, Ho SB, Montgomery CK, Kim YS. 1990. Cell lineage markers in human pancreatic cancer. *Cancer* 66:2134–43

80. Kleinman H, Luckenbill-Edds L, Cannon FW, Sephel GC. 1987. Use of extracellular matrix components for cell culture. *Anal. Biochem.* 166:1–13

81. Kobari M, Matsuno S, Sato T, Kan M, Tachibana T. 1984. Establishment of a human pancreatic cell line and detection of pancreatic cancer associated antigen. *Tohoku J. Exp. Med.* 143:33–46

82. Kudo H, Inada M, Oshio G, Wakatsuki Y, Ogawa K, et al. 1987. Immunohistochemical localization of vitamin B12 R-binder in the human digestive tract. *Gut* 28:339–45

83. Kumpulainen T, Jalovaara P. 1981. Immunohistochemical localization of carbonic anhydrase isoenzymes in the human pancreas. *Gastroenterology* 80:796–99

84. Kyriazis AA, Kyriazis AP, Sternberg CN, Sloane NH, Loveless JD. 1986. Morphological, biological, biochemical and karyotypic characterization of human pancreatic ductal adenocarcinoma Capan-2 in tissue culture and the nude mouse. *Cancer Res.* 46:5810–15

85. Kyriazis AP, McCombs WB3, Sandberg AA, Kyriazis AA, Sloane NH, Lepera R. 1983. Establishment and characterization of pancreatic adenocarcinoma cell line SW-1990 in tissue culture and the nude mouse. *Cancer Res.* 43:4393–401

86. Lan MS, Batra SK, Qi W-N, Metzgar RS, Hollingsworth MA. 1990. Cloning and sequencing of a human pancreatic tumor mucin cDNA. *J. Biol. Chem.* 265:15294–99

87. Lan MS, Hollingsworth MA, Metzgar RS. 1990. Polypeptide core of a human pancreatic tumor mucin antigen. *Cancer Res.* 50:2997–3001

88. Leiter EH, Coleman DL, Eppig JJ. 1979. Endocrine pancreatic cells of postnatal "diabetes" (DB) mice in cell culture. *In Vitro* 15:507–21

89. Levrat JH, Palevody C, Daumas M, Ratovo G, Hollande E. 1988. Differentiation of the human pancreatic cell line (Capan-1) in culture and co-culture with fibroblasts dome formation. *Int. J. Cancer* 42:615–21

90. Lieber M, Mazzetta J, Nelson-Rees W, Kaplan M, Todaro G. 1975. Establishment of a continuous tumor-cell line (PANC-1) from a human carcinoma of the exocrine pancreas. *Int. J. Cancer* 15:741–47

91. Logsdon CD. 1989. Long-term regulation of pancreatic function studied in vitro. See Ref. 21, pp. 515–30

92. Logsdon CD, Williams JA. 1986. Pancreatic acinar cells in monolayer culture: direct trophic effects of caerulein in vitro. *Am. J. Physiol.* 250:G440–47

93. Lojda Z, Gossrau R. 1980. Study on aminopeptidase A. *Histochemistry* 67:267–90

94. Madden ME, Heaton KM, Huff JK, Sarras MPJ. 1989. Comparative analysis of a human pancreatic undifferentiated cell line (MIA PaCa-2) to acinar and ductal cells. *Pancreas* 4:529–37

95. Madden ME, Sarras MP Jr. 1987. Distribution of Na^+,K^+-ATPase in rat exocrine pancreas as monitored by K^+-ATPase cytochemistry and [^{3}H]-ouabain binding: a plasma membrane protein found primarily to be ductal cell associated. *J. Histochem. Cytochem.* 35:1365–74

96. Madden ME, Sarras MP Jr. 1989. The pancreatic ductal system of the rat:

cell diversity, ultrastructure, and innervation. *Pancreas* 4:472–85

97. Madden ME, Sarras MP Jr. 1988. Morphological and biochemical characterization of a human pancreatic ductal cell line (PANC-1). *Pancreas* 3: 512–28

98. Makino T, Usuda N, Rao S, Reddy JK, Scarpelli DG. 1990. Transdifferentiation of ductular cells into hepatocytes in regenerating hamster pancreas. *Lab. Inves.* 62:552–61

99. Malick LE, Tompa A, Kuszynski C, Pour P, Langenbach R. 1981. Maintenance of adult hamster pancreas cells on fibroblastic cells. *In Vitro* 17:947–55

100. Mangino MM, Hubchak S, Scarpelli DG. 1992. Stimulation of DNA synthesis in pancreatic duct cells by gastrointestinal hormones: interaction with other growth factors. *Pancreas* 7:271–79

101. Marino CR, Matovcik LM, Gorelick FS, Cohn JA. 1991. Localization of the cystic fibrosis transmembrane conductance regulator in pancreas. *J. Clin. Invest.* 88:712–16

102. Meitner PA, Kajiji SM, LaPosta-Frazier N, Bogaars HA, Jolly GA, et al. 1983. "COLO-357," a human pancreatic adenosquamous carcinoma: growth in artificial capillary culture and in nude mice. *Cancer Res.* 43:5978–85

103. Metzgar RS, Gaillard MT, Levine SJ, Tuck FL, Bossen EH, Borowitz MJ. 1982. Antigens of human pancreatic adenocarcinoma cells defined by murine monoclonal antibodies. *Cancer Res.* 42:601–8

104. Metzgar RS, Hollingsworth MA, Kaufman B. 1993. Pancreatic mucins. See Ref. 22, pp. 351–67

105. Moll R, Dhouailly D, Sun TT. 1989. Expression of keratin 5 as a distinctive feature of epithelia and biphasic mesotheliomas. An immunohistochemical study using monoclonal antibody AE14. *Virchows Arch. B* 58:129–45

106. Moll R, Franke WW, Schiller DL, Geiger B, Krepler R. 1982. The catalog of human cytokeratin polypeptides: patterns of expression of specific cytokeratins in normal epithelia, tumors and cultured cells. *Cell* 31:11–24

107. Moll R, Schiller DL, Franke WW. 1990. Identification of protein IT of the intestinal cytoskeleton as a novel type I cytokeratin with unusual properties and expression pattern. *J. Cell Biol.* 111:567–80

108. Morgan RT, Woods LK, Moore GE, Quinn LA. 1980. Human cell line (COLO 357) of metastatic pancreatic

adenocarcinoma. *Int. J. Cancer* 25: 591–98

109. Neuwald PD, Anderson, C, Salivar WO, Aldenderfer PH, Dermody WC, et al. 1980. Expression of oncodevelopmental gene products by human tumor cells in culture. *J. Natl. Cancer Inst.* 64:447–59

110. Nishita T, Oshige H, Matsushita H, Kano Y, Asari M. 1989. The immunohistolocalization of carbonic anhydrase III in the submandibular gland of rats and hamsters. *Histochem. J.* 21:8–14

111. Nooter K, Herweijer H. 1991. Multidrug resistance (mdr) genes in human cancer. *Br. J. Cancer* 63:663–69

112. Odin P, Asplund M, Busch C, Obrink B. 1988. Immunohistochemical localization of cell CAM 105 in rat tissues: appearance in epithelia, platelets, and granulocytes. *J. Histochem. Cytochem.* 36:729–39

113. Ohyanagi H, Saitoh Y, Okumura S, Ishida T, Uesaka T, et al. 1987 A new monoclonal-antibody-defined tumor marker (KM01) for pancreatic carcinoma. *Mt. Sinai J. Med. (NY)* 54:393–400

114. Okabe T, Yamaguchi N, Ohsawa N. 1983. Establishment and characterization of a carcinoembryonic antigen (CEA)-producing cell line from a human carcinoma of the exocrine pancreas. *Cancer* 51:662–68

115. Okazaki K, Tamura S, Morita M, Nishimori I, Yamamoto Y, Yamamoto Y. 1989. Interspecies crossreactive antigen of the pancreatic duct cell prepared by monoclonal antibody. A preliminary study of its immunological significance in patients with chronic pancreatitis with Sjogren's syndrome. *Int. J. Pancreatol.* 5:359–77

116. Oliver CS. 1980. Isolation and maintenance of differentiated exocrine gland acinar cells in vitro. *In Vitro* 16:297–305

117. Oliver CS, Waters JF, Tolbert CL, Kleinman HK. 1987. Growth of exocrine pancreatic cells on a reconstituted basement membrane gel. *In Vitro Cell Dev. Biol.* 23:465–73

118. Orci L, Like AA, Amherdt M, Blondel B, Kanazawa Y, et al. 1973. Monolayer cell culture of neonatal rat pancreas: an ultrastructural and biochemical study of functioning endocrine cells. *J. Ultrastruct. Res.* 43: 270–97

119. Park I-S, Bendayan M. 1992. Characterization of the endocrine cells in the pancreatic-biliary duct system of the rat. *Anat. Rec.* 232:247–56

120. Parsa I, Marsh WH, Sutton AL, Butt KMH. 1981. Effects of dimethylnitrosamine on organ-cultured adult human pancreas. *Am. J. Pathol.* 102:403–11
121. Philipsen EK, Jorgensen M, Dabelsteen E. 1991. Expression of blood-group related carbohydrate antigens in normal human pancreatic tissue. *Acta Pathol. Microbiol. Immunol. Scand.* 99:931–40
122. Pileri SA, Sabattini E, Falini B, Zucchini L, Gobbi M, et al. 1991. Immunohistochemical detection of the multidrug transport protein P170 in human normal tissues and malignant lymphomas. *Histopathology* 19:131–40
123. Poulsen MD, Hansen GH, Dabelsteen E, Hoyer PE, Noren O, Sjostrom H. 1993. Dipeptidyl peptidase IV is sorted to the secretory granules in pancreatic islet A-cells. *J. Histochem. Cytochem.* 41:81–88
124. Rafiee P, Ho SB, Bresalier RS, Bloom EJ, Kim J-H, Kim YS. 1992. Characterization of the cytokeratins of human colonic, pancreatic, and gastric adenocarcinoma cell lines. *Pancreas* 7:123–31
125. Rao MS, Reddy JK. 1991. Replicative culture in vitro of pancreatic epithelial oval cells derived from rats after copper deficiency-induced acinar cell depletion. *J. Tissue Culture Meth.* 13:121–24
126. Rao MS, Yeldandi AV, Reddy JK. 1990. Stem cell potential of ductular and periductular cells in the adult rat pancreas. *Cell Diff. Dev.* 29:155–63
127. Resau JH, Hudson EA, Jones RT. 1983. Organ explant culture of adult Syrian golden hamster pancreas. *In Vitro* 19:315–25
128. Resau JH, Marzella L, Trump BF, Jones RT. 1984. Degradation of zymogen granules by lysosomes in cultured pancreatic explants. *Am. J. Pathol.* 115:139–50
129. Rodrigues CJ, Rodrigues-Junior AJ, Sesso A. 1991. Morphometric evaluation of acinar cell number and volume in rat pancreas treated with DL-ethionine. *Braz. J. Med. Biol. Res.* 24:909–17
130. Ruoff NM, Hay RJ. 1979. Metabolic and temporal studies on pancreatic exocrine cells in culture. *Cell Tissue Res.* 204:243–52
131. Saito H, Kasajima T, Nagura H. 1985. An imunocytochemical study on secretory mechanism of IgA in human pancreas. *Acta Pathol. Jpn.* 35:87–101
132. Sakaue M, Saito N, Tanaka C. 1987. Immunohistochemical localization of gamma-aminobutyric acid (GABA) in the rat pancreas. *Histochemistry* 86:365–69
133. Sangadala S, Wallace P, Mendecino J. 1991. Characterization of mucin glycoprotein-specific translation products from swine and human trachea, pancreas, and colon. *Mol. Cell. Biochem.* 106:1–14
134. Sarras MP Jr, Huff JK, Palmiter-Thomas P. 1992. High molecular weight secretory products of the human pancreatic duct epithelium and the effect of secretin on their discharge. *Pancreas* 7:132–43
135. Sato T, Sato M, Hudson EA, Jones RT. 1983. Characterization of bovine pancreatic ductal cells isolated by a perfusion-digestion technique. *In Vitro* 19:651–60
136. Satomura Y, Sawabu N, Takemori Y, Ohta H, Watanabe H, et al. 1991. Expression of various sialylated carbohydrate antigens in malignant and nonmalignant pancreatic tissues. *Pancreas* 6:448–58
137. Schmiegel WH, Kaltoff H, Arndt Rea. 1985. Monoclonal antibody-defined pancreatic cancer-associated antigens. *Cancer Res.* 45:1402–07
138. Schoumacher RA, Ram J, Iannuzzi MC, Bradbury NA, Wallace RW, et al. 1990. A cystic fibrosis pancreatic adenocarcinoma cell line. *Proc. Natl. Acad. Sci. USA* 87:4012–16
139. Schuessler MH, Pintado S, Welt S, Real FX, Xu M, et al. 1991. Blood group and blood-group-related antigens in normal pancreas and pancreas cancer: enhanced expression of precursor type 1, Tn and sialyl-Tn in pancreas cancer. *Int. J. Cancer* 47:180–87
140. Schulte BA, Spicer SS. 1983. Light microscopic detection of sugar residues in glycoconjugates of salivary glands and the pancreas with lectin-horseradish peroxidase conjugates. *Histochem. J.* 15:1217–38
141. Schussler MH, Skovdy A, Ramaekers F, Real FX. 1992. Intermediate filaments as differentiation markers of normal pancreas and pancreatic cancer. *Am. J. Pathol.* 140:559–68
142. Schwenk J, Makovitz J. 1989. Comparative study on expression of Lea, Leb, Lex, Ley, and CA19–9 and CA-50 in chronic pancreatitis and pancreatic carcinoma. *Virchows Arch. A* 414:465–76
143. Sessa F, Bonato M, Frigerio B, Capella C, Solcia E, et al. 1990. Ductal cancers of pancreas frequently express markers of gastrointestinal epithelial cells. *Gastroenterology* 98:1655–65
144. Shepherd JG, Chen J-R, Tsao M-S,

Duguid WP. 1993. Neoplastic transformation of propagable cultured rat pancreatic duct epithelial cells by azaserine and streptozotocin. *Carcinogenesis* 14:1027–33

145. Shibata A, Ludvigsen CWJ, Naber SP, McDaniel ML, Lacy PE. 1976. Standardization of a digestion-filtration method for isolation of pancreatic islets. *Diabetes* 20:667–72

146. Simon-Assman P, Simo P, Bouziges F, Haffen K, Kedinger M. 1990. Synthesis of basement membrane proteins in the small intestine. *Digestion* 46 *(Suppl.)* 2:12–21

147. Skutelsky E, Alroy J, Ucci AA, Carpenter JL, Moore FM. 1987. Modulation of carbohydrate residues in regenerative nodules and neoplasms of canine and feline pancreas. *Am. J. Pathol.* 126:25–32

148. Smith JJ, Derynck R, Korc M. 1987. Production of transforming growth factor alpha in human pancreatic cancer cells: evidence for a superagonist autocrine cycle. *Proc. Natl. Acad. Sci. USA* 84:7567–70

149. Smith ZDJ, Caplan MJ, Forbush BI, Jamieson JD. 1987. Monoclonal antibody localization of Na$^+$,K$^+$-ATPase in the exocrine pancreas and parotid of the dog. *Am. J. Physiol.* 253:G99–109

150. Spicer SS, Ge Z, Tashian RE, Hazen-Martin DJ, Schulte BA. 1990. Comparative distribution of carbonic anhydrase isozymes III and II in rodent tissues. *Am. J. Anat.* 187:55–64

151. Spicer SS, Sens MA, Tashian RE. 1982. Immunocytochemical demonstration of carbonic anhydrase in human epithelial cells. *J. Histochem. Cytochem.* 30:864–73

152. Stoner GD, Harris CC, Bostwick DG, Jones RT, Trump BF, et al. 1978. Isolation and characterization of epithelial cells from bovine pancreatic duct. *In Vitro* 14:581–90

153. Tan MH, Nowak NJ, Loor R, Ochi H, Sandberg AA, et al. 1986. Characterization of a new primary human pancreatic tumor line. *Cancer Invest.* 4:15–23

154. Tanaka K, Akayama M, Yamamoto A, Omori K, Tashiro Y. 1987. Quantitative immunoelectron microscopic localization of (Na$^+$,K$^+$)ATPase on rat exocrine pancreas cells. *J. Histochem. Cytochem.* 35:675–82

155. Thiebaut F, Tsuruo T, Hamada H, Gottesman MM, Pastan I, Willingham MC. 1987. Cellular localization of the multidrug-resistance gene product P-glycoprotein in normal human tissues. *Proc. Natl. Acad. Sci. USA* 84:7735–38

156. Trautmann B, Schlitt H-J, Hahn EG, Lohr M. 1993. Isolation, culture, and characterization of human pancreatic duct cells. *Pancreas* 8:248–54

157. Trezise AEO, Buchwald M. 1991. In vivo cell-specific expression of the cystic fibrosis transmembrane conductance regulator. *Nature* 353:434–37

158. Tsao MS, Duguid WP. 1987. Establishment of propagable epithelial cell lines from normal adult rat pancreas. *Exp. Cell Res.* 168:365–75

159. Tsutsumi Y, Nagura H, Watanabe K, Yanaihara N. 1984. Immunoreactivity of N-terminal fragment of gastrin releasing peptide as histochemical marker for pancreatobiliary duct-type cells. *Lab. Invest.* 50:94–100

160. Vaughan JJ, Pascall JC, James PS, Brown KD. 1991. Expression of epidermal growth factor and its mRNA in pig kidney, pancreas, and other tissues. *Biochem. J.* 279:315–18

161. Verme B, Hootman S. 1990. Regulation of pancreatic duct epithelial growth in vitro. *Am. J. Physiol.* 258:G833–40

162. Walker NI. 1987. Ultrastructure of the rat pancreas after experimental duct ligation. I. The role of apoptosis and intraepithelial macrophages in acinar cell deletion. *Am. J. Pathol.* 126:439–51

163. Walker NI, Winterford CM, Kerr JFR. 1992. Ultrastructure of the rat pancreas after experimental duct ligation. II. Duct and stromal cell proliferation, differentiation, and deletion. *Pancreas* 7:420–34

164. Wallace DH, Hegre OD. 1979. Development in vitro of epithelial-cell monolayers derived from fetal rat pancreas. *In Vitro* 15:270–74

165. Williams JA. 1984. Regulatory mechanisms in pancreas and salivary acini. *Annu. Rev. Physiol.* 46:361–75

166. Xerri L, Payan MJ, Choux R, Gros N, Figarella-Branger D, Sarles H. 1990. Predominance of sialomucin secretion in malignant and premalignant pancreatic lesions. *Hum. Pathol.* 21:927–31

167. Yamaguchi N, Yamamura Y, Koyama K, Ohtsuji E, Imanishi J, Ashihara T. 1990. Characterization of new human pancreatic cancer cell lines which propagate in a protein-free chemically defined medium. *Cancer Res.* 50:7008–14

168. Yonezawa S, Byrd JC, Dahiya R, Ho JJL, Gum JR, et al. 1991. Differential mucin gene expression in human pan-

creas and colon cancer cells. *Biochem. J.* 276:599–605

169. Yuan S-Z, McIntyre LJ, Kim YS. 1987. Monoclonal antibodies to human pancreatic carcinoma. *J. Gastroenterol. Hepatol.* 2:225–31

170. Yuan SZ, Ho JJL, Yuan M, Kim YS. 1985. Human pancreatic cancer-asso-ciated antigens detected by murine monoclonal antibodies. *Cancer Res.* 45:6179–87

171. Yunis AA, Arimura GK, Russin DJ. 1977. Human pancreatic carcinoma (MIA PaCa-2) in continuous culture: sensitivity to asparaginase. *Int. J. Cancer* 19:128–35

Annu. Rev. Physiol. 1994. 56:445–61
Copyright © 1994 by Annual Reviews Inc. All rights reserved

PARIETAL CELL CULTURE:
New Models and Directions

Catherine S. Chew

Institute for Molecular Medicine and Genetics, Medical College of Georgia,
Augusta, Georgia 30912–3100

KEY WORDS: gastric glands, primary culture, HCl secretion, epidermal growth factor,
             cytoskeleton

INTRODUCTION

The gastric parietal cell is highly specialized and appears to be terminally differentiated. In vertebrates, parietal cells are the source of HCl in gastric secretions. In some species including human, monkey, rabbit, cat, guinea pig, and ox, but not rat, mouse and hog, parietal cells also secrete intrinsic factor that is required for absorption of the vitamin, cobalamin (B12), by the distal small intestine (15). Because acid secretion is correlated with peptic ulcer disease and because the parietal cell has such interesting biological properties, there has been considerable interest in defining the inter- and intracellular mechanisms associated with the functions of this cell type. During the late 1970's, two isolated cell models that included gastric glands and enriched parietal cells (5, 31) were developed to facilitate such studies. Further refinements in the purity of isolated parietal cell preparations have led to the more recent development of prototype primary parietal cell culture models that are described below.

BACKGROUND

Parietal cells are localized within well-defined glandular regions in the fundus and corpus regions of the gastric mucosa. Glands containing parietal cells possess lumens that interconnect with macroscopic gastric pits that extend upward into the main gastric lumen thereby providing an outlet for gastric secretions. The luminal surface of the gastric mucosa is lined with surface mucous cells, whereas several different cell types, including mucous

445

0066–4278/94/0315–0445$05.00

neck cells, chief cells, endocrine-like cells, and undifferentiated cells, are present in the glandular area extending from upper third of the gland region to the base. The entire tubular structure is referred to as the oxyntic gland, which is derived from the Greek *oxyntos*, meaning to generate an acidic substance. Parietal describes the physical position of the cells, which bulge out from the glandular wall presumably because of their relatively large size. Parietal cells are frequently referred to as oxyntic cells in the older literature, particularly in amphibian studies. In mammals, parietal cells are most numerous in the glandular neck region, but are also found at the base. Within the neck region, which comprises the upper third of oxyntic glands, there are progenitor cells that presumably develop into parietal and other differentiated cell types. As they mature, parietal cells appear to migrate downward toward the base of the gland. It has been speculated that parietal cells in the basal region secrete HCl less actively than those near the neck region. The life span of parietal cells, which comprise approximately 30–40% of the cell population within the corpus mucosa, appears to range from three months in rodents to one year in humans. (see 16, 18 for reviews).

With respect to the physiologic regulation of parietal cell function, the major in vivo stimulants of HCl secretion are acetylcholine, histamine, and gastrin (see 6 for a recent review). Following appropriate stimulation in vivo or in vitro, parietal cells undergo dramatic morphological transformations in which the resting intracellular tubulovesicular structures appear to fuse with intracellular canaliculi. The current dogma assumes that this membrane fusion process leads to the appearance of elongated microvilli within the canalicular spaces. The H^+, K^+-ATPase or proton pump, which is responsible for H^+ ion secretion, has been immunolocalized to the tubulovesicles with increased staining of the canalicular membrane detectable after stimulation. Activation of the H^+, K^+-ATPase is thought to occur upon fusion of tubulovesicular and canalicular membranes (16, 18, 30). Although the elongated microvilli of canaliculi are frequently referred to as apical membranes, it should be emphasized that this characterization is somewhat misleading. Because of the triangular shape of the parietal cell, there is actually very little membrane area exposed to the glandular lumen on the apical side of the cell (18). Thus canalicular membranes into which proton pumps are inserted may actually arise near the basal pole of the cell and extend through the cell to the apical pole. In vivo, acidic secretions exit the cell via the canalicular space, which communicates with the glandular lumen. Ito (18) has proposed that, at least in some cells, the intracellular canaliculi may become completely closed off from the gland lumen when these cells are not actively secreting. The detection of relatively high concentrations of actin within parietal cells has led to several hypotheses regarding the role of the cytoskeleton in the mediation of the complex membrane rearrangements that occur within parietal cells upon stimulation and following withdrawal of the stimulus (cf 16, 24, 32).

DEVELOPMENT AND CHARACTERISTICS OF CULTURED PARIETAL CELL MODELS

Some years before and during the time isolated parietal cell models were being developed and characterized, a number of attempts were made to establish cultures of gastric epithelial cells (22, 25, 26, 27, 29, 34). The majority of these early studies utilized a mixed population of gastric mucosal epithelial cells, which were grown from explants of the fundic mucosa or from partially enriched isolated parietal cell populations, and few attempts were made to characterize the functionality of parietal cells in the heterogeneous populations. A study by Okada & Ueda (29) did, however, report that parietal cells present in monolayers growing out from explants of 6–8 day old rat fundic mucosae responded to the agonists, histamine, acetylcholine, and gastrin, with hyperpolarization of their resting membrane potential and decreased membrane resistance. In this latter study, parietal cells appeared to survive for approximately one week in culture. They were identified by their ability to accumulate acridine orange into intracellular vesicles and by the detection of a pronounced succinic dehydrogenase activity that was suggestive of the presence of large numbers of mitochondria (a characteristic of parietal cells). In explants these cells cross-reacted with anti-parietal cell antibodies obtained from human patients with pernicious anemia. The cultures contained several different cell types, and the identification of parietal cells was indirect; however, the work was promising and encouraged other laboratories to attempt to develop parietal cell cultures with a longer survival time. Initially, these efforts were unsuccessful, and some workers came to the conclusion that parietal cells de-differentiated when cultured for more than a few days.

In my laboratory, we experienced similar failures because when partially enriched parietal cell preparations were placed in culture, the cultures were rapidly overgrown with mucus-containing cells and cells that had a fibroblast-like morphology (11; CS Chew & MR Brown, unpublished observations). Initially we also thought that the apparent disappearance of parietal cells was due to de-differentiation. It was not until a new method of parietal cell enrichment was adopted that a hormonally-responsive cultured parietal cell model was successfully developed. The enrichment process was based on an initial report by Berglindh (4) that showed improved enrichment/viability of parietal cells through the use of Nycodenz™ density gradients and an older technique developed by Soll (30) that utilized centrifugal elutriation to produce 50–75% enrichment of parietal cells. By combining these two techniques, we were able to obtain parietal cell preparations that approached 100% purity (11). When such highly enriched parietal cells were placed in serum-free culture, there was no disappearance of this cell type and no overgrowth by other cell types (11). Thus we concluded that parietal cells do not de-differentiate in culture, but can become a minor component when co-cultured in the presence of other rapidly dividing cell types.

The use of serum-free culture media and the commercial availability of the basement membrane extract, Matrigel™ (Collaborative Research), were important factors that led to the development of this agonist-responsive model. A variety of attachment matrices were initially tested including fibronectin, laminin, polyarginine, polylysine, collagen types I and IV, Cell-Tak™, as well as different types of cell culture dishes. Although different lots of Matrigel were found to perform more or less well, this relatively crude basement membrane extract allowed for the best overall parietal cell attachment/responsiveness. When either fetal, newborn, or adult calf or horse serum was included in the culture media, the ability of the cells to respond to agonists was suppressed. If bovine serum albumin (BSA) was not used as a serum substitute, parietal cells also became less responsive to agonist stimulation. Presumably, BSA serves as a carrier for essential factors. Serum has been reported to promote growth of fibroblasts and to be cytotoxic for some cell types (3). This may also to be the case with parietal cells. However, there might also be factors present in serum that specifically inhibit parietal cell HCl secretion but are not cytotoxic. This is an important question for future consideration.

Water quality is of the utmost importance for successful parietal cell culture and our unpublished observations (CS Chew & M Ljungström) have shown that only carefully maintained, toxin-free water systems producing water with a resistivity of 18 MΩ/cm will suffice. The inclusion in culture media of antibiotics has been found to be essential, particularly in species such as rabbits, which are coprophagic. In our experience, gastric bacteria of rabbits are highly resistant to penicillin and streptomycin. This may also be the case in other species. The most effective antibiotics we have identified are gentamicin sulfate, novobiocin, and geneticin. Usually these antibiotics can be removed after 3–4 days of culture. There can be problems with yeast contamination, a condition that also plagues primary cultures of other cell types. Interestingly, the problem is rare when gastric glands are placed in culture. Our experience suggests that the differences in yeast contamination are related to the parietal cell enrichment steps including density gradient separation, centrifugal elutriation, and multiple low-speed centrifugations in which yeast appear to co-purify with parietal cells thereby increasing the probability of contamination. In contrast, before glands are placed in culture, they are simply rinsed with antibiotics and antimycotics.

To date, only a few hormones/growth factors have been screened for effects on the cells, and the culture medium most often utilized has been a 1:1 mixture of Ham's F-12 and Dulbecco's modified Eagle's medium with *l*-glutamine and either 15 mM *N*-2-hydroxymethylpiperazine-*N'*-2-ethanesulfonic acid (HEPES) or bicarbonate. A potentially important observation is that when parietal cells are cultured in bicarbonate/CO_2 vs air with HEPES buffer, cells appear healthy by visual criteria and cellular attachment is unchanged; however, basal acid secretion increases to such a degree that agonist-stimulated secretion cannot be reproducibly demonstrated (Figure 1).

The relative success of this recently developed parietal cell culture, as compared to earlier models, relates to the specific criteria used to identify parietal cells and, most importantly, the demonstration of agonist-responsiveness using previously established criteria including accumulation of the weak base, ^{14}C-aminopyrine. The first step in the development of the model was the immunolocalization of the H^+, K^+-ATPase, using a well characterized monoclonal antibody, to the majority of cells cultured from highly

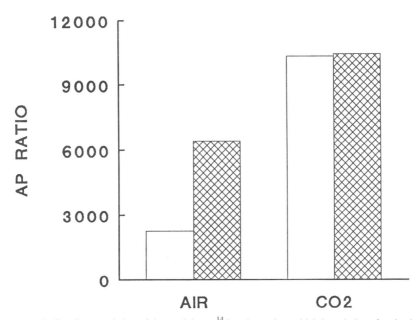

Figure 1   Basal accumulation of the weak base, ^{14}C-aminopyrine, which is an index of parietal cell HCl secretion, is substantially elevated when cells are cultured in bicarbonate/5% CO_2, as compared to air with HEPES buffer. Triplicate data are from a population of cells isolated from the same animal and cultured for three days on Matrigel as described in Reference 11. Similar results were obtained in four other experiments. Open bars, controls; hatched bars, 1 μM histamine, 30 min.

enriched parietal cell populations. It was found that relatively few cells were immunostained with this antibody in heterogeneous cell populations. After it was determined that immunostaining of cells was unchanged after 1–2 weeks of culture, other morphological features of cultured parietal cells were carefully examined using standard light microscopy and then transmission and scanning electron microscopy (TEM, SEM). Although the well-established features of parietal cell morphology were somewhat altered after several days in culture, important characteristics such as the presence of intracellular canaliculi, cytosolic tubulovesicles, and large number of mitochondria were unchanged (7, 11).

Mitochondrial autofluorescence is readily observed when cells on the microscope stage are exposed to fluorescence excitation at wavelengths in the 450 nm range (19; CS Chew, unpublished observations). Similarly, histochemical detection of the mitochondrial enzyme, succinic dehydrogenase, can be used to tentatively identify parietal cells because of the large number of mitochondria present in this cell type. Mitochondrial autofluorescence and histochemistry are useful discriminatory tools, but these techniques alone are not sufficient to unequivocally identify parietal cells in culture. Interestingly, the presumed specific vital fluorescent mitochondrial stain, rhodamine 123, diffusely labels parietal cells as compared to other gastric cell types in which labeling appears to be confined to mitochondria (cf Figure 2). Our unpublished observations (CS Chew & M Scanlon) with stimulated and unstimulated parietal cells suggest that this phenomenon is the result of accumulation of this membrane-potential-sensitive cationic dye in tubulovesicles and intracellular canaliculi as well as in mitochondria.

Stimulation by histamine and, to a lesser extent, by carbachol was found to induce dramatic morphological changes in parietal cells, which are readily observable with a light microscope (Figure 3; 10, 11, 21). Importantly, pre-addition of antagonists (e.g omeprazole, which directly inhibits the H^+, K^+-ATPase, or the histamine H_2-receptor antagonist, cimetidine, when histamine was the stimulant completely blocked the gross morphological changes. Furthermore, secondary addition of these antagonists reversed this response (11; CS Chew, unpublished observations).

Stimulation of cultured parietal cells causes a significant increase in cell size (Figure 4) and the characteristic appearance of elongated canalicular microvilli (11, 21). The TEM images demonstrate the presence of large numbers of mitochondria in stimulated and unstimulated cells and tubulovesicles in unstimulated cells. TEM also suggests that the gross cellular enlargement that occurs upon stimulation of secretion is caused by expansion of the intracellular canaliculi, presumably as a result of the inability of these secretions to readily exit the cell (see below). Following maximal agonist stimulation, the gross enlargement of parietal cells makes it difficult to fix

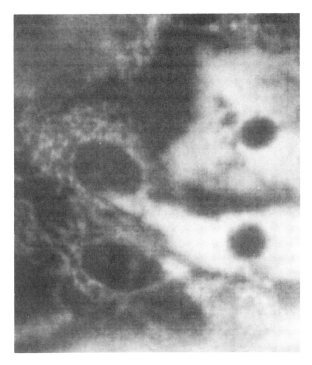

Figure 2 Cultured parietal and other unidentified mucosal cells vitally stained with the mitochondrial stain, rhodamine 123. Parietal cells (*right side*) exhibit diffuse fluorescence as compared to other cell types (*left side*). Unpublished data from stimulated and unstimulated parietal cells suggest that this phenomenon is due to accumulation of this cationic dye not only in mitochondria, but also within tubulovesicles and intracellular canaliculi (CS Chew & M Scanlon, unpublished observation).

these cells using standard EM fixatives, which are hyperosmotic. Better preservation of cellular features can be obtained by adjusting the fixative osmolarity to 300 mOsM (10, 11).

If cells are cultured for several days, both loose association between cells in the form of membrane infoldings and apparent tight junction formations are observed within 24–48 hours of culture (Figure 5).

Other studies of cultured cells utilizing various fluorescently labeled probes for cytoskeletal proteins have demonstrated the presence of, for example, abundant filamentous (F)-actin, which appears to surround the intracellular canaliculi and plasma membrane (24, 32; Figure 6). As can be seen in Figure 6, F-actin associated with intracellular canaliculi appear to project toward the apical surface in cultured cells. It remains to be determined whether these projections are localized to the apical pole of the cell. If so,

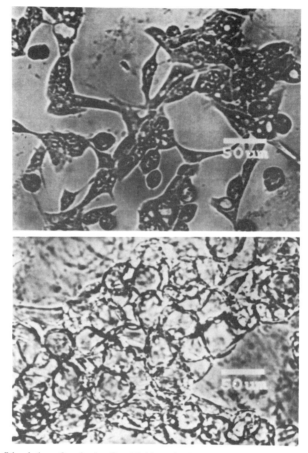

Figure 3 Stimulation of parietal cells with histamine leads to a dramatic increase in cell size within a few minutes of stimulation. These changes are readily visualized with a standard light microscope at magnifications of 200–1000×. Top, unstimulated cells. Bottom, cells from the same population stimulated with 1 μM histamine, 30 min. Adapted from Reference 10 with permission.

they may be the site at which intracellular canaliculi communicate with the external milieu in vivo. It is also unclear whether these projections are associated with mysterious pits on the cell surface that have been observed in some scanning electron micrographs of cultured parietal cells, or as vesicular depressions in Nomarski images (10, 11, 21; Figure 4).

The gross morphological changes detected in living and fixed cells upon stimulation of parietal cells in primary culture suggest that acidic parietal cell secretions might be trapped within intracellular canaliculi that have

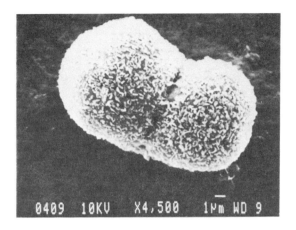

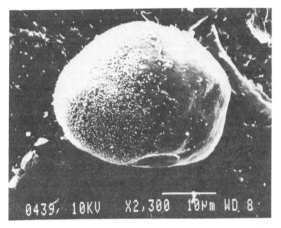

Figure 4   Scanning electron micrograph of parietal cells after two days of culture. Cells were incubated with and without 10 μM histamine for 30 min, then fixed and subjected to scanning electron microscopy as described in Reference 10. Top, unstimulated; bottom, histamine. Note differences in magnification, which are indicated on photomicrographs.

become closed off during cell isolation and have failed to reopen during culture. In acutely isolated cells and gastric glands, increased accumulation of the isotopically labeled weak base, ^{14}C-aminopyrine, in response to agonist stimulation has been established as a semi-quantitative measure of parietal cell acid secretion based on the work of Berglindh and colleagues in glands, and that of Soll and colleagues as well as several other laboratories with isolated cells (5, 6, 16, 31). In order for aminopyrine to accumulate, it is necessary that a membrane-bound acidic cellular compartment be present

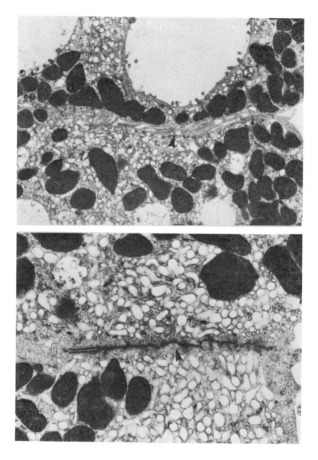

Figure 5   Transmission electron micrograph of parietal cell sections showing formation of loose and tight membrane interconnections. Cells were cultured for three days then fixed with glutaraldehyde, postfixed with osmium tetroxide, and sectioned as described in Reference 10. Arrows are used to indicate loose (*top*) and tight (*bottom*) cellular connections. Other sections (not shown) suggest the presence of desmosomes in some tight junction formations.

to trap the protonated form of the weak base; the unprotonated form is freely permeable across cell membranes.

When cultured parietal cells are stimulated, there is increased accumulation of ^{14}C-aminopyrine. Furthermore, the relative accumulation is substantially higher than in freshly isolated cells, so that acid secretion can be measured in as few as 5–10,000 cells/sample (11; Figure 1). The reason for the large increase in AP accumulation in cultured cells as compared to acutely isolated

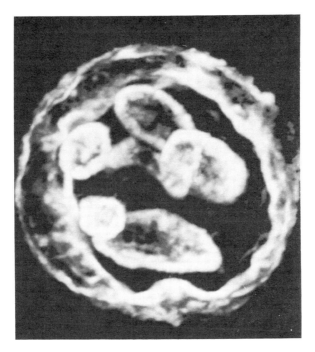

Figure 6   Three-dimensional reconstruction of a cultured parietal cell following simultaneous fixation, permeabilization, and staining for F-actin with rhodamine-labeled phalloidin. Cell was sectioned at 0.2 μm intervals with a Molecular Dynamics Multiprobe 2001 inverted confocal laser scanning microscope. Serial sections were reconstructed with Molecular Dynamics software on a Silicon Graphics Iris computer using a maximal intensity model (courtesy of Dr. David Hanzel). Note interconnections of F-actin, which appears to line intracellular canaliculi and extend toward presumed apical pole of the cell.

parietal cells has not been clearly established, but there is a direct correlation between the appearance of enlarged intracellular vacuoles and increased AP accumulation. These observations have led to the hypothesis that the intracellular canaliculi of cultured cells are more tightly sealed than the canaliculi in acutely isolated cells, and/or acid secretion is more brisk in cultured cells that have had time to recover from the insults associated with cell isolation and enrichment. Although the fluorescent weak base acridine orange has also been used by our laboratory and others (10, 14) to demonstrate the presence of acidic spaces within parietal cells, it should be emphasized that acridine orange is toxic to cells, and can produce significant artifacts. To our knowledge, there is presently no suitable cell permeant, nontoxic fluorescent dye with a pK that is low enough to provide a reasonable kinetic estimate of acid secretory activity. There are injectable, dextran-linked, cell-impermeant fluorescent dyes with pKs of 2–3 that are available from Molecular Probes (Eugene, OR); however, it is unlikely that such dyes will be useful for studies of intracanalicular pH because, to be useful, such dyes must be injected directly into the canalicular space rather than the bulk cytosol.

UTILITY OF CURRENT CULTURED PARIETAL MODELS

A major advantage of primary cultures over transformed cell lines is their phenotypic stability. It is not surprising, therefore, that cultured parietal cells are presently being utilized to define specific intracellular signaling mechanisms and to determine the effects of various agonists and growth factors on cell function. Cultured parietal cells possess several advantages over acutely isolated cells including, for example, improved viability. The ability to visualize agonist-stimulated increases in secretory activity in single cells is another important advantage. Cultured cells can also be loaded with the calcium-sensitive fluorescent probe fura-2, and changes in intracellular calcium can be monitored simultaneously with secretion in single cells using digitized video image analysis techniques (10, 21). From such studies, it has been determined that histamine-stimulated increases in intracellular calcium are not correlated with secretory responses. Both histamine and the hormone gastrin elevate calcium in what appears to be a sub-population of parietal cells representing approximately 70% of the total. In contrast, the cholinergic agonist carbachol elevates intracellular calcium in both gastrin-responsive and -unresponsive parietal cells (10, 12, 21). There also appears to be heterogeneity in cellular sensitivity to gastrin with only 12% of cells that respond to maximal doses of gastrin (10–100 nM) responding to 0.1 nM gastrin. Oscillations in the calcium signal are observed in ~30% of the cells following stimulation with histamine at maximal and sub-maximal concentrations, but are only observed with relatively low doses of carbachol (21). Oscillations in the calcium signal have also been observed with gastrin (12), but are not as well characterized.

Preliminary results suggest that the growth factors, epidermal growth factor (EGF) and transforming growth factor alpha (TGFα), have long-term effects on parietal cell function that are quite different from acute effects. When administered acutely, these growth factors suppress HCl secretion both in vivo and in vitro (measured indirectly as AP accumulation in the latter case), and the inhibition appears to be mediated through the inhibitory protein Gi (2, 6, 20). In contrast, addition of either growth factor to cultured parietal cells leads to enhanced basal and stimulated AP accumulation within 24 hours with an EC_{50} that is six to thirty times lower than the reported IC_{50} for inhibition (2, 9, 20). A select group of tyrosine kinase inhibitors suppresses the stimulatory effect of EGF and inhibits the in situ phosphorylation of a protein that co-migrates with a 44 kd MAP kinase isozyme, ERK1 (28). This enzyme and other members of the ERK enzyme family have been proposed as potential modulators of growth factor-stimulated mitogenesis in proliferating cell types (27). The parietal cell data suggest that growth factors may be involved not only in the modulation of mitogenesis, but also in the regulation of differentiated cell functions.

DEFICIENCIES IN CURRENT MODELS

It would be possible to measure HCl secretion directly if parietal cells could be induced to form a tight monolayer on an appropriate attachment substrate. This is presently not the case. When parietal cells are cultured on Matrigel, they preferentially attach in clumps, not monolayers (11). Moreover, since parietal cells do not proliferate, it is unlikely that a monolayer can be induced to form when highly enriched parietal cells are utilized as a starting material. Although cultured gastric glands do form limited monolayers because one or more dividing cell types are present in glands, the apical canalicular openings of parietal cells in these preparations also appear to close off in culture (13). Thus acidic secretions are trapped within patent canalicular spaces in cultured cells and glands. ^{14}C-aminopyrine (AP) accumulation is a useful tool for measurement of HCl secretion; however, the measurement is indirect and, if not carefully controlled, can lead to erroneous conclusions about the acid secretory status of either acutely isolated or cultured parietal cells. Because AP is a weak base, agents with similar properties will compete with this labeled probe for protons with a resultant decrease in AP accumulation unrelated to the acid secretory status of the cell. As expected, agents with protonophoric properties also reduce AP accumulation. Conversely, when cellular secretions are unable to exit the cells, acid secretion will ultimately be limited by the capacity of the intracellular canaliculus. This limitation probably leads to an underestimation of true acid secretory capacity.

Current morphological and immunohistochemical evidence suggests that, in contrast to acutely isolated cells in which polarity appears to be lost, parietal cells do regain polarity when placed in culture (32). However, the sealing off of the apical membrane, which effectively seals off the intracellular canalaculi, makes it difficult to identify and access the apical end of unfixed cells. Thus attempts to obtain reliable apical membrane patch-clamp measurements have not been successful. Clearly, this problem is not unique to cultured parietal cell models. In isolated glands, where parietal cells do appear to retain appropriate polarity, the apical membrane is not readily accessible because it faces the internal gland lumen. Even if the apical membrane were accessible, as discussed above, most of the apical membrane transporters are buried within the interior of the cell.

Another problem with current cultured parietal cell models is the difficulty in obtaining sufficient cellular material for biochemical measurements. The failure to divide and the progressive decline in parietal cell numbers during culture ($\sim$10% cells lost/day) means that only experimental protocols requiring relatively small amounts of starting material are feasible.

FUTURE DIRECTIONS

Although attempts to create immortal parietal cells that retain phenotypic stability (using, for example, viral transformation techniques) have thus far been unsuccessful, further research in this area is warranted, particularly in light of a recent demonstration that expression of the Simian virus 40 Large Tumor (T) oncogene in chondrocytes induces proliferation without loss of differentiated phenotype (23). Another potential approach is to identify, then isolate, a progenitor cell population that can be induced to differentiate into parietal cells. If either of these approaches proves successful, it should then be possible to characterize the development of cellular signaling pathways involved in the control of HCl secretion as well as those involved in the maintenance of differentiated cellular functions. Intracellular signaling pathways and possible changes in signal transduction mechanisms that occur as the cell matures could also be compared and contrasted with transduction mechanisms in cancer cell lines, for example, to define commonality and divergence of these pathways. With phenotypically stable cell lines, techniques such as site-directed mutagenesis (33) and vector-based gene transfer (17, 23) should provide physiologists with powerful tools for the study of a variety of transport-related activities. Such information may be useful not only for defining specific aberrations associated with uncontrolled cell division, but also for determining which pathways are activated or suppressed during different stages of differentiation.

With existing primary cell culture techniques, it is now possible to study a variety of second messenger-related events using cell-permeant forms of fluorescent probes such as fura-2 and BCECF to measure changes in intracellular calcium and pH, respectively. This work is expected to expand as video cameras with improved sensitivity and response linearity become more generally available and confocal microscopic and atomic force microscopic techniques mature. The utilization of micro-injectable probes such as a fluorescently labeled cAMP-dependent protein kinase regulatory subunit (1), in conjunction with video image analysis and confocal microscopy, may allow the localization and movement of these regulatory subunits following agonist-dependent cell activation. Similarly, a variety of other cellular proteins that are involved in signal transduction pathways may be identified and characterized with these techniques. If the antigenic properties of the external cell membrane change as the parietal cell matures, it may also be possible to develop specific antibodies against cells in different stages of development. Acutely isolated parietal cells could then be separated using fluorescence-activated cell sorting in conjunction with fluorescently labeled antibodies, a technique that has been successful in defining subpopulations of lymphocytes. In this case, the separated parietal cells could be studied and compared in primary culture.

Another important area of research that has, as yet, received little attention is cell-cell interactions within the gastric gland. Now that techniques have been developed that allow recognition of living parietal cells at the light microscopic level, problems associated with the study of these cells in a heterogeneous preparation have been greatly reduced. Preliminary results with cultured gastric glands suggest that cell-cell interactions may be important, for example, in the control of basal HCl secretion; basal AP accumulation is significantly lower in cultured glands than in cultured parietal cells (7, 13). Moreover, cultured glands appear to be much less dependent on exogenous growth factors. These data suggest that there may be important paracrine interactions among different cell types present in glands. Whether these interactions are unique to the gastric mucosa or common to other gastrointestinal organs is an interesting question for future research. With the continuing development of new and powerful molecular biological techniques, approaches such as in situ polymerase chain reaction (ISPCR) and fluorescent in situ hybridization (FISH) are expected to provide new insights into control mechanisms associated with both parietal cell development and differentiated function.

ACKNOWLEDGMENTS

The assistance and collaboration of Drs. Magnus Ljungström, Milton Brown, Anne Petropoulos, Keiya Nakamura, James Goldenring, and Carole Soroka in the development and characterization of the cultured parietal cell model described in this chapter are gratefully acknowledged. Drs. Douglas Benson and David Hanzel also provided invaluable assistance in the development and application of video imaging and confocal microscopic methodologies. This work is supported by National Institutes of Health grant DK31900.

Literature Cited

1. Adams SR, Harootunian AT, Buechler YJ, Taylor SS, Tsein RY. 1991. Fluorescence ratio imaging of cyclic AMP in single cells. *Nature* 349:694–97
2. Atwell MM, Hanson PJ. 1988. Effect of pertussis toxin on the inhibition of secretory activity by prostaglandin E_2, somatostatin, epidermal growth factor and 12-*O*-tetradecanoylphorbol 13-acetate in parietal cells from rat stomach. *Biochim. Biophys. Acta* 971:282–88
3. Barnes D, Sato G. 1980. Serum-free cell culture: a unifying approach. *Cell* 22:649–55
4. Berglindh T. 1985. Improved one-step purification of isolated gastric parietal cells from rabbit and dog. *Fed. Proc.* 440:1203A
5. Berglindh T, Helander HF, Öbrink KJ. 1976. Effects of secretagogues on oxygen consumption, aminopyrine accumulation and morphology in isolated gastric glands. *Acta Physiol. Scand.* 97:401–14
6. Chew CS. 1993. Peptidergic regulation of gastric acid secretion. In *Handbook of Experimental Pharmacology: Gastrointestinal Regulatory Peptides*. ed. D Brown, 106:199–51. Berlin/New York: Springer-Verlag. 446 pp.
7. Chew CS. 1991. Parietal cell functions in culture. *Digestion* 49:2–3
8. Chew CS, Brown MR. 1986. Release of intracellular Ca^{2+} and elevation of inositol trisphosphate by secretagogues in parietal and chief cell isolated from rabbit gastric mucosa. *Biochim. Biophys. Acta* 888:116–25
9. Chew CS, Brown MR. 1989. TGFα and EGF enhance acid secretion in cultured parietal cells. *FASEB J.* 3: A1152
10. Chew CS, Ljungström M. 1990. HCl secretion and $[Ca^{2+}]_i$ in cultured parietal cells. *J. Inter. Med.* 228:9–15 (Suppl. 1)
11. Chew CS, Ljungström M, Smolka A, Brown MR. 1989. Primary culture of secretagogue-responsive parietal cells. *Am. J. Physiol.* 256(19):G254–63
12. Chew CS, Nakamura K, Ljungström, M. 1993. Calcium signaling patterns in the gastric parietal cell. *Yale J. Biol. Med.* 65(5): In press
13. Chew CS, Nakamura K, Petropoulos AC. 1991. Characterization of acid secretory responsiveness of cultured gastric glands. *J. Cell Biol.* 115:401a
14. Dibona, DR, Ito S, Berglindh T, Sachs

G. 1979. Cellular site of gastric acid secretion. *Proc. Natl. Acad. Sci. USA* 76:1689–93
15. Donaldson RM. 1987. Intrinsic factor and transport of cobalamin. In *Physiology of the Gastrointestinal Tract*, ed. LR. Johnson, 2:959–73. New York: Raven. 1780 pp. 2nd. ed.
16. Forte JG, Soll, A. 1989. Cell biology of hydrochloric acid secretion. In *Handbook of Physiology. Section 6: The Gastrointestinal Section*, ed. SG Schultz, JG Forte, III, pp. 207–28. New York: Oxford Univ. Press. 758 pp.
17. Howard BH. 1983. Vectors for introducing genes into cells of higher eukaryotes. *Trends Biochem. Sci.* 8: 209–12
18. Ito S. 1987. Functional gastric morphology. See Ref. 15, pp. 817–51
19. Kohler E, Frömter E. 1985. Identification of mitochondria-rich cells in unstained vital preparations of epithelia by autofluorescence. *Pflügers Arch.* 403:47–49
20. Lewis JJ, Goldenring JR, Asher VA, Modlin IM. 1990. Effects of epidermal growth factor on signal transduction in rabbit parietal cells. *Am. J. Physiol.* 258(21):G476–83
21. Ljungström M, Chew CS. 1991. Calcium oscillations in single cultured gastric parietal cells. *Am. J. Physiol.* 260(29):C67–78
22. Logsdon CD, Bisbee CA, Rutten MA, Machen, TE. 1982. Fetal rabbit gastric epithelial cells cultured on floating collagen gels. *In Vitro* 18:233–42
23. Malleingerin F, Olsen BR. 1993. Expression of Simian Virus Large-T (Tumor) oncogene in mouse chondrocytes induces cell proliferation without loss of the differentiated phenotype. *Proc. Nat. Acad. Sci. USA* 90:3289–93
24. Mangeat P, Gusdinar T, Sahuquet A, Hanzel DK, Forte JG, Magous R. 1990. Acid secretion and membrane reorganization in single gastric parietal cells in primary culture. *Biol. Cell.* 69:223–32
25. Mårdh S, Norberg N, Ljungström M, Humble L, Borg T, Carlsson C. 1984. Preparation of cells from pig gastric mucosa: isolation by isopycnic centrifugation on linear density gradients of Percoll. *Acta Physiol. Scand.* 122:607–13

26. Matuoka K, Tanaka M, Mitsui Y, Murota S. 1983. Cultured rabbit gastric epithelial cells producing prostaglandin I₂. *Gastroenterology* 84:498–505

27. Miller LR, Jacobsen ED, Johnson, LR. 1973. Effect of pentagastrin on gastric mucosal cells grown in tissue culture. *Gastroenterology* 64:254–67

28. Nakamura K, Chew CS. 1993. Parietal cells contain an EGF-sensitive MAP kinase that is inhibited by a subclass of tyrosine kinase inhibitors. *Gastroenterology* 104:A155

29. Okada Y, Ueda S. 1984. Electrical membrane responses to secretagogues in parietal cells of the rat gastric mucosa in culture. *J. Physiol.* 354:109–19

30. Smolka A, Helander HF, Sachs G. 1983. Monoclonal antibodies against gastric H⁺, K⁺ ATPase. *Am. J. Physiol.* 245(8):G589–96

31. Soll AH. 1978. The actions of secretagogues on oxygen uptake by isolated mammalian parietal cells. *J. Clin. Invest.* 61:370–80

32. Soroka CJ, Chew CS, Hanzel DK, Smolka A, Modlin IM, Goldenring JG. 1993. Characterization of membrane and cytoskeletal compartments in cultured parietal cells: Immunofluorescence and confocal microscopy. *Eur. J. Cell Biol.* 60:76–87

33. Stevens CF. 1984. Site-directed mutagenesis. *Trends Neurosci.* 7:306–7

34. Terano A, Ivey KJ, Stachura J, Sekhon S, Hosjima H, et al. 1982. Cell culture of rat gastric fundic mucosa. *Gastroenterology* 83:1280–91

Annu. Rev. Physiol. 1994. 56:463–84
Copyright © 1994 by Annual Reviews Inc. All rights reserved

CONTROL OF CALCIUM RELEASE IN FUNCTIONING SKELETAL MUSCLE FIBERS

Martin F. Schneider

Department of Biological Chemistry, University of Maryland at Baltimore School of Medicine, Baltimore, Maryland 21201

KEY WORDS: ryanodine receptor, intramembrane charge movement, calcium channel, transverse tubule, sarcoplasmic reticulum

INTRODUCTION

This review focuses on the normal physiological mechanisms that control calcium release from the sarcoplasmic reticulum (SR) during electrical depolarization of functioning vertebrate skeletal muscle fibers. Special attention is devoted to questions concerning the functional interactions between components of the calcium release and control system. In vertebrate skeletal muscle the two known components reside in separate but closely apposed membranes: the junctional membrane of the SR, which contains the SR calcium release channel, and the immediately adjacent membrane of the transverse tubules (TT), which contains the TT membrane voltage-sensing elements that control the SR calcium channel. The TT system carries the electrical depolarization signal from the plasma membrane radially into the fiber for near-synchronous initiation of SR calcium release throughout the fiber volume. Several recent reviews have covered various functional aspects of these components as well as their interaction in physiological depolarization-release coupling (6, 23, 35, 43, 65, 86, 108, 109, 110, 111). The restricted length of the present review has required focus on selected areas to the unfortunate neglect of related but peripheral studies and use of only typical examples as references to general points. Molecular, structural, and molecular biological aspects of the calcium release and control system are presented in companion reviews (G Meissner; C Franzini-Armstrong & A Jorgensen, this volume).

463

In order to investigate the normal physiological interaction of various release and control components, it is essential that the TT, SR and any intervening components be maintained as much as possible in their normal structural and functional relationships in the experimental preparations under study. Distortion of the normal structure could alter possible direct interactions between the TT voltage sensor, the SR calcium release channel and other possible membrane or inter-membrane components, as well as altering possible indirect interactions between membrane or inter-membrane elements mediated by any diffusible intermediates in the local micro-environment. Thus identification or verification of normal physiological control mechanisms for SR calcium release needs to be carried out in minimally disrupted fiber preparations such as those considered here. In contrast, detailed characterization of individual components may be best accomplished using more disrupted preparations, ultimately with purified proteins in reconstituted systems. A full understanding of the physiological control requires reconciliation and integration of results from both intact and disrupted preparations. How do the multiple modulators of release, identified and characterized in isolated systems, interact in the control of the fully integrated system? Are there properties of the intact system that lack counterparts or have not been identified in simpler isolated systems? Extensive efforts of several laboratories over the past few years devoted to investigating these and related questions are considered here.

TECHNIQUES AND FIBER PREPARATIONS

Full characterization of the control of SR calcium release in functionally intact muscle fiber preparations requires the use of at least two, and perhaps more, types of measuring systems to monitor events at the TT voltage sensor, the SR release channels, and possible intervening, coupling, or modulating elements. Movements of the TT voltage sensor are monitored as intramembrane charge movement currents (I_Q) detected with voltage-clamp techniques and appropriate procedures for eliminating the larger ionic and linear capacitative currents crossing the fiber external (surface and TT) membranes (110, 113). Since the SR constitutes an internal membrane system electrically uncoupled from the fiber external membranes, no current directly generated by SR calcium release is detected by the voltage-clamp circuit. Therefore, SR calcium release must be detected using a second monitoring system, either one involving fiber contraction (62) as an intrinsic but indirect detector of the elevated myoplasmic $[Ca^{2+}]$ resulting from release or, more quantitatively, one monitoring myoplasmic $[Ca^{2+}]$ transients using optical techniques and calcium indicators introduced into the myoplasm (110). The measured $[Ca^{2+}]$ can then be used with a modeling approach to calculate the change in total myoplasmic calcium (Ca$_T$) bound to various myoplasmic sites. The rate of SR calcium release (R$_{rel}$) is calculated as dCa$_T$/dT (7, 96, 97). Direct or indirect monitoring of other possible fixed or diffusible intermediates in the control process has not yet been achieved, although possible roles of putative diffusible intermediates have been investigated in skeletal muscle fibers by experimental manipulations designed to hold their concentrations constant at various levels (61, 74), or to rapidly alter their concentrations using photorelease methodology (32, 58, 134). Optical techniques and membrane potential-sensitive dyes can also be used to monitor the time course of the TT membrane potential (55, 56), which may differ from the electrically measured voltage between fiber interior and exterior due to current flow within the T system and the resulting voltage gradients.

Several muscle fiber preparations have been developed that maintain to varying extents the normal structural and functional interactions between components of the calcium release and control system. Intact fibers, either dissected out as isolated single fibers or within a muscle or muscle bundle, should manifest physiological coupling. They can be studied electrically using microelectrode (20) or gap (2) techniques, mechanically using force transducers (12, 20), and optically for [Ca^{2+}] monitoring using indicator microinjection (8), or indicator loading with membrane permeant acetoxymethyl esters of the active dyes (21). Isolated single fibers cut at one or both ends can be studied in a single (82) or multiple (81, 131) gap arrangement that isolates the solutions exposed to the cut end(s) of the fiber from those exposed to the intact segment of the fiber under study. Cut fibers with gap electrical recording provide lower noise records of I$_Q$ than those obtained with microelectrode (63, 66), but current flow across membranes within the gap does contribute to and complicate the total recorded current (25, 68, 82). The cut fiber allows modification of the internal medium, including introduction of [Ca^{2+}] indicators, by modification of the cut end solutions. The indicator-containing fiber segment in the experimental pool can then be studied optically. Cut fibers should maintain normal function (82) to the extent that the internal solution applied to the cut ends mimics the rapidly diffusible normal constituents of the myoplasm. Both intact and cut fibers maintain fast electrical propagation of the depolarization signal radially into the fiber via the T system, physiologically by action potential propagation, but by voltage-clamp pulses for experimental study of voltage-dependent processes. Although the Na and K ionic currents underlying the action potential are usually blocked in voltage-clamp studies of calcium release, there is some evidence that Na movements through unblocked Na channels may modulate calcium release (2).

Mechanically skinned fibers, which have the surface membrane peeled off, are a somewhat more disrupted preparation with normal structural and functional interaction between TT and SR possibly still maintained. In mechanically skinned fibers, the T tubules seal at the fiber surface during skinning and form a closed electrically and chemically isolated T system compartment that repolarizes through Na and K gradients generated by the TT Na/K pump (34, 124). The sealed T system can be depolarized either by changes in bathing solution ionic composition (34, 42, 84, 124), or by passing an electrical current between electrodes in the bath or in the myoplasm outside the T system (27), but the T tubules are too small for recording electrical signals by either patch clamp or fine-tipped microelectrodes. The skinned fiber preparation thus lacks the means to monitor charge movement or even to quickly modify the TT voltage by voltage-clamp. However, it does provide a preparation for studying release under conditions where TT and SR may exhibit physiological interaction, but the TT voltage is changed more slowly than in voltage-clamped fibers. Since the rate of calcium release characterized in voltage-clamped fibers exhibits an early peak that inactivates within roughly 50 ms of the onset of an intermediate or relatively large depolarization, leaving only the non-inactivating component remaining (96, 110), the release studied in skinned fibers by ionic depolarizations requiring more than tens of ms for completion would likely correspond to the non-inactivating component of release observed in voltage-clamped fibers.

TRANSVERSE TUBULE VOLTAGE SENSOR

Membrane-sensitive conformational changes of a charged voltage sensor molecule within the TT membrane, detected experimentally as intramembrane charge movement (110, 113), remain the generally accepted initial step in the TT depolarization/SR calcium release coupling process. Many parallels have been found between charge movement (Q) and calcium release, whereas no conditions or procedures have as yet been found that largely suppress Q while still maintaining external membrane potential-dependent SR calcium release.

Components of Intramembrane Charge Movement

The origin of the Q_γ component of charge movement, which is identified kinetically as the delayed "hump" component of I_Q following the faster Q_β component for pulses to the threshold voltage range for release activation, has been the subject of detailed study. Q_γ constitutes the steeply voltage-dependent component of Q over the voltage range near the release threshold (1, 65). Hui & Chandler (68) found that the steady state voltage dependence of total Q was statistically better described by the sum of two Boltzmann distributions, interpreted as arising from the Q_β and Q_γ voltage sensors moving independently within the membrane, rather than by a single Boltzmann distribution. The analyses included a theoretical gap factor to account for contributions of membrane under the Vaseline seals (68) and the possibility of non-linear charge in the control pulse used experimentally for removing linear currents (68, 98). A previously proposed sequential three state (two transition) model for charge movement (98) provided an equally good fit to the voltage dependence of the charge movement observed by Hui & Chandler (69). However, the sequential model was inconsistent with the kinetics of I_Q near -60 mV (69), which is near the calcium release threshold. It was also inconsistent with the voltage dependence of OFF charge movement when various depolarizing pulses were followed by an intermediate off step to -55 or -60 mV for about 100 ms before the final off step to -90 mV (69). In contrast, the model of Q_β and Q_γ moving independently in parallel could account for these observations (69). Similar separations of the Q_β and Q_γ were attained on the basis of sensitivity to tetracaine (which preferentially suppresses Q_γ), voltage dependence or kinetics (71). The properties of Q were shown to be quite similar in cut and intact fibers (66), providing that creatine phosphate (20 mM) was included in the end pool solution for the cut fibers (67), although some difference in temperature sensitivity of the two charge components in cut vs intact fibers was noted (66). The above cut fiber studies included 20 mM EGTA in the cut end solution, which eliminates fiber movement (63), but not Q_γ (63) or calcium transients (51, 103). The studies did not include calcium indicators for monitoring calcium transients.

The calcium feedback hypothesis for the origin of Q_γ, an alternative to the two parallel voltage sensor hypothesis (see above), was supported by a coordinated series of papers from three laboratories (30, 51, 105, 127). This hypothesis assumes a single population of intramembrane charges, but considers that binding of calcium ions to or near the voltage sensors during calcium release causes a secondary further effective TT depolarization. This in turn causes the delayed and steeply voltage-dependent secondary charge movement at and beyond the calcium release threshold, detected experimentally as Q_γ. Both the calcium feedback hypothesis and the two parallel sensor hypothesis are consistent with the frequently observed close correlation of Q_γ and calcium release (110). The parallel sensor model considers that Q_γ (as well as possibly Q_β) is involved in controlling release activation (68). The feedback hypothesis considers Q_γ to be a direct result of release.

The calcium feedback hypothesis predicts that procedures that selectively decrease or eliminate calcium release should decrease or eliminate Q_γ, but they should not decrease the maximum charge Q_{max} moved for large depolarizations. A sufficiently large depolarization would still move all charge either with or without the effective voltage shift hypothesized to accompany calcium release. In contrast, the parallel sensor hypothesis predicts that if Q_γ is truly decreased, there must be an equal decrease of Q_{max}, since Q_γ constitutes an independent sub-component of Q_{max}. Two conditions that suppress the hump component of I_Q, conditioning prepulses or 25 μM tetracaine, were found to cause maximal suppression of the I_Q amplitude for intermediate depolarizations and less suppression for larger depolarizations (71, 105). These findings were used to support the calcium feedback hypothesis (105). However, careful examination of the voltage dependence of total charge movement revealed that Q_γ was still present, but had shifted a few mV in the depolarizing direction in 25 μM tetracaine, which resulted in the observed maximum in the voltage dependence of the suppressed I_Q (71). An unequivocal demonstration of true suppression (not just a shift in voltage dependence) of Q_γ, together with unchanged Q_{max}, which would be inconsistent with the parallel sensor hypothesis, has not yet been achieved.

The calcium feedback hypothesis also predicts a negative phase of I_Q during a depolarizing pulse (105) because of a partial reversal of the effect of locally elevated $[Ca^{2+}]$ if R_{rel} reaches a peak and then declines appreciably during the pulse (96). The parallel sensor model, on the other hand, can only predict outward I_Q during a depolarizing pulse since the driving force on intramembrane charges due to membrane depolarization is always outward. Detection of a delayed inward I_Q during depolarization (105), especially with demonstration of ON/OFF charge equality (118), thus constitutes strong support for the calcium feedback hypothesis. However, the possibility of a residual time-dependent ionic current causing an apparent inward I_Q during depolarization (70) must be unequivocally ruled out.

Dihydropyridine Receptor: Voltage Sensor and/or Calcium Channel

Pharmacological studies with drugs in the dihydropyridine (DHP) and phenylalkylamine classes of calcium channel antagonists, which interact with the DHP receptor (DHPR), led to the suggestion that the DHPR is the intramembrane molecule that serves as the TT voltage sensor for SR calcium release in skeletal muscle (106). The DHPR is well known as the L-type calcium channel in the surface membrane of a variety of cells. DHP and other calcium channel antagonists suppress surface membrane I_{Ca} in these cells by preferential binding to the inactivated state of the L-type calcium channel, thus causing increased occupancy of the inactivated state according to the modulated receptor mechanism (11, 59). In skeletal muscle, the voltage sensors for SR calcium release also exhibit an inactivated state. Depolarizations lasting seconds or tens of seconds inactivate depolarization-contraction coupling (60) and cause transformation of the TT voltage sensors to a modified state (16, 26, 62). Fiber repolarization produces recovery of contraction (60) and charge movement (16, 26, 62). The first indication for a role of the DHPR as a voltage sensor for SR calcium release came from the finding that the phenylalkylamine D600 (gallopamil) blocked recovery of both contractile ability (37) and charge movement (72) during repolarization after prolonged depolarization. Furthermore, during strong hyperpolarization, fibers depolarized in D600 recovered calcium release and charge movement with closely parallel time courses (39). In partially depolarized fibers, the dihydropyridine nifedipine produced similar extents of suppression of calcium release and modification of charge movement (106), consistent with the modulated receptor mechanism for DHP action and with the association of the DHPR with charge movement and control of SR calcium release. Finally, restoration of mechanical activity by expression of the DHPR in dysgenic skeletal myotubes lacking the DHPR clearly identified the DHPR as the voltage sensor for calcium release (129). An interesting aspect of the identification of the voltage sensor with the DHPR is the high susceptibility of L-type (DHPR) calcium channels to run down in the absence of phosphorylation (24), which may point to possible analogous important phosphorylation effects in the DHPR control of calcium release and may explain (102) contradictory reports of calcium channel antagonist effects on contractile activation found in different experimental conditions or preparations.

L-type calcium channel activity is present in skeletal muscle, but the kinetics of channel opening are quite slow (112). Calcium influx through these or other calcium-conducting channels in external (surface or TT) membranes is not involved in activating SR calcium release in skeletal muscle fibers (4, 18, 99). This is in contrast to the situation in cardiac myocytes, where calcium inflow through L-type calcium channels is faster than in skeletal muscle and is necessary for activating SR calcium release (13, 19, 89). Interestingly, fast calcium current activation kinetics can be made to occur in skeletal fibers during a second pulse applied shortly after a conditioning pulse that activates the calcium current (40, 50). The transition to the fast gating mode follows the time course of the initial I_{Ca} activation during the conditioning pulse, but occurs even if I_{Ca} is blocked by nifedipine during conditioning (41). The possible dual or alternative roles of the skeletal DHPR as a voltage sensor for SR calcium release and/or as an external membrane calcium channel with voltage sensor controlling its own voltage-dependent gating naturally gives rise to questions concerning the relative amounts of measured Q that are related to these two possible functions (83, 117) of the same or closely similar (23) TT molecules.

When frog cut fibers were held at -100 mV to minimize depolarization-dependent and drug-induced inactivation, nifedipine caused a 29% decrease in Q with no significant decrease in SR calcium release (106). In rat cut, fast twitch skeletal fibers held at -90 mV, I_{Ca} was completely eliminated by nifedipine and Q was again decreased by about 30% at saturating nifedipine (88). One interpretation of these observations on fully polarized fibers is that up to about 30% of Q could be involved in calcium channel gating and not in voltage sensing for SR calcium release (83, 88), which would be the case if separate voltage sensors controlled I_{Ca} and calcium release and, if at -90 and -100 mV, nifedipine completely and selectively eliminated the I_{Ca} gating component (83). Alternatively, the same voltage sensors could control both I_{Ca} and calcium release. However, at least some transitions of the gating system would have to be involved only in the control of I_{Ca} or only in controlling SR release to account for the different kinetics of the two systems (83). In this case, the modulated receptor model could be modified so that the nifedipine affinity of both the inactivated state (above) and also an intermediate state located between the resting and active states of the voltage sensor would be higher than the nifedipine affinity of the resting state (36, 83, 102). This could explain the observed decrease in charge moved in a depolarizing step from a fully polarized potential in nifedipine (88, 106), since some charge would already be partially moved to the intermediate state as a result of its drug-induced occupancy. I_{Ca} could be eliminated without suppressing calcium release if the drug-occupied intermediate state could still undergo transition to the active, but drug-oc-cupied, state during depolarization (41), and if the drug-occupied active state could activate SR calcium release, but could not function as a conducting calcium channel. This interpretation could also account for the potentiating effect of DHPs on contractile activation (36, 48, 94, 102).

TT TO SR SIGNAL TRANSMISSION

An early proposal for the mechanism whereby the TT voltage sensor could control the SR calcium release channel envisioned a direct mechanical interaction of the two units, with the voltage sensor in its resting confor-mation directly blocking the release channel and with the block removed by voltage-dependent movement of the voltage sensor during TT depolar-ization (26). TT to SR transmission by a diffusible chemical transmitter would be the alternative to direct molecular interaction of the TT voltage sensor with the SR release channel.

Molecular Coupling Models

The SR calcium release channel has now been identified with the relatively high molecular weight ryanodine receptor (RyR), which has a putative intramembrane calcium channel domain in the junctional SR membrane (128), but also has a huge cytoplasmic domain that makes up most or all of the foot structure located between the SR and TT (14, 43, C Franzini-Armstrong & A Jorgensen, this volume). The foot presumably contacts the TT membrane and thus could make direct contact with DHPR molecules in the TT membrane. The original mechanical coupling model can be modified in view of these findings to still provide direct interaction between the DHPR voltage sensor and the RyR, but with the interaction now occurring at a domain of the RyR remote from the calcium channel domain. As in the mechanical blocking model, the DHPR in its resting state could again exert an inhibitory influence on the RyR calcium channel, which could be reversed as a result of the voltage-dependent conformational change of the DHPR voltage sensor during fiber depolarization. Inhibition of the RyR by the DHPR in the resting fiber and its removal during depolarization is attractive because of the general inherent rapidity of removal of inhibition and because the putative positively charged transmembrane helices in the DHPR (130) would move outward in the TT membrane during depolarization, i.e. away from the RyR. However, activation during depolarization is equally possible. The general molecular interaction hypothesis for depolarization-release coupling, including various formally equivalent models involving possible additional interacting, coupling, or linking proteins (22, 79), has not been ruled out and has become a widely recognized working hypothesis for the initiation of SR calcium release by TT depolarization.

Molecular interaction between the DHPR and RyR could involve little or no delay for TT to SR signal transmission. In that case evaluation of predictions of various kinetic models for the relationship between the time courses A(t) of SR channel activation and Q(t) of charge moved is quite straightforward. In the simplest case of a single voltage-dependent transition of the voltage sensor, A(t) would be proportional to Q(t). However, as is the case for gating currents for ionic channels (3), one or more preliminary voltage-dependent charge-moving transitions probably precede the final transition that opens the SR channel, so considerable voltage sensor charge movement could precede the actual channel opening step. In muscle fibers, a subthreshold prepulse, which moves considerable Q but activates minimal release, applied just before a larger test pulse, decreases the pulse duration required for detectable fiber contraction (62) and decreases the latent time before the calcium transient (114). The decrease in time corresponds to the time to move the prepulse charge at the test pulse voltage. The subthreshold Q that moves prior to release activation thus should be included in any release gating model since it appears to arise from precursor transitions in the control mechanism for SR calcium release (and/or from precursor transitions for gating an I_{Ca} that has the same voltage sensor kinetics; see above). Since subthreshold prepulses move predominantly Q_β with little Q_γ (65), Q_β appears to be involved in the SR control mechanism.

Tests of kinetic models for gating of SR release by the TT voltage sensors involve comparison of A(t) with the final SR channel-controlling component $Q_A(t)$ of Q(t). For most of the voltage range, the time course of R_{rel} during a depolarizing pulse exhibits an early peak followed within tens of ms by a rapid phase of decline to a lower but more maintained level (96), which in turn then declines much more slowly as calcium is depleted from the SR (116). The fast decline of R_{rel}, which is independent of inactivation of the voltage sensors and is attributed to calcium-dependent inactivation of the SR release system (7, 115, 121), is distinct from the mechanically refractory condition that also develops during depolarization, but has a time course about 1000 times slower and is associated with marked changes in charge movement (see above). Earlier studies used subthreshold prepulses to minimize precursor charge transitions during a following test pulse and demonstrated a linear relationship between the amount of charge moved and the peak R_{rel} for test pulses of various amplitudes and durations (98). However, for detailed evaluation of kinetic models, a full comparison of the predicted time course of Q_A with the measured A(t) is desirable. The presence of fast inactivation of the SR caclium release system, which presumably depends on an unknown local $[Ca^{2+}]$ in the immediate vicinity of the release channel, complicates the comparison. However, the inactivating component of R_{rel} can be preinactivated by a large conditioning prepulse, after which activation of the remaining non-inactivating component of release during a subsequent test pulse can be compared directly with charge movement, thus avoiding the need to consider inactivation when testing kinetic models for release activation (122).

Using the preinactivation protocol, Simon & Hill (119) found that A(t) was proportional to $[Q(t)]^4$ for both release activation during a pulse and release deactivation after the pulse, as expected if four identical and independent voltage sensors were required to move in the TT membrane to activate a single SR calcium release channel, and if the SR channel opened and closed with negligible delay when any three of the four sensors in an associated group were in the activating state and the fourth sensor moved into or out of the activating state. In this case, Q_A corresponds to the activating movement of the fourth sensor in each group. The four TT voltage sensing units for each SR channel could correspond to the four putative charged transmembrane alpha helices within a single DHPR (130). This would be similar to the gating mechanism of plasma membrane sodium channels (3, 23), which are highly homologous to the DHPR (130). Alternatively, a group of four different but neighboring DHPRs might act together to gate each SR channel, with a single charged transmembrane helix from each DHPR used to gate the SR channel (83). The latter configuration would be consistent with the structural arrangement in toadfish swimbladder skeletal muscle, where a tetrad of TT particles appears to be positioned opposite a single release channel and where each TT particle is believed to be a single DHPR (14). The finding that A(t) is proportional to [Q)t)]^4 also indicates that under the conditions of these experiments (119), there was no major component of Q that had kinetics drastically different from the kinetics consistent with gating the SR channels. Thus gating current for the much faster sodium channels must have been a negligible part of the total measured Q. Since a kinetically distinct hump component of I_Q was not detected in these experiments (119), possible complexity in kinetics due to Q_γ was also absent. Although the observed kinetic agreement of A(t) and [Q(t)]^4 shows that all detected Q has the appropriate time course to gate SR channels by the four sensor mechanism, it does not insure that all of the measured Q was in fact exclusively involved in gating SR release. Some or all of the measured Q could have been exclusively or additionally involved with gating I_{Ca} in the DHPRs themselves, but with the same voltage sensor kinetics as for gating SR calcium release (see above).

The molecular interaction model for TT voltage sensor control of the SR channel has been recently extended by Rios and co-workers (107) to include the possibility that the channel could open either on its own without any of the voltage sensors moved, or with increasing probability, as one to four of the sensors move into their activating position during fiber depolarization. Each of the individual voltage sensors in the activating position is proposed to act as an allosteric ligand for one of the four subunits making up a single SR calcium channel. An allosteric interaction is also proposed to occur among the four channel subunits so the system becomes formally equivalent to the Monod, Wyman, Changeux, model (100) for allosteric regulation of a four subunit enzyme. The allosteric model is qualitatively different from the preceding models, which involve a strict one-to-one correspondence between a particular gating state of the voltage sensors and the open state of the SR channel, since the channel can open with varying numbers of the four voltage sensors having moved. If the allosteric coupling between channel subunits were weak, channel opening could be significant only with all four sensors moved, as found by Simon & Hill (119), but if coupling were stronger, opening could be significant for fewer moved charges.

The allosteric model (107) was formulated to account for the marked effects of perchlorate ion, which in intact and cut fibers shifts the voltage dependence of charge movement (90) and of release activation to more negative potentials (46, 52), and drastically slows the off time course of charge movement after a depolarizing pulse (64, 90). In skinned fibers, perchlorate potentiates depolarization-induced, but not caffeine-induced, calcium release (42). These effects were previously attributed to a direct action of perchlorate on the TT voltage sensor. However, perchlorate also decreased both the threshold charge for release and the apparent numbers of charges that move to open each SR channel (53, 107), which indicates greater coupling efficiency between sensors and release channels. Perchlorate had negligible effect on the activity of purified skeletal muscle DHPR calcium channels in bilayers (192), on cardiac myocytes (92), or on surface or TT membrane calcium currents in crayfish skeletal fibers (53a) where direct TT to SR molecular coupling does not occur. To account for these observations, it was suggested that the primary perchlorate effect could be at the RyR calcium channel, with secondary effects on the voltage sensors as predicted by the allosteric model (107). However, a mathematically identical allosteric model was also applied previously to gating I_{Ca} in the DHPR itself (93), but in that case all allosteric interactions were independent of the RyR and were only among the four membrane-spanning domains within a single DHPR (93). If similar gating steps apply to DHPR control of SR calcium release, but with the SR-activating state of the DHPR now corresponding to the open state of the DHPR calcium channel, the action of perchlorate might similarly occur at the level of the voltage sensor.

Diffusible Mediators or Modulators of SR Calcium Release

CALCIUM IONS   The possibility of DHPR to RyR signal transmission by a diffusible chemical transmitter is the standard alternative to direct molecular interaction between the DHPR and the RyR. Calcium ions have long been considered as a candidate for a diffusible TT to SR transmitter. This would be consistent with the presence of calcium-induced calcium release (CICR) in skinned skeletal muscle fibers, where CICR was first discovered (38, 45), as well as in various fragmented, purified, or reconstituted SR and RyR preparations (G Meissner, this volume). Since in intact fibers calcium release continues for pulses to beyond the reversal potential for I_{Ca} (18), and also during stimulation in the absence of extracellular Ca^{2+} (4, 99), calcium influx across the TT membrane cannot be required for TT to SR transmission, although voltage-dependent liberation of trigger calcium ions from binding sites on the cytosolic surface of the TT membrane might still be involved. However, introduction of sufficient concentrations of the fast high affinity calcium buffers fura-2 or BAPTA into the myoplasm to buffer measured myoplasmic calcium at close to the resting level did not eliminate calcium release on depolarization of intact (61) or cut fibers (28, 74). Thus if calcium ions play a necessary role in TT to SR transmission, the putative trigger calcium must be localized to a restricted space that is not accessible to or controlled by the calcium buffers. Even in the absence of added myoplasmic calcium buffers, a restricted space in which trigger calcium is tightly controlled by the TT voltage sensors would seem to be required if Ca^{2+} were to serve as a necessary TT to SR transmitter, since release can be turned off and on by TT membrane potential even when the average measured myoplasmic $[Ca^{2+}]$ is markedly elevated during and after a large depolarization. No such space has been ultra-structurally identified in the TT/SR junction. In cardiac cells, where the junctional structure is similar to that in skeletal muscle, calcium ions do serve as DHPR to RyR transmitter (19, 89, 126), but the signal may be high local $[Ca^{2+}]$ in the immediate vicinity of the open DHPR calcium channels (125), which in cardiac cells provide the path for entry of trigger calcium into the cell from the extra-cellular medium. Hypothetical voltage-dependent liberation of calcium ions from binding sites on the TT cytoplasmic surface in skeletal muscle could not realistically be expected to produce similarly high local $[Ca^{2+}]$ as found at the cytoplasmic mouth of a conducting calcium channel.

One might speculate that a hypothetical restricted space, consisting of the cytosolic end of the DHPR channel pore and the inner vestibule of the DHPR, could exist largely within the DHPR molecules that control release. If the vestibule abutted a calcium-binding site on the RyR, if the resting DHPR channel contained a trapped Ca^{2+} ion, and if during de-polarization the DHPR channel opened to the RyR but not to the TT lumen, the calcium ion could bind to and activate the RyR without inter-ference from cytosolic calcium ions. The functional properties of this or other imaginable models with similarly restricted calcium spaces of mac-romolecular dimensions (31) become indistinguishable kinetically from models with direct DHPR/RyR interaction. However, the involvement of calcium as a transmitter within the voltage sensor does provide the in-teresting mechanistic possibility that the modulatory role of extracellular $[Ca^{2+}]$ in decreasing the tendency to inactivation of charge movement (15), mechanical activity (91), and calcium release capability (17) could be the result of slow access of the trapped Ca^{2+} to the external solution during prolonged depolarization (31).

Except for the possible localized action within a highly restricted mac-romolecular space (see above), Ca^{2+} ions do not seem to be necessary for TT to SR transmission during initiation of SR calcium release. However, Ca^{2+} could still have a secondary role in augmenting the primary release activated by a calcium-independent mechanism. Based on the structural finding that in swimbladder skeletal muscle every other SR release channel may lack a corresponding TT voltage sensor tetrad (14), it was proposed that only half of the release channels may be directly controlled by the TT voltage sensors and that the other half may be activated secondarily by

CICR driven by the elevated $[Ca^{2+}]$ from the directly activated release (109). Binding studies indicate an excess of RyR Ca channels compared to DHPRs in other less specialized skeletal muscles (G Meissner, this volume), which indicates that lack of direct TT voltage control of some RyR channels may be a general property of skeletal muscle. Potentiation of CICR by sub-mM caffeine did not qualitatively alter the characteristic early peak and subsequent decline of the R_{rel} waveform for long pulses (80), which indicates that CICR is not incompatible with the observed release time courses. The turn off of release was slowed after short pulses in caffeine (80, 120), consistent with an increased calcium sensitivity in the presence of caffeine causing loss of TT control of release due to the positive feedback inherent in CICR driven by global $[Ca^{2+}]$. The relatively rapid turn off of release after short pulses in the absence of caffeine does not rule out involvement of CICR during physiological release if the CICR were driven by a high local $[Ca^{2+}]$ in the immediate vicinity of release channels directly controlled by the TT voltage sensor rather than by global $[Ca^{2+}]$, since such locally elevated $[Ca^{2+}]$ would dissipate almost instantly once the channels closed (80).

Microinjection of sufficient fast calcium buffer into voltage-clamped frog cut fibers to eliminate the $[Ca^{2+}]$ transient selectively eliminated the inactivating component of R_{rel} without decreasing the maintained or non-inactivating component (28, 74). This indicates that the inactivating component (but not the non-inactivating component) might be activated by CICR. The release calculations before and after introduction of extrinsic calcium buffers require different assumptions and may thus involve different scaling errors, but the release records were made comparable by scaling the calculated R_{rel} to the SR calcium content determined respectively before and after injection (28, 74). A possible complicating factor in any experiment demonstrating suppression of peak release due to introduction of calcium buffers is the susceptibility of the peak R_{rel} in cut fibers to run down during the course of an experiment (80). However, in cut fibers, control injections with the non-buffering BAPTA analogue anisidine did not produce the suppression of peak R_{rel} obtained with BAPTA or fura-2 injections (28), thus indicating that run down or injection damage were probably not the cause of the decline in peak R_{rel} observed after calcium buffer injections into voltage-clamped cut fibers.

Simple elimination of calcium-dependent inactivation of release (115, 121) without any suppression of release activation would also eliminate the early peak in the calcium release waveform. But in this case, the maintained release after removal of inactivation would be at least as large as the peak R_{rel} before removal of inactivation, i.e. several times larger than the maintained release in control before adding calcium buffers. An increase in release has been observed with microinjections of fura-2 into intact fibers to concentrations that partially but incompletely suppressed action potential [Ca^{2+}] transients (8). Higher concentrations of fura-2 did cause a suppression of release, which was attributed to a possible pharmacological effect of fura-2 or to injection damage (61). Diffusion of fura-2 from the ends of cut fibers also increased release for action potentials (104) and increased the steady release during voltage-clamp depolarization (77), consistent with removal of calcium-dependent inactivation of release by strong myoplasmic calcium buffering. However, other studies using diffusion of BAPTA from the ends of cut fibers found a suppression of peak release during voltage-clamp depolarization (29). Finally, normal release waveforms exhibiting early peaks followed by a rapid and then a slow phase of decline have been observed in recent experiments in which myoplasmic [Ca^{2+}] was buffered using mM concentrations of quin-2 as both calcium buffer and calcium indicator (31a). These release records first confirm the release waveform previously deduced based on modeling calcium binding to intrinsic myoplasmic sites. They further indicate the possible importance of the local [Ca^{2+}] in the immediate vicinity of the calcium release channels, which could be appreciably higher than the average measured myoplasmic [Ca^{2+}], in controlling the release channel.

INOSITOL 1, 4, 5-TRISPHOSPHATE   In analogy with its role as a messenger for activation of calcium release in smooth muscle and most non-muscle cells, inositol 1, 4, 5-trisphosphate (InsP3) has been considered as a possible candidate for the hypothetical chemical transmitter from the TT to the SR. In this case, InsP3 would be released from the TT by the voltage-dependent activation of phospholipase C and would activate SR calcium release by binding to an InsP3-sensitive release channel (76). The relatively slow rate of SR release activation following photolytic liberation of InsP3 in skeletal muscle fibers (134) argues against its role as a primary activator of SR calcium release. Blinks and colleagues (54) have provided a convincing explanation for the various contradictory reports concerning the effectiveness of InsP3 in releasing calcium and/or activating contraction. They found that microinjection of InsP3 into intact skeletal fibers did not cause contractile activation, whereas similar injections did cause contractions in fibers with T systems partially depolarized either by moderate elevation of K$^+$ in the bathing solution or by TT system disruption by glycerol removal osmotic shock. Full TT depolarization or nifedipine application to fibers with partially depolarized TTs eliminated the InsP3 response (54). These observations are consistent with the idea (54) that InsP3 injection causes a small TT depolarization, presumably by activating DHP-sensitive TT channels (133). The depolarization could activate SR calcium release if the TTs were already partially depolarized to near the calcium release threshold, but not with fully polarized or fully depolarized TTs. According to this interpretation, the calcium release produced by InsP$_3$ injection is not due to any activating effect of InsP$_3$ on the SR, but is simply release by a TT to SR coupling mechanism that does not involve InsP$_3$.

MAGNESIUM IONS   Magnesium ions have a strong inhibitory effect on calcium release in a variety of disrupted skeletal muscle SR membrane and RyR preparations (G Meissner, this volume). Lowering myoplasmic [Mg^{2+}] potentiates SR calcium release activation during ionic depolarization of mechanically skinned fibers (87) and during voltage-clamp depolarization of cut fibers (75), but changes in myoplasmic [Mg^{2+}] are unlikely to be involved in physiological TT to SR signaling since cytosolic Mg^{2+} is present and well buffered in skeletal muscle at a free concentration in the 1 mM range. An interesting possibility proposed by Lamb & Stephenson (87) is that TT to SR signaling could involve removal of Mg^{2+} inhibition of release without a change in [Mg^{2+}] if the conformational change of the TT voltage sensor during depolarization had the allosteric effect of decreasing the affinity of the RyR for Mg^{2+} at an inhibitory site for release. It will be interesting to see if this mechanism proves capable of accounting for a variety of observations on fast voltage-clamp depolarization of intact or cut fibers as well as the observations on the slower ionic depolarization of skinned fibers.

G PROTEINS AND PHOSPHORYLATION   In skinned or split fibers, application of the non-hydrolyzable GTP analogue, GTPγS, has been found to cause calcium release (33, 123), or to potentiate caffeine or calcium-induced release (132), presumably by causing maintained activation of GTP binding (G) proteins. In other studies on skinned fibers, however, GTPγS did not potentiate depolarization-induced release (85). In voltage-clamped cut fibers, GTPγS was reported to increase charge movement (49, 101) and calcium current (49), but in other studies, it was reported to have no effect on charge movement (85). G proteins activate L-type (DHPR) calcium channels in other preparations via DHPR phosphorylation by cAMP-dependent protein kinase (57, 78), and via direct interaction with the channel (73, 136). The observed activation of release by GTPγS in skinned skeletal fibers may be mediated by a direct activation of TT DHPR calcium channels, with release of calcium from the TT lumen initiating further calcium release from the SR via CICR (123). However, phosphorylation does have effects on the TT and SR in skeletal fibers. Activation of cAMP-dependent protein kinase potentiated calcium current via DHPR calcium channels (5, 49), presumably by phosphorylation of the channels, but it did not potentiate SR calcium release (5). Phosphorylation of the SR release channel by calcium/

calmodulin-dependent protein kinase II inhibits SR calcium channel activity (135), whereas phosphorylation by endogenous kinase enhances channel activity by increasing its sensitivity to Ca^{2+} and ATP (56a).

Each of the preceding agents or treatments can clearly modulate SR calcium release in various skeletal fiber preparations. However, compelling evidence for the necessary involvement of any as a diffusible transmitter from TT to SR has not been provided and some indication against necessary participation has been obtained. The direct molecular interaction model would thus seem to be the current hypothesis of choice for the mechanism of TT to SR signal transmission.

Literature Cited

1. Adrian RH, Peres AR. 1979. Charge movement and membrane capacity in frog muscle. *J. Physiol.* 289:83–97
2. Allard B, Rougier O. 1992. Reappraisal of the role of sodium ions in excitation-contraction coupling in frog twitch muscle. *J. Musc. Res. Cell Motil.* 13:117–25
3. Armstrong CM. 1992. Voltage-dependent ion channels and their gating. *Physiol. Rev.* 72:S5–14
4. Armstrong CM, Bezanilla F, Horowicz P. 1972. Twitches in the presence of ethylene glycol bis (β- aminoethyl ether)-N,N'-tetraacetic acid. *Biochem. Biophys. Acta* 267:605–8
5. Arreola J, Calvo J, Garcia MC, Sanchez JA. 1987. Modulation of calcium channels of twitch skeletal muscle fibres of the frog by adrenaline and cyclic adenosine monophosphate. *J. Physiol.* 393:307–30
6. Ashley CC, Mulligan IP, Lea TJ. 1991. Ca^{2+} and activation mechanisms in skeletal muscle. *Q. Rev. Biophys.* 24: 1–73
7. Baylor SM, Chandler WK, Marshall MW. 1983. Sarcoplasmic reticulum calcium release in frog skeletal muscle fibres estimated from Arsenazo III calcium transients. *J. Physiol.* 344: 625–66
8. Baylor SM, Hollingworth S. 1988. Fura-2 Ca^{2+} transients in frog skeletal muscle fibres. *J. Physiol.* 403:151–92
9. Deleted in proof
10. Deleted in proof
11. Bean BP. 1984. Nitrendipine block of cardiac calcium channels: high-affinity binding to the inactivated state. *Proc. Natl. Acad. Sci. USA* 81:6388–92
12. Berwe D, Gottschalk G, Luttgau HC. 1987. Effects of the calcium antagonist

gallopamil (D600) upon excitation-contraction coupling in toe muscle fibres of the frog. *J. Physiol.* 385:693–707
13. Beukelmann DJ, Wier WG. 1988. Mechanism of release of calcium from sarcoplasmic reticulum of guinea-pig cardiac cells. *J. Physiol.* 405:233–55
14. Block BA, Imagawa T, Campbell KP, Franzini-Armstrong C. 1988. Structural evidence for direct interaction between the molecular components of the transverse tubule/sarcoplasmic reticulum junction in skeletal muscle. *J. Cell Biol.* 107:2587–600
15. Brum G, Fitts R, Pizarro G, Rios E. 1988. Voltage sensors of the frog skeletal muscle membrane require calcium to function in excitation-contraction coupling. *J. Physiol.* 398:475–505
16. Brum G, Rios E. 1987. Intramembrane charge movement in frog skeletal muscle fibres. Properties of charge 2. *J. Physiol.* 387:489–517
17. Brum G, Rios E, Stefani E. 1988. Effects of extracellular calcium on calcium movements of excitation-contraction coupling in frog skeletal muscle fibres. *J. Physiol.* 398:441–73
18. Brum G, Stefani E, Rios E. 1987. Simultaneous measurement of Ca current and intracellular Ca concentrations in single skeletal muscle fibres of the frog. *Can. J. Physiol. Pharmacol.* 65:681–85
19. Callewaert G, Cleemann L, Morad M. 1988. Epinephrine enhances Ca^{2+} current-regulated Ca^{2+} release and Ca^{2+} reuptake in rat ventricular myocytes. *Proc. Natl. Acad. Sci. USA* 85:2009–13
20. Caputo C, Bezanilla F, Horowicz P. 1984. Depolarization-contraction coupling in short frog muscle fibers. *J. Gen. Physiol.* 84:133–54

21. Caputo C, Bolanos P. 1992. Fluo-3 calcium transients during potasium contractures of single muscle fibers. *Biophys. J.* 61:159 (Abstr.)

22. Caswell AH, Brandt NR, Brunschwig JP, Purkerson S. 1991. Localization and partial characterization of the oligomeric disulfide-linked molecular weight 95,000 protein (triadin) which binds the ryanodine and dihdropyridine receptors in skeletal muscle triadic vesicles. *Biochemistry* 30:7507–13

23. Catterall WA. 1991. Excitation-contraction coupling in vertebrate skeletal muscle: A tale of two calcium channels. *Cell* 64:871–74

24. Chad JE, Eckert R. 1986. An enzymatic mechanism for calcium current inactivation in dialysed Helix neurones. *J. Physiol.* 378:31–51

25. Chandler WK, Hui CS. 1990. Membrane capacitance in frog cut twitch fibers mounted in a double vaseline-gap chamber. *J. Gen. Physiol.* 96:225–56

26. Chandler WK, Rakowski RF, Schneider MF. 1976. Effects of glycerol treatment and maintained depolarization on charge movement in muscle. *J. Physiol.* 254:285–316

27. Constantin LL, Podolsky RJ. 1967. Depolarization of the internal membrane system in the activation of frog skeletal muscle. *J. Gen. Physiol.* 50:1101–24

28. Csernoch L, Jacquemond V, Schneider MF. 1993. Microinjection of strong calcium buffers suppresses the peak of calcium release during depolarization in frog skeletal muscle fibers. *J. Gen. Physiol.* 101:297–333

29. Csernoch L, Jacquemond V, Schneider MF. 1993. Peak calcium release is suppressed by high affinity calcium buffers applied from the cut ends of frog skeletal muscle fibers. *Biophys. J.* 64:37 (Abstr.)

30. Csernoch L, Pizarro G, Uribe I, Rodriguez M, Rios E. 1991. Interfering with calcium release suppresses I_γ, the delayed component of intramembranous charge movement in skeletal muscle. *J. Gen. Physiol.* 97:845–84

31. Curtis BA. 1988. Na/Ca exchange and excitation-contraction coupling in frog fast fibres. *J. Musc. Res. Cell Motil.* 9:415–27

31a. Dey SK, Klein MG, Schneider MF. 1994. The rate of calcium release in quin-2-buffered frog cut skeletal muscle fibers. *Biophys. J.* 66: In press

32. DiFranco M, Suarez-Isla BA, Vergara J. 1991. Fast detection of Ca-transients elicited by flash photolysis of dm-nitrophen and nitr-5 with the fluorescent indicators rhod-2 and fluo-3. *Biophys. J.* 59:542 (Abstr.)

33. Di Virgilio F, Salviati G, Pozzan T, Volpe P. 1986. Is a guanine nucleotide-binding protein involved in excitation-contraction coupling in skeletal muscle? *Eur. Mol. Biol. J.* 5:259–62

34. Donaldson SK. 1985. Possible stimulation of Ca^{2+} release via a transverse tubule-sarcoplasmic reticulum mechanism. *J. Gen. Physiol.* 86:501–25

35. Dulhunty AF. 1992. The voltage-activation of contraction in skeletal muscle. *Prog. Biophys. Mol. Biol.* 57:181–223

36. Dulhunty AF, Gage PW. 1988. Effects of extracellular calcium concentration and dihydropyridines on contraction in mammalian skeletal muscle. *J. Physiol.* 399:63–80

37. Eisenberg RS, McCarthy RT, Milton RL. 1983. Paralysis of frog skeletal muscle fibres by the calcium antagonist D-600. *J. Physiol.* 341:495–505

38. Endo M, Tanaka M, Ogawa Y. 1970. Calcium-induced release of calcium from the sarcoplasmic reticulum of skinned skeletal muscle fibers. *Nature* 228:34–36

39. Feldmeyer D, Melzer W, Pohl B. 1990. Effects of gallopamil (D600) on calcium release and intramembrane charge movements in frog skeletal muscle fibres. *J. Physiol.* 421:343–62

40. Feldmeyer D, Melzer W, Pohl B, Zollner P. 1990. Fast gating kinetics of the slow Ca^{2+} current in cut skeletal muscle fibres of the frog. *J. Physiol.* 425:347–67

41. Feldmeyer D, Melzer W, Pohl B, Zollner P. 1992. Modulation of calcium current gating in frog skeletal muscle by conditioning depolarization. *J. Physiol.* 457:639–53

42. Fill MD, Best PM. 1990. Effect of perchlorate on calcium release in skinned fibres stimulated by ionic substitution and caffeine. *Pflügers Arch.* 415:688–92

43. Fleischer S, Inui M. 1989. Biochemistry and biophysics of excitation-contraction coupling. *Annu. Rev. Biophys. Biophys. Chem.* 18:333–64

44. Deleted in proof

45. Ford LE, Podolsky RJ. 1970. Regenerative calcium release within muscle cells. *Science* 167:58–59

46. Foulks JG, Miller JAD, Perry FA. 1973. Repolarization-induced reactivation of contracture tension in frog skeletal muscle. *Can. J. Physiol. Pharmacol.* 51:324–34

47. Deleted in proof
48. Gallant EM, Goettl VM. 1985. Effects of calcium antagonists on mechanical responses of mammalian skeletal muscles. *Eur. J. Pharmacol.* 117:259–65
49. Garcia J, Aldeco RG, Stefani E. 1990. Charge movement and calcium currents in skeletal muscle fibres are enhanced by GTPγS. *Pflügers Arch.* 417:114–16
50. Garcia J, Avila-Sakar AJ, Stefani E. 1990. Repetitive stimulation increases the activation rate of skeletal muscle Ca^{2+} currents. *Pflügers Arch.* 416:210–12
51. Garcia J, Pizarro G, Rios E, Stefani E. 1991. Effect of the calcium buffer EGTA on the "hump" component of charge movement in skeletal muscle. *J. Gen. Physiol.* 97:885–96
52. Gomolla M, Gottschalk G, Luttgau HC. 1983. Perchlorate-induced alteration in electrical and mechanical parameters of frog skeletal muscle fibres. *J. Physiol.* 343:197–214
53. Gonzalez A, Rios E. 1993. Perchlorate enhances transmission in skeletal muscle excitation-contraction coupling. *J. Gen. Physiol.* 102:373–422
53a. Gyorke S, Palade P. 1992. Effects of perchlorate on excitation-contraction coupling in frog and crayfish skeletal muscle. *J. Physiol.* 456:443–51
54. Hannon JD, Lee NK-M, Yandong C, Blinks JR. 1992. Inositol trisphosphate (InsP$_3$) causes contraction in skeletal muscle only under artificial conditions: evidence that Ca^{2+} release can result from depolarization of T-tubules. *J. Musc. Res. Cell Motil.* 13:447–56
55. Heiny JA, Jong D-S. 1990. A nonlinear electrostatic potential change in the T-system of skeletal muscle detected under passive recording conditions using potentiometric dyes. *J. Gen. Physiol.* 95:147–75
56. Heiny JA, Vergara J. 1982. Optical signals from surface and T-system membranes in skeletal muscle fibers. *J. Gen. Physiol.* 80:203–30
56a. Herrmann-Frank A, Varsanyi M. 1993. Enhancement of Ca^{2+} release channel activity by phosphorylation of the skeletal muscle ryanodine receptor. *FEBS Lett.* In press
57. Hescheler J, Kameyama M, Trautwein W, Mieskes G, Soeling HD. 1987. Regulation of the cardiac calcium channel by protein phosphatases. *Eur. J. Biochem.* 165:261–66
58. Hill D, Simon BJ. 1991. Use of "caged calcium" in skeletal muscle to study calcium-dependent inactivation of SR calcium release. *Biophys. J.* 59:239 (Abstr.)
59. Hille B. 1977. Local anesthetics: hydrophilic and hydrophobic pathways for the drug-receptor reaction. *J. Gen. Physiol.* 69:497–515
60. Hodgkin AL, Horowicz P. 1960. Potassium contractures in single muscle fibres. *J. Physiol.* 153:386–403
61. Hollingworth S, Harkins AB, Kurebayashi N, Konishi M, Baylor SM. 1992. Excitation-contraction coupling in intact frog skeletal muscle fibers injected with mmolar concentrations of fura-2. *Biophys. J.* 63:224–34
62. Horowicz P, Schneider MF. 1981. Membrane charge moved at contraction thresholds in skeletal muscle fibers. *J. Physiol.* 277:483–506
63. Horowicz P, Schneider MF. 1981. Membrane change movement in contracting and non-contracting skeletal muscle fibres. *J. Physiol.* 314:565–93
64. Huang CLH. 1987. 'Off' tails of intramembrane charge movements in frog skeletal muscle in perchlorate-containing solutions. *J. Physiol.* 384:491–509
65. Huang CLH. 1988. Intramembrane charge movements in skeletal muscle. *Physiol. Rev.* 68:1197–247
66. Hui CS. 1991. Comparison of charge movement components in intact and cut twitch fibers of the frog. *J. Gen. Physiol.* 98:287–314
67. Hui CS. 1991. Factors affecting the appearance of the hump charge movement component in frog cut twitch fibers. *J. Gen. Physiol.* 98:315–47
68. Hui CS, Chandler WK. 1990. Intramembranous charge movement in frog cut twitch fibers mounted in a double vaseline-gap chamber. *J. Gen. Physiol.* 96:257–97
69. Hui CS, Chandler WK. 1991. Q$_β$ and Q$_γ$ components of intramembranous charge movement in frog cut twitch fibers. *J. Gen. Physiol.* 98:429–64
70. Hui CS, Chen W. 1991. Does the hump charge movement component have a negative phase? *Biophys. J.* 59:543 (Abstr.)
71. Hui CS, Chen W. 1992. Separation of Q$_β$ and Q$_γ$ charge components in frog cut twitch fibers with tetracaine. *J. Gen. Physiol.* 99:985–1016
72. Hui CS, Milton RL, Eisenberg RS. 1984. Charge movement in skeletal muscle fibers paralyzed by the calcium-entry blocker D600. *Proc. Natl. Acad. Sci. USA* 81:2582–85
73. Imoto Y, Yatani A, Reeves JP, Codina J, Birnbaumer L, Brown AM. 1988. α-subunit of G$_s$ directly activates car-

diac calcium channels in lipid bilayers. *Am. J. Physiol.* 255:H722–28

74. Jacquemond V, Csernoch L, Klein MG, Schneider MF. 1991. Voltage-gated and calcium-gated calcium release during depolarization of skeletal muscle fibers. *Biophys. J.* 60:867–73

75. Jacquemond V, Schneider MF. 1992. Low myoplasmic Mg^{2+} potentiates calcium release during depolarization of frog skeletal muscle fibers. *J. Gen. Physiol.* 100:137–54

76. Jaimovich E. 1991. Chemical transmission at the triad: $InsP_3$. *J. Musc. Res. Cell Motil.* 12:316–20

77. Jong D-S, Pape PC, Chandler WK, Baylor SM. 1993. Reduction of calcium inactivation of sarcoplasmic reticulum calcium release by fura-2 in voltage-clamped cut twitch fibers from frog muscle. *J. Gen Physiol.* 102:333–70

78. Kameyama M, Hescheler J, Hofmann F, Trautwein W. 1986. Modulation of Ca current during the phosphorylation cycle in the guinea pig heart. *Pflügers Arch.* 407:123–28

79. Kim KC, Caswell AH, Talvenheimo JA, Brandt NR. 1990. Isolation of a terminal cisterna protein which may link the dihydropyridine receptor to the junctional foot protein in skeletal muscle. *Biochemistry* 29:9281–89

80. Klein MG, Simon BJ, Schneider MF. 1990. Effects of caffeine on calcium release from the sarcoplasmic reticulum in frog skeletal muscle fibres. *J. Physiol.* 425:599–626

81. Kovacs L, Rios E, Schneider MF. 1979. Calcium transients and intramembrane charge movement in skeletal muscle fibers. *Nature* 279:391–96

82. Kovacs L, Schneider MF. 1978. Contractile activation by voltage clamp depolarization of cut skeletal muscle fibres. *J. Physiol.* 277:483–506

83. Lamb GD. 1992. DHP receptors and excitation-contraction coupling. *J. Musc. Res. Cell Motil.* 13:394–405

84. Lamb GD, Stephenson DG. 1990. Calcium release in skinned muscle fibres of the toad by transverse tubule depolarization or by direct stimulation. *J. Physiol.* 423:495–517

85. Lamb GD, Stephenson DG. 1991. Excitation-contraction coupling in skeletal muscle fibres of rat and toad in the presence of GTPγS. *J. Physiol.* 444:65–84

86. Lamb GD, Stephenson DG. 1992. Importance of Mg^{2+} in excitation-contraction coupling in skeletal muscle. *News Physiol. Sci.* 7:270–74

87. Lamb GD, Stephenson GD. 1991. Effect of Mg^{2+} on the control of Ca^{2+} release in skeletal muscle fibres of the toad. *J. Physiol.* 434:507–28

88. Lamb GD, Walsh T. 1987. Calcium currents, charge movement and dihydropyridine binding in fast- and slow-twitch muscles of rat and rabbit. *J. Physiol.* 393:595–617

89. London B, Krueger JW. 1986. Contraction in voltage-clamped, internally perfused single heart cells. *J. Gen. Physiol.* 88:475–505

90. Luttgau HC, Kovacs L, Gottschalk G, Fuxreiter M. 1983. How perchlorate improves excitation-contraction coupling in skeletal muscle fibers. *Biophys. J.* 43:247–49

91. Luttgau HC, Spieker W. 1979. The effects of calcium deprivation upon mechanical and electrophysiological parameters in skeletal muscle fibres of the frog. *J. Physiol.* 296:411–29

92. Ma J, Anderson K, Shirokov R, Levis R, Gonzalez A, et al. 1993. Effects of percholarte on the molecules of exitation-contraction coupling of skeletal and cardiac muscle. *J. Gen. Physiol.* 102:423–48

93. Marks TN, Jones SW. 1992. Calcium currents in the A7r5 smooth muscle-derived cell line. *J. Gen. Physiol.* 99:367–90

94. McCleskey EW. 1985. Calcium channels and intracellular calcium release are pharmacologically different in frog skeletal muscle. *J. Physiol.* 361:231–49

95. Deleted in proof

96. Melzer W, Rios E, Schneider MF. 1984. Time course of calcium release and removal in skeletal muscle fibres. *Biophys. J.* 45:637–41

97. Melzer W, Rios E, Schneider MF. 1987. A general procedure for determining calcium release from the sarcoplasmic reticulum in skeletal muscle fibers. *Biophys. J.* 51:849–63

98. Melzer W, Schneider MF, Simon BJ, Szucs G. 1986. Intramembrane charge movement and calcium release in frog skeletal muscle. *J. Physiol.* 373:481–511

99. Miledi R, Parker I, Zhu PH. 1984. Extracellular ions and excitation-contraction coupling in frog twitch muscle fibers. *J. Physiol.* 351:687–710

100. Monod J, Wyman J, Changeux J-P. 1965. On the nature of allosteric transitions: a plausible model. *J. Mol. Biol.* 12:88–118

101. Mouzou A, Poindessault J-P, Raymond G. 1992. Involvement of a pertussis toxin-sensitive G-protein in excitation-

contraction coupling of intact and cut-end voltage-clamped skeletal muscle fibres. *Pflügers Arch.* 421:510–12

102. Neuhaus R, Rosenthal R, Luttgau HC. 1990. The effects of dihydropyridine derivatives on force and Ca^{2+} current in frog skeletal muscle fibres. *J. Physiol.* 427:187–209

103. Palade P, Vergara J. 1982. Arsenazo-III and antipyrylazo III calcium transients in single skeletal muscle fibers. *J. Gen. Physiol.* 79:679–708

104. Pape PC, Jong D-S, Chandler WK, Baylor SM. 1993. Effect of fura-2 on action-potential stimulated calcium release in cut twitch fibers from frog muscle. *J. Gen. Physiol.* 102:295–332

105. Pizarro G, Csernoch L, Uribe I, Rodriguez M, Rios E. 1991. The relationship between Q$_\gamma$ and Ca release from the sarcoplasmic reticulum in skeletal muscle. *J. Gen. Physiol.* 97: 913–47

106. Rios E, Brum G. 1987. Involvement of dihydropyridine receptors in excitation- contraction coupling in skeletal muscle. *Nature* 325:717–20

107. Rios E, Karhanek M, Ma J, Gonzalez A. 1993. An allosteric model of the molecular interaction of excitation-contraction coupling in skeletal muscle. *J. Gen. Physiol.* 102:449–82

108. Rios E, Ma J, Gonzalez A. 1991. The mechanical hypothesis of excitation-contraction (EC) coupling in skeletal muscle. *J. Musc. Res. Cell Motil.* 12:127–35

109. Rios E, Pizarro G. 1988. Voltage sensors and calcium channels of excitation-contraction coupling. *News Physiol. Sci.* 3:223–28

110. Rios E, Pizarro G. 1991. Voltage sensor of excitation-contraction coupling in skeletal muscle. *Physiol. Rev.* 71:849–908

111. Rios E, Pizarro G, Stefani E. 1992. Charge movement and the nature of signal transduction in skeletal muscle excitation-contraction coupling. *Annu. Rev. Physiol.* 54:109–33

112. Sanchez JA, Stefani E. 1983. Kinetic properties of calcium channels of twitch muscle fibres of the frog. *J. Physiol.* 37:1–17

113. Schneider MF, Chandler WK. 1973. Voltage dependent charge movement in skeletal muscle. *Nature* 242:244–46

114. Schneider MF, Rios E, Kovacs L. 1981. Calcium transients and intramembrane charge movement in skeletal muscle. In *The Regulation of Muscle Contraction: Excitation-Contraction Coupling*, ed. AD Grinnell,

MAB Brazier, pp. 131–42. New York: Academic

115. Schneider MF, Simon BJ. 1988. Inactivation of calcium release from the sarcoplasmic reticulum in frog skeletal muscle. *J. Physiol.* 405:727–45

116. Schneider MF, Simon BJ, Szucs G. 1987. Depletion of calcium from the sarcoplasmic reticulum during calcium release in frog skeletal muscle. *J. Physiol.* 392:167–92

117. Schwartz LM, McClesky EW, Almers W. 1985. Dihydropydine receptors in muscle are voltage-dependent but most are not functional calcium channels. *Nature* 314:747–51

118. Shirokova N, Gonzalez A, Rios E. 1993. Three phases in I$_\gamma$, the hump component of charge movement in frog skeletal muscle. *Biophys. J.* 64:240a (Abstr.)

119. Simon BJ, Hill D. 1992. Charge movement and SR calcium release in frog skeletal muscle can be related by a Hodgkin-Huxley model with four gating particles. *Biophys. J.* 61:1109–16

120. Simon BJ, Klein MG, Schneider MF. 1989. Caffeine slows turn-off of calcium release in voltage clamped skeletal muscle fibers. *Biophys. J.* 55: 793–97

121. Simon BJ, Klein MG, Schneider MF. 1991. Calcium dependence of inactivation of calcium release from the sarcoplasmic reticulum in skeletal muscle fibers. *J. Gen. Physiol.* 97:437–71

122. Simon BJ, Schneider MF. 1988. Time course of activation of calcium release from sarcoplasmic reticulum in skeletal muscle. *Biophys. J.* 54:1159–63

123. Somasundaram B, Tregear RT, Trentham DR. 1991. GTPγS causes contraction of skinned frog skeletal muscle via the DHP-sensitive Ca^{2+} channels of the sealed T-tubules. *Pflügers Arch.* 418:137–43

124. Stephenson EW. 1985. Excitation of skinned muscle fibers by imposed ion gradients. *J. Gen. Physiol.* 86:813–32

125. Stern MD. 1992. Theory of excitation-contraction coupling in cardiac muscle. *Biophys. J.* 63:497–517

126. Stern MD, Lakatta EG. 1992. Excitation-contraction coupling in the heart: the state of the question. *FASEB J.* 6:3092–100

127. Szucs G, Csernoch L, Magyar J, Kovacs L. 1991. Contraction threshold and the "hump" component of charge movement in frog skeletal muscle. *J. Gen. Physiol.* 97:897–911

128. Takeshima H, Nishimura S, Matsumoto T, Ishida H, Ueda M, et al. 1989.

Primary structure and expression from complementary DNA of skeletal muscle ryanodine receptor. *Nature* 339:439–45

129. Tanabe T, Beam KG, Povel JA, Numa S. 1987. Restoration of excitation-contraction coupling and slow calcium current in dysgenic muscle by dihydropyridine receptor complementary DNA. *Pflügers Arch.* 410:75–82

130. Tanabe T, Takeshima H, Mikami A, Flockerzi V, Matsuo H, et al. 1987. Primary structure of the receptor for calcium channel blockers from skeletal muscle. *Nature* 328:313–18

131. Vergara J, Caputo C. 1983. Effects of tetracaine on charge movements and calcium signals in frog skeletal muscle fibers. *Proc. Natl. Acad. Sci. USA* 80:1477–81

132. Villaz M, Robert M, Carrier L, Beeler T, Rouot B, et al. 1989. G-protein dependent potentiation of calcium re-lease from sarcoplasmic reticulum of skeletal muscle. *Cell Signal.* 1:493–506

133. Vilven J, Coronado R. 1988. Opening of dihydropyridine calcium channels in skeletal muscle membranes by inositol trisphosphate. *Nature* 336:587–89

134. Walker JW, Somlyo AV, Goldman YE, Somlyo AP, Trentham DR. 1987. Kinetics of smooth and skeletal muscle activation by laser pulse photolysis of caged inositol 1,4,5-trisphosphate. *Nature* 327:249–52

135. Wang J, Best PM. 1992. Inactivation of the sarcoplasmic reticulum calcium channel by protein kinase. *Nature* 359:739–41

136. Yatani A, Codina J, Imoto Y, Reeves JP, Birnbaumer L, Brown, AM. 1987. A G protein directly regulates mammalian cardiac calcium channels. *Science* 238:1288–92

Annu. Rev. Physiol. 1994. 56:485–508
Copyright © 1994 by Annual Reviews Inc. All rights reserved

RYANODINE RECEPTOR/Ca^{2+} RELEASE CHANNELS AND THEIR REGULATION BY ENDOGENOUS EFFECTORS

Gerhard Meissner

Departments of Biochemistry and Biophysics, and Physiology, University of North Carolina, Chapel Hill, North Carolina 27599–7260

KEY WORDS: excitation-contraction coupling, sarcoplasmic reticulum, striated muscle, neuronal tissue, nonexcitable cells

INTRODUCTION

Current evidence suggests that excitable and nonexcitable cells may contain one or both of two intracellular Ca^{2+} release channels. Release of Ca^{2+} from intramembrane compartments can be triggered by the binding of the second messenger inositol 1,4,5-trisphosphate (IP$_3$) to the IP$_3$ receptor/Ca^{2+} release channel (for review, see 6). It also can be mediated by the ryanodine receptor (RyR)/Ca^{2+} release channel in response to a surface membrane action potential and/or a change in the concentration of a second messenger, by a mechanism referred to in muscle as excitation-contraction (E-C) coupling.

In striated muscle, rapid release of Ca^{2+} from the intracellular compartment, sarcoplasmic reticulum (SR), is initiated by a surface membrane action potential that is communicated to the SR at specialized areas where the junctional SR comes in close contact with the surface membrane or tubular infoldings of the surface membrane (T-tubule); at these areas large protein structures are present that span the gap between the two membrane systems. These structures have been termed feet (see C Franzini-Armstrong & A Jorgensen, this volume) and are now commonly known as ryanodine receptor/Ca^{2+} release channels because of the presence of an intrinsic Ca^{2+} channel activity within the feet structures, and their ability to bind the plant

485

0066–4278/94/0315–0485$05.00

alkaloid ryanodine with high affinity and specificity. The RyR ion channel has been purified from muscle and neuronal tissue as a 30 S protein complex comprised of four polypeptides of ~5000 amino acid residues each. The very large subunits presumably allow a complex pattern of regulation, since functional studies have shown that the channel may be regulated by various endogenous effector molecules including Ca^{2+}, ATP, and calmodulin, depending on the isoform. This review summarizes recent studies aimed at elucidating the structure, cellular distribution, and regulation of the RyR/ Ca^{2+} release channels by endogenous effector molecules in vitro. The action of reactive oxygen species (1) and exogenous effectors (91) on the RyR are not detailed here because of space limitations.

EXCITATION-CONTRACTION COUPLING—AN OVERVIEW

The mechanism of RyR/Ca^{2+} release channel activation has been most extensively studied in vertebrate skeletal and cardiac muscle. Cardiac E-C coupling is dependent on extracellular Ca^{2+}. A plasmalemmal dihydropyridine-sensitive Ca^{2+} current repesents a major pathway for the entry of extracellular Ca^{2+} during an action potential (5a). The resulting rise in intracellular Ca^{2+} concentration is thought to trigger the massive release of Ca^{2+} from the SR by opening RyR ion channels (12, 84) closely apposed to the plasmalemma in structural complexes called couplings (110). Morphological (110) and more recent immunocytochemical (54, 55) and [^{3}H] ryanodine binding (55) studies showing the presence of an appreciable portion of RyRs without any plasmalemmal contact in mammalian (corbular SR) and avian (extended junctional SR) heart suggest that the cardiac RyR may be activated by Ca^{2+} or some other effector in the absence of a close association with the cardiac dihydropyridine receptor (DHPR)/Ca^{2+} channel. There is good evidence that the Ca^{2+} trigger mechanism also plays a major role in regulating a Ca^{2+} release channel in crustacean muscle (4, 33, 104). Mammalian smooth muscle (40), and brain (60) also contain Ca^{2+}-activated RyR ion channels. However, it is unclear whether Ca^{2+} is the principal physiological activator of the RyR in these cells.

In vertebrate skeletal muscle, a different mechanism of E-C coupling appears to be in effect that is not dependent on extracellular Ca^{2+}. The mechanical coupling hypothesis for skeletal muscle suggests that the SR RyR/Ca^{2+} release channel is physically linked to a voltage-sensing molecule located in the tubular infoldings of the surface membrane, the transverse (T) tubule. Biophysical and pharmacological evidence and cDNA expression studies suggest that the T-tubule DHPR for calcium channel antagonists is the voltage-sensor in vertebrate skeletal muscle E-C coupling (see review by M Schneider, this volume). There is morphological evidence to suggest that, at least in some skeletal muscle, only a subpopulation of RyRs are mechanically linked to T-tubule sensors (see C Franzini-Armstrong & A Jorgensen, this volume). Ca^{2+} ions released by these channels could serve to amplify further SR Ca^{2+} release by opening the remaining DHPR-unlinked release channels. Several recent observations support the idea of a dual regulation of the SR release channel in skeletal muscle. These include (a) partial inhibition of SR Ca^{2+} release following the microinjection of Ca^{2+} buffers into frog muscle fibers (M Schneider, this volume), and (b) [^{3}H]PN200–110 and [^{3}H]ryanodine binding measurements that suggest a low DHPR/RyR of ~1 and 0.6 for rabbit and frog skeletal muscle, respectively (1a).

STRUCTURE OF RYR/Ca^{2+} RELEASE CHANNEL

The neutral plant alkaloid ryanodine, utilized as a probe in the isolation and subsequent cloning of the RyR ion channel, has had a major impact on the investigation of the mechanism of E-C coupling. Depending on muscle type and activity, ryanodine can either cause contracture or a decline in contractile force (53). Single channel measurements have shown that ryanodine may exert its actions in vertebrate and crustacean muscle by inducing at nanomolar to micromolar concentrations the formation of an open subconductance channel state, whereas at concentrations above 100 μM, ryanodine completely closes the release channel (10, 11, 50, 63, 62, 99, 104). The conductance pathway of the RyR from brain (5, 60, 71) and the nematode C. elegans (57) is modified by ryanodine in an essentially identical manner.

The detergent-solubilized RyR has been purified with retention of its [^{3}H]ryanodine binding and intrinsic channel activities from a variety of tissues including rabbit skeletal muscle (44, 61, 108), canine cardiac muscle (2, 45, 95), mammalian brain (60, 71), amphibian skeletal muscle (62, 83, 89), lobster skeletal muscle (104), and C. elegans (57) (Table 1). In most of these studies, the membrane-bound RyR was solubilized using the zwitterionic detergent CHAPS and high ionic strength (1.0 M NaCl) and then, as shown by density gradient centrifugation (61), purified as a 30 S protein complex. SDS gel electrophoresis suggests that the purified RyRs of mammalian skeletal and cardiac muscle (2, 50, 51, 61), brain (60, 71), crustacean skeletal muscle (104), and C. elegans (57) contain a single major high molecular weight polypeptide with a calculated M_r ~560,000, as determined by cloning and sequencing of the complementary DNA of the mammalian skeletal and cardiac muscle RyR isoforms (87, 90, 117, 132) (Table 1). Reptiles and certain specialized, fast contracting muscles of birds

Table 1 Comparison of properties of 30 S RyR/Ca^{2+} release channel complexes

Property	Mammalian skeletal muscle	Mammalian cardiac muscle	Mammalian vascular muscle	Mammalian brain	Amphibian skeletal muscle	Lobster skeletal muscle	C. elegans
Apparent sedimentation coefficient	30 S	30 S	30 S	30 S	30 S	30 S	~30 S
Number of ~560 kd polypeptides (on SDS gels)	1	1	1	1	2	1	1
Morphology	quatrefoil	quatrefoil	—	quatrefoil	—	—	—
High-affinity ryanodine binding (K_d)	5 nM	2 nM	—	3 nM	4 nM	6 nM	26 nM
Single channel conductance							
in symmetric 0.25 M K$^+$	770 pS	745 pS	370 pS	800 pS	—	775 pS	215 pS
in symmetric 0.5 M Na$^+$	600 pS	550 pS	—	—	600 pS	—	—
in 0.05 M Ca^{2+} trans	145 pS	145 pS	~100 pS	140 pS	110 pS	125 pS	—
Modification by ryanodine	Yes	Yes	Yes	Yes	Yes	Yes	Yes
Activation by							
Ca^{2+}	µM	µM	µM	µM	µM	mM	—
mM ATP	Yes	Yes	Weakly	Yes	Yes	Weakly	—
µM IP$_3$	?	No	—	?	?	—	—
µM acylcarnitines	Yes	—	—	—	—	—	—
µM cyclic ADP-ribose	No	Yes	—	Yes	—	—	—
Inhibition by							
mM Mg^{2+}	Yes	Yes	Yes	—	—	Weakly	—
µM calmodulin	Yes	Yes	—	—	—	—	—
µM sphingosine	Yes	Yes	—	—	—	—	—

For details and references see text.

and fish also express only one RyR isoform (87a). In contrast, the presence of two major, immunologically distinct high molecular weight RyR protein bands (termed α and β) has been described for the main body musculature of chicken, frog, and fish (62, 83, 87a, 89). The two receptor isoforms were shown to be present in chicken and frog as homotetramers (62, 83, 89), and in frog to have immunological properties and an electrophoretic mobility characteristic of the mammalian skeletal or cardiac receptor isoforms (62). Mammalian skeletal muscle RyR activity has been also reported by one laboratory to be associated with a 106 kd protein (43).

Electron microscopy studies have revealed that the purified 30 S RyRs of mammalian skeletal (61, 101) and cardiac (2) muscle and brain (60) have an overall morphology identical to the protein bridges (feet) that span the T-tubule-SR junctional gap in isolated SR fractions of vertebrate skeletal muscle (see review by C Franzini-Armstrong & A Jorgensen, this volume). The four leaf clover-like (quatrefoil) appearance of negative-stained samples, the apparent sedimentation coefficient of 30 S (61), and cross-linking (63) and scanning transmission electron microscopy studies (102) have demonstrated a tetrameric assembly of the high molecular weight subunits of the CHAPS-purified skeletal RyR. Averaged images of negatively stained (125) and frozen hydrated (94) specimens have provided a more detailed view of the structure of the rabbit skeletal muscle RyR (to a resolution of ~3 nm). These studies indicate an overall dimension of $27 \times 27 \times 14$ nm for the skeletal RyR and further suggest the possible presence of an unusual ion-conducting structure comprised of a central (membrane-spanning) channel that branches into four radial channels in the cytoplasmic (foot) region of the complex.

MOLECULAR CLONING AND EXPRESSION OF RYR ISOFORMS

The primary structure of three mammalian RyR isoforms has been determined by cDNA cloning and sequencing. The isoforms are encoded by three different genes coding for a skeletal muscle (RyR1) (117, 132), cardiac muscle (RyR2) (87, 90), and brain (RyR3) (36) RyR. The partial sequence of a TGFβ-regulated RyR expressed in mink lung epithelial cells has been reported (30); however, based on sequence comparison (36), this appears to be the brain isoform. The partial sequences of the RyR from two nonvertebrates, *Drosophilia* (38) and *C. elegans* (57), have also been reported.

Northern blot analysis of mRNA from a variety of mammalian tissues indicates that the skeletal isoform appears to be restricted to fast- and slow-twitch skeletal muscle except that an RNA species with ~2,400 nucleotides hybridizable with the 3'-terminal region of the skeletal muscle

RyR has been shown to be present in rabbit brain (117a). The cardiac isoform is apparently expressed, in addition to the heart, throughout the brain, with the possible exception of the pituitary (36, 60, 87, 90). The brain RyR mRNA was found to be most abundant in certain areas of the brain (corpus striatum, thalamus, and hippocampus) and to be present in tissues containing smooth muscle such as aorta and uterus (36). TGFβ-treated, excitable and nonexcitable mink tissues, expressed with low abundance a caffeine-insensitive RyR (30) which, based on sequence comparison, appeared to be closely related to the brain isoform (see above). Expression studies with the skeletal and cardiac muscle cDNAs in cultured cells and *Xenopus* oocytes suggest that the M_r 560,000 polypeptides are sufficient to form ryanodine-, caffeine- and Ca^{2+}-sensitive Ca^{2+} channels (49, 87, 117).

The skeletal muscle cDNA encodes a protein of 5032–5037 amino acids, whereas the cardiac muscle and brain cDNAs were found to encode proteins of 4968–4976 and 4872 amino acids, respectively. Comparison of the predicted amino acid sequences of the skeletal and cardiac muscle and brain receptors reveals a large number of conserved regions throughout the sequence of the three RyRs with an overall identity of 66–70% and greater than 90% in the 250 amino acid carboxy-terminal portion. The only other protein shown so far to display significant sequence homology with the RyR is the IP_3 receptor ion channel, which is similarly comprised of four polypeptides of 2,701–2,749 amino acids each (6).

Hydropathy plots suggest that the M_r ~560,000 polypeptides consist of two major structural regions: the carboxy-terminal pore region, which is thought to consist of as few as four (117) and as many as ten or possibly twelve (132) putative transmembrane segments, and a large extramembrane region, which is thought to correspond to the cytoplasmic foot structure (Figure 1). Primary sequence predictions also suggest the presence of several potential cytoplasmic Ca^{2+}, nucleotide, and calmodulin binding and phosphorylation sites (36, 87, 90, 117, 132). Of these, however, only one phosphorylation site has been confirmed in vitro. The cardiac RyR was phosphorylated by a calmodulin-dependent protein kinase at Ser2809 (128), whereas the corresponding site in the skeletal RyR (Ser2843) was phosphorylated by cAMP-, cGMP- and calmodulin-dependent protein kinases (115). In addition, experimental evidence for the involvement of two RyR regions in regulating Ca^{2+}-induced Ca^{2+} release in skeletal muscle has been obtained. In malignant hyperthermia-susceptible pigs, the skeletal muscle RyR contains a trypsin-accessible arginine at position 615 (79) which, when mutated to cysteine (28), alters the sensitivity of the Ca^{2+}-induced Ca^{2+} release process. Evidence for a second Ca^{2+}-sensitive region was obtained in $^{45}Ca^{2+}$ and ruthenium red overlay studies with trpE fusion proteins. These findings led to the identification of three Ca^{2+}-binding peptides (amino acid

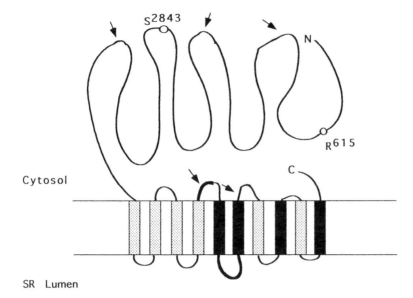

Figure 1   Membrane topology model of mammalian skeletal muscle RyR ion channel. Each of four (only one is shown) polypeptides forming the RyR ion channel consists of ~5035 amino acids with four (*filled segments*; 117) or 10 (132) predicted hydrophobic transmembrane segments at the carboxy-terminus and a large hydrophilic cytoplasmic (foot) domain. Also indicated are a cytoplasmic mutation site (R615C) in malignant hyperthermia-susceptible pigs, cytoplasmic Ser2843 shown to be phosphorylated by protein kinases, five protease-sensitive sites with a high predicted surface probability (*arrows*), and two antibody binding sites accessible from the cytoplasmic and lumenal sides of the SR membrane, respectively (*bold lines*). Binding of Ab(4478-4512) increased the Ca^{2+} sensitivity of the skeletal muscle RyR (for details see text).

residues 4246–4467, 4382–4417, and 4478–4512) (14). An antibody against the 4478–4512 peptide increased the Ca^{2+} sensitivity of the RyR release channels incorporated into planar bilayers without altering channel conductance. Since Ca^{2+} ions were still able to activate the antibody-release channel complex, it was unlikely that the antibody bound directly to a critical Ca^{2+} activation site.

The above mutant, phosphorylation, and antibody studies provide strong evidence for the localization on the cytoplasmic surface of three sites of the skeletal muscle RyR. Surface probability analysis, along with sequence analysis of peptides generated by the two endoproteases Lys-C and Glu-C, have indicated five protease-sensitive regions (1221–1334, 2725–2929, 3713–3714, 4372–4475, and 4676–4683), which correspond to regions of high surface probability (68). Two of these sites (2725–2929 and 4372–4475) correspond to the phosphorylation and antibody-binding sites mentioned above (Figure 1). An antibody directed against residues 4581–4640 in the C-terminal portion of the skeletal RyR showed no significant binding to closed vesicles, but bound to permeabilized vesicles, which supports the predicted lumenal localization of the hydrophilic segment corresponding to M1/M2 and M5/M6 loop, respectively, of the four (117) and ten (132) membrane-spanning topology models based on sequence analysis (32). Further structural studies will be necessary for the localization of the functional domains and determination of the number and configuration of the transmembrane segments of the RyR.

RYR/Ca^{2+} RELEASE CHANNEL CONDUCTS MONO- AND DIVALENT CATIONS

The RyR/Ca^{2+} release channel is a cation-selective channel that displays an unusually large ion conductance for monovalent ($\sim$600 and $\sim$750 pS with symmetric 500 mM Na^+ and 250 mM K^+ as the current carrier, respectively) and divalent ($\sim$100–150 pS with 50 mM Ca^{2+} *trans*) cations (Table 1). The existence of a large Ca^{2+} and Ba^{2+} conductance was originally demonstrated in single channel recordings with skeletal (106, 107) and cardiac (98) muscle SR vesicles fused with planar lipid bilayers. The channel was identified as the SR Ca^{2+} release channel on the basis of its activation by Ca^{2+} and adenine nucleotides, and inhibition by Mg^{2+} and ruthenium red. A caffeine-sensitive, high conductance Ca^{2+} channel was demonstrated in patch-clamp recordings with native frog skeletal muscle "sarcoball" preparations that showed two predominant conductance levels of $\sim$90 and 140 pS (111).

Reconstitution of the CHAPS-purified skeletal muscle RyR channel into planar lipid bilayers reveals several novel features that are not readily observed in studies with the native release channel because of the presence of SR K^+ and Cl^- channels, which are also incorporated into the bilayers during SR vesicle fusion. The purified RyR channel displayed a high conductance for Ca^{2+} and monovalent cations and high selectivity for cations over anions (61, 65, 108). Unit conductances of 26 and 22 pS for choline and Tris, respectively, suggest the presence of a large ion-conducting pore structure in the skeletal muscle SR Ca^{2+} release channel (108), in agreement with earlier vesicle flux studies that provided evidence for a choline (130) and glucose (74) permeable Ca^{2+} release pathway in junctional-derived SR vesicles. Ion conductances have been reported to display simple saturation kinetics with K_m and γ_{max} values, respectively, of 3 mM and 172 pS for Ca^{2+}, 47 mM and 1032 pS for K^+ (108), and 75 mM and 600 pS for Na^+ (65). Under bi-ionic conditions, the skeletal muscle release channel was selectively permeable to Ca^{2+} with permeability ratios (P_{Ca}/P_x) of 5 for Na^+

(65), 6 and 14 (108) and 19 and 2900 (44) for K^+ and $Tris^+$, respectively. A model of the conductance and permeability properties of the cardiac RyR has been published (119).

Under comparable recording conditions, the CHAPS-purified RyR channels of rabbit skeletal, canine cardiac and vascular smooth muscle, bovine brain, and frog and lobster skeletal muscle all have a similar large unitary Ca^{2+} conductance of (120 ± 30) pS (in 50 mM Ca^{2+} *trans* with 0.25 M KCl or NaCl in the *cis* chamber), and can also readily conduct monovalent cations with a main conductance of 550–600 pS for Na^+ (in 0.5 M symmetric Na^+) and 700–800 pS for K^+ (in 0.25 M symmetric K^+) (2, 40, 60, 62, 104) (Table 1). Two exceptions were that the maximal K^+ conductance for the mammalian aorta smooth muscle channel was half of that of the main conductance of the skeletal and cardiac channels (40), and the Ca^{2+} permeable channel of *C. elegans* had only a maximal conductance of 215 pS in 250 mM KCl (57). However, the appearance of multiple subconductances present within the channel tetramer is a frequently observed phenomenon upon reconstitution of the detergent-solubilized purified channel. In symmetric 250 mM KCl, Smith et al (108) observed three distinct conductance levels of 200, 400, and 800 pS. Liu et al (65) found that the purified skeletal release channel could display a maximal conductance of either 300 or 600 pS in symmetric 0.5 M NaCl. For each of these, three subconductances were apparent that corresponded to 1/4, 1/2, and 3/4 of the main conductance level. Similarly, up to four distinct conductances could be detected with Ca^{2+} as the conducting ion. Appearance of multiple conductances has been proposed to be due either to the presence of a channel comprised of four subunits, each containing an individually conducting pore, or a single conducting pore present in several discrete conductance states within the tetrameric assembly of the $M_r560,000$ subunits. In either case, cooperative interactions among the subunits must occur to account for the multiple conductance behavior of the release channel.

The observation of an essentially identical conductance behavior of various RyRs (Table 1) suggests that the pore region of the RyR ion channel is highly conserved. In agreement with this prediction, the putative pore region in the C-terminal domain shows a high extent of sequence similarity among the mammalian skeletal, cardiac, and brain RyR isoforms (36).

THE MAMMALIAN SKELETAL MUSCLE RYR IS ALSO A LIGAND-GATED CHANNEL

Present physiological and biochemical evidence suggests that the vertebrate skeletal muscle RyR ion channel is under the dual control of the T-tubule potential and various endogenous effector molecules. Based on in vitro studies, the latter may include Ca^{2+}, Mg^{2+}, adenine nucleotides, calmodulin, lipid metabolites such as sphingosine, acyl carnitines and IP_3, polyamines such as spermine, and RyR phosphorylation. We do not know at present the way in which linkage to the DHPR in skeletal muscle alters the RyR's regulation by endogenous effectors.

Regulation of the RyR ion channel has been studied in vitro using three complementary techniques. First, the Ca^{2+} efflux behavior of passively or actively (via Ca^{2+} pump) loaded, junctional-derived, T-tubule-attached (triads) or -detached (heavy) SR vesicles has been examined using rapid mixing or filtration devices. Second, regulation of the channel has been investigated in single channel recordings following the incorporation of SR vesicles or purified RyR channels into planar lipid bilayers. Although single channel measurements provide more direct information, an advantage of the vesicle flux technique is that it more readily yields representative data by averaging the kinetic behavior of a large number of channels. Also a possible loss or alteration of function during channel purification and reconstitution into a foreign lipid environment is less likely. Third, [³H]ryanodine binding studies suggest that ryanodine is a sensitive ligand for probing the functional states of the release channel. The in vitro regulation of the mammalian skeletal muscle RyR ion channel by its endogenous effectors will be reviewed first. Difference in the regulation of the mammalian RyR isoforms and non-mammalian RyRs will be described subsequently.

T-Tubule Depolarization-Induced Ca^{2+} Release

Biochemical evidence for a T-tubule regulated release channel activity has been obtained in studies with actively loaded membrane fractions enriched in SR/T-tubule junctional complexes (triads) (20, 48). Rapid ion replacement causing depolarization of the attached T-tubule produced a multiphase Ca^{2+} release pattern consisting of (*a*) a lag period, (*b*) the rapid release of a small amount of Ca^{2+} with a first order rate constant of 100 s^{-1}, and (*c*) the release of a larger amount of Ca^{2+} at a slower rate ($k_1 \sim 1$ s^{-1}) (48). The magnitude and rate of the rapid release phase were dependent on the magnitude of the T-tubule potential change, and Ca^{2+}, ATP, and caffeine concentrations of T-tubule depolarizing media (20, 46, 48). A small but significant amount of Ca^{2+} was released in media containing a "fast" Ca^{2+} buffer (4 mM BAPTA) (3), which suggested that, as observed in recent studies with intact frog skeletal muscle fibers (see review by M Schneider, this volume), Ca^{2+} can be released by Ca^{2+}-dependent and -independent release mechanisms in vertebrate skeletal muscle.

The use of dihydropyridines and specific antibodies suggests an involvement of the DHPR and a second intrinsic membrane protein, triadin, in mediating slow T-tubule depolarization-induced SR Ca^{2+} release, whereas a 28 kd T-tubule protein, which is not part of the DHPR, is implicated in mediating the rapid release phase (9). Involvement of the DHPR in only slow but not fast Ca^{2+} release challenges the concept of a DHPR/RyR mediated T-tubule to SR communication in skeletal muscle.

Regulation by Ca^{2+}, Mg^{2+} and Adenine Nucleotides

In the absence of other regulatory ligands such as Mg^{2+} and ATP, a bell-shaped Ca^{2+} activation curve of Ca^{2+} efflux from heavy SR vesicles has been obtained, with Ca^{2+} efflux being maximal in the micromolar Ca^{2+} concentration range (26, 58, 75, 82, 85). Such a curve suggests that the Ca^{2+} release channel possesses high-affinity activating and low-affinity inhibitory Ca^{2+} binding sites. Observations of the behavior of single channels using the planar lipid bilayer technique have corroborated the vesicle ion flux studies. In single channel measurements, the channel's fraction of open time (P_o) was close to zero with nanomolar free Ca^{2+} on the *cis* (SR cytoplasmic) side of the bilayer (107). The addition of micromolar Ca^{2+} to the *cis* chamber activated the channel and induced rapid channel openings and closings occurring as single events or bursts that could last from less than one to many milliseconds. The presence of millimolar Ca^{2+} *cis* resulted in channel inactivation (67). The effects of *trans* (SR lumenal) Ca^{2+} have been highly variable, showing inhibition at 1 mM (26, 67), but not at 10 (129) or 50 mM (107). In the bilayers, the Ca^{2+}-activated Ca^{2+} release channel activity was only moderately affected by membrane potential and did not demonstrate time-dependent activation or inactivation on a time scale of seconds to minutes. The limited time ($\sim$30 min) of most single channel recordings, as well as the variable extent of channel activation by Ca^{2+}, have so far precluded the formulation of a detailed kinetic scheme of the interaction of Ca^{2+} with the different regulatory sites of the channel.

[^{3}H]ryanodine binding measurements also suggest a bimodal regulation of the skeletal muscle release channel by Ca^{2+}, and further indicate that the affinity and cooperativity of interaction between high- and low-affinity [^{3}H]ryanodine binding sites are dependent on Ca^{2+} concentration and ionic strength (15, 63, 70, 76, 80, 93).

Besides Ca^{2+}, cytoplasmic Sr^{2+} activated the channel, whereas Ba^{2+} and Mg^{2+} were inhibitory (58, 75, 76, 82, 86, 97). Mg^{2+} likely inhibits SR Ca^{2+} release by multiple mechanisms by (a) competing with Ca^{2+} for the Ca^{2+} activation sites, (b) binding to the low-affinity Ca^{2+} inhibitory sites, and (c) sterically blocking the channel as it binds to a site near the conduction pathway (58, 75, 85). In support of the latter suggestion is the finding that Mg^{2+} is a permeant cation and produces a rapid flickering of the Ca^{2+}- and ATP-activated channel (107).

In the absence of Mg^{2+} and ATP at neutral pH, heavy rabbit skeletal muscle SR vesicles released their Ca^{2+} stores with a first-order rate constant of about $1-2 \ s^{-1}$ (58, 75, 86), whereas in vivo SR Ca^{2+} release occurs on a millisecond time scale (M Schneider, this volume). Therefore, an important observation was that Ca^{2+}-induced Ca^{2+} release could be greatly potentiated by relatively high (mM) concentrations of ATP (72, 81, 85, 88). Optimal channel activation was found in the presence of μM Ca^{2+} and mM ATP (AMP-PCP) to give maximal release rates with a first-order rate constant of $20-100 \ s^{-1}$ (75, 82, 85, 116). In single channel measurements, the channel could be activated by either μM Ca^{2+} or mM ATP; however, both were again required to fully activate the channel, i.e. to increase the channel's fraction of open time (P_o) close to one (107).

Various other adenine nucleotides (AMP-PCP, ADP, AMP, cAMP, adenosine, adenine) potentiated Ca^{2+} release, which suggests that activation occurs because of binding to an effector site rather than covalent modification of the channel protein via a phosphorylation reaction. Other trinucleotides (CTP, GTP, ITP, UTP) had no substantial effect on the release of Ca^{2+} (72, 81).

It is likely that MgATP, rather than free ATP, is a major physiological regulator of the RyR ion channel because most of the nucleotide in cells is complexed with Mg^{2+}. However, study of regulation of the channel complex by ATP and MgATP is difficult because of the presence of uncomplexed Mg^{2+} ions, which inhibit the Ca^{2+}- and ATP-activated channel. The addition of Mg^{2+} and adenine nucleotide at concentrations approximating those in muscle (5 mM each, 0.7 mM free Mg^{2+}) was strongly stimulatory at μM $[Ca^{2+}]$ and indicated the existence of a regulatory site that, upon binding of MgATP, rendered the channel more sensitive to activation in a narrower Ca^{2+} concentration range (75). In the presence of μM Ca^{2+} and 5 mM AMP-PCP, a change in free Mg^{2+} concentration from 0.1 to 4 mM had a profound inhibitory effect on Ca^{2+} efflux, which suggests that free Mg^{2+} may be an important efffector of in vivo SR Ca^{2+} release. Although it is unlikely that Mg^{2+} and ATP concentrations in muscle undergo rapid changes during E-C coupling, it is of interest that isolated skeletal muscle triads, due to the presence of glycolytic enzymes, can synthesize ATP, which is not readily exchangeable with the bulk cytoplasmic ATP (37). It is conceivable, therefore, that a change in ATP concentration within the restricted space of the triadic gap, brought about by a change in the metabolic state of muscle, modulates SR Ca^{2+} release activity.

The Ca^{2+}-activated release channel is affected by pH, ionic strength, and anion composition. Ca^{2+} efflux rates were greatly reduced by decreasing the pH from $\sim$7.5 to 6 (72, 116), without an apparent change in the affinity of the high-affinity, Ca^{2+} activating and low-affinity, Ca^{2+} inactivating binding sites of the channel (41). An increase in KCl concentration (76) or replacement of Cl^- by ClO_4^- (66) potentiated, whereas replacement of Cl^- by gluconate$^-$ (39) decreased SR Ca^{2+} release.

Regulation by Lipid and Polycationic Metabolites

Hormone receptor-mediated processes leading to the formation of the second messenger inositol 1,4,5-trisphosphate, and subsequent activation of an intracellular IP_3-sensitive Ca^{2+} release pathway, play a major role in the control of intracellular Ca^{2+} levels in smooth muscle, neurons, and non-excitable cells (6). Two early studies showing that IP_3 promotes the release of Ca^{2+} from skinned skeletal muscle fibers (122) and SR vesicles (124) suggested that IP_3 may also play a central role in the mechanism of E-C coupling. This idea has been extensively examined since then, with disparate results. In favor of a role of IP_3 in E-C coupling are these observations: (a) enzymes involved in metabolism of IP_3 were present in purified T-tubule (42); (b) electrical stimulation of skeletal muscle resulted in an increased turnover of polyphosphates (59); (c) total levels of IP_3 were high (~ 2 μM in muscle) (69) and 300–400 pmol/mg in triad protein (42a) and increased during repetitive stimulation of skeletal muscle (69); and (d) T-tubule depolarization increased the effectiveness of IP_3 in eliciting Ca^{2+} release in peeled skeletal muscle fibers (22). However, the slow response of skinned skeletal muscle fibers to IP_3, generated by the photolysis of caged IP_3 (126), and the inability of microinjected heparin in blocking SR Ca^{2+} release in skeletal muscle fibers (92) have argued against IP_3 as a primary regulatory ligand in E-C coupling.

In studies with isolated SR membranes, IP_3 released Ca^{2+} (120, 121, 124). In one study, the precursor molecule PIP_2, but not IP_3, was effective in eliciting Ca^{2+} release from junctional SR vesicles (16). In planar lipid bilayer experiments, single ryanodine-sensitive skeletal muscle Ca^{2+} release channels were activated by PIP_2 (16) and IP_3 (16, 114, 120) under assay conditions that varied among the investigators. Moreover, IP_3 and its non-hydrolyzable analogue IPS_3 have been shown to activate the T-tubule DHP-sensitive Ca^{2+} channel (123). Clearly, additional studies are required to clarify the role of IP_3 in SR Ca^{2+} release and its involvement in E-C coupling.

Fatty acids and their derivatives are known to be a part of some signal transduction pathways. Several of these cellular processes may have an effect on Ca^{2+} metabolism in cells. It is perhaps not surprising that several lipid metabolites have been found to modulate Ca^{2+} release channel activity. Micromolar concentrations of the fatty acid derivatives palmitoyl carnitine and palmitoyl CoA stimulated [^{3}H]ryanodine binding and Ca^{2+} release channel activity in mammalian (24) and avian (23) skeletal muscle SR. Their action appeared to be highly specific and limited to the skeletal RyR isoform because palmitoic acid and short chain acyl carnitines did not significantly stimulate [^{3}H]ryanodine binding and Ca^{2+} release, whereas palmitoyl carnitine was without an effect on [^{3}H]ryanodine binding to canine cardiac SR. Acyl derivatives are present in micromolar concentrations in muscle cells, and increased levels have been observed in certain metabolic diseases (34) and during cold adaption in ducklings (E Dumonteil & G Meissner, unpublished studies). Accordingly, fatty acid derivatives may play a role in modulating SR Ca^{2+} release activity in certain metabolic and diseased states of muscle that involve changes in Ca^{2+} cycling.

Sphingosine, a long chain amino alcohol and a component of sphingomyelin, is a potent inhibitor of Ca^{2+} release from SR (100). Although sphingosine is known to inhibit several protein kinases, [^{3}H]ryanodine and Ca^{2+} release measurements have provided evidence for a direct action of micromolar concentrations of sphingosine on the RyR (100). Since sphingomyelin and sphingomyelinase are present in isolated T-tubule, sphingosine is another likely candidate for modulating SR Ca^{2+} release in muscle, although its specific role is unknown at present.

Several endogenous polycationic metabolites including spermine have been reported to interact with skeletal RyR. Micromolar concentrations of spermine inhibited caffeine-induced SR Ca^{2+} release (90a), whereas millimolar concentrations stimulated the binding of ryanodine to its receptor (130a).

Regulation by Calmodulin and Phosphorylation

In single channel measurements, calmodulin inhibited the release channel by reducing channel open time without having an apparent effect on single channel conductance (109). Channel inhibition was Ca^{2+}-dependent, reversible, and only partial (two to threefold), rather than complete, inhibition was observed under assay conditions that varied $^{45}Ca^{2+}$ release rates from heavy SR vesicles by > 1000-fold (73). Calmodulin inhibited SR Ca^{2+} release and single channel activities in the absence of ATP, thus suggesting calmodulin binding to the RyR and a direct inhibitory action of calmodulin (73, 109). Sequence analysis of the skeletal muscle RyR identified several candidate calmodulin-binding sites in the C-terminal half of the protein. Takeshima et al (117) predicted two calmodulin sites at residues 3614–3637 and 4295–4325, whereas Zorzato et al (132) predicted three different sites at residues 2807–2840, 2909–2930, and 3031–3049. Photoaffinity labeling studies provided early evidence that at least one of these sites is utilized in vitro by showing binding of calmodulin to high M_r skeletal and cardiac proteins now known to be the RyR polypeptides (103). More recently, calmodulin-binding studies with heavy skeletal muscle SR vesicles have indicated the presence of two classes of sites with K_ds of ~1 and 30 nM (113); however, none of these sites has yet been localized on the channel.

In vitro phosphorylation of a serine residue (Ser2809) by a calmodulin-dependent kinase has been reported to activate the calmodulin-inhibited RyR ion channel isolated from cardiac muscle (128). The site of phosphorylation is close to a possible calmodulin-binding site. Thus it is possible that phosphorylation of this site may antagonize inhibition by calmodulin.

Whereas the cardiac RyR was an excellent substrate for the multifunctional Ca^{2+}/calmodulin protein kinase, phosphorylation of the skeletal muscle RyR by endogenous and exogenous CaM kinases was found to be more variable (17, 112, 115, 128). In the skeletal RyR, Ser2843 was a major target for cAMP-, cGMP- and CaM-dependent kinases (115). This site is homologous to serine 2809 of the cardiac RyR. Investigations of the effects of protein phosphorylation on skeletal muscle SR Ca^{2+} release showed variable effects (15, 29, 56). In one recent patch-clamp study, an inactivation resulting from phosphorylation was observed (127). In contrast, an activation of single channel activities, which was ascribed to removal of block by Mg^{2+}, has been also recently reported (35). Accordingly, there is growing evidence that protein phosphorylation may modulate SR Ca^{2+} release channel activity, although the details are unclear at present.

Other Proteins Interacting with the RyR

Several proteins have been implicated in the regulation of the skeletal muscle SR Ca^{2+} release channel, in addition to the T-tubule DHPR and calmodulin. These include triadin, calsequestrin, annexin VI, S-100, glyceraldehyde 3-phosphate dehydrogenase, aldolase, FK506-binding protein, and calpain.

Triadin is a M_r 90,000 SR membrane protein that may be involved in the functional coupling of the T-tubule DHPR and SR RyR (9, but see also 58a). Calsequestrin is a major mammalian skeletal muscle SR Ca^{2+}-binding protein that is concentrated in the terminal cisternae of SR. Observations of calsequestrin protein conformational changes preceding those of the RyR suggest that calsequestrin, in addition to increasing the Ca^{2+} storing capacity of SR, may have an active role in regulating SR Ca^{2+} release (47). Annexin VI is a minor SR lumenal Ca^{2+}-binding protein that, in single channel measurements at concentrations of 5–40 nM $trans$, modulated Ca^{2+} release channel activity in a Ca^{2+}-dependent manner by increasing the channel's open probability and mean open time (21). S-100, a cytoplasmic M_r 21,000 Ca^{2+}-binding protein, stimulated Ca^{2+}-induced Ca^{2+} release at a concentration of 5 μM (25).

The two glycolytic enzymes, glyceraldehyde 3-phosphate dehydrogenase and aldolase, have been shown to be present in triad-enriched membrane fractions (13). Glyceraldehyde 3-phospate dehydrogenase was found to promote association of isolated T-tubule with junctional SR vesicles to form T-SR junctions. Accordingly, one of its proposed roles is to help to stabilize the linkage between T-tubule DHPR and SR RyR (13). Aldolase binds IP_3, which has been proposed to effect SR Ca^{2+} release (see above). Although a direct functional role of aldolase in SR Ca^{2+} release has not been established, it is of interest that the enzyme can be specifically released from triads by μM IP_3 (118).

Calpain is an endogenous Ca^{2+}-dependent protease that selectively degrades the RyR in heavy SR vesicles (8, 31, 96, 103). Single channel measurements have suggested that treatment of the channel with calpain may impair its inactivation, without an effect on its unitary conductance or requirement of μM Ca^{2+} for activity (96). Lastly, FK506-binding protein is an immunophilin of M_r 12,000 that co-purifies with the skeletal muscle RyR (19, 52). The binding protein may serve as a protein kinase C inhibitor and inhibit calcineuron, a Ca^{2+}- and calmodulin-activated phosphatase, thereby affecting two enzymatic activities that may play a role in SR Ca^{2+} release. A physiological function of the FK506-binding protein in SR Ca^{2+} release has not been demonstrated, however.

Comparative Studies

Table 1 compares several of the properties of the mammalian skeletal and cardiac muscle RyR isoforms, along with those of RyR preparations isolated from mammalian vascular smooth muscle and brain, and amphibian and crustacean skeletal muscle. With the exception of ryanodine, the pharmacological properties of the RyR from *C. elegans* have not been described (57).

The mammalian cardiac muscle isoform can be activated by Ca^{2+}, ATP, and caffeine, and inhibited by Mg^{2+} and calmodulin, similar to the skeletal isoform. Major differences in the sensitivity to these effectors were observed (77, 98, 131). Sphingosine also inhibits both isoforms (7, 100). Other effectors have been found to be specific for one of the two isoforms. Acylcarnitines activated only the skeletal release channel (23, 24), whereas cyclic ADP ribose, a novel Ca^{2+} mobilizing agent in sea urchin eggs (64), stimulated the cardiac, but not skeletal muscle, RyR (78).

Little is known about the regulation of the mammalian brain RyR isoform. The brain RyR isoform is expressed in brain and smooth muscle tissue and appears to be identical with a TGFβ-regulated RyR expressed in excitable and nonexcitable mink tissues (30, 36). In contrast to the mammalian striated muscle RyRs, the TGFβ regulated RyR was found to be caffeine-insensitive (30). Incorporation of mammalian brain microsomes (5) and purified brain RyR preparations (60, 71) resulted in the appearance of ryanodine-sensitive channel conductances that could be activated by Ca^{2+} (60), ATP, caffeine (5, 60, 71), and IP_3 (5, 60). Because of the expression of cardiac and brain isoforms in brain (36), it is not clear at present which isoform was responsible for the observed activities.

Vascular smooth muscle has been reported to express the brain RyR isoform (36), and vascular ryanodine-sensitive Ca^{2+} channels have been recorded following their partial purification and reconstitution into planar lipid bilayers (40). Although only a limited number of single channel measurements were obtained, these studies nevertheless suggest that the vascular RyR exhibits a Ca^{2+}-gated channel activity that could be modified by caffeine and, to a low extent, by ATP. In rat liver, the presence of an atypical high-affinity [^{3}H]ryandine-binding activity has been described that is slightly stimulated by Mg^{2+} and strongly inhibited by caffeine (105). This study raises the possibility that additional RyR isoform(s) are expressed in mammalian tissues.

Amphibian skeletal muscle expresses two homotetrameric RyR isoforms (62, 83, 89). In [^{3}H]ryanodine binding and planar lipid bilayer measurements, the frog RyRs exhibited pharmacological properties similar to those of the mammalian striated muscle release channels (Table 1). Separation of these isoforms and some differences in their Ca^{2+} sensitivity have been recently reported (83).

Study of the crustacean RyR is of interest because SR Ca^{2+} release in crustacean muscle, like that in cardiac muscle, is thought to be triggered by Ca^{2+}, which enters the cell through voltage-sensitive Ca^{2+} channels (4, 33). The isolation of a 30 S RyR protein complex from crayfish (27) and lobster (104) has been described. The lobster channel required millimolar concentrations of Ca^{2+} for activation and was not appreciably affected by ATP, caffeine, and Mg^{2+}. These studies suggest that the lobster RyR exhibits a distinctly different pattern of regulation by Ca^{2+} and other effector molecules than the mammalian muscle channel proteins. Further comparison and identification of additional RyR isoforms should help to better define the mechanism of Ca^{2+} release from intracellular membrane stores.

CONCLUSION

The identification of [^{3}H]ryanodine as a specific probe has enabled the isolation and subsequent cloning of an intracellular 30 S RyR complex comprised of four $\sim$560 kd polypeptides. Current evidence suggests that in mammalian cells at least three distinct RyR genes exist. The mammalian RyRs show a tissue-specific expression, and those isolated from muscle and neuronal tissue have been shown to share several properties. These include an apparent sedimentation coefficient of 30 S, activation by Ca^{2+}, and a high conductance mono- and divalent cation pathway that can be modified by ryanodine in an essentially identical manner. On the other hand, the

RyRs exhibit differences in their sensitivity to regulation by a growing number of putative effector molecules. Further studies are needed to determine the amino acid sequences that are responsible for these differences, as well as to localize the regulatory domains within the large RyR/Ca^{2+} release channel complexes.

ACKNOWLEDGMENTS

I would like to thank Kristin Anderson, Ron Grunwald, and Ashutosh Tripathy for reading the manuscript and their helpful suggestions. Support from United States Public Health Service grants AR18687 and HL27430 is gratefully acknowledged.

Literature Cited

1. Abramson JJ, Salama G. 1989. Critical sulfhydryls regulate calcium release from sarcoplasmic reticulum. *J. Bioenerg. Biomembr.* 21:283–94

1a. Anderson K, Cohn AH, Meissner G. 1994. High affinity [^{3}H]PN200-110 and [^{3}H]ryanodine binding to rabbit and frog skeletal muscle homogenates. *Am. J. Physiol.* In press

2. Anderson K, Lai FA, Liu QY, Rousseau E, Erickson HP, Meissner G. 1989. Structural and functional characterization of the purified cardiac ryanodine receptor-Ca^{2+} release channel complex. *J. Biol. Chem.* 264:1329–35

3. Anderson K, Meissner G. 1993. T-tubule-mediated SR Ca^{2+} release from rabbit skeletal muscle homogenates is not inhibited by BAPTA. *Biophys. J.* 64:A36

4. Ashley CC, Mulligan IP, Lea TJ. 1991. Ca^{2+} and activation mechanisms in skeletal muscle. *Q. Rev. Biophys.* 24:1–73

5. Ashley RH. 1989. Activation and conductance properties of ryanodine-sensitive calcium channels from brain microsomal membranes incorporated into planar lipid bilayers. *J. Membr. Biol.* 111:179–89

5a. Bean BP. 1989. Classes of calcium channels in vertebrate cells. *Annu. Rev. Physiol.* 51:367–84

6. Berridge MJ. 1993. Inositol tris-phosphate and calcium signalling. *Nature* 361:315–25

7. Betto R, Salviati G, Dettbarn C, Palade P, Jenkins G, Sabbadini R. 1993. Endogenous sphingosine controls cardiac SR Ca release. *Biophys. J.* 64: A151

8. Brandt NR, Caswell AH, Brandt T, Brew K, Mellgren RL. 1992. Mapping of the calpain proteolysis products of the junctional foot protein of the skeletal triad junction. *J. Membr. Biol.* 127:35–47

9. Brandt NR, Caswell AH, Brunschwig JP, Kang JJ, Antoniu B, Ikemoto N. 1992. Effects of anti-triadin antibody on Ca^{2+} release from sarcoplasmic reticulum. *FEBS Lett.* 299:57–59

10. Buck E, Zimanyi I, Abramson JJ, Pessah IN. 1992. Ryanodine stabilizes multiple conformational states of the skeletal muscle calcium release channel. *J. Biol. Chem.* 267:23560–67

11. Bull R, Marengo JJ, Suarez IBA, Donoso P, Sutko JL, Hidalgo C. 1989. Activation of calcium channels in sarcoplasmic reticulum from frog muscle by nanomolar concentrations of ryanodine. *Biophys. J.* 56:749–56

12. Cannell MB, Berlin JR, Lederer WJ. 1987. Effect of membrane potential changes on the calcium transient in single rat cardiac muscle cells. *Science* 238:1419–23

13. Caswell AH, Brandt NR. 1989. Triadic proteins of skeletal muscle. *J. Bioenerg. Biomembr.* 21:149–62

14. Chen SRW, Zhang L, MacLennan DH. 1992. Characterization of a Ca^{2+} binding and regulatory site in the Ca^{2+} release channel (ryanodine receptor) of rabbit skeletal muscle sarcoplasmic reticulum. *J. Biol. Chem.* 267:23318–26

15. Chu A, Diaz-Munoz M, Hawkes MJ, Brush K, Hamilton SL. 1990. Ryanod-

ine as a probe for the functional state of the skeletal muscle sarcoplasmic reticulum calcium release channel. *Mol. Pharmacol.* 37:735–41

16. Chu A, Stefani E. 1991. Phosphatidylinositol 4,5-bisphosphate-induced Ca^{2+} release from skeletal muscle sarcoplasmic reticulum terminal cisternal membranes. *J. Biol. Chem.* 266:7699–705

17. Chu A, Sumbilla C, Inesi G, Jay SD, Campbell KP. 1990. Specific association of calmodulin-dependent protein kinase and related substrates with the junctional sarcoplasmic reticulum of skeletal muscle. *Biochemistry* 29:5899–905

18. Deleted in proof

19. Collins JH. 1991. Sequence analysis of the ryanodine receptor: possible association with a 12K, FK506-binding immunophilin/protein kinase C inhibitor. *Biochem. Biophys. Res, Commun.* 178:1288–90

20. Corbett AM, Bian J, Wade JB, Schneider MF. 1992. Depolarization-induced calcium release from isolated triads measured with impermeant Fura-2. *J. Membr. Biol.* 128:165–79

21. Diaz-Munoz M, Hamilton SL, Kaetzel MA, Hazarika P, Dedman JR. 1990. Modulation of Ca^{2+} release channel activity from sarcoplasmic reticulum by annexin VI (67-kDa Calcimedin). *J. Biol. Chem.* 265:15894–99

22. Donaldson SK, Goldberg ND, Walseth TF, Huetteman DA. 1988. Voltage-dependence of inositol 1,4,5-trisphosphate-induced Ca^{2+} release in peeled skeletal muscle fibers. *Proc. Natl. Acad. Sci. USA* 85:5749–53

23. Dumonteil E, Barré H, Meissner G. 1993. Potential role of palmitoyl carnitine modulation of the avian Ca^{2+} release channel in muscular nonshivering thermogenesis. *Biophys. J.* 64:A304

24. El-Hayek R, Valdivia C, Valdivia HH, Hogan K, Coronado R. 1993. Palmitoyl carnitine: Activation of the Ca^{2+} release channel of skeletal muscle sarcoplasmic reticulum by palmitoyl carnitine and related long chain fatty acid derivatives. *Biophys. J.* 65:779–89

25. Fano GMV, Angelella P, Aisa MC, Giambanco I, Donato R. 1989. S-100αo protein stimulates Ca^{2+}-induced Ca^{2+} release from isolated sarcoplasmic reticulum vesicles. *FEBS Lett.* 255:381–84

26. Fill M, Coronado R, Mickelson JR, Vilven J, Ma JJ, et al. 1990. Abnormal ryanodine receptor channels in malig-nant hyperthermia. *Biophys. J.* 57:471–75

27. Formelova J, Hurnak O, Novotova M, Zachar J. 1990. Ryanodine receptor purified from crayfish skeletal muscle. *Gen. Physiol. Biophys.* 9:445–53

28. Fujii J, Otsu K, Zorzato F, de Leon S, Khanna VK, et al. 1991. Identification of a mutation in porcine ryanodine receptor associated with malignant hyperthermia. *Science* 253:448–51

29. Gechtman Z, Orr I, Shoshan-Barmatz V. 1991. Involvement of protein phosphorylation in activation of Ca^{2+} efflux from sarcoplasmic reticulum. *Biochem. J.* 276:97–102

30. Giannini G, Clementi E, Ceci R, Marziali G, Sorrentino V. 1992. Expression of a ryanodine receptor-Ca^{2+} channel that is regulated by TGF-β. *Science* 257:91–94

31. Gilchrist JSC, Wang KKW, Katz S, Belcastro AN. 1992. Calcium-activated neutral protease effects upon skeletal muscle sarcoplasmic reticulum protein structure and calcium release. *J. Biol. Chem.* 267:20857–65

32. Grunwald R, Sealock R, Meissner G. 1993. Membrane topology of the rabbit skeletal muscle ryanodine receptor as determined by site directed antibodies. *Biophys. J.* 64:A152

33. Gyorke S, Palade P. 1992. Calcium-induced calcium release in crayfish skeletal muscle. *J. Physiol.* 457:195–210

34. Haeckel R, Kaiser E, Oellerich M, Siliprandi N. 1990. Carnitine: biochemical, analytical and clinical aspects. *J. Clin. Chem. Clin. Biochem.* 28:289–363

35. Hain J, Schindler H, Nath S, Fleischer S. 1993. Phosphorylation of the skeletal muscle calcium release channel removes block by magnesium ions. *Biophys. J.* 64:A151

36. Hakamata Y, Nakai J, Takeshima H, Imoto K. 1992. Primary structure and distribution of a novel ryanodine receptor/calcium release channel from rabbit brain. *FEBS Lett.* 312:229–35

37. Han JW, Thieleczek R, Varsanyi M, Heilmeyer LMG. 1992. Compartmentalized ATP synthesis in skeletal muscle triads. *Biochemistry* 31:377–84

38. Hasan G, Rosbash M. 1992. *Drosophila* homologs of two mammalian intracellular Ca^{2+}-release channels: identification and expression patterns of the inositol 1,4,5-triphosphate and the ryanodine receptor genes. *Development* 116:967–75

39. Hasselbach W, Migala A. 1992. Mod-

ulation by monovalent anions of calcium and caffeine induced calcium release from heavy sarcoplasmic reticulum vesicles. *Z. Naturforsch. Teil C* 47:440–48

40. Herrmann-Frank A, Darling E, Meissner G. 1991. Functional characterization of the Ca^{2+}-gated Ca^{2+} release channel of vascular smooth muscle sarcoplasmic reticulum. *Pflügers Arch.* 418:353–59

41. Herrmann-Frank A, Meissner G. 1992. Regulation of Ca^{2+} release from skeletal muscle sarcoplasmic reticulum. In *Muscle Fatigue Mechanisms in Exercise and Training*, ed. P Marconnet, PV Komi, B Saltin, OM Serjersted, 34:11–19. Basel: Karger

42. Hidalgo C, Jaimovich E. 1989. Inositol trisphosphate and excitation-contraction coupling in skeletal muscle. *J. Bioenerg. Biomembr.* 21:267–81

42a. Hidalgo C, Jorquera J, Tapia V, Donoso P. 1993. Triads and transverse tubules isolated from skeletal muscle contain high levels of inositol 1,4,5-trisphosphate. *J. Biol. Chem.* 268:15111–17

43. Hilkert R, Zaidi N, Shome K, Nigam M, Lagenaur C, Salama G. 1992. Properties of immunoaffinity purified 106-kDa Ca^{2+} release channels from the skeletal sarcoplasmic reticulum. *Arch. Biochem. Biophys.* 292:1–15

44. Hymel L, Inui M, Fleischer S, Schindler H. 1988. Purified ryanodine receptor of skeletal muscle sarcoplasmic reticulum forms Ca^{2+}-activated oligomeric Ca^{2+} channels in planar bilayers. *Proc. Natl. Acad. Sci. USA* 85:441–45

45. Hymel L, Schindler H, Inui M, Fleischer S. 1988. Reconstitution of purified cardiac muscle calcium release channel (ryanodine receptor) in planar bilayers. *Biochem. Biophys. Res. Commun.* 152:308–14

46. Ikemoto N, Antoniu B, Kang JJ. 1992. Characterization of "depolarization"-induced calcium release from sarcomic reticulum in vitro with the use of membrane potential probe. *Biochem. Biophys. Res. Commun.* 184:538–43

47. Ikemoto N, Antoniu B, Kang JJ, Meszaros LG, Ronjat M. 1991. Intravesicular calcium transient during calcium release from sarcoplasmic reticulum. *Biochemistry* 30:5230–37

48. Ikemoto N, Antoniu B, Meszaros LG. 1985. Rapid flow chemical quench studies of calcium release from isolated sarcoplasmic reticulum. *J. Biol. Chem.* 260:14096–100

49. Imagawa T, Nakai J, Takeshima H, Nagasaki Y, Shigekawa M. 1992. Expression of Ca^{2+}-induced Ca^{2+} release channel activity from cardiac ryanodine receptor cDNA in Chinese hamster ovary cells. *J. Biochem.* 112:508–13

50. Imagawa T, Smith JS, Coronado R, Campbell KP. 1987. Purified ryanodine receptor from skeletal muscle sarcoplasmic reticulum is the Ca^{2+}-permeable pore of the calcium release channel. *J. Biol. Chem.* 262:16636–43

51. Inui M, Saito A, Fleischer S. 1987. Isolation of the ryanodine receptor from cardiac sarcoplasmic reticulum and identity with the feet structures. *J. Biol. Chem.* 262:15637–42

52. Jayaraman T, Brillantes A-M, Timmerman AP, Fleischer S, Erdjument-Bromage H, et al. 1992. FK506 binding protein associated with the calcium release channel (ryanodine receptor). *J. Biol. Chem.* 267:9474–77

53. Jenden DJ, Fairhurst AS. 1969. The pharmacology of ryanodine. *Pharmacol. Rev.* 21:1–25

54. Jorgensen AO, Shen AC-Y, Arnold W, McPherson PS, Campbell KP. 1993. The Ca^{2+} release channel/ryanodine receptor is localized in junctional and corbular sarcoplasmic reticulum in cardiac muscle. *J. Cell Biol.* 120:969–80

55. Junker J, Sommer JR, Sar M, Meissner G. 1994. Extended junctional sarcoplasmic reticulum of avian cardiac muscle contains functional ryanodine receptors. *J. Biol. Chem.* In press

56. Kim DH, Ikemoto N. 1986. Involvement of 60-kilodalton phosphoprotein in the regulation of calcium release from skeletal muscle sarcoplasmic reticulum. *J. Biol. Chem.* 261:11674–79

57. Kim YK, Valdivia HH, Maryon EB, Anderson P, Coronado R. 1992. High molecular weight proteins in the nematode *C. elegans* bind [^{3}H]ryanodine and form a large conductance channel. *Biophys. J.* 63:1379–84

58. Kirino Y, Osakabe M, Shimizu H. 1983. Ca^{2+}-induced Ca^{2+} release from fragmented sarcoplasmic reticulum: Ca^{2+}-dependent passive Ca^{2+} efflux. *J. Biochem.* 94:1111–18

58a. Knudson CM, Stang KK, Moomaw CR, Slaughter CA, Campbell KP. 1993. Primary structure and topological analysis of a skeletal muscle-specific junctional sarcoplasmic reticulum glycoprotein (triadin). *J. Biol. Chem.* 268:12646–54

59. Lagos N, Vergara J. 1990. Phosphoinositides in frog skeletal muscle:

A quantitative analysis. *Biochim. Biophys. Acta* 1043:235–44

60. Lai FA, Dent M, Wickenden C, Xu L, Kumari G, et al. 1992. Expression of a cardiac Ca^{2+} release channel isoform in mammalian brain. *Biochem. J.* 288:553–64

61. Lai FA, Erickson HP, Rousseau E, Liu QY, Meissner G. 1988. Purification and reconstitution of the calcium release channel from skeletal muscle. *Nature* 331:315–19

62. Lai FA, Liu QY, Xu L, El-Hashem A, Kramarcy NR, et al. 1992. Amphibian ryanodine receptor isoforms are related to those of mammalian skeletal or cardiac muscle. *Am. J. Physiol.* 263:C365–72

63. Lai FA, Misra M, Xu L, Smith HA, Meissner G. 1989. The ryanodine receptor-Ca^{2+} release channel complex of skeletal muscle sarcoplasmic reticulum. Evidence for a cooperatively coupled, negatively charged homotetramer. *J. Biol. Chem.* 264:16776–85

64. Lee HC. 1993. Potentiation of calcium- and caffeine-induced calcium release by cyclic ADP-ribose. *J. Biol. Chem.* 268:293–99

65. Liu QY, Lai FA, Rousseau E, Jones RV, Meissner G. 1989. Multiple conductance states of the purified calcium release channel complex from skeletal sarcoplasmic reticulum. *Biophys. J.* 55:415–24

66. Ma J, Anderson K, Shirokov R, Levis R, Gonzalez A, et al. 1993. Effects of perchlorate on the molecules of excitation-contraction coupling of skeletal and cardiac muscle. *J. Gen. Physiol.* 102:423–48

67. Ma J, Fill M, Knudson CM, Campbell KP, Coronado R. 1988. Ryanodine receptor of skeletal muscle is a gap junction-type channel. *Science* 242:99–102

68. Marks AR, Fleischer S, Tempst P. 1990. Surface topography analysis of the ryanodine receptor/junctional channel complex based on proteolysis sensitivity mapping. *J. Biol. Chem.* 265:13143–49

69. Mayr GW, Thieleczek R. 1991. Masses of inositol phosphates in resting and tetanically stimulated vertebrate skeletal muscle. *Biochem. J.* 280:631–40

70. McGrew SG, Wolleben C, Siegl P, Inui M, Fleischer S. 1989. Positive cooperativity of ryanodine binding to the calcium release channel of sarcoplasmic reticulum from heart and skeletal muscle. *Biochemistry* 28:1686–91

71. McPherson PS, Kim YK, Valdivia H,

Knudson CM, Takekura H, et al. 1991. The brain ryanodine receptor: a caffeine-sensitive calcium release channel. *Neuron* 7:17–25

72. Meissner G. 1984. Adenine nucleotide stimulation of Ca^{2+}-induced Ca^{2+} release in sarcoplasmic reticulum. *J. Biol. Chem.* 159:1365–74

73. Meissner G. 1986. Evidence of a role for calmodulin in the regulation of calcium release from skeletal muscle sarcoplasmic reticulum. *Biochemistry* 25:244–51

74. Meissner G. 1986. Ryanodine activation and inhibition of the Ca^{2+} release channel of sarcoplasmic reticulum. *J. Biol. Chem.* 261:6300–6

75. Meissner G, Darling E, Eveleth J. 1986. Kinetics of rapid Ca^{2+} release by sarcoplasmic reticulum. Effects of Ca^{2+}, Mg^{2+}, and adenine nucleotides. *Biochemistry* 25:236–44

76. Meissner G, El-Hashem A. 1992. Ryanodine as a functional probe of the skeletal muscle sarcoplasmic reticulum Ca^{2+} release channel. *Mol. Cell. Biochem.* 114:119–23

77. Meissner G, Henderson JS. 1987. Rapid calcium release from cardiac sarcoplasmic reticulum vesicles is dependent on Ca^{2+} and is modulated by Mg^{2+}, adenine nucleotide, and calmodulin. *J. Biol. Chem.* 262:3065–73

78. Meszaros LG, Bak J, Chu A. 1993. Cyclic ADP-ribose as an endogenous regulator of the non-skeletal type ryanodine receptor Ca^{2+} channel. *Nature* 364:76–79

79. Mickelson JR, Knudson CM, Kennedy CFH, Yang D-I, Litterer LA, et al. 1992. Structural and functional correlates of a mutation in the malignant hyperthermia-susceptible pig ryanodine receptor. *FEBS Lett.* 301:49–52

80. Mickelson JR, Litterer LA, Jacobson BA, Louis CF. 1990. Stimulation and inhibition of [^{3}H]ryanodine binding to sarcoplasmic reticulum from malignant hyperthermia susceptible pigs. *Arch. Biochem. Biophys.* 278:251–57

81. Morii H, Tonomura Y. 1983. The gating behavior of a channel for Ca^{2+}-induced Ca^{2+} release in fragmented sarcoplasmic reticulum. *J. Biochem.* 93:1271–85

82. Moutin MJ, Dupont Y. 1988. Rapid filtration of Ca^{2+}-induced Ca^{2+} release from skeletal sarcoplasmic reticulum. *J. Biol. Chem.* 263:4228–35

83. Murayama T, Ogawa Y. 1992. Purification and characterization of two ryanodine-binding protein isoforms from sarcoplasmic reticulum of bullfrog

skeletal muscle. *J. Biochem.* 112:514–22

84. Nabauer M, Callewaert G, Cleemann L, Morad M. 1989. Regulation of calcium release is gated by calcium current, not gating charge, in cardiac myocytes. *Science* 244:800–3

85. Nagasaki K, Kasai, M. 1983. Fast release of calcium from sarcoplasmic reticulum vesicles monitored by chlortetracycline fluorescence. *J. Biochem.* 94:1101–9

86. Nagasaki K, Kasai M. 1984. Channel selectivity and gating specificity of calcium-induced calcium release channel in isolated sarcoplasmic reticulum. *J. Biochem.* 96:1769–75

87. Nakai J, Imagawa T, Hakamata Y, Shigekawa M, Takeshima H, Numa S. 1990. Primary structure and functional expression from cDNA of the cardiac ryanodine receptor/calcium release channel. *FEBS Lett.* 271:169–77

87a. O'Brien J, Meissner G, Block BA. 1993. The fastest contracting muscle of non-mammalian vertebrates express only one isoform of the ryanodine receptor. *Biophys. J.* In press

88. Ogawa Y, Ebashi S. 1976. Ca-releasing action of β, γ-methylene adenosine triphosphate on fragmented sarcoplasmic reticulum. *J. Biochem.* 80:1149–57

89. Olivares EB, Tanksley SJ, Airey JA, Beck CF, Ouyang Y, et al. 1991. Nonmammalian vertebrate skeletal muscles express two triad junctional foot protein isoforms. *Biophys. J.* 59:1153–63

90. Otsu K, Willard HF, Khanna VK, Zorzato F, Green NM, MacLennan DH. 1990. Molecular cloning of cDNA encoding the Ca^{2+} release channel (ryanodine receptor) of rabbit cardiac muscle sarcoplasmic reticulum. *J. Biol. Chem.* 265:13472–83

90a. Palade P. 1987. Drug-induced Ca^{2+} release from isolated sarcoplasmic reticulum. III. Block of Ca^{2+}-induced Ca^{2+} release by organic polyamines. *J. Biol. Chem.* 262:6149–54

91. Palade P, Dettbarn C, Brunder D, Stein P, Hals G. 1989. Pharmacology of calcium release from sarcoplasmic reticulum. *J. Bioenerg. Biomembr.* 21:295–320

92. Pape PC, Konishi M, Baylor SM, Somlyo AP. 1988. Excitation-contraction coupling in skeletal muscle fibers injected with the InsP₃ block, heparin. *FEBS Lett.* 235:57–62

93. Pessah IN, Stambuk RA, Casida JE. 1987. Ca^{2+}-activated ryanodine binding: mechanisms of sensitivity and intensity modulation by Mg^{2+}, caffeine, and adenine nucleotides. *Mol. Pharmacol.* 31:232–38

94. Radermacher M, Wagenknecht T, Grassucci R, Frank J, Inui M, et al. 1992. Cryo-EM of the native structure of the calcium release channel/ryanodine receptor from sarcoplasmic reticulum. *Biophys. J.* 61:936–40

95. Rardon DP, Cefali DC, Mitchell RD, Seiler SM, Jones LR. 1989. High molecular weight proteins purified from cardiac junctional sarcoplasmic reticulum vesicles are ryanodine-sensitive calcium channels. *Circ. Res.* 64:779–89

96. Rardon DP, Cefali DC, Mitchell RD, Seiler SM, Jones LR. 1990. Digestion of cardiac and skeletal muscle junctional sarcoplasmic reticulum vesicles with calpain II. Effects on the Ca^{2+} release channel. *Circ. Res.* 67:84–96

97. Rousseau E, Pinkos J, Savaria D. 1992. Functional sensitivity of the native skeletal Ca^{2+}-release channel to divalent cations and the Mg-ATP complex. *Can. J. Physiol. Pharmacol.* 70:394–402

98. Rousseau E, Smith JS, Henderson JS, Meissner G. 1986. Single channel and $^{45}Ca^{2+}$ flux measurements of the cardiac sarcoplasmic reticulum calcium channel. *Biophys. J.* 50:1009–14

99. Rousseau E, Smith JS, Meissner G. 1987. Ryanodine modifies conductance and gating behavior of single Ca^{2+} release channel. *Am. J. Physiol.* 253:C364–68

100. Sabbadini RA, Betto R, Teresi A, Fachechi-Cassano G, Salviati G. 1992. The effects of sphingosine on sarcoplasmic reticulum membrane calcium release. *J. Biol. Chem.* 267:15475–84

101. Saito A, Inui M, Radermacher M, Frank J, Fleischer S. 1988. Ultrastructure of the calcium release channel of sarcoplasmic reticulum. *J. Cell Biol.* 107:211–19

102. Saito A, Inui M, Walls JS, Fleischer S. 1989. Mass measurement of the feet structures/calcium release channel of sarcoplasmic reticulum by scanning transmission electron microscopy (STEM). *Biophys. J.* 55:206a

103. Seiler S, Wegener AD, Whang DD, Hathaway DR, Jones LR. 1984. High molecular weight proteins in cardiac and skeletal muscle sarcoplasmic reticulum vesicles bind calmodulin, are phosphorylated, and are degraded by Ca^{2+}-activated protease. *J. Biol. Chem.* 259:8550–57

104. Seok JH, Xu L, Kramarcy NR, Sealock R, Meissner G. 1992. The 30 S lobster

skeletal muscle Ca^{2+} release channel (ryanodine receptor) has functional properties distinct from the mammalian channel proteins. *J. Biol. Chem.* 267: 15893–901

105. Shoshan-Barmatz V, Pressley TA, Higham S, Kraus-Friedmann N. 1991. Characterization of high-affinity ryanodine-binding sites of rat liver endoplasmic reticulum. Differences between liver and skeletal muscle. *Biochem. J.* 276:41–46

106. Smith JS, Coronado R, Meissner G. 1985. Sarcoplasmic reticulum contains adenine nucleotide-activated calcium channels. *Nature* 316:446–49

107. Smith JS, Coronado R, Meissner G. 1986. Single channel measurements of the calcium release channel from skeletal muscle sarcoplasmic reticulum. Activation by Ca^{2+} and ATP and modulation by Mg^{2+}. *J. Gen. Physiol.* 88: 573–88

108. Smith JS, Imagawa T, Ma J, Fill M, Campbell KP, Coronado R. 1988. Purified ryanodine receptor from rabbit skeletal muscle is the calcium-release channel of sarcoplasmic reticulum. *J. Gen. Physiol.* 92:1–26

109. Smith JS, Rousseau E, Meissner G. 1989. Calmodulin modulation of single sarcoplasmic reticulum Ca^{2+}-release channels from cardiac and skeletal muscle. *Circ. Res.* 64:352–59

110. Sommer JR, Johnson EA. 1979. Ultrastructure of cardiac muscle. In *Handbook of Physiology*, ed. RM Berne, Sec. 2, pp. 113–86. Bethesda: Am. Physiol Soc.

111. Stein PG, Palade PT. 1988. Sarcoballs: Direct access to sarcoplasmic reticulum Ca^{2+} channels in skinned frog skeletal muscle fibers. *Biophys. J.* 54:357–63

112. Strand MA, Louis CF, Mickelson JR. 1993. Phosphorylation of the porcine skeletal and cardiac muscle sarcoplasmic reticulum ryanodine receptor. *Biochim. Biophys. Acta* 1175:319–26

113. Strasburg GM, Reedy M, Burke C. 1991. Calmodulin interaction with the sarcoplasmic reticulum Ca^{2+}-release channel from skeletal and cardiac muscle. *Biophys. J.* 59:105a

114. Suarez-Isla BA, Alcayaga C, Marengo JJ, Bull R. 1991. Activation of inositol trisphosphate-sensitive Ca^{2+} channels of sarcoplasmic reticulum from frog skeletal muscle. *J. Physiol.* 441:575–91

115. Suko J, Maurer-Fogy I, Plank B, Bertel O, Wyskovsky W, et al. 1993. Phosphorylation of serine 2843 in ryanodine receptor-calcium release channel of skeletal muscle by cAMP-, cGMP- and CaM-dependent protein kinase. *Biochim. Biophys. Acta* 1175:193–206

116. Sumbilla C, Inesi G. 1987. Rapid filtration measurements of Ca^{2+} release from cisternal sarcoplasmic reticulum vesicles. *FEBS Lett.* 210:31–36

117. Takeshima H, Nishimura S, Matsumoto T, Ishida H, Kangawa K, et al. 1989. Primary structure and expression from complementary DNA of skeletal muscle ryanodine receptor. *Nature* 339:439–45

117a. Takeshima H, Nishimura S, Nishi M, Ikeda M, Sugimoto T. 1993. A brain-specific transcript from the 3'-terminal region of the skeletal muscle ryanodine receptor gene. *FEBS Lett.* 322:105–10

118. Thieleczek R, Mayr GW, Brandt NR. 1989. Inositol polyphosphate-mediated repartitioning of aldolase in skeletal muscle triads and myofibrils. *J. Biol. Chem.* 264:7349–56

119. Tinker A, Lindsay ARG, Williams A. 1992. A model for ionic conduction in the ryanodine receptor channel of sheep cardiac muscle sarcoplasmic reticulum. *J. Gen. Physiol.* 100:495–517

120. Valdivia C, Valdivia HH, Potter BV, Coronado R. 1990. Ca^{2+} release by inositol-trisphosphorothioate in isolated triads of rabbit skeletal muscle. *Biophys. J.* 57:1233–43

121. Valdivia C, Vaughan D, Potter BVL, Coronado R. 1992. Fast release of $^{45}Ca^{2+}$ induced by inositol 1,4,5-trisphosphate and Ca^{2+} in the sarcoplasmic reticulum of skeletal muscle: evidence for two types of Ca^{2+} release channels. *Biophys. J.* 61:1184–93

122. Vergara J, Tsien RY, Delay M. 1985. Inositol 1, 4, 5-trisphosphate: A possible chemical link in excitation-contraction coupling in muscle. *Proc. Natl. Acad. Sci. USA* 82:6352–56

123. Vilven J, Coronado R. 1988. Opening of dihydropyridine calcium channels in skeletal muscle membranes by inositol trisphosphate. *Nature* 336:587–89

124. Volpe P, Salviati G, DiVirgilio F, Pozzan T. 1985. Inositol 1, 4, 5-trisphosphate induces calcium release from sarcoplasmic reticulum of skeletal muscle. *Nature* 316:347–49

125. Wagenknecht T, Grassucci R, Frank J, Saito A, Inui M, Fleischer S. 1989. Three-dimensional architecture of the calcium channel/foot structure of sarcoplasmic reticulum. *Nature* 338:167–70

126. Walker JW, Somlyo AV, Goldman YE, Somlyo AP, Trentham DR. 1987. Kinetics of smooth and skeletal muscle activation by laser pulse photolysis of

caged inositol 1, 4, 5-trisphosphate. *Nature* 327:249–52

127. Wang J, Best PM. 1992. Inactivation of the sarcoplasmic reticulum calcium channel by protein kinase. *Nature* 359: 739–41

128. Witcher DR, Kovacs RJ, Schulman H, Cefali DC, Jones LR. 1991. Unique phosphorylation site on the cardiac ryanodine receptor regulates calcium channel activity. *J. Biol. Chem.* 266: 11144–52

129. Xu L, Jones R, Meissner G. 1993. Effects of local anesthetics on single channel behavior of skeletal muscle calcium release channel. *J. Gen. Physiol.* 101:207–33

130. Yamanouchi H, Kanemasa T, Kasai M. 1984. Effects of adenine nucleotides on the Ca^{2+}-gated cation channel in sarcoplasmic reticulum vesicles. *J. Biochem.* 95:161–66

130a. Zarka A, Shoshan-Barmatz V. 1992. The interaction of spermine with the ryanodine receptor from skeletal muscle. *Biochim. Biophys. Acta* 1108:13–20

131. Zimanyi I, Pessah IN. 1991. Comparison of [^{3}H]ryanodine receptors and Ca^{2+} release from rat cardiac and rabbit skeletal muscle sarcoplasmic reticulum. *J. Pharmacol. Exp. Ther.* 256:938–46

132. Zorzato F, Fujii J, Otsu K, Phillips M, Green NM, et al. 1990. Molecular cloning of cDNA encoding human and rabbit forms of the Ca^{2+} release channel (ryanodine receptor) of skeletal muscle sarcoplasmic reticulum. *J. Biol. Chem.* 265:2244–56

Annu. Rev. Physiol. 1994. 56:509–34
Copyright © 1994 by Annual Reviews Inc. All rights reserved

STRUCTURE AND DEVELOPMENT OF E-C COUPLING UNITS IN SKELETAL MUSCLE

Clara Franzini-Armstrong and Annelise O. Jorgensen

Department of Cell Developmental Biology, University of Pennsylvania, Philadelphia, Pennsylvania 19104–6058, and Department of Anatomy and Cell Biology, University of Toronto, Toronto, Ontario M5S 1A8 Canada

KEY WORDS: feet, tetrads, sarcoplasmic reticulum, transverse tubules, triads

INTRODUCTION

Excitation-contraction (e-c) coupling depends on appropriate communication between the specialized, junctional domains of the sarcolemma/transverse tubules (jSL/jT) and those of the sarcoplasmic reticulum (jSR). Essential events at the SR-T/SL junctions are depolarization of the surface membrane, its detection by voltage sensors, and the resultant release of calcium from jSR. In skeletal muscle, e-c coupling is independent of extracellular calcium (7, 16, 18, 27, 42, 70, 71, 85, 92 for reviews). The nonjunctional components of the two membrane systems, free SL/free T, and free or longitudinal SR, are continuous with the junctional domains, but functionally and structurally distinct from them.

In this chapter we review the structure and protein composition of the membranes involved in e-c coupling and the structure and development of junctions formed by the interaction of jSR with either jT or jSL (e-c units). Structural information provides the framework into which the function of and the interaction between the protein components of these structures must fit. The article is written from the perspective of immunolabeling and electron microscopy (EM). The two morphological approaches complement each other. Immunolabeling approaches assign specific locations within the cell

509

0066–4278/94/0315–0509$05.00

to recognized proteins considered to be relevant to e-c coupling. EM provides high resolution images that reveal the spatial organization of the various components and keeps immunolocalization honest. Both approaches rely on the information gathered from cell fractionation and protein purification techniques.

THE MEMBRANE SYSTEMS AND THEIR INTERACTIONS

Interaction between the SR and SL/T tubules occurs at specialized junctions called peripheral couplings, dyads and triads or, collectively, e-c units. Peripheral couplings are formed between one SR cisterna and the SL. In some fibers they are present only before T tubule formation. Dyads and triads are internal junctions comprised of either one or two jSR cisternae and a jT segment. Different muscle fibers have various combinations of the three types of junctions. Function of peripheral e-c units is demonstrated in muscles that lack T tubules (9). Infiltration techniques, which enhance the shape of T tubules, and immunohistochemistry, have shown that although surface membranes, T tubules, and SR are continuous structures, their junctional domains are discrete.

In the process of e-c coupling, three events must take place: detection of changes in membrane potential of SL (in peripheral couplings) or T tubules (in triads and dyads); transmission of relevant information to the SR; and release of calcium from the SR. All elements necessary for these events are contained within an e-c unit. In addition, the units contain calcium-binding proteins, thus assuring a high local total calcium concentration.

FEET/RYANODINE RECEPTORS: Structure, Disposition and Location

Electron Microscopy

Feet were the first structural components of e-c units to be described. They span the gap between the apposed SR and SL/T tubules and appear to physically connect them while maintaining a gap of constant width (approximately 10 nm) between them. Feet are easily detectable in EMs of tangentially sectioned junctions because they form orderly arrays with a tetragonal arrangement. The plaques or arrays of feet in muscles of invertebrates are extensive, which allows low-resolution reconstruction of feet structure (72). Each foot has four large subunits symmetrically located around a central less dense area, and adjacent feet are closely apposed in orderly arrays (Figure 1e).

Ordered disposition and close proximity between adjacent feet are maintained in isolated vesicles (81), which allow imaging of foot structure and disposition by rotary shadowing (30, 72). In these images, the feet are 25–26 nm on their sides and have a clearly visible depression in the center of the tetrameric structure (quatrefoil) formed by four apparently identical subunits. The center to center distance between feet in arrays is 26–32 nm in muscles of vertebrates and 27–28 nm in invertebrates. The arrangement, although tetragonal in both cases, differs slightly. However, similar macromolecules are involved in all striated muscles, as seen from biochemical data (38, 97). Attempts to obtain higher resolution imaging of the native foot protein in frozen-hydrated triads have not provided sufficient detail to reveal new structural information.

A different view of the feet is seen in sections that cut across the junctional gap. Here feet appear as evenly spaced densities that cross the gap and apparently touch the cytoplasmic surface of T tubules. Views of the foot from different angles are probably responsible for the various appearances described in the literature (e.g. dense parallel lines, pillars, and bridges) (45).

The unusually large size and characteristic shape of the feet have allowed their direct identification with the large spanning proteins (60, 61) or ryanodine receptors, RyR (10, 51, 69), that constitute the channel responsible for release of calcium from the SR (see 78, G Meissner, this volume). Foot-spanning protein, ryanodine receptor (RyR), and SR calcium release channel are alternate names that identify the same molecule on the basis of its structural, biochemical, and functional connotations. We use the term foot when dealing with EM identification and RyR in the case of immunolabeling or biochemical approaches.

Immunolabeling

Immunolabeling at the light microscope level shows location of RYRs at sites where triads are located in adult muscle (Figure 1k) and where peripheral couplings and small triads are located during development (3, 100, 112). ImmunoEM studies show localization of RyRs at the triads in situ (3, 26, 67) (Figure 1o) and at the feet-bearing surfaces of isolated heavy SR and triads (61). Colocalization of RyRs and feet is confirmed by immunoEM studies of rat cardiac muscle (56) in jSR and in corbular SR. The latter has feet but does not form junctions (24, 99). Similarly, identification of feet with RyRs in peripheral couplings is implied by the coincidental absence and presence of feet and RyR mRNA in proliferating and differentiated myoblasts, respectively, from a cell line (76).

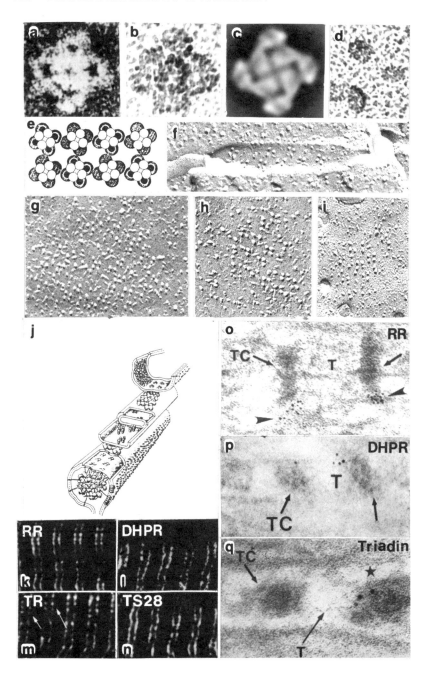

Two recent EM studies (26, 67) note that immunolabeling of the jSR membrane is scarce and that 20–50% of the labeling is apparently non-junctional. One possible explanation for the limited labeling is that antigenic sites are sterically blocked by the narrow junctional gap, but may be exposed in tangential cuts where the SR membrane is not identifiable as junctional. Extrajunctional labeling may indicate the presence of some RyRs (or their subunits) in the free SR. These may be molecules in transit from their site of synthesis to their final junctional location and EM could easily miss them. The local stimulation experiments (49) indicate that no significant release of calcium occurs away from the regions where triads are located, which implies that extrajunctional feet in skeletal muscle may not contribute to calcium release during e-c coupling.

Substructure

The quatrefoil foot structure is readily visible in the isolated RyR molecule, but the latter has an additional feature: a smaller, stain-excluding or raised central platform that also shows a four subunit structure and is rotated by 45° (10, 69) (Figure 1a,b). The platform presumably corresponds to the

---

Figure 1   Structure and location of components of the triads and peripheral couplings. (*a,b*) Images of isolated ryanodine receptors, (*a*) negatively stained, (*b*) rotary shadowed, that show four large equal domains and a central more dense region that is raised. The four large domains constitute the foot region of the molecule, and the raised platform is probably the intramembrane domain. Magnification: ~746,000 (*a*, reproduced from 69; *b*, see 10). (*c*) Central section through the three-dimensionally reconstructed volume of the RYR that shows four radial stain-filled channels (reproduced from 109).

(*d*) Rotary shadowed isolated DHPRs are slightly ovoid in shape. Magnification: × 300,000 (reproduced from Leung AT, Imagawa T, Block B, Franzini-Armstrong C, Campbell KP. 1988. *J. Biol. Chem.* 263:994–1001).

(*e*) Diagram showing relationship of feet and tetrads. Tetrads (*black circles*) are located above alternate feet (*gray, white circles*: cytoplasmic and intramembrane domains of RyRs). (*f*) Freeze-fracture image of tetrads in T tubules of toadfish muscle. Magnification: × 102,000 (reproduced from 10).

(*g,h,i*) Groups of tetrads in the plasmalemma of (*g*) cultured human muscle; (*h*) in vivo developing mouse muscle; (*i*) adult tonic frog muscle fiber. The tetrads are arranged similarly to those in T tubules, but they form more extensive arrays. (*g*, magnification: × 71,600, reproduced from 88; *h*, × 92,000, reproduced from 46; *i*, × 95,000 reproduced from 40).

(*j*) Three-dimensional image of a triad that shows the relationship between calsequestrin, feet, and tetrads (reproduced from 10). (*k-n*) Immunofluorescence localization of RyRs, DHPRs, triadin, and TS28 (a T tubule antigen) in adult rabbit skeletal muscle. The four proteins show punctuate labeling (e.g. *arrows, m*) consistent with a location at T-SR junctions. Magnification: × 2,400 (*k,l,n* reproduced from 112; *m* from 67).

(*o-q*). Immunogold labeling for RR (*arrowheads*), DHPR, and triadin (*asterisk*) at the EM level shows location of all three proteins at the T-SR junction. Terminal cisternae of the SR (TC) and the dilated T tubules (T) are indicated. (*o,p,*) Magnification: × 100,000; *q*, × 180,000. *o,q,* reproduced from 67; *p,* reproduced from 55).

intramembrane domain of the molecule. Indeed, in freeze-fracture replicas of the jSR membrane, a small intramembrane quatrefoil is revealed at the location of each foot (10). Comparison of the in situ and isolated molecules thus indicates a large cytoplasmic hydrophilic domain, the foot, and a smaller intramembrane domain, presumably the calcium release channel. RyRs are homotetramers composed of four identical polypeptide chains (69), each with a large hydrophilic segment and a shorter hydrophobic region (104, 113). Each of the four subunits apparently contributes equally to the formation of the foot and the channel regions, but the complete tetramer is necessary for ryanodine binding and channel activity (69).

Reconstruction of the macromolecules from negatively stained and frozen hydrated specimens at 2.5–3 nm resolution reveals many relevant features (91, 109). A central low density channel is surrounded by the four subunits and is connected to four radial channels which, in turn, open into a larger peripheral vestibule. It is tempting to assume that these areas of low density represent the hydrophilic channels through which calcium exits from the SR, particularly since the channels would seem to be admirably designed for directing the calcium away from the narrow junctional gap (Figure 1c).

A discrepancy exists between the three-dimensional reconstructions from negatively stained images of the isolated RYRs and the shadowed images of feet in SR vesicles: the former have raised central regions on both sides (91, 109), while the latter have a large central depression on the side of the molecule that is in proximity to the T tubules in the junction (10, 30). It is not clear how this discrepancy arises, unless some distortion of the molecule occurs at its site of attachment to the membrane during negative staining.

Conclusions

On the basis of immunocytochemistry and the structural similarity between feet and purified RyR, it is reasonable to assume that all arrays of feet found in EMs of skeletal muscle are composed of RyRs. The converse is not necessarily true, i.e. lack of detection of feet by EM does not exclude the presence of RYRs in cases where the molecules do not form an array, since single feet are difficult to detect in EMs. In cells other than skeletal muscle, further caution is necessary. IP$_3$ receptors (31) are also composed of four subunits and have large cytoplasmic domains similar to feet, although smaller. A structural difference between arrays of IP$_3$ receptors and of RyRs has not been established, and thus discrimination between these two components solely by EM is not yet possible (72).

The purification, characterization, and sequencing of RyRs, their identification with feet, and the demonstration that they are the calcium release channels marked the beginning of a new era in e-c coupling studies (see

G Meissner, this volume). We now know that the SR calcium release channels in skeletal muscle are located in the SR membrane immediately adjacent to the T tubules. Feet have unique large cytoplasmic domains that may directly contact components of the SL/T tubules. Implications of this contact for e-c coupling mechanism are discussed below. An important question remaining is whether calcium release during activity creates a transient spike in calcium concentration within the junctional gap (see M Schneider, this volume).

TETRADS/DIHYDROPYRIDINE RECEPTORS

Two components of the SL/T tubules, dihydropyridine receptors (DHPRs) and tetrads, have been implicated in e-c coupling. Recent ultrastructural evidence indicates that they are reflections of a single entity. We use the term DHPR when dealing with the functionally, biochemically, or immunologically identified molecule, and the term tetrad when dealing with the structure revealed by EM.

Dihydropyridine Receptors (DHPRs)

DHPRs are slowly activating calcium channels responsible for most of the charge movement associated with depolarizations to the contractile threshold. They have been postulated to be the voltage sensors of e-c coupling (8, 92, 105, 106, see M Schneider, this volume). DHPRs are composed of one each of five subunits (α_1, α_2, β, γ, δ; 13a, 18), all of which have been sequenced and expressed (22a, 23, 28a, 52a, 80a, 93a, 106a,b). The structure of the isolated molecule is shown in Figure 1d. Sequence similarity with the sodium channel, functional expression, identification of binding site, and block by antibodies indicate that the α_1 subunit is the channel-forming and DHP-binding portion of the molecule (80a, 82a, 83, 88a, 106b). Three α_1 isoforms have been detected so far in skeletal muscle (23, 75) and one in cardiac muscle (80a). The function of the other units is not fully determined. α_2 aids functional expression of α_1 (28a); β contributes to appropriate kinetics of the skeletal calcium channel (68a), and δ is a fragment of α_2 (22a).

Dysgenic muscle has been an essential tool in understanding the role of DHPRs. Muscular dysgenesis is a recessive lethal mutation (47a), and it was fortunate that the dysgenic mouse colony was maintained for several years. Powell recognized its significance as a tool in e-c coupling research and generously distributed it to several laboratories (8, 89, 90a). The defect is a point mutation in the gene for α_1 subunit of DHPR (19, 106), which results in undetectable levels of the protein (65) and reduction, but not total absence, of specific DHP binding (89, 91a). The correlated decrease in DHP binding, lack of slow calcium currents and charge movement, and interruption of e-c coupling in dysgenic fibers, and the rescue of functions and currents in fibers transfected with the cDNA for the DHPR constitute compelling evidence for identification of DHPRs with the voltage sensors of e-c coupling (1a, 8, 85, 89, 90, 106). cDNA for cardiac DHPR, expressed in dysgenic cells, results in calcium currents with fast cardiac-type kinetics and in e-c coupling that is dependent on extracellular calcium (106a).

In a demanding series of experiments using various skeletal-cardiac cDNA chimeras, the components responsible for the faster kinetics of the cardiac DHPR and for the ability to sustain skeletal muscle type e-c coupling (independent of extracellular calcium) have been identified. The two recognized transcripts of adult skeletal muscle, one short, one long, have dual functions as channels and voltage sensors (7a). The first repeat is mostly responsible for differences between cardiac and skeletal channel kinetics (104a), while the cytoplasmic loop between repeats II and III seems to have a key role in skeletal-type e-c coupling, independent of extracellular calcium (105). This might be the loop that allows interaction with RyRs.

Localization of Dihydropyridine Receptors

Biochemical evidence first indicated that DHPRs were located in T tubules of adult skeletal muscle (39). LM (Figure 1l) and EM (Figure 1p) immunolocalization show α_1 and α_2 subunits of DHPRs at the level of T tubules, and more specifically in segments of T tubules associated with SR in e-c units (34, 55). This is supported by LM immunolabeling of myotubes developing in vivo and in vitro, which shows α_1 and α_2 subunits of DHPRs in discrete foci (35, 112), colocalized with RyRs (112). This association implies a close apposition of membranes containing DHPRs and RyRs. The foci are in areas where either peripheral couplings or triads are expected.

One EM study (55), however, reports that only about 50% of the labeling is confined to the junctional face of the T tubule. This is probably because access to the cytoplasmic region of the DHPR that contains the epitope recognized by the mAB antibody used is limited. However, the possibility that DHPRs are localized to nonjunctional T tubule membrane is consistent with DHPR labeling of subsarcolemmal vesicles possibly corresponding to nonjunctional segments of T tubules near their opening. Extra junctional DHPRs have not been detected by LM, and the possibilities that they are either rare (perhaps less stable) or a different isoform remain to be examined. Thus immunolabeling shows clustering of DHPRs in proximity to RyRs, but does not exclude the presence of some DHPRs at other sites.

Tetrads: Disposition and Identification with DHPRs

Tetrads are groups of four proteins, visible in freeze-fracture replicas, that form orderly clusters either on the surface membrane, presumably at sites of peripheral couplings (Figure 1g,h,i), or in the junctional region of T tubules (Figure 1f). Assemblies of tetrads were first seen in the T tubules of toadfish (45), in the plasmalemma of cultured human muscle (88), and frog tonic fibers (40). Their relevance to e-c coupling became most obvious when their precise spatial relationship to feet was established in the fast-acting muscle of toadfish swimbladder (10). In this muscle, tetrads are located exclusively in jT segments and are arranged in two rows, superimposed on the two rows of feet that occupy the junctional gap (Figure 1f,j). Profiles of feet are characteristically rotated relative to the axis of the T tubules, and tetrads have the same orientation. The images show that the four components of the tetrads are located almost exactly above the four subunits of the feet, which strongly indicates that feet and tetrads can interact with each other (perhaps through some intermediate component).

Several indirect lines of evidence favor identification of tetrads with four DHPRs. (a) DHPRs and tetrads are both located in jLM and jT tubule domains (see above); (b) tetrads are present in the surface membrane of normal mouse myotubes in vivo and in vitro, but are missing in dysgenic myotubes (46), which lack normal DHPRs (19, 90); (c) similarly, immunolabeling for DHPRs reappears in dysgenic fibers rescued by fusion with fibroblasts (35); (d) finally, but most importantly, small clusters of tetrads are present in dysgenic myotubes transfected with the cDNA for the missing DHPRs (101).

E-C Coupling Puzzles

The mechanical hypothesis of e-c coupling (96) proposes that effects of charge movement in the T tubule membrane may induce calcium release from the SR by a direct molecular interaction between components of the two membranes. Thus activation (or derepression; 27) of the calcium release channel would be a direct result of charge movement within the DHPR. Identification of tetrads with DHPRs puts the voltage sensors of e-c coupling in the appropriate position for an interaction with the feet, perhaps via some intermediate component (see below). Assuming a direct interaction, it is unclear why the four subunits of the RyR, acting as single functional unit (15, 80), should need to interact with four DHPRs (see 71 for a review).

Tetrads in toadfish muscle reveal an additional puzzle (10). The distance between tetrads is twice that between adjacent feet, i.e. tetrads are associated with alternate feet (Figure 1e, j). This is confirmed by the increased electron density of alternate feet in thin sections of toadfish muscle, presumably from the superimposition of foot profiles and alternate tetrads (C Franzini-Armstrong, unpublished observations).

The alternate disposition of tetrads is not related to the presence of two feet isoforms, since toadfish swimbladder muscle has a single ryanodine receptor isoform (86). Instead, it might simply be due to the size of the molecules involved. A tetrad, as seen in freeze-fracture, is slightly larger than a foot, and it is possible that steric hindrance limits the ability of tetrads to interact with all feet.

It is obviously important to know whether the alternate disposition of tetrads is unique to toadfish muscle. This simple question has turned out to be difficult to answer because of the uncooperative behavior of the protein constituting the tetrads, which tends to become distorted and often invisible in the fracturing process. At the moment we must rely on a limited number of observations. Ordered arrangements of tetrads have been observed in T tubules and peripheral couplings of frog slow tonic fibers (40) and in peripheral couplings of cultured human muscle (88), and rat (110), mouse (46), and chicken myotubes (102) in vivo. It is more difficult to establish a relationship between the position of tetrads and feet in peripheral couplings than in triads because the junctions are formed between an SR membrane with an ovoidal shape and the flat surface membrane, and the orientation of the array of feet underlying the tetrads is not known. It was initially suggested that tetrads in peripheral couplings of developing mouse muscle have a one-to-one relationship to feet (46). However, closer examination reveals that the disposition of tetrads in all cases cited above is most consistent with the disposition in toadfish muscle, i.e. tetrads are associated with alternate feet. Unfortunately, the ratio of tetrads to feet is not known for fibers for which crucial biochemical and physiological information is available, namely adult frog, rabbit, and rat muscle. The average ratio of DHPRs to RyRs has been reported to be approximately two in a variety of muscles (71, 9a), as expected if tetrads are composed of DHPRs and the disposition is the same as in the toadfish. However, more recent data indicate a considerably lower average ratio (as low as 0.6) in frog and rabbit (19a, see G Meissner, this volume). In addition, two triad fractions from rabbit, which have different mechanical stability, (one weaker and the other stronger), have DHPR/RyR ratios of 0.5 and 7, respectively (63). Does this mean that the disposition of tetrads in rabbit muscle varies in different areas of the same muscle and/or the same fiber? An answer to this question is important because a variable ratio of tetrads to feet would greatly weaken the direct mechanical coupling hypothesis. Clearly more information on disposition of tetrads must be obtained.

For the moment we know that an alternate disposition of tetrads is found in some muscles. The next challenge is to explain this apparent paradox. If tetrad-associated feet are activated by direct molecular interactions, then the other feet are either silent, or activated cooperatively, or activated by a totally different mechanism.

One final structural factor is important in considering the role of feet and tetrads in e-c coupling. In skeletal muscle, all arrays of feet are located at junctional sites, which is consistent with their possible role in direct transduction of the DHPR-generated signal. In muscles that depend on extracellular calcium for e-c coupling (cardiac muscle and muscles of invertebrates), on the other hand, feet may also be found in corbular or extended junctional SR membranes, which do not face surface membrane/T tubules and may be at some distance from either (24, 99). RyR identity of feet on corbular SR has been confirmed by immunolabeling (56). If these free feet participate in e-c coupling, they must be activated by some indirect mechanism. Conversely, the obligatory position of vertebrate feet in the junctional gap would indicate that skeletal muscle e-c coupling, which is independent of extracellular calcium, requires close proximity of feet to DHPR-bearing T tubule membrane.

WHAT HOLDS THE JUNCTIONAL MEMBRANES TOGETHER?

The junction between SR and surface membrane or T tubules is mechanically strong and the spacing between the two apposed membranes does not change with variations in fiber length or swelling of T tubules. Early experiments in Caswell's laboratory directly demonstrated that junctional T and SR membranes tend to adhere to each other (13). One expectation has been that DHPRs and RyRs form a complex spanning the junction. Although co-isolation of the two proteins has been achieved (66, 77), appropriate stoichiometry and structural integrity of the complex have not been demonstrated. Furthermore, interaction between DHPRs and RyRs after solubilization has not been demonstrated (12).

In the search for components of the junction that may be responsible either for holding feet and DHPRs together, or for allowing them to interact with each other, a new protein, appropriately named triadin, has been identified (17, 64). Triadin is a 95 kd glycoprotein and an abundant component of e-c units (approximately 1:1 stoichiometry with the foot protein) that forms multimeric assemblies; it is joined covalently by disulfide bonds. Its location in the terminal cisternae of the SR has been confirmed by immunocytochemistry (14, 67) (Figure 1m,q). However, the results reported by the two laboratories have led to different conclusions regarding the topology of triadin. Caswell and collaborators find that triadin binds to the foot protein and DHPR in overlays (17), that anti-triadin antibodies affect release of calcium from the SR (11), and that the location of at least one site for disulfide bonding is on the cytoplasmic side of the molecule. On that basis, they propose that triadin is the component of the junction that allows interaction between DHPRs and RyRs. Based on biochemical analysis and the deduced amino acid sequence, Campbell and collaborators propose that triadin is an integral membrane glycoprotein with a single transmembrane domain and only a short stretch (47aa) of its N_2 terminus on the cytosolic side (68). The highly basic luminal domain of triadin suggests a possible interaction with calsequestrin, perhaps by forming the strands that join it to the jSR membrane. If correct, this model implies that triadin is an unlikely candidate for mediating interaction between RyR and DHPR.

Three observations are relevant to the question of a possible intermediate component between DHPRs and RyRs, both indicating that the DHPR-RyR complex may need a third component. One such observation comes from dysgenic muscle. Despite the lack of DHPRs, dysgenic myofibers in vivo have some respectable looking triads, complete with ordered, apparently normal rows of feet (46). In addition, cultured dysgenic myotubes show well developed triads under stimulation by CGRP, despite the lack of calcium currents and continued failure of e-c coupling (47). There are two possible explanations for these findings. Either the association between feet and T tubule membrane is mediated by a protein other than DHPRs, or a different calcium channel, such as the one detected by Adams & Beam (1), substitutes for DHPRs in the formation of these triads, although such a channel does not participate in e-c coupling.

A third observation comes from a study of CHO cells co-transfected with the cDNAs for a skeletal-cardiac chimera of the DHPR and for the RyR (103). Calcium currents indicate appropriate insertion of DHPRs in the surface membrane; EM shows correct feet insertion in ER membranes; and caffeine shows function of at least a fraction of the feet. However, no tetrads are seen, and no junction is formed between the DHPR-bearing surface membrane and the feet-bearing ER, which suggests the lack of a component necessary for junction formation.

CALSEQUESTRIN

Calsequestrin, which sequesters calcium, is the major calcium-binding protein present in the lumen of the SR (73, 79). Similarly to other SR proteins, it has only two isoforms, one present in fast-twitch fibers and one present in slow-twitch fibers and cardiac muscle (22, 32). Its preferred location in the jSR cisternae has been demonstrated both by differential fractionation of heavy and light SR vesicles (79) and by in situ immunolocalization at LM and EM levels of resolution (57). Presence of calsequestrin in SR cisternae away from the junctions is rare in skeletal muscle (84), but it is frequent in muscle-derived heater tissue (B Block, this volume). Calsequestrin is bound to the inner surface of the SR by elongated structures that form periodic attachment sites at the junctional membrane (44, 99) (Figure 1j). These are presumably responsible for preventing diffusion away from the junction, as well as for the detergent-resistant association of calsequestrin with the junctional SR membrane (13). Ligand blot analyses indicate that several proteins interact with calsequestrin, but only one is calcium-dependent, a 26 kd protein in cardiac muscle and a 30–31 kd doublet in skeletal muscle (20, 82). Finally, an interaction between triadin and calsequestrin and a direct effect of calsequestrin conformation on activity of the calcium release channel have been postulated (50, 68). Further characterization of the proposed calsequestrin-binding protein(s) and of their interactions is needed before the possible involvement of calsequestrin and its linking proteins in e-c coupling can be fully assessed.

COMPARATIVE ASPECTS

Recent investigations have examined the content of ATPase and feet in three types of fibers: a slow-twitch and a fast-twitch fiber in the guinea pig, and the super-fast fibers of the swimbladder from male and female toadfish (5, 29, 43). The ATPase content rises very steeply when going from slow-twitch to fast-twitch to superfast male and female, the ratios being 1: 2.1: 16: 16.3. The content of feet, on the other hand, increases in approximate proportion to the ATPase in the two guinea pig muscles, but far less steeply in the superfast fibers, even when the myofibril-free volume of the fiber is ignored. The ratios for feet are 1: 2.5: 3.7: 4.7. Finally, the length of T tubule per fiber cross-section, which indicates the density of the network, does not vary much, the ratios being 1:1.1:1.4:1.5. However, the geometry of the fibers is such that the average distance between T tubules and the center of the myofibrils is about threefold larger in fast-twitch fibers than in the superfast ones. We conclude that overall ability to segregate calcium from the cytoplasm is of major importance in the design of muscle fibers capable of repetitive cycles of contraction at a high frequency. Note also that a short distance between T tubules and contractile material is of importance in fast fibers and that it is achieved without a large increase in T tubule surface area and a corresponding increase in capacitance.

An interesting puzzle remains in the relationship between charge movement and transverse tubules in rat muscle. Fast-twitch and slow-twitch fibers in the leg muscles differ by a factor of five to six in the maximum amount of charge movement per fiber capacitance (25, 48), while the ratio of junctional membrane to total external surface area is only a factor of two (4). There are two possibilities for this apparent discrepancy. Either the density of DHPRs (and tetrads) is lower in the jT tubules of slow-twitch vs fast-twitch fibers, or a larger portion of the charge movement results from events other than those related to e-c coupling in the fast fibers (71). This is another situation in which knowledge of the distribution of tetrads in the T tubules is crucial.

DEVELOPMENT

Assembly of E-C Coupling Units

The fairly recent identification and sequencing of several proteins of e-c units have provided new tools for studying the temporal appearance of elements involved in e-c coupling. The major proteins, calsequestrin (74), Ca^{2+}-ATPase (74), RyRs (2, 6, 76), and DHPRs (76) are upregulated at early stages of myogenesis, apparently in response to the same myogenic factors that initiate expression of muscle-specific myofibrillar proteins (6). Concurrently, de novo formation of SR and e-c units is observed, while the onset of T tubule formation occurs later (62, 102). The initial assembly of SR and e-c units, subsequent changes in their distribution, and the coordinated development of T tubules and other components of the SR occurs in several distinct phases.

Ultrastructure

PERIPHERAL COUPLINGS   The first phase, which precedes T tubule formation, is the assembly of a small number of e-c units at the periphery of the myotube. An initial loose connection between membrane elements, often continuous with rough ER, and the surface membrane (SL) has been noted in vivo (28, 102) and in vitro (76). Concurrently with upregulation of DHPR and RyR synthesis and with myofibril assembly, feet appear between apposed SR and SL (76). During in vivo development, arrays of feet and groups of tetrads appear simultaneously, and the SR content (presumably calsequestrin) acquires a specific connection to the junctional SR membrane (28, 102). Thus the formation of a loose complex between SR and SL appears to precede the formation of the peripheral coupling, and the latter involves a fairly simultaneous assembly of its three major proteins. Free SR is clearly present at these early stages (62, 102) and preferentially associated with Z lines (36).

T TUBULES   The second phase is the formation of T tubules. A variable time period (up to 9 days in chick embryos, 36, 102) separates the two phases, which indicates a specific developmental regulation of T tubule formation (36). T tubules are first detected at the periphery as individual tubules, with a predominant longitudinal orientation (Figure 2a,b,c,d,e, f,g,h). They then penetrate fairly rapidly (within 24 hrs in the chick) across the whole fiber and form a network. Caveolae may represent a starting point of T tubule formation (52).

INTERNAL E-C UNITS   The third phase, formation of internal e-c units, starts as soon as T tubules begin to form (41, 62, 102). All triads have well visible assemblies of feet and a density in the lumen of jSR, probably due to the presence of calsequestrin (28, 41, 102). The presence of tetrads has not been verified in these early triads, but the appearance of internal junctions temporally coincides with a marked increase in specific DHP binding in developing chicken muscle (compare 95 and 102) . As internal junctions form, peripheral couplings and groups of tetrads on the plasmalemma decrease dramatically (46, 62, 102).

Immunolocalization

FREE SR AND PERIPHERAL COUPLINGS   Calsequestrin, Ca^{2+}-ATPase, and RyRs appear in this sequence in cultured rat (54) and rabbit (AO Jorgensen, in preparation), mononucleated myoblasts, and in early myotubes in vivo and in vitro before T tubule formation (R Wilson & AO Jorgensen, in preparation). Interestingly, upregulation of mRNA (76), protein expression, as well as temporal appearance and distribution of RYRs and DHPRs (AO Jorgensen, in preparation) coincide. The two proteins co-distribute in discrete foci not related to the myofibril striations in myoblasts and early myotubes (AO Jorgensen, in preparation) (Figure 2 i,j,l,m). Pre-T tubule appearance of nonjunctional SR and its association with Z lines is confirmed either by immunolabeling for Ca^{2+}-ATPase (36, R Wilson & AO Jorgensen, in preparation), or by a lipid soluble fluorescent dye (36, 37).

The EM and immunolabeling results summarized above suggest that the early-formed e-c units and free SR have a structure and protein composition similar to those in the adult muscle and that the potential for internal calcium cycling is present prior to formation of T tubules.

Models of SR and E-C Unit Assembly

The distinct temporal appearance and distribution of Ca^{2+}-ATPase, calsequestrin, and RyRs in the early stages of development suggest that they travel separately to their particular target domains. Indeed, calsequestrin, but not the Ca^{2+}-ATPase, may be transported by coated vesicles (107).

SR assembly may start with the formation of a Ca^{2+}-ATPase and calsequestrin-containing membrane (74, 114), which is in continuity with the ER and contains ER as well as SR proteins (108). Some SR may become loosely apposed to the surface membrane in some parts of the cell and then become an e-c unit by assembly of feet, DHPRs, and calsequestrin (28,

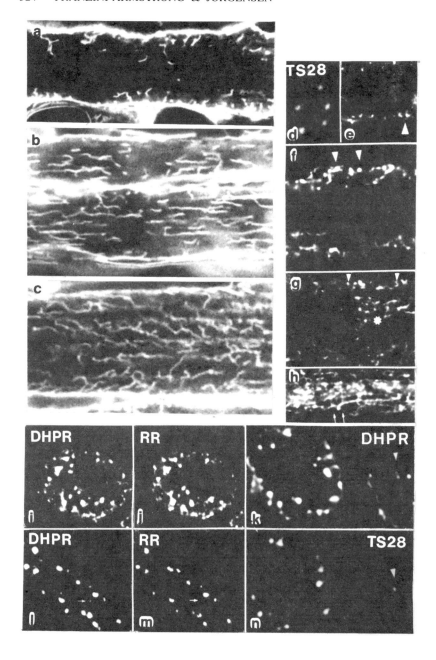

76, 102). We do not know the sequence by which this assembly occurs, but some clues are available. One is the fact that arrays of RyRs may be formed by direct lateral interactions of RyRs with each other, as indicated by the following evidence. (*a*) Arrays are maintained in isolated SR, which has been separated from T tubules, and are present at some sites not facing T tubules in cardiac muscle and muscle of some invertebrates; (*b*) arrays are formed spontaneously, and presumably in the absence of other jSR proteins, in CHO cells transfected with cDNA for RyR (103). The second, third, and fourth clues come from dysgenic muscle and indicate that association between feet and SL/T tubules does not require DHPRs, but that clustering of DHPRs at junctions requires the α_1 subunit (35, 46). Finally, EMs indicate that groups of tetrads and clusters of feet appear at the same developmental stage, and association of calsequestrin with the jSR membrane coincides with clustering of feet (28, 102).

There are at least two possible models for targeting of DHPRs and RyRs to junctional membranes that face each other. One model proposes that a complex between the two vesicles, which contain DHPRs and RyRs respectively, fuses simultaneously with the loosely apposed SR and the SL, thus leading to the assembly of an e-c unit. Visualization of internal foci of apposed RyRs and DHPRs not associated with T tubules (112) (Figure 2k,n) would favor this hypothesis, although α_1 and α_2 DHPR subunits are clearly not essential for the formation of a complex between the two vesicles. The

----

Figure 2   Biogenesis of T tubules and triads in developing skeletal muscle. (*a,b,c*) Gradual formation of T tubules from periphery to center of fiber and longitudinal orientation of early T tubules is demonstrated in scanning confocal images of mouse diaphragm at embryonal day 15 (*a*); 16 (*b*) and 17 (*c*). (*a*) Magnification: × 1400; *b,c* × 2000 (BE Flucher & Franzini-Armstrong, unpublished observations).

(*d,e,f,g,h*) Immunofluorescence imaging of TS28, a T tubule-specific antigen in developing rabbit muscle in vivo. The protein is first seen in discrete loci at the cell surface (*d,e,f, arrowheads*, embryonic day 17) and later in longitudinally oriented internal tubules (*g, asterisk*, embryonic day 24; *h, arrows*, newborn). Similarity between DiI (*a-c*) and TS28 (*d-h*) patterns indicates that TS28 is incorporated in T tubules at the onset of their formation and from the periphery inward. (*d* Magnification: × 2400; *e-h*, × 1700 (*d-g* reproduced from 111; *h* from 112).

(*i-n*) Scanning confocal images showing double labeling for T tubules and junctional proteins. *i,j* and *l,m* show colocalization of DHPR and RyR in discrete foci in developing muscle in vivo (*i,j*, embryonic day 24) and in vitro (*l,m*, day 3 in culture). This suggests that e-c coupling units or their precursors form very early. (*k-n*) Some, but not all, α_1-DHPR positive foci colocalize with TS28-positive structures in early development. This indicates that some RR/DHPR complexes may represent precursors of e-c coupling units that are not associated with T tubules. (*i-k,n* magnification: × 1900; *l,m* × 1200) (*i,j*, W Arnold, AO Jorgensen, unpublished observations; *l,m*, W Arnold, AO Jorgensen, in preparation; *k,n* reproduced from 112).

second model suggests that RyRs and DHPRs are initially inserted in SR and SL membranes independently, at such a low density that they are not detectable by immunolabeling. Formation of an e-c unit would occur when RyRs assemble into arrays, adhere to the SL (perhaps via an intermediate component), and induce clustering of DHPRs and association of calsequestrin with the jSR. The apparent self-assembly capacity of RyRs, and the simultaneous assembly of feet, tetrads, and calsequestrin are consistent with the second model.

T Tubules

Once T tubules form in most vertebrate twitch fibers, there is a shift from peripheral e-c units at the SL, to internal ones at T tubules (41, 62, 102), and DHPRs are relegated to the latter (93). This is part of a common pattern of segregation that results in a unique protein profile for T tubules and SL (53, 87, 111). It is likely that characterization of the structure, function, and temporal appearance of proteins specific to these two domains will provide clues to the mechanisms insuring specific targeting of DHPRs.

On the basis of EM studies, two models have been proposed for the formation of T tubules. One is by direct fusion of vesicles carrying T tubule-specific proteins to preformed caveolae (the "add-on" model, 94). The second is by invagination of the surface membrane (52). Note that the latter mechanism requires a flow of proteins to T tubules via the surface membrane. Comparison of the temporal appearance of a T tubule-specific antigen (TS28) in situ and in vitro with EM images and DiI labeling of the T tubules (112, AO Jorgensen, in preparation), indicates that the antigen is segregated in the T tubules from their onset and thus may be directly incorporated into them. Immunolocalization of other markers of adult T tubules and DHPRs (112, AO Jorgensen, in preparation) indicates different temporal appearances and distributions, which implies that their incorporation in developing T tubules involves distinct transport vesicles and that some mechanism for targeting to specific domains is needed. For DHPRs this may simply be the result of interaction with other components of e-c units.

A third hypothesis of T tubule formation derives from the observation that a polyclonal antibody against T tubules recognizes an internal network in cultured myoblasts and myotubes before a T network continuous with the plasmalemma is demonstrated by DiI labeling (37). This suggests that a preformed internal network would fuse with the plasmalemma to form T tubules. However, the hypothesis is inconsistent with the gradual growth in length of the tubules from the periphery inward.

DHPRs and RyRs colocalize in early stages of myogenesis, and most foci are either located at the periphery, or associated with discrete domains of TS28-positive T tubules (112, AO Jorgensen, in preparation). These represent peripheral couplings and triads respectively. However, some internal foci are not in proximity of a TS28-positive tubule, which suggests a junction between a RyR-containing membrane and an internal DHPR vesicle that is not continuous with a T tubule (AO Jorgensen, in preparation). Such a complex could act as a precursor of an e-c unit, as proposed above.

Dysgenic Muscle

Dysgenic muscle fibers offer some clues to the questions of the role played by DHPRs in the assembly of peripheral couplings and triads. The mutant expresses almost normal levels of α_2DHPR, RyR, Ca^{2+}-ATPase, and calsequestrin, but α_1DHPR is not detectable by antibodies (65), and tetrads are not present (46). Nonetheless, dysgenic muscle fibers form some peripheral couplings at early developmental stages and triads once the T tubules develop (46, 89). Thus α_1DHPR is not needed for formation and targeting of the junctions. So far there is no evidence that any of the three known DHPR isoforms are regulated coincidentally with the transition between peripheral and internal e-c units (23, 75). However, α_1DHPR is apparently needed for targeting of α_2 to the e-c units (35), and the lower density of e-c units in dysgenic muscle suggests a role for α_1 DHPR in stabilizing the junctions.

We do not know whether RyRs play a role in targeting e-c units to SL or T tubules. If a loose association between SR and surface/T tubules precedes clustering of RyRs, then targeting would be independent of either RyRs or DHPRs in both models of junction formation presented above. Developmental regulation of RyR isoforms has so far been demonstrated only in chicken muscles (100).

Maturation

The final step in the development of the membrane system is a rearrangement of the initially disordered SR and T tubules, which results in specific locations of triads, a transverse T network, and a differentiated shape of the free SR and fiber type-specific arrangements of membranes (see 42 for review). This is a slow process, which usually extends through several weeks after birth. Increase in rate of expression of RyR, a marker of jSR membrane, is faster than that of ATPase, a representative of the free SR (58), in early postnatal chicken muscle (21).

Some Remaining Questions

This description of morphogenetic events in the differentiation of muscle membranes raises several questions. We do not know what mechanisms are responsible for assembly of e-c units and for differential targeting of DHPRs once T tubules develop. It is tempting to speculate that some protein uniquely associated with T tubules may be essential for the latter in a manner analogous to that proposed for targeting of synaptic vesicles (98).

Another question is the mechanism of formation of T tubules. Several possibilities have been proposed from the formation of an internal network, which later opens to the outside, to a gradual accrual of lipid and protein-carrying vesicles, which carry newly synthesized product directly to the T tubules, to a simple growth by invagination from the surface membrane. The various hypotheses have important implications for the mechanism whereby the T tubules acquire their unique components and segregate them from those of the surface membrane (53, 87). The current static images do not allow final resolution of this question. Treatment of developing muscle with metabolic inhibitors and antisense mRNAs to proteins considered essential for the formation of e-c units should begin to provide some answers.

A third question not addressed in this review is how the precise location and reorientation of triads is controlled (see 33).

Finally, formation of T tubules coincides with a large increase in the number of calcium release units (28, 41, 62, 102). Is there a burst in expression of the required proteins, or are the proteins available in some internal pool? In chicken the transition is quite abrupt, which suggests that it is a good model for further inquiry.

WHAT REMAINS TO BE DONE?

The next step in the structure-composition-function correlation is the identification and characterization of additional components uniquely associated with the interacting junctional membranes. Comparative and developmental studies suggest that a protein that is a functional component of e-c units should be found in peripheral couplings as well as in triads/dyads. Cherchez la femme!

Literature Cited

1. Adams BA, Beam KG. 1989. A novel calcium current in dysgenic skeletal muscle. *J. Gen. Physiol.* 94:429–44

1a. Adams BA, Tanabe T, Mikami A, Numa S, Beam KG. 1990. Intramembrane charge movement restored in dysgenic skeletal muscle by injection of dihydropyridine receptor cDNAs. *Nature* 346:569–72

2. Airey JA, Baring MD, Sutko JL. 1991. Ryanodine receptor protein is expressed during differentiation in the muscle cell lines BC3H1 and C2C12. *Dev. Biol.* 148:365–74

3. Airey JA, Beck CF, Murakami K, Tanksley SJ, Deerinck J, et al. 1990. Identification and localization of two triad junction foot protein isoforms in mature avian fast twitch skeletal muscle. *J. Biol. Chem.* 265:14187–94

4. Appelt D, Buenviaje B, Champ C, Franzini-Armstrong C. 1989. Quantitation of feet content in two types of muscle fibers from hind limb of the rat. *Tissue Cell* 21:783–94

5. Appelt D, Shen V, Franzini-Armstrong C. 1991. Quantitation of Ca ATPase, feet and mitochondria in super fast

muscle fibres from the toadfish, *Opsanus tau*. *J. Muscle Res. Cell Motil.* 12:543–52

6. Arai M, Otsu K, MacLennan DH, Periasamy M. 1992. Regulation of sarcoplasmic reticulum expression during cardiac and skeletal muscle development. *Am. J. Physiol.* 262:C614–20

7. Ashley CC, Mulligan IP, Lea TJ. 1991. Ca^{2+} and activation mechanisms in skeletal muscle. *Q. Rev. Biophys.* 24:1–73

7a. Beam KG, Adams BA, Niidome T, Numa S, Tanabe T. 1992. Function of a truncated dihydropyridine receptor as both voltage sensor and calcium channel. *Nature* 360:169–71

8. Beam KG, Knudson CM, Powell JA. 1986. A lethal mutation in mice eliminates the slow calcium current in skeletal muscle cells. *Nature* 320:168–70

9. Benterbusch R, Herberg FW, Melzer W, Thieleczek R. 1992. Excitation-contraction coupling in a pre-vertebrate twitch muscle: the myotomes of *Branchiostoma lanceolatum*. *J. Membr. Biol.* 129:237–52

9a. Bers DM, Stiffel VM. 1993 Ratio of ryanodine and dihydropyridine receptors in cardiac and skeletal muscle and implications for excitation-contraction coupling. *Am. J. Physiol.* 264:C1587–93

10. Block BA, Imagawa T, Leung A, Campbell P, Franzini-Armstrong C. 1988. Structural evidence for direct interaction between the molecular components of the transverse tubules/sarcoplasmic reticulum junction in skeletal muscle. *J. Cell Biol.* 107:2587–2600

11. Brandt NR, Caswell AH, Brunschwig JP, Kang JJ, Antoniu B, Ikemoto N. 1992. Effects of anti-triadin antibody on Ca^{2+} release from sarcoplasmic reticulum. *FEBS Lett.* 299:57–59

12. Brandt NR, Caswell AH, Wen SR, Talvenheimo JA. 1990. Molecular interactions of the junctional foot protein and dihydropyridine receptor in skeletal muscle triads. *J. Membr. Biol.* 113:237–51

13. Brunschwig JP, Brandt NR, Caswell AH, Lukeman DS. 1982. Ultrastructural observations of isolated intact and fragmented junctions of skeletal muscle by use of tannic acid mordating. *J. Cell Biol.* 93:533–42

13a. Campbell KP, Leung AT, Sharp AH. 1988. The biochemistry and molecular biology of the dihydropyridine-sensitive calcium channel. *Trends Neurosci.* 11:425–30

14. Carl SL, Caswell AH, Ball JW, Meissner G, Brandt N, et al. 1992. Immunofluorescent localization of triadin, DHP receptor and ryanodine receptor in skeletal and heart muscle. *Biophys. J.* 61:A161

15. Carroll S, Skarmeta JG, Yu X, Collins KD, Inesi G. 1991. Interdependence of ryanodine binding, oligomeric receptor interactions, and Ca^{2+} release regulation in junctional sarcoplasmic reticulum. *Arch. Biochem. Biophys.* 290:239–47

16. Caswell AH, Brandt NR. 1989. Does muscle activation occur by direct mechanical coupling of transverse tubules to sarcoplasmic reticulum? *Trends Biochem. Sci.* 14:161–65

17. Caswell AH, Brandt NR, Brunschwig JP, Purkerson S. 1991. Localization and partial characterization of the oligomeric disulfide-linked molecular weight 95,000 protein (triadin) which binds the ryanodine and dihydropyridine receptors in skeletal muscle triadic vesicles. *Biochemistry* 30:7507–13

18. Catterall WA. 1991. Excitation-contraction coupling in vertebrate skeletal muscle: a tale of two calcium channels. *Cell* 64:871–74

19. Chaudhari N. 1992. A single nucleotide deletion in the skeletal muscle specific calcium channel transcript of muscular dysgenesis (mdg) mice. *J. Biol. Chem.* 267:25636–39

19a. Cohn AH, Anderson K, Meissner G. 1993. High affinity [^{3}H]PN200-100 and [^{3}H]ryanodine binding to rabbit and frog skeletal muscle homogenates. *Biophys. J.* 64:A152

20. Damiani E, Margreth A. 1990. Specific protein-protein interactions of calsequestrin with junctional sarcoplasmic reticulum of skeletal muscle. *Biochem. Biophys. Res. Commun.* 172:1253–59

21. Damiani E, Tarugi P, Calandra S, Margreth A. 1992. Sequential expression during postnatal development of specific markers of junctional and free sarcoplasmic reticulum in chicken pectoralis muscle. *Dev. Biol.* 153:102–14

22. Damiani E, Volpe P, Margreth A. 1990. Coexpression of two isoforms of calsequestrin in rabbit slow-twitch muscle. *J. Muscle Res. Cell Motil.* 11:522–30

22a. DeJongh KS, Warner C, Catterall WA. 1990. Subunits of purified calcium channels. Alpha2 and delta are encoded by the same gene. *J. Biol. Chem.* 265:14738–41

23. DeJongh KS, Warner C, Colvin AA, Catterall WA. 1991. Characterization of the two size forms of the alpha 1 subunit of skeletal muscle L-type calcium channels. *Proc. Natl. Acad. Sci. USA* 88(23):10778–82

24. Dolber PC, Sommer JR. 1984. Corbular sarcoplasmic reticulum of rabbit cardiac muscle. *J. Ultrastruc. Res.* 87:190–96

25. Dulhunty AF, Gage P. 1985. Excitation-contraction coupling and charge movement in denervated rat extensor digitorum longus and soleus muscle. *J. Physiol.* 358:75–89

26. Dulhunty AF, Junankar PR, Stanhope C. 1992. Extra-junctional ryanodine receptors in the terminal cisternae of mammalian skeletal muscle fibres. *Proc. R. Soc. London Ser. B* 247:69–75

27. Ebashi, S. 1991 Excitation-contraction coupling and the mechanism of muscle contraction. *Annu. Rev. Physiol.* 53:1–16

28. Edge MB. 1970. Development of apposed sarcoplasmic reticulum at the T system and sarcolemma and the change in orientation of triads in skeletal muscle. *Dev. Biol.* 23:634–50

28a. Ellis SB, Williams ME, Ways NR, Brenner R, Sharp AH, et al. 1988. Sequence and expression of mRNAs encoding the alpha1 and alpha2 subunits of a DHP-sensitive calcium channel. *Science* 241:1661–64

29. Ferguson DG, Franzini-Armstrong C. 1988. The Ca ATPase content of slow and fast twitch fibers of guinea pig. *Muscle Nerve* 11:561–70

30. Ferguson DG, Schwartz H, Franzini-Armstrong C. 1984. Subunit structure of junctional feet in triads of skeletal muscle. A freeze-drying, rotary-shadowing study. *J. Cell Biol.* 99:1735–42

31. Ferris CD, Snyder SH. 1992. Inositol 1,4,5-trisphosphate activated calcium channels. *Annu. Rev. Physiol.* 54:469–88

32. Fliegel L, Leberer E, Green NM, MacLennan DH. 1989. The fast-twitch muscle calsequestrin isoform predominates in rabbit slow-twitch soleus muscle. *FEBS Lett.* 242:297–300

33. Flucher BE. 1992. Structural analysis of muscle development: transverse tubules, sarcoplasmic reticulum, and the triad. *Dev. Biol.* 154:245–60

34. Flucher BE, Morton ME, Friehner SC, Daniels MP. 1990. Localization of the alpha1 and alpha2 subunits of the dihydropyridine receptor and ankyrin in skeletal muscle. *Neuron* 5:339–51

35. Flucher BE, Phillips JL, Powell JA. 1991. Dihydropyridine receptor alpha subunits in normal and dysgenic muscle in vitro: expression of alpha1 is required for proper targeting and distribution of alpha2. *J. Cell Biol.* 115:1345–56

36. Flucher BE, Takekura H, Franzini-Armstrong C. 1993. Development of the excitation-contraction coupling apparatus in skeletal muscle: II Association of the sarcoplasmic reticulum and transverse tubules with myofibrils. *Dev. Biol.* 160: In press

37. Flucher BE, Terasaki M, Chin HM, Beeler TJ, Daniels MP. 1991. Biogenesis of transverse tubules in skeletal muscle in vitro. *Dev. Biol.* 145:77–95

38. Formelova J, Hurnak O, Novotova M, Zachar J. 1990. Ryanodine receptor purified from crayfish skeletal muscle. *Gen. Physiol. Biophys.* 9:445–53

39. Fosset, M, Jaimovich E, Delpont E, Lazdunski M. 1983. [^{3}H] Nitrendipine receptors in skeletal muscle: properties and preferential location in transverse tubules. *J. Biol. Chem.* 258:6086–92

40. Franzini-Armstrong C. 1984. Freeze-fracture of frog slow tonic fibers. Structure of surface and internal membranes. *Tissue Cell* 16:146–66

41. Franzini-Armstrong C. 1991. Simultaneous maturation of transverse tubules and sarcoplasmic reticulum during muscle differentiation in the mouse. *Dev. Biol.* 146:353–63

42. Franzini-Armstrong C. 1994. The sarcoplasmic reticulum and transverse tubules. In *Myology*, ed. AG Engel, C Franzini-Armstrong. New York: McGraw Hill In press

43. Franzini-Armstrong C, Ferguson DG, Champ C. 1988. Discrimination between fast- and slow-twitch fibres of guinea pig skeletal muscle using the relative surface density of junctional transverse tubule membrane. *J. Muscle. Res. Cell Motil.* 9:403–14

44. Franzini-Armstrong C, Kenney LJ, Varriano-Marston E. 1987. The structure of calsequestrin in triads of vertebrate skeletal muscle: a deep etch study. *J. Cell Biol.* 105:49–56

45. Franzini-Armstrong C, Nunzi G. 1983. Junctional feet and particles in the triads of a fast-twitch muscle fibre. *J. Muscle Res. Cell Motil.* 4:233–52

46. Franzini-Armstrong C, Pincon-Raymond M, Rieger F. 1991. Muscle fibers from dysgenic mouse in vivo lack a surface component of peripheral couplings. *Dev. Biol.* 146:364–76

47. Garcia L, Pincon-Raymond M, Romey G, Changeux JP, Lazdunski M, Rieger F. 1990. Induction of normal ultra-

structure by CGRP treatment in dysgenic myotubes. *FEBS Lett.* 263:147–52

47a. Glueckson-Waelsch S. 1963. Lethal genes and analysis of differentiation. *Science* 142:1269–76

48. Hollingworth S, Marshall MM. 1981. A comparative study of charge movement in frog skeletal muscle fibres. *J. Physiol.* 312:583–602

49. Huxley AF. 1971. The activation of striated muscle and its contractile response. *Proc. R. Soc. London Ser. B* 178:1–27

50. Ikemoto N, Ronjat M, Meszaros LG, Koshita M. 1989. Postulated role of calsequestrin in the regulation of calcium release from sarcoplasmic reticulum. *Biochemistry* 28:6764–71

51. Inui M, Saito A, Fleischer S. 1987. Purification of the ryanodine receptor and identity with foot structure of junctional terminal cisternae of sarcoplasmic reticulum from fast muscle. *J. Biol. Chem.* 262:1740–47

52. Ishikawa H. 1968. Formation of elaborate networks of T-system tubules in cultured skeletal muscle with special reference to the T-system formation. *J. Cell Biol.* 38:51–66

52a. Jay SD, Sharp AH, Kahl SD, Vedvick TS, Harnold MM, Campbell KP. 1991. Structural characterization of the dihydropyridine-sensitive $alpha_2$ subunit and the associated delta peptides. *J. Biol. Chem.* 266:3287–93

53. Jorgensen AO, Arnold W, Shen AC-Y, Yuan S, Gaver M, Campbell KP. 1990. Identification of novel proteins unique to either transverse tubules (TS28) or the sarcolemma (SL50) in rabbit skeletal muscle. *J. Cell Biol.* 110:1173–85

54. Jorgensen AO, Kalnins VI, Zubrzycka E, MacLennan DH. 1977. Assembly of the sarcoplasmic reticulum: localization by immunofluorescence of sarcoplasmic reticulum proteins in differentiating rat skeletal muscle cell cultures. *J. Cell Biol.* 74:287–98

55. Jorgensen AO, Shen AC-Y, Arnold W, Leung AT, Campbell KT. 1989. Subcellular distribution of the 1,4-dihydropyridine receptor in rabbit skeletal muscle in situ: an immunofluorescence and immunogold labeling study. *J. Cell. Biol.* 109:135–47

56. Jorgensen AO, Shen AC-Y, Arnold W, McPherson PS, Campbell KP. 1993. The Ca^{2+}-release channel/ryanodine receptor is localized in junctional and corbular sarcoplasmic reticulum in cardiac muscle. *J. Cell Biol.* 120:969–80

57. Jorgensen AO, Shen AC-Y, Campbell KP, MacLennan DH. 1983. Ultrastructural localization of calsequestrin in rat skeletal muscle by immunoferritin labeling of ultrathin frozen sections. *J. Cell Biol.* 97:1573–81

58. Jorgensen AO, Shen AC-Y, MacLennan DH, Tokuyasu KT. 1982. Ultrastructural localization of the Ca^{2+} + Mg^{2+}-dependent ATPase of sarcoplasmic reticulum in rat skeletal muscle by immunoferritin labeling of ultrathin frozen sections. *J. Cell Biol.* 92:409–16

59. Deleted in proof

60. Kawamoto RM, Brunschwig J-P, Caswell AH. 1988. Localization by immunoelectron microscopy of spanning protein of triad junction in terminal cisternae/triad vesicles. *J. Muscle Res. Cell Motil.* 9:334–43

61. Kawamoto RM, Brunschwig J-P, Kim KC, Caswell AH. 1986. Isolation, characterization and localization of the spanning protein from skeletal muscle triads. *J. Cell Biol.* 103:1405–14

62. Kelly AM. 1971. Sarcoplasmic reticulum and T tubules in differentiating rat skeletal muscle. *J. Cell Biol.* 49:335–44

63. Kim KC, Caswell AH, Brunschwig JP, Brandt NR. 1990. Identification of a new subpopulation of triad junctions isolated from skeletal muscle; morphological correlations with intact muscle. *J. Membr. Biol.* 113:221–35

64. Kim KC, Caswell AH, Talvenheimo JA, Brandt NR. 1990. Isolation of a terminal cisterna protein which may link the dihydropyridine receptor to the junctional foot protein in skeletal muscle. *Biochemistry* 29:9283–89

65. Knudson CM, Chaudari N, Sharp AH, Powell JA, Beam KG, Campbell KP. 1989. Specific absence of the $alpha_1$ subunit of the dihydropyridine receptor in mice with muscular dysgenesis. *J. Biol. Chem.* 264:1345–48

66. Knudson CM, Imagawa T, Kahl SD, Gaver MG, Leung AT, et al. 1988. Evidence for physical association between junctional sarcoplasmic reticulum ryanodine receptor and junctional transverse tubule dihydropyridine receptor. *Biophys. J.* 53:605a

67. Knudson CM, Stang KK, Jorgensen A, Campbell KP. 1993. Biochemical characterization and ultrastructural localization of a major junctional sarcoplasmic reticulum glycoprotein (triadin). *J. Biol. Chem.* 268: In press

68. Knudson CM, Stang KK, Moomaw CR, Slaugther C, Campbell KP. 1993. Primary structure and topological anal-

ysis of a skeletal muscle specific, junctional sarcoplasmic reticulum glycoprotein (triadin). *J. Biol. Chem.* 268: In press

68a. Lacerda AE, Kim HS, Ruth P, Perez-Reyes E, Flockerzi V, et al. 1991. Normalization of current kinetics by interaction between alpha$_1$ and beta subunits of the skeletal muscle dihydropyridine-sensitive calcium channel. *Nature* 352:527–30

69. Lai FA, Erickson HP, Rousseau E, Liu Q-Y, Meissner G. 1988. Purification and reconstitution of the calcium release channel from skeletal muscle. *Nature* 331:315–19

70. Lai FA, Meissner G. 1990. Structure of the calcium release channel of skeletal muscle sarcoplasmic reticulum and its regulation by calcium. *Adv. Exp. Med. Biol.* 269:73–77

71. Lamb DG. 1992. DHP receptors and excitation-contraction coupling. *J. Muscle Res. Cell Motil.* 13:394–405

72. Loesser KE, Castellani L, Franzini-Armstrong C. 1992. Disposition of junctional feet in muscles of invertebrates. *J. Muscle Res. Cell Motil.* 13:161–73

73. MacLennan DH, Wong PTS. 1971. Isolation of a calcium-sequestering protein from sarcoplasmic reticulum. *Proc. Natl. Acad. Sci. USA* 68:1231–35

74. MacLennan DH, Zubrzycka-Gaarn E, Jorgensen AO. 1985. Assembly of the sarcoplasmic reticulum during muscle development. *Curr. Topics Membr. Trans.* 24:337–68

75. Malouf NN, McMahon DK, Hainsworth CN, Kay BK. 1992. A two-motif isoform of the major channel subunit in skeletal muscle. *Neuron* 8:899–906

76. Marks AR, Taubman MB, Saito A, Dai Y, Fleischer S. 1991. The ryanodine receptor/junctional channel complex is regulated by growth factors in a myogenic cell line. *J. Cell Biol.* 114: 303–12

77. Marty I, Robert M, Villaz M, Lai Y, Catterall WA, Ronjat M. 1993. Isolation of a complex of dihydropyridine receptor and ryanodine receptor from triad junctions of skeletal muscle. *Biophys. J.* 65:153a

78. McPherson PS, Campbell KP. 1993. The ryanodine receptor/Ca^{2+} release channel. *J. Biol. Chem.* In press

79. Meissner G. 1975. Isolation and characterization of two types of sarcoplasmic reticulum vesicles. *Biochim. Biophys. Acta* 389:51–68

80. Meissner G. 1992. Ligand binding and cooperative interactions among the subunits of the tetrameric Ca^{2+} release channel complex of sarcoplasmic reticulum. *Adv. Exp. Med. Biol.* 311: 277–87

80a. Mikami A, Imoto K, Tanabe T, Niidome T, Mori Y, et al. 1989. Primary structure and functional expression of the cardiac dihydropyridine-sensitive calcium channel. *Nature* 340:230–36

81. Mitchell RD, Saito A, Palade P, Fleischer S. 1983. Morphology of isolated triads. *J. Cell Biol.* 96:1017–29

82. Mitchell RD, Simmerman HKB, Jones LR. 1988. Ca^{2+} binding affects protein conformation and protein interactions of canine cardiac calsequestrin. *J. Biol. Chem.* 263:1376–81

82a. Morton ME, Caffrey JM, Brown AM, Froehner SC. 1988. Monoclonal antibody to the alpha$_1$ subunit of the dihydropyridine-binding complex inhibits calcium currents in BC3H1 myocytes. *J. Biol. Chem.* 263:613–16

83. Nakayama H, Taki M, Striessnig J, Glossmann H, Catterall WA, Kanaoka Y. 1991. Identification of 1,4-dihydropyridine binding regions within the alpha$_1$ subunit of skeletal muscle Ca^{2+} channels by photoaffinity labeling with diazipine. *Proc. Natl. Acad. Sci. USA* 88:9203–7

84. Nassar R, Wallace NR, Taylor I, Sommer JR. 1986. The quick-freezing of single intact muscle fibers at known time intervals following electrical stimulation. *Scanning EM* I:309–28

85. Numa S, Tanabe T, Takeshima H, Mikami A, Niidome T, et al. 1990. Molecular insights into excitation-contraction coupling. *Cold Spring Harbor Symp. Q. Biol.* 55:1–7

86. O'Brien J, Block BA. 1993. The fastest contracting skeletal muscles of non-mammalian vertebrates express only one isoform of the ryanodine receptor. *Biophys. J.* 64:304a

87. Ohlendieck K, Ervasti JM, Snook JB, Campbell KP. 1991. Dystrophin-glycoprotein complex is highly enriched in isolated skeletal muscle sarcolemma. *J. Cell Biol.* 112:135–48

88. Osame M, Engel AG, Rebouche CJ, Scott RE. 1981. Freeze-fracture electron microscopic analysis of plasma membranes of cultured muscle cells in Duchenne dystrophy. *Neurology* 31: 972–79

88a. Perez-Reyes E, Castellano A, Kim HS, Bertrand P, Baggstrom E, et al. 1992.

Induction of calcium currents by the expression of the alpha$_1$ subunit of the dihydropyridine receptor from skeletal muscle. *J. Biol. Chem* 267:1792–97

89. Pincon-Raymond M, Rieger F, Fosset M, Lazdunski M. 1985. Abnormal transverse tubule system and abnormal amount of receptors for Ca^{2+} channel inhibitors of the dihydropyridine family in skeletal muscle from mice with embryonic muscular dysgenesis. *Dev. Biol.* 112:458–66

90. Powell JA. 1990. Muscular dysgenesis: a model system for studying skeletal muscle development. *FASEB J.* 4: 2798–808

90a. Powell JA, Fambrough DM. 1973. Electrical properties of normal and dysgenic mouse skeletal muscle in culture. *J. Gen. Physiol.* 82:21–38

91. Radermacher M, Wagenknecht T, Grassucci R, Frank J, Inui M, et al. 1992. Cryo-EM of the native structure of the calcium release channel/ryanodine receptor from sarcoplasmic reticulum. *Biophys. J.* 61:936–40

91a. Rieger F, Pincon-Raymond M, Tassin AM, Garcia L, Romey G, et al. 1987. Excitation-contraction uncoupling in the developing skeletal muscle of the muscular dysgenesis mouse embryo. *Biochimie* 69:411–17

92. Rios E, Ma J, Gonzalez A. 1991. The mechanical hypothesis of excitation-contraction coupling. *J. Muscle Res. Cell Motil.* 12:127–35

93. Romey G, Garcia L, Dimitriadou V, Pincon-Raymond M, Rieger F, Lazdunski M. 1989. Ontogensis and localization of the Ca^{2+} channels in mammalian skeletal muscle in culture and role in excitation-contraction coupling. *Proc. Natl. Acad. Sci. USA* 86:2933–37

93a. Ruth P, Rohkasten A, Biel M, Bosse E, Regulla S, et al. 1989. Primary structure of the beta subunit of the DHP-sensitive calcium channel from skeletal muscle. *Science* 245:1115–18

94. Schiaffino S, Cantini M, Sartore S. 1977. T-system formation in cultured rat skeletal tissue. *Tissue Cell* 9:437–46

95. Schmid A, Renaud JF, Fosset M, Meaux JP, Lazdunski M. 1984. The nitrendipine-sensitive Ca^{2+} channel in chick muscle cells and its appearance during myogenesis in vivo and in vitro. *J. Biol. Chem.* 259:11366–72

96. Schneider MF, Chandler, WK.1973. Voltage dependent charge movement in skeletal muscle: a possible step in excitation-contraction coupling. *Nature* 242:747–51

97. Seok JH, Xu L, Kramarcy NR, Sealock R, Meissner G. 1992. The 30S lobster skeletal muscle Ca^{2+} release channel (ryanodine receptor) has functional properties distinct from the mammalian channel proteins. *J. Biol. Chem.* 267: 15893–901

98. Sollner T, Whiteheart W, Brunner M, Erdjumenyt-Bromage H, Geromanso S, et al. 1993. SNAP receptors implicated in vesicle targeting and fusion. *Nature* 362:318–23

99. Sommer JR, Bossen E, Dalen H, Dolber P, High T, et al. 1991. To excite a heart: a bird's view. *Acta Physiol. Scand.* S599:5–21

100. Sutko JL, Airey JA, Murakami K, Takeda M, Beck C, et al. 1991. Foot protein isoforms are expressed at different times during embryonic chick skeletal muscle development. *J. Cell Biol.* 113:793–803

101. Takekura H, Bennett L, Tanabe T, Beam K, Franzini-Armstrong C. 1993. Tetrads are restored in dysgenic myotubes transfected with cDNA for skeletal DHPR. *Biophys. J.* 64:241a

102. Takekura H, Franzini-Armstrong C. 1994. Development of the excitation-contraction coupling apparatus in skeletal muscle. I. Peripheral and internal calcium release units are formed sequentially. *J. Muscle Res. Cell Motil.* In press

103. Takekura H, Takeshima H, Nishimura S, Takahashi M, Tanabe T, et al.1993. Co-expression of ryanodine and dihydropyridine receptors is not sufficient to form a junction. *Biophys. J.* 64:153a

104. Takeshida H, Nishimura S, Matsumoto T, Ishida H, Kangawa, K, et al. 1989. Primary structure and expression from complementary DNA of skeletal muscle ryanodine receptor. *Nature* 339:439–45

104a. Tanabe T, Adams BA, Numa S, Beam KG. 1991. Repeat I of dihydropyridine receptors is critical in determining calcium channel activation kinetics. *Nature* 352:800–3

105. Tanabe T, Beam KG, Adams BA, Nicodome T, Numa S. 1990. Regions of the skeletal muscle dihydropyridine receptor critical for excitation-contraction coupling. *Nature* 346:567–69

106. Tanabe T, Beam KG, Powell JA, Numa S. 1988. Restoration of excitation-contraction coupling and slow calcium current in dysgenic muscle by

dihydropyridine receptor complementary DNA. *Nature* 336:134–39

106a. Tanabe T, Mikami A, Numa S, Beam KG. 1990. Cardiac-type excitation-contraction coupling in dysgenic skeletal muscle injected with cardiac dihydropyridine receptor cDNA. *Nature* 344: 451–53

106b. Tanabe T, Takeshima H, Mikami A, Flockerzi V, Takahashi H, et al. 1987. Primary structure of the receptor for calcium channel blockers from skeletal muscle. *Nature* 328:313–18

107. Thomas K, Navarro J, Benson RJJ, Campbell KP, Rotundo RL, Fine RE. 1989. Newly synthesized calsequestrin, destined for the sarcoplasmic reticulum, is contained in early/intermediate Golgi-derived clathrin-coated vesicles. *J. Biol. Chem.* 264:3140–45

108. Volpe P, Martini A, Nori A. 1992. The sarcoplasmic reticulum of skeletal muscle: a look from inside. *Adv. Exp. Med. Biol.* 311:263–75

109. Wagenknecht T, Grassucci R, Frank J, Saito A, Inui M, Fleischer S. 1989. Three-dimensional architecture of the calcium channel/foot structure of sarcoplasmic reticulum. *Nature* 338:167–70

110. Yiping L, Appelt D, Kelly AM,

Franzini-Armstrong C. 1992. Differences in the histogenesis of EDL and diaphragm in rat. *Dev. Dynamics* 193: 359-369

111. Yuan S, Arnold W, Jorgensen AO. 1990. Biogenesis of transverse tubules: immunocytochemical localization of a transverse tubular protein (SL50) in rabbit skeletal muscle developing in situ. *J. Cell Biol.* 110:1187–98

112. Yuan S, Arnold W, Jorgensen AO. 1991. Biogenesis of transverse tubules and triads: immunolocalization of the 1,4-dihydropyridine receptor, TS28, and the ryanodine receptor in rabbit skeletal muscle developing in situ. *J. Cell Biol.* 112:289–301

113. Zorzato F, Fujii J, Otsu K, Phillips M, Green NM, et al. 1990. Molecular cloning of cDNA encoding human and rabbit forms of the Ca^{2+} release channel (ryanodine receptor) of skeletal muscle sarcoplasmic reticulum. *J. Biol. Chem.* 265:2244–56

114. Zubrzycka-Gaarn E, Campbell KP, MacLennan DH, Jorgensen AO. 1983. Biosynthesis of intrinsic sarcoplasmic reticulum proteins during differentiation of the myogenic cell line L6. *J. Biol. Chem.* 258:4576–81

Annu. Rev. Physiol. 1994. 56:535–77
Copyright © 1994 by Annual Reviews Inc. All right reserved

THERMOGENESIS IN MUSCLE

Barbara A. Block

Stanford University, Department of Biological Sciences, Hopkins Marine Station,
Pacific Grove, California 93950

KEY WORDS: skeletal muscle, thermogenesis, calcium, sarcoplasmic reticulum

INTRODUCTION

Skeletal muscles are most often examined at the cellular level in relationship
to their primary role in force generation. Throughout the animal kingdom,
regardless of phylogeny, muscle generates heat. Exercise, shivering, and
nonshivering thermogenesis provide excess heat in muscle that affords
adaptive significance to a wide variety of organisms. Although there is
reasonable concordance on the mechanisms involved in muscle as a force-
generating cell, the physiological mechanisms for thermogenesis, biological
significance, and evolutionary role of muscle as a heat-producing cell are
not as clearly defined. Heat liberation resulting from contractile activity is
well understood, actively studied, and has been carefully measured by muscle
energeticists. Heat production during periods of nonshivering thermogenesis
(NST) is not as well defined, and its existence is controversial in many
species, despite compelling evidence for NST from fish, birds, and mammals. Investigators interested in the role of heat production in skeletal muscle
primarily focus on the relationship between heat liberation during the
contraction-relaxation cycle (1, 77, 90, 110, 128). Discussions of heat
production independent of contractile activity usually focus on mammals
where extensive reviews exist (44, 46, 47, 83, 86, 95). Despite major
efforts to understand how muscle contributes to basal metabolic rate (BMR)
and to cold-induced thermogenesis in endotherms, the mechanistic basis of
such activity remains poorly defined. The fundamental mechanisms for heat
generation without contractile activity have not been elucidated. This review
examines skeletal muscle in light of its secondary role as a furnace and

535

0066–4278/94/0315–0535$05.00

examines the cellular basis for the role of skeletal muscle in heat production from several taxa. As with the mechanics of force generation, functional similarities in the use of muscle for thermogenesis should be apparent across phyla. The goal is to use a comparative approach to determine if common physiological and molecular pathways are utilized in muscular thermogenesis in the animal kingdom.

THERMOGENESIS IN FISH MUSCLES

Thermogenic Organs Modified From Muscle

Most fish are ectothermic with body temperatures within a degree or two of ambient water temperature, the result of respiration with a gill. Endothermy, the ability to elevate body temperature by internal heat generation occurs in one group of teleosts, the Scombroidei (20, 40). The two forms of endothermy, systemic and cranial, have linkages to oxidative phenotypes of skeletal muscle. Thus the few endothermic fish provide one of the best model systems to study the properties of skeletal muscle that are selected for heat generation.

Tunas (Scombridae: *Euthynnus, Auxis, Katsuwonus* and *Thunnus*) are systemic endotherms and raise their body temperature in a fashion similar to mammals: elevated metabolism is coupled with reduced whole body thermal conductance. Muscle, brain, and viscera temperatures in tuna are elevated above water temperature. Billfishes (Xiphiidae: *Xiphias,* and Istiophoridae: *Istiophorus, Makaira, Tetrapturus*) and a single species of mackerel from the family Scombridae, *Gasterochisma melampus,* have evolved the minimum required endothermic capacity; a brain heater that warms the central nervous system (17, 37). The thermogenic organs of billfishes and *Gasterochisma* provide a unique system for identifying the key components of muscle-based thermogenesis. In the early 1980's, Carey discovered that swordfish and other closely related species of billfishes had a specialized thermogenic organ derived from extraocular muscles beneath the brain (37). Swordfish range through daily vertical excursions in the water column and experience changes in temperature as much as 19°C in 2 hr (38, 39). During the daily fluctuations in temperature, the swordfish reduces the temperature change experienced by the brain and retina by warming these tissues with the heater organ. The evolution of cranial endothermy in fish has been linked with selection for thermal niche expansion (23).

Heater organs, modified from extraocular muscles, have been identified in ten species of fishes from three families (Xiphiidae, Istiophoridae, and Scombridae). Sequencing of the cytochrome b gene to establish phylogenetic relationships (22, 23) indicates the billfishes share a common ancestor to the exclusion of other scombroids, which indicates that a thermogenic organ associated with the superior rectus eye muscle is a synapomorphy of these taxa. However, the heater organ is an independently acquired specialization of the butterfly mackerel, *Gasterochisma melampus*. *Gasterochisma* is more closely related to primitive mackerels and tunas, which indicates that the thermogenic cell type of *Gasterochisma* is not homologous with that of the billfishes. The heater organ of *Gasterochisma* is derived from the lateral rectus eye muscle that supports a separate evolutionary origin of the thermogenic cell type. The phylogenetic resolution of relationships among fishes with heater organs permits distinction between cellular differences that are the result of physiological adaptation from differences due to separate evolutionary histories. For example, cellular differences between the heater organs of the butterfly mackerel and billfishes can be attributed to each lineage having independently evolved the heater system. Because of the shared common ancestry in billfishes (Istiophoridae, Xiphiidae), variation in structure and function of heater organs can be attributed to adaptive changes rather than different origins of the heater phenotype. For example, the amount of muscle modified into heater cells varies between billfishes, yet the oxidative capacity of a gram of heater tissue is relatively similar between species (17, 157). Species having the largest thermal ecological range (swordfish) have a larger proportion of extraocular fibers expressing the thermogenic phenotype than fishes that are more tropical and warm temperate in their habitat (19). Morphometric data indicate that swordfish have two to three times as much heater tissue expressed as a blue marlin of similar body size (17, 19). This additional thermogenic capacity reflects the larger thermal needs of the swordfish over the blue marlin. Telemetry studies examining the ecologies of both species support the adaptive argument (23, 38, 39, 89). Blue marlin remain in the top 200 meters of the water column and range in temperature from 17–27°C. Swordfish range to depths greater than 600 meters, experience temperatures from 6–27°C, and encounter temperature changes of 19°C in daily dives.

Structure and Metabolism of Heater Cells

The modified muscle cells of the fish heater organ are unique because the force-producing machinery of the cells, the contractile proteins, are few while the internal membranes that regulate Ca^{2+} ion movements in normal muscle cells are hypertrophied (17, 24). In normal muscle, intracellular Ca^{2+} is controlled by the T-tubule and sarcoplasmic reticulum (SR) membranes that trigger contraction when Ca^{2+} is released. Heater cells have a unique structure compared to all other muscle cells; foremost is the lack of organized myofibrillar elements. Monoclonal antibodies to skeletal isoforms of actin and myosin demonstrate a loose disposition of the myofibrillar proteins in the heater cell cytoplasm. Gel electrophoresis confirms the presence of small amounts of myosin and actin in heater cells. The heater cell volume is primarily composed of mitochondria, SR, and T-tubules (17, 24). Stereological analysis of the mitochondrial fiber volume has been completed on five species of billfishes (20; B Block, unpublished results). Mean mitochondrial volumes (mt,f) range from 60–63% of the cell volume. Among four of five genera (*Xiphias, Makaira nigricans, Tetrapturus angustirostris, Istiophorus*) there are no statistically significant differences if the fish are compared from the same ocean basin (i.e. water temperatures influences structure and physiology). A rich network of smooth membranes, identified as the SR and T-tubule membranes by a variety of electron microscopy techniques, are situated between the mitochondria (24). The membrane systems are so extensive that free cytoplasmic space has been difficult to identify in electron micrographs. The SR is often found in pancake-like stacks, an unusual disposition of SR in normal muscle cells. Freeze-fracture has revealed a carpet of intramembrane particles on the cytoplasmic surface of the SR similar in size (18 nm) to the Ca^{2+} ATPase (24). The disposition of the SR in stacks throughout the cytoplasm most likely increases the surface area of SR and hence the available space for packing of the Ca^{2+} ATPase.

Certain skeletal muscles from other animals occasionally have a stereological profile similar to the heater cell phenotype of fish. Such muscles are commonly used for sound production and recruited for high frequency contractions over sustained periods of time (105, 145). Muscles with hypertrophied SR and high mitochondria volumes include a variety of sound-producing muscles that operate at high frequencies (90–550 Hz, e.g. toadfish swimbladder, rattlesnake tail rattle, cicada synchronous tymbal muscles). Electron microscopy and morphometry indicate the muscles have hypertrophied SR and mitochondria volumes. This structural make-up of the muscle cells used for sound production reflects selection for rapid Ca^{2+} release and reuptake, high levels of oxidative phosphorylation potential for generation of ATP, and comparatively low levels of force production (due to reduction of the myofibrillar volume). In the specialized muscles of toadfish, cicadas, and rattlesnakes, the increased SR volume is associated primarily with increased surface area for the Ca^{2+} ATPase, the rate-limiting enzyme of Ca^{2+} sequestration (4, 21). Similarly, the morphology of the heater cells, in particular the hypertrophy of the SR membrane, is a specialization for increasing the available surface area for the Ca^{2+} ATPase, the key protein in the proposed heat generation pathway of the thermogenic cells (21, 24).

Measurements of key metabolic enzyme activities indicate that heater tissue has a high aerobic capacity (6, 157). Citrate synthase activities at saturating substrate concentrations are among the highest reported for vertebrate tissues (136–290 units per gram tissue at 25°C). High levels of hexokinase activity indicate that glucose is an important source of fuel for energy metabolism in heater tissue (6, 157). Low glycolytic capacities are indicated by the low levels of pyruvate kinase and lactate dehydrogenase. High rates for enzyme activities associated with fatty acid metabolism (3-hydroxyacyl-CoA dehydrogenase) and carnitine transport across the mitochondrial membrane (carnitine palmitoyltransferase) also demonstrate that free fatty acids (FFAs) play a key role in thermogenesis. These results, when combined with the mitochondrial respiration experiments, indicate a high capacity for substrate oxidation and ATP generation. Other indicators of above average oxidative capacity in fish thermogenic organs include measurements of myoglobin and cytochrome C. Myoglobin in blue marlin heater organs is threefold higher (377–411 μmol/kg wet wt) than the muscles from terrestrial amniotes (21). Cytochrome C content in swordfish heater organs (35 ±3 nmol/g) is similar to the range reported for mammalian brown fat (22–35 nmol/g), another thermogenic cell that approaches the physiological limits of mitochondrial packing (37).

The enzymatic studies and morphometric data on mitochondrial volume coincide on an important point, the similarity of the aerobic capacity of heater cells among billfishes (e.g. swordfish and blue marlin). Both studies indicate that a gram of heater tissue from either billfish taken from the same water mass (i.e. Pacific or from the Mediterranean) has the same heat-generating capacity. Interestingly, citrate synthase activities in heater organs were substantially higher in fishes that were captured from water masses with colder waters. For example, swordfish from the Mediterranean sea (sea surface temperature of 23°C and a mixed layer extending 50 meters), had heater cells with a higher oxidative capacity than swordfish from warm waters off Hawaii (sea surface temperatures 27°C, mixed layer 26°C for 100 meters). This result suggests that thermal ecology may regulate expression of the oxidative capacity of the heater phenotype. Thus to keep the brain and eyes warm over the larger thermal gradient experienced by a swordfish in comparison to blue marlin, there must be more of the heater phenotype expressed. This has been documented comparatively between the two species. Swordfish have a considerably higher number of muscle fibers expressing the heater phenotype than do blue marlin (17, 19). Biochemical data on *Gasterochisma*, a fish from the coldest thermal environments (50° S latitude 11–12° sea surface temperature), demonstrate a significantly higher aerobic capacity of the heater cell than comparable measurements from warm and cold temperate billfishes. The 63% packing of the heater cell volume with mitochondria and the high enzymatic activities of citrate synthase in billfish heater cells may not represent the limitation for either mitochondria packing or aerobic enzymes. *Gasterochisma* has citrate synthase activities significantly higher than billfishes (290 vs 166 units of enzyme activity per gram at 25°C).

Metabolic studies (6, 21, 132, 157) of the properties of mitochondria isolated from heater tissue support the findings of the enzymatic profiles of aerobic metabolism, fatty acid oxidation, and carbohydrate metabolism. These studies have examined the capacity of isolated mitochondria for coupled respiration and substrate oxidation rates, and have assessed the maximal in vitro activities of key enzymes involved in aerobic metabolic pathways. Additionally, the role of Ca^{2+} ions for stimulating mitochondrial oxidative metabolism, as well as a possible role of Ca^{2+} ions for uncoupling respiration, have been examined. Three independent studies on isolated mitochondria from blue marlin, sailfish, and swordfish heater organs indicate that respiration is tightly coupled (6, 20, 132). Maximal respiration rates of isolated heater organ mitochondria at 20 and 25°C are the highest of any vertebrate tissue (Table 1). The highest respiratory control ratios in the presence of ADP were obtained in swordfish (9.8 ± 3, n=4). The isolated mitochondrial respiration measurements have established that heater cells can oxidize a wide variety of fatty acid fuels including octanoyl and palmitoyl carnitine, as well as the carnitine esters of stearic, decanoic, and hexanoic acids. Oxidation rates are also high with carbohydrate substrates.

Free cytoplasmic Ca^{2+} ions are known to act as a second messenger significantly affecting mitochondrial metabolism (123, 124). The stimulatory role of Ca^{2+} on mitochondrial metabolism is important when considering the models for thermogenesis in the fish heater organs described below.

Table 1 Mitochondrial oxygen consumption rates in muscle

Animal	Tissue	Substrate	State-3 respiration rate ($nmol_{O_2}$/min/mg protein)
Swordfish[6][a]	Heater	Glutamate	167 ± 48 (4)[b]
Swordfish[6]	Heater	Palmitoyl carnitine	144 ± 50 (4)
Blue Marlin[20]	Heater	Pyruvate + malate	125 ± 25 (5)
Locust[152]	Muscle	Pyruvate	598 ± 35 (7)
Locust[152]	Muscle	Palmitoyl carnitine	316 ± 8 (7)
Hummingbird[151]	Muscle	Pyruvate + malate	159 ± 10 (4)
Hummingbird[151]	Muscle	Palmitoyl-CoA + carnitine + malate	138 ± 16 (4)
Tuna[128]	Red muscle	Palmitoyl carnitine	$104 + 29$ (9)
Carp[5]	Red muscle	Lauroyl carnitine	$84 + 12$ (6)

All fish mitochondrial respiration rates are reported at 25°C. Insect respiration rates are at 30°C. Hummingbird muscle mitochondria are at 40°C. [a] Reference. [b] Number of individual preparations examined.

These models are based on stimulation of heat generation by release of Ca^{2+} from the SR membranes surrounding the heater cell mitochondria. In isolated heart mitochondria, nanomolar Ca^{2+} results in significant stimulation of state-3 respiration primarily through activation of matrix dehydrogenases (57). Nanomolar changes in cytosolic concentration of Ca^{2+} have been shown to activate several key mitochondrial dehydrogenases, the respiratory chain enzymes, and fatty acid oxidation rates in vertebrate mitochondria. Three matrix enzymes, pyruvate, NAD^+-isocitrate and 2-oxoglutarate dehydrogenases can be activated by increases in extramitochondrial concentrations of Ca^{2+} within a physiological range for vetebrate mitochondria (0.05–2 μmol; 123). Thus Ca^{2+} release in the cytoplasm plays a key role in altering the NADH supply to the respiratory chain, which affects the rate of oxidative metabolism and ATP production (56, 124). These findings have led to the hypothesis that Ca^{2+} is a metabolic stimulator capable of enhancing the rate of ATP supply to match demand.

In swordfish heater cells, Ballentyne et al (6) investigated the effects of Ca^{2+} on mitochondrial metabolism. The oxidation of α-glycerolphosphate by isolated swordfish mitochondria could be stimulated fourfold by the addition of 1 mM $CaCl_2$. This addition of Ca^{2+} is far from physiological, thus the results, while of interest, are difficult to interpret. Despite the ambiguity of these results, a possible linkage was hypothesized to exist (6) between Ca^{2+} stimulation of mitochondrial respiration and the SR futile Ca^{2+} cycling hypothesis of Block (18). A potent nonshivering thermogenic mechanism is apparent if Ca^{2+} released in the heater cell cytoplasm stimulates oxidative processes. O'Brien et al (132) further investigated this question of a stimulatory induced metabolic coupling or, conversely, an uncoupling effect of Ca^{2+}, on blue marlin heater mitochondria. As in other vertebrate tissues, isolated heater mitochondria have active mechanisms for rapid Ca^{2+} uptake and a sodium-induced egress pathway. In blue marlin, P/O ratios remain relatively insensitive to free Ca^{2+} concentrations in the physiological range (132). The results for this species indicate that uncoupling by Ca^{2+} is not a significant process and that the heater mitochondria maintain a high oxidative ATP output in its presence. Further studies should test the hypothesis that Ca^{2+} in the heater cell cytoplasm elicits a stimulatory effect on oxidative process that would promote heat generation by increasing flux through oxidative metabolic pathways.

Specialized Membranes of the Heater Cells

The properties of the SR membrane system in the heater cell have been intensively studied using conventional techniques developed for isolation and characterization of mammalian SR (24, 25, 26, 125). The biochemical studies have established that the isolated SR of the billfish heater organs contains the Ca^{2+} ATPase calsequestrin and the Ca^{2+} SR release channel. Relatively low amounts of the L-type Ca^{2+} channel (DHP receptor) have been identified using [^{3}H] PN200 binding in T-tubule fractions of heater cells (106). Parvalbumin, a calcium-binding protein found in other SR enriched fish skeletal muscles, is not present in a high concentration in heater cells (K Rodnick, personal communication). While normal skeletal muscle can be biochemically separated into two distinct fractions (heavy and light SR, depending upon the constituent SR proteins) by sucrose gradient centrifugation, heater tissue SR cannot be separated into distinct fractions. As discussed below, this is because heater SR has a homogeneous distribution of SR proteins throughout the SR membrane (26). It is thought that this distribution is associated with the different physiological constraints on Ca^{2+} release for contraction vs Ca^{2+} release for thermogenesis. The primary need for morphologically separated sites of release in skeletal muscle is to reduce diffusion distances and obtain a synchronous contraction throughout the muscle fiber. This is brought about by the even spacing of the triads throughout the sarcomeres of skeletal muscle fibers. Heater cells lack myofibrils and sarcomeres, and junctional triads are difficult to identify (24).

The Ca^{2+} ATPase is the most prominent protein in isolated SR of blue marlin and swordfish. A wide variety of antisera have been used, but fail to recognize the specific isoform of the Ca^{2+} ATPase expressed in scombroid fish skeletal muscle or heater tissue. However, freeze-fracture studies have revealed a dense set of particles on the cytoplasmic leaflet of the SR that correspond to the appearance of the Ca^{2+} ATPase in nonjunctional SR regions of normal skeletal muscle. Recently, A Tullis (personal communication) amplified 700 bp of the Ca^{2+} ATPase message from heater tissue and determined its isoform identity. Using amino acid substitutions found in the phosphorylation and nucleotide-binding domains as markers for the slow or fast form of the Ca^{2+} ATPase, the analysis indicates that heater cells primarily express the fast-twitch form of the Ca^{2+} ATPase. Extraocular muscle from which the heater tissue is derived also expresses the fast-twitch isoform of the pump.

Protein gels and immunological techniques have identified significant amounts of calsequestrin in billfish heater cells (23). The mobility of the calsequestrin isoform expressed in these cells is similar to the extraocular muscle calsequestrin. Due to a unique mobility of the fish eye muscle and heater calsequestrin isoform, when compared to either mammalian fast or slow-twitch skeletal isoforms, it remains difficult to assign the fish extraocular calsequestrin to one of these two classes of isoforms. Electron microscopy and light level immunofluorescence studies indicate a distribution of the calsequestrin throughout the SR membrane system. This is in striking contrast to skeletal muscle where the calsequestrin is localized in a recognizable morphological structure, the triad. Similarly, the SR Ca^{2+} release channel also has a homogenous rather than punctate distribution in the heater cell SR. This too is in contrast to the inhomogenous distribution of the Ca^{2+} release channel in skeletal muscle. In heater cells, the SR Ca^{2+} release channel and calsequestrin co-localize and have a relatively homogenous distribution throughout the SR membrane system, which indicates their localization in the spaces between the mitochondria. Taken together the results indicate that the SR in between the mitochondria is highly enriched in the protein components required for Ca^{2+} uptake, sequestration, and release.

Immunological studies of the SR proteins involved in Ca^{2+} cycling indicate a close relationship between isoforms of SR proteins expressed in heater and the isoforms expressed in the muscle precursor, the superior rectus eye muscle (131). The most interesting case of the linkage between isoforms of SR proteins expressed in eye muscles and heater tissue is found in the SR Ca^{2+} release channel. The heater cell has a unique expression pattern of the SR Ca^{2+} release channel that is shared with the precursor eye muscle fibers. While mammalian skeletal muscles express a single isoform of the SR Ca^{2+} release channel, avian, amphibian, reptilian, and fish skeletal muscles have been shown to express two isoforms, α and β, in the skeletal muscles (3, 112, 131, 134). Biochemical studies (112) demonstrate similarity between the two nonmammalian isoforms, co-expressed within a single muscle fiber, and the mammalian skeletal and cardiac Ca^{2+} release channels. The skeletal isoform of mammals runs similarly on SDS gels with the α isoform of nonmammals. The mammalian cardiac form of the SR Ca^{2+} release channel has a similar mobility to the β isoform. Immunoblot analyses have recently shown that only the skeletal or α isoform of the SR Ca^{2+} release channel is expressed in the extraocular muscles of fish, while two forms are found in the swimming muscles (131). SDS-PAGE gels also reveal one high molecular weight polypeptide in heater, while two polypeptides are seen in the body musculature. The fastest contracting twitch fibers in vertebrates are the extraocular muscles (5). O'Brien et al (131) have hypothesized that the α isoform of the SR release Ca^{2+} channel has certain characteristics of activation or inactivation that are advantageous for high frequency contraction and speed. A predisposition toward the use of extraocular muscle fibers as the heater phenotype may be the expression of only the skeletal-like form of the SR Ca^{2+} release channel.

Models for Nonshivering Thermogenesis in the Heater Cell

Biochemical measurements of enzymatic activities along with physiological data indicate a high heat generating potential (250 $W \cdot kg^{-1}$) of the modified billfish eye muscles (157). Although the exact molecular mechanism of thermogenesis in the heater cells has not fully been elucidated, biochemical and structural data suggest that heat production is linked to the release of Ca^{2+} from internal cytoplasmic stores. Thermogenesis is hypothesized to be associated with stimulation of catabolic processes and mitochondrial respiration via Ca^{2+}. The simplest hypothesis is that stimulation of the heater cell occurs via the cranial nerve (a unique branch of III) supplying the thermogenic portion of the extraocular muscle. Stimulation is presumed to lead to depolarization and Ca^{2+} release. The structural components for such an excitation pathway are present in the heater cells (26, 106). Changes in the concentration of intracellular Ca^{2+} are hypothesized to trigger thermogenesis. Whether this occurs because of a prolonged nervous stimulation or a series of excitatory stimulatory events (such as in a fast-twitch fiber recruited continuously) is not known. However, both mechanisms of stimulation would result in an increase flux of Ca^{2+} across the SR and a rise in cytoplasmic $[Ca^{2+}]$. Ca^{2+} entry into the small heater cell cytoplasmic space would occur without the usual binding to troponin or parvalbumin, effective Ca^{2+} buffers that are absent in heater cells. This suggests a rapid rise in cytoplasmic $[Ca^{2+}]$ would occur after stimulation of the heater cell. Ca^{2+} transport by the pump that is densely spread throughout the SR would result in rapid ATP hydrolysis. Splitting of ATP would lower cytoplasmic ATP levels and increase [ADP] and $[P_i]$. Increased cytosolic [ADP] would subsequently stimulate the mitochondrial adenylate transporter, and ADP would be imported into the mitochondrial matrix thus increasing the ADP/ATP levels, which would result in stimulation of oxidative processes and substrate catabolism (Figure 1a). This basic pathway would be stimulated by any process that prolongs a cytoplasmic Ca^{2+} transient in the heater cell cytoplasm. A single point mutation in a gene coding for either the Ca^{2+} ATPase, the SR Ca^{2+} release channel, the T-tubule L-type Ca^{2+} channel, or any other protein involved in Ca^{2+} sequestration or release could raise sarcoplasmic Ca^{2+}, hence Ca^{2+} cycling, and stimulate thermogenesis (Figure 1b). Elevated levels of cytoplasmic Ca^{2+} would also be possible if prolonged stimulation of Ca^{2+} release occurred through a ligand or hormone that would potentiate the probability of opening of the SR release channel (Figure 1c). The SR Ca^{2+} release channels are activated by Ca^{2+} at physiological concentrations, and the opening of the channel is affected by ligands such as Mg^{2+} and adenine nucleotides. Alternatively, the SR could be the storage site for intracellular Ca^{2+}, and nervous stimulation could simply result in Ca^{2+} release, reuptake, and stimulation of mitochondrial oxidation via $Ca^{2+}/H+$ exchange (Figure 1d).

EXCITATION-THERMOGENIC COUPLING Three of the four thermogenic pathways outlined in Figure 1 involve the normal pathway for triggering Ca^{2+}

release in skeletal muscles cells. Skeletal muscles have an exquisite mechanism for depolarization-induced Ca^{2+} release, and Block (18, 20, 21) has hypothesized that such control can be combined with stimulation of oxidative phosphorylation and substrate catabolism (heat-generating processes) via Ca^{2+} release and reuptake at the SR in the heater cell. The process, called excitation-thermogenic coupling, simply implies that depolarization-induced Ca^{2+} release can trigger thermogenesis without contraction. The exact nature of the signal that leads to metabolic stimulation of heater tissue is not known but, as indicated above, structural results indicate that initiation of thermogenesis in the heater cell could occur via the normal cholinergic pathway found in skeletal muscle cells.

Such a thermogenic pathway in fish, with thermogenesis resulting from increased permeability of the heater cell SR to Ca^{2+}, has striking similarities to the proposed mechanism of thermogenesis in malignant hyperthermia (116), a condition involving abnormalities in the Ca^{2+} release channel of skeletal muscle in mammals. The condition in pigs has been genetically linked to the ryanodine receptor gene (RYR1) coding for the skeletal isoform of the SR Ca^{2+} release channel (154). A point mutation is presumed to underlie the presence of a hyperactive Ca^{2+} release channel, which is insensitive to closing. Under certain physiological stresses, such genetically predisposed pigs enter into a hyper-metabolic state that results in excessive catabolic activity in muscles and fatal levels of heat generation (154).

Research into the exact mechanisms of thermogenesis in heater cells has been influenced by the recent discoveries in malignant hyperthermia (MH). A current focus is to identify whether a normal molecular pathway for excitation-thermogenic coupling exists in these cells. A mutation that would result in increased SR Ca^{2+} permeability or leakiness to Ca^{2+} (Ca^{2+}ATPase, or SR Ca^{2+} release channel) or increased Ca^{2+} influx across the cell surface and T-tubule membrane (DHP receptor) could be the causative agent of the thermogenesis. The goal of current research on the heater organ is to define whether the proteins involved in this pathway are similar to mammalian junctional SR proteins, or if this unique adaptation is associated with a mutation of key proteins involved in the Ca^{2+} release pathway.

The presence of a unique expression pattern of the SR Ca^{2+} release channel in the extraocular muscles may be the prediposition required for the evolution of the unique thermogenic phenotype. One hypothesis is that fast-twitch oxidative, glycolytic (FOG) fibers of extraocular muscles in fish are enriched in the SR Ca^{2+} release channel and SR Ca^{2+} ATPase to begin with. Recent results indicate expression of only the fast, direct mechanically coupled isoform (skeletal) in extraocular muscle and heater cells. Direct sequencing of the cDNA for the fish SR Ca^{2+} release channel should reveal whether the fish have a normal extraocular isoform and release channel, or

a

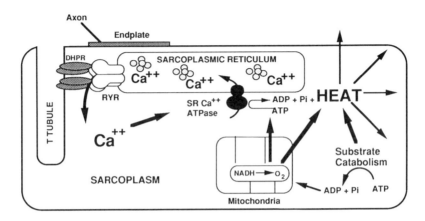

b

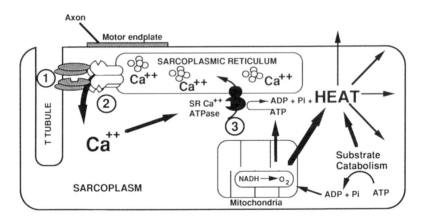

whether the key specialization is the high expression of the Ca^{2+} release channel throughout the heater cell SR.

As discussed above, any endogenous metabolite or ligand that increases the permeability of the SR to Ca^{2+} will increase thermogenesis according to the model (Figure 1c). Similarly, any increase in sarcoplasmic Ca^{2+} transients (due to depolarization) will stimulate thermogenesis. Evidence for pathways that increase SR permeability has been found in other endotherms and is discussed in more detail below, but the results from these studies could apply to the heater system. Ligands that prolong the open time of

c

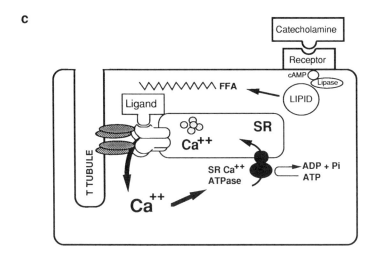

d

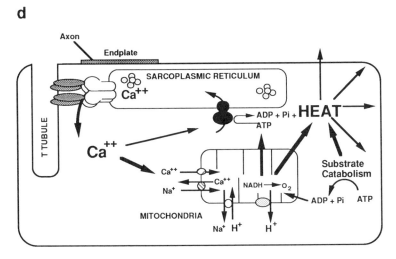

Figure 1   Models for nonshivering thermogenesis in skeletal muscle. See text for details. DHPR, dihydropyridine receptor, RYR, SR Ca^{2+} release channel.

the SR Ca^{2+} release channel, such as long chain FFAs released in the cytoplasm during lipid oxidation, could stimulate thermogenesis in the heater organ (62). Inefficiency in SR Ca^{2+} uptake caused by a reduction in the cations pumped per ATP by the SR Ca^{2+} ATPase could also be a source of increased stimulation for thermogenesis. Finally, if the stimulatory pathway for thermogenesis in the heater organ is via the normal pathway found in skeletal muscle, it is possible that prolonging the open time of the L-type Ca^{2+} channel, for example by phosphorylation, would in turn increase sarcoplasmic Ca^{2+} transients by effectively opening the SR Ca^{2+} release channel.

MITOCHONDRIAL THERMOGENESIS   The hypothesis of excitation-thermogenic coupling assumes that heat generation is stimulated by cytoplasmic processes associated with hydrolysis of ATP. This is based on two results discussed above: the presence of large amounts of the Ca^{2+} ATPase, and the coupled nature of heater cell mitochondria. Thermogenesis in any cell has two possible sources: mitochondrial uncoupling or cytoplasmic-based ATP utilization. To establish the cellular site of thermogenesis, it is necessary to compare the extent of heat generation from the changes in the mitochondrial coupling ratios, or the leak of protons across the mitochondrial membrane, to capacity for thermogenic stimulation from cytoplasmic processes (i.e. ATP hydrolysis). Both processes would generate heat and are not mutually exclusive. Cytoplasmic-based heat production requires delivery of ATP to the cytoplasm via the mitochondrial ATPase, whereas mitochondrial uncoupling does not require this step. The latter thermogenic process requires the presence of a specific uncoupler. The billfish thermogenic organ has a high density of mitochondria just as does other aerobic and thermogenic tissue [e.g mammalian brown adipose tissue (BAT)]. As in BAT, the focus of a thermogenic mechanism could be on a mitochondrial uncoupling mechanism rather than a cytoplasmically based stimulus for increasing oxidative processes in the heater cells. While numerous hypotheses for uncoupling mitochondria exist and include FFAs, Ca^{2+} ions, and differences in the efficiency of proton translocation, only the BAT uncoupling protein has been widely accepted as a designated thermogenic proton leakage pathway (130). BAT mitochondria possess a specialized uncoupling protein that is a major protein component of their inner membrane. The uncoupling protein is capable of dissipating the electrochemical gradient generated across the inner mitochondrial membrane during respiration as heat (85, 130). Immunological studies have ruled out the expression of this protein in the heater cells (18). From an evolutionary perspective there is no reason, a priori, to hypothesize that the fish thermogenic system, which evolved prior to the mammalian BAT, should have independently derived the same mechanism. However, as in questions surrounding endothermic metabolism in birds and mammals, it is important to discern if there is clear way to distinguish between the two modes of heat production.

The elucidation of some details of molecular regulation of the BAT uncoupling protein has provided insight as to key differences in mitochondrial-based thermogenesis vs cytoplasmically based thermogenic mechanisms. One of the most interesting findings is the relationship between expression of F_1F_0 ATPase and uncoupling protein in BAT mitochondria (92, 141). Stimulation of BAT via chronic cold exposure leads to an increase in expression of uncoupling protein and a simultaneous decrease in expression of F_1F_0 ATPase. Thus when heat is being generated at the level of the mitochondria, ATP delivery to the cytoplasm is down-regulated. Using this paradigm for analysis of the fish thermogenic tissues is relatively easy. Examination of SDS-PAGE gels in swordfish and marlin indicate that the most intense proteins in the profile of all membranous components of the heater cell are two bands with apparent molecular weights of 55,000 and 50,100 kd. These correspond to the alpha and beta subunits of the mitochondrial F_1F_0 ATPase. Although identification of these protein bands requires immunological confirmation, the results suggest that a cytoplasmically based mechanism for stimulating oxidation rates is the basis for heat production in the fish thermogenic organs.

Future Directions

THE ORIGIN OF THE HEATER PHENOTYPE   Studies of vertebrate extraocular muscles reveal an unusual and complex morphology and physiology. The muscles contain a variety of multiply and singly innervated fibers, whereas in vertebrate limb muscles, singly innervated fibers predominate. The cellular diversity of extraocular muscle has been linked in part to the physiology of the fibers. Several fiber populations have been identified via electrophysiology. Most extraocular fibers are categorized as being comparable to twitch fibers, singly innervated with action potentials (43). These fibers are capable of superfast contraction (5). Another population of fibers is associated with tonic fibers and generates graded tension, and appears to be equivalent to the tonic population of fibers in frogs. Histochemical, molecular, and immunological studies indicate a predominance of muscle fibers in fish extraocular muscles most phenotypically similar to twitch fibers (156).

Block (17) and Block & Franzini-Armstrong (24) have hypothesized that the heater phenotype is a product of one particular muscle fiber type. Rather than considering that the fiber phenotype (thermogenic) has arisen de novo, they suggest there is a predisposed fiber type that has a high aerobic capacity and ample SR. No study to date has unequivocally demonstrated if all extraocular muscle fibers are capable of expressing the phenotype, or if certain physiological properties of a fiber phenotype would predispose the muscle cell for becoming a heat-generating cell. Physiological arguments have been put forth for fast-twitch, slow-twitch, and tonic fibers that emphasize aspects of calcium transients, calcium cycling abilities, and hence protein machinery for these processes and aerobic capacity. Recent work has identified the isoforms of SR proteins expressed in heater (131) and indicates linkage between the heater phenotype and fast-twitch extraocular muscle fibers (A Tullis, personal observation).

Elucidation of the nervous or hormonal control of the heater cell requires further work. In mammals, nonshivering as well as shivering thermogenesis (NST) is tightly linked to the sympathetic nervous system activity (85). A calorigenic response to catecholamines underlies the increased thermogenesis in the skeletal muscles of cold-acclimated mammals (83, 84). Similarly, in BAT, direct noradrenergic innervation of the cells causes release of norepinephrine from sympathetic nerve endings and stimulation of thermogenesis. Additionally, in mammals, chronic cold acclimation increases the sympathetic innervation to BAT, presumably increasing the ability for NST. While immunological studies have demonstrated the presence of skeletal muscle-like cholinergic nerve endings on the surface of heater cells, the potential role of sympathetic innervation should be explored in detail. It is possible that simple excitation of the muscle cell sarcolemma results in release of Ca^{2+} by the heater cell. Whether input is from the unique cranial nerve supplying this portion of the heater organ, or whether there is electrical continuity between the intact skeletal muscle portion of the extraocular muscle and the heater portion (e.g. gap junctions) remains to be determined.

In summary, two independent evolutions of a thermogenic tissue in fish demonstrate unequivocally that muscle is an important nonshivering heat source in vertebrates. In the conversion of muscle to a thermogenic organ, there has been evolutionary selection on the energetically costly pathway of Ca^{2+} cycling by the SR as the raw material for a thermogenic process, rather than harnessing the energetic potential of the cross-bridge apparatus (imagine a heater cell packed full of myosin heads). Immunological results indicate that the precursor muscle source is linked to the FOG fiber type. This fiber prior to modification is enriched in mitochondria and SR in most vertebrates. Apparently, a source of heat is readily available in all skeletal muscle fibers that cycle Ca^{2+} for continuous contraction for sustained periods of time.

The Role of Muscle in Tuna Endothermy

Tunas are able to elevate muscle, viscera, brain, and eye tissue temperatures significantly above water temperature (40, 70). They lack specialized thermogenic organs and instead conserve heat in tissues with high aerobic capacities by use of vascular counter-current heat exchangers. Several studies have demonstrated that tunas have high standard metabolic rates that presumably underlie their capacity for endothermy (29, 69). While it is clear that the metabolic costs are elevated at rest, it is difficult to explain why this is so. Most likely it reflects the numerous physiological and metabolic adaptations underlying the increased aerobic capacity of tunas (29). Aspects of tuna energetics were reviewed in a previous volume (150), thus only the contribution of the skeletal muscle to whole body metabolism and thermogenesis is considered in the following framework. (*a*) What contribution does skeletal muscle have in the elevation of metabolic rates of tunas? (*b*) Do tunas per kilogram body mass have a higher aerobic capacity in their slow oxidative (red) and fast-twitch (white) muscles than closely related ectothermic taxa? (*c*) Is the recruitment of both slow and fast-twitch fibers for continuous swimming occurring more frequently in tunas as a result of the numerous morphological specializations of the body plan than in ectothermic taxa and thus contributing to a higher rate of heat production from the muscles?

The metabolic rate of a tuna swimming at low speeds is significantly higher than other fishes (salmon) and may be correlated with increased aerobic costs of the tuna skeletal muscle machinery (69). Metabolic comparisons should only be made between the tuna and closely related ectothermic taxa such as the bonitos and mackerels. However, until such data exist, comparisons between the oxygen consumption rate of swimming tunas and salmonids will have to provide the basis for discussions of metabolism. In most fish, the swimming muscles are segregated into anatomically distinct zones consisting of two major fiber types, red and white, with an intermediate pink fiber often interspersed among the white fibers of many species (27). At low speeds, fish generate power only with the aerobic fibers (red), while at high speeds anaerobic fast-twitch (white) fibers are recruited (27, 142). The pink fibers are also fast-twitch fibers, but the nature of their recruitment order, especially in larger fishes such as tunas, is not clearly defined.

Endothermy in tunas is correlated with a unique positioning of the red muscle mass within the body plan of the tunas (71, 107). In contrast to all other teleosts, tunas have a more deeply situated red muscle mass along the horizontal septum and close to the axial skeleton. The deep red muscle is linked by a complex series of robust tendons to the caudal peduncle and tail. Both features, endothermy and central positioning of red muscle, also appear at the same time as a novel, more stiff-bodied swimming form, thunniform swimming (23, 71). Thunniform swimming generates forward propulsion, without the lateral undulation characteristic of many fishes, and concentrates the forces generated by contracting muscles on the tail. Thunniform swimming may reduce drag and increase the efficiency of movement through the water at higher speeds as indicated in the early metabolic measurements (69). Linkages between the novel swimming form, red muscle positioning, and endothermy have been hypothesized, but not tested (23).

Electromyograph (EMG) data on lightly anaesthetized tunas (*Katsuwonus pelamis*) have shown deep red muscle contracting at slow tail beat frequencies (140) without recruitment of the white muscle. Higher tail beat frequencies (e.g. burst activity) elicit activity from both muscle groups. Thus limited experimental evidence demonstrates that tunas recruit their slow and fast-twitch muscles in a similar fashion to other fishes. More extensive EMG recordings are required on free-swimming tunas of a wider variety of species and size before conclusions about muscle recruitment patterns can be made. One key question is whether the white muscle, in particular the FOG or pink fibers, are recruited during periods of continuous swimming.

The contribution in tunas of the deep red muscle, a highly aerobic tissue, to metabolic rate is not known, but hypothesized to be high. Microsphere measurements in nonswimming albacore tuna, *Thunnus alalunga,* provide values for the distribution of cardiac output to the muscles in a restrained tuna (163). The skeletal muscles of 10 kg albacore received 64% of the cardiac output, which indicates a key role in oxygen consumption and heat generation. Red muscle receives the highest percentage of the cardiac output (36%), although the tissue comprises only 4.5% of the total body mass in this species (163). The white muscle has the smallest relative blood flow; however, the large muscle mass as a percent of total mass (59%) results in a significant percentage of the cardiac output (28%) going to the white muscle. The microsphere studies provide the best evidence to date that the skeletal muscle of tunas, examined under basal conditions, consumes a large portion of the oxygen distributed to the whole animal and thus must be responsible for elevation of aerobic capacity as well as considerable heat generation. Further studies should follow up on these preliminary findings and methodology.

Does an extraordinary oxidative capacity of red muscle underlie the capacity for tuna endothermy? The aerobic capacity of tuna red muscle has been examined in several studies (73, 129). The literature is somewhat conflicting with some authors indicating high levels of aerobic activity, whereas others recognize similarities between red muscle of tunas and ectothermic fishes (22, 58). The phylogenetically correct comparisons will be made only if aerobic activity of red muscle, determined by enzymatic data or mitochondrial oxidation rates, is compared between closely related endothermic and ectothermic taxa (22). Recent investigations (129) have systematically re-examined the aerobic capacity of the muscles in the skipjack tuna, *Katsuwonus pelamis*. This study provides evidence for some of the highest oxidative enzyme capacities ever measured in tuna red muscle (for example citrate synthase activity equals 80 units per gram tissue at 25°C). However, a more comprehensive comparison among closely related ecto-thermic and endothermic tunas and their relatives (58) demonstrates that high aerobic activity is present in the red muscles of both endothermic and ectothermic scombrid fish. Thus although some tuna species have extraordinarily high aerobic capacity of the slow-twitch red muscle fibers (e.g. skipjack tuna), in other species this capacity is not significantly different from closely related ectothermic species. Block & Finnerty (22) have used parsimony analyses to demonstrate that the high oxidative capacity of red muscle of fishes is a predisposition for the evolution of thermogenesis and endothermy in these species. Fish swim continuously in a viscous medium, a constraint to locomotion that is not encountered by terrestrial animals. Differences in red muscle mitochondrial properties between fish species are modest and demonstrate that substrate oxidation rates per milligram of mitochondrial protein are relatively similar among actively swimming teleosts (129).

Morphometric analysis (121) of skipjack tuna muscle has also demonstrated a high mitochondrial volume, V_v (mt,f), on average 29–32% V_v (mt,f). Although elevated, the tuna value is similar to red muscle mitochondrial V_v reported for other fishes. Mitochondrial volumes between 20–45.5% of fiber volume have been reported in a variety of fish species including shark (109), eel (93), trout (101), and anchovy red muscle (100). The recent morphometric investigation established that the inner mitochondrial surface area (63–70 m^2/cm^3; S_v im,m) in skipjack tuna red muscle is high for vertebrate muscle tissues (one and one-half to twofold higher than for a wide variety of mammals). Skipjack tuna red muscle appears to be pushing the theoretical limit of the maximal packing of mitochondrial inner membrane, S_v (im,m) of 83 m^2/cm^3, in vertebrates (129). The similarity in maximal packing of mitochondria in oxidative red muscle fibers among fish species and the high inner mitochondrial membrane values suggest that skipjack tunas have achieved one of the highest possible aerobic capacities of force-generating red muscle. The fish appear to have reached a constraint for increasing mitochondrial volume; more (40% or so) would result in myofibrillar volume reduction and loss of force-generating capacity (129).

If tuna red muscle has a higher (as in skipjack) or similar oxygen consumption as a gram of red muscle from other closely related ectothermic species, how does it play a role in thermogenesis? Do tunas have a larger volume of recruitable red muscle tissue? Do they activate red fibers more often? Does this tissue receive a higher percentage of cardiac output than in teleosts of similar size? The respiration studies and enzymatic data indicate the tissue has a relatively high rate of oxygen consumption. The microsphere study indicates that red muscle tissue of tunas during periods of low electrical stimulation receives a high amount of blood flow (163). Thus red muscle must be the site of considerable heat generation. As an obligate ram ventilator, these fish are constantly swimming to breathe, hence standard metabolic rate can be postulated to be elevated due, in part, to the aero- bic cost of propulsion required for respiration (29). Further studies will need to compare the metabolic cost of swimming between closely related endothermic and ectothermic taxa (bonitos) who swim in a comparable fashion.

One way that muscle will increase the metabolic heat output of the fish is if there is a significant increase in the volume of red muscle. Several studies have carefully examined the relative distribution of red muscle in tunas (58, 71). Three of the smaller tuna species (*Auxis, Euthynnus, Katsuwonus*) have a high red muscle mass (7–13%), but some of the larger species (*Thunnus*) have a red muscle mass similar to other fishes (4–6%). The smaller tunas have significantly higher relative red muscle masses than closely related, similarly sized ectothermic taxa such as the bonito (*Sarda chiliensis,* 4.5%) and more distantly related taxa such as mackerel (*Scomber japonicus,* 6%). In *Auxis* and *Euthynnus,* the hypothesis that the high metabolic rates of tunas are associated with greater quantities of red muscle per unit body mass, in comparison with ectothermic sister taxa, is apparently true. Among the larger tunas, which have the most wide-ranging thermal ecologies, the red muscle volume is similar to closely related ectothermic taxa. Further studies on a wider range of body sizes are needed to examine this question more carefully and with phylogenetic considerations.

The microsphere measurements indicate the white muscle receives a considerable proportion of the cardiac output due to the total mass, thus it has the potential for a significant contribution to heat production. Two properties of white muscles that may increase the total aerobic capacity of the skeletal muscles and hence heat generation are (*a*) higher aerobic capacity and (*b*) higher frequency of recruitment. Several studies have demonstrated a large potential for aerobic metabolism in white muscle of tunas (58, 129). A higher aerobic capacity in tuna white muscle could be attributed to increasing the FOG fiber contribution in this muscle (B Block, personal observation). If this is the case, such fiber types may be recruited more frequently during steady-state swimming. While electrophysiological data have shown a clear division of labor in species of fishes between the slow and fast-twitch red and white muscle fiber populations (142), data on tunas indicate a possible contribution of the white muscle fibers to a wider range of swimming activity (30). This could be associated with a high aerobic fast-twitch fiber population (FOG or pink) being present in white muscle. It remains possible that the thunniform locomotory mode results in a continuous recruitment of a higher proportion of aerobic fibers throughout the body plan (slow and fast-twitch muscle masses) at all cruising velocities.

This could be tested with EMG studies aimed at determining the frequency of red and white muscle activity at a variety of swimming speeds. Appropriate comparative data should be obtained from ectothermic mackerels or bonitos.

TUNA BURN   Heat production in endothermic tunas has been linked with activity-related muscle metabolism. Tunas and their close relatives in comparison to taxa other than the Scombroidei, appear to have a higher aerobic content of muscle fibers in their body musculature (22, 58, 129). The increased aerobic capacity has been coupled to the evolution of heat retention systems that are essential for elevation of body temperatures (70). Tunas under adverse conditions of capture on hook and line often generate large amounts of heat in their muscles in a syndrome that parallels malignant hyperthermia (MH), or porcine stress syndrome (116). The highly profitable tuna fishery has commonly reported this condition known as "tuna burn," which has a dramatic effect on the quality of the tuna product that is most prized for raw consumption as sashimi. Interestingly, the literature on the etiology of tuna burn parallels MH, reported to occur with relative frequency in domestic mammals such as swine. Pigs experience the fatal syndrome, often as a reaction to the acute stress prior to slaughter. This parallels the physiological stresses for a tuna fighting capture by hook and line. However, little in the way of recent research on MH and excitation-contraction coupling has led to a cross-over of research ideas and etiology into the burnt tuna arena. This most likely is due to the relatively recent discovery of the SR Ca^{2+} release channel (111) and its only recent connection to the MH syndrome (88, 116).

Tuna muscle that has been burnt has a poor quality resulting primarily from degradation processes in the skeletal muscles that are initiated during the period of capture and continue after death. Descriptions of burnt tuna muscle are virtually identical to the descriptions of the quality of muscle after a porcine attack of MH (51). The problem in the tuna population is most often associated with certain fishing practices (hand-lines, rod and reels), which in most cases involve intense struggle for the fish. Thus as in MH in swine, a stressful situation brings about a syndrome that leads to destruction of the muscle tissue, a lower quality product for market, and economic losses. While the cause of the burnt tuna syndrome has not been unequivocally identified, most studies have suggested a variety of etiologies including low pH, high muscle temperature, lysosomal proteolytic activities, and calcium activation of proteases (reviewed in 160). Several studies have suggested that burnt tuna is associated with fish that experience the greatest stress during short-term capture procedures, and it is well established that the quality of the tuna muscle can be preserved if the fishermen can pith the tuna after capture, a difficult procedure in such large-bodied fish.

Morphological studies of burnt tuna muscle indicate irregularities of the muscle cells. However, separating postmortem effects from actual causal changes related to the syndrome remains challenging for experimentation is extremely limited in these fishes. Postmortem burnt muscle provides evidence that there is a process of degradation similar in nature to reports of Ca^{2+} toxicity that occurs in the mammalian skeletal muscles. However, while this is certainly the problem associated with the decline in the quality of the meat, it is probably not the cause (51). Early hypotheses linked the burnt tuna syndrome to Ca^{2+} leakage in muscle (160). The causative agent for the leakage of Ca^{2+} in the hypothesis was low cellular ATP, which would bring about increases of sarcoplasmic Ca^{2+} from metabolic collapse and decreased cellular ATP for pumping Ca^{2+} back into the SR. This in turn was proposed to lead to a cascade of events associated with proteolytic activity of the muscles from Ca^{2+}-activated proteases. Recently, Watson et al (160) suggested that the types of postmortem changes described in the literature, which included selective destruction of Z-discs and irregularities of the SR, are associated specifically with Ca^{2+}-activated neutral proteases. The most recent hypothesis for the syndrome has added catecholamines as the key factor involved in initiation of burnt tuna. The stimulatory factor for the syndrome is stress, which leads to norepinephrine release and subsequent increase of activity of Ca^{2+}-activated neutral proteases, thus resulting in breakdown of sarcomere structure. Figure 2 takes this tuna burn hypothesis and places the model in the context of what we now understand about the EC coupling processes. The stress associated with the intense activity surrounding capture induces increased levels of circulating catecholamines that would lead to prolonged cytoplasmic Ca^{2+} transients, possibly by sympathetically mediated phosphorylation of the DHP receptor. This would in turn be associated with the increase of $[Ca^{2+}]$ in the sarcoplasm from the prolonged opening of the SR Ca^{2+} release channel. Increased catabolism would be associated with the calcium transient. This in turn could also lead to the Ca^{2+}-activated proteolytic breakdown associated with the earlier hypotheses. Whether it is necessary to include a mutant SR Ca^{2+} release channel, as in porcine MH, remains questionable.

An additional factor that should be investigated in relationship to this new model is the consideration of the fiber type affected in burnt tunas vs unburnt tunas. A complication in fish is that two isoforms of the SR Ca^{2+} release channel, α and β, are expressed in their swimming musculature (131). Recent work (B Block, unpublished observations) indicates that many

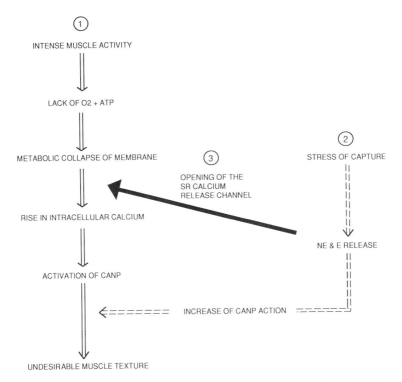

Figure 2 Models for tuna burn. Previous explanations for the increased heat production and damage caused by tuna burn suggested involvement of Ca^{2+} (1) and catecholamines (2) as potentiators of the syndrome (159). The hypothesis presented here incorporates the SR Ca^{2+} release channel into the previous models.

large yellowfin and big-eye tunas have a large number of fast-twitch oxidative fibers mixed in with the fast-twitch glycolytic population. Both fiber types are enriched in SR and thus have a high content of the SR Ca^{2+} release channel. Such a high content of aerobic fast-twitch fibers (58) is unusual in fish and may be an important component of why and how these fish get burnt, whereas other large game fish caught under similar conditions (blue marlin) do not. The current hypothesis suggests that it is the prevalence of these fiber types, enriched with SR and the Ca^{2+} release channel that is the causative agent for the burnt tuna syndrome. An abnormality (genetic mutation) in the tuna SR Ca^{2+} release channel of skeletal muscle may account for the disruption in SR Ca^{2+} homeostasis in the tuna muscle. In this model, as suggested by earlier models, stress and the effects of catecholamines are the major cause of the syndrome. However, it remains possible that as in the mammalian MH syndrome reviewed below, a genetic predisposition for the tuna burn syndrome involves a mutation in the SR Ca^{2+} release channel. The capacity to link polymorphisms in the skeletal SR Ca^{2+} release channel to wild populations of tunas would be an arduous task. However, amplifying and sequencing a 1 kb region around the porcine mutation might be a quick way to discern if there is a key amino acid difference in this region of the tuna SR Ca^{2+} release channel. A complication of this strategy would be the need to acquire fish sequences from normal RYRs to ensure establishing phylogenetic-specific substitutions. Initial studies could focus on the properties of the isolated SR Ca^{2+} release channel in normal and burnt tunas to establish if there are differences in the probability of the open state of the channel and ligand binding properties as was done on porcine MH.

Ca^{2+}-MEDIATED THERMOGENESIS IN MAMMALS

Long term exposure to cold temperatures has been shown to significantly increase BMR in mammals (42, 76, 161). This increase in metabolic rate of cold-acclimated mammals has been linked to nonshivering thermogenesis due in part to skeletal muscle (95). In mammals, the control of nonshivering thermogenesis has been shown to be regulated through the sympathetic nervous system, although the cellular basis for this remains unclear (95, 96, 97). For example, a calorigenic response to catecholamines in cold-acclimated mammals increases metabolic rate as much as five times the BMR (83). The first response to cold exposure in mammals is to shiver and increase heat production through muscle contractions that produce no useful work. Long-term cold exposure results in further elevation of whole body metabolism; shivering subsides and nonshivering thermogenesis is the cause for the increased energy expenditure (95, 97, 98, 126). The increased heat production from norepinephrine appears to be closely associated with the level of nonshivering thermogenesis (97). There are numerous hypotheses about the organs responsible and the mechanistic basis for nonshivering thermogenesis in mammals. Blood flow measurements have established that most nonshivering thermogenesis in small mammals is associated with brown adipose tissue (85, 130). While brown adipose tissue (BAT) elicits a large proportion of the metabolic response to cold in small mammals, calculations of the total heat production of BAT fall short of accounting for all the nonshivering thermogenesis heat production (48, 94). Additionally, BAT is less than 0.3% of the body mass of most large mammals and cannot by size alone be the only site of nonshivering thermogenesis. The controversy as to how much and by what means skeletal muscle contributes to nonshivering thermogenesis has not been settled. Long-term cold exposure induces numerous alterations in skeletal muscles that result in an increase of oxygen demand and elevation of serum free fatty acids (31, 32, 33, 146). The large mass of muscle as a percent of mammalian body mass, and the metabolic stimulation evident in response to thyroid hormone as well as catecholamines, are suggestive of a key thermogenic role for this tissue during long-term cold exposure.

Clausen et al (47) provide an extensive review of the significance of cation transport in skeletal muscle metabolism under a variety of conditions. At rest, ATPases such as the Ca^{2+} ATPase and the Na^+,K^+ ATPase consume only a small portion of the skeletal muscle resting metabolism. However, during stimulation associated with contraction, the metabolic rate of muscle rises quickly through ATP consuming processes, cross-bridge cycling, and Ca^{2+} cycling. Calculations of the costs of Ca^{2+} cycling are obtained in stretched muscle where myofilament overlap is small and the energy released is measured as heat liberated (47, 139). Activation heat measurements (heat produced at zero force) from contracting muscles indicate that 20–50% of the energetic turnover is associated with SR Ca^{2+} cycling. Muscles with a higher proportion of fast-twitch fibers, and thus SR, consume a larger fraction of the total energy from the relative contribution of Ca^{2+} cycling than do muscles composed of slow-twitch fibers with lower SR content (113). Thus a major energy consuming pathway of the skeletal muscle cell, Ca^{2+} cycling, is implicated as a mechanism for heat generation in working muscles. This is significant given that nonshivering thermogenesis, by definition, implies that the myofibrillar component (actomyosin ATPase) of a muscle cell is not involved in heat generation. However, models for nonshivering thermogenesis must reconcile the relatively low cost of maintaining ionic balance when muscle is not contracting. That is, there must be some stimulatory event that enhances cation turnover (i.e. prolonged stimulation or leak of sarcoplasmic Ca^{2+} release channel and elevation of cytoplasmic Ca^{2+} below contraction threshold) if Ca^{2+} cycling is a significant thermogenic source when muscle is not contracting.

Cold acclimation studies in mammals indicate that there is a generalized increase in the ion permeability of membranes in a variety of tissues (42). The increased active transport required to balance increases in membrane permeability could serve as one of the effectors stimulating cellular metabolism. Cold acclimation, as well as thyroxine, in mammals results in significant increases in the Ca^{2+} transport properties of skeletal muscle SR (2, 47, 148). Although such changes are suggestive of a major role for Ca^{2+} transport and cycling in skeletal muscle energy turnover and thermogenesis, doubt remains. Interestingly, the components of the muscle cell responsible for Ca^{2+} cycling, the Ca^{2+} release channel, and Ca^{2+} ATPase have homologues in liver endoplasmic reticulum, a tissue long thought to have a role in NST. The best evidence of a cellular pathway in mammalian skeletal muscle capable of extraordinary thermogenesis and associated with Ca^{2+} cycling in muscle has been found in the elucidation of the molecular cause of mammalian MH (72, 116).

MALIGNANT HYPERTHERMIA   The role of Ca^{2+} and its stimulatory effect on muscle metabolism and thermogenesis in mammals is best illustrated in MH, where a rapid and often lethal rise in body temperature is linked to abnormalities of Ca^{2+} regulation in muscle cell cytoplasm. The proposed mechanism for thermogenesis in MH (116) bears striking resemblance to the proposed mechanism of thermogenesis in the fish heater organs (Figure 1). In humans and mammals with the genetic disorder, the syndrome is characterized by a rapid increase in muscle temperature and muscle rigidity under certain types of stresses (72). MH in humans is a syndrome that is most often triggered with volatile anesthetics. The syndrome characteristically is associated with thermogenesis in muscle leading to hyperthermia, metabolic acidosis, rhabdomyolysis, myoglobinuria, and elevated plasma creatine phosphokinase (72, 88). Altered biochemical and physiological properties of the isolated SR Ca^{2+} release channel have been detected in SR isolated from MH pigs vs normal pigs, which indicates a possible defect of the SR Ca^{2+} release channel (108, 127). Similarly, high rates of Ca^{2+}-induced Ca^{2+} release and increased sensitivity to caffeine were observed in human heavy SR preparations enriched in the release channel from MH patients (65). Trypsin digestion of the porcine Ca^{2+} release channel suggested an alteration in the primary sequence (108). Linkage between polymorphic markers and porcine MH led to the identification of the locus for MH pigs to chromosome 6 (115, 122). The gene encoding skeletal SR Ca^{2+} release channel, RYR1, also mapped to a related region of chromosome 19 in humans and became a suspect in the cause of MH (115). The biochemical results suggesting a hyperactive or leaky SR calcium release channel (65) and the genetic results indicating possible linkage of MH with the channel led to a large sequencing effort of porcine RYR1 cDNAs to discern whether a mutation was associated with the condition (67, 116). Porcine MH has been genetically linked to a single point mutation of RYR1. A substitution of a cysteine for arginine (i.e. substitution of cytosine for thymine at nucleotide position 1843), in the porcine SR calcium release channel is presumed to be the primary defect. Similarly, a C (nucelotide 1840) for T substitution in the human RYR1 gene was found in a few patients susceptible to MH; however, numerous human MH-susceptible patients do not show this substitution, which indicates that it is not the mutation associated with the syndrome in humans (68a). Thus hypersensitive gating of the SR Ca^{2+} release channel underlies the defect of MH responsible for thermogenesis. The discovery of the mutation and linkage to SR Ca^{2+} cycling provides clear evidence for the molecular pathway increasing energy utilization and thermogenesis in skeletal muscle.

ROLE OF FREE FATTY ACIDS ON RYANODINE RECEPTOR   The MH syndrome in humans is also thought to be linked with other defects such as a deficiency in the enzyme, carnitine palmitoyl transferase, which catalyzes the transport of long chain acyl carnitines into the matrix of the mitochondria (158). The etiology of transferase deficiencies indicates that Ca^{2+} toxicity may be occurring in the muscle cell cytoplasm; however, until recently, a mechanistic basis for this etiology was not clearly defined. Palmitoyl carnitine and esterified long chain fatty acids (FFA) have been shown to selectively activate the SR Ca^{2+} release channel in mammals and frogs in a physiological range (62). The increase in SR permeability in response to the long chain length FFAs provides a possible pathway for myoplasmic Ca^{2+} concentrations to increase in response to a local build up of FFA in the myoplasm. El-Hayek et al (62) have proposed that palmitoyl carnitine binds to and modulates gating of the SR Ca^{2+} release channel and is capable of increasing the Ca^{2+} permeability of the skeletal muscle SR reticulum by direct interaction with a functionally important region of the molecule (Figure 3). Interestingly, only long chain acyl carnitines of a certain length (C_{14}, C_{16}, C_{18}) induce SR Ca^{2+} release. This newly identified interaction of a substrate metabolite with the Ca^{2+} release channel is a strong candidate for the endogenous thermogenic factor linking Ca^{2+} cycling, β-oxidation, and muscle cell metabolism for heat generation. More research is required to resolve whether the interactions arise from the fatty acids interacting with the channel protein itself through an actual fatty acid binding domain, or from a partitioning of the FFAs into the membrane and a resultant alteration of the properties of the membrane surrounding the protein. Lipid metabolites have been shown to mobilize Ca^{2+} from intracellular stores and have been implicated as second messengers in a variety of signal transduction pathways involving ion channels (16, 45, 135).

The clear effect of FFAs on the Ca^{2+} permeability of SR suggests that an increase in acyl carnitine production during exercise or nonshivering thermogenesis could effectively increase Ca^{2+} release and muscle cell metabolic processes that are activated by Ca^{2+}. Elevation of cytoplasmic $[Ca^{2+}]$ is a potent stimulator of mitochondrial oxidative processes (56). Fatty acid mobilization occurs by a variety of mechanisms (epinephrine, glucagon, growth factors), and substrates can be found either in the cytoplasm or the blood. Additionally, the plasmalemma contains a rich source of phospholipids that can be released via the action of cellular phos-

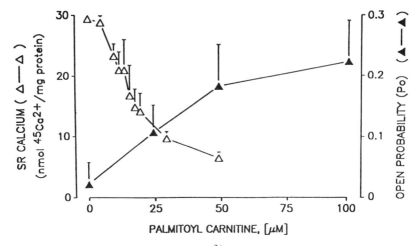

Figure 3   FFAs activate the skeletal muscle Ca^{2+} release channel in mammals. Certain long chain fatty acids prolong the open time of the SR calcium release channel in mammals. Open triangles correspond to vesicles of porcine skeletal muscle SR loaded with $^{45}Ca^{2+}$ and exposed to solutions containing various palmitoyl carnitine concentrations at room temperature. Ca^{2+} release in the presence of uM palmitoyl carnitine occurs. This is indicated by the reduction of $^{45}Ca^{2+}$ in vesicles after a filtration assay (*open triangles*). Filled triangles correspond to open time of Ca^{2+} release channels from porcine SR at the indicated palmitoyl carnitine concentrations (from 61a).

pholipases. A heat-generating cycle could commence with hydrolysis of triacylglycerol by lipases in the cell cytoplasm. Accumulation of long chain fatty acids in the cytoplasm would increase myoplasmic Ca^{2+} and generate considerable heat from futile Ca^{2+} cycling. Lipolysis could, in fact, be the stimulatory event that then leads to Ca^{2+} release and increased cycling. SR $Ca^{2+}ATP$ turnover by the Ca^{2+} ATPase would increase cytoplasmic adenylates and stimulate mitochondrial respiration. The increased demand for FFAs from the oxidative processes within the mitochondria would feedback and stimulate cytoplasmic demand for increased lipolysis. A plausible link (or pathway) thus exists between the increase in FFAs that occurs during cold acclimation (7) to a change in the permeability of the SR membrane that leads to increased energy utilization and heat production. Lipolysis brought about by norepinephrine control is the stimulatory event in brown adipose tissue thermogenesis. Given the well demonstrated role of catecholamines in nonshivering thermogenesis, it remains possible that a FFA-mediated futile Ca^{2+} cycling pathway in skeletal muscle could be initiated with catecholamines (Figure 1c).

NONSHIVERING THERMOGENESIS IN BIRDS: A Role for Muscle?

Endothermy in mammals and birds has many features in common including the physiological responses to cold stress (42, 52, 83). Although regulatory thermogenesis in mammals has been the subject of intense investigation for decades, the physiological responses and adaptations of birds to cold has received less study; this despite the impressive thermoregulatory abilities of small birds and in particular the model they represent for skeletal muscle-based thermogenesis. Many small birds winter in high latitudes and encounter cold temperatures that require elevations in thermogenic capacities on seasonal time scales. The thermogenic capabilities of birds of the avian subfamily Carduelinae (goldfinches, house finches redpolls) are impressive and in many cases exceed the abilities of mammals. For example, goldfinches can maintain a metabolic rate of five times standard metabolic rate for 6–8 hr during ambient temperatures of −70°C in winter (53). The same birds in the springtime will become hypothermic after only a few minutes of exposure (53). This change occurs without any change in aerobic capacity of the skeletal muscles, which are the major thermogenic tissues in birds (35, 119).

The cold-induced metabolic scope has been examined in a few studies and has been shown to range three to eight times BMR (164). Metabolic scope during flight can range five to ten times BMR and thus exceeds maximum metabolism elicited by cold (28, 120). Rates of oxygen consumption by birds during sustained flying are among the highest reported for vertebrates. Flight muscles, particularly the pectoralis and supercoracoideus, of birds reflect this intense metabolic demand with adaptations that facilitate uptake and utilization of oxygen and energy substrates. Mass-specific aerobic capacities are among the highest in the animal kingdom (35, 119, 152). The extraordinary metabolic demands for flight in birds select for skeletal muscle fiber types with high rates of substrate utilization, and predispose the use of these muscles in birds as thermogenic organs. Histochemical studies have demonstrated that the flight muscle of birds are composed predominantly of fast glycolytic and fast-oxidative-glycolytic fiber types (35, 68, 117, 155). The latter fibers are rich in mitochondria, SR, and T-tubules and have high substrate oxidation rates (118, 119).

Birds meet the bulk of the increased thermogenic needs in response to cold stress with shivering thermogenesis (162). Electromyograms indicate shivering at all temperatures below the thermal neutrality zone. The relative importance of shivering thermogenesis vs nonshivering thermogenesis in birds, as in mammals, is still a matter of active debate (11, 50). Two questions that have been raised in the avian literature and have been well examined are still unresolved. (*a*) Is there a cold-induced facultative non-shivering thermogenesis in birds? (*b*) Is skeletal muscle the main site of NST in birds?

Early studies by El Halawani et al (62a) demonstrated an increased capacity for nonshivering thermogenesis in cold-acclimated birds. Similarly, Barré et al (9) demonstrated a large increase in the metabolic rate of cold-acclimated muscovy ducklings that could not be attributed to shivering activity. These two studies demonstrate a nonshivering thermogenic component to cold adaptation in birds, although the site of this response remains controversial. The key role of a specialized thermogenic organ in mammals (BAT) has continually led to a search for a similar tissue in birds. The issue of whether or not BAT is present in birds has been addressed morphologically and biochemically by numerous studies (9, 114, 133, 143, 144). Although birds have been reported to have a multiocular adipose tissue, with some similarities to mammalian brown adipose tissue, it lacks the key biochemical features (presence of uncoupling protein) and thus is functionally white adipose tissue (144). From the reported morphological and biochemical evidence, one must reject the hypothesis that birds have brown adipose tissue and look elsewhere for the cold-induced increased heat production. This is expected from an evolutionary standpoint. It would be highly unlikely that birds would independently evolve the exact same specialized adipose tissues of mammals. Thus a major difference in cold defense between mammals and birds is the lack of a specialized thermogenic organ. However, as discussed above, the high oxidative capacity of the flight muscles may preclude the need for such a thermogenic organ. As in the tuna example of endothermy, it is quite clear that the presence of a highly oxidative muscle phenotype for locomotion predisposes the use of this tissue as a furnace.

How Do Birds Stay Warm?

Dawson and colleagues have shown that passerines and birds of the family Carduelidae, which overwinter in cold latitudes, undergo a pronounced seasonal acclimatization involving an increased resistance to cold (55). Birds overwintering in northern latitudes have been shown to have a substantial increase in their thermogenic capacities and withstand cold exposure far longer than summer birds (55). This physiological response involves enhanced abilities for increasing heat production for sustained periods (119). Thermoregulatory stresses are more severe for many of these small birds (10–20g) because of the decreased amounts of insulation associated with their small size (34). The metabolic processes of acclimatization involve numerous biochemical changes in the flight muscles, which comprise 15–25% of body mass in adult birds (53, 54, 55, 75). Acclimatization involves increasing energy reserves (lipid), improved mobilization of substrates to fuel thermogenesis, and a greater reliance on lipid metabolism during cold stress (119). In most cases documented, aerobic capacity as determined by marker enzymes for aerobic catabolism does not change much in flight muscles, but can be augmented in leg muscles, which contribute to shivering at low temperatures (36). The metabolic demands of flight are greater than the aerobic demands of cold exposure. The lack of change in aerobic capacity within the major muscle masses associated with thermogenesis has led to a focus on the change in energy substrate utilization during cold exposure, given the result that lipid metabolism appears to be playing a key role in the process of metabolic acclimatization (120). The specific activity of β-hydroxyacyl-CoA dehydrogenase in pectoralis muscles, a key enzyme in the β-oxidation pathway, increases 50–100% in cold-acclimated American goldfinches (120). The exact role of seasonally enhanced levels of increased β-oxidative capacity is not entirely clear from the existing literature, but may be involved with a role of FFA in augmenting thermogenesis. However, recent studies indicate that house finches do not undergo a seasonal change in the capacity to oxidize lipid, which complicates the interpretation of a role for lipid in stimulating thermogenesis (T O'Connor, personal communication).

The research programs on cold acclimation in overwintering birds assume that shivering thermogenesis is the major source of enhanced muscle-based heat production during winter. Nonshivering thermogenesis in winter-acclimatized birds remains subject to debate (52). Although the exact thermogenic mechanism (in wild birds) remains unclear, the seasonal changes in metabolic heat production and the well documented increased capacity for shivering thermogenesis (162) point to the flight muscles as the major source of heat. What remains to be resolved is whether the muscles are contributing via both pathways (shivering and nonshivering thermogenesis). The two are not mutually exclusive, and the basic enhancements required for energy consumption via nonshivering thermogenic pathways would indeed increase the energy consumption during shivering thermogenesis. Thus the issue is not whether muscle is involved, most research in this area would support the role of skeletal muscle involvement. What is at issue is how it is involved, and an objective view would suggest that both mechanisms are at work.

A MECHANISM FOR THERMOGENESIS IN AVIAN SKELETAL MUSCLE   In ducklings, Barré et al (12) demonstrated that cold exposure induces the development of nonshivering thermogenesis of muscular origin. The exact pathway for this response is currently being elucidated and appears to involve free fatty acids (FFAs) and possibly futile Ca^{2+} cycling. Prolonged cold exposure in birds has long been linked to increases in FFA levels in the plasma (13, 66, 99, 136, 159). Barré et al (12) demonstrated that FFAs increased respiration in skeletal muscle mitochondria from cold-acclimated ducklings, but did not effect membrane potential. A potent calorigenic effect of glucagon in birds, similar in scope to the norepinephrine-induced thermogenesis in mammals, has also been documented (10). Glucagon results in release of FFA in birds, and it is postulated that in response to the hormone, increases of cytoplasmic FFA would result in partial uncoupling of skeletal muscle mitochondria with a concomitant increase of respiration and heat production.

Dumonteil et al (61) recently provided evidence supporting the idea that increased ATP-dependent cycling of Ca^{2+} may underlie the nonshivering thermogenesis of muscular origin in birds. The role of futile Ca^{2+} cycling of the SR in muscular nonshivering thermogenesis was determined by examining the Ca^{2+} transport activities of muscle homogenates and heavy SR microsomal fractions from thermoneutral and cold-acclimated ducklings. As in cold-acclimated mammals (2), these studies demonstrate increased Ca^{2+} loading capabilities in direct response to cold adaptation. The studies indicate that the Ca^{2+} transporting system of skeletal muscle SR undergoes a significant increase in activity associated with cold stimulation. Importantly, cold-acclimated ducklings show an increase in SR Ca^{2+} release channel content in the cold. The result is suggestive of a role of Ca^{2+} cycling in nonshivering thermogenesis of muscular origin. Future studies should decipher whether such qualitative increases in the properties of Ca^{2+} transport and release are due to changes in SR volume in specific muscle fibers or due to increased packing of the proteins within the same SR volume. Dumonteil et al (60) have also shown a potential role of FFAs for potentiating SR Ca^{2+} cycling. Palmitoyl carnitine stimulated [³H] ryanodine binding in cold-acclimated SR isolated from muscovy duckling muscle in a concentration-dependent manner. Palmitoyl carnitine also induced rapid Ca^{2+} release from passively loaded SR vesicles. The two results suggest that a FFA-mediated thermogenic pathway involving ATP-dependent Ca^{2+} cycling may exist between the SR and cytoplasm (as in model Figure 1c and mammals, Figure 3).

The cold acclimation response is evolutionarily conserved in vertebrates, and the results for birds as well as mammals must be examined with this in mind. Numerous vertebrates in response to cold acclimation increase the mitochondrial and SR volume, as well as Ca^{2+} ATPase content in certain muscle fiber types (2, 61, 147). For ectotherms, the cellular adaptations are hypothesized to increase the ATP delivery and relaxation components of the muscle cells and thus power output in the face of decreasing diffusion potential due to cold. In endotherms, one has to decipher whether the increased Ca^{2+} transport properties of the SR and increased mitochondrial content of the muscle fibers in response to cold (33, 49, 61) are just an evolutionary vestige of this primitive vertebrate response. Based on the above discussion, there remains a possible link between cold acclimation in vertebrates and the increased substrate mobilization that may ultimately lead to the explanation of how nonshivering thermogenesis evolved in birds and mammals. The ancestral physiological response of certain ectothermic vertebrates to cold is to increase SR volume in certain muscle fibers and hence increase the surface area of the Ca^{2+} ATPase, the limiting step in muscle relaxation times (147). This adaptive response could have been present in the reptilian ancestors of birds and mammals. It is possible that the ectothermic vertebrate physiological response to cold (increasing the aerobic capacity of the fiber, SR volume, and Ca^{2+} release and sequestering proteins, and substrate mobilization) were modified more for wasting of energy or futile cycling, and hence heat production, rather than for the earlier function of maintaining muscle power output. This latter function would not be a problem given that birds and mammals maintain their body temperatures at elevated temperatures. The process of cold acclimation may be hardwired into the evolutionary program of some vertebrates and has since been modified (perhaps hormonally or sympathetically) to increase the level of energetic turnover, and thus thermogenesis during cold stress periods in endotherms. It remains possible that endotherms may have evolved an endogenous agonist (thyroid hormone, glucagon, epinephrine) that stimulates aerobic metabolism through the Ca^{2+} cycling pathway (i.e. opening of the SR Ca^{2+} release channel and possibly liver ryanodine receptors) in response to cold.

HEAT GENERATION IN INSECT MUSCLES

Within the class insecta, endothermy of muscular origin is widespread. Thermogenesis occurs during a wide variety of activities including flying, running, singing, pre-flight warm up, and social activities (64, 79, 80, 82). Flying insects achieve the highest mass-specific rates of aerobic energy expenditure in the animal kingdom (14, 15) and are able to harness exogenous heat from the high rates of substrate flux occurring in their muscles during periods of activity (81). Insect muscle efficiencies range from 4–11% and thus liberate substantial heat as a byproduct of the inefficient coupling of chemical energy into mechanical work. Heat generation is substantial enough in insects that over-heating is a problem during flight, and elaborate strategies for heat dissipation have evolved (80).

The high oxidative capacity of insect flight muscles is made possible by the direct delivery of oxygen by the tracheal system. Mitochondrial morphometric measurements demonstrate higher inner mitochondrial surface densities in bees and blowflies than in mammals of similar size (41, 91, 153). Marker enzymes for aerobic metabolism are two to threefold higher per volume of mitochondria than in vertebrate mitochondria (153). Insects are able to access oxygen and generate ATP at a rate that exceeds limits possible in a similar volume of vertebrate mitochondria. Suarez & Moyes (153) examined respiration in isolated coupled mitochondria from locust flight muscle and found oxygen consumption rates that exceed by threefold published values obtained in the most oxidative vertebrate muscle mitochondria (Table 1). The best explanation for this capability is the difference in oxygen delivery to the muscle cell. The high rates of oxygen consumption and substrate oxidation, along with the low efficiency of myofibrillar muscle (63), indicate that heat production occurs as a by-product of substrate flux stimulated by the hydrolysis of ATP, the result of cross-bridge cycling and Ca^{2+} cycling.

The muscle efficiency of insects during flight or stridulation is substantially lower than estimates for vertebrate muscle efficiency (63, 103, 151). Two types of muscle tissue power activities in insects, and they are classified as asynchronous and synchronous muscles (137) on the basis of the neural control of contraction. Synchronous and asynchronous muscles are capable of oscillating at high frequencies with asynchronous muscles reaching contraction frequencies of 1000 Hz (149) and synchronous muscles operating as high as 550 Hz during sound production in certain cicadas (105). Synchronous muscles are similar to vertebrate skeletal muscle; each action potential results in depolarization and contraction. Asynchronous muscle differs significantly from the vertebrate skeletal muscles in that rapid contraction oscillations are obtained from a single action potential. Asynchronous muscles structurally offer a paradox when considering how and why so much heat is generated. The muscle is characterized by an almost complete lack of SR and transverse T-tubules, the energetically costly (and thus thermogenic) components of most vertebrate muscles that operate at high frequencies for long periods. Morphometric analysis suggests that asynchronous muscle appears to offer the advantage of high frequency operation without the high operating costs of synchronous muscles. In synchronous muscle, high frequency operation is obtained by expanding the surface area available for the proteins that sequester and release calcium. Hypertrophy of the SR is associated with a reduction of myofibrillar volume (22% myofibril in *O. vanduzeei*). Comparison of similar frequency tymbal muscles, one asynchronous and the other synchronous, indicates that the fibrillar muscle has more myofibrillar cross-section (49% myofibril; 3% SR) by volume than the cicada using synchronous muscles (104, 105). Thus although it costs more metabolically for Ca^{2+} cycling in the synchronous muscle, cross-bridge cycling in the asynchronous muscle, because of a larger component of myofibrils, must be significantly higher. Both types of muscles presumably have high operating costs, and this is reflected in the high mitochondria volumes of both muscle fiber types (39–42% of fiber volume). The mitochondrial volumes reflect substantial capacities for adenylate turnover, and it would be interesting to determine whether similar amounts of heat are generated as a consequence of their use.

In synchronous muscles, as in vertebrate fast-twitch oxidative muscles, a large fraction of the muscle cell volume is devoted to SR packed with the Ca^{2+} ATPase (102, B Block, personal observation). The mitochondrial volume is also large (44% of myofibril volume) as a result of the metabolic expense of cycling Ca^{2+}. The overall result is a reduction in available myofibrillar volume. Stridulation requires less tension development, and thus the reduction of contractile protein can be tolerated. Although the volume of muscle associated with cross-bridge cycling has been reduced, the energetic cost of achieving high frequency is shifted to the use of SR Ca^{2+} cycling, and the energetic expense is relatively high as evidenced by the numerous mitochondria, as discussed above. As in vertebrate FOG fibers, the cost of producing sustained high frequency contraction is elevated because of Ca^{2+} transport demands. Temperature recordings of singing Katydids indicate the large amounts of heat generated during singing when contraction frequencies are 150 s^{-1}. Such muscles, with their low myofibrillar volumes and high SR and mitochondrial content, provide a model system for studying the thermogenic output associated with Ca^{2+} cycling.

CONCLUSION

This brief review of muscular thermogenesis in animals leads to the question as to whether there are any indications of similar thermogenic mechanisms across the animal kingdom? Other than shivering, there remains some doubt. However, a common theme is that ATP-dependent cycling of Ca^{2+} between the SR and the cytosol is emerging as a key pathway for muscular thermogenesis. The discovery of the SR Ca^{2+} release channel, and more recently the role of ligands that may alter the permeability of SR to Ca^{2+}, provide an interesting direction for future research into muscular as well as non-muscular thermogenesis. There is substantial evidence suggesting that thermogenesis in skeletal muscle may be linked to aerobic fast-twitch fiber types, changes in the permeability of SR membrane to cations and ATP utilization by the Ca^{2+} pump, and increased substrate oxidation rates in the mitochondria. As power requirements for locomotion increase with continual need for speed, a general reliance among animals on the fast-twitch, FOG fiber type (or similar phenotype such as the synchronous muscle fibers of insects) is apparent. Similarly, the use of FFA as a fuel increases. Aerobic fiber types are predisposed for ATP production required for sustained thermogenesis. The preferential use of FFAs by such fiber types may be the endogenous thermogenic effector that links the ATP-generating potential with a stimulatory effector (Figure 1c). FFAs have often been hypothesized to be the second messenger for activation of thermogenesis. In mammalian thermogenesis studies, FFAs were originally proposed to have had uncoupling effects on mitochondria (87, 138). In mammalian BAT, norepinephrine stimulates lipolysis that results in the release of FFAs. The FFAs regulate, or act, as endogenous agents controlling the activity of the uncoupling protein, a proton translocator. Similarly, recent research is suggestive of a role of FFAs in regulating thermogenesis in cold-acclimated bird muscle via the SR Ca^{2+} release channel.

In certain vertebrates there is a generalized physiological set of responses to cold acclimation (42, 78). In cold-acclimated animals, whether they are fish or mammals, mitochondrial volume, lipid content, and sarcoplasmic reticulum volume change in a fiber-type dependent manner (8, 33, 59, 147). The morphological changes are associated in ectothermic animals with maintaining the ATP supply as temperature declines. Such changes would have less importance for endotherms maintaining a constant temperature. The increase of oxidative capacity and SR volume in endotherms may promote heat production via shivering and nonshivering thermogenesis. Thermogenic mechanisms in muscle tissue may be built upon a phylogenetically primitive physiological response in vertebrates (increase of cytoplasmic SR and mitochondrial components in response to cold) and a modification of the pathway for wasting energy as heat may be occurring in endotherms (7). Current knowledge of the role of FFAs on increasing the permeability of SR in mammals suggests that a basic thermogenic pathway is available if long chain fatty acids are, in fact, stimulating the open probability of the SR Ca^{2+} release channel. While Ca^{2+} release increases catabolic processes that may be important for delivering ATP for power, there must be a simultaneous increase in heat production. Whether there is an endogenous thermogenic effector in muscle (hormonally or sympathetically mediated) that, when released, increases the permeability of the SR via the SR Ca^{2+} release channel, thereby increasing the heat production via futile calcium cycling during periods of rest for thermogenic purposes (i.e. nonshivering thermogenesis), remains to be elucidated.

Several lines of evidence point to a common pathway of thermogenesis in skeletal muscle involving the proteins responsible for Ca^{2+} release and reuptake, lipids and mitochondria. Within the next decade, our current knowledge of the molecular channels and pumps in muscle cell Ca^{2+} homeostasis should permit the deciphering of the exact pathway for nonshivering thermogenesis in skeletal muscle. Muscles are built along a similar plan across animals. As we define the pathways and generate hypotheses, we should use the power of the comparative method for strengthening our knowledge of the role of muscle as a furnace.

ACKNOWLEDGMENTS

Work in the author's laboratory was supported by National Institutes of Health grant AR 40246 and National Science Foundation grant IBN 895-8225. I thank Mark Beamsley, John O'Brien, John Finnerty, Alexa Tullis, and Tim O'Connor for discussions and help in preparation of the manuscript.

Literature Cited

1. Abbott BC, Howarth JV. 1973. Heat studies in excitable tissues. *Physiol. Rev.* 53:120–58
2. Agostini B, Demartino L, Soltau B, Hasselbach W. 1991. The modulation of the calcium transport by skeletal muscle sarcoplasmic reticulum in the hibernating European hamster. *Z. Naturforsch.* 46:1109–26
3. Airey JA, Beck CF, Murakami K, Tanksley SJ, Deerinck TJ, et al. 1990. Identification and localization of two triad junctional foot protein isoforms in mature avian fast twitch skeletal muscle. *J. Biol. Chem.* 265:14187–94
4. Appelt D, Shen V, Franzini-Armstrong C. 1991. Quantitation of Ca ATPase, feet and mitochondria in superfast muscle fibers from the toadfish, *Opsanus tau. J. Mus. Res. Cell Motil.* 12:543–52
5. Bach-y-Rita P, Ito F. 1966. In vivo studies of fast and slow muscle fibers in cat extraocular muscle. *J. Gen. Physiol.* 49:1177–98
6. Ballantyne JS, Chamberlin ME, Singer TD. 1992. Oxidative metabolism in thermogenic tissues of the swordfish and mako shark. *J. Exp. Zool.* 261:110–14
7. Ballantyne JS, George JC. 1977. The effects of long chain fatty acids on the respiration of liver mitochondria of cold and warm acclimated rat, pigeon and trout. *J. Thermal Biol.* 2:239–45
8. Ballantyne JS, George JC. 1978. An ultrastructural and histological analysis of the effects of cold acclimation on vertebrate skeletal muscle. *J. Thermal Biol.* 3:109–16
9. Barré H, Cohen-Adad F, Duchamp C, Rouanet J. 1986. Multilocular adipocytes from muscovy ducklings differentiated in response to cold acclimation. *J. Physiol.* 375:27–38
10. Barré H, Cohen-Adad F, Rouanet J. 1987. Two daily glucagon injections induce nonshivering thermogenesis in Muscovy ducklings. *Am. J. Physiol.* 252:E616–20
11. Barré H, Duchamp C, Rouanet J-L, Dittmar A, Delhomme G. 1989. Muscular nonshivering thermogenesis in cold-acclimated ducklings. In *Physiology of Cold Adaptation in Birds,* ed. C Bech, RE Reinertsen, pp. 49–58. New York: Plenum
12. Barré H, Geloen A, Chatonnet J, Dittmar A, Rouanet J. 1985. Potentiated muscular thermogenesis in cold-acclimated muscovy duckling. *Am. J. Physiol.* 249:R533–38
13. Barré H, Nedergaard J, Cannon B. 1986. Increased respiration in skeletal muscle mitochondria from cold-acclimated ducklings: uncoupling effect of free fatty acids. *Comp. Biochem. Physiol.* 85B:343–348
14. Bartholomew GA. 1981. A matter of size: an examination of endothermy in insects and terrestrial vertebrates. In *Insect Thermoregulation,* ed. B Heinrich, pp. 45–78. New York: Wiley & Sons
15. Bartholomew GA, Casey TM. 1973. Oxygen consumption of moths during rest, pre-flight warm-up, and flight in relation to body size and wing morphology. *J. Exp. Biol.* 76:11–25
16. Berridge MJ, Irvine RF. 1989. Inositol phosphates and cell signalling. *Nature* 341:187–204
17. Block BA. 1986. Structure of the brain and eye heater tissue in marlins, sailfish and spearfish. *J. Morphol.* 190:169–89
18. Block BA. 1987. The billfish brain

and eye heater: a new look at non-shivering thermogenesis. *News Physiol. Sci.* 2:208–13

19. Block BA. 1990. Phylogeny and ecology of brain and eye heaters in billfishes. In *Planning the Future of Billfishes,* ed. RH Stroud, pp. 123–36. Savannah, GA: National Coalition for Marine Conservation

20. Block BA. 1991. Endothermy in fish: thermogenesis, ecology and evolution. In *Biochemistry and Molecular Biology of Fishes,* ed. PW Hochachka, TP Mommsen, 1:269–311. New York: Elsevier

21. Block BA. 1991. Evolutionary novelties: how fish have built a heater out of muscle. *Am. Zool.* 31:726–42

22. Block BA, Finnerty JR. 1993. Endothermic strategies in fishes; A phylogenetic analysis of constraints, predispositions, and selective pressures. *Environ. Biol. Fish.* In press

23. Block BA, Finnerty JR, Stewart AFR, Kidd J. 1993. Evolution of endothermy in fish: mapping physiological traits on a molecular phylogeny. *Science* 260:210–14

24. Block BA, Franzini-Armstrong C. 1988. The structure of the membrane systems in a novel muscle cell modified for heat production. *J. Cell Biol.* 107:1099–112

25. Block BA, Franzini-Armstrong C, Lai FA, Meissner G. 1988. Identification of the triad and isolation of the ryanodine receptor from the thermogenic muscle tissue of fish. *Biophys. J.* 53(2):A470 (Abstr.)

26. Block BA, Kim SY. 1992. Localization of junctional SR proteins in the thermogenic heater cells of billfish. *Biophys. J.* 61(2):A429 (Abstr.)

27. Bone Q. 1978. Locomotor muscle. In *Fish Physiology,* ed. WS Hoar, DJ Randall, 361–424. New York/San Francisco/London: Academic

28. Brackenbury J. 1984. Physiological responses of birds to flight and running. *Biol. Rev.* 59:559

29. Brill RW. 1987. On the standard metabolic rates of tropical tunas, including the effect of body size and acute temperature change. *Fish. Bull.* 85:25–35

30. Brill RW, Dizon AE. 1979. Red and white muscle fibre activity in swimming skipjack tuna *Katsuwonus pelamis. J. Fish Biol.* 15:679–85

31. Bukowiecki L, Himms-Hagen J. 1971. Decreased half-life of some mitochondrial proteins in skeletal muscle and brown adipose tissue of cold-acclimated rats. *Can. J. Physiol. Pharmacol.* 49:1015–18

32. Bukowiecki L, Himms-Hagen J. 1976. Alterations of mitochondrial protein metabolism in liver, brown adipose tissue and skeletal muscle during cold acclimation. *Biochim. Biophys. Acta* 428:491–599

33. Buser KS, Kopp B, Gehr P, Weibel ER, Hoppler H. 1982. Effect of cold environment on skeletal muscle mitochondria in growing rats. *Cell Tissue Res.* 225:427–36

34. Calder WA, King JR. 1974. Thermal and caloric relations of birds. In *Avian Biology,* ed. DS Farner, JR King, pp. 259–413. New York: Academic

35. Carey C, Dawson WR, Maxwell LC, Faulkner JA. 1978. Seasonal acclimatization to temperature in cardueline finches. II. Changes in body composition and mass in relation to season and acute cold stress. *J. Comp. Physiol.* 125:101–13

36. Carey C, Marsh RL, Bekoff A, Johnston RM, Olin AM. 1989. Enzyme activities in muscles of seasonally acclimatized house finches. See Ref. 11, pp. 95–104

37. Carey FG. 1982. A brain heater in the swordfish. *Science* 216:1327–29

38. Carey FG. 1990. Further observations on the biology of the swordfish. See Ref. 19, pp. 103–22

39. Carey FG, Robison BH. 1981. Daily patterns in the activities of swordfish, *Xiphias gladius,* observed by acoustic telemetry. *Fish. Bull.* 79:277–92

40. Carey FG, Teal JM, Kanwisher JW, Lawson KD. 1971. Warm-bodied fish. *Am. Zool.* 11:137–45

41. Casey TM, Ellington CP. 1989. Energetics of insect flight. In *Energy Transformation in Cells and Animals,* ed. W Weiser, E Gnaiger, pp. 200–10. Stuttgart: Thieme

42. Chaffee RRJ, Roberts JC. 1971. Temperature acclimation in birds and mammals. *Annu. Rev. Physiol.* 33:155–202

43. Chiarandini DJ, Davidowitz J. 1979. Structure and function of extraocular muscle fibers. In *Current Topics in Eye Research,* ed. JA Zadunaisky, H Davson, pp. 91–142. New York: Academic

44. Chinet A, Giovannini P. 1989. Evidence by calorimetry for an activation of sodium-hydrogen exchange of young rat skeletal muscle in hypertonic media. *J. Physiol.* 415:409–22

45. Chow SC, Jondal M. 1990. Polyunsaturated free fatty acids stimulate an increase in cytosolic Ca^{2+} by mobiliz-

ing the inositol 1,4,5-triphosphate-sensitive Ca^{2+} pool in T cells through a mechanism independent of phosphoinositide turnover. *J. Biol. Chem.* 265: 902–7

46. Clausen T. 1986. Regulation of active Na^+-K^+ transport in skeletal muscle. *Physiol. Rev.* 66:542–74

47. Clausen T, Hardeveld CV, Everts ME. 1991. Significance of cation transport in control of energy metabolism and thermogenesis. *Physiol. Rev.* 71:733–74

48. Colquhoun EQ, Clark MG. 1991. Open question: has thermogenesis in muscle been overlooked and misinterpreted? *News Physiol. Sci.* 6:256–59

49. Conley KE, Weibel ER, Taylor CR, Hoppeler H. 1985. Aerobic capacity estimated by exercise vs cold-exposure: endurance training effects in rats. *Respir. Physiol.* 62:273–80

50. Connolly E, Nedergaard J, Cannon B. 1989. Shivering and nonshivering thermogenesis in birds: A mammalian view. See Ref. 11, pp. 37–48

51. Davie PS, Sparksman RI. 1986. Burnt tuna: an ultrastructural study of postmortem changes in muscle of yellowfin tuna (*Thunnus albacares*) caught by rod and reel and southern bluefin tuna. *J. Food Sci.* 51:1122–28

52. Dawson WR. 1975. Avian physiology. *Annu. Rev. Physiol.* 37:441–65

53. Dawson WR, Carey C. 1976. Seasonal acclimatization to temperature in cardueline finches. I. Insulative and metabolic adjustments. *J. Comp. Physiol.* 112:317–33

54. Dawson WR, Marsh RL. 1989. Metabolic acclimatization to cold and season in birds. See Ref. 11, pp. 83–94

55. Dawson WR, Marsh RL, Buttemer WA, Carey C. 1983. Seasonal and geographic variation of cold resistance in house finches. *Physiol. Zool.* 56: 353–69

56. Denton RM, McCormack JG. 1985. Ca^{2+} transport by mammalian mitochondria and its role in hormone action. *Am. J. Physiol.* 249:E543–54

57. Denton RM, McCormack JG. 1990. Ca^{2+} as a second messenger within mitochondria of the heart and other tissues. *Annu. Rev. Physiol.* 52:451–66

58. Dickson KA. 1993. Unique adaptations of the metabolic biochemistry of tunas and billfishes for life in the pelagic environment. *Environ. Biol. Fish.* In press

59. Duchamp C, Cohen-Adad F, Rouanet J, Barré H. 1992. Histochemical arguments for muscular non-shivering thermogenesis in muscovy ducklings. *J. Physiol.* 457:27–45

60. Dumonteil E, Barré H, Meissner G. 1993. Potential role of palmitoyl carnitine modulation of the avian Ca^{2+} release channel in muscular nonshivering thermogenesis. *Biophys. J.* 2(2): A304 (Abstr.)

61. Dumonteil E, Barré H, Meissner G. 1993. Sarcoplasmic reticulum Ca^{2+} ATPase and ryanodine receptor in cold-acclimated ducklings and thermogenesis. *Am. J. Physiol.* 265:C507–13

61a. El Halawani MES. 1970. Cold acclimation and the role of catecholamines in body temperature regulation in male leghorns. *Poultry Sci.* 49:621–32

62. El-Hayek R, Valdivia C, Valdivia HH, Coronado R. 1993. Activation of the Ca^{2+} release channel of skeletal muscle sarcoplasmic reticulum by palmitoyl carnitine. *Biophys. J.* 65:779–89

63. Ellington CP. 1985. Power and efficiency of insect flight muscle. *J. Exp. Biol.* 115:293–304

64. Esch H, Goller F. 1991. How do bees shiver? *Naturwissenschaften* 78:325–28

65. Fill M, Coronado R, Mickelson JR, Vilven J, Ma J, et al. 1990. Abnormal ryanodine receptor channels in malignant hyperthermia. *Biophys. J.* 50:471–75

66. Freeman BM. 1967. Some effects of cold on the metabolism of the fowl during the perinatal period. *Comp. Biochem. Physiol.* 20:179–93

67. Fujii J, Otsu K, Zorzato F, Leon SD, Khanna VK, et al. 1991. Identification of a mutation in porcine ryanodine receptor associated with malignant hyperthermia. *Science* 253:448–51

68. George JS, Berger AJ. 1966. *Avian Myology.* New York: Academic. 160 pp.

68a. Gillard EF, Otsu K, Fujii J, Khanna VK, De Leon S, et al. 1990. A substitution of cysteine for arginine 614 in the ryanodine receptor is potentially causative of human malignant hyperthermia. *Genomics* 11:751–55

69. Gooding RM, Neill WH, Dizon AE. 1981. Respiration rates and low-oxygen tolerance limits in skipjack tuna, *Katsuwonus pelamis. Fish. Bull.* 79: 31–48

70. Graham JB. 1973. Heat exchange in the black skipjack, and the blood-gas relationship of warm-bodied fishes. *Proc. Natl. Acad. Sci. USA* 70:1964–67

71. Graham JB, Koehrn FJ, Dickson KA. 1983. Distribution and relative proportions of red muscle in scombrid fishes: Consequences of body size and rela-

574   BLOCK

tionships to locomotion and endothermy. *Can. J. Zool.* 61:2087–96
72. Gronert G. 1980. Malignant hyperthermia. *Anaesthesiology* 53:395–423
73. Guppy M, Hulbert WC, Hochachka
PW. 1979. Metabolic sources of heat
and power in tuna muscles. II. Enzyme
and metabolite profiles. *J. Exp. Biol.*
82:303–20
74. Deleted in proof
75. Hart JS. 1962. Seasonal acclimatization
in four species of small wild birds.
Physiol. Zool. 35:224–36
76. Hart JS, Héroux O, Depocas F. 1956.
Cold acclimation and the electromyo-
gram of unanaesthetised rats. *J. Appl.
Physiol.* 9:404–8
77. Hasselbach W, Oetliker H. 1983. Energetics and electrogenicity of the sarcoplasmic reticulum calcium pump.
Annu. Rev. Physiol. 45:325–39
78. Hazel JR, Prosser CL. 1974. Molecular
mechanisms of temperature compensation in poikilotherms. *Physiol. Rev.*
54:620–77
79. Heinrich B. 1987. Thermoregulation
by winter-flying endothermic moths.
J. Exp. Biol. 127:313–32
80. Heinrich B. 1993. *The Hot-Blooded
Insects.* Cambridge, MA: Harvard
Univ. Press. 601 pp.
81. Heinrich B, Casey TM. 1973. Metabolic rate and endothermy in sphinx
moths. *J. Comp. Physiol.* 82:195–
206
82. Heinrich B, Mommsen TP. 1985.
Flight of winter moths at 0°C. *Science*
228:177–79
83. Himms-Hagen J. 1976. Cellular thermogenesis. *Annu. Rev. Physiol.* 38:
315–51
84. Himms-Hagen J. 1984. Nonshivering
thermogenesis. *Brain Res. Bull.* 12:
151–60
85. Himms-Hagen J. 1990. Brown adipose
tissue thermogenesis: interdisciplinary
studies. *FASEB J.* 4:2890–98
86. Himms-Hagen J, Behrens W, Muirhead
M, Hbous A. 1975. Adaptive changes
in the calorigenic effect of catecholamines: role of changes in the adenyl
cyclase system and of changes in the
mitochondria. *Mol. Cell. Biochem.* 6:
15–31
87. Hittelman KJ, Lindberg O. 1969. Oxidative phosphorylation and compart-
mentation of fatty acid metabolism in
brown fat mitochondria. *Eur. J. Biochem.* 11:183–92
88. Hogan K, Fergus C, Powers PA, Gregg
RG. 1992. A cysteine-for-arginine substitution (R614C) in the human skeletal
muscle calcium release channel cos-

egregates with malignant hyperthermia.
Anesth. Analg. 75:441–48
89. Holland KN, Brill RW, Chang RKC.
1990. Horizontal and vertical movements of Pacific blue marlin captured
and released using sportfishing gear.
Fish. Bull. 88:397–402
90. Homsher E, Kean CJ. 1978. Skeletal
muscle energetics and metabolism.
Annu. Rev. Physiol. 40:93–131
91. Hoppeler H, Lindstedt SL. 1985. Mal-
leability of skeletal muscle in over-
coming limitations: structural elements.
J. Exp. Biol. 115:355–64
92. Houstek J, Kopecky J, Baudysova M,
Janikova D, Pavelka S, Kelment P.
1990. Differentiation of brown adipose
tissue and biogenesis of thermogenic
mitochondria in situ and in cell culture. *Biochim. Biophys. Acta* 1018:
243–47
93. Hulbert WC, Moon TW. 1978. A
histochemical, light, and electron microscopic examination of eel, *Anguilla
rostrata*, red and white muscle. *J. Fish
Biol.* 13:527–33
94. Imai Y, Horwitz BA, Smith RE. 1968.
Calorigenesis of brown adipose tissue
in cold exposed rats. *Proc. Soc. Exp.
Biol.* 127:717–19
95. Jansky L. 1973. Non-shivering thermogenesis and its thermoregulatory significance. *Biol. Rev.* 48:85–132
96. Jansky L, Bartunkova R, Zeisberger
E. 1967. Acclimation of the white rat
to cold: noradrenaline thermogenesis.
Physiol. Bohemoslov. 16:366–71
97. Jansky L, Bartunkova R, Mejsnar J,
Zeisberger E. 1969. Interspecies differences in cold adaptation and nonshivering thermogenesis. *Fed. Proc.*
28:1053–58
98. Jansky L, Hart JS. 1963. Participation
of skeletal muscle and kidney during
nonshivering thermogenesis in cold-acclimated rats. *Can. J. Biochem. Physiol.* 41:953–64
99. Jeronen E, Isometsä P, Hissa R,
Pyörnilä A. 1976. Effect of acute
temperature stress on the plasma catecholamine, corticosterone and metabolite levels in the pigeon. *Comp. Biochem. Physiol.* 55C:17–22
100. Johnston IA. 1982. Quantitative analysis of ultrastructure and vasculariza-
tion of the slow muscle fibres of the
anchovy. *Tissue Cell* 14:319–28
101. Johnston IA, Moon TW. 1981. Fine
structure and metabolism of multiple
innervated fast muscle fibres in teleost
fish. *Cell Tissue Res.* 219:93–109
102. Josephson RK. 1985. Mechanical
power output from striated muscle dur-

ing cyclic contraction. *J. Exp. Biol.* 114:493–513

103. Josephson RK, Stevenson RD. 1991. The efficiency of a flight muscle from the locust *Schistocerca americana*. *J. Physiol.* 442:413–29

104. Josephson RK, Young D. 1981. Sychronous and asychronous muscles in cicadas. *J. Exp. Biol.* 91:219–37

105. Josephson RK, Young D. 1985. A synchronous insect muscle with an operating frequency greater than 500 Hz. *J. Exp. Biol.* 118:185–208

106. Kim SY, Block BA. 1992. Excitation-thermogenic coupling: localization of the acetylcholine receptor and dihydropyridine receptor in heater cells. *Biophys. J.* 61(2):A165 (Abstr.)

107. Kishinouye K. 1923. Contributions to the comparative study of the so-called scombroid fishes. *J. Coll. Agric. Tokyo Imp. Univ.* 8:293–475

108. Knudson CM, Mickelson JR, Louis CF, Campbell KP. 1990. Distinct immunopeptide maps of the sarcoplasmic reticulum Ca^{2+} release channel in malignant hyperthermia. *J. Biol. Chem.* 265:2421–24

109. Kryvi H. 1977. Ultrastructure of the different fibre types in axial muscle of the sharks *Etmopterus spinax* and *Galeus melastomus*. *Cell Tissue Res.* 184:287–300

110. Kushmerick MJ. 1983. Energetics of muscle contraction. In *Handbook of Physiology*, ed. LD Peachey, RH Adrian, SR Greiger, pp. 189–236. Bethesda: Am. Physiol. Soc.

111. Lai FA, Erickson HP, Rousseau E, Liu QY, Meissner G. 1988. Purification and reconstitution of the calcium release channel from skeletal muscle. *Nature* 331:315–19

112. Lai FA, Liu Q, Xu L, El-Hashem A, Kramarcy NR, et al. 1992. Amphibian ryanodine receptor isoforms are related to those of mammalian skeletal and cardiac muscle. *Am. J. Physiol.* 263: C365–72

113. Leijendekker WJ, Hardeveld CV, Kassenaar AAH. 1987. Heat production during contraction in skeletal muscle of hypothyroid mice. *Am. J. Physiol.* 253:E214–20

114. Luckenbill LM, Cohen AS. 1966. The association of lipid droplets with cytoplasmic filaments in avian subsynovial adipose cells. *J. Cell Biol.* 31:195–99

115. MacLennan DH, Duff C, Zorzato F. 1990. Ryanodine receptor gene is a candidate for predisposition to malignant hyperthermia. *Nature* 343:559–61

116. MacLennan DH, Phillips MS. 1992. Malignant hyperthermia. *Science* 256: 789–94

117. Marsh RL. 1979. PhD thesis. *Seasonal adjustment in size and biochemistry of the flight muscles in a long-distance migrant, the gray catbird (Dumetella carolinensis)*. Univ. Mich. Ann Arbor

118. Marsh RL. 1981. Catabolic enzyme activities in relation to premigratory fattening and muscle hypertrophy in the gray catbird (*Dumetella carolinensis*). *J. Comp. Physiol.* 141:417–23

119. Marsh RL, Dawson WR. 1982. Substrate metabolism in seasonally acclimatized American goldfinches. *Am. J. Physiol.* 242:R563–69

120. Marsh RL, Dawson WR. 1989. Energy substrates and metabolic acclimatizatin in small birds. See Ref. 11, pp. 105–114

121. Mathieu-Costello O, Agey PJ, Logemann RB, Brill RW, Hochachka PW. 1992. Capillary-fiber geometrical relationships in tuna red muscle. *Can. J. Zool.* 70:1218–29

122. McCarthy TV, Healy JMS, Heffron JJA. 1990. Localization of the malignant hyperthermia susceptibility locus to human chromosome 19q12–13.2. *Nature* 343:562–64

123. McCormack JG, Denton RM. 1989. The role of Ca^{2+} ions in the regulation of intramitochondrial metabolism and energy production in rat heart. *Mol. Cell. Biochem.* 89:121–25

124. McCormack JG, Halestrap AP, Denton RM. 1990. Role of calcium ions in regulation of mammalian intramitochondrial metabolism. *Physiol. Rev.* 70:391–425

125. Meissner G. 1984. Adenine nucleotide stimulation of Ca^{2+}-induced Ca^{2+} release in sarcoplasmic reticulum. *J. Biol. Chem.* 259:2365–74

126. Mejsnar J, Jansky L. 1971. Nonshivering thermogenesis and calorigenic action of catecholamines in the white mouse. *Physiol. Bohemoslov.* 20:157–62

127. Mickelson JR, Gallant EM, Litterer LA, Johnson KM, et al. 1988. Abnormal sarcoplasmic reticulum ryanodine receptor in malignant hyperthermia. *J. Biol. Chem.* 263:9310–15

128. Mommaerts WFHM. 1969. Energetics of muscular contraction. *Physiol. Rev.* 49:427–508

129. Moyes CD, Mathieu-Costello OA, Brill RW, Hochachka PW. 1992. Mitochondiral metabolism of cardiac and skeletal muscles from a fast (*Katsuwonus pelamis*) and a slow

576   BLOCK

(*Cyprinus carpio*) fish. *Can. J. Zool.*
70:1246–53
130. Nicholls DG, Locke RM. 1984. Thermogenic mechanisms in brown fat. *Physiol. Rev.* 64:1–64
131. O'Brien J, Meissner G, Block BA. 1993. The fastest contracting muscles of non-mammalian vertebrates express only one isoform of the ryanodine receptor. *Biophys. J.* 65:1–10
132. O'Brien J, Tullis A, Block BA. 1992. Role of mitochondria in heat production by a muscle derived thermogenic organ in fish. *Biophys. J.* 61(2):A297 (Abstr.)
133. Oliphant LW. 1983. First observations of brown fat in birds. *Condor* 85:350–54
134. Olivares EB, Tanksley SJ, Airey JA, Beck C, Ouyang Y, et al. 1991. Nonmammalian vertebrate skeletal muscles express two triad junctional foot protein isoforms. *Biophys. J.* 59:1153–63
135. Ordway RW, Singer JJ, Walsh JV. 1991. Direct regulation of ion channels by fatty acids. *Trends Neurosci.* 14:96–100
136. Parker GH. 1978. Changes in muscle, liver, and plasma free fatty acid levels in the pigeon on acute exposure to cold. *Arch. Int. Physiol. Biochim.* 86:771–77
137. Pringle JWS. 1981. The evolution of fibrillar muscle in insects. *J. Exp. Biol.* 94:1–14
138. Prusiner SB, Cannon B, Lindberg O. 1968. Oxidative metabolism in cells isolated from brown adipose tissue. I. Catecholamine and fatty acid stimulation of respiration. *Eur. J. Biochem.* 6:15–22
139. Rall JA. 1982. Energetics of Ca^{2+} cycling during skeletal muscle contraction. *FASEB J.* 41:155–60
140. Rayner MD, Keenan MJ. 1967. Role of red and white muscles in the swimming of the skipjack tuna. *Nature* 214:392–93
141. Ricquier D, Bouillaud F, Toumelin P, Mory G, Bazin R, et al. 1986. Expression of uncoupling protein mRNA in thermogenic or weakly thermogenic brown adipose tissue. *J. Biol. Chem.* 261:13905–10
142. Rome LC, Loughna PT, Goldspink G. 1985. Temperature acclimation: improved sustained swimming performance in carp at low temperatures. *Science* 228:194–96
143. Saarela S, Hissa R, Pyörnilä A, Harjula R, Ojanen M, Orell M. 1989. Do birds possess brown adipose tissue? *Comp. Biochem. Physiol.* 92A:219–228

144. Saarela S, Keith JS, Hohtola E, Trayhurn P. 1991. Is the mammalian brown fat-specific mitochondrial uncoupling protein present in adipose tissues of birds. *Comp. Biochem. Physiol. B* 100:45–49
145. Schaeffer P, Lindstedt SL. 1992. Structure-function coupling in the fastest-contracting vertebrate muscle: the rattlesnake tail-shaker muscle. *Physiologist* 35:224
146. Seitz HS, Krone W, Wile H, Tarnowski W. 1981. Rapid rise in plasma glucagon induced by acute cold exposure in man and rat. *Pflügers Arch.* 389:115–20
147. Sidell BD, Moerland TS. 1989. Effects of temperature on muscular function and locomotory performance in teleost fish. In *Advances in Comparative and Environmental Physiology*, ed. CP Magnum, 5:115–56. Berlin/Heidelberg: Springer-Verlag
148. Simonides WS, Hardeveld CV. 1986. Effects of the thyroid status on the sarcoplasmic reticulum in slow skeletal muscle of the rat. *Cell Calcium.* 7:147–60
149. Sotavalta O. 1953. Recordings of high wing-stroke and thoracic vibration frequency in some midges. *Biol. Bull.* 104:439–44
150. Stevens ED, Dizon AE. 1982. Energetics of locomotion in warm-bodied fish. *Annu. Rev. Physiol.* 44:121–31
151. Stevenson RD, Josephson RK. 1990. Effects of operating frequency and temperature on mechanical power output from moth flight muscle. *J. Exp. Biol.* 149:61–78
152. Suarez RK, Lighton JRB, Brown GS, Mathieu-Costello O. 1991. Mitochondrial respiration in hummingbird flight muscles. *Proc. Natl. Acad. Sci. USA* 88:4870–73
153. Suarez RK, Moyes CD. 1992. Mitochondrial respiration in locust flight muscles. *J. Exp. Zool.* 263:351–55
154. Takeshima H, Nishimura S, Matsumoto T, Ishida H, Kangawa K, et al. 1989. Primary structure and expression from complementary DNA of skeletal muscle ryanodine receptor. *Nature* 339:439–45
155. Talesara GL, Goldspink G. 1978. A combined histochemical and biochemical study of myofibrillar ATPase in pectoral, leg, and cardiac muscle of several species of bird. *Histochem. J.* 10:695–710
156. Tullis A, Block BA. 1992. On the origin of the billfish heater cell phenotype. *Am. Zool.* 32:68A
157. Tullis A, Block BA, Sidell BD. 1991.

Activities of key metabolic enzymes in the heater organs of scombroid fishes. *J. Exp. Biol.* 161:383–403

158. Vladutiu GD, Hogan K, Saponara I, Tassini L, Conroy J. 1993. Carnitine palmitoyl transferase deficiency in malignant hyperthermia. *Muscle Nerve* 16:485–91

159. Wagner WD, Peterson RA, Cenedella RJ. 1971. The effects of cold and prostaglandin E1 on lipid mobilization in the chicken. *Can. J. Physiol. Pharmacol.* 49:394–98

160. Watson C, Bourke RE, Brill RW. 1988. A comprehensive theory on the etiology of burnt tuna. *Fish. Bull.* 86:367–72

161. Weiss K. 1954. Adaptation of rats to cold air and effects on tissue oxygen consumptions. *Am. J. Physiol.* 177: 201–7

162. West GC. 1965. Shivering and heat production in wild birds. *Physiol. Zool.* 38:111

163. White FC, Kelly R, Kemper S, Schumacker PT, Gallagher KR, Laurs RM. 1988. Organ blood flow haemodynamics and metabolism of the albacore tuna *Thunnus alalunga* (Bonnaterre). *Exp. Biol.* 47:161–69

164. Withers PC. 1977. Respiration, metabolism, and heat exchange of euthermic and torpid poorwills and hummingbirds. *Physiol. Zool.* 50:43

Annu. Rev. Physiol. 1994. 56:579–621
Copyright © 1994 by Annual Reviews Inc. All rights reserved

EVOLUTIONARY PHYSIOLOGY

T. Garland, Jr. and P. A. Carter

Department of Zoology, 430 Lincoln Drive, University of Wisconsin, Madison, Wisconsin 53706

KEY WORDS: adaptation, allozyme, comparative methods, fitness, locomotion, natural
            selection, quantitative genetics

INTRODUCTION

"The objectives of comparative physiology are: (*1*) to describe the diverse ways in which different kinds of animals meet their functional requirements; (*2*) to elucidate evolutionary relationships of animals by comparing physiological and biochemical characteristics; (*3*) to provide the physiological basis of ecology . . .; (*4*) to call attention to animal preparations particularly suitable for demonstrating specific functions; and (*5*) to lead to broad biological generalizations arising from the use of kind of animal as one experimental variable." (337, p. v)

"Physiological ecology is concerned with the way that physiological traits fit organisms for the ecological circumstances in which they live, so there is always, by definition, an implicit evolutionary component to it." (67, back cover)

"The field of physiological ecology...is...fundamentally evolutionary to the extent that it considers how organisms came to be the way they are and how they might change in the future." (39, p. 251)

The 1950 volume edited by Prosser outlined a broad agenda for comparative physiology (337). The purpose of the present paper is to alert physiologists to the development of a new subdiscipline, evolutionary physiology, which incorporates much of what is contained in Prosser's five objectives (see above) and a substantial fraction of what is generally termed physiological ecology (39, 61, 62, 67, 68, 135, 136, 155, 391, 421, 422). Following this introductory section, we highlight several crosscutting themes in evolutionary physiology, then describe and illustrate five major approaches for addressing such questions (ranging from quantitative genetics to interspecific comparison), and close with some ideas for integrating these approaches.

579

0066–4278/94/0315–0579$02.00

Our paper is selective in its coverage, and we devote little space to Prosser's third objective, i.e. ecological implications of physiological and biophysical variation and evolution (see 1, 11, 24, 25, 65, 78, 81, 113, 114, 119, 137, 153, 189, 205, 209, 212, 220, 223, 229, 232, 236, 240, 241, 274, 283, 284, 310, 313, 320, 327, 329, 330, 346, 352, 377, 394, 405, 407, 422, 423, 428, 432, 431, 444).

Modern evolutionary physiology seems to have its origins in the late 1970's, which witnessed debates concerning the metabolic and thermoregulatory status of dinosaurs and mammal-like reptiles (35, 42, 43, 101, 102, 303, 368, 383, 417). The next major impetus came from attempts to integrate quantitative genetic perspectives into behavioral and physiological ecology (9–11). These efforts were reflected in explicit attempts to document the magnitude and causes of physiological variation among individuals within populations (14, 15, 28, 30, 31, 33, 56, 58, 114, 143, 148, 149, 160, 161, 166, 167, 171, 189, 190, 216, 217, 226, 228, 256, 257, 311, 329, 376, 377, 401, 405, 426, 431, 462, 463), and whether this individual variation was correlated with behavior, life history traits, or ecology (56, 81, 143, 161, 190, 227, 249, 306, 311, 329, 332, 377, 401, 405, 435, 439, 447, 462, 463). Other studies tested whether individual variation in physiological traits had any genetic basis (55, 57, 58, 150, 154, 157, 158, 226, 260, 278-281, 402, 410, 424, 427), or could be molded by laboratory selective-breeding studies (37, 40, 41, 87, 179, 215, 218, 219, 278, 279, 360-362). Most recently, phylogenetically-based comparative studies have come to the fore (27, 50, 88, 164, 165, 213, 218, 265-267, 274, 336, 406, 437). Interestingly, the use of physiological information for reconstructing evolutionary relationships is not presently receiving much attention (but see 21, 289, and compare 106, 364).

Thinking about evolution is not new to physiologists (95, 135, 155, 242–245, 290, 316, 337, 371, 383, 456, 457, 460, 464; references therein). Nonetheless, at the risk of failing to appreciate sufficiently the accomplishments of past evolutionary-thinking physiologists, we see contemporary evolutionary physiology as fundamentally different from most of what came before. Many current practitioners began their studies as evolutionary biologists, or were formally trained in both evolutionary biology and physiology. Others represent physiologists who have moved forcefully in an evolutionary direction, often taking up formal collaborations with evolutionary biologists. Whatever their genesis, today's evolutionary physiologists try to do state-of-the-art physiology and state-of-the-art evolutionary biology; the evolutionary interpretation is no longer an afterthought. As in behavioral ecology (345), part of this increase in evolutionary rigor came in response to Gould & Lewontin's (175) criticisms of "the adaptationist programme" (36, 135, 262). Evolutionary physiologists now use a range of tools to test a priori hypotheses. Previously, evolutionary conclusions usually were inductive and followed the accumulation of considerable data (e.g. the basal metabolic rates of many species); such an "encyclopedic" approach (135) has been criticized as "stamp collecting." The switch from an inductive to a hypothetico-deductive model of analysis reflects some maturity in the field (61, 62, 135, 364); it is difficult to phrase non-trivial a priori hypotheses about processes until patterns have been thoroughly documented.

The 1987 publication of the results of a National Science Foundation-sponsored workshop on "New Directions in Ecological Physiology" (135), with an emphasis more evolutionary than ecological (e.g. 134), heralded the field (see also 34, 35, 39, 61, 62, 155, 214). The "Evolutionary Physiology" symposium held at the 1993 meetings of the Society for the Study of Evolution helped to advertise the field to nonphysiologists, and the formation in 1992 of a National Science Foundation panel in "Functional and Physiological Ecology," now renamed "Ecological and Evolutionary Physiology," will help to maintain this marriage (cf 135, 136, 237). Although current practitioners have various origins, many of the next generation will begin their graduate careers aspiring towards becoming evolutionary physiologists.

EVOLUTION FROM A PHYSIOLOGICAL PERSPECTIVE AND VICE VERSA

Physiologists are interested in how organisms work (231, 380). A subset of physiologists also wants to know why organisms are designed to work in particular ways. Unless one assumes special creation of all organisms, an understanding of such why questions requires an evolutionary perspective (134, 299, 308, 460). In this section we briefly review some of the recurring evolutionary questions and related principles that have been considered in the physiological literature. The following five sections cover complementary approaches to studying physiological evolution.

How Do Different Kinds of Organisms Work?

Physiologists have always sought to discover general principles of organismal function, such as homeostasis, or the scaling of metabolic rate with body mass (25, 32, 100, 134, 290, 337, 339, 456, 457). Faced with the tremendous diversity of living organisms, both in terms of numbers of species and their behavioral and ecological variation, physiologists have asked what general principles apply to all or most organisms, how common are exceptions to the rules, and whether there exist multiple solutions to a given adaptive problem, such as life in hot, arid environments (24, 25). Because all organisms on this planet are descended from common ancestors (and perhaps from a single common ancestor), general biological principles (e.g. use of DNA as a genetic material; structure of eukaryotic cell membranes; responses to changes in ambient temperature by mammals) are likely to occur in a strongly hierarchical—that is, phylogenetic—pattern.

Extremes of Adaptation, Model Species, and the August Krogh Principle

Identification of similarities among species allows the possibility that certain species may be able to serve as model systems for studying basic physiological processes (33, 62, 100, 456, 457). Krogh noted that for any physiological principle there exists an organism especially well suited for its study [259: e.g. giant axons of squid, 'gas windows' of crab legs (288); scallop muscles (292); rattlesnake tail muscles (375)]. Similarly, physiologists (including plant physiologists, 310) have long been aware that organisms living in extreme environments are especially likely to exhibit clear examples of evolutionary adaptation because of the presumably intense past selective pressures (24, 25, 155, 380). Organisms adapted to extreme environments can serve to illustrate the range of evolutionary possibilities (62, 456, 457), but we must be mindful that the organisms alive today—and hence available for physiological study—are but a small fraction of what has existed. Thus there is no guarantee that we can observe the range of possibilities even among the most extreme of living species. For example, the largest terrestrial mammal that ever lived (*Baluchitherium*) was much larger than living elephants, or mammoths, or mastodons (references in 165). Although the proposition is seductively appealing, little evidence exists that today's species are any better adapted than those of a million or 100 million years ago (174, 224, 225). We must also remember that behavioral adaptation can go a long way towards ameliorating the need for physiological evolution (24, 25, 52, 209). In any case, species displaying extreme development of a particular physiological property can also prove useful as model systems (e.g. locomotor abilities: 153, 231).

Are Species Differences in Physiology Adaptive?

"Four legs may be optimal, but we have them by conservative inheritance, not selected design." (173, p. 44)

The neo-Darwinian synthesis (77b, 144, 350), including its emphasis on natural selection as the major driving force in evolution, led inevitably to the view that virtually all features of organisms are adaptive. Comparative physiologists have routinely viewed any differences among species as adaptations to their different life styles (60, 118, 126, 133, 172, 202, 290, 337-339, 382, 425, 449, 455, 467), and have provided many examples that clearly represent strong evidence for adaptation (32, 95, 371; see also 6).

Nonetheless, not all features of organisms represent adaptations to current environmental conditions (26, 36, 59, 175, 187, 272, 275, 454, 455, 460). Some, for example, represent simple inheritance from ancestors. A current thrust in evolutionary biology aims to develop rigorous methods for studying adaptation (see below), including ways to formally test hypotheses about the adaptive nature of organismal features (1, 6, 26, 50, 51, 59, 175, 182, 187, 239, 263, 265-267, 274, 275, 278, 307, 345, 349, 350, 394, 459).

The operational definition of evolutionary adaptation is quite controversial (36, 182, 345), but revolves mainly around the distinction between origin and maintenance of a trait. Some traits are maintained by current selection, but did not originate in response to the same selective pressures. For example, as noted by Darwin, the sutures between bones in the mammalian skull may now be adaptive for allowing the birth of relatively large-brained offspring in some species (humans), but they arose long ago in evolutionary history (144, p. 257). Other traits arose because of natural selection, but are now present for other reasons, such as "phylogenetic inertia," which may be attributable to developmental or genetic constraints in addition to selection (e.g. see 187). Thus the origin (evolutionary history) and/or the current maintenance (phenotype existence sensu 345) of a trait may be adaptive, and both are worthy topics of study. Phylogenetic comparative studies of interspecific variation can address historical origins, and measurement of selection within populations can address current maintenance (see below).

Imprecise usage of the term adaptation (36, 345, 454, 455) has led to many confusions in the physiological literature:

> "Physiologists have used the term 'adaptation' in two entirely different ways. First, adaptation is used to describe compensatory, short-term changes to environmental or organismic disturbance. Such control systems are phenotypic and reveal the plasticity of physiological systems generally. Second, adaptation is used in the genetic and evolutionary sense of describing a trait or feature that has been cemented into the genotype through the pressure of natural selection. Comparing the acclimatory changes in erythrocyte phosphates of fish or humans with traits like the high-affinity Hb systems of the high-altitude-dwelling llamas, amphibians, and so on is clearly a category mistake." (454, p. 244)

Regardless of methodological or semantic debates, studies of adaptation will continue their prominence in both evolutionary biology and comparative physiology. Physiology can contribute something special to the study of adaptation: an understanding of mechanism (50, 70, 95, 239, 367, 371). An understanding of biochemical and biophysical mechanisms can help to define what is theoretically possible for organisms to achieve (the phenotype-set sensu 345), if selection were to favor it, and thus aid in the identification of constraints on evolution [30, 71, 72, 100, 342 (but see 302); 367, 388, 396, 459, 465].

Are Organisms Optimally Designed?

"We do not think a functional explanation complete until we can show that a structure or movement is optimal (by some plausible criterion) for the proposed function." (5, p. 237)

In addition to presuming that most if not all features of organisms represent adaptations, a common perspective in comparative physiology is to view organisms as more-or-less optimally designed (3–5, 363). Reasons why organisms may not be optimally designed and why optimality perspectives in general may not be the best way to study evolution have been discussed at length elsewhere (24, 25, 36, 77a, 79, 92, 124, 175, 182, 321, 361, 459; but see 241, 354, 390). With regard to this debate, we emphasize two points. First, a fundamental reason for a lack of optimal solutions to adaptive problems is that natural selection—the only known mechanism for adaptive phenotypic evolution—can only work on existing phenotypic variation that is at least partly heritable; thus some possible solutions to selective problems will most likely never be accessible within a given lineage (36, 175, 222). Second, a major problem with testing optimality predictions is the lack of a suitable null model (see 182); using the optimal solution, e.g. perfect matching, as a null model (see 109 on symmorphosis), is counter to the way most biological and statistical inference is performed, e.g. no matching as a null model.

The concept of symmorphosis is a recent example of an optimal design perspective on animal morphology and physiology (451, 452). Favorable discussions and criticisms of symmorphosis have appeared elsewhere (35, p. 13; 65, 108–110, 117, 163, 231, 273, 381, 392), and casual references appear frequently (35, 93, 134, 209). Qualitatively, the likelihood of a match between biological structures and their functional requirements is intuitively obvious; exactly how good this match should be is less obvious. Moreover, adequacy or sufficiency, rather than optimality, is the most likely evolutionary outcome (11, 24, 25, 145, 147, 460, p. 17) because natural selection tends to maximize relative, not absolute, fitness.

Trade-offs and Constraints: Why Do Traits Evolve in a Correlated Fashion?

Constraints or trade-offs can be identified and studied at several different levels of biological organization (12, 30, 67, 173, 218, 302, 374, 396, 459). The environment and its associated selective regime (26, 275) impose constraints on what types of physiological variants and on what kinds of organisms can survive and reproduce, both within populations at the level of individual variation, and over long term evolutionary time (258). Although selection sets ultimate limits on the dimensions of an allowable multidimensional phenotypic space, organisms will not necessarily ever reach those limits. Instead, fundamental properties of biological systems can preclude some variants, such as titanium in tortoise shells. Constraints set by inherent organismal properties can be elucidated through biochemistry and physiology [30, 71, 72, 342 (but see 302), 374, 388, 396], or through developmental (465) biology. Alternatively, they can be evidenced as a lack of genetic variation in certain phenotypic dimensions. For example, non-zero genetic correlations are often interpreted as indicating evolutionary constraints (12), but genetic correlations (see below) can sometimes facilitate response to natural selection (154, 279) and can themselves be molded by selection (55–58); moreover, their interpretation can be very complicated (77a, 354). Wherever a constraint is identified, a fundamental question is whether it is absolute or could possibly be overcome (e.g. by a new mutation); physiology should address such questions.

What is the Origin of Allometric Relationships?

Allometric patterns and equations describing them have long fascinated physiologists (65, 66, 149, 187, 196, 274, 313, 320, 346, 351, 381, 414, 419, 450). Within a clade, and on a log-log scale, variation in body mass can explain more than 90% of the variation in a variety of physiological traits, such as basal metabolic or heart rate. Even with such a high coefficient of determination (r^2), variation of individual points about a linear regression can be substantial, both among individuals within species (38, 148, 160, 226) and among species (151, 304, 342, 399, 400). However, not all physiological traits vary strongly with body mass; examples include hematocrit, blood oxygen carrying capacity, and normal body temperatures of birds and mammals (160, 336, 381).

Ignoring variation about a regression line, an obvious question is whether the slope of the line itself (the allometric scaling exponent), or its intercept (196), represent general physical and biochemical constraints placed on organisms as opposed to adaptive evolutionary responses. For example, Weibel et al (452) categorize variation among species as "allometric...reflect(ing) intrinsic properties of the organism, particularly the size dependence of rate constants, such as stride frequency, heart rate, etc" or as "adaptive...relat(ing) to behavioral traits and to the ecological conditions to which the species are adapted by evolutionary selection..."

The dichotomy between allometric and adaptive variation is imprecise (and analogous to the quantitative genetic problem of trying to separate genetic from environmental effects when genotype-by-environment interaction exists). Interspecific allometric patterns can themselves be adaptive in the sense that they are maintained by natural selection. In some cases, the adaptiveness of allometric relationships is subject to experimental evolutionary tests. For example, Weber (448) observed a fairly tight allometric relationship between wing proportions and body size among populations and species of *Drosophila*. Did this represent an ineluctable con- straint on the shapes of fruit flies that could be produced? Did the existing phenotypic diversity indicate what was possible? To test this, Weber artificially selected on wing proportions and succeeded in producing lines of flies that exceeded the limits seen in nature (GS Wilkinson, personal communication, has done similar experiments with another species of fly). Thus the allometric pattern seen in nature did not reflect an unconditional genetic or developmental constraint on the shape of flies. Instead, it must have been maintained by natural selection.

Artificial selection experiments (see below) will not be practical for studying most examples of allometry in physiological traits. Another way to alter allometric relationships, one that relies on proximate rather than ultimate mechanisms, is "allometric engineering," as applied by Sinervo and colleagues to lizard eggs to alter characteristics of hatchling lizards (393–396). Alternatively, an understanding of physiological mechanisms can help in determining whether a particular pattern of phenotypic variation or covariation (e.g. an allometric relationship) represents what could possibly exist or just what selection has allowed.

QUANTITATIVE GENETIC ANALYSES

"...species represent the product of evolution, whereas the process can only be studied within species....For the physiological ecologist, heritability is the most useful piece of genetic information since it is both descriptive and predictive." (278, p. 497)

Most traits studied by physiologists show continuous variation (body temperature, metabolic rate, blood pressure, blood hemoglobin levels, enzyme activites). Quantitative genetics was developed early in this century for studying the genetic basis of traits that showed more-or-less continuous, as opposed to discrete, variation (references in 9, 10, 13, 51, 58, 127, 132, 180, 183, 261, 262, 297, 323, 453). The general assumption is that such traits are affected by alleles segregating at many loci and that each locus has a relatively small effect on the phenotype. Quantitative genetics has a long history of application in plant and animal breeding, but a recent revival for application to problems in evolutionary biology began in about 1980 (14, 260–262, 357, 402).

Quantitative genetics uses observed phenotypic variation among individuals of known relationship (e.g. parents and their offspring, full- and half-sibs) to estimate the relative magnitudes of genetic and environmental effects on the phenotypic variation observed within a population (i.e. variation among individuals). Thus it traditionally does not attempt to identify the effects of variation at single gene loci. Instead, it allows estimation of summary statistics, such as heritability, that are both descriptive and predictive. When more than one trait is studied, estimates of shared genetic and environmental effects are available. Quantitative genetics is actually a broad collection of tools that can address topics including whether the phenotypic variation in a single trait (e.g. differences in resting blood pressure among individuals within a population) is to any extent genetically based; whether selection on a trait could lead to improvement; whether different traits are genetically coupled such that selection on one would necessarily produce a correlated response in another (including the nature of allometric relationships, e.g. 448); how many genes are responsible for the phenotypic differences between populations of the same or of closely related species; whether one or more "major genes" are segregating within a population; whether gene action is entirely additive or includes dominance or epistasis; and the direction and magnitude of past natural selection. Recent marriages of quantitative genetics with molecular marker techniques are allowing the actual identification of specific loci with relatively large effects, termed quantitative trait loci (230, 324).

Only if a trait under selection is to some extent genetically based will natural selection result in evolution. The equation, $R = h^2 s$, is used to describe the evolutionary response of the mean value of a single phenotypic trait to natural (or artificial) selection, where R = the genetic response to selection, s = the selection differential (difference in means of selected and unselected individuals), and h^2 = the narrow-sense heritability (ratio of additive genetic variance to total phenotypic variance, ranging between zero and one). Narrow-sense heritability can be estimated by measuring the phenotypes of related individuals, such as offspring and their parents (13, 51, 58, 132, 180, 297, 323, 410, 453), or through artificial selection experiments. A multivariate version of the foregoing equation substitutes a matrix of additive genetic variances and covariances for h^2 (13, 51, 56–58, 261, 262).

Physiological traits are highly susceptible to a variety of environmental effects, both acute and chronic (e.g. acclimation and acclimatization): "Much of the intraspecific physiological variation encountered by physiologists is a result of short-term physiological acclimation..." (62, p. 203). Therefore, one might expect that physiological traits would often exhibit low or even zero narrow-sense heritabilities. Until recently, comparative physiologists simply did not address such questions empirically (e.g. discussion following Reference 25). However, available empirical studies indicate that physiological traits often do show substantial heritabilities (37, 40, 41, 58, 127, 132, 158, 178–180, 203–205, 215, 219, 260, 278–281; 312, 328, 355, 360–362, 402, 410, 420, 461). Some measures of locomotor performance in lizards and snakes (55, 57, 150, 226, 424, 427) and even maximal oxygen consumption in garter snakes (157) seem to show very high heritabilities (0.5–0.9) based on comparisons of families of full-siblings. Unfortunately, these estimates can be inflated by non-additive genetic effects or maternal effects, and more sophisticated breeding designs are required to estimate narrow-sense heritabilities. Other physiological traits, such as basal metabolic rate in house mice (278, 279; T Garland, Jr et al, unpublished), show very low (< 0.05) narrow-sense heritabilities.

Genetic correlations are the two-trait analogue of heritabilities; they indicate the extent to which the phenotypic covariance of two traits is genetically based. Although genetic correlations can be caused by linkage disequilibrium (for example, from physical linkage of genes), pleiotropy is a more typical cause. Pleiotropy simply refers to one gene affecting more than one trait. Shared biochemical, physiological, or developmental pathways are likely to be reflected as pleiotropic gene action. Thus genetic correlations may be particularly interesting to physiologists because of what they can suggest about physiological mechanisms (10, 279, 360). Conversely, knowledge of physiological mechanisms can be used to predict genetic correlations (154, 318). For example, Garland (150) predicted a necessary trade-off between speed and stamina, based on the fast-twitch, slow-twitch dichotomy (an oversimplification) of muscle fiber types. In contrast, the genetic correlation estimated from measurements of full-sibling families of garter snakes was actually positive (for possible explanations, see 154, 436). Rather than constrain, this positive correlation could facilitate genetic response if natural selection favored increased overall locomotor abilities (150, 154, 166; cf 279, 360). Dohm & Garland (115) looked to differences in developmental timing to predict genetic correlations between numbers of scales in different regions of a snake's body; empirically, this prediction was only partially supported. In *D. melanogaster,* artificial selection on desiccation resistance increased longevity and depressed early fecundity both in stocks that were originally selected for delayed reproduction and in control lines (360, 362). Other physiological performance characters also responded to these selection regimes, including flight duration and ethanol tolerance (increased by desiccation but not by starvation selection). Graves et al (179) studied the underlying mechanisms and found that desiccation tolerance was reduced substantially in flies depleted of glycogen reserves by flight in both selected and control lines; thus variation in the amount of glycogen reserves was at least partly responsible for the correlation between seemingly unrelated physiological traits. This is an example of how antagonistic pleiotropy between genes that have differential effects on early fitness can create physiological correlations observed during selection.

Both heritabilities and genetic correlations can be used to predict responses to selection, although the number of generations over which such predictions will be accurate depends on the constancy of the genetic parameters (12, 51, 132, 261). Traits with low heritabilities are often inferred to have been subject to intense past selection, although a number of tenuous assumptions are involved (51, 158). The presence of dominance or epistasis can also be used to draw inferences about how past selection has acted on a trait (54, 132, 158, 193, 197, 279, 297). To investigate the nature of genetic variation, such as whether it is entirely additive or includes dominance or epistasis, crosses of selected lines, inbred lines, subspecies, or even closely related species can be used (278, 279, 297, 347). Such crosses also form the basis for estimating the minimum number of independently segregating genetic factors required to account for a difference in phenotypic mean (469).

ARTIFICIAL SELECTION EXPERIMENTS

Selection experiments are one form of genetic manipulation (51, 127, 132, 180, 183, 200, 201, 297, 323, 353, 453) that has intuitive appeal for evolutionary physiologists. They are in some sense more natural than are more modern alternatives such as the production of transgenic organisms (136, 263; J Breslow, this volume; M Paul et al, this volume). Of course, selection in the laboratory cannot entirely mimic selection in nature because the former generally involves much more specific targets of selection (single characters), higher selection intensities (and often truncation selection), smaller populations, and much shorter time scales (360, 361, 397), although these limitations do not necessarily apply to study organisms such as microorganisms.

Two general kinds of selection experiments can be distinguished (360). Traditional artificial selection involves laboratory or barnyard populations in which each individual in each generation is scored for some phenotypic trait (or combination of traits) of interest. Some top or bottom percentage of individuals from the distribution of phenotypic scores is then selected as the parents for the next generation; this is termed truncation selection (for physiological examples, see 74, 90, 91, 203–205, 215, 378). Variations on this theme are used routinely in plant and animal breeding, such as taking at least one male and female from each family to reduce inbreeding (132, 200, 201, 297, 353: e.g. 278, 279). In laboratory natural selection, freely breeding populations are exposed to intentionally altered environmental conditions, such as different temperatures, or to a laboratory or other environment that is novel as compared with nature (22, 23, 37, 40, 41, 219, 269, 362, 420; references therein), or to husbandry conditions changed so as to favor altered demographic schedules, such as delayed reproduction (179, 360–362; references therein).

Artificial selection can be a sharper experimental instrument because it is more precise and allows one to select a particular physiological trait (cf 36, 218, 219, 360). It is also useful for estimating realized heritabilities and genetic correlations (132, 200, 201, 261, 278, 279, 297, 323, 353). Laboratory natural selection, on the other hand, may allow clearer insight as to what might occur in nature; only the environment is specified, and the adaptive solution is left up to the organism (36). In theory, either protocol can yield multiple solutions; in practice, the number of ways in which a selective problem will be solved in a particular organism is an empirical issue that has been little studied.

Selection experiments will reveal traits that evolve as correlated responses, thus indicating the interdependence of aspects of the phenotype (51, 278, 279). For example, artificial selection on maximal sprint running speed might divulge that leg length evolved as a correlated response. Such a result would suggest that leg length was causally related to speed (6). Our laboratory is currently conducting artificial selection for voluntary wheel-running behavior in mice and will monitor correlated changes in physiological and hormonal traits.

Mechanistic inferences derived from correlated responses to selection can be greatly strengthened by subsequently doing the converse experiment; for example, selecting directly on leg length to see if sprint speed evolves as a correlated response. Experiments of this nature have been done on aging and its correlates in *D. melanogaster* (179, 358, 360–362, 384), and this genetic model species has served as subject for a number of other long-term selection experiments involving physiological characteristics (128, for 250–300 generations: some bacterial selection experiments have exceeded 2,000 generations, 269). In these selection experiments, replicate control and selected lines are required (i.e. at least two of each) in order to make inferences about correlated responses (194, 279, 362). In general, the design of selection experiments is complicated (see references cited herein).

Some physiological traits are too difficult to measure on hundreds of individual organisms each generation. Some measurements may not be sufficiently reproducible to allow effective artificial selection. Others require sacrifice of the organism (e.g. heart size, although even this might be accomplished nondestructively with ultrasonic imaging techniques). For traits that require destructive sampling (e.g. brain mass: references in 261), artificial selection is still possible, for example, through the use of sibling selection (see 132, 297). But many physiological measurements can be automated (215), or are relatively simple; mice, for example, have been successfully selected for hematocrit (378) and for thyroid function (74).

An interesting question for physiologists is whether selection yields repeatable results at the level of physiological mechanism. If selection to increase some organismal trait is imposed on several different replicate lines drawn from the same homogeneous base population, does the trait increase via the same physiological or morphological mechanism? For example, would all lines of mice selected for higher sprint speed respond with an increase in leg length, or an increase in the percentage of fast twitch muscle fibers, or an increase in muscle mass? Alternatively, would different solutions appear in each line? The optimality perspective on physiological evolution might suggest a single solution (but see 408), as appears to have occurred in early comparisons between stocks of *D. melanogaster* selected for delayed reproduction (276, 357). Most geneticists and evolutionary biologists, on the other hand, would not be surprised to see multiple solutions and unpredictable responses (82, 90, 91, 179, 203, 204, 269, 299, 319, 362); in the jargon of quantitative genetics, the answer will depend on whether genetic correlations between the trait being selected and other traits remain the same in all replicate selection lines. If several lower-level traits change in response to organismal selection, then another intriguing question is whether they all change in parallel (as symmorphosis would suggest: cf 134), or one at a time (suggesting a sequential series of limiting factors). A third question of interest is whether evolution follows the principle of "last hired, first fired." That is, if one selects for improved performance, then relaxes or reverses selection, do the mechanistic components decrease in the same order as they increased?

Evidence from *D. melanogaster* can address the foregoing questions. Service et al (385) utilized reverse selection to examine the nature of genetic and phenotypic correlations in stocks produced by selection for delayed reproduction. In reverse-selected lines (selected for early reproduction from delayed regime), longevity fell while early reproduction increased; starvation resistance also fell, while ethanol and desiccation tolerance remained unaltered during the first 20 generations of reverse selection. Graves et al (179) reexamined these same stocks after 100 generations of reversed selection, and found that starvation, desiccation, and ethanol resistance had dropped further than at generation 20. Leroi et al (270) have now found a shifting of the nature of the original genetic correlations uncovered in the Rose postponed-aging stocks [e.g. (357); early fecundity B > O]. After ten years of laboratory evolution, the pattern of early fecundity observed in the standard assay environment now favors the O lines. The B lines still preserve their early fecundity advantage in the B culture regime, which is slightly different from that used to maintain the O stocks. In addition, in the standard environment, the development time of the delayed reproduction vs early reproduced control group now favors the early reproduced line, such that the early fitness trade-off now resides in the development time component as opposed to early fecundity. These results seem to indicate that although life history trade-offs may be inevitable, the nature of the genetic correlations that control them are plastic, such that selection may have more leeway than we imagine to create solutions to adaptive problems.

In most laboratory experiments, selection operates on preexisting genetic variation. However, for those experiments (e.g. involving microorganisms) that extend hundreds or thousands of generations and/or involve very large population sizes, new mutations can also be important. Changes in the frequencies of preexisting genes can lead to changes in genetic correlations (and heritabilities), but where new mutations are possible, changes in genetic correlations are particularly likely.

BIOCHEMICAL AND PHYSIOLOGICAL STUDIES OF ALLOZYME VARIATION

"Metabolic control theory, including both experimental and theoretical extensions, provides a 'glue' to hold physiology and genetics together." (86, p. 193)

Following the advent of protein electrophoresis in the mid-1960's, numerous studies demonstrated correlations between genotype or allele frequencies (actually, protein phenotypes representing alternative alleles) and environmental or ecological factors, such as habitat temperature, seasonality, latitude, or altitude (271). Many workers interpreted such correlations as indicating the action of natural selection. These interpretations were criticized for being based on correlational data and for not assigning a more important role to random mutation and genetic drift (169, 175, 271). Several research groups, therefore, developed a biochemical and physiological approach to studying the evolutionary significance of genetic variation at specific loci (89, 137, 247–250, 331, 334, 439, 441, 443, 444). Examples include work by Powers and colleagues on killifish lactate dehydrogenase (Ldh) (98, 111, 112, 322, 332–334); Watt and colleagues on sulfur butterfly phosphoglucose isomerase (Pgi) (439, 440, 445–447); Koehn and colleagues on mussel leucine aminopeptidase (Lap) (29, 199, 248, 251–254); van Delden and many others on *Drosophila* alcohol dehydrogenase (Adh) (2, 8, 48, 73, 80, 268, 315, 429); Hartl, Dykhuizen, and Dean on several loci in *E. coli* (103, 104, 121, 123, 124, 185, 186); Burton and colleagues on copepod glutamate-pyruvate transaminase (Gpt) (63, 64); Hoffman on sea anemone Pgi (206–208); and Snyder and colleagues on *Peromyscus* hemoglobins (75, 76,

402–404). Many other studies have correlated multi-locus heterozygosity with measures of physiological performance in an attempt to explain levels of genetic variation, without considering functional differences among allozymes; these have been reviewed elsewhere (169). Here we attempt to clarify several issues concerning the rationale, assumptions, and empirical measures involved in functional studies of variation at single loci.

For genotypic variation to affect fitness, two requirements must be met. First, the allozymes produced by the different genotypes must exhibit functional differences; second, the functional differences among allozymes must cause biochemical or physiological differences that are detectable at the organismal level (Figure 1). Thus a convincing research program must

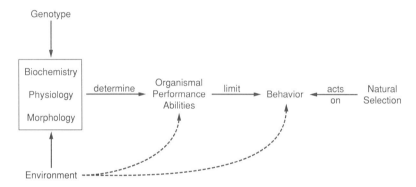

Figure 1   The centrality of organismal performance paradigm, much of which was developed in relation to studies of locomotor performance (see 9, 39, 154, 166, 210, 220, 431). Both genetic and environmental effects act through development and ontogeny to determine an organism's primary phenotypic characteristics, which often are categorized as biochemical, physiological or morphological. Acting in concert, these traits determine whole-organism performance abilities, such as maximal sprint running speed or stamina (153, 166, 231) or perhaps ability to raise offspring (110). In practice, behavior, e.g. motivation, can also affect measurements of performance, which are typically obtained in the laboratory by forcing the organism to perform at its maximum capacity for the trait of interest (6, 34, 137, 231). Performance defines the extent or limits of an organism's capabilities, whereas behavior indicates how an organism actually uses (or fails to use) these capacities. Selection acts most directly on behavior, but behavior is limited by performance. Thus, genotypic or biochemical variation (e.g. allozyme variants identified by protein electrophoresis) should only be subject to selection if they have effects at the level of organismal performance and hence behavior (89, 248). It is absolutely critical that the appropriate ecological context of the organism be considered when determining a performance to measure in the laboratory; the performance must relate to behavior in the field to have any relevance to natural selection (9, 14, 34, 35, 113, 114, 137, 153, 154, 158, 166, 220, 227, 439, 442). Natural selection is defined operationally as a correlation between fitness and phenotype. Dashed arrows indicate the possibility of direct environmental effects on performance (e.g. the effects of substrate on sprinting ability) or behavior (e.g. temperature-dependent switches in antipredator behavior) (references in 58, 154, 166). The inseparability of physiology, behavior, and environment has long been a central tenant of physiological ecology (1, 24, 25, 52, 78, 81, 205, 209, 210, 212, 223, 241, 258, 284, 291, 313, 327, 329, 330, 380, 382, 421, 422, 432, 435).

first measure the appropriate characteristics of enzyme function and then relate the observed variation to whole-organism performance and/or behavior.

Functional Differences Among Allozymes

Three measures of enzyme function are common, each of which can be influenced by structural differences among allozymes. The Michaelis constant, K_m, is the substrate concentration that yields a reaction velocity equal to one half of the maximum reaction velocity, V_{max}. K_m is generally considered to be a measure of substrate binding affinity (202, but see 140). The catalytic rate constant, K_{cat}, is a measure of the amount of product produced per active site on an enzyme per unit time. Thus it is a measure of the speed with which an enzyme functions, standardized to the number of active sites contained by the enzyme. The third measure, V_{max}, is the product of K_{cat} and enzyme concentration, [E], and is the maximum reaction velocity at saturating levels of substrate. Values of these enzymatic parameters are specific to the reaction conditions used; thus in vitro reaction conditions must be chosen that match or approximate the ecological context indicated by field studies. For example, it was vital to Powers' work on Ldh in killifish (see references above) that the biochemical studies be conducted at the temperatures suggested by his field studies: as it turned out, no differences in Ldh function existed at temperatures convenient for biochemical work (25°C), but significant differences existed at temperatures relevant to the natural environment of killifish (5 and 30°C)!

For selection to act on allozymes, they must differ in at least one of the foregoing functional parameters. For a given set of reaction conditions, differences among allozymes in K_m or in K_{cat} can only be caused by differences in structure; therefore, if selection acts on either one of these functional properties, it also acts on the locus that produces the allozymes. However, two different factors can influence V_{max}.

First, V_{max} can be affected by differences in allozyme structure. As noted above, allozyme differences in K_{cat} are caused by differences in allozyme structure; any such changes in K_{cat} would result in a change in V_{max} (332). V_{max} can also differ among allozymes because of allozyme-specific differences in [E] caused by differential stability of the allozymes [an enzyme's stability is a function of its structure (202)]; any such changes in [E] would also result in a change in V_{max} (440). In both instances, selection acting on V_{max} would be acting directly on the locus of interest.

Second, V_{max} can be affected by changes in [E] caused by genetic factors unrelated to allozyme structure. Allozyme-specific differences in [E] can be the result of a control locus that differentially affects the allozymes. Laurie et al (268) demonstrated that some activity differences among Adh allozymes in *Drosophila* are caused not by the Adh alleles themselves, but by linked variants of controlling regions of the chromosome. In this example, selection on V_{max} might actually be acting on the controlling gene(s) rather than on the Adh locus.

Despite such potential complexities in interpreting the origins of variation in V_{max}, it is a most useful measure of enzymatic activity. First, V_{max}, as compared to K_{cat}, is the better measure of enzymatic activity with regard to the whole-organism phenotype simply because it measures maximal activity, not just substrate turnover/active site. (The converse of this is also true; K_{cat} is a better measure of activity at the level of the enzyme molecule itself because it does not include [E].) Second, the ratio of V_{max} to K_m is a good approximation of enzyme velocity at low substrate concentrations, which are usually the physiologically-relevant conditions (440). In fact, V_{max}/Km ratios have typically been used as the measure of enzymatic effectiveness (332, 440). Finally, questions about the origins of variation in V_{max} can be addressed by measuring K_{cat} (440); in this way, differences in V_{max} among allozymes can be ascribed to differences in either K_{cat} or [E]. Determination of K_{cat} requires a completely purified enzyme, which is a non-trivial task. In any case, V_{max} is an enzymatic measure of potentially great functional and hence evolutionary significance. V_{max} has routinely been measured by physiological ecologists (and by exercise physiologists) as a simple indicator of biochemical functional capacities (83, 84, 87, 88, 148, 158, 160, 171, 184, 202, 228, 257, 291, 293, 329, 330, 339, 467).

Organismal Effects of Differences in Allozyme Function

For selection to "see" differences in functional characteristics of allozymes, they must cause variation at the level of the whole organism (Figure 1). In other words, allozymes that differ in function must also cause differences in the rate of flux, the efficiency of flux, and/or amounts of a given substrate (86, 250). Such differences in metabolic pathway characteristics can directly or indirectly influence fitness through their impact on energy supply, availability, and/or use (86, 442, 443).

The traditional view of metabolic pathways suggests that all control of flux through a pathway resides only with rate limiting regulatory enzymes (18, 19). However, quantitative theories of metabolic control, in which flux control potentially resides at all steps in a pathway, have been developed by Kacser (metabolic control analysis: 233–235; see also 125, 192), Savageau (biochemical systems theory: 372–374), Crabtree (flux oriented theory: 96, 97), and their colleagues. Each of these theories has its own array of assumptions and characteristics, and excellent reviews are available elsewhere (94, 138).

In metabolic control theory, control of flux through a pathway can be shared by all enzymes in the pathway; control coefficients can be calculated for each enzymatic step in a pathway for any given set of reaction conditions. The control coefficient of an enzyme actually measures the sensitivity of the flux through the pathway to any changes in the functional capabilities of that enzyme, and is inversely proportional to the V_{max}/K_m ratio. Furthermore, control coefficients of all enzymes in a pathway are interrelated, so that changing the control coefficient of one enzyme will change the control coefficients of one, some, or all of the other enzymes in the pathway. But, a change in the functional characteristics of an enzyme may or may not result in changes in its own control coefficient; this is a question that must be answered empirically for each enzyme in a pathway and for every set of reaction conditions of interest.

Much resistence to metabolic control theory has come from those unwilling to discard the traditional idea of metabolic control by one or a few key regulatory enzymes (18, 19). It is important to realize that metabolic control theory does not necessarily preclude the traditional view of rate limiting regulatory enzymes (198). Metabolic control theory does, however, provide a methodology by which control of flux can be empirically measured at the different steps in a metabolic pathway; the traditional view of metabolic control is but one possible evolutionary outcome. That metabolic control theory is tenable and useful is shown by the fact that some of its parameters have been empirically estimated for a variety of loci in several pathways in diverse taxa (44, 103, 168, 191, 246, 398, 466) and that it has been used successfully to develop quantitative genetic analyses of metabolic pathways (85, 104, 238, 413, 438) (see also 110 on a possible link to symmorphosis).

Several different, but not exclusive, scenarios describe how selection might affect flux-dependent measures of organismal performance. Selection might simply affect the rate of flux through a pathway, and so select for allozymes that either maximize flux or do not limit it. Empirical measurements in various systems have shown allozyme-dependent rates of flux (103, 122, 446). Selection might also affect the different impact of allozymes on the efficiency of flux (86, 250); in this untested scenario, the selective advantage of a high rate of flux in a pathway is tempered by the energetic cost of the maintenance of enzyme pools used in that pathway. Finally, selection can affect the differential impact that allozymes can have on pools of substrates in a pathway; deleterious effects of enzyme deficiency diseases are usually caused by substrate accumulation (86, 460).

MEASURING SELECTIVE IMPORTANCE IN THE FIELD

"Natural selection acts on phenotypes, regardless of their genetic basis, and produces immediate phenotypic effects within a generation that can be measured without recourse to principles of heredity or evolution. In contrast, evolutionary response to selection, the genetic change that occurs from one generation to the next, does depend on genetic variation.... Upon making this critical distinction...precise methods can be formulated for the measurement of phenotypic natural selection." (262, p. 1210)

Natural selection has been defined in various and sometimes overly complex ways (129). The simplest and operationally most useful definition of natural selection is variation in Darwinian fitness that is correlated with variation in one or more phenotypic traits. This definition emphasizes that natural selection is a purely phenotypic phenomenon that occurs and can be measured within generations (58, 99, 166, 177, 262, 309, 344, 379, 394, 430). Moreover, it emphasizes that selection acts on phenotypic variation, without regard to its genetic basis, and thus can be futile in the sense of leading to no improvement in a population. The realization that repeatable, individual variation is the most fundamental requirement for natural selection to occur has stimulated many recent studies of the magnitude and correlates of individual variation in physiological, performance, and behavioral traits (see references in Introduction).

Quantifying selection in nature requires measurement of individual differences in fitness, e.g. lifetime reproductive success, and in some trait of interest, e.g. standard metabolic rate. A correlation between fitness and the phenotypic trait equals selection. Because true fitness is exceedingly difficult to measure, such components of fitness as survivorship or clutch size are usually measured as a substitute (129, 262, 345). Incomplete measures of fitness will limit inferences that can be drawn, but are an important first step. To date, only a handful of studies have specifically addressed whether natural selection acts on individual variation in physiological traits in natural populations. For example, Jayne & Bennett (227) demonstrated a correlation between survivorship and speed or stamina in garter snakes (see also 56, 229, 232, 352: reviews in 35, 39, 58, 166).

The foregoing approach to quantifying selection in nature is a "black box" in the following sense. Into the black box goes a known number of individuals with a known distribution of phenotypes (e.g. sprint speeds of hatchling lizards) and out comes a smaller number of individuals with a possibly altered distribution. The alteration of the distribution is attributable to the effects of natural selection, assuming no differential immigration or emigration with respect to the phenotypic trait being studied, no ontogenetic changes in the phenotype, etc (129, 262). The nature of the selective agent(s) is, however, unknowable from such information. For example, if faster lizards survived longer, it would not be known whether this was because (a) they were better able to escape from predators, (b) they were better able to catch insects and hence less likely to starve to death, or (c) maximal sprint speed was phenotypically correlated with some other trait (stamina?) that was the actual target of selection. Thus correlational studies of selection in nature are an important first step, but they are incomplete with respect to understanding the causes of selection. Elucidation of the causes of selection requires additional information, such as direct observations of animals in nature (e.g. observations of predator-prey interactions) (39, 153, 166, 180, 227, 329: see also 24, 25). Once the mechanism of selection is understood, more concrete interpretations can be made about the original field data suggesting selection on genotype-related behaviors (Figure 1). Furthermore, predictions about other selective effects can be made and tested (in the case of allozyme variation, see 440, 444, 447).

Correlational studies of selection in the wild (129) can be enhanced by experimental manipulations (166, 309). Because selection in nature will often be weak, extremely large sample sizes can be required to detect its action. This is a problem of statistical power. A standard way to increase power in correlation or regression analyses is to increase the range of variation in the independent variable (e.g. maximal sprint speed). Sinervo and colleagues (393–396) have used this approach, via experimental manipulation of eggs and dams, to study selection on offspring size and clutch size in lizards. Artificial selection experiments could also be used to extend variation beyond the natural range (318), and crossbreeding or direct genetic manipulation might be used to alter expression of allozymes, followed by release of manipulated individuals into natural populations. Finally, field transplants (241) can be performed to determine the relative fitness of varying phenotypes under different environmental conditions.

INTERSPECIFIC COMPARATIVE METHODS

"...we must learn to treat comparative data with the same respect as we would treat experimental results..." (298, p. vii)

Interspecific comparisons are a long-standing tradition in physiology (6, 20, 126, 172, 338, 380, 382, 383, 464). For example, broad surveys of data compiled primarily from the literature, then plotted on log-log axes vs body mass, have provided a plethora of descriptive and predictive interspecific allometric equations (see references in *What is the Origin of Allometric Relationships?*).

At the opposite extreme in terms of sample size, two species, differing in behavior or ecology often have been chosen and compared to determine whether they show phenotypic differences that could be interpreted as adaptations to the presumably different selective regimes (26, 275) imposed by the differences in behavior or ecology. Garland & Adolph (156) have argued that extreme caution must be used when attempting to infer adaptation from two-species comparative studies. Any two species are likely to show differences in almost any phenotypic trait that one might choose to measure. These differences are almost guaranteed by random mutation and genetic drift acting independently in the lineages leading to the two study species, unless counteracted by uniform stabilizing selection. Thus given a sufficient sample size of individuals from each of the two study species, a statistically significant difference will probably be found; that is, the null hypothesis of no difference in physiology will likely be rejected. About 50% of the time the difference will, by chance, be in the same direction as that predicted by the alternative hypothesis (adaptation to the environmental factor). Thus the chance of rejecting the null hypothesis of no adaptive differences in physiology can be as high as 50%; α, the Type I error rate, may be closer to 0.50 than to the nominal 0.05!

Garland & Adolph (156) argue that, at a minimum, three species are required for a comparative study that aims to make inferences about adaptation, and the more species the better. But multi-species data sets bring with them numerous statistical complications. In brief, species (and some-times populations within a species) related by a hierarchical phylogeny cannot be assumed to represent statistically independent data points (Figure 2). Species inherit both their genome and their environment (unless a dispersal event or rapid climatic change has occurred) from their immediate ancestor. Closely related species (i.e. species that diverged relatively re-cently) will therefore tend to be quite similar with respect to most aspects of their genotype, environment, and phenotype (139, 176, 187).

The most obvious problem with species non-independence is that it lowers the degrees of freedom available for hypothesis testing. For example, suppose one wished to correlate blood hemoglobin level with altitude for a series of three species. Assume that species mean values were available for both hemoglobin level and altitude (perhaps we would be dealing with species that presently exist as only single populations, each with a narrow altitudinal distribution). The sample size is thus three species' means, and the null hypothesis would be no correlation between hemoglobin level and altitude. The 1-tailed alternative hypothesis would be a positive correlation between hemoglobin level and altitude. Because altitude is the independent variable (the presumed selective regime), we could compute a least-squares linear regression of hemoglobin level on altitude. Assuming we judge statistical significance at an a priori $\alpha = 0.05$, then with one degree of freedom, the critical value for the t statistic is 6.314 (from Table 12 of 356) or 39.9 for the equivalent F statistic (from Table 16 of 356). (In terms of hypothesis testing, we could equivalently look up the critical value for the Pearson

What Conventional Statistics Assumes

What Evolution Provides

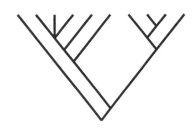

Figure 2 Diagrammatic representation of the statistical problems caused by the hierarchical nature of evolutionary relationships and descent with modification. Typically, the field of statistics assumes that data points are independent, as would be the case if we studied 10 species that were related as shown on the left; here, instantaneous speciation resulted in 10 independent lineages that led to 10 living species that might be studied by a physiologist. Thus if we were to test for a correlation between species mean values for two phenotypes (e.g. size-corrected heart mass and maximal oxygen consumption) of these 10 species, or perhaps between one phenotype and an environmental factor (e.g. blood hemoglobin concentration and altitude), we could claim the nominal N-2 = 8 degrees of freedom for hypothesis testing. If, instead, the 10 species were actually related as shown on the right, we would have something fewer than 8 d.f. available for hypothesis testing. Although no simple correction factor for degrees of freedom is available, various methods exist that explicitly use the phylogenetic topology and branch lengths to allow valid hypothesis testing (see text).

product-moment correlation coefficient with 1 d.f., which is ±0.988 for the 1-tailed test) (from Table B.16 of 468).

If our three study species were the result of one ancestral lineage splitting simultaneously into three daughters, the foregoing procedure would be perfectly acceptable. If, on the other hand, two of our species were very close relatives, then we would have something fewer than three independent data points and hence something less than one degree of freedom. In the limit, if two of our species had diverged only yesterday, then we would have only two independent data points and hence no degrees of freedom for hypothesis testing! In effect, this brings us back to a two-species comparison and illustrates another perspective on why two-species comparisons are inadequate for inferring adaptation-inadequate d.f. (156).

Interspecific Comparisons in a Phylogenetic Context

"If we assume that the...cladogram...is correct, we can then hypothesize what the particular common ancestor must have been like." (20, p. 14)

Incorporation of a phylogenetic perspective into comparative studies is essential from a statistical perspective (see above, below, and Figure 2) and moreover allows one to address questions that simply cannot be considered in the absence of phylogenetic information (59, 187, 211, 213, 265–267, 275, 302). For example, if one has data for the mean phenotypes (character states) of a series of species and some estimate of their evolutionary relationships, then one can use a parsimony algorithm (59, 142, 213, 274, 285–287, 296, 409, 411, 458) to infer the likely phenotype of ancestors, that is, nodes on the phylogenetic tree (78, 119, 213, 465). Thus parsimony reconstructions allow one to infer where in a clade a particular feature arose (35, 62, 69, 71, 72, 107, 130, 294, 365, 366, 370), if it has arisen more than once and, if so, the minimum number of times it has arisen (49, 105, 130, 264, 301, 349, 387), such as how many times air breathing evolved in fishes (62), toe fringes evolved in lizards (277), or the ability to produce benzaldehyde arose and/or was lost in tiger beetles (7). Once nodal values have been estimated, the inferred changes that have occurred along each branch segment of the phylogenetic tree can be computed, thus allowing inferences about the directions of past evolutionary change, tests for correlations in the changes of two or more characters (59, 78, 164, 165, 187, 213, 274, 277, 335), elucidation of the sequence of changes that occurred during the evolution of a complex trait (49, 134, 239, 265–267, 301), and tests for whether the presence of a particular state in one character or environmental feature predisposes some other trait to change in a particular direction (7, 187, 285, 287). If associations between characters and environmental factors are established (see 162, pp. 29, 30), then inferences about adaptation are possible (11, 26, 50, 59, 156, 175, 182, 187, 239, 265–267, 274, 275, 277, 302, 307, 345, 349, 350, 415, 416). If independent information on divergence times is available, then rates of evolution can be studied (152, 210, 465: of 408).

Phylogenetically-Based Statistical Methods

The foregoing uses of phylogenetic information to study variation among species are not statistical in any formal sense; that is, P-values or confidence intervals are not being assigned to the estimates of ancestral states, inferred changes, or correlations of inferred changes across traits. But phylogenetic analyses of character evolution can also be explicitly statistical with formal estimation and/or hypothesis testing. Since 1985 a number of phylogenetically-based statistical methods have been proposed. Of the available alternatives, Felsenstein's (139) method of phylogenetically independent contrasts is the best understood and is applicable to a wide range of questions, including correlation, principal components analysis, regression, multiple regression, ANOVA, and ANCOVA (152, 159, 162, 164, 176, 295, 296, 341). This method was designed for use with traits exhibiting continuous variation, such as body size or metabolic rate (for applications with physiological traits see 27, 88, 156, 164, 188, 213, 218, 274, 336, 386, 406, 437). The simplest use of phylogenetically independent contrasts is to study correlated evolution, such as the allometry of some trait in relation to body size (165). Both PC-based (159, 296) and MacIntosh-based (162, 340) computer programs to conduct independent contrasts analyses and various other comparative methods are available.

In many cases, statistical analyses done by a method that allows for phylogenetic non-independence will indicate that relationships between variables (as judged by correlation or regression: 164, 187, 188), or differences among groups [as judged by analysis of variance (ANOVA) or covariance (ANCOVA): 159], indicate weaker and hence less significant relationships. Such is not always the case, however (27, 156, 274, 348, 437).

Can one predict whether a phylogenetic statistical analysis will yield an answer that is different from a conventional, non-phylogenetic method? In general, if the phenotypic data being analyzed (e.g. basal metabolic rate, sprint speed) follow the phylogeny—if species strongly resemble their close relatives for the traits being tested for a correlation—then a statistical method that allows for phylogenetic relationships will indicate a weaker relationship than one that assumes all species to be related as by a star (*left* in Figure 2). In other words, if it is phylogenetic resemblance of species values that is driving an apparently significant correlation between traits, then a phylogenetically based statistical method, such as independent contrasts, will indicate a weaker and less statistically significant relationship.

Other phylogenetically based statistical methods, including squared-change parsimony and some techniques for discrete traits, are discussed elsewhere (152, 170, 187, 213, 274, 275, 282, 285-287, 296, 307, 335). Estimates of phylogenetic relationships are becoming more widely available (131, 389, 412). Most of the methods can deal with unresolved nodes in phylogenies (see 159, 170, 176, 187, 341).

INTEGRATING MICRO- AND MACROEVOLUTIONARY APPROACHES

To understand the hows and whys of evolutionary change at the phenotypic level (e.g. physiological traits), multiple valid approaches exist that can converge on the same endpoint. Because microevolutionary (within-species) phenomena can be studied experimentally, as through artificial selection experiments, physiologists may find them particularly attractive. But motivation can come from either direction. The senior author, for example, undertook quantitative genetic analyses of basal metabolic rates of mice in hopes of better understanding the (in)famous mouse-elephant curve (cf 261). Similarly, Bennett's bacterial selection experiments (37, 40, 41) and Huey's

Drosophila selection experiments (215, 218, 219) were preceded by studies of interspecific variation in thermal physiology of lizards (31, 164, 195, 210, 213: cf 39, 213, 214, 218), which are not ideally suited to artificial selection. Finally, microevolutionary analyses of the correlated evolution of snake color patterns and antipredator behaviors, including locomotor abilities, were motivated by interspecific patterns (see 55–58).

Comparative approaches focus on the endpoints of evolutionary processes. Because of the non-independence of species values caused by hierarchical descent with modification, statistical methods that allow for phylogenetic relatedness are required to determine whether the (co)variation observed among species represents more of a pattern than could have arisen simply by chance processes, such as random mutation and genetic drift. If an appropriate statistical method confirms that the observed pattern is really unusual, then—and only then—do the data call for an explanation, such as adaptation by natural selection.

Given that a statistically significant pattern is observed for among-species variation (e.g. group differences) or covariation (e.g. correlations between two physiological traits), then at least three processes (mechanisms) might account for it: (*a*) selection acting within species; (*b*) genetic couplings of characters; and (*c*) higher-level phenomena such as species selection or lineage sorting (references in 77b, 120, 134, 144, 166, 305, 350, 418, 459). Mechanisms *(a)* and *(b)* are familiar to physiologists, but *(c)* covers phenomena that are less well understood. In some cases biogeographic, paleoclimatological, and/or fossil information can be used to help construct scenarios for the evolution of physiological (or other) traits (78, 107, 225, 284, 302, 314, 342, 367, 369).

Some organisms are particularly suitable both for comparative phylogenetic analyses [including comparisons of natural populations, subspecies, or laboratory strains with known relationships (16, 141, 155, 162)] and for quantitative genetic analyses, including artificial selection experiments [*Drosophila* (82–85, 87, 88, 128, 179, 184, 203–205, 214, 215, 218, 219, 255, 317, 355, 358–362, 384, 420, 448); and *Mus* (16, 17, 22, 23, 45–47, 141, 143, 190, 230, 260, 278–281, 300, 324, 325, 410)]. Whatever the choice as to organism, analytical mode or physiological system, a plurality of approaches will be necessary to understand any large question in evolutionary physiology (51, 146, 166, 218, 223, 275, 308, 318, 329, 418, 432, 433, 434, 465). Comparative studies, for example, indicate what did happen during evolution, but not necessarily what had to happen; similarly, "selection experiments indicate what might happen in nature, but not necessarily what will happen" (219, p. 755). Understanding the ultimate causes and proximate mechanisms of the evolution of endothermy is a good example of a long-standing problem in evolutionary physiology that calls for multidisciplinary approaches (B Block, this volume; 35, 42, 43, 50, 53, 101, 102, 130, 148, 160, 189, 221, 225, 303, 326, 368, 383, 406, 417, 437; references therein). For example, our laboratory is currently analyzing the genetic correlation between minimal and maximal rates of oxygen consumption and beginning selection experiments on voluntary activity levels in *Mus* (see also 143, 190, 347).

CONCLUSION AND FUTURE PROSPECTS

Evolution and physiology have much to offer each other (36, 61, 62, 71, 72, 108, 135, 155, 214, 339, 342, 343, 388). Knowledge of physiological mechanisms can allow much deeper insight into possible reasons for evolutionary correlations and constraints than is possible for many of the traits typically studied by evolutionary biologists (e.g. morphology). A comparative perspective can even enlighten biomedical and clinical issues (460). For example, Rose and colleagues have provided clear evidence that an evolutionary perspective can (or at least should!) alter accepted views on aging (179, 357–362, 384, 460). Similarly, Kluger's (242–245) studies of fever and White's (456, 457) comparative perspective on acid-base balance during hypothermia have affected the way physicians view and treat human patients. "Those who see the body as a machine designed by a careless engineer are prone to therapeutic hubris. The antidote is a deep understanding of each organ's phylogeny and functions, as well as its ontogeny and structure." (460, p. 18)

We see evolutionary physiology moving forward on many fronts during the next decade. Which of the several promising areas, such as phylogenetically-based comparative studies, artificial selection studies in the laboratory, or physiological analyses of single-gene products will yield the greatest insights is difficult to predict. Perhaps the most illuminating studies will be those that apply several complementary approaches (35, 36, 39, 43, 51, 88, 155, 166, 214, 218, 302, 308, 345, 423, 432) to an ecologically and phylogenetically well-known group of species that is tractable for physiological studies. Such studies will not be easy, quick, or inexpensive, but they may yield understanding that is greater than any equivalent series of piecemeal studies done on several different species.

The tools now exist to permit comprehensive studies of physiological evolution. Such studies will be greatly facilitated by interactions of physiologists with biochemists, morphologists, ethologists, ecologists, geneticists, and systematists. We envision studies in which knowledge of biochemistry, physiology, biomechanics, and/or developmental biology is first used to predict trade-offs between various physiological functions. These hypothesized constraints are then tested in at least two ways, by quantification of genetic correlations within populations and of evolutionary correlations through interspecific comparative studies. Whatever approaches are used, the framework (Figure 1) that envisions measures of whole-animal performance as central for attempting to link morphological, physiological, or biochemical variation with behavior, fitness, or ecology should be a guiding principle for ecological and evolutionary physiologists.

ACKNOWLEDGMENTS

TG thanks RB Huey for many helpful discussions over the years and for bringing various references and quotations to our attention. SC Adolph, AF Bennett, JL Graves, RE Jung, and WB Watt commented on part or all of the manuscript, and several of our colleagues sent us reprints or preprints. Supported by National Science Foundation grants IBN-9157268, IBN-9111185, and DEB-9220872 to TG, and by a Michael Guyer Postdoctoral Fellowship from the Department of Zoology, University of Wisconsin-Madison to PAC.

Literature Cited

1. Adolph SC, Porter WP. 1993. Temperature, activity, and lizard life histories. *Am. Nat.* 142:273–95
2. Alahitois SN. 1982. Adaptation of *Drosophila* enzymes to temperature. IV. Natural selection at the alcohol dehydrogenase locus. *Genetica* 59:81–87
3. Alexander RMcN. 1982. *Optima for Animals*. London: Edward Arnold
4. Alexander RMcN. 1984. Optimal strengths for bones liable to fatigue and accidental fracture. *J. Theor. Biol.* 109:621–36
5. Alexander RMcN. 1988. Why mammals gallop. *Am. Zool.* 28:237–45
6. Alexander RMcN. 1991. Apparent adaptation and actual performance. *Evol. Biol.* 25:357–73
7. Altaba CR. 1991. The importance of ecological and historical factors in the production of benzaldehyde by tiger beetles. *Syst. Zool.* 40:101–05
8. Anderson PR, Knibb WR, Oakeshott JG. 1987. Observations on the extent and temporal stability of latitudinal clines for alcohol dehydrogenase allozymes and four chromosome inversions in *Drosophila melanogaster*. *Genetica* 75:81–88
9. Arnold SJ. 1983. Morphology, performance and fitness. *Am. Zool.* 23:347–61

10. Arnold SJ. 1987. Genetic correlation and the evolution of physiology. See Ref. 135, pp. 189–215
11. Arnold SJ. 1988. Behavior, energy and fitness. *Am. Zool.* 28:815–27
12. Arnold SJ. 1992. Constraints on phenotypic evolution. *Am. Nat.* 140:S85–107 (Suppl.)
13. Arnold SJ. 1994. Multivariate inheritance and evolution: a review of concepts. See Ref. 51, In press
14. Arnold SJ, Bennett AF. 1984. Behavioural variation in natural populations. III. Antipredator displays in the garter snake *Thamnophis radix*. *Anim. Behav.* 32:1108–18
15. Arnold SJ, Bennett AF. 1988. Behavioral variation in natural populations. V. Morphological correlates of locomotion in the garter snake *Thamnophis radix*. *Biol. J. Linn. Soc.* 34:175–90
16. Atchley WR, Fitch WM. 1991. Gene trees and the origins of inbred strains of mice. *Science* 254:554–58
17. Atchley WR, Logsdon TE, Cowley DE, Eisen EJ. 1991. Uterine effects, epigenetics and postnatal skeletal development in the mouse. *Evolution* 45:891–909
18. Atkinson DE. 1990. What should a theory of metabolic control offer to the experimenter? See Ref. 94, pp. 3–28

19. Atkinson DE. 1990. An experimentalist's view of control analysis. See Ref. 94, pp. 413–28
20. Atz JW, Epple A, Pang PKT. 1980. Comparative physiology, systematics, and the history of life. See Ref. 316, pp. 7–15
21. Barker WC, Dayhoff MO. 1980. Evolutionary and functional relationships of homologous physiological mechanisms. *BioScience* 30:593–600
22. Barnett SA, Dickson RG. 1985. A paternal influence on survival of wild mice in the nest. *Nature* 317:617–18
23. Barnett SA, Dickson RG. 1989. Wild mice in the cold: some findings on adaptation. *Biol. Rev.* 64:317–40
24. Bartholomew GA. 1986. The role of natural history in contemporary biology. *BioScience* 36:324–29
25. Bartholomew GA. 1987. Interspecific comparison as a tool for ecological physiologists. See Ref. 135, pp. 11–37
26. Baum DA, Larson A. 1991. Adaptation reviewed: a phylogenetic methodology for studying character macroevolution. *Syst. Zool.* 40:1–18
27. Bauwens D, Garland T Jr, Castilla AM, Van Damme R. 1994. Evolution of sprint speed in lacertid lizards: morphological, physiological, and behavioral coadaptation. *Evolution.* In press
28. Bauwens D, Van Damme R, Vanderstighelen D, Thoen C, Sanders D, et al. 1987. Individuality in common lizards (*Lacerta vivipara*): a provisional review. In *Proc. 4th Ordinary Gen. Meet. Soc. Eur. Herpetol.*, ed. JJ van Gelder, H Strijbosch, PJM Bergers, pp. 55–58. Nijmegen, The Netherlands: Facul. Sci.
29. Bayne BL. 1987. Genetic aspects of physiological adaptation in bivalve molluscs. See Ref. 67, pp. 169–89
30. Beeby R, Kacser H. 1990. Metabolic constraints in evolution. In *Organizational Constraints on the Dynamics of Evolution*, ed. J Maynard Smith, G Vida, pp. 55–75. Manchester: Manchester Univ. Press
31. Bennett AF. 1980. The thermal dependence of lizard behaviour. *Anim. Behav.* 28:752–62
32. Bennett AF. 1987. The accomplishments of physiological ecology. See Ref. 135, pp. 1–10
33. Bennett AF. 1987. Inter-individual variability: an underutilized resource. See Ref. 135, pp. 147–69
34. Bennett AF. 1989. Integrated studies of locomotor performance. See Ref. 433, pp. 191–202
35. Bennett AF. 1991. The evolution of activity capacity. *J. Exp. Biol.* 160:1–23
36. Bennett AF. 1994. Adaptation and the evolution of physiological characters. In *Handbook of Comparative Physiology*, ed. WH Dantzler, Oxford: Oxford Univ. Press. In press
37. Bennett AF, Dao KM, Lenski RE. 1990. Rapid evolution in response to high-temperature selection. *Nature* 346:79–81
38. Bennett AF, Garland T Jr, Else PL. 1989. Individual correlation of morphology, muscle mechanics and locomotion in a salamander. *Am. J. Physiol.* 256(25):R1200–8
39. Bennett AF, Huey RB. 1990. Studying the evolution of physiological performance. In *Oxford Surveys in Evolutionary Biology*, ed. DJ Futuyma, J Antonovics, 7:251–84. Oxford: Oxford Univ. Press
40. Bennett AF, Lenski RE. 1993. Evolutionary adaptation to temperature II. Thermal niches of experimental lines of *Escherichia coli*. *Evolution* 47:1–12
41. Bennett AF, Lenski RE, Mittler JE. 1992. Evolutionary adaptation to temperature. I. Fitness responses of *Escherichia coli* to changes in its thermal environment. *Evolution* 46:16–30
42. Bennett AF, Ruben JA. 1979. Endothermy and activity in vertebrates. *Science* 206:649–54
43. Bennett AF, Ruben JA. 1986. The metabolic and thermoregulatory status of therapsids. In *The Ecology and Biology of Mammal-like Reptiles*, ed. N Hotton, PD MacLean, JJ Roth, EC Roth, pp. 207–18. Washington, DC: Smithsonian Institution
44. Berry MN, Gregory RB, Grivell DC, Henley DC, Phillips JW, et al. 1990. Constraints in the application of control analysis to the study of metabolism in hepatocytes. See Ref. 94, pp. 343–49
45. Berry RJ. 1981. Town mouse, country mouse: adaptation and adaptability in *Mus domesticus (M. musculus domesticus)*. *Mamm. Rev.* 11:91–136
46. Berry RJ, Berry AJ, Anderson TJC, Scriven P. 1992. The house mice of Faray, Orkney. *J. Zool.* 228:233–46
47. Berry RJ, Jakobson ME, Peters J. 1987. Inherited differences within an island population of the house mouse. *J. Zool.* 211:605–18
48. Bijlsma-Meeles E, Bijlsma R. 1988. The alcohol dehydrogenase polymorphism in *Drosophila melanogaster:* fit-

ness measurements and predictions under conditions with no alcohol stress. *Genetics* 120:743–53

49. Blackburn DG. 1992. Convergent evolution of viviparity, matrotrophy, and specializations for fetal nutrition in reptiles and other vertebrates. *Am. Zool.* 32:313–21

50. Block BA, Finnerty JR, Stewart AFR, Kidd J. 1993. Evolution of endothermy in fish: mapping physiological traits on a molecular phylogeny. *Science* 260:210–14

51. Boake CRB, ed. 1994. *Quantitative Genetic Studies of Behavioral Evolution.* Chicago: Univ. Chicago Press. In press

52. Bradley WG, Yousef MK. 1972. Small mammals in the desert. In *Physiological Adaptations: Desert and Mountain,* ed. MK Yousef, SM Horvath, RW Bullard, pp. 127–42. New York: Academic

53. Brand MD, Couture P, Else PL, Withers KW, Hulbert AJ. 1991. Evolution of energy metabolism. *Biochem. J.* 275:81–86

54. Broadhurst PL, Jinks JL. 1974. What genetical architecture can tell us about the natural selection of behavioral traits. In *The Genetics of Behaviour,* ed. JHF van Abeelen, pp. 43–63. Amsterdam: North-Holland

55. Brodie ED III. 1989. Genetic correlations between morphology and antipredator behaviour in natural populations of the garter snake *Thamnophis ordionoides. Nature* 342: 542–43

56. Brodie ED III. 1992. Correlational selection for color pattern and antipredator behaviour in the garter snake *Thamnophis ordionoides. Evolution* 46: 1284–98

57. Brodie ED III. 1993. Homogeneity of the genetic variance-covariance matrix for antipredator traits in two natural populations of the garter snake *Thamnophis ordinoides. Evolution.* 47: 844–54

58. Brodie ED III, Garland T Jr. 1993. Quantitative genetics of snake populations. In *Snakes: Ecology and Behavior,* ed. RA Seigel, JT Collins, pp. 315–62. New York: McGraw Hill

59. Brooks DR, McLennan DA. 1991. *Phylogeny, Ecology, and Behavior. A Research Program in Comparative Biology.* Chicago: Univ. Chicago Press

60. Buddington RK, Chen JW, Diamond JM. 1991. Dietary regulation of intestinal brush-border sugar and amino acid

transport in carnivores. *Am. J. Physiol.* 261(30):R793–801

61. Burggren WW. 1991. Does comparative respiratory physiology have a role in evolutionary biology (and vice versa)? In *Physiological Strategies for Gas Exchange and Metabolism,* ed. AJ Worlies, MK Grieshaber, CL Bridges, pp. 1–14. Cambridge: Cambridge Univ. Press

62. Burggren WW, Bemis WE. 1990. Studying physiological evolution: paradigms and pitfalls. In Evolutionary Innovations, ed. MH Nitecki, pp. 191–238. Chicago: University of Chicago Press

63. Burton RS, Feldman MW. 1982. Changes in free amino acid concentrations during osmotic response in the intertidal copepod Tigriopus californicus. *Comp. Biochem. Physiol.* 73A:441–45

64. Burton RS, Feldman MW. 1983. Physiological effects of an allozyme polymorphism: Glutamate-pyruvate transaminase and response to hyperosmotic stress in the copepod *Tigriopus californicus. Biochem. Genet.* 21:239–51

65. Calder WA III. 1984. *Size, Function and Life History.* Cambridge: Harvard Univ. Press

66. Calder WA III. 1987. Scaling energetics of homeothermic vertebrates: an operational allometry. *Annu. Rev. Physiol.* 49:107–20

67. Calow P, ed. 1987. *Evolutionary Physiological Ecology.* Cambridge: Cambridge Univ. Press

68. Calow P, Berry RJ, eds. 1989. *Evolution, Ecology, and Environmental Stress.* London: Academic

69. Campbell JW, Smith DD Jr, Vorhaben JE. 1985. Avian and mammalian mitochondrial ammonia-detoxifying systems in tortoise liver. *Science* 228: 349–51

70. Carothers JH. 1986. An experimental confirmation of morphological adaptation: toe fringes in the sand-dwelling lizard *Uma scoparia. Evolution* 40: 871–74

71. Carrier DR. 1987. The evolution of locomotor stamina in tetrapods: circumventing a mechanical constraint. *Paleobiology* 13:326–41

72. Carrier DR. 1991. Conflict in the hypaxial musculo-skeletal system: documenting an evolutionary constraint. *Am. Zool.* 31:644–54

73. Cavener DR, Clegg MT. 1981. Multigenic response to ethanol in *Drosophila melanogaster. Evolution* 35:1–10

74. Chai CK. 1970. Selective breeding for

131I thyroid uptake in mice. *Genetics* 64:29–40

75. Chappell MA, Hayes JP, Snyder LRG. 1988. Hemoglobin polymorphisms in deer mice (*Peromyscus maniculatus*): physiology of beta-globin variants and alpha-globin recombinants. *Evolution* 42:681–88

76. Chappell MA, Snyder LRG. 1984. Biochemical and physiological correlates of deer mouse alpha-chain hemoglobin polymorphisms. *Proc. Natl. Acad. Sci. USA* 81:5484–88

77a. Charlesworth B. 1990. Optimization models, quantitative genetics, and mutation. *Evolution* 44:520–38

77b. Charlesworth B, Lande R, Slatkin M. 1982. A neo-Darwinian commentary on macroevolution: the plain truth. *Evolution* 36:474–98

78. Chevalier CD. 1991. *Aspects of thermoregulation and energetics in the Procyonidae (Mammalia: Carnivora)*. PhD thesis. Univ. Calif. Irvine. 202 pp.

79. Cheverud JM, Moore AJ. 1994. Quantitative genetics and the role of the environment provided by relatives in behavioral evolution. See Ref. 51, In press

80. Choudhary M, Laurie CC. 1991. Use of in vitro mutagenesis to analyze the molecular basis of the difference in *Adh* expression associated with the allozyme polymorphism in *Drosophila melanogaster*. *Genetics* 129:481–88

81. Christian KA, Tracy CR. 1981. The effect of the thermal environment on the ability of hatchling Galapagos land iguanas to avoid predation during dispersal. *Oecologia* 49:218–23

82. Clark AG. 1987. Senescence and the genetic-correlation hang-up. *Am. Nat.* 129:932–40

83. Clark AG. 1989. Causes and consequences of variation in energy storage in *Drosophila melanogaster*. *Genetics* 123:131–44

84. Clark AG. 1990. Genetic components of variation in energy storage in *Drosophila melanogaster*. *Evolution* 44:637–50

85. Clark AG. 1991. Mutation-selection balance and metabolic control theory. *Genetics* 129:909–23

86. Clark AG, Koehn RK. 1992. Enzymes and adaptation. In *Genes in Ecology*, ed. RJ Berry, TJ Crawford, GM Hewitt, pp. 193–228. Boston: Blackwell Scientific

87. Clark AG, Szumski FM, Bell KA, Keith LE, Houtz S, Merriwether DA. 1990. Direct and correlated responses to artificial selection on lipid and glycogen contents in *Drosophila melanogaster*. *Genet. Res. Cambridge* 56:49–56

88. Clark AG, Wang L. 1994. Comparative evolutionary analysis of metabolism in nine *Drosophila* species. *Evolution*. In press

89. Clarke B. 1975. The contribution of ecological genetics to evolutionary theory: Detecting the direct effects of natural selection on particular polymorphic loci. *Genetics* 79:101–13

90. Cohan FM, Hoffmann AA. 1989. Uniform selection as a diversifying force in evolution: evidence from *Drosophila*. *Am. Nat.* 134:613–37

91. Cohan FM, Hoffmann AA, Gayley TW. 1989. A test of the role of epistasis in divergence under uniform selection. *Evolution* 43:766–74

92. Congdon JD, Gibbons JW. 1987. Morphological constraint on egg size: A challange to optimal egg size theory? *Proc. Natl. Acad. Sci. USA* 84:4145–47

93. Cooper DM, Weiler-Ravell D, Whipp BJ, Wasserman K. 1984. Growth-related changes in oxygen uptake and heart rate during progressive exercise in children. *Pediat. Res.* 18:845–51

94. Cornish-Bowden A, Cardenas ML, ed. 1990. *Control of Metabolic Processes*. New York: Plenum

95. Cowles RB. 1958. The evolutionary significance of the scrotum. *Evolution* 12:417–18

96. Crabtree B, Newsholme EA. 1985. A quantitative approach to metabolic control. *Curr. Top. Cell. Reg.* 25:21–75

97. Crabtree B, Newsholme EA. 1987. A systematic approach to describing and analyzing metabolic control systems. *Trends Biol. Sci.* 12:4–12

98. Crawford DL, Powers DA. 1989. Molecular basis of evolutionary adaptation at the lactate dehydrogenase-B locus in the fish *Fundulus heteroclitus*. *Proc. Natl. Acad. Sci. USA* 86:9365–69

99. Crespi BJ. 1990. Measuring the effects of natural selection on phenotypic interaction systems. *Am. Nat.* 135:32–47

100. Crews D. 1992. Behavioural endocrinology and reproduction: an evolutionary perspective. In *Oxford Reviews of Reproductive Biology,* ed. SR Milligan, 14:303–70. Oxford: Oxford Univ. Press

101. Crompton AW, Taylor CR, Jagger JA. 1978. Evolution of homeothermy in mammals. *Nature* 272:333–36

102. Daniels CB, Pratt J. 1992. Breathing in long necked dinosaurs: did the sauropods have bird lungs? *Comp. Biochem. Physiol.* 101A:43–46

103. Dean AM. 1990. Molecular adaptations in the lactose operon. See Ref. 94, pp. 389–98

104. Dean AM, Dykhuizen DE, Hartl DL. 1988. Theories of metabolic control in quanitative genetics. See Ref. 453, pp. 536–48

105. de Fraipont M, Clobert J, Barbault R. 1994. The evolution of oviparity with egg guarding and viviparity in lizards and snakes: a phylogenetic analysis. *Evolution.* In press

106. de Queiroz A, Wimberger PH. 1993. The usefulness of behavior for phylogeny estimation: levels of homoplasy in behavioral and morphological characters. *Evolution* 47:46–60

107. Dial BE, Grismer LL. 1992. A phylogenetic analysis of physiological-ecological character evolution in the lizard genus *Coleonyx* and its implications for historical biogeographic reconstruction. *Syst. Biol.* 41:178–95

108. Diamond JM. 1991. Evolutionary design of intestinal nutrient absorption: enough but not too much. *News Physiol. Sci.* 6:92–96

109. Diamond JM. 1992. The red flag of optimality. *Nature* 355:204–06

110. Diamond JM, Hammond K. 1992. The matches, achieved by natural selection, between biological capacities and their natural loads. *Experientia* 48:551–57

111. DiMichele L, Powers DA. 1982. LDH-B genotype-specific hatching times of *Fundulus heteroclitus* embryos. *Nature* 296:563–64

112. DiMichele L, Powers DA. 1982. Physiological basis for swimming endurance differences between LDH-B genotypes of *Fundulus heteroclitus. Science* 216:1014–16

113. Djawdan M. 1993. Locomotor performance of bipedal and quadrupedal heteromyid rodents. *Funct. Ecol.* 7:195–202

114. Djawdan M, Garland T Jr. 1988. Maximal running speeds of bipedal and quadrupedal rodents. *J. Mamm.* 69:765–72

115. Dohm MR, Garland T Jr. 1993. Quantitative genetics of scale counts in the garter snake *Thamnophis sirtalis. Copeia.* 1993:987–1002

116. Dudley EC, ed. 1991. The unity of evolutionary biology. *Proc. Fourth Int. Congr. Systematic Evolutionary Biology.* Portland, OR: Dioscorides

117. Dudley R, Gans C. 1991. A critique of symmorphosis and optimality models in physiology. *Physiol. Zool.* 64:627–37

118. Duman JG, Wu DW, Xu L, Tursman D, Olsen TM. 1991. Adaptations of insects to subzero temperatures. *Quart. Rev. Biol.* 66:387–10

119. Dunson WA, Travis J. 1991. The role of abiotic factors in community organization. *Am. Nat.* 138:1067–91

120. Dupre J, ed. 1987. *The Latest on the Best: Essays on Evolution and Optimality.* Cambridge MA: MIT Press

121. Dykhuizen DE, Dean AM. 1990. Enzyme activity and fitness: evolution in solution. *Trends Ecol. Evol.* 5:257–62

122. Dykhuizen DE, Dean AM, Hartl DL. 1987. Metabolic flux and fitness. *Genetics* 115:25–31

123. Dykhuizen DE, Hartl DL. 1980. Selective neutrality of 6PGD allozymes in *E. coli* and the effects of genetic background. *Genetics* 96:801–17

124. Dykhuizen DE, Hartl DL. 1983. Functional effects of PGI allozymes in *E. coli. Genetics* 105:1–18

125. Easterby JS. 1973. Coupled enzyme assays: a general expression for the transient. *Biochim. Biophys. Acta* 293:552–58

126. Eckert R, Randall D, Augustine G. 1988. *Animal Physiology: Mechanism and Adaptation.* New York: Freeman. 3rd Ed.

127. Ehrman L, Parsons PA. 1981. *Behavior Genetics and Evolution.* New York: McGraw-Hill

128. Ehrman L, White MM, Wallace B. 1991. A long-term study involving *Drosophila melanogaster* and toxic media. *Evol. Biol.* 25:175–209

129. Endler JA. 1986. *Natural Selection in the Wild.* Princeton: Princeton Univ. Press

130. Eppley ZA. 1991. *The ontogeny of endothermy in charadriiform birds: functional bases, ecological adaptations and phylogenetic constraints.* PhD thesis. Univ. Calif. Irvine. 192 pp.

131. Estes R, Pregill G. 1988. *Phylogenetic Relationships of the Lizard Families.* Stanford: Stanford Univ. Press

132. Falconer DS. 1989. *Introduction to Quantitative Genetics.* London: Longman. 3rd Ed.

133. Faraci FM. 1991. Adaptations to hypoxia in birds: how to fly high. *Annu. Rev. Physiol.* 53:59–70

134. Feder ME. 1987. The analysis of physiological diversity: the prospects for pattern documentation and general questions in ecological physiology. See Ref. 135, pp. 38–70

135. Feder ME, Bennett AF, Burggren WW, Huey RB, eds. 1987. *New Directions in Ecological Physiology.* New York: Cambridge Univ. Press

136. Feder ME, Block BA. 1991. On the future of animal physiological ecology. *Funct. Ecol.* 5:136–44

137. Feder ME, Watt WB. 1992. Functional biology of adaptation. In *Genes in Ecology,* ed. RJ Berry, TJ Crawford, GM Hewitt, pp. 365–92. Boston: Blackwell Scientific

138. Fell DA. 1992. Metabolic control analysis: a survey of its theoretical and experimental development. *Biochem. J.* 286:313–30

139. Felsenstein J. 1985. Phylogenies and the comparative method. *Am. Nat.* 125:1–15

140. Fersht AR. 1985. *Enzyme Structure and Mechanism.* New York: Freeman

141. Fitch WM, Atchley WR. 1987. Divergence in inbred strains of mice: a comparison of three different types of data. In *Molecules and Morphology in Evolution: Conflict or Compromise?* ed. C Patterson, pp. 203–16. Cambridge: Cambridge Univ. Press

142. Forey PL, Humphries CJ, Kitching IJ, Scotland RW, Siebert DJ, Williams DM. 1992. *Cladistics: A Practical Course in Systematics.* Oxford: Clarendon

143. Friedman WP, Garland T Jr, Dohm MR. 1992. Individual variation in locomotor behavior and maximal oxygen consumption in mice. *Physiol. Behav.* 52:97–104

144. Futuyma DJ. 1986. *Evolutionary Biology.* Sunderland MA: Sinauer

145. Gans C. 1983. On the fallacy of perfection. *Perspectives on Modern Auditory Research,* ed. RR Fay, G Gourevitch, pp. 101–12. Groton, CT: Amphora

146. Gans C. 1989. Stages in the origin of vertebrates: analysis by means of scenarios. *Biol. Rev.* 64:221–68

147. Gans C. 1991. Efficiency, effectiveness, perfection, optimization: their use in understanding vertebrate evolution. In *Efficiency and Ecomomy in Animal Physiology,* ed. RW Blake, pp. 1–11. Cambridge: Cambridge Univ. Press

148. Garland T Jr. 1984. Physiological correlates of locomotory performance in a lizard: an allometric approach. *Am. J. Physiol.* 247(16):R806–15

149. Garland T Jr. 1985. Ontogenetic and individual variation in size, shape and speed in the Australian agamid lizard *Amphibolurus nuchalis. J. Zool. Lond. (A)* 207:425–39

150. Garland T Jr. 1988. Genetic basis of activity metabolism. I. Inheritance of speed, stamina, and antipredator dis-

plays in the garter snake *Thamnophis sirtalis. Evolution* 42:335–50

151. Garland T Jr. 1994. Phylogenetic analyses of lizard endurance capacity in relation to body size and body temperature. In *Lizard Ecology: The Third Generation,* ed. LJ Vitt, ER Pianka. Princeton: Princeton Univ. Press. In press

152. Garland T Jr. 1992. Rate tests for phenotypic evolution using phylogenetically independent contrasts. *Am. Nat.* 140:509–19

153. Garland T Jr. 1993. Locomotor performance and activity metabolism of *Cnemidophorus tigris* in relation to natural behaviors. In *Biology of Whiptail Lizards (Genus Cnemidophorus),* ed. JW Wright, LJ Vitt, pp. 163–210. Norman OK: Oklahoma Museum Natural History

154. Garland T Jr. 1994. Quantitative genetics of locomotor behavior and physiology in a garter snake. See Ref. 51, In press

155. Garland T Jr, Adolph SC. 1991. Physiological differentiation of vertebrate populations. *Annu. Rev. Ecol. Syst.* 22:193–28

156. Garland T Jr, Adolph SC. 1994. Why not to do two-species comparative studies: limitations on inferring adaptation. *Physiol. Zool.* In press

157. Garland T Jr, Bennett AF. 1990. Quantitative genetics of maximal oxygen consumption in a garter snake. *Am. J. Physiol.* 259(28):R986–92

158. Garland T Jr, Bennett AF, Daniels CB. 1990. Heritability of locomotor performance and its correlates in a natural population. *Experientia* 46:530–33

159. Garland T Jr, Dickerman AW, Janis CM, Jones JA. 1993. Phylogenetic analysis of covariance by computer simulation. *Syst. Biol.* 42:265–92

160. Garland T Jr, Else PL. 1987. Seasonal, sexual, and individual variation in endurance and activity metabolism in lizards. *Am. J. Physiol.* 252(21):R439–49

161. Garland T Jr, Hankins E, Huey RB. 1990. Locomotor capacity and social dominance in male lizards. *Funct. Ecol.* 4:243–50

162. Garland T Jr, Harvey PH, Ives AR. 1992. Procedures for the analysis of comparative data using phylogenetically independent contrasts. *Syst. Biol.* 41:18–32

163. Garland T Jr, Huey RB. 1987. Testing symmorphosis: does structure match functional requirements? *Evolution* 41:1404–9

164. Garland T Jr, Huey RB, Bennett AF.

1991. Phylogeny and thermal physiology in lizards: a reanalysis. *Evolution* 45:1969–75

165. Garland T Jr, Janis CM. 1993. Does metatarsal/femur ratio predict maximal running speed in cursorial mammals? *J. Zool.* 229:133–51

166. Garland T Jr, Losos JB. 1994. Ecological morphology of locomotor performance in squamate reptiles. See Ref. 432, In press

167. Gatten RE Jr, Congdon JD, Mazzotti FJ, Fischer RU. 1991. Glycolysis and swimming performance in juvenile American alligators. *J. Herp.* 25:406–11

168. Giersch C, Lammel D, Steffen K. 1990. Application of metabolic control analysis to photosynthesis: the problem of getting data for an impressive algorithm. See Ref. 94, pp. 351–62

169. Gillespie JH. 1991. *The Causes of Molecular Evolution.* New York: Oxford Univ. Press

170. Gittleman JL, Kot M. 1990. Adaptation: statistics and a null model for estimating phylogenetic effects. *Syst. Zool.* 39:227–41

171. Gleeson TT, Harrison JM. 1988. Muscle composition and its relation to sprint running in the lizard *Dipsosaurus dorsalis.* *Am. J. Physiol.* 255(24):R470–77

172. Gordon MS, Bartholomew GA, Grinnell AD, Jorgensen CB, White FN. 1982. *Animal Physiology: Principles and Adaptations.* New York: MacMillan. 4th Ed.

173. Gould SJ. 1980. The evolutionary biology of constraint. *Daedalus* 109:39–52

174. Gould SJ 1989. *Wonderful Life. The Burgess Shale and the Nature of History.* New York: Norton

175. Gould SJ, Lewontin RC. 1979. The spandrels of San Marco and the Panglossian paradigm: a critique of the adaptationist programme. *Proc. R. Soc. London Ser. B* 205:581–98

176. Grafen A. 1989. The phylogenetic regression. *Phil. Trans. R. Soc. London Ser. B* 326:119–57

177. Grant PR. 1986. *Ecology and Evolution of Darwin's Finches.* Princeton: Princeton Univ. Press

178. Graves JL, Luckinbill LS, Nichols A. 1988. Flight duration and wing beat frequency in long- and short-lived *Drosophila melanogaster.* *J. Insect Physiol.* 34:1021–26

179. Graves JL, Toolson EC, Jeong C, Vu LN, Rose MR. 1992. Desiccation, flight, glycogen, and postponed senescence in *Drosophila melanogaster.* *Physiol. Zool.* 65:268–86

180. Greene HW. 1986. Natural history and evolutionary biology. In *Predator-Prey Relationships: Perspectives and Approaches from the Study of Lower Vertebrates,* ed. ME Feder, GV Lauder, pp. 99–108. Chicago: Univ. Chicago Press

181. Hahn ME, Hewitt JK, Henderson ND, Benno RH, eds. 1990. *Developmental Behavior Genetics: Neural, Biometrical, and Evolutionary Approaches.* New York: Oxford Univ. Press

182. Hailman JP. 1988. Operationalism, optimality, and optimism: suitabilities versus adaptations of organisms. In *Evolutionary Processes and Metaphors,* ed. MW Ho, SW Fox, pp. 85–116. Chichester UK: Wiley & Sons

183. Harris RA, Allan AM. 1989. Alcohol intoxication: ion channels and genetics. *FASEB J.* 3:1689–95

184. Harshman LG, Ottea JE, Hammock BD. 1991. Evolved environment-dependent expression of detoxification enzyme activity in *Drosophila melanogaster.* *Evolution* 45:791–95

185. Hartl DL, Dykhuizen DE. 1981. Potential for selection among nearly neutral allozymes of 6-phosphogluconate dehydrogenase in *Escherichia coli.* *Proc. Natl. Acad. Sci. USA* 78:6344–48

186. Hartl DL, Dykhuisen DE, Dean AM. 1985. Limits of adaptation: the evolution of selective neutrality. *Genetics* 111:655–74

187. Harvey PH, Pagel MD. 1991. *The Comparative Method in Evolutionary Biology.* Oxford: Oxford Univ. Press

188. Harvey PH, Pagel MD, Rees JA. 1991. Mammalian metabolism and life histories. *Am. Nat.* 137:556–66

189. Hayes JP. 1989. Altitudinal and seasonal effects on aerobic metabolism of deer mice. *J. Comp. Physiol. B* 159:453–59

190. Hayes JP, Garland T Jr, Dohm MR. 1992. Metabolic rates and reproduction of *Mus:* are energetics and life history linked? *Funct. Ecol.* 6:5–14

191. Heinrich R. 1990. Metabolic control analysis: principles and applications to the erythrocyte. See Ref. 94, pp. 329–42

192. Heinrich R, Rapoport SM. 1983. The utility of mathematical models for the understanding of metabolic systems. *Trans. Biochem. Soc.* 11:31–35

193. Henderson ND. 1981. Genetic influences on locomotor activity in 11-day-old housemice. *Behav. Genet.* 11:209–25

194. Henderson ND. 1989. Interpreting studies that compare high- and low-selected lines on new characters. *Behav. Genet.* 19:473–502

195. Hertz PE, Huey RB, Nevo E. 1983. Homage to Santa Anita: thermal sensitivity of sprint speed in agamid lizards. *Evolution* 37:1075–84

196. Heusner AA. 1987. What does the power function reveal about structure and function in animals of different size? *Annu. Rev. Physiol.* 49:121–34

197. Hewitt JK, Fulker DW, Broadhurst PL. 1981. Genetics of escape-avoidance conditioning in laboratory and wild populations of rats: A biometrical approach. *Behav. Genet.* 11:533–44

198. Higgins J. 1990. History and original thoughts on the control theoretic approach. See Ref. 94, pp. 41–50

199. Hilbish TJ, Koehn RK. 1985. Dominance in physiological phenotypes and fitness at an enzyme locus. *Science* 229:52–54

200. Hill WG, Caballero A. 1992. Artificial selection experiments. *Annu. Rev. Ecol. Syst.* 23:287–310

201. Hill WG, Mackay TFC, ed. 1989. *Evolution and Animal Breeding: Reviews on Molecular and Quantitative Approaches in Honour of Alan Robertson.* Wallingford UK: Oxon

202. Hochachka PW, Somero GN. 1984. *Biochemical Adaptation.* Princeton: Princeton Univ. Press

203. Hoffman AA, Parsons PA. 1989. An integrated approach to environmental stress tolerance and life history variation in *Drosophila. Biol. Bull. Linn. Soc.* 37:117–36

204. Hoffman AA, Parsons PA. 1989. Selection for increased desiccation resistance in *Drosophila melanogaster:* additive genetic control and correlated responses for other stresses. *Genetics* 122:837–45

205. Hoffman AA, Parsons PA. 1991. *Evolutionary Genetics and Environmental Stress.* Oxford: Oxford Univ. Press

206. Hoffman RJ. 1981. Evolutionary genetics of *Metridium senile.* I. Kinetic differences in phosphoglucose isomerase allozymes. *Biochem. Genet.* 19: 129–44

207. Hoffman RJ. 1981. Evolutionary genetics of *Metridium senile.* II. Geographic patterns of allozyme variation. *Biochem. Genet.* 19:145–54

208. Hoffman RJ. 1983. Temperature modulation of the kinetics of phosphoglucose isomerase genetic variants from the sea anemone *Metridium senile. J. Exp. Zool.* 227:361–70

209. Hofmann RR. 1989. Evolutionary steps of ecophysiological adaptation and diversification of ruminants: a comparative view of their digestive system. *Oecologia* 78:443–57

210. Huey RB. 1982. Temperature, physiology, and the ecology of reptiles. In *Biology of the Reptilia, Physiology (C),* ed. C Gans, FH Pough, 12:25–91. London: Academic

211. Huey RB. 1987. Phylogeny, history, and the comparative method. See Ref. 135, pp. 76–98

212. Huey RB. 1991. Physiological consequences of habitat selection. *Am. Nat.* 137:S91–115 (Suppl.)

213. Huey RB, Bennett AF. 1987. Phylogenetic studies of coadaptation: preferred temperatures versus optimal performance temperatures of lizards. *Evolution* 41:1098–115

214. Huey RB, Bennett AF. 1990. Physiological adjustments to fluctuating thermal environments: an ecological and evolutionary perspective. In *Stress Proteins in Biology and Medicine,* ed. R Morimoto, A Tissieres, pp. 37–59. Cold Spring Harbor NY: Cold Spring Harbor Lab.

215. Huey RB, Crill WD, Kingsolver JG, Weber KE. 1992. A method for rapid measurement of heat or cold resistance of small insects. *Funct. Ecol.* 6:489–94

216. Huey RB, Dunham AE. 1987. Repeatability of locomotor performance in natural populations of the lizard *Sceloporus merriami. Evolution* 41: 1116–20

217. Huey RB, Dunham AE, Overall KL, Newman RA. 1990. Variation in locomotor performance in demographically known populations of the lizard *Sceloporus merriami. Physiol. Zool.* 63:845–72

218. Huey RB, Kingsolver JG. 1993. Evolution of resistance to high temperature in ectotherms. *Am. Nat.* 142:521–46

219. Huey RB, Partridge L, Fowler K. 1991. Thermal sensitivity of *Drosophila melanogaster* responds rapidly to laboratory natural selection. *Evolution* 45:751–56

220. Huey RB, Stevenson RD. 1979. Integrating thermal physiology and ecology of ectotherms: a discussion of approaches. *Am. Zool.* 19:357–66

221. Hulbert AJ, Else PL. 1990. The cellular basis of endothermic metabolism: a role for "leaky" membranes? *News Physiol. Sci.* 5:25–28

222. Jacob F. 1977. Evolution and tinkering. *Science* 196:1161–66

223. James FC. 1991. Complementary de-

scription and experimental studies of clinal variation in birds. *Am. Zool.* 31:694–705

224. Janis CM. 1994. Do legs support the arms race hypothesis in mammalian predator/prey relationships? In *Vertebrate Behaviour as Derived from the Fossil Record*, ed. JR Horner, L Ellis, New York: Columbia Univ. Press. In press

225. Janis CM, Damuth J. 1990. Mammals. See Ref. 305, pp. 301–45

226. Jayne BC, Bennett AF. 1990. Scaling of speed and endurance in garter snakes: a comparison of cross-sectional and longitudinal allometries. *J. Zool.* 220:257–77

227. Jayne BC, Bennett AF. 1990. Selection on locomotor performance capacity in a natural population of garter snakes. *Evolution* 44:1204–29

228. John-Alder HB. 1984. Seasonal variations in activity, aerobic energetic capacities, and plasma thyroid hormones (T3 and T4) in an iguanid lizard. *J. Comp. Physiol. B* 154:409–19

229. John-Alder HB, Joos B. 1991. Interactive effects of thyroxine and experimental location on running endurance, tissue masses, and enzyme activities in captive versus field-active lizards *(Sceloporus undulatus)*. *Gen. Comp. Endocrinol.* 81:120–32

230. Johnson TE, DeFries JC, Markel PD. 1992. Mapping quantitative trait loci for behavioral traits in the mouse. *Behav. Genet.* 22:635–53

231. Jones JH, Lindstedt SL. 1993. Limits to maximal performance. *Annu. Rev. Physiol.* 55:547–69

232. Joos B, John-Alder HB. 1990. Effects of thyroxine on standard and field metabolic rates in the lizard, *Sceloporus undulatus*. *Physiol. Zool.* 63:873–85

233. Kacser H, Burns JA. 1973. The control of flux. *Symp. Soc. Exp. Biol.* 27:65–104

234. Kacser H, Burns JA. 1979. Molecular democracy: who shares the controls? *Biochem. Soc. Trans.* 7:1149–61

235. Kacser H, Porteous JW. 1987. Control of metabolism: what do we have to measure? *Trends Biol. Sci.* 12:5–14

236. Karasov WH. 1992. Daily energy expenditure and the cost of activity in mammals. *Am. Zool.* 32:238–48

237. Kaufman DW, Courtney MW, Chu PR. 1982. The first three years of NSF's Population Biology and Physiological Ecology Program. *Bioscience* 32:51–53

238. Keightley PD. 1989. Models of quantitative variation of flux in metabolic pathways. *Genetics* 121:869–76

239. King DG. 1991. The origin of an organ: phylogenetic analysis of evolutionary innovation in the digestive tract of flies (Insecta: Diptera). *Evolution* 45:568–88

240. Kingsolver JG. 1989. Weather and the population dynamics of insects: integrating physiological and population ecology. *Physiol. Zool.* 62:314–34

241. Kingsolver JG, Watt WB. 1984. Mechanistic constraints and optimality models: thermoregulatory strategies in *Colias* butterflies. *Ecology* 65:1835–39

242. Kluger MJ. 1979. *Fever, Its Biology, Evolution and Function.* Princeton: Princeton Univ. Press

243. Kluger MJ. 1986. Fever: a hot topic. *News Physiol. Sci.* 1:25–27

244. Kluger MJ. 1991. Fever: role of pyrogens and cryogens. *Physiol. Rev.* 71:93–127

245. Kluger MJ. 1991. The adaptive value of fever. In *Fever: Basic Mechanisms and Management*, ed. P Mackowiak, pp. 105–24. New York: Raven

246. Knowles RG, Pogson CI, Salter M. 1990. Application of control analysis to the study of amino acid metabolism. See Ref. 94, pp. 377–84

247. Koehn RK. 1969. Esterase heterogeneity: dynamics of a polymorphism. *Science* 163:943–44

248. Koehn RK. 1978. Physiology and biochemistry of enzyme variation: The interface of ecology and population genetics. In *Ecological Genetics: The Interface*, ed. P Brussard, pp 51–72. New York: Springer Verlag

249. Koehn RK. 1987. The importance of genetics to physiological ecology. See Ref. 135, pp. 170–85

250. Koehn RK. 1991. The cost of enzyme synthesis in the genetics of energy balance and physiological performance. *Biol. J. Linn. Soc.* 44:231–47

251. Koehn RK, Hilbish TJ. 1987. The adaptive importance of genetic variation. *Am. Sci.* 75:134–40

252. Koehn RK, Newell RIE, Immermann F. 1980. Maintenance of an aminopeptidase allele frequency cline by natural selection. *Proc. Natl. Acad. Sci. USA* 77:5385–89

253. Koehn RK, Shumway SE. 1982. A genetic/physiological explanation for differential growth rate among individuals of the American oyster, *Crassostrea virginica* (Gmelim). *Mar. Biol. Lett.* 3:35–42

254. Koehn RK, Zera AJ, Hall JG. 1983. Enzyme polymorphism and natural se-

lection. In *Evolution of Genes and Proteins*, ed. M Nei, RK Koehn, pp 115–36. Sunderland MA: Sinauer

255. Kohane MJ, Parsons PA. 1988. Domestication: evolutionary changes under stress. *Evol. Biol.* 23:31–48

256. Kolok AS. 1992. The swimming performances of individual largemouth bass (*Micropterus salmoides*) are repeatable. *J. Exp. Biol.* 170:265–70

257. Kolok AS. 1992. Morphological and physiological correlates with swimming performance in juvenile largemouth bass. *Am. J. Physiol.* 263(32):R1042–48

258. Kramer DL. 1983. The evolutionary ecology of respiratory mode in fishes: an analysis based on cost of breathing. *Environ. Biol. Fishes* 9:145–58

259. Krebs HA. 1975. The August Krogh principle: "For many problems there is an animal on which it can be most conveniently studied." *J. Exp. Zool.* 194:221–26

260. Lacy RC, Lynch CB. 1979. Quantitative genetic analysis of temperature regulation in *Mus musculus*. I. Partitioning of variance. *Genetics* 91:743–53

261. Lande R. 1979. Quantitative genetic analysis of multivariate evolution, applied to brain:body size allometry. *Evolution* 33:402–16

262. Lande R, Arnold SJ. 1983. The measurement of selection on correlated characters. *Evolution* 37:1210–26

263. Landel CP, Chen S, Evans GA. 1990. Reverse genetics using transgenic mice. *Annu. Rev. Physiol.* 52:841–51

264. Lanyon SM. 1992. Interspecific brood parasitism in blackbirds (*Icterinae*): a phylogenetic perspective. *Science* 255:77–79

265. Lauder GV. 1990. Functional morphology and systematics: studying functional patterns in an historical context. *Annu. Rev. Ecol. Syst.* 21:317–40

266. Lauder GV. 1991. Biomechanics and evolution: integrating physical and historical biology in the study of complex systems. In *Biomechanics in Evolution*, ed. JMV Rayner, RJ Wooten, pp. 1–19. Cambridge: Cambridge Univ. Press

267. Lauder GV. 1991. An evolutionary perspective on the concept of efficiency: how does function evolve? In *Efficiency and Economy in Animal Physiology*, ed. RW Blake, pp. 169–84. Cambridge: Cambridge Univ. Press

268. Laurie CC, Bridgham JT, Choudhary M. 1991. Associations between DNA sequence variation and variation in expression of the *Adh* gene in natural populations of *Drosophila melanogaster*. *Genetics* 129:489–99

269. Lenski RE, Rose MR, Simpson SC, Tadler SC. 1991. Long term experimental evolution in *Escherichia coli*. I. Adaptation and divergence during 2,000 generations. *Am. Nat.* 138:1315–41

270. Leroi A, Chen WR, Rose MR. 1994. Long-term laboratory evolution of a genetic trade-off in *Drosophila melanogaster* 2. Stability of genetic correlations. *Evolution.* 48:In press

271. Lewontin RC. 1974. *The Genetic Basis of Evolutionary Change*. New York: Columbia Univ. Press

272. Lewontin RC. 1978. Adaptation. *Sci. Am.* 239:156–69

273. Lindstedt SL, Jones JH. 1987. Symmorphosis: The concept of optimal design. See Ref. 135, pp. 289–309

274. Losos JB. 1990. Ecomorphology, performance capability, and scaling of West Indian Anolis lizards: an evolutionary analysis. *Ecol. Monogr.* 60:369–88

275. Losos JB, Miles DB. 1994. Adaptation, constraint, and the comparative method: phylogenetic issues and methods. See Ref. 432, In press

276. Luckinbill LS, Arking R, Clare MJ, Cirocco WC, Buck SA. 1984. Selection for delayed senescence in *Drosophila melanogaster*. *Evolution* 35:969–1003

277. Luke C. 1986. Convergent evolution of lizard toe fringes. *Biol. J. Linn. Soc.* 27:1–16

278. Lynch CB. 1986. Genetic basis of cold adaptation in laboratory and wild mice, *Mus domesticus*. In *Living in the Cold: Physiological and Biochemical Adaptations*, ed. HC Heller, XJ Musacchia, LCH Wang, pp. 497–540. New York: Elsevier

279. Lynch CB. 1994. Evolutionary inferences from genetic analyses of cold adaptation in laboratory and wild populations of the house mouse, *Mus domesticus*. See Ref. 51, In press

280. Lynch CB, Sulzbach DS. 1984. Quantitative genetic analysis of temperature regulation in *Mus musculus*. II. Diallel analysis of individual traits. *Evolution* 38:527–40

281. Lynch CB, Sulzbach DS, Connolly MS. 1988. Quantitative-genetic analysis of temperature regulation in *Mus domesticus*. IV. Pleiotropy and genotype-by-environment interactions. *Am. Nat.* 132:521–37

282. Lynch M. 1991. Methods for the analysis of comparative data in evolutionary ecology. *Evolution* 45:1065–80

283. MacMillen RE, Garland T Jr. 1989. Adaptive physiology. In *Advances in the Study of Peromyscus (Rodentia)*. ed. JN Lane, GL Kirkland, Jr, pp. 143–68. Lubbock TX: Texas Tech. Univ. Press

284. MacMillen RE, Hinds DS. 1983. Water regulatory efficiency in heteromyid rodents: a model and its application. *Ecology* 64:152–64

285. Maddison WP. 1990. A method for testing the correlated evolution of two binary characters: Are gains or losses concentrated on certain branches of a phylogenetic tree? *Evolution* 44:539–57

286. Maddison WP. 1991. Squared-change parsimony reconstructions of ancestral states for continuous-valued characters. *Syst. Zool.* 40:304–14

287. Maddison WP, Maddison DR. 1992. *MacClade. Analysis of Phylogeny and Character Evolution. Version 3*. Sunderland MA: Sinauer

288. Maitland DP. 1986. Crabs that breathe air with their legs—*Scopimera* and *Dotilla*. *Nature* 319:493–95

289. Mangum CP. 1990. The fourth annual Riser lecture: The role of physiology and biochemistry in understanding animal phylogeny. *Proc. Biol. Soc. Wash.* 103:235–47

290. Mangum CP, Towle D. 1977. Physiological adaptation to unstable environments. *Am. Sci.* 65:67–75

291. Marsh RL, Dawson WR. 1989. Avian adjustments to cold. In *Advances in Comparative and Environmental Physiology*, ed. CH Wang, 4:204–53. Berlin: Springer-Verlag

292. Marsh RL, Olson JM, Guzik SK. 1992. Mechanical performance of scallop adductor muscle during swimming. *Nature* 357:411–13

293. Martinez del Rio C. 1990. Dietary, phylogenetic, and ecological correlates of intestinal sucrase and maltase activity in birds. *Physiol. Zool.* 63:987–1011

294. Martinez del Rio C, Baker HG, Baker I. 1992. Ecological and evolutionary implications of digestive processes: Bird preferences and the sugar constitutions of floral nectar and fruit pulp. *Experientia* 48:544–51

295. Martins EP. 1994. A comparative study of the evolution of the *Sceloporus* push-up display. *Am. Nat.* In press

296. Martins EP, Garland T Jr. 1991. Phylogenetic analyses of the correlated evolution of continuous traits: a simulation study. *Evolution* 45:534–57

297. Mather K, Jinks JL. 1982. *Biometrical Genetics: The Study of Continuous Variation*. London: Chapman & Hall, 3rd Ed.

298. Maynard Smith J, Halliday TR. 1979. Preface. In *The Evolution of Adaptation by Natural Selection*, ed. J Maynard Smith, TR Halliday, pp. v-vii. London: The Royal Society

299. Mayr E. 1961. Cause and effect in biology. *Science* 134:1501–6

300. McCarthy JC. 1982. The laboratory mouse as a model for animal breeding: a review of selection for increased body weight and litter size. *Proc. 2nd World Congr. Genet. Applied Livestock Production*, 5:66–83

301. McKitrick MC. 1992. Phylogenetic analysis of avian parental care. *Auk* 109:828–46

302. McKitrick MC. 1993. Phylogenetic constraint in evolutionary theory: has it any explanatory power? *Annu. Rev. Ecol. Syst.* 24:

303. McNab BK. 1978. The evolution of endothermy in the phylogeny of mammals. *Am. Nat.* 112:1–21

304. McNab BK. 1992. Rate of metabolism in the termite-eating sloth bear *(Ursus ursinus)*. *J. Mamm.* 73:168–72

305. McNamara KJ, ed. 1990. *Evolutionary Trends*. Tucson AZ: Univ. Arizona Press

306. Miles DB. 1989. Selective significance of locomotory performance in an iguanid lizard. *Am. Zool.* 29:146A

307. Miles DB, Dunham AE. 1993. Historical perspectives in ecology and evolutionary biology: the use of phylogenetic comparative analyses. *Annu. Rev. Ecol. Syst.* 24:

308. Mitchell SD. 1992. On pluralism and competition in evolutionary explanations. *Am. Zool.* 32:135–44

309. Mitchell-Olds T, Shaw RG. 1987. Regression analysis of natural selection: statistical and biological interpretation. *Evolution* 41:1149–61

310. Mooney HA. 1991. Plant physiological ecology—determinants of progress. *Funct. Ecol.* 5:127–35

311. Moore MC, Marler CA. 1987. Effects of testosterone manipulations on non-breeding season territorial aggression in free-living male lizards, *Sceloporus jarrovi*. *Gen. Comp. Endocr.* 65:225–32

312. Mousseau TA, Roff DA. 1987. Natural selection and the heritability of fitness components. *Heredity* 59:181–97

313. Nagy KA. 1987. Field metabolic rate and food requirement scaling in mammals and birds. *Ecol. Monogr.* 57:111–28

314. Norris KS. 1958. The evolution and

systematics of the iguanid genus *Uma* and its relation to the evolution of other North American desert reptiles. *Bull. Am. Mus. Nat. Hist.* 114:251–326

315. Oudman L, van Delden W, Bijlisma R. 1991. Polymorphism at the Adh and alpha-Gpdh loci in *Drosophila melanogaster:* effects of rearing temperature on development rate, body weight, and some biochemical parameters. *Heredity* 67:103–15

316. Pang PKT, Epple A, ed. 1980. *Evolution of Vertebrate Endocrine Systems. Graduate Studies No. 21.* Lubbock TX: Texas Tech. Press

317. Parsons PA. 1982. Evolutionary ecology of Australian *Drosophila:* a species analysis. *Evol. Biol.* 14:297–350

318. Partridge L. 1994. Genetic and nongenetic approaches to questions about sexual selection. See Ref. 51, In press

319. Partridge L, Fowler K. 1992. Direct and correlated responses to selection on age at reproduction in *Drosophila melanogaster. Evolution* 46:76–91

320. Peters RH. 1983. *The Ecological Implications of Body Size.* Cambridge: Cambridge Univ. Press

321. Pierce GJ, Ollason JG. 1987. Eight reasons why optimal foraging theory is a complete waste of time. *Oikos* 49:111–18

322. Place AR, Powers DA. 1979. Genetic variation and relative catalytic efficiencies: the LDH-B allozymes of *Fundulus heteroclitus. Proc. Natl. Acad. Sci. USA* 76:2354–58

323. Plomin R, DeFries JC, McClearn GE. 1990. *Behavioral Genetics: A Primer.* New York: Freeman. 2nd Ed.

324. Plomin R, McClearn GE, Gora-Maslak G, Neiderhiser JM. 1991. Use of recombinant inbred strains to detect quantitative trait loci associated with behavior. *Behav. Genet.* 21:99–116

325. Pomp D, Eisen EJ, Ziecik AJ. 1988. LH receptor induction and ovulation rate in mice selected for litter size and body weight. *J. Reprod. Fert.* 84:601–10

326. Porter RK, Brand MD. 1993. Body mass dependence of H⁺ leak in mitochondria and its relevance to metabolic rate. *Nature* 362:628–30

327. Porter WP. 1989. New animal models and experiments for calculating growth potential at different elevations. *Physiol. Zool.* 62:286–13

328. Posthuma L, Hogervorst RF, Joosse ENG, Van Straalen NM. 1993. Genetic variation and covariation for characteristics associated with cadmium tolerance in natural populations of the springtail *Orchesella cincta* (L.). *Evolution* 47:619–31

329. Pough FH. 1989. Organismal performance and Darwinian fitness: Approaches and interpretations. *Physiol. Zool.* 62:199–236

330. Pough FH, Magnusson WE, Ryan MJ, Wells KD, Taigen TL. 1992. Behavioral energetics. In *Environmental Physiology of the Amphibia,* ed. ME Feder, WW Burggren, pp. 395–436. Chicago: Univ. Chicago Press

331. Powers DA. 1987. A multidisciplinary approach to the study of genetic variation within species. See Ref. 135, pp 102–34

332. Powers DA, DiMichele L, Place AR. 1983. The use of enzyme kinetics to predict differences in cellular metabolism, developmental rate, and swimming performance between LDH-B genotypes of the fish, *Fundulus heteroclitus. Isozymes: Curr. Top. Biol. Med. Res.* 10:147–70

333. Powers DA, Greaney GS, Place AR. 1979. Physiological correlation between lactate dehydrogenase genotype and haemoglobin function in killifish. *Nature* 277:240–41

334. Powers DA, Place AR. 1978. Biochemical genetics of *Fundulus heteroclitus.* I. Temporal and spatial variation in gene frequencies of Ldh-B, Mdh-A, Gpi-B, and Pgm-A. *Biochem. Genet.* 16:593–607

335. Proctor HC. 1991. The evolution of copulation in water mites: a comparative test for nonreversing characters. *Evolution* 45:558–67

336. Promislow DEL. 1991. The evolution of mammalian blood parameters: patterns and their interpretation. *Physiol. Zool.* 64:393–431

337. Prosser CL, ed. 1950. *Comparative Animal Physiology.* Philadelphia: Saunders

338. Prosser CL, ed. 1973. *Comparative Animal Physiology.* Philadelphia: Saunders. 3rd Ed.

339. Prosser CL. 1986. *Adaptational Biology: Molecules to Organisms.* New York: Wiley & Sons

340. Purvis A. 1992. *Comparative methods: theory and practice.* PhD thesis. Univ. Oxford. 149 pp.

341. Purvis A, Garland T Jr. 1993. Polytomies in comparative analyses of continuous characters. *Syst. Biol.* 42:569–75

342. Ramsay MA, Dunbrack RL. 1986. Physiological constraints on life history phenomena: the example of small bear cubs at birth. *Am. Nat.* 127:735–43

343. Randall D. 1986. The next 25 years: vertebrate physiology and biochemistry. *Can. J. Zool.* 65:794–96

344. Rausher MD. 1992. The measurement of selection on quantitative traits: biases due to environmental covariances between traits and fitness. *Evolution* 46:616–26

345. Reeve HK, Sherman PW. 1993. Adaptation and the goals of evolutionary research. *Quart. Rev. Biol.* 68:1–32

346. Reiss MJ. 1989. *The Allometry of Growth and Reproduction.* Cambridge: Cambridge Univ. Press

347. Richardson CS, Dohm MR, Garland T Jr. 1994. Metabolism and thermoregulation in crosses between wild and laboratory house mice. *Physiol. Zool.* In press

348. Richman AD, Price T. 1992. Evolution of ecological differences in the Old World leaf warblers. *Nature* 355:817–21

349. Ridley M. 1983. *The Explanation of Organic Diversity: The Comparative Method and Adaptations for Mating.* Oxford: Clarendon

350. Ridley M. 1993. *Evolution.* Boston: Blackwell Scientific

351. Riska B. 1991. Regression models in evolutionary allometry. *Am. Nat.* 138:283–99

352. Robb LA, Martin K, Hannon SJ. 1992. Spring body condition, fecundity and survival in female willow ptarmigan. *J. Anim. Ecol.* 61:215–23

353. Robertson A, ed. 1980. *Selection Experiments in Laboratory and Domestic Animals.* Slough UK: Commonwealth Agricultural Bureau

354. Roff DA. 1994. Quantitative genetic versus optimality models in behavioral evolution. See Ref. 51, In press

355. Roff DA, Mousseau TA. 1987. Quantitative genetics and fitness: lessons from *Drosophila. Heredity* 58:103–18

356. Rohlf FJ, Sokal RR. 1981. *Statistical Tables.* San Francisco: Freeman. 2nd Ed.

357. Rose MR. 1984. Laboratory evolution of postponed senescence in *Drosophila melanogaster. Evolution* 38:1004–10

358. Rose MR. 1991. *The Evolutionary Biology of Aging.* New York: Oxford Univ. Press

359. Rose MR, Graves JL Jr. 1989. Minireview: What evolutionary biology can do for gerentology. *J. Geront.* 44:B27–29

360. Rose MR, Graves JL Jr, Hutchinson EW. 1990. The use of selection to probe patterns of pleiotropy in fitness characters. In *Insect Life Cycles: Genetics, Evolution and Co-ordination,* ed. F Gilbert, pp 29–42. London: Springer-Verlag

361. Rose MR, Service PM, Hutchinson EW. 1987. Three approaches to tradeoffs in life-history evolution. In *Genetic Constraints on Adaptive Evolution,* ed. V Loeschcke, pp. 91–105. Berlin: Springer-Verlag

362. Rose MR, Vu LN, Park SU, Graves JL Jr. 1992. Selection on stress resistance increases longevity in *Drosophila melanogaster. Exper. Geront.* 27:241–50

363. Rosen R. 1967. *Optimality Principles in Biology.* London: Butterworths

364. Ross DM. 1981. Illusion and reality in comparative physiology. *Can. J. Zool.* 59:2151–58

365. Ruben JA, Bennett AF. 1980. The vertebrate pattern of activity metabolism: Its antiquity and possible relation to vertebrate origins. *Nature* 286:886–88

366. Ruben JA, Bennett AF. 1981. Intense exercise, bone structure and blood calcium levels in vertebrates. *Nature* 291:411–13

367. Ruben JA, Bennett AF. 1987. The evolution of bone. *Evolution* 41:1187–97

368. Ruben JA, Bennett AF, Hisaw FL. 1987. Selective factors in the origin of the mammalian diaphragm. *Paleobiology* 13:54–59

369. Ruben JA, Boucot AJ. 1989. The origin of the lungless salamanders (Amphibia: Plethodontidae). *Am. Nat.* 134:161–69

370. Ruben JA, Parrish JK. 1990. Antiquity of the chordate pattern of exercise metabolism. *Paleobiology* 16:355–59

371. Ruibal R. 1957. The evolution of the scrotum. *Evolution* 11:376–78

372. Savageau MA. 1976. *Biochemical Systems Analysis.* Reading MA: Addison Wesley

373. Savageau MA. 1990. Biochemical systems theory: alternative views of metabolic control. See Ref. 94, pp. 69–88

374. Savageau MA, Sorribas A. 1989. Constraints among molecular and systemic properties—implications for physiological genetics. *J. Theor. Biol.* 141:93–115

375. Schaeffer P, Lindstedt SL. 1992. Structure-function coupling in the fastest-contracting vertebrate muscle: the rattlesnake tail-shaker muscle. *Physiologist* 35:224

376. Schall JJ, Bennett AF, Putnam RW. 1982. Lizards infected with malaria:

physiological and behavioral consequences. *Science* 217:1057–59

377. Schall JJ, Dearing MD. 1987. Malarial parasitism and male competition for mates in the western fence lizard, *Sceloporus occidentalis*. *Oecologia* 73: 389–92

378. Schlager G, Weibust RS. 1976. Selection for hematocrit percent in the house mouse. *J. Hered.* 67:295–99

379. Schluter D. 1988. Estimating the form of natural selection on a quantitative trait. *Evolution* 42:849–61

380. Schmidt-Nielsen K. 1972. *How Animals Work.* Cambridge: Cambridge Univ. Press

381. Schmidt-Nielsen K. 1984. *Scaling: Why Is Animal Size So Important?* Cambridge: Cambridge Univ. Press

382. Schmidt-Nielsen K. 1990. *Animal Physiology: Adaptation and Environment.* Cambridge: Cambridge Univ. Press. 4th Ed.

383. Schmidt-Nielsen K, Bolis L, Taylor CR, ed. 1980. *Comparative Physiology: Primitive Mammals.* Cambridge: Cambridge Univ. Press

384. Service PM. 1987. Physiological mechanisms of increased stress resistance in *Drosophila melanogaster* selected for postponed senescence. *Physiol. Zool.* 60:321–26

385. Service PM, Hutchinson EW, Rose MR. 1988. Multiple genetic mechanisms for the evolution of senescence in *Drosophila melanogaster*. *Evolution* 42:708–16

386. Sessions SK, Larson A. 1987. Developmental correlates of genome size in plethodontid salamanders and their implications for genome evolution. *Evolution* 41:1239–51

387. Shaffer HB. 1984. Evolution in a paedomorphic lineage. I. An electrophoretic analysis of the Mexican ambystomatid salamanders. *Evolution* 38: 1194–206

388. Shine R, Guillette LJ. 1988. The evolution of viviparity in reptiles: a physiological model and its ecological consequences. *J. Theor. Biol.* 132:43–50

389. Sibley CG, Ahlquist JE. 1991. *Phylogeny and Classification of Birds.* New Haven: Yale Univ. Press

390. Sibly RM. 1989. What evolution maximizes. *Funct. Ecol.* 3:129–35

391. Sibly RM, Calow P. 1986. *Physiological Ecology of Animals: An Evolutionary Approach.* Oxford: Blackwell Scientific

392. Sillau AH. 1985. Capillarity and oxygen diffusion distances of the soleus muscle of guinea pigs and rats. Effects of hyperthyroidism. *Comp. Biochem. Physiol.* 82A:471–78

393. Sinervo B. 1990. The evolution of maternal investment in lizards: an experimental and comparative analysis of egg size and its effect on offspring performance. *Evolution* 44:279–94

394. Sinervo B, Doughty P, Huey RB, Zamudio K. 1992. Allometric engineering: a causal analysis of natural selection on offspring size. *Science* 258:1927–30

395. Sinervo B, Huey RB. 1990. Allometric engineering: an experimental test of the causes of interpopulational differences in performance. *Science* 248: 1106–9

396. Sinervo B, Licht P. 1991. Proximate constraints on the evolution of egg size, number, and total clutch mass in lizards. *Science* 252:1300–2

397. Slatkin M, Kirkpatrick M. 1986. Extrapolating quantitative genetic theory to evolutionary problems. In *Evolutionary Genetics of Invertebrate Behavior: Progress and Prospects*, ed. MD Huettel, pp. 283–93. New York: Plenum

398. Smith GK, Knowles RG, Pogson CI, Salter M, Hanlon M, Mullin R. 1990. Flux control coefficients of glycinamide ribonucleotide transformylase for de novo purine biosynthesis. See Ref. 94, pp. 385–88

399. Smith RJ. 1984. Determination of relative size: the "criterion of subtraction" problem in allometry. *J. Theor. Biol.* 108:131–42

400. Smith RJ. 1984. Allometric scaling in comparative biology: problems of concept and method. *Am. J. Physiol.* 246(15):R152–60

401. Snell HL, Jennings RD, Snell HM, Harcourt S. 1988. Intrapopulation variation in predator-avoidance performance of Galapagos lava lizards: the interaction of sexual and natural selection. *Evol. Ecol.* 2:353–69

402. Snyder, LRG. 1982. 2,3-Diphosphoglycerate in high- and low-altitude populations of the deer mouse. *Resp. Physiol.* 48:107–23

403. Snyder LRG, Born S, Lechner AJ. 1982. Blood oxygen affinity in high- and low-altitude populations of the deer mouse. *Resp. Physiol.* 48:89–105

404. Snyder LRG, Hayes JP, Chappel MA. 1988. Alpha-chain hemoglobin polymorphisms are correlated with altitude in the deer mouse, *Peromyscus maniculatus*. *Evolution* 42:689–97

405. Sorci G, Massot M, Clobert J. 1994. Maternal parasite load predicts off-

spring sprint speed in the philopatric sex. *Am. Nat.* In press

406. Sparti A. 1992. Thermogenic capacity of shrews (Mammalia, Soricidae) and its relationship with basal rate of metabolism. *Physiol. Zool.* 65:77–96

407. Spotila JR, O'Connor MP. 1992. Introduction to the workshop: biophysical ecology: methods, microclimates, and models. *Am. Zool.* 32:151–53

408. Stewart CB, Schilling JW, Wilson AC. 1987. Adaptive evolution in the stomach lysozymes of foregut fermenters. *Nature* 330:401–04

409. Strauss RE. 1994. Optimal mapping of continuous characters onto evolutionary trees for studies of character evolution. *Paleobiology.* In press

410. Sulzbach DS, Lynch CB. 1984. Quantitative genetic analysis of temperature regulation in *Mus musculus*. III. Diallel analysis of correlations between traits. *Evolution* 38:541–52

411. Swofford DL, Olsen GJ. 1990. Phylogeny reconstruction. In *Molecular Systematics,* ed. DM Hillis, C Moritz, pp. 411–501. Sunderland MA: Sinauer

412. Szalay FS, Novacek MJ, McKenna MC, ed. 1993. *Mammal Phylogeny.* New York: Columbia Univ. Press

413. Szathmary E. 1993. Do deleterious mutations act synergistically? Metabolic control theory provides a partial answer. *Genetics* 133:127–32

414. Taylor CR. 1987. Structural and functional limits to oxidative metabolism: insights from scaling. *Annu. Rev. Physiol.* 49:135–46

415. Taylor PJ. 1987. Historical versus selectionist explanations in evolutionary biology. *Cladistics* 3:1–13

416. Telenius A, Angerbjorn A, Eriksson O. 1989. On phylogenetic ecology. *Evol. Theory* 8:351–56

417. Thomas DK, Olson EC, eds. 1980. *A Cold Look at the Warm-Blooded Dinosaurs.* Boulder CO: Westview

418. Thomson KS. 1992. Macroevolution: the morphological problem. *Am. Zool.* 32:106–12

419. Tomasi TE, Geit AS. 1992. The allometry of thyroxine utilization rates. In *Mammalian Energetics: Interdisciplinary Views of Metabolism and Reproduction,* ed. TE Tomasi, TH Horton, pp.64–82. Ithaca NY: Cornell Univ. Press

420. Toolson EC, Kuper-Simbron R. 1989. Laboratory evolution of epicuticular hydrocarbon composition and cuticular permeability in *Drosophila* pseudoobscura: effects on sexual dimorphism

and thermal-acclimation ability. *Evolution* 43:468–73

421. Townsend CR, Calow P. 1981. *Physiological Ecology: An Evolutionary Approach to Resource Use.* Sunderland MA: Sinauer

422. Tracy CR, Turner JS. 1982. What is physiological ecology? *Bull. Ecol. Soc. Am.* 63:340–47

423. Tracy CR, Turner JS, Huey RB. 1986. A biophysical analysis of possible thermoregulatory adaptations in sailed pelycosaurs. In *The Ecology and Biology of Mammal-Like Reptiles,* ed. N Hotton, PD MacLean, JJ Roth, EC Roth, pp. 195–206. Washington DC: Smithsonian Institution

424. Tsuji JS, Huey RB, van Berkum FH, Garland T Jr, Shaw RG. 1989. Locomotor performance of hatchling fence lizards (*Sceloporus occidentalis*): quantitative genetics and morphometric correlates. *Funct. Ecol.* 3:240–52

425. Ulmasov KA, Sammakov S, Karaev K, Evgen'ev MB. 1992. Heat shock proteins and thermoresistance in lizards. *Proc. Natl. Acad. Sci. USA* 89:1666–70

426. van Berkum FH, Huey RB, Tsuji JS, Garland T Jr. 1989. Repeatability of individual differences in locomotor performance and body size during early ontogeny of the lizard *loporus occidentalis* (Baird & Girard). *Funct. Ecol.* 3: 97–105

427. van Berkum FH, Tsuji JS. 1987. Interfamilial differences in sprint speed of hatchling *Sceloporus occidentalis. J. Zool.* 212:511–19

428. Van Damme R, Bauwens D, Castilla AM, Verheyen RF. 1989. Altitudinal variation in the thermal biology and running performance in the lizard *Podarcis tiliguerta. Oecologia* 80:516–24

429. van Delden W. 1982. The alcohol dehydrogenase polymorphism in *Drosophila melanogaster.* Selection at an enzyme locus. *Evol. Biol.* 15:187–222

430. Wade MJ, Kalisz S. 1990. The causes of natural selection. *Evolution* 44:1947–55

431. Wainwright PC. 1991. Ecomorphology: experimental functional anatomy for ecological problems. *Am. Zool.* 31: 680–93

432. Wainwright PC, Reilly SM, ed. 1994. *Ecological Morphology: Integrative Organismal Biology.* Chicago: Univ. Chicago Press

433. Wake DB, Roth G, eds. 1989. *Complex Organismal Functions: Integration and*

Evolution in Vertebrates. Chichester UK: Wiley & Sons

434. Wake MH. 1992. Evolutionary scenarios, homology and convergence of structural specializations for vertebrate viviparity. *Am. Zool.* 32:256–63

435. Waldschmidt S, Tracy CR. 1983. Interactions between a lizard and its thermal environment: implications for sprint performance and space utilization in the lizard *Uta stansburiana. Ecology* 64:476–84

436. Wallace B. 1991. The manly art of self-defense: on the neutrality of fitness components. *Quart. Rev. Biol.* 66:455–65

437. Walton M. 1993. Physiology and phylogeny: the evolution of locomotor energetics in hylid frogs. *Am. Nat.* 141:26–50

438. Ward PJ. 1990. The inheritance of metabolic flux: expressions for the within-sibship mean and variance given the parental genotypes. *Genetics* 125:655–67

439. Watt WB. 1977. Adaptation at specific loci. I. Natural selection on phosphoglucose isomerase of *Colias* butterflies: biochemical and population aspects. *Genetics* 87:177–94

440. Watt WB. 1983. Adaptation at specific loci. II. Demographic and biochemical elements in the maintenance of the *Colias* PGI polymorphism. *Genetics* 103:691–724

441. Watt WB. 1985. Allelic isozymes and the mechanistic study of evolution. *Isozymes: Curr. Top. Biol. Med. Res.* 12:89–132

442. Watt WB. 1985. Bioenergetics and evolutionary genetics—opportunities for new synthesis. *Am. Nat.* 125:118–43

443. Watt WB. 1986. Power and efficiency as indexes of fitness in metabolic organization. *Am. Nat.* 127:629–53

444. Watt WB. 1991. Biochemistry, physiological ecology, and evolutionary genetics—the mechanistic tools of evolutionary biology. *Funct. Ecol.* 5:145–54

445. Watt WB. 1992. Eggs, enzymes, and evolution: natural genetic variants change insect fecundity. *Proc. Natl. Acad. Sci. USA* 89:10608–12

446. Watt WB, Boggs CL. 1987. Allelic isozymes as probes of the evolution of metabolic organization. *Isozymes: Curr. Top. Biol. Med. Res.* 15:27–47

447. Watt WB, Carter PA, Donohue K. 1986. Females' choice of "good genotypes" as mates is promoted by an insect mating system. *Science* 233:1187–90

448. Weber KE. 1990. Selection on wing allometry in *Drosophila melanogaster. Genetics* 126:975–89

449. Weber RE, Wells RMG. 1989. Hemoglobin structure and function. In *Comparative Pulmonary Physiology: Current Concepts,* ed. SC Wood, pp. 279–310. New York: Dekker

450. Weibel ER. 1987. Scaling of structural and functional variables in the respiratory system. *Annu. Rev. Physiol.* 49:147–59

451. Weibel ER, Taylor CR, eds. 1981. Design of the mammalian respiratory system. *Resp. Physiol.* 44:1–164

452. Weibel ER, Taylor CR, Hoppeler H. 1991. The concept of symmorphosis: A testable hypothesis of structure-function relationship. *Proc. Natl. Acad. Sci. USA* 88:10357–61

453. Weir BS, Eisen EJ, Goodman MJ, Namkoong G, eds. 1988. *Proc. Second Int. Conf. Quant. Genet.* Sunderland MA: Sinauer

454. Wells RMG. 1989. The control of hemoglobin-oxygen binding in vertebrate animals. *News Physiol. Sci.* 4:242–45

455. Wells RMG. 1990. Hemoglobin physiology in vertebrate animals: a cautionary approach to adaptationist thinking. In *Advances in Comparative and Environmental Physiology. Vertebrate Gas Exchange,* ed. RG Boutilier, 6:143–61. Heidelberg: Springer-Verlag

456. White FN. 1981. A comparative physiological approach to hypothermia. *J. Thor. Cardiovas. Surg.* 82:821–31

457. White FN. 1989. Temperature and acid-base regulation. *Adv. Anesth.* 6:67–96

458. Wiley EO, Seigel-Causey D, Brooks DR, Funk VA. 1991. *The Compleat Cladist: A Primer of Phylogenetic Procedures.* Lawrence KS: Univ. Kansas Museum Natural History Special Publication No. 19

459. Williams GC. 1992. *Natural Selection. Domains, Levels, and Challenges.* New York: Oxford Univ. Press

460. Williams GC, Nesse RM. 1991. The dawn of Darwinian medicine. *Quart. Rev. Biol.* 66:1–22

461. Willis MB. 1989. *Genetics of the Dog.* London: HF & G Witherby

462. Wilson MA, Gatten RE Jr. 1989. Aerobic and anaerobic metabolism of paired male lizards *(Anolis carolinensis). Physiol. Behav.* 46:977–82

463. Wilson MA, Gatten RE Jr, Greenberg N. 1989. Glycolysis in *Anolis car-*

olinensis during agonistic encounters. *Physiol. Behav.* 48:139–42

464. Wood SC, Lenfant C, ed. 1979. *Evolution of Respiratory Processes: A Comparative Approach.* New York: Dekker

465. Wray GA. 1992. Rates of evolution in developmental processes. *Am. Zool.* 32:123–34

466. Wright BE, Albe KR. 1990. A new method for estimating enzyme activity and control coefficients in vivo. See Ref. 94, pp. 317–28

467. Yacoe ME, Cummings JW, Myers P, Creighton KG. 1982. Muscle enzyme profile, diet, and flight in South American bats. *Am. J. Physiol.* 242(11): R189–94

468. Zar JH. 1984. *Biostatistical Analysis.* Englewood Cliffs NJ: Prentice-Hall. 2nd Ed.

469. Zeng ZB. 1992. Correcting the bias of Wright's estimates of the number of genes affecting a quantitative character: a further improved method. *Genetics* 131:987–1001

Annu. Rev. Physiol. 1994. 56:623–47
Copyright © 1994 by Annual Reviews Inc. All rights reserved

AMMONIUM TRANSPORT BY THE THICK ASCENDING LIMB OF HENLE'S LOOP

David W. Good

Departments of Internal Medicine and Physiology and Biophysics, University of Texas Medical Branch, Galveston, Texas 77555

KEY WORDS: epithelial NH_4^+ transport, intracellular pH, Na^+-K^+-$2Cl^-$ cotransport, renal NH_4^+ excretion, NH_3 transport

INTRODUCTION

In addition to its central role in NaCl reabsorption and the excretion of a concentrated or dilute urine, the thick ascending limb of the loop of Henle (TAL) also influences urinary net acid excretion by reabsorbing ammonium.[1] Over the past several years, studies of ammonium transport by the TAL have provided new insights into two important issues. First, they identified the key ammonium transport event that drives countercurrent multiplication of ammonium and generates high concentrations of ammonium in the renal medulla. Second, they uncovered a complex ammonium transport process that does not conform to the classical principles of epithelial ammonium transport and that has greatly expanded our understanding of how ammonium may be transported across epithelial cell membranes. The main purpose of this review is to summarize recent work on the cellular mechanisms of ammonium transport in the mammalian TAL. In addition, the functional role of TAL ammonium absorption in promoting medullary ammonium accumulation and urinary ammonium excretion is briefly discussed.

---

[1] The terms ammonium and total ammonia are used interchangeably to indicate the sum of NH_4^+ and NH_3. When mechanisms of transport are discussed, the chemical formulas NH_4^+ and NH_3 are used to indicate the specific chemical species transported.

623

0066–4278/94/0315–0623$02.00

BASIC TRANSPORT FUNCTIONS OF THE TAL EPITHELIUM

Absorption of NaCl and $NaHCO_3$ comprise the bulk of transcellular ion transport in TAL segments (see 24, 30, 37, 77 for reviews). These processes are summarized briefly below to provide background for evaluating mechanisms of ammonium transport.

Cl^- absorption is a secondary-active process mediated by apical membrane Na^+-K^+-$2Cl^-$ cotransport. The basolateral Na^+-K^+ ATPase provides energy for Cl^- absorption by extruding Na^+ and maintaining the apical Na^+ gradient that drives the Na^+-K^+-$2Cl^-$ cotransporter. Cl^- exits the basolateral membrane through Cl^- channels and possibly via KCl cotransport. Most of the K^+ taken up via the Na^+-K^+-$2Cl^-$ cotransporter recycles back into the tubule lumen through apical membrane K^+ channels, thus resulting in little net transepithelial K^+ flux. The movements of K^+ from cell to lumen and of Cl^- from cell to blood generate a transepithelial voltage-oriented lumen-positive with respect to blood. Net Cl^- absorption is inhibited virtually completely by sulfonamide-type loop diuretics such as furosemide and bumetanide, which inhibit the Na^+-K^+-$2Cl^-$ cotransporter.

Absorption of HCO_3^- occurs in TALs of some species and involves H^+ secretion across the apical membrane and HCO_3^- efflux across the basolateral membrane. Proton secretion is mediated by apical membrane Na^+/H^+ exchange and therefore depends on the apical Na^+ gradient generated by the Na^+-K^+ ATPase. Several basolateral HCO_3^- transporters have been identified in TAL segments, including electrogenic $NaHCO_3$ cotransport, electroneutral $KHCO_3$ cotransport, and Cl/HCO_3 exchange; however, the contributions of these transporters to transcellular HCO_3^- absorption have not been clearly defined. In the isolated, perfused TAL of the rat, rates of net HCO_3^- absorption (10–20 pmol/min/mm) are approximately 10 to 20% of the rates of net Cl^- absorption. Except for their dependence on the basolateral Na^+-K^+ ATPase, HCO_3^- and Cl^- absorption occur via separate mechanisms and can be regulated independently (1, 21, 24). Absorption of either NaCl or $NaHCO_3$ decreases the osmolality of the luminal fluid because the TAL is virtually impermeable to H_2O.

GENERAL FEATURES OF TAL AMMONIUM ABSORPTION

Classical Concept of Epithelial Ammonium Transport

Transepithelial ammonium transport generally has been explained on the following bases (40, 57): (a) cell membranes are highly permeable to the uncharged, lipid-soluble NH$_3$, which results in rapid NH$_3$ diffusion that precludes the development of sizeable NH$_3$ concentration differences between tissue compartments; (b) due to its charge, NH$_4^+$ permeates cell membranes much more slowly than NH$_3$; and (c) because the NH$_3$ concentration is virtually equal in all compartments (lumen, cell, and interstitial space), the NH$_4^+$ concentration in each compartment (x) is directly proportional to the H$^+$ concentration ([NH$_4^+$]$_x$ = [H$^+$]$_x$ •([NH$_3$]/K_a, where K_a is the dissociation constant for the ammonium buffer reaction and [NH$_3$] is the NH$_3$ concentration). Because the pK_a for ammonium is ~9, NH$_4^+$ concentrations are ~100 × NH$_3$ concentrations at physiological pH, which results in high concentrations of NH$_4^+$ in acidic fluids such as the urine. The predominance of NH$_3$ diffusion over transport of NH$_4^+$ has best been illustrated by the response of intracellular pH (pH$_i$) of cells to ammonium (4, 60). Exposure to ammonium causes a rapid intracellular alkalinization because NH$_3$ enters the cells and combines with intracellular H$^+$ to form NH$_4^+$. This process continues until [NH$_3$]$_i$ = [NH$_3$]$_o$. The rapid alkalinization is followed by a slow plateau phase acidification that results in part from much slower entry of NH$_4^+$ (acidification occurs because NH$_4^+$ that enters the cell dissociates to release protons when NH$_3$ exits to maintain NH$_3$ diffusion equilibrium) (4). As discussed in detail in the following sections, transport of ammonium by the TAL does not conform to any of the classic principles outlined above.

Evidence For Direct Absorption of NH$_4^+$

The TAL is not accessible on the kidney surface and cannot be studied directly in vivo. Consequently, direct information on its ammonium transport properties has been obtained mostly through the technique of isolated tubule perfusion (6). Absorption of ammonium was first demonstrated in TALs from rats perfused and bathed in vitro with 4 mM NH$_4$Cl (27). This ammonium concentration approximates that which normally surrounds the medullary portion of the TAL in vivo. In both cortical (CTAL) and medullary (MTAL) thick ascending limbs, the ammonium concentration in collected tubule fluid was well below that in the perfusate and bath, thus indicating net ammonium absorption (27). The physiologic significance of this absorption process has been supported by several observations: (a) the ammonium absorption appears to be a generalized process since it occurs in TALs from rats, which normally excrete an acidic, ammonium-rich urine, and rabbits (16), which normally excrete an alkaline urine containing little ammonium; (b) the rates of ammonium absorption measured in the TAL in vitro are sufficient to account for net ammonium absorption measured across the entire loop of Henle of the rat in vivo (27); and (c) the ammonium absorption is regulated homeostatically, which permits the TAL to contribute to changes in urinary ammonium excretion in conditions such as chronic metabolic acidosis (see below).

In principle, absorption of ammonium by the TAL could be the result of transport of NH_4^+, NH_3, or both. Further studies revealed, however, that both cortical and medullary TALs from rats also absorbed HCO_3^- and acidified the luminal fluid (24, 27). As a combined result of the fall in luminal total ammonia concentration and the fall in luminal pH, the calculated luminal NH_3 concentration was only half that in the peritubular bath (27, 47). Thus the TAL was able to generate and maintain a large NH_3 concentration difference across its epithelium, and the net ammonium flux occurred in a direction opposite to the transepithelial NH_3 concentration difference. It was concluded, therefore, that the ammonium absorption could not have occurred by NH_3 diffusion and must have resulted from the direct transport of NH_4^+ (27). In the steady state, net ammonium absorption results because the net flux of NH_4^+ from lumen to bath exceeds the net backflux of NH_3 into the tubule lumen.

Active vs Passive NH_4^+ Absorption

Both active and passive mechanisms contribute to NH_4^+ absorption, with active transport of NH_4^+ accounting for most of the ammonium absorptive flux.

Passive absorption of NH_4^+ occurs by paracellular diffusion, driven by the lumen-positive transepithelial voltage. The paracellular pathway of the TAL is cation-selective and is permeable to a variety of cations, including Na^+, K^+, Ca^{2+}, and Mg^{2+} (29, 30). It is likely that NH_4^+ also shares this transport pathway. In the rabbit MTAL, the flux-voltage relationship for passive NH_4^+ transport appeared linear when the transepithelial voltage was clamped chemically to positive or negative values, consistent with paracellular movement (16). The transepithelial permeability of the MTAL to NH_4^+ is relatively high (0.6 to 1.4 $\times$ 10^{-4}cm/sec) (16, 20), and is similar to permeabilities reported for K^+ and Na^+(29, 37, 67). In both rat and rabbit MTALs, calculation of the passive NH_4^+ flux using the spontaneous transepithelial voltage measured at physiologic flow rates revealed that NH_4^+ diffusion could account only for 10–30% of the net ammonium flux (16, 20). Passive absorption could contribute to a greater extent in vivo if a sizeable lumen to interstitial NH_4^+ concentration difference was present across the TAL epithelium.

The first evidence for active transport of NH_4^+ was obtained from studies of the K^+ dependence of ammonium absorption in the rat MTAL (19, 20). Increasing the K^+ concentration in perfusate and bath reduced the net ammonium absorptive flux by half with no effect on the NH_4^+ permeability or the transepithelial driving forces for NH_4^+ or NH_3 diffusion, consistent with an active component of NH$_4^+$ absorption that was inhibited by K$^+$. Active transport of NH$_4^+$ was confirmed directly by two studies demonstrating that NH$_4^+$ could be absorbed against a transepithelial electrochemical potential difference. (*a*) In the rat MTAL, the maximum transepithelial voltage generated by the tubules was not sufficient to account for the limiting transepithelial NH$_4^+$ concentration difference (20). (*b*) In the rabbit MTAL, net ammonium absorption persisted when the driving force for passive NH$_4^+$ absorption was eliminated or reversed by chemically clamping the transepithelial voltage to zero or lumen-negative values (16). In the latter study, the ammonium absorption rate at zero voltage was ~65% of the rate measured in the presence of the spontaneous transepithelial voltage. Thus this observation was consistent with the conclusion obtained from analysis of the driving forces for NH$_4^+$ diffusion, namely, that active transport of NH$_4^+$ accounts for the majority of ammonium absorption (16, 20). Before discussing the mechanisms of active NH$_4^+$ absorption, it is necessary to review the effects of ammonium transport on intracellular pH, since these effects have been important in identifying the pathways of NH$_4^+$ transport.

NH$_4^+$ TRANSPORT AS A DETERMINANT OF INTRACELLULAR pH

Luminal Ammonium Addition

The unusual ability of the TAL to transport NH$_4^+$ more rapidly than NH$_3$ is reflected in its pH$_i$ response to ammonium exposure.

In the isolated, perfused mouse (41) or rat (74) MTAL, addition of ammonium to the tubule lumen results in a rapid intracellular acidification (Figure 1a, *control*). The acidification is observed in tubules studied in 25 mM HCO$_3^-$ solutions (i.e. under conditions of physiologic cell buffering) and is sustained for as long as ammonium is present in the luminal fluid (74). This pH$_i$ response is opposite to that observed in virtually all other mammalian cell types (which alkalinize when exposed to ammonium because of rapid entry of NH$_3$) and indicates that NH$_4^+$ is transported across the apical membrane more rapidly than NH$_3$. These findings are consistent with the results of the transepithelial transport studies demonstrating that active transport of NH$_4^+$ predominates over diffusion of NH$_3$ to result in net ammonium absorption (16, 20, 26, 47). Recent preliminary studies indicate that the NH$_3$ permeability of the apical membrane of the rat MTAL is similar to NH$_3$ permeabilities measured for other cell membranes (see below). Thus the property of the apical membrane that distinguishes it from other cell membranes and that accounts for the predominance of NH$_4^+$ entry over

a.

Lumen

20 mM NH$_4^+$

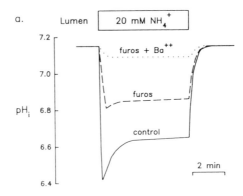

furos + Ba^{++}

furos

control

2 min

pH$_i$

b.

Bath

4 mM NH$_4^+$

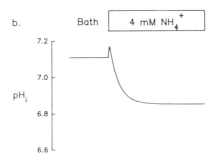

pH$_i$

c.

Bath

4 mM NH$_4^+$

Lumen

4 mM NH$_4^+$

furos

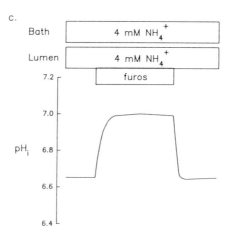

pH$_i$

NH$_3$ entry is the presence of transport pathways that mediate rapid uptake of NH$_4^+$, not the absence of a significant NH$_3$ permeability.

It is clear from the studies described above that uptake of NH$_4^+$ across the apical membrane is associated with a large and continuous acid load to the TAL cell. However, the mechanisms of the intracellular acidification have not been clearly defined. It is important to note that apical uptake and cellular accumulation of NH$_4^+$, by itself, cannot account for the pronounced fall in pH$_i$. This is because the pK_a for the ammonium buffer reaction is ~2 pH units above the cell pH. Consequently, only about 1% of the NH$_4^+$ inside the cell would dissociate to release a proton, resulting in a negligibly small cell acid load given the buffering power of the cell (74). Therefore, processes in addition to apical NH$_4^+$ uptake must play a role in the intracellular acidification. Possible explanations include (a) apical NH$_4^+$ entry coupled with basolateral (or apical) NH$_3$ efflux, which results in the net deposition of H$^+$ inside the cells; (b) efflux of NH$_4^+$ across the basolateral membrane in exchange for H$^+$ or by cotransport with base; (c) inhibition by ammonium of H$^+$ or base transporters responsible for pH$_i$ regulation; and (d) an effect of ammonium on metabolic acid production. Further study of these issues should enhance our understanding of the complex interactions between NH$_4^+$ transport, H$^+$ and HCO$_3^-$ transport, and intracellular pH regulation in epithelial cells.

Basolateral Ammonium Addition

Only limited information is available on the effects of basolateral ammonium addition on pH$_i$ in the TAL. In mouse MTALs studied in HEPES-buffered solutions, addition of ammonium to the peritubular bath resulted in an abrupt intracellular alkalinization, followed by a slow return of pH$_i$ toward its initial control value (41). In rat MTALs studied in HCO$_3^-$-buffered solutions, basolateral ammonium addition caused an initial rapid rise in pH$_i$, followed by a secondary acidification that reduced the steady-state pH$_i$ to a value below that measured prior to ammonium addition (Figure 1b). The response

←——

Figure 1 Effects of ammonium on intracellular pH (pH$_i$) in the isolated, perfused medullary thick ascending limb of the rat. (a) Addition of 20 mM NH$_4^+$ to the luminal perfusate under control conditions (*solid line*), in the presence of 10^{-4} M luminal furosemide (*dashed line*), or in the presence of 10^{-4} M luminal furosemide plus 12 mM luminal barium (*dotted line*). (b) Addition of 4 mM NH$_4^+$ to the peritubular bath. (c) Addition of furosemide (10^{-4} M) to the luminal perfusate in MTAL perfused and bathed with 4 mM NH$_4$Cl. All tubules were perfused and bathed in vitro at pH 7.4 with 25 mM HCO$_3^-$-buffered solutions. pH$_i$ was measured using the fluorescent dye BCECF. In experiment (b), luminal furosemide and barium were present to block apical NH$_4^+$ uptake that could occur secondary to diffusional entry of NH$_4^+$ into the luminal fluid. Tracings in panels (a) and (c) are adapted from data in reference 74; panel (b), BA Watts & DW Good, unpublished data.

of pH_i to basolateral ammonium addition thus appears to follow a more conventional pattern in which diffusional entry of NH_3 initially predominates over entry of NH_4^+ to result in intracellular alkalinization. Pathways for significant NH_4^+ uptake also appear to be present, however, as evidenced by the pronounced secondary acidification observed in the rat MTAL. As discussed below, the basolateral NH_4^+ transport pathways are poorly understood.

Symmetric Ammonium Addition

In vivo, the MTAL is surrounded by fluids containing millimolar concentrations of ammonium due to the high ammonium levels generated in the renal medulla by countercurrent multiplication (9, 23, 25, 47, 56, 66). Therefore, to assess the potential significance of ammonium as a determinant of pH_i, it is necessary to assess the effect of a physiologic concentration of ammonium in both the luminal and peritubular fluids. In rat MTALs perfused and bathed in vitro with 25 mM HCO_3^--buffered solutions, the mean pH_i was 7.16. In contrast, in tubules studied under identical conditions but with 4 mM NH_4Cl in the perfusate and bath, the mean steady-state pH_i was 6.61 (74). Qualitatively similar results were reported for mouse MTALs studied in HEPES-buffered solutions (41). Thus the pronounced intracellular acidification observed in response to luminal ammonium addition persists under the more physiologic condition of bilateral ammonium exposure.

The results presented above demonstrate that ammonium transport is a critical determinant of pH_i in the TAL. The marked intracellular acidification associated with ammonium indicates that the acid-loading effects of NH_4^+ transport predominate over the acid-extruding mechanisms responsible for pH_i regulation, thereby resetting the steady-state pH_i to a much lower value. These findings predict that factors that regulate NH_4^+ absorption may have a profound impact on pH_i. As discussed below, the effects of furosemide or an increase in luminal $[K^+]$ to cause marked intracellular alkalinization in association with inhibition of active NH_4^+ absorption validate this prediction.

MECHANISMS OF NH_4^+ TRANSPORT

Pathways of NH_4^+ transport have been identified in TALs from the effects of inhibitors or ion replacements on net ammonium absorption and ammonium-dependent changes in pH_i. The evidence indicates that NH_4^+ shares a number of transport pathways with other monovalent cations. There is no convincing evidence for transport pathways specific for NH_4^+.

Apical Membrane

Na$^+$-K$^+$-2Cl$^-$ COTRANSPORT   The possibility that NH$_4^+$ could replace K$^+$ on the apical membrane Na$^+$-K$^+$-2Cl$^-$ cotransporter was first proposed based on the observation that luminal furosemide inhibited NH$_4^+$ absorption in the rat TAL (27). There is now strong evidence supporting the cotransport hypothesis.

A major role for the Na$^+$-K$^+$-2Cl$^-$ cotransporter in NH$_4^+$ absorption has been deduced from the actions of the diuretic furosemide. This agent (a) abolishes net ammonium absorption in the rat TAL (27, 74), (b) inhibits active NH$_4^+$ absorption in the rabbit MTAL independently of effects on transepithelial voltage (16), and (c) inhibits by 55–70% the initial rate of cell acidification observed with luminal addition of NH$_4^+$ (Figure 1a, *furos*) (42, 74). The luminal addition of furosemide also causes an abrupt intracellular alkalinization in MTALs perfused and bathed with 4 mM NH$_4$Cl (Figure 1c). The latter result is best explained as follows: Furosemide blocks apical NH$_4^+$ uptake via the Na$^+$-NH$_4^+$-2Cl$^-$ cotransporter. This eliminates the intracellular acid load that results from transcellular ammonium absorption, thereby permitting pH$_i$ to recover to a value (~7.0) similar to that observed in TALs studied in ammonium-free solutions (74). When furosemide is removed from the lumen, the restoration of apical Na$^+$-NH$_4^+$-2Cl$^-$ uptake again results in rapid intracellular acidification (Figure 1c). Luminal addition of furosemide has no effect on pH$_i$ in the absence of ammonium (74). Thus these findings underscore the critical importance of apical membrane Na$^+$-NH$_4^+$-2Cl$^-$ cotransport as a determinant of pH$_i$ in the MTAL.

Although the above results support a major role for Na$^+$-K$^+$-2Cl$^-$ cotransport in NH$_4^+$ absorption, they do not identify the nature of the interaction between NH$_4^+$ and the cotransporter. Direct support for the Na$^+$-NH$_4^+$-2Cl$^-$ cotransport hypothesis was obtained from kinetic studies on plasma membrane vesicles from rabbit MTALs (43). Key findings were that (a) interaction between NH$_4^+$ and K$^+$ at the K$^+$ binding site was fully competitive with a 1:1 stoichiometry, (b) a NH$_4$Cl gradient could drive bumetanide-sensitive translocation of Na$^+$ across the vesicle membrane, and (c) NH$_4^+$ did not bind to the Na$^+$ site[2]. The apparent affinity of the cotransporter for NH$_4^+$ was high (K_m = 1.9 mM), similar to the K_m estimated in the same study for K$^+$ (≤1 mM). These values are consistent with the K$^+$ affinity of 1–2 mM reported for the rabbit CTAL (30), and with the low luminal NH$_4^+$ concentration (0.5 mM) at which apical NH$_4^+$ uptake was half-maximal in the mouse MTAL (42). In the rat in vivo, the NH$_4^+$ concentration of

[2] Different results were obtained in experiments with plasma membrane vesicles from the shark rectal gland in which NH$_4^+$ was accepted by both the K$^+$ and Na$^+$ sites of the cotransporter (44).

fluid delivered to the ascending limb of Henle's loop ranges from 3 to 20 mM (5, 9, 25) and the K^+ concentration ranges from 5 to 35 mM (see 19). Thus the affinity of the cotransporter for NH_4^+ is well within the range of NH_4^+ concentrations encountered physiologically. In addition, as discussed below, the competitive interaction between NH_4^+ and K^+ permits the luminal K^+ concentration to act as an effective physiologic modulator of MTAL NH_4^+ absorption.

Functional evidence for competition between NH_4^+ and K^+ on the apical Na^+-K^+-$2Cl^-$ cotransporter was obtained from studies of the K^+-dependence of ammonium absorption in the isolated, perfused rat MTAL (19, 20). With 4 mM NH_4^+ in perfusate and bath, increasing the luminal K^+ concentration from 4 to 24 mM inhibited net ammonium absorption by 50%. Potassium specifically inhibited the active component of NH_4^+ absorption, with no effect on paracellular NH_4^+ diffusion (20). The inhibition of NH_4^+ absorption could be accounted for by a simple model assuming pure competitive interaction between NH_4^+ and K^+ on the apical Na^+-K^+-$2Cl^-$ cotransporter. (20). Increasing the luminal K^+ concentration also caused an abrupt and pronounced intracellular alkalinization that was dependent on the presence of ammonium and virtually identical to the alkalinization observed with luminal furosemide (see Figure 1c) (74). The effects of K^+ could not be attributed to membrane depolarization since addition of luminal barium (another maneuver that results in rapid depolarization) (31) did not reproduce either the rapid intracellular alkalinization or the inhibition of NH_4^+ absorption observed with increasing luminal $[K^+]$ (74). Thus the effects of luminal K^+ on active NH_4^+ absorption and pH_i are most likely the result of competitive inhibition of NH_4^+ uptake on the apical membrane Na^+-NH_4^+ (K^+)-$2Cl^-$ cotransport system. An important implication of the effects of $[K^+]$ and furosemide to increase pH_i by inhibiting Na^+-NH_4^+-$2Cl^-$ cotransport is that factors that control TAL Cl^- absorption through modulation of the Na^+-K^+-$2Cl^-$ cotransporter (peptide hormones, prostaglandins, etc) would be expected to have a much greater influence on pH_i when NH_4^+ is present.

In conclusion, these studies demonstrate that apical membrane Na^+-NH_4^+-$2Cl^-$ cotransport mediates most or all of active NH_4^+ absorption in the TAL and that uptake of NH_4^+ via the cotransporter is responsible for the intracellular acidification that accompanies transcellular ammonium absorption under symmetric ammonium conditions.

K^+ CHANNEL   The apical membrane of the TAL is largely, if not exclusively, K^+ conductive and contains K^+ channels that are Ba^{2+}-inhibitable, ATP-regulated, and pH_i-sensitive (3, 30, 32, 37, 42, 55, 70, 77). The apical K^+ conductance functions to recycle K^+ taken up by the Na^+-K^+-$2Cl^-$ cotransporter into the tubule lumen (30, 37). The first indication that

NH$_4^+$ may permeate TAL K$^+$ channels was obtained in mouse MTAL suspensions in which Ba^{2+} blocked most of the intracellular acidification evoked by addition of NH$_4^+$ to the suspension medium (41). Subsequent studies in isolated, perfused rat (74) and mouse (42) MTALs showed that furosemide did not completely prevent the intracellular acidification induced by luminal ammonium addition and that the residual acidification observed with furosemide was inhibited by luminal Ba^{2+} (Figure 1a). Thus apical NH$_4^+$ uptake occurred via both furosemide- and Ba^{2+}-sensitive pathways. Based on previous observations that NH$_4^+$ permeates K$^+$ channels in a variety of cell types, including the ATP-sensitive K$^+$ channels of pancreatic β cells (47, 61), it is likely that Ba^{2+}-sensitive NH$_4^+$ entry in the TAL occurs via apical membrane K$^+$ channels. This conclusion was supported by the finding of Kikeri et al (42) that the Ba^{2+}-sensitive transepithelial conductance and the Ba^{2+}-sensitive NH$_4^+$ influx had similar pH$_i$-sensitivities, consistent with transport of NH$_4^+$ and K$^+$ via the same Ba^{2+}-sensitive pathway.

Although apical K$^+$ channels appear to contribute significantly to NH$_4^+$ uptake in response to luminal NH$_4^+$ addition, i.e. in response to the imposition of a large lumen-to-cell NH$_4^+$ concentration difference, their contribution to net ammonium absorption appears to be minimal under physiologic conditions in which ammonium is present in both the luminal and peritubular solutions. In the rat MTAL, luminal furosemide abolished net ammonium absorption even though this agent neither blocks apical K$^+$ channels nor reduces the apical membrane voltage that would drive conductive NH$_4^+$ entry (30, 36, 39, 70). In addition, adding Ba^{2+} to the tubule lumen reduced net ammonium absorption only by 14%, a result that could be explained by secondary effects of luminal Ba^{2+} to diminish the driving forces for apical Na$^+$-NH$_4^+$-2Cl$^-$ uptake and/or paracellular NH$_4^+$ absorption (74). It is possible that rapid uptake of NH$_4^+$ via Na$^+$-NH$_4^+$-2Cl$^-$ cotransport limits uptake of NH$_4^+$ via K$^+$ channels through two effects: (a) by elevating the intracellular NH$_4^+$ concentration above that in the luminal fluid, and (b) through intracellular acidification (Figures 1a, c), which inhibits the apical K$^+$ conductance (3, 42, 55, 70). It should be noted, however, that in the rabbit MTAL, approximately 25% of net ammonium absorption persisted in the presence of luminal furosemide (16). Whether this NH$_4^+$ flux occurred through apical K$^+$ channels was not investigated. It is possible that channel-mediated NH$_4^+$ uptake may have been unmasked or accelerated in the presence of furosemide by this agent's ability to reduce cell [NH$_4^+$], hyperpolarize the apical membrane, and/or increase the apical K$^+$ conductance through intracellular alkalinization (39).

The conclusion from the pH$_i$ experiments that NH$_4^+$ permeates apical K$^+$ channels is at variance with results of patch-clamp experiments on single apical K^+ channels in rat TALs (3). In the patch-clamp study, a single type of K^+ channel was observed in cell-attached or cell-excised patches, with a conductance of 60 to 70 pS at zero clamp voltage and 145 mM NaCl-Ringer in either the pipette or bath solution. In cell-excised (inside-out) patches with 145 mM KCl in the pipette and 145 mM NH_4Cl in the bath, no NH_4^+ conductance was observed. However, under virtually identical conditions with 145 mM KCl in both pipette and bath, the channel also did not conduct K^+, even when a large voltage was applied across the patch (3). The latter result suggests that some critical regulatory factor necessary for channel activity was absent under the conditions used to test for NH_4^+ conductance, which makes the results of the NH_4^+ conductance experiments difficult to interpret. Clearly, further studies are needed to clarify the NH_4^+ transport properties of TAL K^+ channels.

Na^+/H^+ EXCHANGE   Studies in renal microvillus membrane vesicles and intact proximal tubules have demonstrated that NH_4^+ can replace Na^+ or H^+ on the brush border Na^+/H^+ exchanger and that Na^+/NH_4^+ exchange may be an important mechanism for proximal tubule ammonium secretion (45, 47, 54, 58). Apical Na^+/H^+ exchange also is present in segments of the TAL (13, 18, 24, 41, 68, 71, 73), and a significant rate of either Na^+/NH_4^+ exchange or NH_4^+/H^+ exchange would be expected to influence the net ammonium absorptive flux. In addition, it was proposed that apical Na^+/H^+ exchange was necessary for ammonium absorption in the mouse MTAL by virtue of its action to extrude H^+ generated intracellularly as a result of NH_4^+ uptake (41).

Direct assessment of the role of apical membrane Na^+/H^+ exchange in ammonium absorption in the isolated, perfused rat MTAL yielded the following results. (a) Addition of amiloride to the lumen at a concentration that inhibits apical membrane Na^+/H^+ exchange by 80 to 90% (1 mM) had no effect on net ammonium absorption (71). (b) Luminal furosemide abolishes net ammonium absorption, but does not inhibit apical Na^+/H^+ exchange (18, 24, 27, 74). (c) Symmetric addition of 4 mM NH_4^+ reduces net luminal H^+ secretion by 20% despite a decrease in pH_i from 7.1 to 6.7 (28); thus the increased intracellular acid load generated by NH_4^+ uptake is not extruded by the apical membrane Na^+/H^+ exchanger. (d) Luminal amiloride had no effect on the initial rate of cell alkalinization when ammonium was added to the tubule lumen under conditions in which NH_4^+ transport pathways and pH_i-regulatory mechanisms were inhibited (see below). Thus amiloride-sensitive NH_4^+/H^+ exchange did not contribute significantly to the intracellular alkalinization, in contrast to results obtained in the rat proximal convoluted tubule (58). Taken together, these results indicate that apical membrane Na^+/H^+ exchange is not necessary for ammonium absorption in the MTAL and that this exchanger is not a quantitatively significant pathway for NH_4^+ transport across the apical membrane.

Basolateral Membrane

To complete its transcellular absorption, NH_4^+ must exit the basolateral membrane either directly or by the combination of NH_3 diffusion and H^+ extrusion. Little information is currently available on the mechanisms of basolateral NH_4^+ transport. The only pathway identified conclusively to mediate transport of NH_4^+ across the basolateral membrane is the Na^+-K^+ ATPase.

Na^+-K^+ ATPASE   In a variety of cell types, NH_4^+ can replace K^+ on the Na^+-K^+ ATPase (see 47 for review). NH_4^+ supports both the enzymatic activity and the transport function of the Na^+ pump in TAL segments (14, 16, 43). In the isolated, perfused rabbit MTAL, active Cl^- absorption was sustained when NH_4^+ replaced K^+ completely in the perfusion and bath solutions (16). Because Cl^- absorption depends ultimately on energy provided by the Na^+ pump, it was concluded that NH_4^+ could support primary active transport of Na^+ across the basolateral membrane. As discussed above, basolateral addition of ammonium in the rat MTAL results in a large secondary intracellular acidification, most likely from basolateral uptake of NH_4^+ (Figure 1b). In mouse MTAL suspensions, the intracellular acidification in response to ammonium addition was partially attenuated by ouabain (42), which suggests that a portion of the NH_4^+ entry occurs via the Na^+-K^+ ATPase.

In plasma membranes isolated from rabbit renal outer medulla, the apparent K_m of the Na^+ pump for NH_4^+ was 10 mM, compared with 2 mM for K^+ (43). The lower affinity for NH_4^+ partially may explain the observation in rabbit MTAL that the rate of active Cl^- absorption with 5 mM NH_4^+ was only 60% of that observed with 5 mM K^+ (16). The relatively low affinity for NH_4^+ makes it unlikely that NH_4^+ uptake would be significant in the renal cortex where extracellular NH_4^+ concentrations are low (~0.1 to 0.3 mM). However, as discussed previously by Kurtz & Balaban (51), significant cellular uptake of NH_4^+ may occur in segments of the renal medulla where interstitial NH_4^+ concentrations may reach 8–20 mM because of countercurrent multiplication by the loop segment (10, 47, 66). It should be noted, however, that the kinetics of NH_4^+ transport by the Na^+ pump have not been examined in intact TAL cells, where the presence of separate cytoplasmic and extracellular domains may result in ion-binding kinetics that differ from those observed in homogenized cell membranes (47).

Because the Na^+-K^+ ATPase acts as a primary active NH_4^+ pump moving

NH_4^+ from the peritublar blood into the cell, this process would be counterproductive for transcellular NH_4^+ absorption. A possible physiologic role for the active NH_4^+ uptake may be to reduce NH_4^+ absorption as the medullary interstitial ammonium concentration rises, thereby limiting further medullary ammonium accumulation. An increase in basolateral NH_4^+ uptake via the Na^+ pump presumably would elevate the intracellular NH_4^+ concentration, thereby reducing apical NH_4^+ uptake and net ammonium absorption. Consistent with this prediction, elevating the NH_4^+ concentration from 4 to 20 mM in lumen and bath diminished net ammonium absorption in the rat MTAL (72).

NH_4^+ EFFLUX PATHWAYS The extent to which direct transport of NH_4^+ contributes to basolateral ammonium efflux is not known. There are, however, a number of basolateral transport pathways that could mediate NH_4^+ exit. First, in keeping with the ability of NH_4^+ to replace K^+ on the Na^+-K^+-$2Cl^-$ cotransporter and the Na^+-K^+ ATPase, NH_4^+ could share pathways that mediate basolateral K^+ exit. These may include K^+ channels (38), KCl cotransport (30), and $KHCO_3$ cotransport (52). In each case, a cell to blood NH_4^+ concentration difference would be required to drive NH_4^+ exit (efflux of NH_4^+ through channels would be opposed by the basolateral membrane voltage; efflux via the electroneutral cotransporters would be opposed by the extracellular to intracellular Cl^- and HCO_3^- concentration differences). However, this does not necessarily preclude a contribution of these pathways, since it is virtually certain that intracellular $[NH_4^+]$ exceeds extracellular $[NH_4^+]$ in TAL segments (see below).

A second pathway capable of mediating NH_4^+ efflux would be basolateral Na^+/H^+ exchange, which has been identified in both mouse and rat TALs (35, 49, 68, 75). In this case, the transmembrane Na^+ gradient would be the primary driving force for NH_4^+ exit (via Na^+/NH_4^+ exchange). The finding that NH_4^+ does not appear to be transported effectively by the apical Na^+/H^+ exchanger does not rule out NH_4^+ transport via the basolateral exchanger, since the apical and basolateral exchangers may be isoforms with different kinetic and regulatory properties. We have demonstrated recently that inhibition of the basolateral Na^+/H^+ exchanger markedly reduces ammonium absorption in the rat MTAL (75). Whether this reflects movement of NH_4^+ on the exchanger is not known.

NH3 TRANSPORT

In the TAL, two transport processes cause the luminal NH_3 concentration to fall below that in the peritubular fluid: (a) absorption of NH_4^+, which reduces the luminal NH_4^+ concentration and secondarily lowers the luminal

NH$_3$ concentration as luminal NH$_3$ combines with H$^+$ to maintain the equilibrium state of the ammonium buffer reaction; and (b) active H$^+$ secretion (24, 27), which acidifies the luminal fluid and reduces the NH$_3$ concentration at any given total ammonia concentration. The net result is the generation of a transepithelial NH$_3$ concentration difference that drives an NH$_3$ backflux, which opposes net ammonium absorption. The magnitude of the backflux depends on the NH$_3$ concentration difference across the epithelium and the NH$_3$ permeability. In the rabbit MTAL, the transepithelial NH$_3$ permeability was $\sim 3 \times 10^{-3}$cm/sec (16), a value similar to NH$_3$ permeabilities reported for medullary collecting ducts ($2-4 \times 10^{-3}$cm/sec) (11, 12, 33), but an order of magnitude less than NH$_3$ permeabilities measured in segments of the proximal tubule ($2-6 \times 10^{-2}$cm/sec) (15, 34, 58, 64). The higher NH$_3$ permeability of the proximal segments is likely because of the greater membrane surface area due to the presence of the apical brush border (58, 65). In the isolated, perfused rabbit MTAL, the calculated NH$_3$ backflux was only $\sim 10\%$ of the net ammonium absorptive flux (16). Thus the transepithelial NH$_3$ permeability is sufficiently low (and the rate of active NH$_4^+$ absorption is sufficiently high) to permit net ammonium absorption to proceed at physiologically significant rates. The rate of NH$_3$ backflux also is limited by the low absolute NH$_3$ concentrations (micromolar) present in the kidney at physiologic pH.

Little information is available on NH$_3$ permeabilities of the apical and basolateral membranes. In both mouse (41) and rat (74) MTALs, addition of 20 mM ammonium to the tubule lumen did not result in intracellular alkalinization, even when apical NH$_4^+$ entry was blocked with luminal furosemide and barium (Figure 1a). This observation originally was interpreted to indicate that the apical membrane was impermeable to NH$_3$ (41). However, several factors in these experiments may have precluded the detection of cell alkalinization from NH$_3$ entry. These include an effect of unblocked pH$_i$ regulatory mechanisms to minimize changes in pH$_i$, and rapid efflux of NH$_3$ out of the cells due to a basolateral membrane surface area 13 times greater than the apical surface area (48), thereby minimizing the amount of NH$_3$ present in the cells to bind protons (74). In recent studies in the rat MTAL, a sharp intracellular alkalinization was observed in response to luminal ammonium addition when additional steps were taken to inhibit apical and basolateral pH$_i$ regulatory mechanisms, and the luminal NH$_3$ concentration was elevated to increase the magnitude of apical NH$_3$ entry (Figure 2). The apparent apical membrane NH$_3$ permeability, calculated from the initial rate of cell alkalinization, averaged 7×10^{-3}cm/sec (BA Watts & DW Good, unpublished observations). This value is similar to the apical membrane NH$_3$ permeability (8×10^{-3}cm/sec) measured in a canine distal nephron cell line (MDCK) (17) and to the NH$_3$ permeability of

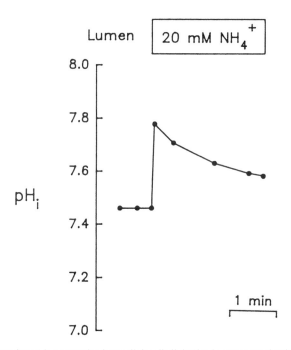

Figure 2   Experiment demonstrating intracellular alkalinization in response to luminal ammonium addition in the isolated, perfused medullary thick ascending limb of the rat. The tubule was perfused and bathed in HEPES-buffered solutions, bath pH 7.4, luminal pH 8.0. Apical NH_4^+ entry was blocked with luminal furosemide plus barium. pH_i regulatory mechanisms were inhibited with lumen and bath amiloride and K^+-free bath. pH_i was measured using the fluorescent dye BCECF; filled circles are single pH_i values determined at selected time points from fluorescence excitation ratios.

1×10^{-2} cm/sec measured for the red blood cell plasma membrane (46). A higher apical NH_3 permeability (7×10^{-2} cm/sec) was reported for the rat proximal convoluted tubule, again most likely reflecting the greater degree of apical membrane amplification. For two membranes in series, each with an NH_3 permeability equal to that measured for the MTAL apical membrane (7×10^{-3} cm/sec), the calculated transcellular NH_3 permeability is 3.5×10^{-3} cm/sec, a value in close agreement with the transepithelial NH_3 permeability measured in MTAL segments. It appears, therefore, that the relatively low transepithelial NH_3 permeability of the MTAL is due to a relatively limited apical membrane surface area available for NH_3 diffusion, and not to an intrinsic property of the membrane that renders it impermeable to NH_3.

Currently there are no estimates of NH_3 permeability for the basolateral membrane. In mouse (41) and rat (Figure 1b) MTALs, addition of NH_4Cl

to the peritubular bath results in a rapid intracellular alkalinization, which indicates that NH$_3$ permeates the basolateral membrane at a rate that initially exceeds the rate of uptake of NH$_4^+$. If the intrinsic NH$_3$ permeability of the lipid-phase of apical and basolateral membranes is similar, then the apical membrane should be rate limiting for NH$_3$ diffusion because of its much smaller surface area. It is also possible that differences in lipid composition or in the density of integral membrane proteins could influence the relative diffusive properties of the apical and basolateral membranes. As discussed below, more rapid diffusion of NH$_3$ across the basolateral membrane may be important for vectorial ammonium transport since the NH$_3$ generated in the cells secondary to apical NH$_4^+$ uptake would preferentially exit the basolateral membrane (along with H$^+$) to complete transcellular NH$_4^+$ absorption.

INTEGRATED MODEL OF TAL AMMONIUM ABSORPTION

A model summarizing key elements of NH$_4^+$ absorption by the TAL is shown in Figure 3. Most of the NH$_4^+$ absorption occurs by secondary-active transport, with a minor portion occurring by paracellular electrodiffusion. Apical NH$_4^+$ entry is mediated predominantly by Na$^+$-NH$_4^+$-2Cl$^-$ cotransport. Thus the energy for ammonium absorption is derived from the basolateral Na$^+$-K$^+$ATPase, which maintains the apical Na$^+$ gradient that is the primary driving force for Na$^+$-NH$_4^+$-2Cl$^-$ cotransport. Uptake of NH$_4^+$ on the cotransporter results in a pronounced and sustained intracellular acidification, resulting in part from NH$_4^+$ dissociating in the cell to release H$^+$ when NH$_3$ exits the basolateral (or apical) membrane. Maneuvers that inhibit uptake of NH$_4^+$ on the cotransporter (furosemide; competitive inhibition by an increase in luminal [K$^+$]) reduce or abolish both the net ammonium absorptive flux and the intracellular acidification that accompanies NH$_4^+$ absorption. Basolateral NH$_4^+$ efflux may occur either by direct transport of NH$_4^+$ and/or by the combination of NH$_3$ diffusion and active H$^+$ extrusion. The relative contributions of these two mechanisms and the possible pathways for basolateral NH$_4^+$ transport are not known. NH$_4^+$ also permeates a barium-sensitive apical pathway, presumably apical K$^+$ channels. However, this does not appear to be a quantitatively important pathway for ammonium absorption, possibly because channel activity is inhibited by the intracellular acidification that results from apical Na$^+$-NH$_4^+$-2Cl$^-$ uptake. Uptake of NH$_4^+$ via the basolateral Na$^+$-K$^+$ ATPase does not contribute directly to NH$_4^+$ absorption, but may serve as a feedback mechanism that slows net ammonium reabsorption as the medullary interstitial NH$_4^+$ concentration increases. Finally, in the rat MTAL, apical Na$^+$/H$^+$ exchange does not

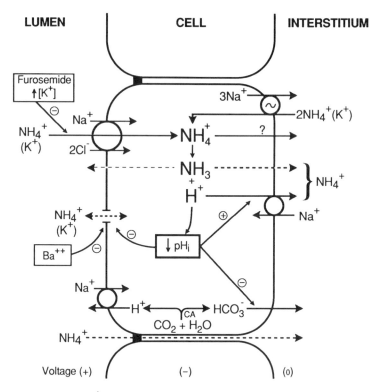

LUMEN   CELL   INTERSTITIUM

Figure 3   Model for NH_4^+ absorption by the thick ascending limb. See text for details. Broken lines indicate diffusion $\oplus$ indicates stimulation and $\ominus$ inhibition of transport pathways. CA, carbonic anhydrase.

significantly influence ammonium absorption, either by directly transporting NH_4^+ or by extruding H^+ generated in the cells by dissociation of NH_4^+. Additional points about the model are noteworthy.

1. The intracellular NH_4^+ concentration exceeds that in the peritubular fluid. This conclusion follows directly from the fact that in the presence of ammonium the cell pH is much lower than the peritubular pH (41, 74), and the assumption that the intracellular $[NH_3]$ is equal to or greater than the peritubular $[NH_3]$. For rat MTALs perfused and bathed in vitro at pH 7.4 with 4 mM total ammonia, the calculated intracellular $[NH_4^+]$ (assuming $[NH_3]_{cell} = [NH_3]_{bath}$) is $\sim$25 mM. Thus a substantial NH_4^+ concentration difference favoring basolateral NH_4^+ efflux is present under steady-state transporting conditions.

2. In the rat MTAL, protons generated in the cell by apical NH$_4^+$ uptake and basolateral NH$_3$ efflux are extruded preferentially across the basolateral membrane rather than across the apical membrane. Evidence against extrusion of the protons via the apical Na$^+$/H$^+$ exchanger includes the fact that luminal H$^+$ secretion as assessed by net HCO$_3^-$ absorption is not accelerated in the presence of ammonium (28); and the activity of the apical Na$^+$/H$^+$ exchanger does not increase with decreasing pH$_i$ over the pH$_i$ range normally measured in MTAL cells (6.5 to 7.1) (73). The net increase in basolateral H$^+$ efflux that presumably accompanies transcellular ammonium absorption could occur equivalently as an increase in H$^+$ extrusion (e.g. via basolateral Na$^+$/H$^+$ exchange), or a decrease in HCO$_3^-$ efflux.

3. The combination of apical NH$_4^+$ uptake and back diffusion of NH$_3$ from cell to tubule lumen would transfer protons from lumen to cell. In the steady state, this process would result in luminal alkalinization (when coupled with extrusion of the protons across the basolateral membrane, see above). This mechanism may contribute to the effect of bilateral ammonium addition to inhibit net HCO$_3^-$ absorption in the rat MTAL. It is likely, however, that the bulk of NH$_3$ diffusion occurs across the basolateral membrane because of the greater membrane surface area and, possibly, a higher intrinsic NH$_3$ permeability.

PHYSIOLOGIC SIGNIFICANCE OF TAL AMMONIUM ABSORPTION

Role in Urinary Ammonium Excretion

The role of TAL ammonium absorption in renal ammonium excretion has been discussed previously (23, 26, 47) and is outlined here only briefly. Changes in renal net acid excretion that maintain systemic acid-base balance occur primarily through controlled changes in the rate of urinary ammonium excretion. The ammonium excreted in the urine is produced in cells of the proximal tubule from glutamine and secreted into the proximal tubule lumen. Absorption of ammonium by the TAL provides a mechanism by which the ammonium delivered out of the proximal tubule is transferred to collecting ducts in the renal medulla for excretion in the final urine. Active absorption of NH$_4^+$ by the MTAL drives an ammonium countercurrent multiplier that causes ammonium to accumulate in the medullary interstitial fluid to concentrations up to two orders of magnitude higher than values in arterial plasma or structures of the renal cortex. The high interstitial ammonium levels are primarily responsible for the transepithelial NH$_3$ concentration difference that drives secretion of NH_3 into medullary collecting ducts in parallel with H^+ secretion. Changes in the rate of TAL NH_4^+ absorption thus influence urinary ammonium excretion by controlling ammonium levels in the medullary interstitium, and thereby regulating the driving force for collecting duct ammonium secretion.

Regulation

Regulation of ammonium absorption by the TAL involves both acute responses to changes in luminal and peritubular fluid composition and adaptive changes in tubule transport capacity in response to chronic perturbations in systemic acid-base or electrolyte balance. In the following sections, an example of each type of regulation is presented to illustrate how the control of ammonium absorption in the TAL may participate in the regulation of urinary ammonium excretion.

POTASSIUM CONCENTRATION   As discussed in the preceding sections, increasing luminal K^+ concentration markedly inhibits active ammonium absorption in the MTAL, most likely as a result of competition between NH_4^+ and K^+ on the apical membrane Na^+-K^+-$2Cl^-$ cotransporter (19, 20, 43). The inhibition of MTAL NH_4^+ absorption by potassium in vitro correlates with a decrease in accumulation of ammonium in the renal medulla during hyperkalemia in vivo. Specifically, chronic dietary potassium loading in rats is associated with a decrease in the ammonium concentration in medullary interstitial fluid, a decrease in the NH_3 concentration difference across the medullary collecting duct, and a decrease in the rate of collecting duct ammonium secretion (10). It is likely that these changes are the result of high medullary K^+ levels, which inhibit active NH_4^+ absorption in the MTAL and thereby reduce countercurrent accumulation of ammonium in the renal medulla. Thus regulation of NH_4^+ absorption in the MTAL appears to play an important role in mediating the decrease in urinary ammonium excretion commonly associated with systemic hyperkalemia.

CHRONIC METABOLIC ACIDOSIS (CMA)   In CMA, production and secretion of ammonium by the proximal tubule increase dramatically, which results in an increase in delivery of ammonium to the loop of Henle (47, 69). CMA also induces an adaptive increase in the capacity of the MTAL to absorb ammonium. MTALs from rats with CMA, ingesting NH_4Cl for 5–8 days, absorbed ammonium in vitro at a rate 40% greater than tubules from normal rats studied under identical conditions (22). This adaptation in the MTAL is associated with the following changes in vivo: (*a*) an increase in net ammonium absorption by the loop of Henle (5), (*b*) an increase in NH_3 concentration difference across the medullary collecting duct that is due entirely to an increase in NH$_3$ concentration in the medullary interstitial fluid (25), and (c) an increase in collecting duct ammonium secretion (2, 25, 62). Thus by enhancing accumulation of ammonium in the renal medulla, the adaptive increase in ammonium absorption by the MTAL during acidosis helps to ensure that the increased load of ammonium delivered to the loop of Henle from the proximal tubule is transferred efficiently to the collecting ducts for excretion in the final urine. The mechanism of the adaptation in MTAL ammonium absorption has not been determined.

Effects of Ammonium on Ion Transport

Relatively little is known about the possible interactions between ammonium transport and the transport of other ions. In principle, NH$_4^+$ could influence ion transport processes directly (e.g. by competitive binding) or indirectly via effects on intracellular pH or cell metabolism. The following sections briefly summarize and speculate on possible effects of ammonium on NaCl and NaHCO$_3$ reabsorption in the TAL.

NaCl REABSORPTION   Reabsorption of NaCl by the TAL plays a critical role in renal NaCl conservation and is essential for the excretion of a concentrated or dilute urine. Several observations suggest that absorption of NaCl by the TAL is inhibited by intracellular acidification. (a) In the isolated, perfused rabbit CTAL, increasing the ambient PCO$_2$, or decreasing the bath HCO$_3^-$ concentration, inhibited net Cl$^-$ absorption (76). (b) In the amphibian diluting segment (a segment functionally homologous to the mammalian TAL in which Cl$^-$ absorption is mediated by apical Na$^+$-K$^+$-2Cl$^-$ cotransport), intracellular acidification induced by a high PCO$_2$, or by the addition of luminal amiloride to block apical Na$^+$/H$^+$ exchange, reduced Cl$^-$ reabsorption (53). (c) In isolated, perfused mouse MTALs switched from HEPES-buffered to CO$_2$/HCO$_3^-$-buffered solutions, a decrease in pH$_i$ correlated with a decrease in net Cl$^-$ absorption (42). The inhibition of Cl$^-$ absorption by acidosis likely occurs in part because intracellular acidification inhibits apical membrane K$^+$ channels, thereby depolarizing the cell and reducing the driving force for basolateral Cl$^-$ exit (30, 37, 53). Based on these findings, it is likely that NH$_4^+$ would inhibit both net NaCl absorption and apical K$^+$ recycling in TAL segments as a result of intracellular acidification. These predictions have not been tested directly; however, such actions of NH$_4^+$ on the TAL could contribute to the natriuretic effect of acidosis (8, 63), and to the effect of NH$_4^+$ to reduce urinary K$^+$ excretion (69).

NaHCO3 ABSORPTION   Although ammonium and HCO$_3^-$ absorption occur via different pathways and can be regulated independently (19, 21, 47, 71), interactions between their transport have been observed. Addition of 4 mM NH_4^+ to perfusion and bath solutions reduced net HCO_3^- absorption by 20% in rat MTALs, despite a reduction in pH_i that would be expected to stimulate luminal acidification (28). In addition, when the NH_4^+ concentration in perfusate and bath was increased from 4 to 20 mM, net HCO_3^- absorption was stimulated with no change in pH_i (28). The mechanisms of these effects have not been identified, although apical membrane NH_4^+-NH_3 recycling may contribute to the inhibition of HCO_3^- absorption seen with NH_4^+ addition (see above). These results illustrate, however, that NH_4^+ influences HCO_3^- transport through factors other than intracellular pH. Unraveling the mechanisms of interaction between NH_4^+ transport and the transport of ions such as H^+, HCO_3^-, K^+, Na^+, or Cl^- across cell membranes may be important for understanding the possible role of ammonium in pathogenic processes such as hepatic encephalopathy (59), renal cell growth and hypertrophy (50), and complement-activated tubulointerstitial injury (7).

ACKNOWLEDGMENTS

The important contribution of BA Watts, III to the work described in this article is gratefully acknowledged. I also thank Drs. L Reuss, M Knepper, and I Kurtz for helpful comments on the manuscript. Work in the author's laboratory was supported by National Institutes of Health Grants DK38217 and DK01745.

Literature Cited

1. Beach RE, Good DW. 1992. Effects of adenosine on ion transport in rat medullary thick ascending limb. *Am. J. Physiol.* 263(32):F482–87
2. Bengele HH, Schwartz JH, McNamara ER, Alexander EA. 1986. Chronic metabolic acidosis augments acidification along the inner medullary collecting duct. *Am. J. Physiol.* 250(19):F690–94
3. Bleich M, Schlatter E, Greger R. 1990. The luminal K^+ channel of the thick ascending limb of Henle's loop. *Pflügers Arch.* 415:449–60
4. Boron WF. 1983. Transport of H^+ and of ionic weak acids and bases. *J. Membr. Biol.* 72:1–16
5. Buerkert J, Martin D, Trigg D. 1983. Segmental analysis of the renal tubule in buffer production and net acid formation. *Am. J. Physiol.* 244(13):F442–54
6. Burg MB. 1982. Introduction: Background and development of micro-perfusion technique. *Kidney Int.* 22:417–24
7. Clark EC, Nath KA, Hostetter MK, Hostetter TH. 1991. Role of ammonia in progressive interstitial nephritis. *Am. J. Kidney Dis.* 17:15–19
8. Cogan MG, Mueller MR. 1983. Na therapy corrects increased urinary Na, K, Cl, and H_2O excretion induced by Cl. *Miner. Electrolyte Metab.* 9:132–36
9. DuBose TD Jr, Caflisch CR. 1988. Effect of selective aldosterone deficiency on acidification in nephron segments of the rat inner medulla. *J. Clin. Invest.* 82:1624–32
10. DuBose TD Jr., Good DW. 1992. Chronic hyperkalemia impairs ammonium transport and accumulation in the inner medulla of the rat. *J. Clin. Invest.* 90:1443–49
11. Flesser MF, Wall SM, Knepper MA. 1991. Permeabilities of rat collecting

duct segments to NH_3 and NH_4^+. *Am. J. Physiol.* 260(29):F264–72

12. Flessner MF, Wall SM, Knepper MA. 1992. Ammonium and bicarbonate transport in rat outer medullary collecting ducts. *Am. J. Physiol.* 262(31):F1–7

13. Friedman PA, Andreoli TE. 1982. CO_2-stimulated NaCl absorption in the mouse renal cortical thick ascending limb of Henle. *J. Gen. Physiol.* 80:683–711

14. Garg LC, Knepper MA, Burg MB. 1981. Mineralocorticoid effects on Na-K-ATPase in individual nephron segments. *Am. J. Physiol.* 240(9):F536–44

15. Garvin JL, Burg MB, Knepper MA. 1987. NH_3 and NH_4^+ transport by rabbit renal proximal straight tubules. *Am. J. Physiol.* 252(21):F232–39

16. Garvin JL, Burg MB, Knepper MA. 1988. Active NH_4^+ absorption by the thick ascending limb. *Am. J. Physiol.* 255(24):F57–65

17. Golchini K, Kurtz I. 1988. NH_3 permeation through the apical membrane of MDCK cells is via a lipid pathway. *Am. J. Physiol.* 255(24):F135–41

18. Good DW. 1985. Sodium-dependent bicarbonate absorption by cortical thick ascending limb of rat kidney. *Am. J. Physiol.* 248(17):F821–29

19. Good DW. 1987. Effects of potassium on ammonia transport by medullary thick ascending limb of the rat. *J. Clin. Invest.* 80:1358–65

20. Good DW. 1988. Active absorption of NH_4^+ by rat medullary thick ascending limb: Inhibition by potassium. *Am. J. Physiol.* 255(24):F78–87

21. Good DW. 1990. Inhibition of bicarbonate absorption by peptide hormones and cyclic adenosine monophosphate in rat medullary thick ascending limb. *J. Clin. Invest.* 85:1006–13

22. Good DW. 1990. Adaptation of HCO_3^- and NH_4^+ transport in rat MTAL: effects of chronic metabolic acidosis and Na^+ intake. *Am. J. Physiol.* 258(27):F1345–53

23. Good DW. 1990. Ammonium transport by the loop of Henle. *Miner. Electrolyte Metab.* 16:291–98

24. Good DW. 1993. The thick ascending limb as a site of renal bicarbonate reabsorption. *Sem. Nephrol.* 13:225–35

25. Good DW, Caflisch CR, DuBose TD Jr. 1987. Transepithelial ammonia concentration gradients in inner medulla of the rat. *Am. J. Physiol.* 252(21):F491–500

26. Good DW, Knepper MA. 1990. Mechanisms of ammonium excretion: role of the renal medulla. *Sem. Nephrol.* 10:166–73

27. Good DW, Knepper MA, Burg MB. 1984. Ammonia and bicarbonate transport by thick ascending limb of rat kidney. *Am. J. Physiol.* 247(16):F35–44

28. Good DW, Watts BA III. 1991. Regulation of HCO_3^- absorption by ammonium in rat medullary thick ascending limb. *J. Am. Soc. Nephrol.* 2:701

29. Greger R. 1981. Cation selectivity of the isolated perfused cortical thick ascending limb of Henle's loop of rabbit kidney. *Pflügers Arch.* 390:30–37

30. Greger R. 1985. Ion transport mechanisms in thick ascending limb of Henle's loop of mammalian nephron. *Physiol. Rev.* 65:760–97

31. Greger R, Schlatter E. 1983. Properties of the lumen membrane of the cortical thick ascending limb of Henle's loop of rabbit kidney. *Pflügers Arch.* 396:315–24

32. Guggino WB. 1991. Regulation of K^+ channels in the thick ascending limb. In *Nephrology*, ed. M Hafano, II:1685–97. Tokyo: Springer-Verlag

33. Hamm L. 1986. Ammonia transport in the rabbit medullary collecting tubule. *Kidney Int.* 29:367

34. Hamm LL, Trigg D, Martin D, Gillespie C, Buerkert J. 1985. Transport of ammonia in the rabbit cortical collecting tubule. *J. Clin. Invest.* 75:478–85

35. Hebert S. 1986. Hypertonic cell volume regulation in mouse thick limbs II. Na^+-H^+ and Cl^--HCO_3^- exchange in basolateral membranes. *Am. J. Physiol.* 250(19):C920–31

36. Hebert SC, Andreoli TE. 1984. Effects of antidiuretic hormone on cellular conductive pathways in mouse medullary thick ascending limbs of Henle: II. Determinants of the ADH-mediated increases in transepithelial voltage and in net Cl^- absorption. *J. Membr. Biol.* 80:221–33

37. Hebert SC, Reeves WB, Molony DA, Andreoli TE. 1987. The medullary thick ascending limb: Function and modulation of the single-effect multiplier. *Kidney Int.* 31:580–88

38. Hurst AM, Duplain M, Lapoint J-Y. 1992. Basolateral membrane potassium channels in rabbit cortical thick ascending limb. *Am. J. Physiol.* 263(32):F262–67

39. Hurst AM, Hunter M. 1992. Apical membrane potassium channels in frog diluting segment: stimulation by furo-

semide. *Am. J. Physiol.* 262(31):F606–14

40. Jacobs MH. 1940. Some aspects of cell permeability to weak electrolytes. *Cold Spring Harbor Symp. Quant. Biol.* 8:30–39

41. Kikeri D, Sun A, Zeidel ML, Hebert SC. 1989. Cell membranes impermeable to NH_3. *Nature* 339:478–80

42. Kikeri D, Sun A, Zeidel ML, Hebert SC. 1992. Cellular NH_4^+/K^+ transport pathways in mouse medullary thick limb of Henle. *J. Gen. Physiol.* 99:435–61

43. Kinne R, Kinne-Saffran E, Schutz H, Scholermann B. 1986. Ammonium transport in medullary thick ascending limb of rabbit kidney: involvement of the Na^+, K^+, Cl^--cotransporter. *J. Membr. Biol.* 94:279–84

44. Kinne R, Koenig B, Kinne-Saffran E, Scott DM, Zierold K. 1985. The use of membrane vesicles to study the NaCl/KCl cotransporter involved in active transepithelial chloride transport. *Pflügers Arch.* 405(Suppl. 1):S101–5

45. Kinsella JL, Aronson PS. 1981. Interaction of NH_4^+ and Li^+ with the renal microvillus membrane Na^+-H^+ exchanger. *Am. J. Physiol.* 241(10):C220–26

46. Klocke RA, Andersson KK, Rotman HH, Forster RE. 1972. Permeability of human erythrocytes to ammonia and weak acids. *Am. J. Physiol.* 222:1004–13

47. Knepper MA, Packer R, Good DW. 1989. Ammonium transport in the kidney. *Physiol. Rev.* 69:179–249

48. Kone BC, Madsen KM, Tisher CC. 1984. Ultrastructure of the thick ascending limb of Henle in the rat kidney. *Am. J. Anat.* 17:217–26

49. Krapf R. 1988. Basolateral membrane $H/OH/HCO_3$ transport in the rat cortical thick ascending limb. Evidence for an electrogenic Na/HCO_3 cotransporter in parallel with a Na/H antiporter. *J. Clin. Invest.* 82:234–41

50. Kurtz I. 1991. Role of ammonia in the induction of renal hypertrophy. *Am. J. Kidney Dis.* 17:650–53

51. Kurtz I, Balaban RS. 1986. Ammonium as a substrate for Na^+-K^+-ATPase in rabbit proximal tubules. *Am. J. Physiol.* 250(19):F497–502

52. Leviel F, Borensztein P, Houillier P, Paillard M, Bichara M. 1992. Electroneutral K^+/HCO_3^- cotransport in cells of medullary thick ascending limb of rat kidney. *J. Clin. Invest.* 90:869–78

53. Munich G, Dietl P, Oberleithner H. 1986. Chloride transport in the diluting segment of the K^+-adapted frog kidney: effect of amiloride and acidosis. *Pflügers Archiv.* 407(Suppl. 2):S60–65

54. Nagami GT. 1988. Luminal secretion of ammonia in the mouse proximal tubule perfused in vitro. *J. Clin. Invest.* 81:159–64

55. Oberleithner H, Kersting U, Hunter M. 1988. Cytoplasmic pH determines K^+ conductance in fused renal epithelial cells. *Proc. Natl. Acad. Sci. USA* 85:8345–49

56. Packer RK, Desai SS, Hornbuckle K, Knepper MA. 1991. Role of countercurrent multiplication in renal ammonium handling: Regulation of medullary ammonium accumulation. *J. Am. Soc. Nephrol.* 2:77–83

57. Pitts RF. 1973. Production and excretion of ammonia in relation to acid-base regulation. In *Handbook of Physiology, Section 8, Renal Physiology*, ed. J Orloff, RW Berliner, pp. 455–96. Washington, DC: Am. Physiol. Soc.

58. Preisig PA, Alpern RJ. 1990. Pathways for apical and basolateral membrane NH_3 and NH_4^+ movement in rat proximal tubule. *Am. J. Physiol.* 259(28):F587–93

59. Raabe W. 1990. Effects of NH_4^+ on the function of the CNS. In *Cirrhosis, Hepatic Encephalopathy, and Ammonium Toxicity*, ed. S Grisolia pp. 99–120. New York: Plenum

60. Roos A, Boron W. 1981. Intracellular pH. *Physiol. Rev.* 61:296–434

61. Rosario LM, Rojas E. 1986. Potassium channel selectivity in mouse pancreatic β cells. *Am. J. Physiol.* 250(19):C90–94

62. Sajo IM, Goldstein MB, Sonnenberg H, Stinebaugh BJ, Wilson DR, Halperin ML. 1981. Sites of ammonia addition to tubular fluid in rats with chronic metabolic acidosis. *Kidney Int.* 20:353–58

63. Sartorius OW, Roemmelt JC, Pitts RF. 1949. The renal regulation of acid-base balance in man. IV. The nature of the renal compensations in ammonium chloride acidosis. *J. Clin. Invest.* 28:423–39

64. Simon EE, Fry B, Hering-Smith K, Hamm LL. 1988. Ammonia loss from rat proximal tubule in vivo: effects of luminal pH and flow rate. *Am. J. Physiol.* 255(24):F861–67

65. Star RA, Kurtz I, Mejia R, Burg MB, Knepper MA. 1987. Disequilibrium pH and ammonia transport in isolated, perfused cortical collecting ducts. *Am. J. Physiol.* 253(22):F1232–42

66. Stern L, Backman KA, Hayslett JP.

1985. Effect of cortical-medullary gradient for ammonia on urinary excretion of ammonia. *Kidney Int.* 27:652–61

67. Stokes JB. 1982. Consequences of potassium recycling in the renal medulla. Effects on ion transport by the medullary thick ascending limb of Henle's loop. *J. Clin. Invest.* 70:219–29

68. Sun AM, Kikeri D, Hebert SC. 1992. Vasopressin regulates apical and basolateral Na$^+$/H$^+$ exchangers in mouse medullary thick ascending limbs. *Am. J. Physiol.* 262(31):F241–47

69. Tannen RL. 1992. Renal ammonia production and excretion. In *Handbook of Physiology. Section 8: Renal Physiology,* ed. EE Windhager, pp. 1017–59. New York: Oxford

70. Wang W, Sackin H, Giebisch G. 1992. Renal potassium channels and their regulation. *Annu. Rev. Physiol.* 54:81–96

71. Watts BA III, Good DW. 1991. Functional role of apical membrane Na$^+$/H$^+$ exchange in rat medullary thick ascending limb. *J. Am. Soc. Nephrol.* 2:715

72. Watts BA III, Good DW. 1991. Effects of NH$_4^+$ concentration on cell pH, NH$_4^+$ absorption, and HCO$_3^-$ absorption in rat medullary thick ascending limb. *Clin. Res.* 39:363A

73. Watts BA III, Good DW. 1992. Effects of intracellular pH and osmolality on apical Na$^+$/H$^+$ exchange in rat medullary thick ascending limb. *J. Am. Soc. Nephrol.* 3:790

74. Watts BA III, Good DW. 1994. Effects of ammonium on intracellular pH in rat medullary thick ascending limb: mechanisms of apical membrane NH$_4^+$ transport. *J. Gen. Physiol.* In press

75. Watts BA III, Good DW. 1993. Basolateral membrane Na$^+$/H$^+$ exchange enhances HCO$_3^-$ and NH$_4^+$ absorption in rat medullary thick ascending limb. *J. Am. Soc. Nephrol.* 3:849

76. Wingo CS. 1986. Effect of acidosis on chloride transport in the cortical thick ascending limb of Henle perfused in vitro. *J. Clin. Invest.* 78:1324–30

77. Winters CJ, Reeves WB, Andreoli TE. 1991. A survey of transport properties of the thick ascending limb. *Sem. Nephrol.* 11:236–47

Annu. Rev. Physiol. 1994. 56:649–69
Copyright © 1994 by Annual Reviews Inc. All rights reserved

NOVEL ASPECT OF ANGIOTENSIN RECEPTORS AND SIGNAL TRANSDUCTION IN THE KIDNEY

Janice G. Douglas and Ulrich Hopfer

Departments of Medicine and Physiology and Biophysics, Division of Endocrinology and Hypertension, Case Western Reserve University School of Medicine and University Hospitals of Cleveland, Cleveland, Ohio 44106–4982

KEY WORDS: losartan, AT_1, AT_2, adenyl cyclase, phospholipase, cytochrome P450, proximal tubular epithelium, glomerular mesangium

THE PHARMACOLOGICAL BASIS FOR PROPOSING NOVEL AII-RECEPTOR SUBTYPES

The involvement of the renin-angiotensin system in regulation of cardiovascular and renal function during health and disease remains under intense investigation. New and exciting developments have emerged in angiotensin receptor subtypes, signal transduction mechanisms, modulators such as GTP binding and regulatory proteins (G proteins), as well as multiple protein kinases and phosphatases. Developments in the receptor field have been facilitated by the discovery of a new class of selective angiotensin II (AII) receptor antagonists, the nonpeptide selective, imidazole derivatives originally reported by Furukawa et al (25). These compounds distinguish separate classes of AII receptors; some have the important property of being potent antihypertensive agents (AT_1 antagonists), while others define a class of receptors for AII that do not seem to be directly involved in blood pressure control (AT_2). This latter group appears to modulate potassium permeability and guanyl cyclase through protein tyrosine phosphorylation in neuronal

649

0066–4278/94/0315–0649$02.00

tissues (3, 74). These compounds have also permitted pharmacological classification of AII receptors into subtypes in a manner analogous to the adrenergic, histaminergic, muscarinic, and dopaminergic receptor systems in which receptor classification was achieved by the use of high-affinity-specific antagonists.

Several years ago, this laboratory proposed a new classification of receptors of the kidney cortex based on receptor affinity, differential binding, biological actions of AII and angiotensin III (AIII), antagonist analogues, regulatory mechanisms, and signal transduction pathways (17). We proposed classifications within the kidney as Types A and B, wherein the receptor of the glomerular mesangium classified as Type A was characterized by high affinity for AII and AIII, down-regulation with high ambient concentrations of AII, and signal transduction mediated primarily by phospholipase C-induced Ca^{2+} transients. By contrast, tubular epithelial receptors were classified as Type B and characterized by lower affinity for AIII, up-regulation by high levels of AII, and signal transduction mediated by adenyl cyclase and phospholipase A_2 (17, 19). This classification has been modified based on new observations.

Glomerular Mesangium

The emergence of a new class of AII antagonists, the nonpeptide imidazole derivatives, has provided additional tools for classification of receptors (25). Thus the classification of AT_1 and AT_2 subtypes emerged based on classical pharmacological criteria (7). One receptor subtype (AT_1), distinguished by low dose losartan sensitivity, has been cloned simultaneously from bovine adrenal cortex, rat vascular smooth muscle, rat kidney, and rabbit proximal tubule (8, 35, 51, 62). As predicted from the pharmacology of this receptor, it shares many characteristics with other G protein-coupled receptors (e.g. seven *trans*-membrane spanning domains) yet has a peptide recognition site unique to AII agonist and antagonist analogues, e.g. losartan and not other vasoactive agonists. The second receptor subtype, AT_2, is distinguished by high affinity for PD123319, low affinity for losartan, and a lack of G protein coupling. AT_2 sites are primarily localized in the CNS, adrenal medulla, uterus, and ovarian granulosa cells (7, 12, 13, 20, 57, 72, 80). Of interest is the fact that fetal kidney expresses AT_2 sites, but there is a change to the AT_1 phenotype at birth (30). While earlier observations in this laboratory suggested only a single class of AII receptors in glomerular mesangium (6) despite multiple signaling mechanisms (18, 40, 55, 56, 64), new insight has emerged. We recently published observations, using peptide and nonpeptide antagonists, that at least two pharmacologically distinct classes of receptors exist in the adult rat kidney: AT_{1A}, which is similar to the vascular AT_1 site, and AT_{1B}, which is not identical to either classical AT_1 or AT_2 subtypes (Figure 1) (24). The nomenclature that we have adapted for the renal receptor subtype described, herein, should not be confused with that used for the highly homologous cloned AT_{1B} receptors (rat genomic library, rat adrenal cDNA library, rat anterior pituitary cDNA library), with pharmacological properties identical to the rat vascular smooth muscle AT_1 (AT_{1A}) receptor (23, 34, 38). This novel AT_{1B} site is expressed in glomerular mesangium and tubular epithelium. The observations from mesangial cells, which formed the basis of the hypothesis, are summarized briefly. The inhibition of AII binding by losartan was biphasic and could be analyzed assuming two types of sites (Figure 2), with the most abundant site (AT_{1A}) showing high affinity for losartan (nM) and low affinity for PD123319 (μM) and CGP42112A (mM). Conversely, the least abundant site (AT_{1B}) displayed a high affinity for PD123319 (nM) and low affinity for losartan (μM) and CGP42112A (μM). Since AII showed a fivefold higher affinity for the AT_{1B} site, the proportion of this subtype decreased with increasing radioligand concentration from a maximum of 25% (Figure 2). However, the true proportion of this site as determined by the ratio of estimated B_{max} values was 14%. A recent report employing autoradiography described PD121918-inhibited AII binding to arterial smooth muscle and juxtaglomerular apparatus of rhesus monkey kidney (28). The site may well be analogous to the recently observed AT_{1B} site. AII and the heptapeptide agonist des Asp[1] AII (AIII) both showed a preference for the AT_{1B} site (PD-sensitive site) with K_ds of 0.25 and 0.2 nM, respectively, as compared to the 6 to 600-fold higher K_d for the AT_{1A} (losartan-sensitive) site. The fact that the potent AT_2 antagonist CGP42112A showed low affinity for the AT_{1B} site (μM), provides a further distinction from the classical AT_2 site where nM affinity is expressed (76).

The classical AT_2 site is not G protein-coupled, thus GTP analogues do not interfere with agonist binding (7). Unlike AT_2, AT_{1B} binding is inhibited dose-dependently by GTPγS. Furthermore, the inhibition curves for GTPγS differ between the AT_{1A} and AT_{1B} sites, as evidenced by significantly greater inhibition of specific [^{125}I]Sar[1] AII binding by 10 μM GTPγS after masking AT_{1B} sites with 0.5 μM PD123319 (40$\pm$9.5%) than after masking AT_{1A} sites with 0.1 μM losartan (19$\pm$9%; $P<0.05$ by paired t-test). The K_i for GTPγS was fourfold higher for the AT_{1B} sites as compared to the AT_{1A} sites. Of interest is the fact that pertussis toxin interferes with binding to both sites (24). No convincing evidence is available to determine whether the fourfold differences in K_i is consistent with different G proteins coupling to these receptor subtypes.

Proximal Tubular Epithelium

The proximal tubule represents an important location where low concentrations of AII regulate salt and water transport. We were the first laboratory to document that AII receptors were present on both the apical and basolateral

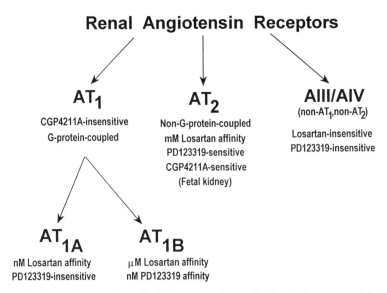

Figure 1 Proposed nomenclature for AII receptor subtypes (7). Renal subtypes are subdivided further into AT_{1A} and AT_{1B} (24). Both renal subtypes are coupled to the same signal transduction pathways (14, 45, 86), but not in epithelial cell lines derived from opossum kidney (36a).

membranes (4, 5), unlike other receptors that were exclusively expressed on basolateral membranes (BLM), e.g. PTH. One rabbit proximal tubular AII receptor subtype has been confirmed as an isoreceptor of the cloned vascular receptor (8). Recent studies from this laboratory aimed at evaluating receptor subtype distribution in basolateral membranes suggest a higher proportion of AT_{1B} sites (40%) than mesangial cells (14). Similar criteria were used to pharmacologically classify this site as for mesangial cells, which include high affinity for PD123319, but not for CGP42112A. In addition, the losartan affinity for the two basolateral membrane sites is similar to mesangial cells (7.9 and 650 nM, respectively).

Of additional interest is the observation that recent measurements of AIII/AIV binding (des-Asp^{1}AII/des Asp^1,Arg^{2}AII) and cytosolic Ca determinations in proximal tubular opossum kidney cell line (OK7A) and rabbit brush border membranes suggest the existence of non-AT$_1$, non-AT$_2$ receptors (21, 22). Assessment of direct AII fragment binding grew out of several observations: (a) AII binding to brush border was very low affinity (μM); and (b) AII was degraded within minutes despite abundant protease inhibitors and a plateau in binding between 30–60 min. This suggested that smaller peptide fragments may be binding to specific receptors. The high affinity binding of AIV and AIII to OK7A cells and rabbit brush border membranes

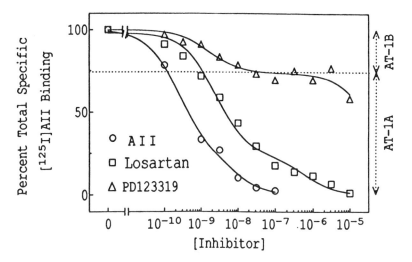

Figure 2 Dose-dependent inhibition of $[^{125}I]AII$ binding to rat mesangial cell membranes by nonpeptide antagonists. Low concentrations of losartan inhibited ~80% of binding (K_i = 8 μM), while higher concentrations inhibited ~20% of binding (K_i = 0.65 μM). Low concentrations of PD123319 inhibited ~20% of binding (K_i = 2.2 nM). The high affinity losartan site is classified as AT$_{1A}$, while the high affinity PD123319 site is classified as AT$_{1B}$. From Ernsberger et al (24) with permission.

is not competed for by losartan or PD123319 (21, 22). These observations support the existence of a novel non-AT$_1$, non-AT$_2$ site specific for AII fragments (AIII/AIV).

These observations allow us to draw the following conclusions: (*a*) AII receptors of the AT$_{1A}$ subtype and a novel subtype, AT$_{1B}$, are present in glomerular mesangium and proximal tubular epithelial cells; (*b*) binding at both sites is inhibited by GTPγS, although type AT$_{1A}$ appears more sensitive; (*c*) pertussis toxin interferes with binding to both sites; and (*d*) a non-AT$_1$, non-AT$_2$ site is expressed in proximal tubule specific for AII fragments (AIII/AIV). Our AT$_{1B}$ subtype (Douglas B) differs pharmacologically from the classical AT$_2$ by virtue of G protein interaction, μM as opposed to nM affinity for the selective antagonist CGP42112A, and μM as opposed to mM K_i for losartan. These represent important new findings that have significant implications for analysis of AII binding and G protein interactions within the kidney.

AII-RECEPTOR/G PROTEIN INTERACTIONS

The multiplicity of G proteins raises important questions as to tissue and cellular distribution, functional consequences of the heterogeneity and importance to the pathophysiology of cardiovascular and renal dysfunction. We evaluated the patterns at the level of expression of these proteins in glomerular mesangium and mesenteric vasculature and have begun to investigate the roles in coupling to AII receptors and various signal transduction pathways.

Studies from this and other laboratories have documented that modest elevation in AII levels via low dose infusion produces a sustained blood pressure elevation with a delayed onset and facilitates reductions in glomerular capillary ultrafiltration coefficient (2, 15, 18). We have examined the effects of short-term AII infusion as a model to evaluate changes at the cellular-molecular level preceding the development of frank hypertension. This is in distinct contrast to the desensitization that accompanies exposure to high doses of AII and is analogous in many respects to acute induction of high affinity adrenergic receptor sites by epinephrine (77). Accompanying low dose AII infusion in vivo, we observed in vitro that the sensitivity and magnitude of AII-induced decrements in glomerular surface area was enhanced (18). This action is mediated by mesangial cell contraction and provides an important physiological correlate to observations on receptor-effector coupling. In addition, there was a moderate increase (33%) in binding affinity and a marked enhancement of AII-induced decrements in adenyl cyclase. We hypothesized that because G proteins regulate binding affinity as well as effector coupling, an alteration in the amount or coupling efficiency of G proteins may have occurred as a consequence of AII-infusion in vivo and might be responsible for the enhanced signal transduction. We focused on resistance vessels and glomerular mesangium. During analysis of the molecular mechanism, we identified a 168 and 465% increase in pertussis toxin-catalyzed ADP-ribosylation of the 40–41 kd α-subunits of glomerular and mesenteric vascular membranes, respectively. On immunoblotting with peptide-specific antisera, we observed regulation of several G_i isoforms; α_{i2} increased 250%, α_{i3} increased 35%, and α_{i1} decreased 53%. Thus the induction of two G_i isoforms may have provided the molecular mechanism (at least in part) that accounted for enhanced and/or sustained AII-induced signal transduction and biological responses reported from this and other laboratories during administration of low doses of AII, sodium depletion, and in a nephrotoxic model (18, 58, 67, 68, 81). Of interest is the fact that the decrease in α_{i1} in this model suggests that differential regulation of the proportions of G protein, rather than an increase in overall levels of G protein, may have been responsible for enhanced signal transduction. This implies that G protein subtypes may differ in their coupling efficiency. Other studies have documented increases or decreases in the mass of G proteins with insulin, IGF-1, glucocorticoids, and thyroid hormone that account for modulation in signaling pathways primarily through the adenyl cyclase system (26, 29, 41, 42, 60, 61). However, none has reported differential regulation of G_i isoforms (α_{i1}, α_{i2}, and α_{i3}) as was observed following short-term exposure to AII in vivo. This observation suggests that all three G_is may be coupled to one or more AII receptor subtypes through one or multiple signaling pathways. To date, the isoforms appear to have overlapping biological effects because all three α_i proteins have similar efficacy to open atrial K^+ channels when employed in their persistently activated forms (85). However, one difference that has emerged in their function is the fact that α_{i2} binds GTPγS many times faster than α_{i1} and α_{i3} and, similarly, α_{i2} displays the fastest rate of GDP release (10). Since agonist G protein interaction involves GDP release and GTP binding to activate effector function, these data suggest that the relative proportion of G_{i2} as compared to G_{i1} and 3 has important implications for facilitation of agonist-mediated signal transduction. Furthermore, the large increase in G_{i2} in this model of AII-induced hypertension may facilitate the rate and magnitude of signal transduction in this and other models of hypertension. These observations on isoform regulation suggest that the AII receptor of glomerular mesangium may be linked to all three G_i isoforms, but that AII can discriminate between the G protein subtypes despite sequence homology of 87–95%. Another recent study demonstrated a link between α_{i2} and the AII receptor of hepatocytes (9). In this latter study, AII elicited a time- and dose-dependent increase in the phosphorylation of α_{i2} that coincided with the loss of ability of Gpp[NH]p to inhibit forskolin-stimulated adenyl cyclase activity. Despite the fact that the exact mechanism of agonist-mediated decrements in adenyl cyclase has not been resolved (e.g. whether $\beta\gamma$ subunit mediates decrements in adenyl cyclase vs a direct mediation through α_i analogous to α_s-mediated stimulation of adenyl cyclase), several recent studies employing other receptor systems have linked α_{i2} to inhibition of adenyl cyclase (47, 48). In addition, mutations in α_{i2} that convert it to a dominantly acting gene (gip 2) display constitutive inhibition of cAMP accumulation in transfected cells (82). Thus it seems likely that the observed increase in α_{i2} in vasoactive tissues accompanying AII infusion in vivo in rats may mediate the enhanced inhibition of cAMP production and mesangial cell contraction reported previously (18). The significance of the decrease in α_{i1} and the modest increase in α_{i3} for AII-induced signal transduction remains to be determined.

Toxin catalyzed ribosylation of G proteins frequently has been used to provide supporting evidence for G protein interaction with receptor systems. AII-interactions are coupled to various signal transduction pathways through pertussis toxin-sensitive and -insensitive G proteins (18, 27, 32, 39, 40, 55, 56, 64, 84). The major signal transduction pathway for AII in a variety of sites is phospholipase C, not adenyl cyclase. While agonist-mediated decrements in adenyl cyclase are classically pertussis toxin-sensitive, phos- pholipase C-induced signaling can be either pertussis toxin-sensitive or -insensitive, thereby evoking the involvement of two G proteins. The same holds for AII in glomerular mesangium. One such G protein may represent a member(s) of the newly described G_q family that lacks the cysteine four amino acids from the carboxy terminus, thereby rendering it insensitive to pertussis toxin (73). The ability of G_q to function in a reconstituted system and to activate partially purified phospholipase C from bovine brain has recently been described (70). Specifically which G protein mediates pertussis toxin-sensitive phospholipase C activation remains to be determined.

Pertussis toxin-catalyzed ADP ribosylation has also been employed to investigate the involvement of G proteins in AII-induced stimulation of PLA_2 in renal epithelial cells. In this location, AII effects on sodium transport have been linked (at least in part) to PLA_2 activation (17, 19, 50). Employing brush border membrane vesicles (BBMV), Morduchowicz et al demonstrated a temporal and dose-dependent correlation between AII stimulation of PLA_2 and activation of the Na^+/H^+ antiporter system, effects that are potentiated by GTP analogues (50). By contrast, inhibition of PLA_2 by pretreatment with mellitin abrogates AII's effects on arachidonic acid release and Na^+ uptake in BBMV. In an analogous manner, pertussis toxin pretreatment of BBMV abolishes AII-induced arachidonic acid release and Na^+ transport, which implicates a G protein in this signaling and transport pathway. Specifically, which G protein is involved has as yet to be determined. Moreover, controversy exists as to which component of the heterotrimeric G protein mediates PLA_2-induced signaling (α vs $\beta\gamma$) (1).

We have observed differential phenotypic regulation of the levels of three G_i isoforms of renal vasculature in a model of AII-induced hypertension. This observation combined with other evidence from the literature suggests that there may be at least five G proteins coupled to the AII receptors of renal vasculature. Furthermore, G_is and other pertussis toxin-sensitive G proteins have also been implicated in AII-induced signaling in proximal tubule epithelium as modulators of Na^+/H^+ exchange.

SIGNAL TRANSDUCTION PATHWAYS

Adenyl Cyclase

Adenyl cyclase is an important mediator of AII-induced effects on proximal tubular transport and glomerular mesangial vasoreactivity (17–19). This appears to be unique to the kidney because phosphoinositide-specific phospholipase C (PLC) is the major signaling system in other AII target tissues.

AII inhibits adenyl cyclase by activating an inhibitory G protein (one of the G_i-isoforms, probably α_{i2}) in both renal locations. In epithelial cells, adenyl cyclase is localized to the basolateral membrane (87) as AII and other agonists fail to regulate brush border membrane cAMP (50, 87). There is an inverse relationship between cAMP and Na^+ and bicarbonate reabsorption (43). It has been presumed that decrements in cAMP decrease the activity of protein kinase A and in turn decrease phosphorylation of the Na^+/H^+ exchanger on the luminal cell surface, thereby facilitating Na and bicarbonate reabsorption (Figure 3). Despite the fact that earlier studies suggested that only μM concentrations of AII decrease adenyl cyclase activity in the kidney (75, 83), more recent studies document that pM concentrations of AII are effective (17, 19, 59). For example, Figure 4 illustrates that the EC_{50} for AII-induced decreases in cAMP is 10^{-11} in proximal tubular cells in tissue culture. Furthermore, pertussis toxin that ADP-ribosylates G_is completely abolishes AII-induced reductions in cAMP levels in epithelial cells (17, 19, 59). Thus there is general agreement that an AII-induced decline in adenyl cyclase activity is the primary signaling mechanism responsible for enhancing epithelial cell salt reabsorption through stimulation of the Na^+/H^+ exchanger on the luminal cell surface.

Under usual circumstances, AII-induced decreases in adenyl cyclase are relatively ineffective in modulating glomerular hemodynamics. However, in a rat model of AII-induced hypertension, nM concentrations of AII inhibit cAMP (18). Such an action would potentiate vasoconstrictor responses and thus amplify biological responses mediated through phosphoinositide-specific PLC. As reviewed above, this augmented sensitivity appears to be mediated by enhanced signaling facilitated by induction of several G_i-isoforms linked to adenyl cyclase (67, 73). This enhanced signaling correlates with potentiated effects on AII-induced decrements in glomerular surface area in vitro (18).

Recent studies have focused on gaining a better understanding of which AII receptor mediates signal transduction through the adenyl cyclase system since two G protein-coupled receptors have been characterized in glomerular mesangium (Figure 1) (24). Employing glomerular mesangial cells in tissue culture, AII inhibits adenyl cyclase in a dose-dependent manner with an EC_{50} of 35 nM and a maximal response of 44% inhibition (86). Both losartan and PD123319 antagonized AII-induced decrements in adenyl cyclase consistent with the fact that there are two G protein-coupled AII receptor subtypes in the kidney (Table 1). Thus this signal transduction pathway does not discriminate between these receptor subtypes in mesangial cells. In contrast, studies with opossum kidney cells (strains OK-VD and OK-RR) indicate that different receptors are associated with different signaling pathways and functions: PD123319-sensitivity of the AII receptor

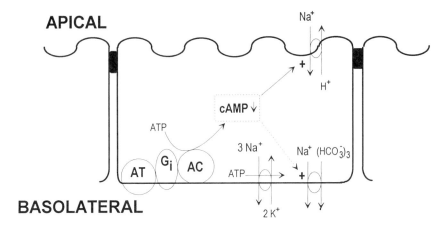

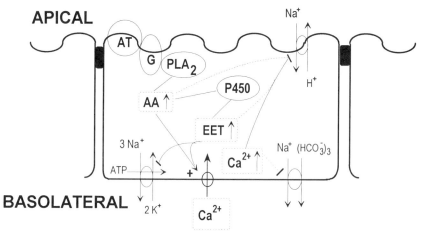

Figure 3   Hypothetical models whereby AII regulates sodium transport in proximal tubular epithelial cells. Solid connections indicate established biochemical pathways; broken ones are hypothetical. The symbols + and indicate stimulation and inhibition, respectively. (*top*) Stimulatory effects on sodium and bicarbonate reabsorption. AII is one of the regulators of cAMP levels. High-affinity AT receptors at the basolateral plasma membrane inhibit adenyl cyclase (AC) through a pertussis-sensitive G_i protein. The resulting decrease in cAMP levels releases the inhibition of the luminal Na^+/H^+ exchanger, which is caused by other hormones, and stimulates basolateral Na^+-bicarbonate co-transport, Na^+-$(HCO_3^-)_3$. (*bottom*) Inhibitory effects on sodium reabsorption. Luminal AT receptors stimulate the release of arachidonic acid (AA) by activation of a phospholipase A_2 (PLA2), which is mediated by a G protein. The AA is predominantly metabolized by a cytochrome P450 epoxygenase (P450) to epoxy-eicosa-trienoic acids (EET). EET and AA directly or indirectly stimulate elevated cytosolic Ca^{2+} levels, in large part through activation of voltage-sensitive Ca^{2+} channels in the plasma membrane. The elevated cytosolic Ca^{2+} and, possibly, AA and EET inhibit the luminal Na^+/H^+ exchanger. EET may also inhibit the Na,K-ATPase ($3Na^+/2K^+$) in the basolateral plasma membrane (adapted from Romero et al, 59).

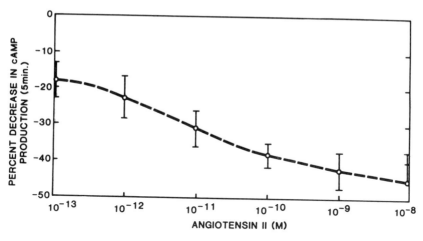

Figure 4   Dose-dependent inhibition of adenyl cyclase in rabbit proximal tubular epithelia cells as per cent inhibition below basal levels. Cells were pretreated with isobutylmethyl xanthine (250 μM) and intracellular cAMP measured by RIA (n = 5 experiments).

(AT_{1B}) is associated with inhibition of adenyl cyclase through a pertussis toxin-sensitive G_i protein, while the losartan-sensitive receptor (AT_{1A}) inhibits Na^+/H^+ exchange through a different pathway that does not involve cAMP (36a).

Table 1

	AII	Losartan	PD123319	CG42112A
Receptor binding:				
AT_{1A} n = 6	8.55 ± 0.10[a]	8.10 ± 0.08[a]	4.67 ± 0.15[a]	3.78 ± 0.1[a]
AT_{1B} n = 6	9.40 ± 0.09[b]	5.93 ± 0.27[b]	8.80 ± 0.19[b]	5.56 ± 0.24[b]
AT_2 n = 8 (reference 76)	8.35 ± 0.06[a]	3.52 ± 0.05[c]	6.40 ± 0.10[a]	9.22 ± 0.05[c]
Functional responses:				
PLC-mediated				
$[Ca^{2+}]_i$ mobilization n = 10	8.87 ± 0.16[a]	10.2 ± 0.3[d]	10.7 ± 0.9[c]	9.01 ± 0.41[c]
Adenyl cyclase inhibition n = 3	7.45 ± 0.08[c]	6.30 ± 0.15[b]	5.92 ± 0.12[a]	5.24 ± 0.11[b]

Values are the negative log of either the ED_{50} or K_d (for AII) or the IC_{50} (for losartan, PD123319, or CGP42112A) ± the standard error of the estimate. The n in the left column refers to the number of independent experiments. Binding affinities at the AT_{1A} or AT_{1B} subtypes were determined by iterative nonlinear curve-fitting with the LIGAND program with derivation of IC_{50} values by using the Cheng-Prusoff equation as described elsewhere (49). ED_{50} and IC_{50} values for functional assays were estimated by iterative curve-fitting to a logistic equation using InPlot (GraphPAD software, San Diego, CA). Affinity and efficacy estimates were compared by analysis of variance with post-hoc Bonferroni tests to determine the significance of individual comparisons (InStat, GraphPAD software). Values with differing superscripts in a vertical column are significantly different. From Madhun et al (45) with permission.

In summary, many observations implicate adenyl cyclase as an important mediator of AII effects on glomerular hemodynamics and ion transport in the kidney. Furthermore, insight into enhanced AII-mediated signal transduction in pathophysiological models is provided.

Phospholipase A₂ (PLA₂)

Eicosanoid biosynthesis plays an important role in modulating ion transport in the kidney and has been implicated as a mediator of AII-induced natriuresis that occurs in the nM to μM range of the peptide. The primary mediators of arachidonic acid release are phosphoinositide-specific PLC and PLA_2. Several studies point to a lack of coupling of epithelial cell AII receptor to PLC (17, 19, 50, 66, 79), thus a role for PLA_2 has been sought. This latter pathway results in release of arachidonic acid and lysophospholipid from a variety of membrane phospholipids (e.g. phosphatidylycholine and phosphatidylethanolamine). The EC_{50} for AII-stimulated PLA_2 is nM, consistent with a physiologically significant effect on ion transport (19, 50, 59). An interesting aspect of arachidonic acid metabolism in proximal tubular epithelium is that it occurs via cytochrome P450-dependent pathways, namely epoxygenase and ω-hydroxylase, as cyclooxygenase and lipoxygenase are not present in this location (36, 69). Eicosanoid products of the cytochrome P450 pathway appear to have a variety of biological actions in the kidney, namely regulation of voltage-sensitive Ca channels, inhibition of Na-K-ATPase, inhibition of renin release, and stimulation of mitogenesis (19, 46, 31, 33, 59, 65). Furthermore, they have been implicated in the pathophysiology of hypertension in SHR (53). While AII stimulates metabolism of arachidonic acid to one or more epoxides (7, 19, 54, 59), different agonists, epidermal growth factor (EGF) and PTH, stimulate product formation to an ω-hydroxylase product(s) in the same cells (54). These observations suggest that different phospholipases may be activated, thereby, channeling arachidonic acid through different pathways for oxidation in the same cell type (epoxygenase vs ω-hydroxylase). Product formation is inhibited by ketoconazole, an inhibitor of cytochrome P450-dependent epoxygenases and ω-hydroxylases, also consistent with oxidation of arachidonic acid by these NADPH-dependent pathways. A further link between epithelial AII receptors and this pathway has been provided by studies of $[Ca^{2+}]_i$ mobilization. Since 5,6-EET (epoxy-eicosa-trienoic acid) has been documented to induce $[Ca^{2+}]_i$ mobilization in pituitary cells (71), we reasoned that AII-induced $[Ca^{2+}]_i$ mobilization in epithelial cells might be mediated by such a mechanism. We observed that AII-induced $[Ca^{2+}]_i$ mobilization is augmented by pretreatment of epithelial cells with arachidonic acid and abrogated by ketoconazole (Figure 5) (46). Moreover, 5,6-EET mimics AII-induced $[Ca^{2+}]_i$ mobilization and the responses to both AII and 5,6-EET

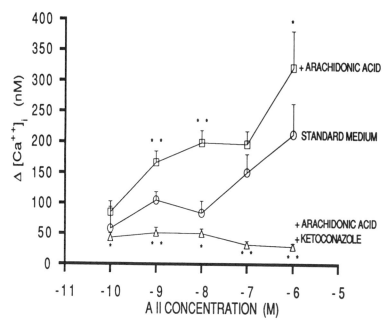

Figure 5 Dose-response relationship of angiotensin II (AII) and $[Ca^{2+}]_i$. $[Ca^{2+}]_i$ was measured first in the absence and then in presence of AII in the perfusion medium at the indicated concentrations. Peak $[Ca^{2+}]_i$ minus basal $[Ca^{2+}]_i$ was averaged for cells incubated in standard medium (*circles*); cells incubated in standard medium plus 3 µM arachidonate for 3 hr (*squares*); cells incubated in standard medium plus 100 µM ketoconazole and 3 µM arachidonate for 3 hr (*triangles*). Data are given as mean ±SEM. *P<0.05, **P<0.005, relative to cells grown in standard medium alone at the same AII concentration. From Madhun et al (46) with permission.

are abolished by dihydropyridine-sensitive Ca channel blockers (Figure 6). The hypothetical model that links this signaling pathway to ion transport is illustrated in Figure 3b.

We have also evaluated the effect of the newer AII antagonists to compete for AII-induced $[Ca^{2+}]_i$ mobilization in epithelial cells. The rank order of potency for inhibition of AII-induced $[Ca^{2+}]_i$ mobilization was PD123319 > losartan > CGP42112A (44). These observations provide additional support for the existence of multiple receptor subtypes in kidney epithelial cells and underscore the functional significance of both receptor subtypes (AT_{1A} and AT_{1B}) in epithelial cells.

Phospholipase C (PLC)

In the majority of AII target tissues, PLC-induced $[Ca^{2+}]_i$ mobilization, diacylglycerol release, and activation of protein kinase C represent the most

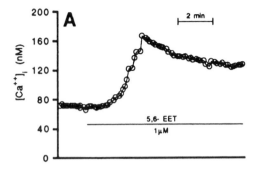

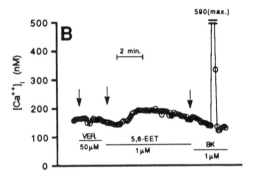

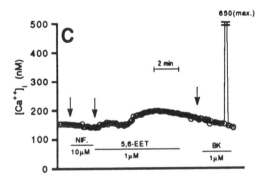

Figure 6   Attenuation of 5,6-EET-induced $[Ca^{2+}]_i$ increases by the Ca channel blockers nifedipine (NIF) and verapamil (VER). $[Ca^{2+}]_i$ was measured as in Figure 5. Typical cell responses to 5,6-EET are shown (*A*), and in the presence of 50 μM verapamil (*B*), or 10 μM nifedipine (*C*). Horizontal bars indicate additions to the perfusion medium. Cells were perfused with the blockers for 2 min as indicated by the horizontal bars, and then with 1 μM 5,6-EET for an additional 6 min. Subsequently, cells were challenged with 1 μM bradykinin (BK) for release of Ca from intracellular IP3-sensitive stores. From Madhun et al (46) with permission.

important mediators of biological responses (55, 64). Within the kidney, there is no question of the importance of this pathway as a modulator of glomerular hemodynamics; however, there is no sound evidence linking this pathway to AII-mediated effects on ion transport (17, 19, 50, 66, 79) despite agreement that AII induces Ca mobilization (11, 16, 37, 52, 79). AII-induced increments in $[Ca^{2+}]_i$ in transporting epithelium appear to be secondary to activation of PLA_2 and arachidonic acid release (see above) rather than through activation of phosphoinositide-specific PLC. One study that recently readdressed this question demonstrated only a small increase in PLC activity (10–25%) and no dose-dependent effect of AII (63). Typically, agonists that are directly linked to PLC induce at least a twofold increase in enzyme activity. Small increments are likely from agonist-mediated influx of Ca and secondary stimulation of PLC since this enzyme is responsive to changes in $[Ca^{2+}]_i$. Moreover, it could explain why 8-(N,N-diethylamino)-octyl-3,4,5-trimethoxybenzoate (TMB-8), a blocker of $[Ca^{2+}]_i$ mobilization, abolished AII's effect on transport in this latter study and in a study by Wang & Chan (63, 78). Thus a role for changes in $[Ca^{2+}]_i$, but not PLC activation, has been reaffirmed as a mediator of proximal tubular transport responses to AII.

Recent attention has focused on which AII receptor subtype mediates mesangial cell $[Ca^{2+}]_i$ mobilization. AII increases mesangial $[Ca^{2+}]_i$ in a dose-dependent manner with an EC_{50} of 1.33 nM and a maximum response at 1 μM of 106 ±6 nM (n = 25) above basal $[Ca^{2+}]_i$. For AII itself there is excellent agreement between the ED_{50} value for $[Ca^{2+}]_i$ mobilization and the binding affinity for either AT_{1A} or AT_{1B} sites (Table 1) (45). Comparing antagonist IC_{50} values, the relative order of potency was PD123319 > losartan > CGP42112A. Collectively, the pIC_{50}s for inhibition of calcium mobilization were lower than the pIC_{50}s for either of the receptor subtypes, consistent with the presence of spare receptors. The best agreement for losartan was with the AT_{1A} subtype, while the best agreement for PD123319 was with the AT_{1B} subtype.

CGP42112A potency in reversing calcium responses most closely matched binding affinity at classical AT_2 receptors (76), even though this subtype was not detected in rat mesangial cells (Table 1). The sensitivity of CGP42112A competition for $[Ca^{2+}]_i$ mobilization was at least three log orders greater than its pIC_{50} for binding to either AT_{1A} or AT_{1B}. Thus it appears possible that AT_{1A}, AT_{1B}, and perhaps even AT_2 receptor subtypes may participate in calcium signaling.

BIOLOGICAL RESPONSES

Ion Transport

The ultimate goal in such studies as described herein is to relate the information gained on AII-mediated signaling to important physiological

Table 2 Apical-to-basal sodium flux in primary proximal tubular cells (J_{Na})

Stimulus	Side of Application	% Change J_{Na}[2] mean ± SEM	(n)
Cells without pretreatment			
Forskolin (100 μM)	A	-12.7 ± 3.3	(11)
AII (10 pM)	BL	$+27.3 \pm 6.0$	(191)
AII (50 nM)	A	-13.0 ± 3.2	(13)
5,6-EET (2 μM)	A	-10.7 ± 4.2	(10)
Ketoconazole (100 μM) pretreatment			
AII (50 nM)	A	-7.8 ± 2.0	(7)
5,6-EET (2 μM)	A	-18.7 ± 3.3	(10)
Inhibitor studies[1]			
AII (10 pM)	BL	$+41.9 \pm 16.0$[3]	(16)
+ EIPA (10 μM)	A	$+12.4 \pm 9.6$	(16)
AII (10 pM)	BL	$+76.8 \pm 33.9$[4]	(5)
+P.tox. (.1 μg/ml)	BL	$+18.8 \pm 11.0$	(5)

[1]Each monolayer was treated first with AII alone and on a subsequent day treated with EIPA or pertussis toxin and rechallenged with AII. [2]Change relative to control period directly preceding exposure to hormones or other agents. [3]Apical (A), basolateral (BL0, epoxy-eicosa-trienoic acid (EET), ethyl-isopropyl-amiloride (EIPA), Pertussis toxin (P.tox) significantly different at P < 0.01 from AII following EIPA. [4]Significantly different at P < 0.05 from AII following pertussis toxin (adapted from 58a).

responses. We have employed rabbit proximal tubular epithelial cells, maintained short-term in tissue culture on porous support, to assess unidirectional apical-to-basolateral Na^+ flux (J_{Na}) to integrate signaling and transport. A role for cAMP in modulation of Na transport has been documented by demonstrating that forskolin decreases J_{Na} by 13% (Table 2). Low doses of AII (pM) that inhibit adenyl cyclase have the opposite effect and increase J_{Na} by 27%. In support of a role for G_i-mediated signal transduction, pertussis toxin significantly attenuates this response from a 77% change in J_{Na} to 19% in paired experiments. A number of studies have implicated cAMP-induced increases or decreases in protein kinase A as the relevant modulator of Na^+/H^+ exchange (17, 43). Thus AII-induced reductions in cAMP levels would relieve this inhibition (Figure 3a). Ethylisopropyl amiloride (ElPA), which inhibits luminal Na^+/H^+ exchange, blocks AII-mediated Na^+ reabsorption (J_{Na}) in support of this hypothesis (Table 2). A number of laboratories have documented that nM and higher concentrations of AII inhibit Na^+ reabsorption in proximal tubular epithelial cells. Of interest is the fact that while PTH inhibits Na reabsorption through stimulation of adenyl cyclase, this signaling pathway does not mediate the natriuretic response to AII. AII (50 nM) inhibits J_{Na} to the same degree as forskolin, an effect that is mimicked by 5,6-EET. As one would predict, ketoconazole inhibits the ability of nM AII to decrease J_{Na}, with a decrease in J_{Na} to -7.8% below basal from -13% with AII alone. Thus dual signaling through G_i-mediated adenyl cyclase inhibition and stimulation of phospholipase A_2 account for AII-induced Na^+ reabsorption and natriuresis, respectively.

This article has reviewed the novel aspects of AII receptor subtypes, signal transduction, and their implications for regulation of renal hemodynamics and ion transport. Of particular interest is the novel G protein-coupled PD123319-sensitive receptor subtype (AT_{1B}) and the possibility of a specific AIII/AIV receptor(s) that has not been described in other locations than the kidney. In addition, G protein isoforms, adenyl cyclase, and the cytochrome P450 system as modulators of glomerular hemodynamics and ion transport in physiological and pathophysiological states are of significant interest.

ACKNOWLEDGMENTS

These studies were supported by the following grants: National Institutes of Health HL22990 and HL41618.

Literature Cited

1. Axelrod J. 1990. Receptor-mediated activation of phospholipase A_2 and arachidonic acid release in signal transduction. *Biochem. Soc. Trans.* 18:503–07

2. Blantz RC, Pelayo JC, Tucker BJ. 1976. AII effects upon the glomerular microcirculation and ultrafiltration coefficient of the rat. *J. Clin. Invest.* 57:419–34

3. Bottari SP, King IN, Reichlin S, Dahlstroem I, Lydon N, de Gasparo M. 1992. The angiotensin AT_2 receptor stimulates protein tyrosine phosphatase activity and mediates inhibition of particulate guanylate cyclase. *Biochem. Biophys. Res. Commun.* 183:206–11

4. Brown GP, Douglas JG. 1982. Angiotensin II binding sites on isolated rat renal brush border membranes. *Endocrinology* 111:1830–36

5. Brown GP, Douglas JG. 1983. Angiotensin-II binding sites in rat and primate isolated renal tubular basolateral membranes. *Endocrinology* 112:2007–14

6. Brown G, Douglas JG, Krontiris-Litowitz J. 1980. Properties of angiotensin II receptors of isolated rat glomeruli: factors influencing binding affinity and comparative binding of angiotensin analogs. *Endocrinology* 106:1923–29

7. Bumpus FM, Catt KJ, Chiu AT, de Gasparo M, Goodfriend T, et al. 1991. Nomenclature for angiotensin receptors: a report of the nomenclature committee. *Council High Blood Pressure Res. Hypertension* 17:720–21

8. Burns KD, Inagami T, Harris RC. 1993. Cloning of a rabbit kidney cortex AT_1 angiotensin II receptor that is present in proximal tubule epithelium. *Am. J. Physiol.* 264:F645–54

9. Bushfield M, Murphy GJ, Lavan BE, Parker PJ, Hruby VJ, et al. 1990. Hormonal regulation of G_i2 α-subunit phosphorylation in intact hepatocytes. *Biochem. J.* 268:449–57

10. Carty DJ, Padrell E, Codina J, Birnbaumer L, Hildebrandt JD, Iyengar R. 1990. Distinct guanine nucleotide binding and release properties of the three G_i proteins. *J. Biol. Chem.* 265:6268–73

11. Chan YL, Chatsudtripone V, Wang T. 1988. Angiotensin receptor mediated regulation of transport in the rat proximal tubule. In *Membrane Biophysics III. Biological Transport*, ed. MA

Dinno, WM Armstrong, pp. 149–60. New York: Liss

12. Chiu AT, Herblin WF, McCall DE, Ardecky RJ, Carini DJ, et al. 1989. Identification of angiotensin II receptor subtypes. *Biochem. Biophys. Res. Comm.* 165:196–203

13. Cook VI, Wright JW, Wright SA, Harding JW. 1990. Comparison of angiotensin metabolism by brain membranes from SHR and WKY rats. *Brain Res.* 529:320–23

14. Damon TH, Ernsberger P, Douglas JG. 1992. Angiotensin II (AII) receptor subtypes in renal cells: proposed AT_{1A} and AT_{1B} receptors. *FASEB J.* 6:A1013 (Abstr.)

15. Diz D, Baer PG, Nasjletti A. 1983. Angiotensin II-induced hypertension in the rat. Effects on the plasma concentration, renal excretion, and tissue release of prostaglandins. *J. Clin. Invest.* 72:466–77

16. Dominguez JH, Snowdowne KW, Freudenrich CC, Brown T, Borle AB. 1987. Intracellular messenger for action of angiotensin II on fluid transport in rabbit proximal tubule. *Am. J. Physiol.* 252:F423–28

17. Douglas JG. 1987. Angiotensin receptor subtypes of the kidney cortex. *Am. J. Physiol.* 253:F1–7

18. Douglas JG. 1987. Subpressor infusions of angiotensin II alter glomerular binding, prostaglandin E_2 and cyclic AMP production. *Hypertension* 9(Suppl. III):49–56

19. Douglas JG, Romero M, Hopfer U. 1990. Signaling mechanisms coupled to the angiotensin receptor of proximal tubular epithelium. *Kidney Int.* 38:S43–47

20. Dudley DT, Panek PL, Major TC, Lu GH, Bruns RF, et al. 1990. Subclasses of angiotensin II bindings sites and their functional significance. *Mol. Pharmacol.* 38:370–77

21. Dulin N, Ernsberger P, Douglas JG. 1993. Rabbit renal epithelial angiotensin receptors. *Hypertension* 22:409 (Abstr.)

22. Dulin N, Ernsberger P, Madhun Z, Douglas JG. 1993. Identification of des-Asp^1,Arg^2 angiotensin II receptors. *Hypertension* 22:444 (Abstr.)

23. Elton TS, Stephan CC, Taylor GR, Kimball MG, Martin MM, et al. 1992. Isolation of two distinct type 1 angiotensin II receptors genes. *Biochem. Biophys. Res. Commun.* 184:1067–73

24. Ernsberger P, Zbou J, Damon TH, Douglas JG. 1992. Angiotensin II receptor subtypes in cultured rat renal mesangial cells. *Am. J. Physiol.* 263: F411–16

25. Furukawa Y, Kishimoto S, Nishikawa K. 1982. *US Patent No. 4,340,598; US Patent No. 4,355,040*

26. Garcia-Sainz JA, Huerta-Bathena ME, Malbon CC. 1989. Hepatocyte β-adrenergic responsiveness and guanine nucleotide-binding regulatory proteins. *Am. J. Physiol.* 256:C384–89

27. Gaul G, Gierschik P, Marmé D. 1988. Pertussis toxin inhibits angiotensin II-mediated phosphatidylinositol breakdown and ADP-ribosylates a 40 KD protein in cultured smooth muscle cells. *Biochem. Biophys. Res. Commun.* 150: 841–47

28. Gibson RE, Thorpe HH, Cartwright ME, Frank JD, Schorn TW, et al. 1991. Angiotensin II receptor subtypes in renal cortex of rats and rhesus monkeys. *Am. J. Physiol.* 261:F512–18

29. Gowler D, Milligan G, Spiegel AM, Denson CG, Housley MD. 1987. Abolition of the expression of inhibitory guanine nucleotide regulatory protein G_i activity in diabetes. *Nature* 327:229–32

30. Grady EF, Sechi LA, Griffin CA, Schambelan M, Kelinyaak JE. 1991. Expression of AT_2 receptors in the developing rat fetus. *J. Clin. Invest.* 88:921–33

31. Harris RC, Homma T, Jacobson HR, Capdevila J. 1990. Epoxyeicosatrienoic acids activate Na^+/H^+ exchange and are mitogenic in cultured rat glomerular mesangial cells. *J. Cell. Physiol.* 144: 429–37

32. Hausdorff WP, Sekura RD, Aguilera G, Catt KJ. 1987. Control of aldosterone production by angiotensin II is mediated by two guanine nucleotide regulatory proteins. *Endocrinology* 120: 1668–78

33. Henrich WL, Falck JR, Campbell WB. 1990. Inhibition of renin release by 14,15-epoxyeicosatrienoic acid in renal cortical slices. *Am. J. Physiol.* 258: E269–74

34. Iwai N, Inagami T. 1992. Identification of two subtypes in the rat type 1 angiotensin II receptor. *FEBS Lett.* 298:257–60

35. Iwai N, Yamano Y, Chaki S, Konishi F, Bardhan S, et al. 1991. Rat angiotensin II receptor: cDNA sequence and regulation of the gene expression. *Biochem. Biophys. Res. Comm.* 177: 299–304

36. Jim K, Hassid A, Sun F, Dunn MJ. 1982. Lipoxygenase activity in rat kidney glomeruli, glomerular epithelial

cells, and cortical tubules. *J. Biol. Chem.* 257:10294–99

36a. Jourdain M, Amiel C, Friedlander G. 1992. Modulation of Na-H exchange activity by angiotensin II in opossum kidney cells. *Am. J. Physiol.* 263: C1141–46

37. Jung KY, Endou H. 1989. Biphasic increasing effect of angiotensin II on intracellular free calcium in isolated rat early proximal tubule. *Biochem. Biophys. Res. Commun.* 165:1221–28

38. Kakar SS, Sellers JC, Devor DC, Musgrove LC, Neil JD. 1992. Angiotensin II type-1 receptor subtype cDNAs: differential tissue expression and hormonal regulation. *Biochem. Biophys. Res. Commun.* 183:1090–96

39. Kojima I, Shikata H, Ogata E. 1986. Pertussis toxin blocks angiotensin II-induced calcium influx but not inositol trisphosphate production in adrenal glomerulosa cell. *FEBS Lett.* 204:347–51

40. Kremer SG, Breuer WV, Skorecki KL. 1989. Vasoconstrictor hormones depolarize renal glomerular mesangial cells by activating chloride channels. *J. Cell Physiol.* 138:97–105

41. Langlois D, Hinsch KD, Saez JM, Begeot M. 1990. Stimulatory effect of insulin and insulin-like growth factor I on G_i proteins and angiotensin-II-induced phosphoinositide breakdown in cultured bovine adrenal cells. *Endocrinology* 126:1264–67

42. Levine MA, Feldman AM, Robishaw JD, Ladenson PW, Ahn TG, et al. 1990. Influence of thyroid hormone status on expression of genes encoding G protein subunits in the rat heart. *J. Biol. Chem.* 265:3553–60

43. Liu F-Y, Cogan MG. 1989. Angiotensin II stimulates early proximal bicarbonate absorption in the rat by decreasing cyclic adenosine monophosphate. *J. Clin. Invest.* 84:83–92

44. Madhun ZT, Douglas JG, Ernsberger P, Hopfer U. 1992. Angiotensin II (AII) receptor subtypes linked to Ca^{2+} mobilization in renal sites. *FASEB J.* 6:A1012 (Abstr.)

45. Madhun ZT, Ernsberger P, Ke F-C, Zhou J, Hopfer U, Douglas JG. 1993. Signal transduction mediated by angiotensin II receptor subtypes expressed in rat renal mesangial cells. *Regul. Peptides* 44:149–57

46. Madhun ZT, Goldthwait DA, McKay D, Hopfer U, Douglas JG. 1991. An epoxygenase metabolite of arachidonic acid mediates angiotensin II-induced rises in cytosolic calcium in rabbit

proximal tubule epithelial cells. *J. Clin. Invest.* 88:456–61

47. McClue SJ, Milligan G. 1990. The α_2B adrenergic receptor of undifferentiated neuroblastoma x glioma hybrid NG108–15 cells, interacts directly with the guanine nucleotide binding protein, G_i2. *FEBS Lett.* 269:430–34

48. McKenzie FR, Milligan G. 1990. δ-Opioid-receptor-mediated inhibition of adenylate cyclase is transduced specifically by the guanine-nucleotide-binding protein G_i2. *Biochem. J.* 267: 391–98

49. McPherson GA. 1985. Analysis of radioligand binding experiments: A collection of computer programs for the IBM-PC. *J. Pharmacol. Methods* 14: 213–28

50. Morduchowicz GA, Sheikh-Hamad D, Dwyer BE, Stern N, Jo OD, Yanagama N. 1991. Angiotensin II directly increases rabbit renal brush-border membrane sodium transport: presence of local signal transduction system. *J. Membr. Biol.* 122:43–53

51. Murphy TJ, Alexander RW, Griendling KK, Runge MS, Bernstein KE. 1991. Isolation of a cDNA encoding the vascular type-1 angiotensin II receptor. *Nature* 351:233–36

52. Norman J, Badie-Dezfooly B, Nord EP, Kurtz I, Schlosser J, et al. 1987. EGF-induced mitogenesis in proximal tubular cells: potentiation by angiotensin II. *Am. J. Physiol.* 253-F299–309

53. Omata K, Abraham NG, Escalaute B, Schwartzmann ML. 1992. Age-related changes in renal cytochrome P-450 arachidonic acid metabolism in spontaneously hypertensive rats. *Am. J. Physiol.* 262:F8–16

54. Omata K, Abraham NG, Schwartzmann ML. 1992. Renal cytochrome P-450-arachidonic acid metabolism: localization and hormonal regulation in SHR. *Am. J. Physiol.* 262:F591–99

55. Pfeilschifter J, Bauer C. 1986. Pertussis toxin abolishes angiotensin II-induced phosphoinositide hydrolysis and prostaglandin synthesis in rat renal mesangial cells. *Biochem. J.* 236:289–94

56. Pfeilschifter J, Huwiler A, Merriweather C, Briner VA. 1992. Angiotensin II stimulation of phospholipase D in rat renal mesangial cells is mediated by the AT_1 receptor subtype. *Eur. J. Pharmacol. Mol. Pharmacol.* 225:57–62

57. Pucell AG, Hodges JC, Sen I, Bumpus FM, Husain A. 1991. Biochemical properties of the ovarian granulosa cell

type 2-angiotensin II receptor. *Endocrinolgy* 128:1947–59

58. Ridge S, Patak RV, Savin VJ. 1984. Decreased ultra filtration coefficient of glomeruli isolated from volume-depleted rats. *J. Lab. Clin. Med.* 103: 363–72

58a. Romero MF. 1992. *Angiotensin II regulation of ion transport in the rabbit proximal tubule.* PhD thesis. Case Western Reserve Univ. Cleveland, OH

59. Romero MF, Hopfer U, Madhun ZT, Zhou J, Douglas JG. 1991. Angiotensin II actions in the rabbit proximal tubule. Angiotensin II mediated signaling mechanisms and electrolyte transport in the rabbit proximal tubule. *Renal Physiol. Biochem.* 14:199–207

60. Ros M, Northuyp JK, Malbon CC. 1989. Adipocyte G-proteins and adenylate cyclase. Effects of adrenalectomy. *Biochem. J.* 257:737–44

61. Saitom N, Guitart X, Hayward M, Tallman JF, Duman RS, Nestler EJ. 1989. Corticosterone differentially regulates the expression of $G_{s\alpha}$ and $G_{i\alpha}$, messenger RNA and protein in rat cerebral cortex. *Proc. Natl. Acad. Sci. USA* 86:3906–10

62. Sasaki K, Yamano Y, Bardhan S, Iwai N, Murray JJ, et al. 1991. Cloning and expression of a complementary DNA encoding a bovine adrenal angiotensin II type-1 receptor. *Nature* 351:230–33

63. Schelling JR, Hanson AS, Marzec R, Linas SL. 1992. Cytoskeleton-dependent endocytosis is required for apical type 1 angiotensin receptor-mediated phospholipase C activation in cultured rat proximal tubule cells. *J. Clin. Invest.* 90:2472–80

64. Schlondorff D, Singhal P, Itassid A, Satriano JA, DeCandido S. 1987. Relationship of GTP-binding proteins, phospholipase C, and PGE_2 synthesis in rat glomerular mesangial cells. *Am. J. Physiol.* 256:F171–78

65. Schwartzmann ML, Ferreri N, Carroll M, Songu-Mize E, McGiff JC. 1985. Renal cytochrome P450-related arachidonate metabolite inhibits (Na^+, K^+)ATPase. *Nature* 314:620–22

66. Sekar MC, Yang M, Meezan E, Pillion DJ. 1990. Angiotensin II and bradykinin stimulate phosphoinositide breakdown in intact rat kidney glomeruli but not in proximal tubules: glomerular response modulated by phorbol ester. *Biochem. Biophys. Res. Commun.* 166: 373–79

67. Sims C, Ashby K, Douglas JG. 1992. Angiotensin II-induced changes in gua-

nine nucleotide binding and regulatory proteins. *Hypertension* 19:146–52

68. Skorecki KL, Ballermann BJ, Rennke HJ, Brenner BM. 1983. Angiotensin II receptors in isolated rat glomeruli. *Fed. Proc.* 42:3064–70

69. Smith WL, Bell TG. 1978. Immunohistochemical localization of the prostaglandin-forming cyclooxygenase in renal cortex. *Am. J. Physiol.* 235: F451–57

70. Smrcka AV, Hepler JR, Brown KO, Sternweis PC. 1991. Regulation of polyphosphoinositide-specific phospholipase C activity by purified G_q. *Science* 251:804–7

71. Snyder G, Lattanzio F, Yadagiri P, Falck JR, Capdevila J. 1986. 5,6-epoxyeicosatrienoic acid mobilizes Ca^{2+} in anterior pituitary cells. *Biochem. Biophys. Res. Commun.* 139: 1188–94

72. Speth RC, Kim KH. 1990. Discrimination of two angiotensin II receptor subtypes with a selective agonist analogue of angiotensin II, p-amino-phylalanine[6] angiotensin II. *Biochem. Biophys. Res. Comm.* 169:997–1006

73. Strathmann M, Simon MI. 1990. G protein diversity: A distinct class of α subunits is present in vertebrates and invertebrates. *Proc. Natl. Acad. Sci. USA* 87:9113–17

74. Sumners C, Tang W, Zelezna B, Raizada MK. 1991. Angiotensin II receptor subtypes are coupled with distinct signal-transduction mechanisms in neurons and astrocytes from rat brain. *Proc. Natl. Acad. Sci. USA* 88:7567–71

75. Torres VE, Northrup TE, Edwards RM, Shah SV, Dousa TP. 1978. Modulation of cyclic nucleotides in isolated rat glomeruli. *J. Clin. Invest.* 62:1334–43

76. Tsutsumi K, Saavedra JM. 1991. Quantitative autoradiography reveals different angiotensin II receptor subtypes in selected rat brain nuclei. *J. Neurochem.* 56:348–51

77. U'Prichard DC, Perry BD, Wang CH, Mitrius JC, Kahn DJ. 1983. Molecular aspects of regulation of α_2-adrenergic receptors. In *Frontiers in Neuropsychiatric Research,* ed. E Usdin, pp. 65–82. London: Macmillan

78. Wang T, Chan YL. 1991. The role of phosphoinositide turnover in mediating the biophasic effect of angiotensin II on renal tubular transport. *J. Pharmacol. Exp. Ther.* 256:309–17

79. Welsh C, Dubyak G, Douglas JG. 1988. Relationship between phospho-

lipase C activation and prostaglandin E_2 and cyclic adenosine monophosphate production in rabbit tubular epithelial cells. *J. Clin. Invest.* 81:710–19

80. Whitebread S, Mele M, Kamber B, de Gasparo M. 1989. Preliminary biochemical characterization of two angiotensin II receptor subtypes. *Biochem. Biophys. Res. Comm.* 163: 284–91

81. Wilkes BM, Bellucci A. 1983. Properties of glomerular angiotensin receptors in acute renal failure in the rat. *J. Lab. Clin. Med.* 102:909–17

82. Wong YH, Federman A, Pace AM, Zachary I, Evans T, et al. 1991. Mutant α subunits of G_{i2} inhibit cyclic AMP accumulation. *Nature* 351:63–65

83. Woodcock EA, Johnston Cl. 1982. Inhibition of adenylate cyclase by angiotensin II in rat renal cortex. *Endocrinology* 111:1687–91

84. Wright GB, Alexander RW, Sekstein L, Gimbrone MA. 1982. Sodium, divalent cations, and guanine nucleotides regulate the affinity of the rat mesenteric artery angiotensin II receptor. *Circ. Res.* 50:462–69

85. Yatani A, Mattera R, Codina J, Graff R, Okabe K, et al. 1988. The G protein-gated atrial K^+ channel is stimulated by three distinct $G_i\alpha$-subunits. *Nature* 336:680–82

86. Zhou J, Ernsberger P, Douglas JG. 1993. Proposed AT_{1A} and AT_{1B} angiotensin receptor subtypes in rat mesangial cells: coupling to adenylyl cyclase. *Hypertension.* In press

87. Zhou J, Sims C, Chang C-H, Berti-Mattera L, Hopfer U, Douglas JG. 1990. Proximal tubular epithelial cells possess a novel 42-kilodalton guanine nucleotide-binding regulatory protein. *Proc. Natl. Acad. Sci. USA* 87:7532–35

Annu. Rev. Physiol. 1994. 56:671–89
Copyright © 1994 by Annual Reviews Inc. All rights reserved

RENAL STEM CELLS AND THE LINEAGE OF THE NEPHRON

D. Herzlinger

Department of Physiology and Biophysics, Cornell University Medical College, New York, New York 10021

KEY WORDS: nephrogenesis, renal progenitors, renal induction, metanephric blastema, ureteric bud

INTRODUCTION

Regulation of the volume and composition of body fluids in multicellular organisms is mediated by at least 14 distinct transporting renal cell types. These heterogeneous epithelial cell types are not randomly distributed throughout the kidney, but are organized into identical functional units called uriniferous tubules. Each uriniferous tubule contains all renal epithelial cell types, and for the purposes of this review, the segmental organization of the uriniferous tubule will be described according to anatomical conventions (1). That is, the uriniferous tubule is composed of a long convoluted portion, the nephron (glomerulus through distal convoluted tubule), and the collecting tubule system (Figure 1a). The complex architecture of the uriniferous tubule is a requisite for normal renal function. Renal morphogenesis must be tightly regulated during development so that the correct renal cell type comes to reside in its appropriate nephron segment, and each segment of all uriniferous tubules align to form the gross anatomical compartments of the organ.

The metanephric kidney develops from an embryonic rudiment composed of two tissue layers, the epithelial ureteric bud and the mesenchyme of the metanephric blastema (Figure 1b). These two embryonic primordia give rise to separate parts of the uriniferous tubule. The ureteric bud, a caudal outgrowth of the Wolffian duct, forms the collecting tubule system by undergoing branching morphogenesis (32). Grobstein, in his classic exper-

671

0066–4278/94/0315–0671$05.00

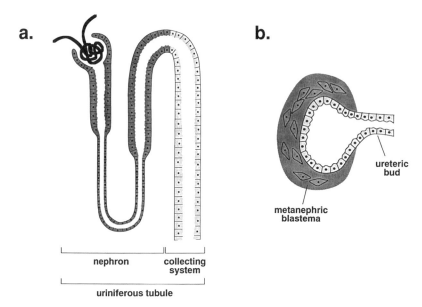

Figure 1   Schematic models of the mature uriniferous tubule and the embryonic rudiment from which it is derived. (*a*) The mature uriniferous tubule is the functional unit of the kidney. According to anatomical conventions, the uriniferous tubule is composed of two parts, the nephron and collecting tubule. The nephron contains at least 14 different renal epithelial cell types organized into segments. The order of segments starting from the end of the nephron that encloses the vascular tuft is glomerulus, proximal tubule, loop of Henle, and distal tubule. The collecting tubule is contiguous with the distal tubule of the nephron. (*b*) The metanephric kidney rudiment is composed of two tissue primordia. The epithelia of the ureteric bud surrounded by mesenchymal cells of the metanephric blastema. The ureteric bud gives rise to, at a minimum, the collecting tubule system. The diverse epithelia of the nephron form from the metanephric blastema.

iments, demonstrated that the metanephric blastema forms the diverse epithelia of the nephron (12–16). The metanephric blastema, an aggregate of cells condensed around the ureteric bud, was isolated free of the ureteric bud and cultured in vitro. These metanephric blastema organ cultures were shown to differentiate into renal tubules only when grown in the presence of several embryonic tissues. Embryonic spinal cord was shown to be the most potent inducer of tubulogenesis. This induction-dependent tubulogenesis exhibited by the metanephric blastema has been extensively characterized by Grobstein, Saxen, and Ekblom (12–16, 46, 8). Renal developmental research for the last 30 years has focused on the cell biological transitions undergone by the metanephric blastema during its induction-dependent differentiation into the epithelia of the nephron. The biochemical signals that direct this process remain unknown.

Although the phenomenology of the transitions undergone by the metanephric blastema during its course of differentiation has been extensively described, the embryonic events leading to the establishment of this tissue primordium have not been examined in amniotes since the late 1800's (28). The metanephric blastema is proposed to be derived directly from intermediate mesoderm located in the nephrogenic cord. These intermediate mesodermal cells are thought to reside in the caudal aspect of the embryo, waiting for ureteric bud contact prior to aggregating around the tip of the bud to form the metanephric blastema. After receiving an inductive stimulus from the ureteric bud, these naive cells of the intermediate mesoderm are believed to differentiate into the epithelia of the nephron. According to this hypothesis, the ureteric bud and metanephric blastema are two histogenetically unrelated tissues (Figure 2a). Although both are originally derived from intermediate mesoderm, the cells of neither primordium are proposed to be immediate descendants of the other. This review focuses on the experimental data that support this contention. Recent studies disproving this hypothesis will be presented (23) and utilized to support the following alternative model describing metanephric blastema formation: nephrogenic progenitors populating the metanephric blastema are derived from the ureteric bud (Figure 2b). This model implies that the ureteric bud epithelial cell is a multipotent renal stem cell. The ureteric bud undergoes an epithelial to mesenchymal transition generating mesenchymal nephron progenitors of the metanephric blastema; these ureteric bud-derived cells then differentiate into diverse renal epithelia after induction.

Although discrimination between these two models of metanephric blastema formation may seem to be a minor point, it has major implications for understanding the signals that initiate and guide renal development. If, as generally accepted, the metanephric blastema is derived exclusively from naive intermediate mesodermal cells, then the signals initiating renal development must induce naive intermediate mesoderm to epithelialize and form the diverse epithelia of the nephron. If, on the other hand, the metanephric blastema is not exclusively derived from intermediate mesoderm, but must incorporate ureteric bud-derived cells prior to becoming competent for metanephric nephron differentiation, then renal development must consist of two stages guided by two sets of regulatory signals. First, a metanephric blastema that contains progenitors competent to differentiate into the epithelia of the metanephric nephron must be formed. Second, metanephrogenic-competent progenitors must undergo the well characterized mesenchymal to epithelial transition leading the generation of diverse renal epithelial cell types.

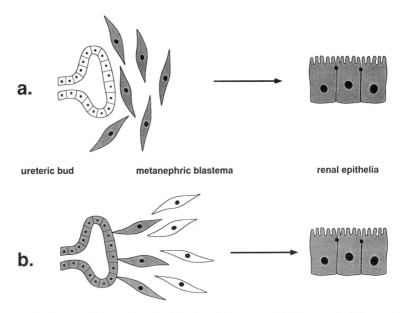

Figure 2   Two models describing the derivation of the metanephric blastema. (*a*) It is currently accepted that the metanephric blastema is derived from intermediate mesoderm of the caudal aspect of the nephrogenic cord. This model implies that the metanephric blastema and ureteric bud are distinct, unrelated tissues. According to this hypothesis, the ureteric bud induces naive mesodermal cells aggregated around its tip to differentiate into the diverse epithelia of the nephron. (*b*) An alternative model proposes that the ureteric bud produces and induces metanephrogenic progenitors. The ureteric bud gives rise to mesenchymal nephron progenitors populating the metanephric blastema by undergoing an epithelial-to-mesenchymal transition followed by delamination. The ureteric bud then induces its immediate descendants to differentiate into the diverse epithelia of the nephron.

EARLY RENAL DEVELOPMENT

Intermediate Mesoderm Gives Rise to the Urogenital System

This review is focused on the embryonic events that lead to the establishment of the two tissue primordia that give rise to the metanephric kidney; the ureteric bud and metanephric blastema. To address this topic, the earliest embryonic cells that give rise to the kidney first must be identified, and their fate followed up to the establishment of these metanephric primordia. The classic experiments performed by Rawles, which analyzed the differentiative potential of cells comprising the head process chick embryo, a stage just prior to gastrulation, demonstrate that lateral and medial aspects of the blastoderm are competent to differentiate into renal tubule-like structures in vitro (43). After gastrulation, when cells of the early embryo segregate into three tissue layers, progenitor cells that give rise to the urogenital system are localized to a specific area of the middle germ layer, the intermediate mesoderm (37, 45). In lower vertebrates this population of mesodermal cells gives rise to a transitional renal structure, the pronephros, and a final mesonephric kidney. In amniotes, a third and final kidney, the metanephros, forms and replaces the mesonephros. No vertebrate utilizes a pronephric kidney, and its function, if any, during amniote development is controversial.

Two Tissue Primordia Are Formed from Intermediate Mesoderm

The importance of the earliest stage of vertebrate renal development, whether true pronephric tubules form and/or function, is that early in embryogenesis two distinct tissue primordium are formed: the nephric duct and the nephrogenic cord. The nephric duct becomes the mesonephric and/or Wolffian duct as it extends along the cranial-caudal axis of the embryo, and gives rise to the ureteric bud. All these duct-derived structures are integral to meso- and metanephric kidney formation. The nephrogenic cord is proposed to give rise to mesonephric and metanephric nephrons after being contacted by the mesonephric duct and ureteric bud, respectively.

Pronephric Duct Formation and Growth

The manner by which the primary nephric duct forms may differ among species (9, 51). Current embryology texts state that the nephric duct forms in conjunction with pronephric tubules from segmented intermediate mesoderm (37, 45). This segmented intermediate mesoderm first forms a series of pronephric tubules, aligned along the cranial-caudal axis of the embryo. The distal ends of successive, segmented pronephric tubules are proposed to fuse, thus forming the pronephric duct. This model describing nephric duct formation was formulated from morphological studies performed on developing chicks (47, 48).

However, it is clear that the nephric duct can form independently from intermediate mesoderm without the establishment of fully formed pronephric tubules (9, 51). As reviewed by Fox (9), studies in amphibians demonstrate that the primary nephric duct originates from intermediate mesoderm posterior to the mesoderm that gives rise to the pronephric tubules. This view is substantiated not only by morphological analyses, but also by experimental embryology. When vital dyes were locally applied to distinct areas of intermediate mesoderm, pronephric tubules were shown to arise from intermediate mesoderm anterior to the intermediate mesoderm that gave rise to the nephric duct. Additional experiments demonstrated that removal of these

different areas of intermediate mesoderm prevented formation of the pronephros and nephric duct independently (5, 10, 26, 38). In humans, Torrey
demonstrated that the primary nephric duct forms by delaminating from the
dorsal-lateral side of intermediate mesoderm between the 9th and 13th somite
and argues that no fully formed pronephric tubules have ever been documented (52). This model of nephric duct formation seems to be true in the
rat embryo as well (53). Thus the primary nephric duct can form directly
from a specified population of intermediate mesoderm, distinct from the
mesoderm that gives rise to pronephric tubules.

A substantial literature describes the mode of caudal nephric duct extension
during embryogenesis (9). The cells of the nephric duct give rise to caudal
extensions of the duct; it does not form in situ from mesoderm. Experiments
performed to reach this conclusion include morphological analyses of duct
growth, extirpation of the primordial duct prior to outgrowth, blockage or
reorientation of the duct, localized vital staining, and explantation. Although
it is clear that the duct itself gives rise to its terminal extensions, this caudal
growth is not accomplished by active division of cells located at the caudal
terminus of the duct. The mitotic indexes of cells comprising the duct are
homogeneous along the entire length of the duct (40). Rather, the duct
elongates by a migratory process, where cells at its terminal tip migrate out
of the duct towards the caudal aspect of the embryo and reassemble into
the duct (40). Whether these cells migrating from the nephric duct form
the nephric duct exclusively, or also give rise to the nephrogenic cord, is
unknown.

Nephrogenic Cord Formation and Growth

Although the formation of the nephric duct has been extensively studied,
the derivation, formation, and mode of extension of the nephrogenic cord
have never been examined. This embryonic primordium can be morphologically identified only after the nephric duct has been formed and appears
caudal to the newly formed duct. The cord extends along the cranial-caudal
axis of the embryo in parallel with the nephric duct, but always precedes
duct extension in the caudal direction. How the nephrogenic cord forms
and extends is completely unknown. Two hypotheses can be formulated.
First, the nephrogenic cord is a continuation of segmented intermediate
mesoderm. In other words, the cells comprising the cord are daughters of
undifferentiated intermediate mesoderm, the same mesoderm that gave rise
to the pronephric tubules and duct. This currently accepted hypothesis implies
that the nephric duct and nephrogenic cord are two independent primordium,
i.e. neither tissue gives rise to cells of the other. Second, the nephrogenic
cord incorporates a population of cells derived from the nephric duct, or is
formed from nephric duct-derived cells during cranial-caudal growth. Since

the nephrogenic cord always precedes the caudal growth of the nephric duct, it is possible that cells migrating from the distal tip of the duct contribute to both primordia. A single experiment performed on the amphibian, *Pleuodeles waltlii,* in 1939 demonstrates that nephrogenic cord extension is inhibited in the absence of the primary nephric duct (39). Obviously a direct relationship between nephric duct growth and nephrogenic cord formation or extension can not be based on results from a single experiment. This author mentions the experiment only to remind the reader of the complete dearth of information describing nephrogenic cord formation and extension.

THE MESONEPHROS

In humans, as the nephric duct forms or reaches the 9th somite, mesonephric tubules begin to appear in the area occupied by the nephrogenic cord (41, 52). The mesonephric nephron is composed of a glomerulus and two segments that join to a collecting tubule. The collecting tubule joins the nephric duct, which is now called the mesonephric or Wolffian duct. All descriptive histological analyses of mesonephron formation, in all species, demonstrate that differentiation of mesonephric tubules occurs only when the mesonephric duct reaches the level at which the tubules are forming (8, 37, 41, 46, 51).

Extensive experimental embryological studies, performed on amphibian and chicken embryos, have analyzed the dependence of mesonephric tubule formation on nephric duct ingrowth (see review by Torrey, 51). In such experiments, the nephric duct is either removed or blocked so that contact between the nephrogenic cord and the mesonephric duct is prevented. Mesonephric nephron formation in these altered embryos is variable. Specifically, the work of Gruenwald demonstrated that when the distal growing end of the nephric duct was destroyed by cautery, removed, or blocked in chick embryos of approximately 40–48 hrs of gestation, substantial mesonephric nephron formation occurred in areas adjacent to duct perturbation, where no morphologically identifiable duct was observed (18, 19). Gruenwald termed this phenomenon "nephric duct-independent" mesonephric nephron formation. His experiments clearly demonstrated, however, that mesonephric nephron formation was completely inhibited in areas greatly distanced from the site of duct perturbation.

The simplest interpretation of these results is that duct-derived cells are still present in areas adjacent to duct perturbation that undergo nephric duct-independent differentiation. Even sophisticated microsurgery may not remove all cells derived from the nephric duct owing to its mode of elongation (40). As reviewed in the previous section, substantial data now demonstrate that the nephric duct elongates by issuing migratory cells from its distal terminus. Thus perturbation of the caudal aspect of the duct, defined by its gross anatomical borders, may not insure complete removal of all duct-derived cells. Until markers specific for all the progeny derived from the ingrowing nephric duct are available, this simple interpretation can not be ruled out.

Gruenwald suggested that tissues other than the mesonephric duct induced the formation of the nephric duct-independent mesonephric nephrons. He went on to substantiate this interpretation with a series of experiments analyzing metanephric kidney formation (19, 20) (see below). However, if the nephrogenic cord is competent to be induced by another tissue, why is nephric duct-independent tubulogenesis active only in sites of the nephrogenic cord adjacent to duct removal? Gruenwald could not answer this question and concluded from these early experiments that the ingrowing nephric duct must change the differentiative potential of the nephrogenic cord. That is, the duct allows or directs the nephrogenic cord to become competent to differentiate into mesonephrons. Is this competence because the duct directs a distinct, unrelated population of cells to differentiate into the mesonephric nephron? Or, is this competence because the duct produces progenitor cells that give rise to mesonephric nephrons?

Although the experiments described above document the importance of the mesonephric duct for mesonephric nephron development, they do not in any way elucidate the mechanism by which the duct allows the cord to become differentiation-competent. Until now, it has been accepted that the duct induces the cord to differentiate without contributing cells that form mesonephric nephrons. Simply put, the duct directs mesonephric progenitors of the nephrogenic cord to differentiate, it does not produce such differentiation-competent cells. The only experiments supporting this contention are a series of experimental embryological studies performed by Croiselle and her colleagues (3, 4, 21, 35, 36). These experiments are quoted extensively, but are inconclusive. A system devised by Le Douarin was utilized to examine the lineage of the epithelia comprising the mesonephric nephron (33). This system relies on the ability to discriminate between chick and quail cells by a nuclear marker. Chimeric embryos can be formed from embryonic primordia taken from each bird, and these chimeric embryos will develop. After development, the lineage of differentiated cells can then be traced back to chick or quail origin. Thus the lineage of differentiated cells can be traced back to the embryonic primordium from which they were derived.

Croiselle and her colleagues formed chick/quail chimeras from embryos of approximately 2 days of gestation, the same stage utilized by Gruenwald (17–20) in his experiments. At this stage, the nephrogenic cord has just extended into the caudal half of the embryo, while the gross anatomical border of the nephric duct is still in the cranial aspect of the embryo. The cranial half of a quail embryo containing the nephric duct and caudal half of a chick embryo containing only the nephrogenic cord were grafted together and allowed to develop (Figure 3a). Mesonephric kidney formation was analyzed and seen to be incomplete, both in tubule organization and the number of mesonephric nephrons formed. However, the epithelia of the rudimentary mesonephric tubules that formed were shown to be derived exclusively from the caudal graft (2, 3, 4, 35). These investigators concluded that cells of the mesonephric nephron are exclusively derived from the nephrogenic cord. Conversely, the mesonephric duct does not give rise to progeny that develop into mesonephric nephrons. What follows then, is that the mesonephric duct must act by inducing a distinct, unrelated population of cells from the nephrogenic cord to differentiate into mesonephric tubules.

However, it appeared that the caudal graft of these chimeras included the area of the nephrogenic cord that Gruenwald demonstrated undergoes nephric duct-independent mesonephric nephron formation (17, 18). Thus it cannot be ruled out that the rudimentary mesonephrons that formed exclusively from cells of the posterior graft did so in a nephric duct-independent fashion. The appropriate control experiment, analyzing mesonephric nephron formation in the posterior graft alone, without any nephric duct or cranial graft present, was not performed in this early series of experiments.

This control was performed in a later, more sophisticated series of experiments with chick/quail chimeric explants described in Figure 3b,c (36). The nephrogenic cord was crudely dissected from the caudal portion of a chicken embryo devoid of Wolffian duct at the same stage utilized to construct the chimeric embryos described in the previous experiments. This nephrogenic cord tissue was combined with quail Wolffian duct, spinal cord, or cultured alone for 18 hrs prior to grafting into the coelom of a chick to facilitate explant development. Not surprisingly, 43% of the control explants, composed only of the nephrogenic cord, developed rudimentary mesonephric nephrons. These results, then, invalidate the original set of experiments. Since the caudal tissue utilized in all these experiments was capable of forming nephric duct-independent mesonephric nephrons, how can these experiments reveal the mechanism by which the nephric duct promotes mesonephric tubule formation? The central question posed by this review has not been resolved in the context of mesonephric kidney development. Does the nephric duct enable the nephrogenic cord to differentiate into mesonephric tubules by induction or by production of mesonephric tubule progenitors?

This question can only be resolved by direct lineage analysis techniques. Cells of the mesonephric duct must be labeled with a heritable tag prior to

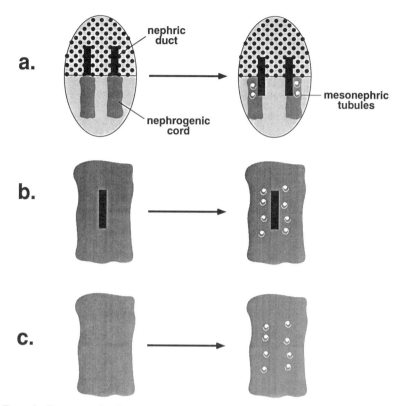

Figure 3   Data supporting the contention that the epithelia of mesonephric tubules are exclusively derived from the nephrogenic cord are inconclusive. (*a*) Chimeric embryos were formed from the cranial portion of a quail embryo containing the nephric duct and the caudal portion of a chick embryo, prior to nephric duct ingrowth, containing only the nephrogenic cord. Mesonephric nephrons that formed in such chimeric embryos formed in the caudal graft and were derived exclusively from chick nephrogenic cord. (*b*) Crudely dissected chick nephrogenic cord was combined with quail mesonephric duct and cultured. Mesonephric tubules formed solely from chick tissue. (*c*) The control for experiments (*a*) and (*b*) was performed as follows. Crudely dissected chick nephrogenic cord was cultured in the absence of the mesonephric duct. Mesonephric tubules formed from the chick nephrogenic cord in the absence of the mesonephric duct. Thus the nephrogenic cord contained in caudal grafts was capable of self-differentiation. These experiments can not possibly determine the mechanism by which the mesonephric duct induces the nephrogenic cord since the nephrogenic cord was competent to self-differentiate (see text).

the nephrogenic cord gaining competence for self-differentiation (nephric duct-independent tubule formation). After development, the fate of the tagged nephric duct-derived progenies must be characterized. Do such mesonephric duct-derived cells exclusively give rise to the mesonephric duct, or do they also give rise to cells of mesonephric nephron?

THE METANEPHROS

In amniotes, the metanephros is formed from the ureteric bud, a caudal outgrowth of the Wolffian duct, and the metanephric blastema, a cap of mesenchymal cells surrounding the tip of the ureteric bud. The ureteric bud gives rise to, at a minimum, the collecting system (32). The metanephric blastema gives rise to the metanephric nephron, which matures into a more functionally diverse nephron than the mesonephric nephron (8, 12–16, 46). The derivation of the ureteric bud is easily understood by morphological analyses; it is a caudal outgrowth of the Wolffian duct (32). It is clear from the work of Grobstein, Saxen, and Ekblom that once formed, the metanephric blastema gives rise to the diverse epithelia of the metanephric nephron (8, 12–16, 46). However, these studies describe only what the formed metanephric blastema gives rise to, not its derivation.

All cells that form the metanephric blastema are proposed to be direct descendants of intermediate mesoderm located in the caudal-most aspect of the nephrogenic cord. When the ureteric bud contacts this naive mesoderm, the naive mesodermal cells are proposed to aggregate around its ingrowing tips and form the metanephric blastema (Figure 2a). This model describing the derivation of the metanephric blastema is based on morphological experiments performed in the late 1800's. Forty-four morphological analyses of metanephric kidney development were performed between 1855 and 1904. As reviewed by Huber in 1905 (28), 17 studies concluded that the blastema and ureteric bud are histogenetically unrelated; cells of neither primordium are direct descendants of the other. This is the presently accepted hypothesis. Four investigations concluded that the ureteric bud gives rise to a mesenchymal cell population, the metanephric blastema, which then forms metanephric nephrons (Figure 2b) (11, 25, 44, 47). Twenty-three investigations concluded that the metanephric nephron forms by direct branching from the ureteric bud (28). The inconsistencies presented by these investigations demonstrate that morphology alone can not be utilized to determine the derivation of the metanephric blastema. These inconsistencies also suggest that the formation of the uriniferous tubule from the metanephric blastema and ureteric bud may be a complex process.

It is now clear that the metanephric nephron does not form by direct branching from the ureteric bud. Microdissection studies show that the renal vesicle, the earliest structural unit of the metanephric nephron, develops without any tubular connections to the ureteric bud (41). Grobstein's experiments (12–16) document that the metanephric blastema, defined as a population of mesenchymal cells removed from the tip of the ureteric bud, gives rise to nephrons. These studies disprove the hypotheses that metanephric nephrons form by direct branching from the ureteric bud. However, this work does not elucidate the manner by which the metanephric blastema forms. Does the ureteric bud give rise to cells of the metanephric blastema, or is the blastema exclusively derived from naive intermediate mesoderm?

Although these questions have been directly addressed by only one renal developmental study (23), data from several classical renal embryological studies suggest that the accepted model describing metanephric blastema formation is not satisfactory. Instead of forming exclusively from naive intermediate mesoderm, it is likely that the metanephric blastema must incorporate ureteric bud-derived cells to be competent to differentiate into the epithelia of the metanephric nephron (Figure 2a).

While probing the dependence of mesonephron formation on nephric duct ingrowth, Gruenwald observed an interesting phenomenon (18–20). When the path of the ingrowing nephric duct was experimentally blocked, sometimes the nephric duct detoured the obstruction, bypassed the majority of the nephrogenic cord, and established contact with the caudal-most aspect of the nephrogenic cord. This phenomenon occurred in embryos that did not issue a ureteric bud. The caudal aspect of the nephrogenic cord is proposed to give rise to the metanephric blastema once contacted by the ureteric bud. However, this area of the embryo, the presumptive metanephric blastema, differentiated into mesonephric tubules when contacted by the mesonephric duct (Figure 4a). Importantly, Gruenwald demonstrated that the caudal aspect of the nephrogenic cord (the presumptive metanephric blastema) in embryos lacking a ureteric bud, reproducibly formed mesonephric nephrons when nervous tissue was placed in close proximity (Figure 4a). Thus although the caudal-most aspect of the nephrogenic cord is proposed to form the metanephric blastema, this area of the embryo gave rise to mesonephric tubules when induced by mesonephric duct or nervous tissue. Metanephric nephrons formed from the caudal aspect of the nephrogenic cord only after ureteric bud ingrowth (Figure 4b). Gruenwald concluded that the role of the nephric duct is directive. The mesonephric duct directs the nephrogenic cord to form mesonephric nephrons. Only the ureteric bud can direct similar cells to form metanephric nephrons.

Similar experiments were extended in the developing mouse embryo (12–16). Grobstein demonstrated that the formed metanephric blastema, defined as an aggregate of cells dissected from the tip of the ureteric bud, could be cultured in vitro. The isolated metanephric blastema could be induced to form metanephric renal tubules by nervous tissue (Figure 4c). Thus Grobstein showed that the metanephric blastema, once formed, could be induced to generate metanephric nephrons by tissues other than the ureteric bud. These results are incompatible with Gruenwald's suggestion that the mesonephric duct and ureteric bud play a directive role. Again, Gruenwald concluded that only the ureteric bud could induce metanephric nephron formation. The question now is, why did nervous tissue induce

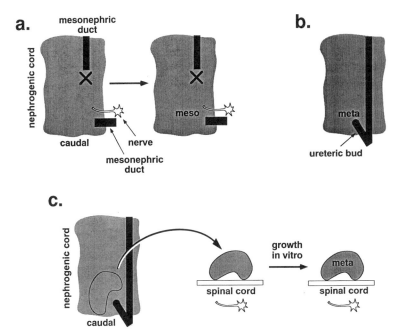

Figure 4   Signals issued by the mesonephric duct and ureteric bud may not be directive. (*a*) The caudal aspect of the nephrogenic cord in embryos lacking a ureteric bud formed mesonephric tubules when induced by mesonephric duct or nerve. (*b*) The caudal aspect of the nephrogenic cord only formed metanephric nephrons when induced by the ureteric bud. From these results (*a* and *b*), Gruenwald concluded that the mesonephric duct or nerve could direct intermediate mesoderm to form mesonephric nephrons, while only the ureteric bud could direct this cell population to form metanephric nephrons. (*c*) When the caudal aspect of the nephrogenic cord is removed after ureteric bud ingrowth (area of nephrogenic cord outlined) and induced with spinal cord, metanephric nephrons form. The work of Grobstein demonstrates that spinal cord (nerve) can direct the formation of metanephric nephrons from tissue isolated from the caudal aspect of the nephrogenic cord at a later stage of development.

mesonephric tubule formation in the area of the embryo proposed to form the metanephric blastema (Gruenwald's experiments) and metanephric nephron formation in the formed metanephric blastema (Grobsteins's experiments)?

One possibility is that the tubules that form in the Grobstein system are mesonephric, although there are no indications that this is the case. The other possibility, favored by this author, is that the caudal aspect of the nephrogenic cord, the presumptive derivative of the metanephric blastema, is not competent to generate metanephric nephrons unless it incorporates cells derived from the ureteric bud. Thus the classical model stating that the metanephric blastema is derived exclusively from naive intermediate mesoderm located in the caudal aspect of the nephrogenic cord may be incorrect. Over the past several years, my laboratory has been analyzing renal development utilizing morphological, immunocytochemical, and recently developed lineage tracing techniques (23, 24, 30, 31). Our recent work (23) directly addresses the questions posed by this review. Do cells derived from the terminal growing tips of the ureteric bud give rise to cells of the metanephric blastema? If so, do such ureteric bud-derived cells ultimately differentiate into the epithelia comprising the metanephric nephron?

Upon close examination, the terminal growing tips of the ureteric bud exhibit morphological characteristics consistent with a delaminating epithelium (22, 23, 34). The basement membrane of the ureteric bud is continuous except at its terminal branching tips where it appears degraded and discontinuous (23, 34). Additionally, ureteric bud cells located within the confines of the discontinuous basement membrane appear to undergo an epithelial-to-mesenchymal transition (23). Cells of the metanephric kidney rudiment have been extensively characterized; ureteric bud cells exhibit an epithelial phenotype (8, 46, 23). However, cells at the terminal tips of the bud, within the confines of the discontinuous basement membrane, exhibit a mesenchymal phenotype identical to the cells comprising the metanephric blastema (23). Additionally, several newly identified transcription factors thought to participate in renal morphogenesis have been localized to the ureteric bud and cells of the metanephric blastema immediately surrounding the ureteric bud (6, 7, 49). These morphological and marker studies do not definitively prove a histogenetic relationship between cells of the ureteric bud and metanephric blastema. They strongly suggest the following: (a) the morphology of the bud is consistent with the bud giving rise to cells of the blastema, and (b) identical proteins are expressed by cells of the ureteric bud and mesenchyme immediately surrounding the bud.

Extensive lineage analysis studies examining the relationship between cells of the ureteric bud and metanephric blastema demonstrate that the ureteric bud gives rise to cells of the metanephric blastema. Additionally, these studies show that such ureteric bud-derived cells populating the metanephric blastema differentiate into the epithelia of the metanephric nephron (23).

Pure ureteric bud preparations from rat embryonic kidney rudiments (gestation day 13) were judged to be free of contaminating metanephric mesenchymal cells by light and electron microscopy. Such isolated bud preparations were tagged with the lineage tracking dye (27), 1, 1 dio-actadecyl-3, 3, 3′, 3′-tetramethylindocarbocyanine perchlorate (DiI), recombined with unlabeled metanephric blastema, and grown organotypically to facilitate renal differentiation. Converse cultures containing DiI-labeled metanephric blastema and unlabeled ureteric bud were established as controls. The location and phenotype of DiI-labeled cells were assessed by immunocytochemistry on frozen sections of recombination organ cultures over time. Markers specific for ureteric bud epithelia, as well as terminal differentiation antigens specific for three distinct nephron segments, were utilized to assess the fate of DiI-tagged cells. The DiI label was never observed in ureteric bud epithelia in control cultures (DiI-labeled blastema, unlabeled bud). However, experimental cultures (DiI-labeled bud, unlabeled metanephric blastema) exhibited DiI-labeled ureteric bud epithelia and DiI-labeled cells in the metanephric blastema by 24 hrs of growth. These results prove that the DiI label is not being passed by cell-cell contact in the recombination organ culture format, since the DiI label is moving in one direction only (from ureteric bud to cells comprising the metanephric blastema). Further analysis of experimental cultures over time demonstrates that DiI-labeled cells derived from the ureteric bud quickly populate the metanephric blastema and ultimately differentiate into diverse renal epithelia. We have demonstrated, utilizing DiI as a lineage marker, that cells of the ureteric bud give rise to mesenchymal nephron progenitors that populate the metanephric blastema. Ultimately such ureteric bud-derived cells differentiate into the epithelia of the metanephric nephron.

An independent lineage analysis technique, retroviral-mediated gene transfer, was utilized to corroborate these results (24, 29, 42). Pure ureteric bud preparations, characterized to be free of adherent mesenchyme by light and electron microscopy, were incubated with decreasing concentrations of the BAG retrovirus (42). This retrovirus transfers the exogenous *lac-z* gene (encoding β-galactosidase) into cells it infects and is replication-defective, therefore infected cells do not produce more virus than would be capable of infecting and transferring the *lac-z* gene into neighboring cells. Thus an infected cell incorporates the *lac-z* gene into its genome and passes this gene in a heritable manner to all of its daughters. Lineage analysis utilizing this method of gene transfer is dependent on infecting a single progenitor cell in the primordium under study. If the *lac-z* gene is transferred to a single progenitor cell within an embryonic primordium by BAG infection, after development, the only cells expressing the *lac-z* gene product (β-galactosidase) will be daughters of the originally infected progenitor. The dilution of retrovirus resulting in a single infected cell per ureteric bud was determined, and ureteric buds containing single infected cells were cultured with metanephric blastema to facilitate renal differentiation. Recombination cultures were fixed and processed for β-galactosidase activity and the binding of a ureteric bud-specific lectin (peroxidase-conjugated Dolichos Biflors) (DB) after different times of culture. Cultures were embedded in plastic and serial sections prepared. Ureteric bud epithelia were identified by peroxidase-DB binding and *lac-z* tagged cells identified by β-galactosidase histochemistry. Cells expressing β-galactosidase were characterized. All β-galactosidase-positive cells were contained in focal growths characteristic of clonally derived cells. Additionally, the number of cells per focal growth increased over time in culture, although the number of focal growths per culture was constant. These results combined with viral titration studies, demonstrate that all β-galactosidase-expressing cells within individual cultures are derived from a single progenitor and are clonally related. All such clonally derived colonies contained ureteric bud founder cells defined by morphology, as well as by the binding of the ureteric bud-specific lectin, DB. The majority of β-galactosidase-expressing cell colonies included immature forming metanephric nephron segments, defined by morphology and absence of DB binding. Several tagged colonies exhibited cells throughout the uriniferous tubule, from the ureteric bud through to the glomerulus. These results conclusively demonstrate that the ureteric bud gives rise to all epithelial cell types comprising the metanephric uriniferous tubule.

Thus we have shown that mesenchymal progenitors of the metanephric nephron delaminate from the ureteric bud. This finding confirms a direct histogenetic relationship between the ureteric bud and metanephric blastema as originally suggested by a sub-set of morphological studies performed during the late 19th century (11, 25, 44, 47). We also demonstrate that the mesenchymal progenitors derived from ureteric bud epithelia give rise to all epithelial cell types of the uriniferous tubule, from the collecting tubule through to the glomerulus. Thus cells of the ureteric bud epithelia are multipotent renal stem cells. A new model of nephrogenesis can now be formulated. As the ureteric bud, the renal stem cell primordium, first branches off the Wolffian duct, it begins to delaminate, generating the first mesenchymal metanephric progenitors. Thus the metanephric blastema is not competent to differentiate into metanephric nephrons until these ureteric bud-derived cells are present. These mesenchymal intermediaries derived from the ureteric bud populate the metanephric blastema and elaborate factors to keep the ureteric bud stem cell population expanding, branching and delaminating towards the periphery of the forming organ. As the ureteric bud continues to branch, the first-born mesenchymal intermediaries, now in contact with the distal portion of the ureteric bud, are induced to differentiate into the epithelia of the nephron—the glomerulus, proximal and distal tubule and ultimately the loop of Henle will be formed. Subsequently, at the proximal branching tips of the bud, more mesenchymal intermediaries are delaminated. These recently delaminated cells support further peripheral branching and delamination of the ureteric bud prior to their terminal differentiation. Repetition of this process will produce a radially growing kidney that has a gradient of nephron maturity, with the least mature nephrons located at the periphery of the organ. Such a gradient of maturity in developing kidneys has been documented by morphological analysis (28, 46, 51).

A major point of this new model describing renal morphogenesis is that ureteric bud branching accomplishes much more than just elaboration of the renal collecting system. The model implies that continued ureteric bud branching leads to expansion of the renal stem cell population during active nephrogenesis. Additionally, continuous delamination from the terminal tips of the ureteric bud leads to continuous production of mesenchymal nephron progenitors throughout nephrogenesis.

In conclusion, the differentiation of the epithelia of the metanephric nephron may now be divided into two distinct steps. First, the ureteric bud stem cell population undergoes an epithelial to mesenchymal transition, delaminating mesenchymal nephrogenic progenitors into the metanephric blastema. Second, mesenchymal nephrogenic progenitors receive signals to undergo the well characterized mesenchymal-to-epithelial transition leading to the generation of diverse renal epithelia. The production of mesenchymal nephron progenitors and their subsequent differentiation occurs throughout nephrogenesis. Inhibition of either of these steps will lead to renal developmental anomalies such as renal dysplasia, aplasia, or agenesis. These defects have previously been attributed to only abnormal induction of the metanephric blastema by the ureteric bud (50). Thus the biochemical and genetic regulators of renal morphogenesis must mediate both the production and induction of metanephric mesenchymal progenitors throughout active nephrogenesis.

ACKNOWLEDGMENT

The work performed in the author's laboratory was supported by National Institute of Health Research grant RO1 DK45218 and a New York Heart Association Investigatorship. I thank Drs. David Cohen, Richard Abramson, and Qais Al-Awqati for their critiques of this manuscript. I thank Ms. Annie Gero for her dedication to my children.

Literature Cited

1. Bulger RE 1987. The urinary system. In *Histology*. ed. L Weiss, RO Greep, pp. 831–88. New York: McGraw-Hill
2. Croiselle Y. 1969. Detection et localization de constituants specifiques de rein a des stades precoces de la tubulogenese chez embryos de poulet et caille. *Bull. Biol. Fr. Belg.* 103:339–73

3. Croiselle Y. 1970. Appearance and disappearance of organ-specific components during kidney tubulogenesis in chick and quail embryos. In *Protides of the Biological Fluids*, ed. H Peters, pp. 79–85. Oxford: Pergamon
4. Croiselle Y, Gumpel-Pinot M, Martin C. 1976. Embryologie experimentale. La differenciation des tubes secreteurs

du rein chez les oiseaux: effects des inducteurs heterogenes. *C.R. Acad. Sci. Paris Series D* 282:1987–90

5. Dalaq A. 1942. Contribution a l'etude morphogenetique chez les anoures III. Operations visant l'eubache pronephretique au seuile gastrulation. *Arch. Biol.* 53:1–124

6. Dressler GR, Deutsch U, Chowdhury K, Nornes HO, Gruss P. 1990. *Pax2*, a new murine paired-box-containing gene and its expression in the developing excretory system. *Development* 109:787–95

7. Dressler GR, Wilkinson JE, Rothenpieler UW, Patterson LT, Williams-Simons L, Westphal H. 1993. Deregulation of *Pax-2* expression in transgenic mice generates severe kidney abnormalities. *Nature* 362:65–67

8. Ekblom P. 1992. Renal development. In *The Kidney: Physiology and Pathophysiolgy*, ed. DW Seldin, G Giebisch, pp. 475–501. New York: Raven

9. Fox H. 1963. The amphibian pronephros. *Quart. Rev. Biol.* 38:1–25

10. Geertruyden J van. 1942. Quelques preacutecisions sur le development du proneacutephros et de l'uretere primaire chez les amphibiens anoures. *Ann. Soc. Roy. Belg.* 73:180–95

11. Gregory ER. 1900. Observations on the development of the excretory system in turtles. *Zool. Jahrbücher Abt. F. Anat. Ontog. Thiere.* BD XIII

12. Grobstein C. 1953. Morphogenetic interaction between embryonic mouse tissues separated by a membrane filter. *Nature* 172:869–71

13. Grobstein C. 1953. Inductive epithelio-mesenchymal interaction in cultured organ rudiments of the mouse. *Science* 118:52–55

14. Grobstein C. 1955. Inductive interaction in the development of the mouse metanephros. *J. Exp. Zool.* 130:319–40

15. Grobstein C. 1956. Trans-filter induction in mouse metanephrogenic mesenchyme. *Exp. Cell Res.* 10:424–40

16. Grobstein C. 1957. Some transmission characteristics of the tubule-inducing influence on mouse metanephrogenic mesenchyme. *Exp. Cell Res.* 13:575–87

17. Gruenwald P. 1937. Zur Entwicklungsmechanik des Urogenital-Systems beim Huhn. *Arch. Entwicklungsmech.* 136:786–813

18. Gruenwald P. 1942. Experiments on the distribution and activation of nephrogenic potency in the embryonic mesenchyme. *Physiol. Zool.* 15:396–409

19. Gruenwald P. 1943. Stimulation of nephrogenic tissues by normal and abnormal inductors. *Anat. Rec.* 86:321–39

20. Gruenwald P. 1952. Development of the excretory system. *Ann. NY Acad. Sci.* 55:142–46

21. Gumpel-Pinot M, Martin C, Croiselle Y. 1971. Sur l'organogenese du mesonephros chez les oiseaux: realisation in vitro de mesonephros chimeres caille-poulet. *C.R. Acad. Sci. Paris Series D* 272:737–39

22. Hay ED. 1990. Epithelial-mesenchymal transitions. *Semin. Dev. Biol.* 1:347–56

23. Herzlinger D, Cohen D, Abramson R. 1993. Nephrogenic progenitors delaminate from the ureteric bud. *J. Cell Sci.* In press

24. Herzlinger D, Koseki C, Mikawa T, Al-Awqati Q. 1992. The metanephric mesenchyme contains multipotent stem cells whose fate is restricted after induction. *Development* 114:565–72

25. Hoffman CK. 1889. Zur Entwicklungsgeschichte der Urogenitalorgane bei den Reptilien. *Z. Wiss. Zool.* BD: XLVIII

26. Holfreter J. 1944. Experimental studies on the development of the pronephros. *Rev. Can. Biol.* 3:220–50

27. Honig MG, Hume RI. 1989. DiI and DiO: versatile fluorescent dyes for neuronal labeling and tracing. *Trends Neurosci.* 12:333–41

28. Huber GC. 1905. On the development and shape of uriniferous tubules of certain higher mammals. *Am. J. Anat.* IV:1–98 (Suppl.)

29. Jaenisch R, Soriano P. 1986. Retroviruses as probes for mammalian development. *Cell* 46:19–29

30. Koseki C, Herzlinger D, Al-Awqati Q. 1991. Integration of embryonic nephrogenic cells carrying a reporter gene into functioning nephros. *Am. J. Physiol.* 261:C550–54

31. Koseki C, Herzlinger D, Al-Awqati Q. 1992. Apoptosis in metanephric development. *J. Cell Biol.* 119(5):1327–33

32. Kupffer C. 1865. Untersunchungen uber die Entwicklung des Harn- und Geschlechtsystems. *Arch Micro. Anat.* BD.I

33. Le Douarin N. 1973. A biological cell labeling technique and its use in experimental embryology. *Dev. Biol.* 30:217–22

34. Lehtonen E. 1975. Epithelio-mesenchymal interface during mouse kidney tubule induction in vivo. *J. Embryol. Exp. Morphol.* 34:695–705

35. Martin C. 1976. Etude chez les oiseaux

de l'influence du mesenchyme nephrogene sur le canal de Wolff a l'aide d'associations heterospecifiques. *J. Embryol. Exp. Morphol.* 35:485–95

36. Martin C, Croiselle Y, Gumpel-Pinot M. 1971. Sur l'organogenese du mesonephros chez les oiseaux; potentialities evolutives du mesenchyme mesonephrogene de l'embryo de poulet. *C.R. Acad. Sci. Paris* 272:863–64

37. Moore KL, Persand TVN. 1993. *The Developing Human: Clinically Oriented Embryology*, pp. 265–303. Philadelphia: Saunders

38. O'Conner RJ. 1938. Experiments on the development of the pronephric duct. *J. Anat.* 73:145–54

39. O'Conner RJ. 1939. Experiments on the development of the amphibian mesonephros. *J. Anat.* 74:33–44

40. Overton J. 1959. Studies on the mode and outgrowth of the amphibian pronephric duct. *J. Embryol. Exp. Morphol.* 7:86–93

41. Potter EL. 1972. *Normal and Abnormal Development of the Kidney*, pp. 1–79. Chicago: Year Book Medical

42. Price J, Turner D, Cepko C. 1987. Lineage analysis in the vertebrate nervous system by retrovirus-mediated gene transfer. *Proc. Natl. Acad. Sci. USA* 84:156–60

43. Rawles M. 1936. A study in the localization of organ-forming areas in the chick blastoderm of the head-process stage. *J. Exp. Zool.* 72:271–315

44. Riede K. 1887. Untersuchungen zur Entwicklung der bleibenden Niere. Inaug. Diss. Munchen

45. Sadler TW. 1990. *Langman's Medical Embryology*, ed. J Gardner, VM Vaughn, pp. 260–96. New York: Williams & Wilkins

46. Saxen L. 1987. *Organogenesis of the Kidney*, ed. PN Barlow, PB Green, CC Wylie. Cambridge: Cambridge Univ. Press

47. Sedgewick A. 1880. Development of the kidney in its relation to the Wolffian body in the chick. *Quart. J. Micro. Sci.* XX

48. Sedgewick A. 1897. On the existence of a head-kidney in the chick-embryo and on certain points in the development of the Mullerian duct. *Quart. J. Micro. Sci.* 19:1–20

49. Sonnenberg E, Godecke A, Walter B, Bladt F, Birchmeier C. 1991. Transient and locally restricted expression of the ros1 protooncogene during mouse development. *EMBO J.* 10(12) 3693–702

50. Stevens FD. 1983. *Congenital Malformations of the Urinary Tract*, pp. 381–482. New York: Praeger

51. Torrey TW. 1965. Morphogenesis of the vertebrate kidney. In *Organogenesis*, ed. RL DeHahn, H Ursprung, pp. 559–79. New York: Holt, Rinehart and Winston

52. Torrey TW. 1954. The early development of the human nephros. *Contrib. Embryol. Carnegie Inst. Wash.* 35:175–97

53. Torrey TW. 1943. The development of the urinogenital system of the albino rat. I. The kidney and its ducts. *Am. J. Anat.* 72:113–47

Annu. Rev. Physiol. 1994. 56:691–709
Copyright © 1994 by Annual Reviews Inc. All rights reserved

MATHEMATICAL MODELS OF TUBULAR TRANSPORT

Alan M. Weinstein

Department of Medicine and Department of Physiology and Biophysics, Cornell
University Medical College, New York, New York 10021

KEY WORDS: proximal tubule, cortical collecting duct, sodium transport, potassium
               transport, acid-base transport

MATHEMATICAL MODELS OF TUBULAR TRANSPORT

Mathematical models of the renal tubule are classified as epithelial, tubular,
or multitubular. The simplest epithelial models are single equations that
represent the overall transepithelial solute and water fluxes as functions of
the luminal and peritubular bath conditions. More detailed models represent
both luminal and peritubular cell membranes, in parallel with a tight junction,
all in series with an epithelial basement membrane. In these models, the
presence of transport components in series renders the cell and interspace
concentrations unknown variables that must be determined via solution of
a set of conservation equations. The tubular models allow prediction of the
effect of epithelial transport to modify the luminal solution and, conversely,
the effect of altered luminal composition on transepithelial fluxes. Here the
conservation equations constitute a set of ordinary differential equations,
with initial data that must be integrated along the tubule length. The lining
epithelium may be represented by single flux equations, or by a compart-
mental model. The multitubular models are mathematically the most complex
and have the character of boundary value problems, where transport along
an entire tubule contributes to the interstitial composition. Thus computational effort (i.e. repeated tubule integration) is required to determine
interstitial concentrations compatible with all contributing tubule fluxes.

The aims for the development of models of renal tubules have been either
to illustrate proposed transport mechanisms, or to identify specific model
parameters from experimental data. For example, the first detailed models

691

0066–4278/94/0315–0691$05.00

of a renal epithelium were for the proximal tubule and were used to see whether plausible parameter sets could be developed that would yield isotonic water transport (36, 66, 67, 77). Although these models were compatible with overall epithelial fluxes and permeabilities, none claimed to have uniquely defined the intraepithelial water fluxes by a fit to data. Parenthetically, in each of these models, substantial reabsorptive water flow traversed the tight junction. Thus far none but the simplest (single equation) representations of the epithelium have been utilized in experimental data analysis. In what follows, we examine many of the models of renal tubular transport and several examples of multitubular models. The special mathematical features of these efforts will be indicated, but the principal focus will be on the physiological questions addressed with each modeling effort.

Model Equations

In general, the geometry of renal tubule models has been rather uniform among investigators (Figure 1). In the detailed epithelial models there is a cellular compartment, bounded by luminal and basolateral membranes, and a paracellular compartment, bounded by tight junction and epithelial basement membrane. The epithelial basement membrane together with the interstitial tissue constitute a diffusion barrier between lateral interspace (LIS) and capillary, so that LIS solute concentrations may be distinct from those within the peritubular capillary or peritubular bath. The models distinguish themselves according to the number of solute species considered. For the early models concerned with osmotic water flow, one or two nonelectrolytes (e.g. NaCl and urea) were considered. More detailed representation of renal tubule function has since required electrolyte species, including protons and multiple buffers. The unknown model variables are the solute concentrations and electrical potential along the tubule lumen, and for the detailed epithelia, the concentrations and potentials within cell and LIS. The model equations are those for mass conservation and electroneutrality. For any point, x, and time, t, in a tubule of cross section area A, solute i is at concentration $c_i(x,t)$ and flowing at $F_i(x,t)$. Especially for the representation of buffer systems, it has proven convenient to formulate the mass conservation equations in terms of the generation of solute, $s_i(x,t)$, namely

$$s_i(x,t) = \frac{\partial F_i}{\partial x}(x,t) + \sum_\beta J_i^\beta(x,t) + \frac{\partial}{\partial t}[Ac_i(x,t)], \qquad 1.$$

in which, $\dfrac{\partial F_i}{\partial x}$ is the increment in axial flow, $\displaystyle\sum_\beta J_i^\beta$ is the total reabsorptive flux across cells and tight junctions, and $\dfrac{\partial [Ac_i]}{\partial t}$ is the local accumulation

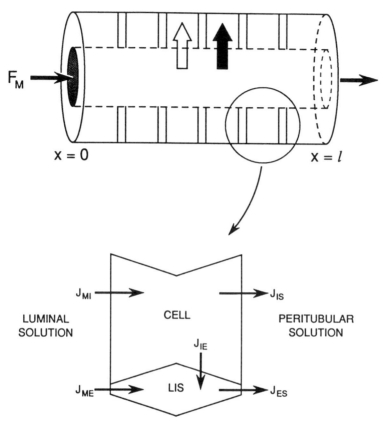

Figure 1   Schematic representation of proximal tubule as a cylinder with inlet at $x = 0$ and outlet at $x = 1$. F_M is luminal perfusion. Transmural fluxes (J) from lumen to peritubular solution are specified by an epithelial model comprised of cellular and lateral intracellular (LIS) compartments. Fluxes across luminal, lateral, and basal cell membranes are denoted J_{MI}, J_{IE}, and J_{IS}; fluxes across the tight junction and interspace basement membranes are J_{ME} and J_{ES}.

of solute. Equation 1 is itself a simplification of mass conservation within the tubule in that it implicitly averages any radial concentration differences into $c_i(x,t)$. In general this is valid when the resistance to diffusion across the luminal membranes is much greater than within the tubule fluid. More detailed considerations of intratubule gradients have been undertaken in the description of CO_2 flux across proximal tubule (e.g. 74, 92) or collecting duct (79). For each of the cellular and paracellular epithelial compartments, the analogue of Equation 1 is

$$s_i^\alpha (t) = \sum_\beta J_i^{\alpha\beta} (t) + \frac{d}{dt} [V^\alpha(t)c_i^\alpha (t)], \qquad 2.$$

where $J_i^{\alpha\beta}$ is the flux of i out of compartment α into β and V^α is the volume of α. With these expressions for the generation of species i, the mass conservation equations for the non-reacting species (e.g. Na^+, K^+, Cl^-, glucose) are simply

$$s_i\,(x,t) = 0 \quad \text{or} \quad s_i^\alpha(t) \;\; = 0. \tag{3.}$$

For a buffer pair, B^- and HB, one equation is the conservation of total buffer

$$s_B + s_{HB} = 0, \tag{4.}$$

and the second is a kinetic relation for s_B in terms of the species concentrations. Corresponding to proton conservation, is the electroneutrality relation for all of the reactions:

$$\sum z_i s_i = 0, \tag{5.}$$

where z_i is the valence of species i. This is distinct from the electroneutrality among the concentrations at each point along the lumen or within the cells:

$$\sum z_i c_i\,(x,t) = 0 \quad \text{or} \quad \sum z_i c_i^\alpha(t) = 0. \tag{6.}$$

Completion of the model equations entails specification of the axial flows and of the transmembrane fluxes. The axial solute flow along renal tubules is accurately represented as the convective flow

$$F_i\,(x,t) = F_v\,(x,t)\,c_i\,(x,t), \tag{7.}$$

in which $F_v(x,t)$ is the volume flow. However, in models of the renal medullary core (interstitial plus vascular compartments), the importance of electrodiffusive flows must be acknowledged by using the full Nernst-Planck equation (81):

$$F_i\,(x,t) = F_v\,(x,t)\,c_i\,(x,t) - D_i A \left[\frac{dc_i}{dx} + \frac{z_i F}{RT}\,c_i\,\frac{d\psi}{dx}\right], \tag{8.}$$

where D_i is the diffusion coefficient of species i, F is the Faraday constant, R is the gas constant, T is the absolute temperature, and ψ is the electrical potential along the tubule or core. For the transepithelial flux of solute i, J_i, the simple epithelial models generally use some form of the Kedem-Katchalsky equation (39, 73),

$$J_i = J_v\,(1 - \sigma_i)\,\bar{c}_i + \sum_{j=1}^{n} L_{ij}\,\Delta\bar{\mu}_j + J_i^a. \tag{9.}$$

The first term is convective solute reabsorption where J_v is transepithelial volume flux, σ_i is the reflection coefficient, and $\overline{c}_i$ is a mean epithelial solute concentration. The second term incorporates both electrodiffusive and coupled transport. The sum is over all solute species, with $\Delta\overline{\mu}_j$ the transepithelial electrochemical potential difference of species i ($RT\Delta\ln c_i + z_iF\Delta\psi$), and L_{ij} a matrix of transport coefficients. Straight permeabilities (or conductances) appear as diagonal entries, L_{ii}, while coupled transport is represented by non-zero cross terms, L_{ij}. The last term, J_i^a, represents any fluxes that result from active transport. In the absence of coupled transport, the solute flux may be written

$$J_i = J_v \, (1 - \sigma_i) \, \overline{c}_i + P_i \left[\Delta c_i + \left(\frac{z_iF}{RT}\right) \overline{c}_i\Delta\psi + J_i^a\right]$$ 10.

in which P_i is the conventional permeability. The equation for transepithelial volume flux, J_v, is a sum of hydrostatic and osmotic terms

$$J_v = L_p\left[\Delta p - RT\sum_{i=1}^{n} \sigma_i\Delta c_i\right] = v_wP_f\left[\frac{\Delta p}{RT} - \sum_{i=1}^{n} \sigma_i\Delta c_i\right],$$ 11.

in which $\overline{V}_w$ is the partial molar volume of water, and L_p [ml/s•cm^2•(mOsm/cm^3)] or P_f (cm/s) are water permeability coefficients. The detailed epithelial models have generally been built up using modifications of these transport equations for each of the cellular and paracellular membranes. At this level, nonlinear (i.e. Goldman) channel fluxes can be included along with nonconstant (or regulated) permeabilities. For coupled solutes fluxes, specific kinetic descriptions have been employed.

Proximal Tubule

The proximal tubule has been the most extensively modeled nephron segment. The issues addressed include the routes and driving forces for water reabsorption, regulation of sodium transport by peritubular protein vis-à-vis glomerulotubular balance, regulation of proton secretion, and mechanisms for proximal chloride transport. The earliest experimental observations on epithelial water transport were made in the intestine and gallbladder. The two salient features were (a) the capability of water reabsorption against an adverse osmotic gradient (lumen hypertonic to serosa), i.e. uphill water transport, and (b) rapid water reabsorption in the absence of any substantial luminal hypotonicity, i.e. isotonic transport (reviewed in 101). The first mathematical models of epithelial transport focused on uphill water transport by the gastrointestinal epithelia driven by salt transport into an intraepithelial middle compartment (54, 56). Although the capability of these models to simulate isotonic transport was initially questioned (20, 22), these doubts were prompted by the unfortunate identification of the cell membrane water permeability with the overall epithelial L_p. When it was recognized that intraepithelial solute polarization effects could render epithelial L_p a small fraction of the cell membrane L_p, gallbladder models were constructed that simulated both the observed uphill and isotonic transport (100).

With respect to proximal tubule, isotonic transport was established experimentally via micropuncture (53, 107), and the early focus of proximal tubule models was the identification of the transepithelial driving forces for water reabsorption. These included peritubular oncotic pressure (66), small degrees of luminal hypotonicity (3, 4, 69), and a reflection coefficient for HCO_3^-, greater than that of Cl^- across the proximal tubule (67, 68). The latter effect refers to the rapid bicarbonate depletion within proximal tubule fluid, and with reference to Equation 11, the greater transepithelial osmotic effect of peritubular HCO_3^- compared with luminal Cl^-. In the face of an abundance of transepithelial driving forces, it remained an open question whether proximal tubule could transport water against an adverse osmotic gradient, i.e. whether intraepithelial solute-solvent coupling via an intraepithelial compartment provided an important force for water reabsorption. Mathematical models of rat proximal tubule suggested that such coupled transport was important and perhaps accounted for two thirds of the isotonic water reabsorption (94, 96). As with the gallbladder, this implied that the overall L_p of proximal tubule could be substantially less than that of the cell membranes and could be modified via changes in the dimensions of the paracellular pathway (95). A recent micropuncture investigation, with perfusion of rat proximal tubule lumen and peritubular capillaries, was designed explicitly to assess the magnitude of coupled water transport (29). Transepithelial volume flows were measured in response to changes in transtubular driving forces and the results fit to a modified form of Equation 11

$$J_v = L_p \left[\Delta \pi - RT \, \sigma_{NaCl} \, \Delta \, c_{NaCl} \right] + J_v^a \, ,$$

which acknowledges the possibility of a coupled water flux, J_v^a. Indeed, it was found that the coupled water flux by these tubules was approximately 75% of the rate of isotonic transport. In rabbit proximal tubule, it had been observed that epithelial L_p decreased with the application of large osmotic gradients (9). This result was congruent with earlier observations in gallbladder (21) and also suggested the presence of an internal compartment or, equivalently, an internal diffusion barrier whose resistance increased along with the ambient osmolality. In most of these models it was assumed that the middle compartment mediating solute-solvent coupling was the lateral intercellular space. Williams & Schafer (106) emphasized that the renal cortical interstitium may also serve as the site for solute polarization. In their model of rabbit proximal tubule, an epithelium (represented by Equations 9 and 11) is placed in series with an interstitial compartment, and thus has its overall water permeability reduced by half.

A number of workers have addressed the issue of whether there is significant water flux across the tight junction. Indirect experimental observations supporting such flux include whole epithelial solvent drag of ionic species (5, 10, 27) and streaming potentials with the application of an impermeant osmotic agent (16, 26, 89). Either streaming potentials or solvent drag can result from a solute polarization effect within the interspace. With solute polarization, water flux across the cell and through the lateral interspace alters interspace ion concentrations, thus promoting either a diffusion potential or diffusive flux across the tight junction (63). These concerns pose a quantitative problem as to whether one could construct a model of proximal tubule with just the right solute polarization to yield the observed reflection coefficients and L_p. So far this has not been achieved. For the rat, the data of Frömter et al (27) were used to determine interspace models for this epithelium (97). It was found that all of the compatible interspace models required substantial tight junction convective chloride flux. Serious objections to the tight junction as a water pathway have been raised through the application of pore theory (8). Preisig & Berry (62) measured the permeation of sucrose and mannitol across rat proximal tubule (tight junction), calculated the equivalent pore dimensions using the Renkin equations, and then estimated the water permeability of this pathway to be at most 2% of tubule water permeability. An important contribution to this discussion came with the suggestion of Fraser & Baines (25) that the tight junction might be more realistically represented as a fiber matrix rather than as a collection of pores. The critical feature of the fiber matrix equations (18) is that for a given solute permeability, the water permeability can be substantially greater than that predicted from the Renkin equations. Such a fiber matrix formulation could yield solute and water permeabilities compatible with data from rat proximal tubule (25). Implicit in these considerations is the assumption that the reflection coefficients of the cellular pathway are unity. Although Welling et al (102, 103) found osmotic reflection coefficients for NaCl and KCl less than 1.0 across peritubular membrane of rabbit proximal tubule, these results have not been confirmed by others either in vesicles (90, 57) or in whole tubules (76).

With the recognition that the tight junction could be an important route for sodium flux, Lewy & Windhager (47) postulated that modulation of junctional fluxes could be important in the regulation of proximal tubule sodium reabsorption. In their scheme, increases in peritubular protein (i.e. oncotic pressure) via decreases in renal interstitial pressure would enhance water and sodium removal from lateral interspaces and thus decrease backflux of sodium across the tight junction into the tubule lumen. In this way, increases in glomerular filtration, which were achieved by increases in filtration fraction (and thus a greater concentration of capillary protein), could be expected to incur a concomitant increase in proximal sodium reabsorption. Such proportional changes in filtration had been observed experimentally (72) and termed glomerulotubular balance (28). Experimental support for this scheme came with observations on aortic constriction, where there is a near perfect balance between declines in glomerular filtration and decreases in proximal reabsorption. When the associated decrease in peritubular protein was prevented (by capillary perfusion), the decrease in proximal reabsorption was also prevented (12). Direct demonstration of peritubular control of proximal sodium reabsorption came with the simultaneous perfusion of tubule lumen and peritubular capillaries with solutions of varying protein concentration (31). The susceptibility of tight junctional permeability to changes in renal interstitial pressure was documented in observations on saline-expanded animals, including decreases in tubule electrical resistance (11, 75) and decreases in NaCl reflection coefficient (6). Thus Deen et al (19) incorporated peritubular control of proximal tubule sodium transport into a model of peritubular capillary, but this was not a detailed epithelial model and did not address the mechanism of modulating the sodium flux. In the detailed epithelial models in which epithelial parameters were fixed, the effect of peritubular protein on sodium transport was negligible. Even interspace compliance, which influenced coupled water transport, did not impact significantly on the magnitude of isotonic sodium reabsorption (95). To rationalize the effect of peritubular protein, an empirical model of a compliant tight junction was formulated in which junctional permeabilities increased and salt reflection coefficient decreased in response to interspace hydrostatic pressure (98). With such a tight junction, the scheme of peritubular control of proximal sodium reabsorption could be realized and, in particular, the data of Green et al (31) could be simulated. Unfortunately, the model seemed to predict massive-junctional disruption with small decreases in peritubular oncotic force. There is no compelling evidence, however, that such large epithelial permeability changes occur under normal circumstances (7, 29, 75). Thus one is left to consider the possibility that interstitial pressure may have a direct cellular effect on the rate of active sodium transport. Indeed, Green et al (29) observed that in the transition from low to high peritubular protein, there was a doubling of isotonic volume reabsorption, with no discernible effect on L_p or the salt reflection coefficient.

Perhaps the most important issue confronting models of glomerulotubular balance is that increases in glomerular filtration may occur secondary to changes in plasma flow, with no change in filtration fraction, and thus no change in peritubular protein concentration. In this case, glomerulotubular balance, or more precisely perfusion-absorption balance (105), is still observed. Simply put, increases in luminal flow enhance sodium reabsorption. Mathematically, glomerulotubular balance may be factored into luminal and peritubular components (98). Glomerulotubular balance, B_G, may be defined as the fractional change in proximal reabsorption, APR, with changes in filtration, GFR:

$$B_G = \frac{GFR}{APR} \frac{dAPR}{dGFR} .$$
                                                                          12.

Since GFR is the product of filtration fraction, FF, and glomerular plasma flow, GPF,

$$GFR = FF \cdot GPF ,$$
                                                                          13.

it is natural to consider filtration balance, B_F, and flow velocity balance, B_V, as the impact of each variable separately

$$B_F = \frac{FF}{APR} \frac{dAPR}{dFF} ,$$
$$B_V = \frac{GPF}{APR} \frac{dAPR}{dGPF} .$$
                                                                          14.

Then for any perturbation of GFR, B_G is the weighted average of B_F and B_V,

$$B_G = B_F \left[1 - FF \frac{dGPF}{dGFR} \right] + B_V \left[1 - GPF \frac{dFF}{dGFR} \right] ,$$
                                                                          15.

in which the coefficients in brackets sum to 1.0. Experimentally, perfusion absorption balance has been verified most thoroughly for $NaHCO_3$ reabsorption (1, 13), but is also reported for NaCl reabsorption (30). To a certain extent, enhanced bicarbonate reabsorption will follow the perfusion dependent increases in luminal bicarbonate. Nevertheless, even when changes in concentration profile are accounted for, there are still substantial flow-dependent effects. Alpern & Rector (2) developed a schematic model of $NaHCO_3$ reabsorption by proximal tubule, in which proton secretion was represented as a Michaelis-Mentin expression. In this formulation, the $K_{1/2}$ for $NaHCO_3$ reabsorption was fashioned empirically, so that it decreased exponentially with increasing luminal flow. The V_{max} was unaffected, and the conceptual underpinning was that the flow was decreasing an unstirred layer. This prediction has received recent support in the experimental study of Preisig (60), in which she demonstrated enhanced luminal membrane

Na^+/H^+ exchange activity with higher luminal perfusion rates. Further, this enhanced activity was shown to be an affinity effect and not an influence on maximal transport. Parenthetically, Verkman & Alpern (91) developed a detailed model of acid/base transport by proximal tubule epithelium, in which the individual membrane coupled transporters received kinetic descriptions. In contrast to the nonequilibrium thermodynamic formulation, this type of model would be amenable to representing flow-dependent affinity changes. Such a model has recently been extended to a whole tubule model (88), but flow-dependent affinities have not yet been explored.

The magnitude of the diffusion barrier of the proximal tubule brush-border has recently drawn additional attention in relation to chloride transport. Reabsorptive chloride entry across the luminal membrane of proximal tubule cells, long thought to be a Cl^-/HCO_3^- exchange process, has also been shown to occur via Cl^-/HCO_2^- (38). In the Cl^- entry step, formate moves from cell to lumen, where it is protonated to formic acid, which recycles to the cell interior via nonionic diffusion. Evidence for this proposed scheme includes the presence of the exchanger in membrane vesicles (38) and, with application of formate to whole tubules, enhancement of NaCl reabsorption (71) in association with proximal tubule cell swelling (70). One difficulty with this proposed scheme came with the determination of the luminal cell membrane formic acid permeability and the finding that it was not even close to being large enough to sustain sufficient formic acid recycling (61). In a mathematical model of rat proximal tubule, which represented Cl^-/HCO_2^- exchange, it was found that a membrane formic acid permeability nearly two orders of magnitude greater than reported was required to sustain one third of the reabsorptive chloride flux (99). It had been speculated that the proximal tubule brush border, as a diffusion barrier or unstirred layer, might have produced an underestimate of the luminal membrane formic acid permeability. This issue was addressed in a mathematical model of the brush border (42). In essence this was a multitubular model, with electrolyte flows along villous and intervillous spaces and with fluxes across the villous membrane. In examining transport of buffers in a villous system, this work extended earlier treatments of buffered species across a flat membrane (32) and neutral species across a villous membrane (108). Although the villous system provided a diffusion barrier, the excess of buffer acted to enhance transport of the acid species. Ultimately it was concluded that the impact of the unstirred layer was likely to be less than a 25% reduction in the measured (relative to the true) cell membrane formic acid permeability. A second point of concern for the formate recycling scheme was the model prediction that even with high cell membrane formic acid permeability, the impact of formate application on overall NaCl transport would still be smaller than reported (99). Thus the mechanism of proximal chloride reabsorption remains an active area of investigation, in which input from model calculations has been helpful in highlighting areas in which our understanding is incomplete.

Thin Descending Limb

Interest in modeling this nephron segment derived initially from its importance in the renal concentrating mechanism. Indeed, all of the models of the renal medulla have necessarily included models of the thin descending limb. Electrolyte models (representing Na^+, K^+, Cl^-, and urea) of rabbit descending limb have been developed, either as a single tubule model in which peritubular concentration profiles are assumed (87), or as part of a multitubule model of the renal medulla, where the peritubular environment is computed to achieve consistency with all transport into the renal interstitium at each medullary level (81). In either case, the transport equations were those of a simple epithelium and, using similar transport parameters, both models predicted that increases in tubule NaCl concentration occurred principally by water abstraction. Although mass flow for NaCl showed little fractional change along descending limb, flow of both KCl and urea increased substantially (87). More recently, an electrolyte model of descending limb has been developed that includes HCO_3^- as well as the $HPO_4^=$/ $H_2PO_4^-$ and NH_3/NH_4^+ buffer pairs (50). For this model, it could not be assumed that dissolved CO_2 and H_2CO_3 are at equilibrium in view of the absence of carbonic anhydrase. Thus the equation for generation of H_2CO_3 is

$$s_{H_2CO_3}(x) = k_1 c_{CO_2}(x) - k_{-1} c_{H_2CO_3}(x), \qquad 16.$$

where k_1 and k_{-1} are the rate constants for hydration and dehydration. These workers developed their model to examine the mechanisms responsible for the increase in luminal HCO_3^- along the length of descending limb: water abstraction, diffusive HCO_3 entry, or NH_3 entry. Their calculations indicate that there is considerable interplay among these mechanisms, insofar as a decrease in one produces conditions that enhance the operation of the others. Under baseline conditions, however, the most important component was NH_3 addition. What was particularly attractive in the development of this model was the coordinated experimental effort to determine the tubule permeabilities to HCO_3^-, NH_3, and NH_4^+ (24). In this work, a clever experimental design using isolated perfused descending limbs permitted the measurement of luminal CO_2 and total ammonia to be translated into net fluxes of NH_3 and NH_4^+, and thus the tubule permeabilities of both of these species.

Thick Ascending Limb

Despite its quantitative importance to transport along the nephron, the effort to model the thick ascending limb has not been extensive. A simple epithelial model of Na^+, K^+, Cl^- and urea transport was fashioned by Stephenson et al (81) in conjunction with their electrolyte model of the renal medulla. Of particular interest was their observation that, in the physiological range of tubule flows, the end-tubule sodium concentration was a steep function of perfusion rate. These considerations take on importance with respect to the sensitivity of tubuloglomerular feedback (see below). To examine acid/base transport by this segment, a simple epithelial model was fashioned that included the HCO_3^-/H_2CO_3 and NH_3/NH_4^+ buffer pairs, along with the uncatalyzed hydration of CO_2 (51). With this model, the tubule ammonia profile showed that roughly 90% of reabsorption occurred within the medullary portion of the thick limb, thus trapping ammonia within the medulla and leaving it available for buffering collecting duct proton secretion. The first detailed epithelial model of the ascending limb was fashioned by Fernandes & Ferreira (23). The model included only Na^+, K^+, and Cl^- as solute species, but permitted the simulation of time-dependent experiments. First, model parameters were chosen to achieve congruence of steady state model predictions with known epithelial properties. Then, using these parameters, they simulated the time course of furosemide or ouabain administration and obtained an enviable reproduction of observed epithelial and cellular electrical potentials.

Collecting Duct

Every multitubular model of the renal concentrating mechanism has included a simple epithelial model of collecting duct, and such models have been utilized for the analysis of experimental data (e.g. 41). In their broad effort to characterize acid/base transport throughout the nephron, Knepper and colleagues developed a simple model of the cortical collecting tubule that included several buffers, as well as the uncatalyzed hydration of CO_2 (79). Model predictions were fit to data to estimate the tubule NH_3 permeability. This effort also yielded the rate constant for the uncatalyzed dehydration of H_2CO_3 in the isolated perfused tubule, virtually identical to that in free solution. A detailed epithelial model of the cortical collecting tubule (CCT) was recently developed by Strieter et al (83, 85). This work built upon a rather extensive effort to simulate the sodium transporting (principal) cell of frog skin and toad urinary bladder (15, 37, 46, 84). One aim of this work was to examine the factors contributing to the constancy of CCT sodium reabsorption and potassium secretion over a wide range of luminal sodium concentrations. In this regard, it was found that a collecting duct with fixed permeabilities failed to deplete luminal sodium to the extent observed. Only when the principal cell luminal membrane sodium permeability was permitted to increase in response to both luminal and cytosolic sodium depletion, could model predictions become congruent with experiment. This sodium-dependent sodium permeability had been described previously in several epithelia, and an empirical mathematical representation had been proposed by Civan & Bookman (15). Mechanisms that might underly this variable Na^+ permeability have not yet been pursued in any modeling study. A second application of the CCT model was to examine enhanced potassium secretion by this nephron segment in conditions of peritubular alkalosis (78, 86). It was found that such a pH effect could only be accommodated through the incorporation of pH-dependent permeabilities. The transmission of peritubular pH to the interior of the principal cell occurred via a basolateral membrane Na^+/H^+ exchanger. Although pH-dependent luminal membrane K^+ channels have been documented in CCT (93), their presence alone (in the model) was not sufficient to modulate K^+ transport. (Without significant shifts in either Na^+ or Cl^- fluxes, electroneutrality required that isolated changes in K^+ permeability could only readjust K^+ driving forces.) Rather, alkalosis mediated increase in luminal membrane Na^+ channel permeability (55) appeared to provide a powerful force for enhancing K^+ secretion. With this mechanism, however, alkalosis increased Na^+ reabsorption unrealistically. Thus, in addition to the documented influence of pH on the principal cell cation channels, Strieter et al (85) proposed an alkalosis-induced decrease in tight junctional Cl^- permeability. In the model, the concerted effect of all three pH-dependent pathways was to enhance K^+ secretion in alkalosis, with stable Na^+ reabsorption. The predicted pH effect on the tight junction remains to be explored experimentally.

Tubuloglomerular Feedback

The analysis of tubuloglomerular feedback (TGF) requires some representation of glomerulus, proximal tubule, and loop of Henle, along with a feedback signal from macula densa to afferent arteriole. The tubule models used in these efforts have been simple epithelial models of nonelectrolyte fluxes (or even more schematic). With regard to steady-state operation of TGF, one interesting use of a model was to assess the impact of pressure natriuresis on the feedback signal. The specific question was whether pressure-dependent inhibition of proximal reabsorption could increase TGF sufficiently to account for homeostasis of GFR under swings of perfusion pressure (autoregulation). Although qualitatively this appeared plausible, model calculations indicated that within a physiological range of pressures, the effect would be small (17). More intensive use of TGF models has emerged from the effort to understand oscillations of glomerular filtration that have been observed in some experimental circumstances (33, 48). This required the development of time-dependent models of tubule flow and transport, and indeed it was found that these simulations could exhibit oscillatory behavior (34, 35, 58). In an elegant analysis of this system, Layton et al (45) rationalized the appearance of TGF oscillations according to the situation of the model within a two-dimensional (τ-γ) parameter space. The first parameter, τ, is simply the signal delay from macula densa to afferent arteriole. The parameter γ is the product of two terms: (a) the steady-state strength of the macula densa signal on thick ascending limb fluid flow, and (b) the axial concentration gradient of salt along the ascending limb at the macula densa. This latter term determines how variations in ascending limb flow will be perceived at the macula densa as variations in luminal concentration. The requirement for accurate solutions to the time-dependent equations of tubule transport also prompted these workers to identify suitable differencing schemes for numerical solution of these differential equations (44, 59). Rich & Moore (64) have represented the macula densa as a simple epithelial model in series with an interstitium and have examined the hypothesis that interstitial composition may be an intermediate signal in the TGF response. Among the model predictions, it was found that although macula densa water permeability led to dilution of the interstitium, it also acted to enhance the sensitivity of interstitial salt concentration as a function of luminal salt concentration.

Concentrating Mechanism

Modeling the renal concentrating mechanism led to the development of a number of multitube models of either renal medulla or entire kidney. The state of the vigorous effort to simulate the antidiuretic kidney was recently reviewed in detail and cannot be repeated here (40, 65, 80). Suffice it to say that no mathematical model of the concentrating renal medulla has succeeded in simulating the observed interstitial solute profiles while staying true to observed tubule permeabilities and transport rates. This difficulty has fueled the effort to obtain a secure data base, as well as the recent efforts to incorporate even more physiological and anatomical detail into the computer simulations. This detail includes axial heterogeneity of transport along the collecting duct (14), variable Henle limb depth into the medulla (43, 49), electrolyte effects (81, 82), and the anatomical organization of medullary structures (104). As a byproduct of this effort, numerical techniques have been developed for the efficient handling of large multi-nephron boundary value problems, and models have been developed that can be applied to the examination of other multi-tubule phenomena. As an example, Mejia et al (52) utilized a five-nephron kidney model to simulate the impact of atrial natriuretic factor, both to enhance glomerular filtration and to decrease collecting duct NaCl reabsorption. Although increases in urinary sodium secretion could be achieved by either glomerular or collecting duct effects of ANF, the collecting duct effect was required for simulating the observed increases in urinary NaCl concentration.

FUTURE DIRECTIONS

The current status of modeling renal tubules is such that one expects to encounter few mathematical difficulties, either in formulating the model equations or in obtaining numerical solutions at relatively small cost. The quality of the models depends upon the accuracy with which experimental data permit the definition of the important transport pathways and of the kinetics of those pathways. In the future, one may expect these models to grow—both in detail and in scope. New information on the multiplicity of ion channels and their regulation has barely begun to be included in tubule models. One can anticipate that as molecular biological techniques allow for the large-scale synthesis of coupled transporters, their kinetics will also be more precisely established and thus become susceptible to inclusion in epithelial models. Clearly as multiple transport pathways are identified, assigning quantitative importance requires the context of a model. With the development of accurate tubule models, the concatenation of these models into a nephron can become a meaningful endeavor. Beyond TGF and the concentrating mechanism, renal electrolyte metabolism (e.g. potassium and acid excretion) requires the creation of multisegmental models. Only with these models can one represent both the primary effect of a defective transporter (either through disease or drug) as well as its secondary downstream consequences. In this way, mathematical models of tubule transport will continue to serve as a repository for our understanding of renal function.

ACKNOWLEDGMENT

This work was supported by Public Health Service Grant 1-R01-DK-29857 from the National Institute of Arthritis, Diabetes, and Digestive and Kidney Disease. AM Weinstein is the recipient of an Irma T. Hirschl Career Scientist Award.

Literature Cited

1. Alpern RJ, Cogan MG, Rector FC Jr. 1983. Flow dependence of proximal tubular bicarbonate absorption. *Am. J. Physiol.* 245:F478–84
2. Alpern RJ, Rector FC Jr. 1985. A model of proximal tubular bicarbonate absorption. *Am. J. Physiol.* 248:F272–81
3. Andreoli TE, Schafer JA. 1978. Volume absorption in the pars recta. III.

Luminal hypotonicity as a driving force for isotonic volume absorption. *Am. J. Physiol.* 234:F349–55

4. Andreoli TE, Schafer JA. 1979. Effective luminal hypotonicity: The driving force for isotonic proximal tubular fluid absorption. *Am. J. Physiol.* 236:F89–96

5. Andreoli TE, Schafer JA, Troutman SL, Watkins MI. 1979. Solvent drag component of Cl⁻ flux in superficial proximal straight tubules: evidence for a para-cellular component of isotonic fluid absorption. *Am. J. Physiol.* 237:F455–62

6. Bentzel CJ, Reczek PR. 1978. Permeability changes in *Necturus* proximal tubule during volume expansion. *Am. J. Physiol.* 234:F225–34

7. Berry CA. 1983. Lack of effect of peritubular protein on passive NaCl transport in the rabbit proximal tubule. *J. Clin. Invest.* 71:268–81

8. Berry CA. 1983. Water permeability and pathways in the proximal tubule. *Am. J. Physiol.* 245:F279–94

9. Berry CA, Verkman AS. 1988. Osmotic gradient dependence of osmotic water permeability in rabbit proximal convoluted tubule. *J. Membr. Biol.* 105:33–43

10. Bomsztyk K, Wright FS. 1986. Dependence of ion fluxes on fluid transport by rat proximal tubule. *Am. J. Physiol.* 250:F680–89

11. Boulpaep EL. 1972. Permeability changes of the proximal tubule of *Necturus* during saline loading. *Am. J. Physiol.* 222:517–31

12. Brenner BM, Troy JL. 1971. Postglomerular vascular protein concentration: Evidence for a causal role in governing fluid reabsorption and glomerulotubular balance by the renal proximal tubule. *J. Clin. Invest.* 50: 336–49

13. Chan YL, Biagi B, Giebisch G. 1982. Control mechanisms of bicarbonate transport across the rat proximal convoluted tubule. *Am. J. Physiol.* 242:F532–43

14. Chandhoke PS, Siadel GM, Knepper MA. 1985. Role of inner medullary collecting duct NaCl transport in urinary concentration. *Am. J. Physiol.* 249:F688–97

15. Civan MM, Bookman RJ. 1982. Transepithelial Na transport and the intracellular fluids: a computer study. *J. Membr. Biol.* 65:63–80

16. Corman B. 1985. Streaming potentials and diffusion potentials across rabbit proximal convoluted tubule. *Pflügers Arch.* 403:156–63

17. Cupples WA, Wexler AS, Marsh DJ. 1990. Model of TGF-proximal tubule interactions in renal autoregulation. *Am. J. Physiol.* 259:F715–26

18. Curry FE, Michel AE. 1980. A fiber matrix control of capillary permeability. *Microvasc. Res.* 20:96–99

19. Deen WM, Robertson CR, Brenner BM. 1973. A model of peritubular capillary control of isotonic fluid reabsorption by the renal proximal tubule. *Biophys. J.* 13:340–58

20. Diamond JM. 1964. The mechanism of isotonic water transport. *J. Gen. Physiol.* 48:15–42

21. Diamond JM. 1966. Non-linear osmosis. *J. Physiol.* 183:58–82

22. Diamond JM, Bossert WH. 1967. Standing-gradient osmotic flow. A mechanism for coupling of water and solute transport in epithelia. *J. Gen. Physiol.* 50:2061–83

23. Fernandes PL, Ferreira HG. 1991. A mathematical model of rabbit cortical thick ascending limb of the Henle's loop. *Biochim. Biophys. Acta* 1064: 111–23

24. Flessner MF, Mejia R, Knepper MA. 1993. Ammonium and bicarbonate transport in isolated perfused rodent long-loop thin descending limbs. *Am. J. Physiol.* 264:F388–96

25. Fraser WD, Baines AD. 1989. Application of a fiber-matrix model to transport in renal tubules. *J. Gen. Physiol.* 94:863–79

26. Frömter E, Gessner K. 1974. Free-flow potential profile along rat kidney proximal tubule. *Pflügers Arch.* 351:69–83

27. Frömter E, Rumrich G, Ullrich KJ. 1973. Phenomenologic description of Na⁺, Cl⁻ and HCO₃⁻ absorption from proximal tubules. *Pflügers Arch.* 343: 189–220

28. Gertz KH, Boylan JW. 1973. Glomerular-tubular balance. In *Handbook of Physiology*, ed. J Orloff, RW Berliner, pp. 763–90. Washington, DC: Am. Physiol. Soc.

29. Green R, Giebisch G, Unwin R, Weinstein AM. 1991. Coupled water transport by rat proximal tubule. *Am. J. Physiol.* 261:F1046–54

30. Green R, Moriarty RJ, Giebisch G. 1981. Ionic requirements of proximal tubular fluid reabsorption: flow dependence of fluid transport. *Kidney Int.* 20:580–87

31. Green R, Windhager EE, Giebisch G. 1974. Protein oncotic pressure effects on proximal tubular fluid movement in the rat. *Am. J. Physiol.* 226:265–76

32. Gutknecht J, Tosteson DC. 1973. Dif-

fusion of weak acids across lipid bilayer membranes: effects of chemical reactions in the unstirred layers. *Science* 182:1258–61

33. Holstein-Rathlou N-H, Leyssac PP. 1987. Oscillations in the proximal intratubular pressure: a mathematical model *Am. J. Physiol.* 252:F560–72

34. Holstein-Rathlou N-H, Marsh DJ. 1989. Oscillations of tubular pressure, flow and distal chloride concentration in rats. *Am. J. Physiol.* 256:F1007–14

35. Holstein-Rathlou N-H, Marsh DJ. 1990. A dynamic model of the tubuloglomerular feedback mechanism. *Am. J. Physiol.* 258:F 1448–59

36. Huss RE, Marsh DJ. 1975. A model of NaCl and water flow through paracellular pathways of renal proximal tubules. *J. Membr. Biol.* 23:305–47

37. Hviid Larsen E. 1978. Computed steady-state ion concentrations and volume of epithelial cells. Dependence on transcellular Na transport. *Alfred Benzon Symp. XI Copenhagen, Munksgaard*, pp. 438–56

38. Karniski LP, Aronson PS. 1985. Chloride/formate exchange with formic acid recycling: a mechanism of active chloride transport across epithelial membranes. *Proc. Natl. Acad. Sci. USA* 82(18):6362–65

39. Katchalsky A, Curran PF. 1967. *Nonequilibrium Thermodynamics in Biophysics.* Cambridge: Harvard Univ. Press

40. Knepper MA, Chou C-L, Layton HE. 1993. How is urine concentrated by the renal inner medulla? In *Contributions to Nephrology*, ed. GM Berlyne, S Giovannetti, 102:144–60. Basel: Karger

41. Knepper MA, Sands JM, Chou C-L. 1989. Independence of urea and water transport in rat inner medullary collecting duct. *Am. J. Physiol.* 256:F610–21

42. Krahn TA, Aronson PS, Weinstein AM. 1993. Weak acid permeability of a villous membrane: formic acid transport across rat proximal tubule. *Bull. Math. Biol.* In press

43. Layton HE. 1986. Distribution of Henle's loops may enhance urine concentrating capability. *Biophys. J.* 49:1033–40

44. Layton HE, Pitman EB. 1993. A dynamic numerical method for models of renal tubules. *Bull. Math Biol.* In press

45. Layton HE, Pitman EB, Moore LC. 1991. Bifurcation analysis of TGF-mediated oscillations in SNGFR. *Am. J. Physiol.* 261:F904–19

46. Lew VL, Ferreira HG, Moura T. 1979. The behaviour of transporting epithelial cells: I. Computer analysis of a basic model. *Proc. R. Soc. London Ser. B* 206:53–83

47. Lewy JE, Windhager EE. 1968. Peritubular control of proximal tubular fluid reabsorption in the rat kidney. *Am. J. Physiol.* 214:943–54

48. Leyssac PP, Baumbach L. 1983. An oscillating intratubular pressure response to alterations in the loop of Henle flow in the rat kidney. *Acta Physiol. Scand.* 117:415–19

49. Lory P. 1987. Effectiveness of a salt transport cascade in the renal medulla: computer simulations. *Am. J. Physiol.* 252:F1095–1102

50. Mejia R, Flessner MF, Knepper MA. 1993. Model of ammonium and bicarbonate transport along LDL: implications of alkalinization of luminal fluid. *Am. J. Physiol.* 264:F397–403

51. Mejia R, Knepper MA. 1990. Acid-base transport in the renal thick ascending limb. *Math. Comput. Modelling* 14:538–42

52. Mejia R, Sands JM, Stephenson JL, Knepper MA. 1989. Renal actions of atrial natriuretic factor: a mathematical modeling study. *Am. J. Physiol.* 257:F1146–57

53. Morel F, Murayama Y. 1970. Simultaneous measurement of unidirectional and net sodium fluxes in microperfused rat proximal tubules. *Pflügers Arch.* 320:1–23

54. Ogilvie JT, McIntosh JR, Curran PF. 1963. Volume flow in a series-membrane system. *Biochim. Biophys. Acta* 66:441–44

55. Palmer LG, Frindt G. 1987. Effects of cell Ca and pH on Na channels from rat cortical collecting tubule. *Am. J. Physiol.* 253:F333–39

56. Patlak CS, Goldstein DA, Hoffman JF. 1963. The flow of solute and solvent across a two-membrane system. *J. Theoret. Biol.* 5:426–42

57. Pearce D, Verkman AS. 1989. NaCl reflection coefficients in proximal tubule apical and basolateral membrane vesicles. Measurement by induced osmosis and solvent drag. *Biophys. J.* 55:1251–59

58. Pitman EB, Layton HE. 1989. Tubuloglomerular feedback in a dynamic nephron. *Comm. Pure Appl. Math.* 42:759–87

59. Pitman EB, Layton HE, Moore LC. 1993. Numerical simulation of propa-

gating concentration profiles in renal tubules. *Bull. Math Biol.* In press

60. Preisig PA. 1992. Luminal flow rate regulates proximal tubule H-HCO$_3$ transporters. *Am. J. Physiol.* 262:F47–54

61. Preisig PA, Alpern RJ. 1989. Contributions of cellular leak pathways to net NaHCO$_3$ and NaCl absorption. *J. Clin. Invest.* 83:1859–67

62. Preisig PA, Berry CA. 1985. Evidence for transcellular osmotic water flow in rat proximal tubules. *Am. J. Physiol.* 249:F124–31

63. Reuss L, Simon B, Cotton CU. 1992. Pseudo-streaming potentials in *Necturus* gallbladder epithelium. III. The mechanism is a junctional diffusion potential. *J. Gen. Physiol.* 99:317–38

64. Rich A, Moore LC. 1989. Transport-coupling hypothesis of tubuloglomerular feedback signal transmission. *Am. J. Physiol.* 257:F882–92

65. Roy DR, Layton HE, Jamison RL. 1992. Countercurrent mechanism and its regulation. In *The Kidney: Physiology and Pathophysiology,* ed. DW Seldin, G Giebisch, pp. 1649–92. New York: Raven. 2nd Ed.

66. Sackin H, Boulpaep EL. 1975. Models for coupling of salt and water transport. *J. Gen. Physiol.* 66:671–733

67. Schafer JA, Patlak CS, Andreoli TE. 1975. A component of fluid absorption linked to passive ion flows in the superficial pars recta. *J. Gen. Physiol.* 66:445–71

68. Schafer JA, Patlak CS, Andreoli TE. 1977. Fluid absorption and active and passive ion flows in the rabbit superficial pars recta. *Am. J. Physiol.* 233:F154–67

69. Schafer JA, Patlak CS, Troutman SL, Andreoli TE. 1978. Volume absorption in the pars recta. II. Hydraulic conductivity coefficient. *Am. J. Physiol.* 234:F340–48

70. Schild L, Aronson PS, Giebisch G. 1990. Effects of apical membrane Cl$^-$-formate exchange on cell volume in rabbit proximal tubule. *Am. J. Physiol.* 258:F530–36

71. Schild L, Giebisch G, Karniski L, Aronson P. 1987. Effect of formate on volume reabsorption in the rabbit proximal tubule. *J. Clin. Invest.* 79:32–38

72. Schnermann J, Wahl M, Liebau G, Fischbach H. 1968. Balance between tubular flow rate and net fluid reabsorption in the proximal convolution of the rat kidney. *Pflügers Arch.* 304:90–103

73. Schultz SG. 1980. *Basic Principles of Membrane Transport.* New York: Cambridge Univ. Press

74. Schwartz GJ, Weinstein AM, Steele RE, Stephenson JL, Burg MB. 1981. Carbon dioxide permeability of rabbit proximal convoluted tubules. *Am. J. Physiol.* 240:F231–44

75. Seely JF. 1973. Effects of peritubular oncotic pressure on rat proximal tubule electrical resistance. *Kidney Int.* 4:28–35

76. Shi L-B, Fushimi K, Verkman AS. 1991. Solvent drag measurement of transcellular and basolateral membrane NaCl reflection coefficient in kidney proximal tubule. *J. Gen. Physiol.* 98:379–98

77. Spring KR. 1973. A parallel path model for *Necturus* proximal tubule. *J. Membr. Biol.* 13:323–52

78. Stanton BA, Giebisch G. 1982. Effect of pH on potassium transport by renal distal tubule. *Am. J. Physiol.* 242:F544–51

79. Star RA, Kurtz I, Mejia R, Burg MB, Knepper MA. 1987. Disequilibrium pH and ammonia transport in isolated perfused cortical collecting ducts. *Am. J. Physiol.* 253:F1232–42

80. Stephenson JL. 1992. Urinary concentration and dilution: models. In *Handbook of Physiology-Renal Physiology,* ed. EE Windhager, pp. 1350–408. New York: Oxford Univ. Press

81. Stephenson JL, Zang Y, Eftekhari A, Tewarson R. 1987. Electrolyte transport in a central core model of the renal medulla. *Am. J. Physiol.* 253:F982–97

82. Stephenson JL, Zang Y, Tewarson R. 1989. Electrolyte, urea, and water transport in a two-nephron central core model of the renal medulla. *Am. J. Physiol.* 257:F399–413

83. Strieter J, Stephenson JL, Giebisch G, Weinstein AM. 1992. A mathematical model of the rabbit cortical collecting tubule. *Am. J. Physiol.* 263:F1063–75

84. Strieter J, Stephenson JL, Palmer LG, Weinstein AM. 1990. Volume-activated chloride permeability can mediate cell volume regulation in a mathematical model of a tight epithelium. *J. Gen. Physiol.* 96:319–44

85. Strieter J, Weinstein AM, Giebisch G, Stephenson JL. 1992. Regulation of K transport in a mathematical model of the cortical collecting tubule. *Am. J. Physiol.* 263:F1076–86

86. Tabei K, Muto S, Furuya H, Asano Y. 1991. Intracellular alkalosis stimulates net potassium (K) secretion in

rabbit cortical collecting ducts (CCD). *J. Am. Soc. Nephrol.* 2:752 (Abstr.)

87. Taniguchi J, Tabei K, Imai M. 1987. Profiles of water and solute transport along long-loop descending limb: analysis by mathematical model. *Am. J. Physiol.* 252:F393–402

88. Thomas SR, Dagher G. 1993. A kinetic model of rat proximal tubule transport—load-dependent bicarbonate reabsorption along the tubule. *Bull. Math. Biol.* In press

89. Tripathi S, Boulpaep EL. 1988. Cell membrane water permeabilities and streaming currents in *Ambystoma* proximal tubule. *Am. J. Physiol.* 255:F188–203

90. Van der Goot FG, Podevin RA, Corman BJ. 1989. Water permeabilities and salt reflection coefficients of luminal, basolateral and intracellular membrane vesicles isolated from rabbit kidney proximal tubule. *Biochim. Biophys. Acta.* 986:332–40

91. Verkman AS, Alpern RJ. 1987. Kinetic transport model for cellular regulation of pH and solute concentration in the renal proximal tubule. *Biophys. J.* 51:533–46

92. Wang KW, Deen WM. 1980. Chemical kinetic and diffusional limitations on bicarbonate reabsorption by the proximal tubule. *Biophys. J.* 31:161–82

93. Wang W, Schwab A, Giebisch G. 1990. Regulation of small conductance K^+ channel in apical membrane of rat cortical collecting tubule. *Am. J. Physiol.* 259:F494–502

94. Weinstein AM. 1983. A nonequilibrium thermodynamic model of the rat proximal tubule epithelium. *Biophys. J.* 44:153–70

95. Weinstein AM. 1984. Transport by epithelia with compliant lateral intercellular spaces: asymmetric oncotic effects across the rat proximal tubule. *Am. J. Physiol.* 247:F848–62

96. Weinstein AM. 1986. A mathematical model of the rat proximal tubule. *Am. J. Physiol.* 250:F860–73

97. Weinstein AM. 1987. Convective paracellular solute flux: A source of ion-ion interaction in the epithelial

transport equations. *J. Gen. Physiol.* 89:501–18

98. Weinstein AM. 1990. Glomerulotubular balance in a mathematical model of the proximal nephron. *Am. J. Physiol.* 258:F612–26

99. Weinstein AM. 1992. Chloride transport in a mathematical model of the rat proximal tubule. *Am. J. Physiol.* 263:F784–98

100. Weinstein AM, Stephenson JL. 1981. Models of coupled salt and water transport across leaky epithelia. *J. Membr. Biol.* 60:1–20

101. Weinstein AM, Stephenson JL, Spring KR. 1981. The coupled transport of water. In *Membrane Transport,* ed. SL Bonting, JJHHM de Pont, pp. 311–51. Amsterdam: Elsevier/North-Holland

102. Welling LW, Welling DJ, Ochs T. 1987. Video measurement of basolateral NaCl reflection coefficient in proximal tubule. *Am. J. Physiol.* 253:F290–98

103. Welling LW, Welling DJ, Ochs T. 1990. Relative osmotic effects of raffinose, KCl, and NaCl across basolateral cell membrane. *Am. J. Physiol.* 259:F594–97

104. Wexler AS, Kalaba RE, Marsh DJ. 1991. Three-dimensional anatomy and renal concentrating mechanism. I. Modeling results. *Am. J. Physiol.* 260:F368–83

105. Wilcox CS, Baylis C. 1985. Glomerular-tubular balance and proximal regulation. In *The Kidney, Physiology and Pathophysiology,* ed. DW Seldin, G Giebisch, pp. 985–1012. New York: Raven

106. Williams JC, Schafer JA. 1988. Cortical interstitium as a site for solute polarization during tubular absorption. *Am. J. Physiol.* 254:F813–23

107. Windhager EE, Whittembury G, Oken DE, Schatzmann HJ, Solomon AK. 1959. Single proximal tubules of the *Necturus* kidney. III. Dependence of H_2O movement on NaCl concentration. *Am. J. Physiol.* 197:313–18

108. Winne D. 1978. The permeability coefficient of the wall of a villous membrane. *J. Math. Biol.* 6:95–108

Annu. Rev. Physiol. 1994. 56:711–39
Copyright © 1994 by Annual Reviews Inc. All rights reserved

HORMONAL SIGNALING AND REGULATION OF SALT AND WATER TRANSPORT IN THE COLLECTING DUCT

Matthew D. Breyer and Yasuhiro Ando

Division of Nephrology and Departments of Medicine and Molecular Physiology and Biophysics, Veterans Administration Medical Center and Vanderbilt University, Nashville Tennessee, and Division of Nephrology, Jichi Medical School, Kawachi-gun, Tochigi, Japan

KEY WORDS: protein kinase C, calcium, cyclic AMP, sodium, vasopressin

INTRODUCTION

The collecting duct is a major site of hormonally regulated water and ion transport. It is the major intra-renal target for vasopressin action, as well as an important site of action for catecholamines, atrial natriuretic peptide, prostaglandin E_2, and mineralocorticoids. The purpose of this review is to summarize the current understanding of the hormonal signaling mechanisms that regulate water and ion transport in the collecting duct.

Cellular Components of the Collecting Duct

Collecting ducts are classified by their location within the kidney: cortical, outer medullary (outer stripe and inner stripe), and inner medullary segments. The collecting duct is a heterogeneous epithelium consisting of three cell types: principle cells, and α and β intercalated cells (107, 118). Principal cells are thought to be primarily responsible for water and cation transport, while intercalated cells play roles in acid-base, K^+, and anion transport (35, 56, 140). The water transport effect of vasopressin is thought to be primarily mediated by principal cells (33, 98), although it remains possible

711

0066–4278/94/0315–0711$05.00

that intercalated cells also participate (99, 194). The reader is referred to the previous year's *Annual Review of Physiology* for a review of intercalated cell function (172). Of relevance to the present considerations is the recent observation that, in cell culture, the β intercalated cell may convert to a principal cell (57). These studies suggest that the functional distinction between these cells may not be static. This review focuses on the coupling between signaling and water and cation transport in the principal cell. Before discussing the cellular signaling mechanisms that modulate water and salt transport in the collecting duct, we briefly discuss the transporters that are thought to be the major targets for these signaling mechanisms.

WATER CHANNELS   It is well established that vasopressin-stimulated water absorption involves the exocytic insertion of water-selective channels into the apical membrane of the collecting duct (32, 74, 77). This process is accompanied by the reorganization of an apical actin web (82). Inhibitors of microtubule and microfilament formation, such as colchicine or cyto-chalasin B, block vasopressin-stimulated water flow (147, 210). In contrast to other exocytic processes such as peptide hormone secretion, where release of the vesicular contents is important, the salient feature of vasopressin-stimulated water permeability is the insertion of the limiting vesicle membrane (which contains water channels) into the cell membrane.

A recently cloned 28 kd erythrocyte-membrane protein (channel-forming integral membrane protein; CHIP28) has been demonstrated to be a water channel (149, 150). Another water channel, designated WCH-CD, has now been isolated from the rat kidney by homology with CHIP28 (63). WCH-CD consists of 270 amino acids and has six putative transmembrane domains. There is 42% amino acid sequence homology to CHIP28. Expression of WCH-CD in *Xenopus* oocytes increases osmotic water permeability. This was inhibited by $HgCl_2$, a characteristic of water-permeable endosomes from the collecting duct (74).

In the kidney, CHIP28 is expressed mainly in the proximal tubule and the thin descending limb of loop of Henle, whereas WCH-CD mRNA is exclusively expressed in the collecting duct, especially in the inner medullary portion (63, 162, 164). WCH-CD is localized predominantly in the apical membrane. WCH-CD mRNA expression, but not that of CHIP28, is enhanced by dehydration (164). These data suggest that WCH-CD is the water channel responsible for vasopressin-stimulated water transport. The water and urea permeability pathways appear to be distinct, since in the cortical collecting duct, vasopressin exclusively stimulates water transport without changing urea permeability. Furthermore, although vasopressin increases both water and urea permeabilities, phloretin has been shown to selectively inhibit urea transport without affecting water transport (102).

Ion Transporters

Na CHANNELS   Amiloride-inhibitable Na^+ channels mediate the electrogenic transport of Na^+ across the apical cortical collecting duct (CCD) membrane, into the cell, and down its electrochemical gradient. Patch-clamp studies of the collecting duct document the existence of at least three functionally different amiloride-inhibitable Na^+ channels (142). These include a 4–5 pS channel that is highly selective for Na:K>10, a 7–10 pS channel that is three to four times more selective for Na>K, and a 28 pS channel that is non-selective for Na^+ and K^+ (142). Since most evidence suggests that electrogenic Na^+ absorption is highly Na^+ selective, the 4–5 pS channel is the most likely candidate for mediating electrogenic Na^+ absorption in the CCD.

The mechanisms regulating Na^+ channel activity appear to be diverse and include modulation of channel density by exocytic insertion (120), as well as altered channel gating, influenced by G proteins (38), protein kinase C (PKC), (114), protein kinase G, cGMP (110), and modulation by the actin filament polymerization (39). An amiloride-binding protein has been purified from A6 cells and bovine kidney (17, 100). In the absence of reducing agents, this protein migrates as a single broad band of approximately 700 kd. When treated with reducing agents, the protein separates into five distinct bands of 315, 150, 95, 70, and 55 kd. The 315 kd subunit has been found to be phosphorylated in response to vasopressin (17, 143, 163, 166). Recently a cDNA has been cloned from rat colon that expresses an amiloride-sensitive Na^+ conductance in oocytes (37, 115). The predicted molecular weight of this protein is 79 K and in vitro translation yields a protein that migrates at 75 kd and after glycosylation, at 92 kd. Interestingly, the predicted amino-acid sequence of this protein includes consensus phosphorylation sites for PKA, PKC, and casein kinase II. It remains unclear exactly how this cloned protein corresponds to the multimeric protein purified from bovine kidney. Both proteins are candidates for mediating electrogenic Na^+ absorption in the collecting duct.

K^+ CHANNELS   Vasopressin stimulates K^+ secretion in the distal tubule and collecting duct (60). In the collecting duct, K^+ is secreted via an apical conductive pathway. Patch-clamp studies have identified several functionally distinct apical K^+ channels in this nephron segment (214) These include a 80–140 pS K^+ channel that is Ca^{2+}-dependent, a small, outward rectifying K^+ channel observed in cultured CCDs (113), and an inward rectifying 35 pS K^+ channel that is regulated by ATP (81, 214). It has been suggested that this latter channel provides the major route for K^+ secretion in the collecting duct (214).

The open probability of the 35 pS apical K^+ channel is markedly increased by PKA and ATP in excised patches (212). In agreement with these observations, the predicted amino acid sequence of an ATP-regulated K^+ channel recently cloned from rat renal medulla contains two consensus sequences for PKA phosphorylation (81). These results suggest that vasopressin and cAMP, through PKA phosphorylation, could activate K^+ secretion via this channel.

NaCl SYMPORT   It remains unclear whether electroneutral NaCl transport exists in the CCD. While there is evidence that a thiazide-sensitive NaCl symport mechanism is present in the rat CCD (201), this has not been uniformly observed (161). Thiazide-sensitive NaCl symport appears to be absent from the rabbit CCD, but present upstream in the connecting segment (179). A cDNA encoding a thiazide-inhibited NaCl symporter has recently been cloned from the urinary bladder of the winter flounder (64). This 112 kd protein possess 12 putative membrane-spanning regions and has several potential protein kinase phosphorylation sites. It remains to be determined whether a homologue is expressed along the mammalian nephron.

Na/K ATPASE   The favorable electrochemical gradients mediating Na^+ absorption and K^+ secretion by the collecting duct are generated by the Na/K-ATPase. Immunohistochemical studies of the CCD demonstrate that Na/K-ATPase selectively localizes to the basolateral domain of principal cells. No labeling of intercalated cells was seen (94). This ATPase exists as a heterodimer with the α-subunit possessing the catalytic activity and oubain binding site. The β-subunit is a glycoprotein required for enzymatic activity. The Na/K ATPase α-subunit is a substrate for both protein kinase A and protein kinase C (43), and phosphorylation of the α-subunit inhibits Na/K-ATPase activity (21). There are three isoforms of the α-subunit and possibly two isoforms of the β-subunit (195). Most evidence suggests α1 is the major isoform in the kidney; however, variable renal expression of α2 and α3 isoforms has also been reported (54). These isozymes display different affinities for ouabain, Na^+, and K^+ (195), and it is thought that different isozymes may be subject to differential regulation both at the level of gene expression and by protein kinases (51, 195).

V_2/CYCLIC AMP-MEDIATED SIGNALING

Arginine vasopressin (AVP) is the single most important hormone regulating urine volume. The primary physiologic action of AVP, antidiuresis, is mediated through the V_2 receptor located in the collecting duct (and in some rodents in medullary thick ascending limb) (125). AVP not only enhances water reabsorption in the collecting duct, but also enhances Na reabsorption and K secretion. This section reviews how the V_2-mediated signal modulates water and salt transport in the collecting duct.

Water Transport

It is generally accepted that AVP stimulates osmotic water permeability in collecting ducts through the V_2 receptor, which stimulates adenylate cyclase and cyclic AMP (cAMP) generation and results in the activation of cAMP-dependent protein kinase (PKA) (1, 77, 163, 185). This activation causes increased water permeability of the apical epithelial membrane of the collecting duct (Figure 1). Each element of this process is discussed below.

The V_2 Receptor

The complementary DNA and the predicted amino acid sequence for the renal V_2 receptor and hepatic V_{1a} receptor have recently been reported (22, 116, 124). The rat liver V_{1a} and renal V_2 receptors are 394 (44 kd) and 370 amino acid proteins (40.5 kd), respectively. Like other G protein-coupled receptors, these receptor proteins display three intra- and three extracellular loops with seven transmembrane domains. The V_{1a} and the V_2 receptors are 60% homologous.

While the V_{1a} receptor mRNA is expressed in multiple organs including liver, spleen, brain, and kidney, V_2 receptor mRNA is almost exclusively expressed in the kidney. In situ hybridization demonstrates V_2 expression in the cortical and medullary collecting duct and the medullary thick

BLOOD

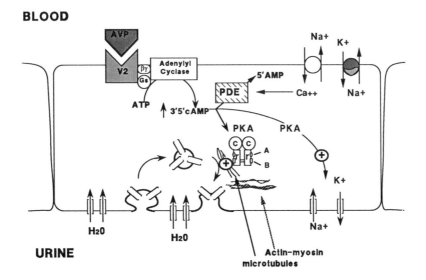

URINE

ascending limb (116). In the collecting duct, V_2 receptors are thought to reside on the basolateral membrane. Apical V_2 receptors may also exist in cultured rat inner medullary collecting duct cells (219), which produce cAMP in response to apical nanomolar AVP. Nevertheless, in the native rabbit cortical collecting duct perfused in vitro, luminal AVP, even in nanomolar concentrations, did not increase water permeability (10, 70). Thus functional V_2 receptors, which mediate the stimulation of water transport, are restricted to the basolateral side of the collecting duct.

G Proteins

STIMULATORY G PROTEINS   Binding of AVP to the V_2 receptor leads to activation of adenylyl cyclase via a stimulatory heterotrimeric G protein, G_s (α_s and $\beta\gamma$-subunits) (22, 123). Immunohistochemical studies of rat kidney show a distinct basolateral localization of $G\alpha_s$ within the collecting duct (in contrast to the proximal tubule where apical localization is seen) (193). AVP and β-adrenergic agonists are the major stimulators of basolateral adenylyl cyclase activity in the collecting duct (125). Association of these hormones with their respective receptors favors $G\alpha_s$ dissociation from $\beta\gamma$, frees $G\alpha_s$, interacts with, and stimulates adenylyl cyclase (19). Free $\beta\gamma$-subunits are also capable of regulating adenylyl cyclase. For instance, $G\alpha_s$ activation of purified type I adenylyl cyclase (a brain-specific isoform) was inhibited by $\beta\gamma$-subunits, while $\beta\gamma$ augmented the $G\alpha_s$ activation of purified type II adenylyl cyclase (197). Other adenylyl cyclase isoforms appear to be insensitive to the effects of $\beta\gamma$.

INHIBITORY G PROTEINS   Inhibitory G proteins (G_is) counteract the stimulatory effects of G_s on cAMP production (123, 180). $G\alpha_{i2}$ appears to be the major isoform present in the rat collecting duct and displays basolateral and cytoplasmic localization (34, 193). While the inhibitory effects of G_i on cAMP generation are clear, the molecular mechanisms whereby this effect occurs is somewhat controversial. Evidence exists for direct inhibitory effects of the α_i-subunit, as well as inhibitory effects of free $\beta\gamma$ (123). The inhibitory effects of $\beta\gamma$ may be mediated by their association with free α_s thereby decreasing the amount of α_s available to stimulate adenylyl cyclase (123).

Whatever the precise mechanism, G_i activation appears to be an important target for several hormones and autacoids that antagonize the G_s-coupled effects of vasopressin. A hallmark of G_i-mediated inhibition of adenylyl cyclase is that it can be experimentally blocked by pertussis toxin (see Figure 2), which irreversibly ADP ribosylates $G\alpha_i$ (129). Furthermore, inhibitory effects mediated by G_i can be experimentally bypassed by administration of cell-permeable cAMP analogues. Based on these criteria, several hormones and autacoids, including PGE_2 (79, 187, 188), epinephrine (67, 155), acetylcholine (67), and endothelin (130), have been shown to antagonize the G_s-coupled effect of vasopressin via G_i-dependent mechanisms. Adenylyl cyclase-independent effects of $G\alpha_i$ on ion channels in the collecting duct have also been proposed (38).

Adenylyl Cyclase

Hormone-stimulated adenylyl cyclase regulates the intracellular level of $3',5'$-cAMP by catalyzing its generation from ATP. Adenylyl cyclases are now known to comprise a family of eight proteins, each characterized by twelve putative membrane-spanning regions and approximate molecular mass of 120–150 kd ($\sim$1200 amino acid residues). Of the eight isoforms of adenylyl cyclase, seven were detected in rat kidney (104). Not only may specific G proteins couple to distinct adenylyl cyclase isoforms (68), but it has also been demonstrated that some adenylyl cyclase isoforms are modulated by $\beta\gamma$-subunits of heterotrimeric G proteins (see above), and by Ca^{2+} and/or Ca^{2+}/calmodulin (75). The adenylyl cyclase isoforms present in the collecting duct have not been characterized. However, both type V and type VI appear to be highly expressed in rat kidney (148). Of interest, both adenylyl cyclase isoforms are directly inhibited by submicromolar Ca^{2+} in a calmodulin-independent fashion (95, 104, 221). If these Ca^{2+}-sensitive isoforms are present in the collecting duct, it would provide a potentially important site for cross-talk between the Ca^{2+}-coupled V_1 and cAMP-coupled V_2 systems.

cAMP Phosphodiesterase

Cytosolic cAMP levels are also regulated by cAMP-phosphodiesterase (cAMP-PDE), which hydrolyzes $3',5'$-cAMP to $5'$-AMP. PDE isozymes have been tentatively classified according to their affinity for cyclic nucleotides (cAMP and cGMP), dependence on calmodulin, and sensitivity to selective inhibitors, such as rolipram and cilostamide (15). The primary structures of several PDE isozymes have been deduced (15, 18, 92, 153) and reveal an amino-terminal regulatory domain and a mid-molecule catalytic domain (18, 92). The cAMP-binding region of the catalytic domain is homologous to that of the regulatory subunit of protein kinase A, although the mode of cAMP binding may be distinct (92).

Although the intra-nephron distribution of PDE isozymes is largely unknown, rolipram-sensitive PDE and calmodulin-dependent PDE, which are low K_m phosphodiesterases, appear to play significant roles in mouse and rat collecting duct (18, 84). Enhanced activity of a specific rolipram-sensitive cAMP-PDE in the collecting duct is known to cause hereditary nephrogenic diabetes insipidus in mice (45, 84, 196). This highlights the importance of PDE as a regulator of the antidiuretic action of AVP. Recent studies also suggest that PDE activity might be regulated by a receptor G protein-coupled mechanism in hepatocytes (119).

cAMP-dependent Protein Kinase (PKA)

There is evolving evidence that vasopressin and cAMP-stimulated water flow are mediated, in part, by PKA. PKA exists as a heterotetramer comprised of two catalytic (C) subunits and two regulatory (R) subunits. Each R subunit possesses two cAMP-binding sites (site A and site B) (Figure 1). Dissociation of R and C subunits occurs when cAMP binds to both the A and B sites on the regulatory subunit (16). The free C subunit is released from tonic inhibition by R. Two major holoenzyme isoforms of PKA exist and are distinguished by their regulatory subunits (RI and RII). RII is larger than RI (monomer molecular weight = 54–59 K vs 49 K). RII exists as a dimer formed by a disulfide bridge and contains an autophosphorylation site (16, 173). The type I isoform of PKA is primarily cytosolic, while the type II isoform is associated with the cytoskeleton and appears to specifically bind to acidic amphipathic helical protein sequences (41, 173, 174). These protein kinase anchoring sequences undoubtedly play an important role in targeting PKA activity to specific protein substrates. While equal amounts of PKA type I and II exist in the rat medullary thick ascending limb, the rat medullary collecting duct predominantly contains type I PKA (65). The selective expression of the type II isozyme, coupled with its specific intracellular localization, may serve as a mechanism for generating tissue-selective effects of cAMP. There are also α and β isoforms of RI and RII regulatory subunits and at least three isoforms of the catalytic subunit (Cα, Cβ, and Cγ) (173). This heterogeneity allows for further selectivity of action.

Although it has been assumed that PKA is essential for the induction of water permeability (1, 52), a direct relationship between PKA activation and the exocytic insertion of water channels into the apical membrane remains only partially established. Some studies have suggested a discrepancy between PKA activation and the hydroosmotic effect of AVP. For example, we have observed that several inhibitors of protein kinase A (H-8, K252a, KT5720) enhanced rather than inhibited the hydroosmotic effect of AVP (6). More recently Snyder et al suggested an integral role of PKA in mediating the hydroosmotic effect of AVP (185). In this study, site A- and site B-selective cAMP analogues synergistically stimulated water transport in the isolated perfused rabbit CCD. Also, two different PKA inhibitors (Rp-cAMPS, H-89) inhibited the AVP and cAMP-induced water transport.

Vasopressin-stimulated PKA-induced phosphorylation of intrinsic protein substrates has been demonstrated in the collecting duct, although the substrate protein has not been specified (53, 85). Therefore, despite the inconsistent actions of several kinase inhibitors, PKA appears to be involved in stimulating water transport. It remains unclear whether different PKA isoforms are more-or-less susceptible to these different inhibitors, which accounts for these apparently discrepant results.

It is conceivable that there are also direct effects of the R subunit of PKA distinct from kinase activity. In prokaryotes such as *E. coli*, cAMP exerts its actions through binding to cAMP receptor protein (CRP), which lacks protein kinase activity (131). Considerable structural homology exists between CRP and R subunit of PKA. In addition, the cAMP-regulatory subunit complex, but not the catalytic subunit, appears to be a potent inhibitor of a phosphoprotein phosphatase (176) and to induce protein synthesis in SV40-3T3 fibroblasts (135). cAMP may also directly bind to other proteins such as the cation channel observed in olfactory epithelium, which is directly gated by cAMP (117, 132). Thus kinase-independent effects of cAMP either via the PKA R subunit or binding to other acceptor proteins could participate in collecting duct signal transduction.

Modulation of Water Permeability at the Apical Membrane

The final step of V_2-mediated signaling is insertion of water channels into the apical plasma membrane. In toad urinary bladder, particle aggregates, which contain water channels, are arrayed linearly in the membrane of a cylindrical organelle termed the aggrephore (77). Upon vasopressin stimulation, aggrephores fuse with the apical plasma membrane and the integral membrane proteins aggregate in clusters. In the mammalian collecting duct, intracellular aggrephores are observed less frequently (48). In this tissue, a sub-population of endosomal vesicles is assumed to deliver the water channels. Once inserted into the apical membrane, water channels localize in clathrin-coated pits (33). With AVP removal, endocytic retrieval of the water channel from the apical surface is observed and water permeability declines (32, 74, 77, 209).

Cytoskeleton elements are presumed to play critical roles in the movement of vesicles and water channels (198). Roles for microtubules and actin filaments in aggrephore movement and insertion of water channels into apical membrane, respectively, have been suggested (128, 147, 210). Upon AVP-stimulation, disruption of actin filament network appears to precede the delivery of water channels (48, 82). However, the precise mechanism is not yet defined. It is also unknown whether the AVP-sensitive water channels display gating similar to ion channels.

V_2 Effects on Cation Transport

Na^+ AND K^+ Vasopressin stimulates both Na^+ absorption and K^+ secretion (61, 83, 166, 214). These effects may be species-dependent, since in the rabbit, this stimulation is transient, whereas in the rat, the stimulatory effect of vasopressin is persistent. Most evidence suggests that vasopressin and cAMP stimulate Na^+ absorption by increasing the density of Na^+ channels in the apical membrane of the collecting duct (120, 166, 167). While cAMP has been shown to inhibit Na^+/K^+ATPase in broken cells (21, 165), the major effect of vasopressin and cAMP appears to be stimulation of Na^+ absorption. Following treatment with vasopressin or cAMP, intracellular sodium increases through enhanced luminal Na^+ entry (30, 156). Patch-clamp studies fail to demonstrate an effect of vasopressin or cAMP on open probability or channel conductance; however, channel number appears to increase following vasopressin treatment (120). By analogy with the process of vasopressin-stimulated water permeability, it may be that stimulation of Na^+ absorption occurs via the exocytic insertion of amiloride-sensitive Na^+ channels (166).

In contrast to its effects on sodium absorption, the cellular mechanisms by which vasopressin stimulates K^+ secretion is less firmly established. cAMP and PKA increase the open probability (P_o) of a 35 pS K^+ channel (212) (in contrast to the lack of effect of cAMP on P_o of the amiloride-sensitive sodium channel). It remains uncertain whether the stimulation of K^+ secretion results secondarily from increased apical K^+ conductance, or simply arises from an enhanced electrochemical gradient for K^+ secretion, the result of the primary effects on Na^+ transport (168). A role for exocytic insertion of K^+ channels in response to cAMP remains purely speculative.

cAMP STIMULATION OF BASOLATERAL Na^+/Ca^{2+} EXCHANGE   Although it has been suggested that vasopressin increases CCD intracellular Ca^{2+} via a V_1 receptor, there is also evidence that vasopressin may increase $[Ca^{2+}]_i$ via a V_2/cAMP-dependent mechanism (28). This effect appears to involve activation of a basolateral Na^+/Ca^{2+} exchanger. As vasopressin or cAMP activates apical Na^+ entry, intracellular Na^+ concentration increases (above approximately 15 mM), and Ca^{2+} can then enter the cell via the Na^+/Ca^{2+} exchanger (27, 28, 183). The Ca^{2+} increase results in feedback inhibition of vasopressin-stimulated Na^+ permeability, possibly contributing to the sustained inhibition of Na^+ transport produced by vasopressin in the rabbit (28, 83). It is also evident that as luminal Na^+ delivery falls, the absolute increase in cell Na^+ and intracellular Ca^{2+} falls. In this manner, decreased luminal Na^+ delivery could convert the net effect of vasopressin in the rabbit CCD from inhibition of Na^+ absorption to stimulation.

V_1/Ca^{2+}-COUPLED SIGNALING

Several hormones and autacoids including vasopressin, PGE_2, acetylcholine, and endothelin have been reported to modulate the AVP-induced water transport in the collecting duct via a signaling mechanism coupled to phospholipid turnover and increased cell Ca^{2+} (1, 29) (Figure 2). While cooperative effects of the V_2/cAMP and Ca^{2+}-coupled pathways remain an attractive possibility, the majority of studies suggest that the Ca^{2+}-coupled pathway inhibits vasopressin action.

Vasopressin Receptor-Stimulated Phospholipid Breakdown

V_1 RECEPTOR AND G PROTEIN COUPLING   The cDNA for the V_{1a} receptor has been cloned from rat liver. The message encodes a 394 amino acid protein. The expressed protein preferentially binds AVP>oxytocin = dDAVP (a V_2-selective analogue) (124). Genomic southern hybridization suggests the existence of multiple members of this receptor family. There is accumulating evidence for a Ca^{2+}-coupled vasopressin receptor in the collecting duct; however, the precise subtype is not well defined (3, 5, 28, 36, 190, 191). There is evidence supporting roles for V_1 and V_2 receptors (3, 28, 190). In the case of the V_2 receptor, it is conceivable that high concentrations of AVP release enough G protein $\beta\gamma$ subunits to activate phospholipase C and phosphatidylinositol hydrolysis (22a). In contrast, G_α subunits may mediate the effects of the V_{1a} receptor. Typically, as in hepatocytes, the V_{1a} receptor (124) couples to a

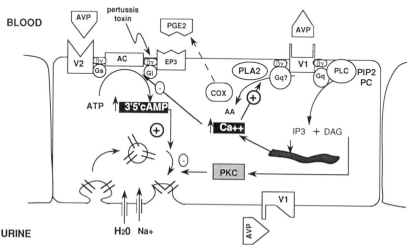

Figure 2   Interaction between cAMP and Ca^{2+}/phospholipase-coupled signaling systems in the collecting duct.

phosphoinositide-specific phospholipase C (PLC) through a pertussis toxin-insensitive, heterotrimeric GTP-binding protein designated G_q (46, 182, 199). Three other G proteins, $G\alpha11$, $G\alpha14$, and $G\alpha15$ (or $\alpha16$ in human) also fall into the G_q family (216). G_q, $G\alpha11$, and $G\alpha14$ are present in mouse kidney (216), and a preliminary report suggests both $G\alpha11$ and $G\alpha14$ are present in the rat collecting duct (175) Other pertussis toxin-sensitive G proteins such as G_o may also participate in phosphatidylinositol hydrolysis (126); however, in the collecting duct, agonist-stimulated Ca^{2+} transients are typically pertussis toxin-insensitive (79, 130).

PHOSPHATIDYLINOSITOL BREAKDOWN   Vasopressin increases collecting duct cell Ca^{2+} by releasing calcium from intracellular stores, an effect dependent upon IP_3 generation (28, 36). G protein-coupled receptors typically activate PLC-β, whereas PLC-γ is activated by tyrosine kinase-coupled receptors (154). PLC hydrolyzes phosphatidylinositol bisphosphate (PIP_2), a minor constituent of cell membrane phospholipids, thereby initiating two major intracellular signal transduction events: the activation of protein kinase C (PKC) and the mobilization of Ca^{2+} from an intracellular store (20, 136). Two PIP_2 breakdown products, diacylglycerol (DAG) and inositol-1,4,5-triphosphate (IP_3), are responsible for these signals (20, 136). Diacylglycerols in the presence of Ca^{2+} directly bind to and activate PKC. The increase in Ca^{2+} may also lead to activation of Ca^{2+}/calmodulin-dependent protein kinases or other Ca^{2+}-dependent protein kinases. Phosphorylation of substrate proteins by these activated protein kinases is believed to be essential to complete signal transduction. As is the case with PKA-mediated signaling, the PKC substrate proteins and their functional roles have not been clearly identified in the collecting duct; however, cytoskeletal elements are candidate targets for PKC or PKC-activated kinases (76, 177).

PHOSPHATIDYLCHOLINE TURNOVER   Although phospholipase-mediated PIP_2 breakdown is a major initial pathway for DAG formation in intact cells, it is transient even in the continued presence of agonist, and other phospholipases may be responsible for sustained DAG formation (55, 136). Numerous studies have documented the importance of phosphatidylcholine as a source for DAG formation (24, 55). A phospholipase C activity that hydrolyzes phosphatidylcholine to diacylglycerol and phosphocholine has been observed in cultured MDCK cells (146). It remains unclear whether a similar activity is present in the collecting duct.

Vasopressin may activate not only phospholipase C, but also phospholipase D (12, 24, 55). Phospholipase D (PLD) hydrolyzes phosphatidylcholine (PC), the major component of membrane phospholipid, which yields phosphatidic acid and choline (24, 87). Phosphatidic acids may be converted to DAG by the action of phosphatidic acid phosphatase (23). In the rabbit CCD, we have demonstrated that exogenous phosphatidic acids inhibit AVP-induced water transport through a protein kinase-dependent mechanism (9). DAG production via PLD is more sustained than the transient increase in DAG that results from PIP_2 breakdown and could be responsible for prolonged activation of PKC in the continued presence of hormone (136). Indeed, there is good evidence that PKC itself may activate PLD (136) thereby perpetuating its own activation.

PROTEIN KINASE C   The ultimate consequence of DAG formation is to activate PKC. There are at least ten different PKC isoforms (136). To date, three isoforms, α, β, and ζ, have been detected in the kidney (50, 103). In the case of α, β, and γ isoforms, both micromolar Ca^{2+} and diacylglycerols are required to activate protein kinase C (PKC). Other PKC isoforms including ζ exhibit Ca^{2+}-independent activation (136). The specific and hormonally activated PKC isoforms in the collecting duct have not yet been identified. There is also the possibility that diacylglycerol action is mediated by PKC-independent mechanisms related to alterations in actin structure (177).

INOSITOL PHOSPHATES   Nanomolar concentrations of vasopressin, PGE_2, muscarinic cholinergic agonists, and endothelin all produce a prompt biphasic increase in collecting duct calcium (28, 67, 79, 130, 190). After reaching a peak (in the range of $1\,\mu M$), Ca^{2+} falls to new but persistently elevated values. This latter phase is associated with increased Ca^{2+} influx. The initial Ca^{2+} increase results from release of Ca^{2+} from intracellular stores and influx of extracellular Ca^{2+} (20). It is well established that V_1 receptor activation generates IP_3 formation from PIP_2 hydrolysis (2, 36). Increased cytosolic IP_3 binds to its receptor located in the endoplasmic reticulum. The IP_3 receptors comprise a family of Ca^{2+} channels, which upon binding IP_3, open and release Ca^{2+} from intracellular stores (20, 59). IP_3 may not only participate in the initial increase in $[Ca^{2+}]_i$, but it has been suggested that some inositol phosphate-sensitive calcium channels may also reside in the plasma membrane and mediate agonist-stimulated Ca^{2+} influx (20, 96). It has been proposed that inositol-1,3,4,5-tetrakisphosphate (IP_4), which is generated from 1,4,5-IP_3 in response to AVP, may promote Ca^{2+} influx through such a Ca^{2+} channel (109). The existence of voltage or ligand-operated Ca^{2+} channels in the collecting duct remains speculative. Alternatively, $[Ca^{2+}]_i$ influx may also be increased by modulation of the basolateral Na^+/Ca^{2+} exchanger (28).

Phospholipase A_2 and Prostaglandin Synthesis

In addition to stimulating phosphatidylinositol (PI) breakdown, vasopressin and several other agonists (including endothelin, bradykinin, and epidermal growth factor) stimulate arachidonic acid release and prostaglandin synthesis in the collecting duct. PGE_2 is the major cyclooxygenase product of arachidonate metabolism in the collecting duct, and it is a major inhibitor of water and sodium absorption in this segment (25). Stimulation of PGE_2 production by vasopressin appears to constitute a feedback regulatory system. Arachidonic acid release may also participate in PKC-dependent signaling since many *cis*-unsaturated fatty acids, including arachidonate, may activate PKC either by themselves, or in cooperation with diacyclglycerols (136).

The major route of arachidonate release is via the action of cytosolic phospholipase A_2 (PLA_2) (88). These enzymes hydrolyze phospholipids (including phosphatidylcholine, phosphatidylethanolamine, and phosphatidylserine, as well as phosphatidylinositol) at the sn-2 position, which selectively releases arachidonic acid (14, 26). While an arachidonate-selective cytosolic PLA_2 has recently been cloned (44), there are many types of PLA_2 including some that are not arachidonate-selective. It remains uncertain which PLA_2 is relevant for hormone action in the collecting duct.

EGF, bradykinin, vasopressin, and endothelin activate PLA_2 and arachidonic acid release in the collecting duct (11, 91, 170, 178, 200, 222). Several of these agents also activate PIP_2 hydrolysis and PKC, which stimulates prostaglandin synthesis in AVP-sensitive cells (139, 169). While agonists that signal via Ca^{2+}/PKC have been demonstrated to stimulate PLA_2, MAP kinase appears to be the primary activator and may mediate the Ca^{2+}/PKC activation of PLA_2 (111, 134).

G protein-coupled receptors also stimulate $cPLA_2$, although the precise molecular mechanism remains unclear (14, 26, 71, 218). There is evidence that a G protein-coupled mechanism, distinct from that involved in phospholipase C activation, is involved (71, 181). Of relevance to this review are the observations that bradykinin-stimulated PGE_2 production was blocked by pertussis toxin, and bradykinin inhibited AVP-stimulated water flow via a pertussis toxin-sensitive, cyclooxygenase-dependent process (171, 178). However, bradykinin does not increase intracellular calcium or act through PKC (80), which suggests that, at least in the collecting duct, the bradykinin receptor is selectively coupled to PLA_2 activation.

Functional Consequences of Phospholipid Hydrolysis in the Collecting Duct

Schlondorff & Levine first demonstrated that PKC was present in toad bladder and that its activation inhibited AVP-sensitive water transport (169). Subsequently, PKC activity has been demonstrated in primary cultured rabbit cortical-collecting duct cells (49). $PKC\alpha$ has also been detected in situ in the collecting duct (50). As mentioned above, vasopressin-stimulated $[Ca^{2+}]_i$

and PIP_2 hydrolysis have also been demonstrated in the mammalian-collecting duct (36).

The functional role of PIP_2 breakdown in modulating AVP-sensitive water transport in the collecting duct has also been examined (9). PKC activators such as phorbol myristate acetate (PMA) and dioctanoylglycerol inhibit AVP-induced water transport in rabbit CCD (8, 169). This inhibition was independent of cyclooxygenase metabolites. Peritubular PMA (10^{-9} to 10^{-7}) potently blocked the hydroosmotic effect of AVP or a cell-permeable cAMP analogue in an equivalent and concentration-dependent fashion (7). This suggests that PKC primarily interferes with AVP-stimulated water flow at post-cAMP step(s). In cultured rabbit CCD cells, PMA was also reported to inhibit AVP-sensitive adenylate cyclase (pre-cAMP inhibition) (49). The mechanisms of both pre- and post-cAMP inhibition of AVP-induced water transport by PKC are undetermined.

Maneuvers that increase cytosolic Ca^{2+} also modulate AVP action. However, conflicting results have been reported depending on the experimental condition, the procedure used to increase $[Ca^{2+}]_i$, and the animal species. In toad urinary bladder, simultaneous administration of the Ca^{2+}-ionophore A23187 together with AVP enhanced the AVP-induced water transport, while A23187 pretreatment suppressed AVP action (73). The effect of $[Ca^{2+}]_i$ on vasopressin action may also be temperature-dependent (8). At 37°C, 10 nM A23187 inhibits AVP-stimulated water permeability in the CCD, while at 25°C, it stimulates water permeability. The primary site of the inhibitory effect appears to be at a pre-cAMP site, although significant inhibition of cAMP-stimulated water flow was observed when A23187 concentration was increased to 1 μM (8, 93). This difference may reflect differences in the magnitude of the $[Ca^{2+}]_i$ increase.

There are several potential mechanisms by which increased cytosolic Ca^{2+} might inhibit AVP-stimulated water flow. As discussed above, a Ca^{2+}-inhibited adenylyl cyclase is present in rat kidney (95, 104, 221). Ca^{2+} has also been shown to stimulate PDE activity in the collecting duct, consistent with the presence of Ca-calmodulin-stimulated PDE (105). Preliminary studies in the rat medullary collecting duct suggest that either AVP itself or PKC activators can stimulate PDE activity (86, 204). Increased PDE activity has also been suggested to mediate the inhibitory effect of PGE_2 on cAMP generation in the rat collecting duct (205).

Increased Ca^{2+} also stimulates formation of endogenous cyclooxygenase products (44, 170), an effect that may be functionally relevant since cyclooxygenase inhibitors reverse the inhibitory effect of A23187 (8). In contrast, indomethacin had no effect on phorbol ester inhibition of water flow, while a PKC inhibitor, staurosporine, blocked the PMA inhibition, but not that observed with 10 nM A21387. Synergy between the Ca^{2+} and protein kinase C-mediated pathways was also observed (8).

Ca^{2+}/PKC Effects on Cation Transport

There is good evidence that Ca^{2+}/PKC-coupled signaling not only inhibits water flow, but also modulates transepithelial Na^+ absorption and K^+ secretion. Exogenous diacylglycerols and phorbol esters potently inhibit both Na^+ absorption and K^+ secretion in the collecting duct (78, 220). Cell attached patch-clamp studies suggest PKC activation decreases the open probability of a 4 pS amiloride-sensitive Na^+ channel in the apical membrane of cultured rabbit-collecting ducts (114). Similarly, maneuvers that increase intracellular Ca^{2+} inhibit sodium absorption in the collecting duct, apparently by reducing Na^+ permeability of the apical membrane (62). Cell attached patch-clamp studies demonstrate increased cell calcium inhibits Na^+ channel activity in the rat cortical collecting duct (144). In contrast, increasing bath $[Ca^{2+}]$ had no effect on channel activity when added to cell-excised inside-out patches, which suggests that the effect of increased Ca^{2+} was indirect and dependent on some intracellular effector (144). PKC activation has also been shown to reduce the open probability of the 35 pS ATP-sensitive K^+ channel in the apical membrane of the rat cortical collecting duct (213). Increasing bath $[Ca^{2+}]$ in cell-excised patches enhanced PKC-induced reduction of channel open probability. Thus PKC-induced phosphorylation reduces the open probability of apical cation channels in the collecting duct.

The above results suggest that agonists that stimulate PIP_2 hydrolysis in the collecting duct should inhibit cation transport in this segment. In support of this, it has been demonstrated that the inhibitory effect of PGE_2 on Na^+ transport is coupled to the release of Ca^{2+} from intracellular stores, and that reducing bath $[Ca^{2+}]$ prevents this Ca^{2+} increase and the inhibition of Na^+ transport (79). The mechanism of PGE_2-mediated inhibition of Na^+ transport may involve both inhibition of apical Na^+ conductance and inhibition of the basolateral Na^+/K^+ ATPase (90, 114, 215). Similarly, muscarinic receptor activation appears to activate PKC, release Ca^{2+} from intracellular stores, and depolarize transepithelial voltage in the cortical collecting duct, which suggests that it may also inhibit Na^+ transport via enhanced PIP_2 hydrolysis (184). These data are in agreement with a predominant inhibitory role for PIP_2 hydrolysis in the collecting duct, with respect to cation transport.

Basolateral V_1 and V_2 Receptors

Vasopressin increases collecting duct $[Ca^{2+}]_i$, which suggests the presence of basolateral V_1 receptors (28, 190). Receptor binding assays also suggest the presence of collecting duct V_1 receptors, especially in the cortical portion

(3). Since stimulation of the major V_1 signaling pathways, PLC and PLA_2, appear to inhibit AVP-stimulated water flow, AVP might inhibit its own V_2-mediated hydroosmotic effect via V_1 receptors. This would be consistent, at least in part, with prostaglandin-mediated regulation of antidiuresis observed in the whole kidney (4, 211). We evaluated the functional role of basolateral V_1 receptors in the rabbit CCD (6). The dose-response relationship of the AVP-stimulated hydraulic conductivity (Lp) showed that between 1 and 230 pM AVP progressively increased Lp, while increasing the concentration to 23 nM produced a significant decline in the Lp(vs 230 pM AVP). The water permeability response to 23 nM AVP was enhanced by pretreatment with either a PKC inhibitor or indomethacin. Staurosporine or indomethacin did not augment the water flow response to 23 or 230 pM AVP. These observations are consistent with studies showing that nanomolar AVP is required to release Ca^{2+} from intracellular stores or for stimulation of PGE_2 synthesis (27, 39, 107, 182, 202). The results suggest that V_1-mediated autoinhibition is only activated at nanomolar vasopressin concentrations.

Autoinhibition of water transport by nanomolar AVP has been recently reported in anuran urinary bladder and rat CCD (133, 152). Interestingly, recent reports from the same laboratory suggest that neither prostaglandins, phorbol esters, nor maneuvers that increase Ca^{2+} inhibit AVP-stimulated Na^+ and water transport in the rat cortical collecting duct (42, 160). In contrast, Han et al reported similar self-inhibition of the water transport by nanomolar AVP in the rat inner medullary collecting duct via V_1-like receptors (72). The V_1-receptor subtypes in the collecting duct could be unique since the spike-like Ca^{2+} response can be induced not only by AVP, but also by the V_2-selective agonist dDAVP (30, 72, 190). Alternatively, as discussed above, V_2-mediated release of $G_{\beta\gamma}$ could account for these effects (22a).

Circulating AVP, the major determinant of distal nephron water reabsorption in vivo, is ~ 1 pM in euhydrated mammals (47, 157). Severe dehydration or hypovolemia only raises circulating AVP level to 50–100 pM. Nevertheless, no evidence for V_1 activation (including PGE_2 synthesis) can be demonstrated using picomolar vasopressin in the isolated collecting duct. While this might seem inconsistent with the established role of endogenous prostaglandins in regulating AVP antidiuresis in vivo (4, 211), these studies did not address the site of prostaglandin production in response to physiological concentrations of AVP. Picomolar AVP might stimulate renal prostaglandin synthesis at some other site than the collecting duct (e.g. interstitial cells). Alternatively, picomolar AVP might induce the release of other autacoids such as kinins (58), which in turn stimulate collecting duct prostaglandin synthesis. These considerations raise the question of what physiological role the Ca^{2+}-coupled vasopressin receptor(s) play in the collecting duct.

In addition to the inhibitory action of increased $[Ca^{2+}]_i$, lowering $[Ca^{2+}]_i$ below a certain level interferes with the hydroosmotic effect of AVP (13, 89, 105, 108). It has been suggested that an optimum range of $[Ca^{2+}]_i$ is required for the full development of water transport in response to AVP. Similarly a facilitory role for protein kinase C in the movement of water channels has been suggested (121). In this study, while the hydroosmotic effect of AVP was inhibited by apical PMA pretreatment, apical PMA alone induced exocytosis and endocytosis, which appeared to be associated with a slow and slight increase in osmotic water permeability. This suggested that localized activation of PKC might mediate the movement of water channels. However, generalized activation is inhibitory to AVP-induced water transport.

LUMINAL ACTION OF AVP   AVP stimulates water and Na transport from the basolateral, but not the apical, side (70, 106, 141). However, some studies suggest that AVP may act from the apical side as well. It is of note that urine contains much higher concentrations of intact AVP than plasma (97, 127, 151). Apical AVP stimulated prostaglandin synthesis in primary cultured canine CCD cells (66). Furthermore, it is evident that AVP exerts non-classical Ca^{2+}-coupled effects, and the activation of these effects by luminal AVP has recently been examined (5, 10). Luminal nanomolar AVP hyperpolarized transepithelial voltage without a significant change in Na or K transport. This hyperpolarization is inhibited by acetazolamide, but not by ouabain. The luminal action of AVP appears to be mediated by an apical V_1 receptor, but not by a V_2 or an oxytocin receptor (5). While luminal AVP does not enhance osmotic permeability, it inhibits the hydroosmotic effect of basolateral AVP. The cellular mechanism of the apical V_1 receptor remains to be elucidated. It is of interest that while luminal dDAVP had no effect, basolateral dDAVP was roughly equipotent with AVP in raising intracellular calcium (5, 28), which suggests that basolateral and luminal V_1 receptors may be different subtypes. Although self-inhibition of basolateral AVP-induced water transport is not experimentally demonstrable, even at the maximal concentration of plasma AVP, luminal AVP-induced inhibition is demonstrable and could be significant in view of high urinary AVP concentrations. While the physiological significance of luminal and basolateral AVP receptors is unknown, one possibility is that luminal AVP may prevent excessive antidiuresis when AVP is inappropriately high, as in SIADH (122) or physical stress.

TYROSINE KINASES

Epidermal growth factor (EGF) potently inhibits both vasopressin-stimulated water permeability and Na^+ transport in the rabbit cortical collecting duct (31, 207). The EGF receptor is a tyrosine kinase that has been shown to phosphorylate several critical signal transduction proteins including phospholipase C γ (40). The activation of PIP_2 hydrolysis by PLC-γ may display delayed kinetics as compare with PLC-β (20). It has also been suggested that activation of phosphatidylcholine-specific PLC requires tyrosine phosphorylation by growth factor-like receptors (136). Tyrosine kinase-coupled receptors also initiate a complex phosphorylation cascade leading to the activation of MAP kinases (145) which, as discussed above, activate PLA_2 and gene transcription (145). Although the precise mechanism by which EGF inhibits water and salt transport is not well established, it appears that the inhibition of water permeability is at a post-cAMP step that involves protein kinase (possibly PKC) activation (31). EGF also inhibits apical Na^+ entry in the cortical collecting duct via a mechanism that requires calcium (208, 215), but unlike PGE_2, it may not inhibit the Na/K ATPase. The basis for these unique effects is unknown, but it is tempting to speculate that re-organization of the apical actin web could play an important role (69, 82).

cGMP   Multiple forms of guanylyl cyclase exist (217), and recent interest in the role of cGMP in the regulation of Na^+ and water transport has surged. At least two general forms of guanylyl cyclase exist in the collecting duct: a particulate form that is an ANP receptor (202), and a soluble form that is stimulated by nitric oxide (203, 206). Important roles for cGMP stimulation of pathways in regulating collecting duct water and salt transport have been suggested.

ANP inhibits Na^+ absorption and vasopressin-stimulated water permeability in the collecting duct; however, the mechanism of these effects remains unclear. Given the existence of a cGMP-activated cyclic nucleotide phosphodiesterase in rat renal medulla (186), it seems plausible that at least one mechanism by which ANP inhibits water permeability is via increased cAMP catabolism. If this were the operative mechanism, then cGMP should not inhibit the effects of cAMP analogues on transport. However, two studies provide apparently conflicting results with respect to the mechanism of ANP; one demonstrating inhibition (137) and one a lack of inhibition (159) of cAMP-stimulated water flow. Alternative molecular mechanisms of cGMP action are only beginning to be defined (see review in this volume by S Francis & J Corbin).

Most data suggest that the ANP receptor is predominantly expressed in the inner medullary rather than the cortical collecting duct (138, 202). However, effects in both portions of the collecting duct have been reported. ANP may inhibit electroneutral, but not electrogenic, NaCl transport in the rat CCD (101). ANP also inhibits Na^+ absorption in the rat inner medullary collecting duct (158). Possible mechanisms include direct inhibitory effects of cGMP or PKG on open probability of an apical amiloride-sensitive cation channel (110, 189). ANP has also been demonstrated to stimulate NaCl secretion in the rat IMCD, an effect mimicked by cGMP and one that is opposite of the cAMP-mediated effects of vasopressin (158). It is intriguing that the effect is accompanied by an enhanced lumen-negative voltage, which suggests that electrogenic Cl^- secretion may be the primary event. Protein kinase G may activate a 10 pS Cl^- channel that resembles the cystic fibrosis transmembrane conductance regulator, as has been observed in T-84 cells, a colonic epithelial cell line that secretes Cl^- (112). It is conceivable that a similar mechanism operates in the collecting duct.

Recently it was suggested that nitric oxide may stimulate cGMP accumulation and inhibition of Na^+ absorption in the collecting duct in a manner similar to ANP (192). In co-culture experiments, pulmonary endothelial cells were required for bradykinin-stimulated NO synthesis and for stimulation of cGMP generation and inhibition of sodium transport in co-cultured mouse collecting duct cells (192). The recent identification of both NO synthase and soluble guanylyl cyclase in rat cortical and medullary collecting duct (203, 206) supports the possibility that this cGMP-generating pathway plays an important role in modulating collecting duct transport.

SUMMARY

The regulation of transport in the collecting duct is under multi-hormonal control. Vasopressin stimulates water and cation transport, primarily through a V_2/G_s-coupled receptor that activates adenylyl cyclase, which raises cAMP. These stimulatory effects are damped by the action of several hormones, including vasopressin itself, which activate inhibitory G proteins, stimulate phospholipid breakdown, increase prostaglandin production, raise intracellular Ca^{2+}, activate protein kinase C, stimulate tyrosine kinases, and raise cGMP. These inhibitory signals interact with the stimulatory, cAMP-coupled signaling pathway at multiple levels. The balance between these pathways controls net salt and water transport in the collecting duct.

Literature Cited

1. Abramow M, Beauwens R, Cogan E. 1987. Cellular events in vasopressin action. *Kidney Int.* 32:S56–66
2. Aiyar N, Nambi P, Stassen FL, Crooke ST. 1986. Vascular vasopressin receptors mediate phosphatidylinositol turnover and calcium efflux in an established smooth muscle cell line. *Life Sci.* 39:37–45
3. Ammar A, Roseau S, Butlen D. 1992. Pharmacological characterization of V1a vasopressin receptors in the cortical collecting duct. *Am. J. Physiol.* 262:F546–53
4. Anderson RJ, Berl T, McDonald KM, Schrier RW. 1975. Evidence for an in vitro antagonism between vasopressin and prostaglandin in the mammalian kidney. *J. Clin. Invest.* 56:420–26
5. Ando Y, Asano Y. 1993. Functional evidence for an apical V1 receptor in the rabbit cortical collecting duct. *Am. J. Physiol.* 264:F467–71
6. Ando Y, Jacobson H, Breyer M. 1989. Does cyclic AMP-dependent protein kinase (PKA) mediate the hydroosmotic effect of vasopressin (AVP) in rabbit cortical collecting duct (CCD)? *Kidney Int.* 37:576 (Abstr.)
7. Ando Y, Jacobson HR, Breyer MD. 1987. Phorbol myristate acetate, dioctanoylglycerol, and phosphatidic acid inhibit the hydroosmotic effect of vasopressin on rabbit cortical collecting tubule. *J. Clin. Invest.* 80:590–93
8. Ando Y, Jacobson HR, Breyer MD. 1988. Phorbol ester and A23187 have additive but mechanistically separate effects on vasopressin action in rabbit cortical collecting tubule. *J. Clin. Invest.* 81:1578–84
9. Ando Y, Jacobson HR, Breyer MD. 1989. Phosphatidic acids inhibit vasopressin-induced water transport via protein kinase C activation. *Am. J. Physiol.* 257:F524–30
10. Ando Y, Tabei K, Asano. Y. 1991. Luminal vasopressin modulates transport in the rabbit cortical collecting duct. *J. Clin. Invest.* 88:952–59
11. Aramori I, Nakanishi S. 1992. Coupling of two endothelin receptor subtypes to differing signal transduction in transfected Chinese hamster ovary cells. *J. Biol. Chem.* 267(18):12468–74
12. Augert G, Bocckino SB, Blackmore PF, Exton JH. 1989. Hormonal stimulation of diacylglycerol formation in hepatocytes: evidence for phosphatidylcholine breakdown. *J. Biol. Chem.* 264(36):21689–98
13. Ausiello DA, Hall D. 1981. Regulation of vasopressin sensitive adenylate cyclase by calmodulin. *J. Biol. Chem.* 256:9796–98
14. Axelrod J. 1990. Receptor-mediated activation of phospholipase A2 and arachidonic acid release in signal transduction. *Biochem. Soc. Trans.* 18(4):503–7
15. Beavo JA, Reifsnyder DH. 1990. Primary sequence of cyclic nucleotide phosphodiesterase isozymes and the design of selective inhibitors. *Trends Pharmacol. Sci.* 11:150–55
16. Beebe SJ, Blackmore BF, Chrisman TD, Corbin JD. 1988. Use of synergistic pairs of site-selective cAMP analogs in intact cells. In *Methods in Enzymology: Initiation and Termination of Cyclic Nucleotide Action,* ed. JD Corbin, RA Johnson, pp. 118–39. New York: Academic
17. Benos DJ, Saccomani G, Sariban-Sohraby S. 1987. The epithelial sodium channel: subunit number and location of amiloride binding site. *J. Biol. Chem.* 262:10613–18
18. Bentley JK, Kadlecek A, Sherbert CH, Seger D, Sonnenburg WK, et al. 1992. Molecular cloning of cDNA encoding a "63-kDa calmodulin-stimulated phosphodiesterase from bovine brain. *J. Biol. Chem.* 267:18676–82
19. Berlot CH, Bourne HR. 1992. Identification of effector-activating residues of Gs$_\alpha$. *Cell* 68:911–22
20. Berridge MJ. 1993. Inositol trisphosphate and calcium signalling. *Nature* 361:315–25
21. Bertorello AM, Aperia A, Walaas SI, Nairn A, Greengard P. 1991. Phosphorylation of the catalytic subunit of Na$^+$, K$^+$-ATPase inhibits the activity of the enzyme. *Proc. Natl. Acad. Sci. USA* 88:11359–62
22. Birnbaumer M, Seibold A, Gilbert S, Ishido M, Barberis C, et al. 1992. Molecular cloning of the receptor for human antidiuretic hormone. *Nature* 357:333–35
22a. Birnbaumer L. 1992. Receptor-to-effector signaling through G proteins: Roles for βγ dimers as well as α subunits. *Cell* 71:1069–72
23. Bishop WR, Bell RM. 1988. Assembly of phospholipids into cellular membranes: biosynthesis, transmembrane

movement and intracellular translocation. *Annu. Rev. Cell Biol.* 4:579–610

24. Bocckino SB, Blakemore PF, Wilson
PB, Exton JH. 1987. Phosphatidate
accumulation in hormone-treated hepatocytes via a phospholipase D mechanism. *J. Biol. Chem.* 262:15309–15

25. Bonvalet JP, Pradelles P, Farman N.
1987. Segmental synthesis and actions
of prostaglandins along the nephron.
Am. J. Physiol. 253:F377–87

26. Bonventre JV. 1992. Phospholipase A2
and signal transduction. *J. Am. Soc.
Nephrol.* 3(2):128–150

27. Bourdeau JE, Lau K. 1990. Basolateral
cell membrane Ca-Na exchange in
single rabbit connecting tubules. *Am.
J. Physiol.* 258:F1497–1503

28. Breyer M. 1991. Feedback inhibition
of cyclic adenosine monophosphate
stimulated Na transport in the rabbit
cortical collecting duct via Na^+ dependent basolateral Ca^{2+} entry. *J. Clin.
Invest.* 88:1502–10

29. Breyer MD. 1991. Regulation of water
and salt transport in collecting duct
through calcium-dependent signaling
mechanisms. *Am. J. Physiol.* 260:F1-
F11

30. Breyer MD, Fredin D. 1991. Cyclic
AMP regulates intracellular sodium
concentration ($[Na^+]$) in the rabbit
cortical collecting duct (CCD). *J. Am.
Soc. Nephrol.* 2(3):732 (abstract)

31. Breyer MD, Jacobson HR, Breyer JA.
1988. Epidermal growth factor inhibits
the hydroosmotic effect of vasopressin
in the isolated perfused rabbit cortical
collecting tubule. *J. Clin. Invest.*
82:1313–20

32. Brown D. 1989. Membrane recycling
and epithelial cell function. *Am. J.
Physiol.* 256:F1–12

33. Brown D, Orci L. 1983. Vasopressin
stimulates formation of coated pits in
rat kidney collecting ducts. *Nature*
302:253–55

34. Brunskill N, Bastani B, Hayes C,
Morrissey J, Klahr S. 1991. Localization and polar distribution of several
G-protein subunits along nephron segments. *Kidney Int.* 40:997–1006

35. Burnatowska-Hledin MA, Spielman
WS. 1988. Immunodissection of mitochondria-rich cells from rabbit outer
medullary collecting tubule. *Am. J.
Physiol.* 254:F907–11

36. Burnatowska-Hledin MA, Spielman
WS. 1989. Vasopressin V1 receptors
on the principal cells of the rabbit
cortical collecting tubule: stimulation
of cytosolic free calcium and inositol
phosphate production via coupling to

a pertussis toxin substrate. *J. Clin.
Invest.* 83:84–89

37. Canessa CM, Horisberger J-D, Rossier
BC. 1993. Epithelial sodium channel
related to proteins involved in neu-
rodegeneration. *Nature* 361:467–70

38. Cantiello HF, Patenaude CR, Codina
J, Birnbaumer L. 1990. G alpha i-3
regulates epithelial Na^+ channels by
activation of phospholipase A2 and
lipoxygenase pathways. *J. Biol. Chem.*
265:21624–28

39. Cantiello HF, Stow JL, Prat AG,
Ausiello DA. 1991. Actin filaments
regulate epithelial Na^+ channel activity. *Am. J. Physiol.* 261:C882–88

40. Carpenter G, Cohen S. 1990. Epidermal growth factor. *J. Biol. Chem.*
265(14):7709–12

41. Carr DW, Stofko-Hahn RE, Fraser
IDC, Cone RD, Scott JD. 1992. Localization of the cAMP-dependent protein kinase to the postsynaptic densities
by A-Kinase anchoring proteins: characterization of AKAP 79. *J. Biol.
Chem.* 267:16816–23

42. Chen L, Reif MC, Schafer JA. 1991.
Clonidine and PGE2 have different
effects on Na^+ and water transport in
rat and rabbit CCD. *Am. J. Physiol.*
261:F126–136

43. Chilablin AV, Vasilates LA, Hennekes
H, Prolong D, Geering K. 1992. Phosphorylation of Na,K-ATPase α-sub-
units in microsomes and in homogenates of *Xenopus* oocytes resuting
from the stimulation of protein kinase
A and protein kinase C. *J. Biol. Chem.*
267(31):22378–84

44. Clark JD, Lin L-L, Kriz RW, Ramesha
CS, Sultzman LA, et al. 1991. A
novel arachidonic acid-selective cytosolic PLA2 contains a Ca^{2+}-dependent
translocation domain with homology
to PKC and GAP. *Cell* 65:1043–51

45. Coffey AK, O'Sullivan DJ, Homma
S, Dousa TP, Valtin H. 1991. induction of intramembranous particle
clusters in mice with nephrogenic
diabetes insipidus. *Am. J. Physiol.*
261:F640–46

46. Conklin BR, Chabre O, Wong YH,
Federman AD, Bourne HR. 1992.
Recombinant Gqα. *J. Biol. Chem.*
267:31–34

47. Cort JH., Schück O, Stribrna J, Skop-
kova J, Jost K, Mulder JL. 1975. Role
of the disulfide bridge and the C-terminal tripeptide in the antidiuretic action of vasopressin in man and the
rat. *Kidney Int.* 8:292–302

48. Ding G, McGovern B, Singhal P,
Hays RM. 1989. Aggrephores have

little, if any role in water channel delivery in rat collecting duct. *Kidney Int.* 35:305

49. Dixon BS, Breckon R, Burke C, Anderson RJ. 1988. Phorbol esters inhibit adenylate cyclase activity in cultured collecting tubular cells. *Am. J. Physiol.* 254:C183-91

50. Dong L, Stevens JL, Jaken S. 1991. Biochemical and immunological characterization of renal protein kinase C. *Am. J. Physiol.* 261:F678-87

51. Doucet A, Barlet C. 1986. Evidence for differences in the sensitivity to ouabain of Na/K-ATPase along the nephrons of rabbit kidney. *J. Biol. Chem.* 261:993-95

52. Dousa TP, Valtin H. 1976. Cellular actions of vasopressin in the mammalian kidney. *Kidney Int.* 10:46-63

53. Edwards RM, Jackson BA, Dousa TP. 1980. Protein kinase activity in isolated tubules of rat medulla. *Am. J. Physiol.* 238:F269-78

54. Emanuel JR, Garetz S, Sone L, Levenson R. 1987. Differential expression of Na-K-ATPase alpha and beta subunit mRNAs in rat tissues and cell lines. *Proc. Natl. Acat. Sci. USA* 84:9030-34

55. Exton JH. 1990. Signaling through phosphatidylcholine breakdown. *J. Biol. Chem.* 265(1):1-4

56. Fejes-Tóth G, Náray-Fejes-Tóth A. 1987. Differentiated transport functions in primary cultures of rabbit collecting ducts. *Am. J. Physiol.* 253: F1302-7

57. Fejes-Tóth G, Náray-Fejes-Tóth A. 1992. Differentiation of β-intercalated cells (β-ICC) in culture into α-ICC and principal cells (PC) via asymmetric cell division. *J. Am. Soc. Nephrol.* 3:838 (Abstr.)

58. Fejes-Tóth G, Zahajszky T, Filep J. 1980. Effect of vasopressin on kallikrein excretion. *Am. J. Physiol.* 239: F388-92

59. Ferris CD, Huganir RL, Supattapone S, Snyder SH. 1989. Purified inositol 1,4,5-trisphosphate receptor mediates calcium flux in reconstituted lipid vesicles. *Nature* 342:87-89

60. Field MF, Stanton BA, Giebisch GH. 1984. Influence of ADH on renal potassium handling: a micropuncture and microperfusion study. *Kidney Int.* 25:502-11

61. Frindt G, Burg MB. 1972. Effect of vasopressin on sodium transport in renal cortical collecting tubules. *Kidney Int.* 1:224-31

62. Frindt G, Windhager EE. 1990. Ca^{2+}-dependent inhibition of sodium transport in rabbit cortical collecting tubules. *Am. J. Physiol.* 258:F568-82

63. Fushimi K, Uchuda S, Hara Y, Hirata Y, Marumo F, Sasaki S. 1993. Cloning and expression of apical membrane water channel of rat kidney collecting tubule. *Nature* 361:549-52

64. Gamba G, Saltzberg SN, Lombardi M, Miyanoshita A, Lytton J, et al. 1993. Primary structure and functional expression of a cDNA encoding the thiazide-sensitive, electroneutral sodium-chloride cotransporter. *Proc. Natl. Acad. Sci. USA* 90:2749-53

65. Gapstur SM, Homma S, Dousa TP. 1988. cAMP-binding proteins in medullary tubules from rat kidney: effect of ADH. *Am. J. Physiol.* 255:F292-300

66. Garcia-Perez A, Smith WL. 1984. Apical-basolateral membrane asymmetry in canine cortical collecting tubule cells. *J. Clin. Invest.* 74:63-74

67. Garg LC. 1992. Actions of adrenergic and cholinergic drugs on renal tubular cells. *Pharmacol. Rev.* 44(1): 81-102

68. Glatt CE, Snyder SH. 1993. Cloning and expression of an adenylyl cyclase localized to the corpus striatum. *Nature* 361:536-38

69. Goldschmidt-Clermont P, Kim JW, Machesky LM, Rhee SG, Pollard TD. 1991. Regulation of phospholipase C-γ1 by profilin and tyrosine phosphorylation. *Science* 251:1231-33

70. Grantham JJ, Burg MB. 1966. Effect of vasopressin and cyclic AMP on permeability of isolated collecting tubules. *Am. J. Physiol.* 211:255-59

71. Gupta SK, Diez E, Heasley LE, Osawa S, Johnson GL. 1990. A G protein mutant that inhibits thrombin and purinergic receptor activation of phospholipase A2. *Science* 249:662-66

72. Han JS, Maeda Y, Knepper MA. 1992. High concentration of vasopressin inhibit vasopressin-stimulated water transport in rat terminal IMCD. *J. Am. Soc. Nephrol.* 3:793 (Abstr.)

73. Hardy MA. 1978. Intracellular calcium as a modulator of transepithelial permeability to water in frog urinary bladder. *J. Cell Biol.* 76:787-91

74. Harris HW, Strange K, Zeidel ML. 1991. Current understanding of the cellular biology and molecular structure of the antidiuretic hormone-stimulated water transport pathway. *J. Clin. Invest.* 88:1-8

75. Harrison JK, Hewlett KGH, Gnegy ME. 1989. Regulation of calmodulin-sensitive adenylate cyclase by the stim-

ulatory G-protein, Gsα. *J. Biol. Chem.* 264:15880–85

76. Hartwig JH, Thelen M, Rosen A, Janmey PA, Nairn AC, Aderem A. 1992. MARCKS is an actin filament crosslinking protein regulated by protein kinase C and calcium-calmodulin. *Nature* 356:618–22

77. Hays RM. 1991. Cell biology of vasopressin. In *The Kidney,* ed. BM Brenner, FC Rector, pp. 424–44. Philadelphia: Saunders

78. Hays SR, Baum M, Kokko JP. 1987. Effects of protein kinase C activation on sodium, potassium, chloride, and total CO_2 transport in the rabbit cortical collecting tubule. *J. Clin. Invest.* 80: 1561–70

79. Hebert RL, Jacobson HR, Breyer MD. 1991. Prostaglandin E2 inhibits sodium transport in the rabbit CCD by raising intracellular calcium. *J. Clin. Invest.* 87:1992–98

80. Hebert RL, Jukic D, Regoli D. 1992. Mediation of bradykinin (BDK) actions in rabbit cortical collecting duct (CCD) via a specific BDK-B2 receptor. *J. Am. Soc. Nephrol.* 3(3):493

81. Ho K, Nichols CG, Lederer WJ, Lytton J, Vassilev PM, et al. 1993. Cloning and expression of an inwardly rectifying ATP-regulated potassium channel. *Nature* 362:31–38

82. Holmgren K, Mugnusson K-E, Franki N, Hays RM. 1992. ADH-induced depolymerization of F-actin in the toad bladder granular cell: a confocal microscope study. *Am. J. Physiol.* 262: C672–77

83. Holt WF, LeChene C. 1981. ADH-PGE2 interactions in cortical collecting tubule. I. Depression of sodium transport. *Am. J. Physiol.* 241:F452–60

84. Homma S, Gapstur SM, Coffey A, Valtin H, Dousa TP. 1991. Role of cAMP-phosphodiesterase isozymes in pathogenesis of murine nephrogenic diabetes insipidus. *Am. J. Physiol.* 261:F345–53

85. Homma S, Gapstur SM, Yusufi ANK, Dousa TP. 1988. In situ phosphorylation of proteins in MCTs microdissected from rat kidney: effect of AVP. *Am. J. Physiol.* 254:F512–20

86. Homma S, Takeda S, Tetsuka T, Kusano E, Asano Y. 1991. Vasopressin (AVP) stimulates low-K_m cAMP phosphodiesterase (PDE) in medullary collecting ducts (MCD). *J. Am. Soc. Nephrol.* 2:723

87. Huang C, Cabot MC. 1990. Vasopressin-induced polyphosphoinositide and phosphatidylcholine degradation in fibroblasts. *J. Biol. Chem.* 265:17468–73

88. Irvine RF. 1982. How is the level of free arachidonic acid controlled in mammalian cells? *Biochem. J.* 204:3–16

89. Ishikawa S, Saito T. 1990. Optimal concentration of cellular free calcium for AVP-induced cAMP in collecting tubules. *Kidney Int.* 37:1060–66

90. Jabs K, Zeidel ML, Silva P. 1989. Prostaglandin E2 inhibits Na^+-K^+-ATPase activity in the inner medullary collecting duct. *Am. J. Physiol.* (257): F424-F430

91. Jassier F, Bugeon L, Blot-Chabaud M, Bonvalet JP, Farman N. 1989. Effects of AVP and dDAVP on PGE2 synthesis in superfused cortical collecting tubules. *Am. J. Physiol.* 256:F1044–50

92. Jin S-LC, Swinnen JV, Conti M. 1992. Characterization of the structure of a low K_m rolipram-sensitive cAMP phosphodiesterase. *J. Biol. Chem.* 267: 18929–39

93. Jones SM, Frindt G, Windhager EE. 1988. Effect of peritubular [Ca] or ionomycin on hydrosmotic response of CCTs to ADH or cAMP. *Am. J. Physiol.* 254:F240–53

94. Kashgarian M, Diemsderfer D, Caplan M, Forbush B. 1985. Monoclonal antibody to Na,K-ATPase: immunocytochemical localization along nephron segements. *Kidney Int.* 28:899–913

95. Katsushika S, Chen L, Kawabe J-I, Nilakantan R, Halnon NJ, et al. 1992. Cloning and characterization of a sixth adenylyl cyclase isoform: Types V and VI constitute a subgroup within the mammalian adenylyl cyclase family. *Proc. Natl. Acad. Sci. USA* 89:8774–78

96. Khan AA, Steiner JP, Klein MG, Schneider MF, Snyder SH. 1992. IP3 receptor: localization to plasma membrane of T cells and cocapping with the T cell receptor. *Science* 257:815–18

97. Kimura T, Share L. 1981. Characterization of the renal handling of vasopressin in the dog by stop-flow analysis. *Endocrinology.* 109:2089–94

98. Kirk KL. 1988. Binding and internalization of a fluorescent vasopressin analogue by collecting duct cells. *Am. J. Physiol.* 255:C622–32

99. Kirk KL. 1988. Origin of ADH-induced vacuoles in rabbit cortical collecting tubule. *Am. J. Physiol.* 254: F719–33

100. Kleyman TR, Kraehenbuhl J-P, Ernst SA. 1991. Characterization and cellular localization of the epithelial Na^+ chan-

nel: studies using an anti-Na$^+$ channel antibody raised by an antiidiotypic route. *J. Biol. Chem.* 266(6):3907–15

101. Knepper MA, Lankford SP, Tereda Y. 1991. Renal tubular actions of ANF. *Can. J. Physiol. Pharmacol.* 69:1537–45

102. Knepper MA, Star RA. 1990. The vasopressin-regulated urea transporter in renal inner medullary collecting duct. *Am. J. Physiol.* 259:F393–401

103. Kosaka Y, Ogita K, Ase K, Nomura H, Kikkawa U, Nishizuka Y. 1988. The heterogeneity of protein kinase C in various rat tissues. *Biochem. Biophys. Res. Comm.* 151:973–81

104. Krupinski J, Lehman TC, Frankenfield CD, Zwaagstra JC, Watson PA. 1992. Molecular diversity in the adenyly-cyclase family: evidence for eight forms of the enzyme and cloning of type VI. *J. Biol. Chem.* 267(34):24858–62

105. Kusano E, Murayama N, Werness JL, Christensen S, Homma S, et al. 1985. Effects of calcium on the vasopressin-sensitive cAMP metabolism in medullary tubules. *Am. J. Physiol.* 249:F956–66

106. Leaf A, Anderson J, Page LB. 1958. Active sodium transport by the isolated toad bladder. *J. Gen. Physiol.* 41:657–68

107. Lefurgey A, Tisher CC. 1979. Morphology of the rabbit collecting tubule. *Am. J. Anat.* 155:111–24

108. Leite JM, Rouse D, Lederer E, Abramowitz J, Suki WN. 1991. TMB-8 prevents the hydroosmotic response to ADH in rabbit cortical collecting tubules. *Kidney Int.* 40:434–40

109. Li G, Pralong W-F, Pittet D, Mayr GW, Schlegel W, Wollheim CB. 1992. Inositol tetrakisphosphate isomers and elevation of cytosolic Ca^{2+} in vasopressin-stimulated insulin-secreting RINm5F cells. *J. Biol. Chem.* 267: 4349–56

110. Light DB, Corbin JD, Stanton BA. 1990. Dual ion-channel regulation by cyclic GMP and cyclic-GMP dependent protein kinase. *Nature* 344:336–39

111. Lin L-L, Wartmann M, Lin AY, Knopf JL, Seth A, Davis RJ. 1993. cPLA2 is phosphorylated and activated by MAP kinase. *Cell* 72:269–78

112. Lin M, Nairn AC, Guggino SE. 1992. cGMP-dependent protein kinase regulation of a chloride channel in T-84 cells. *Am. J. Physiol.* 262:C1304–12

113. Ling BN, Hinton CF, Eaton DC. 1991. Potassium permeable channels in primary cultures of rabbit cortical collecting tubule. *Kidney Int.* 40:441–52

114. Ling BN, Kokko KE, Eaton DC. 1992. Inhibition of apical Na$^+$ channels in rabbit cortical collecting tubules by basolateral prostaglandin E2 is modulated by protein kinase C. *J. Clin. Invest.* 90:1328–34

115. Lingueglia E, Voilley N, Waldmann R, Lazdunski M, Barbry P. 1993. Expression cloning of an epithelial amiloride-sensitive Na$^+$ channel. *FEBS Lett.* 318:95–99

116. Lolait SJ, O'Carrol A-M, McBride OW, Konig M, Morel A, Brownstein MJ. 1992. Cloning and characterization of a vasopressin V2 receptor and possible link to nephrogenic diabetes insipidus. *Nature* 357:336–39

117. Ludwig J, Margalit T, Eismann E, Lancet D, Kaupp UB. 1990. Primary structure of cAMP-gated channel from bovine olfactory epithelium. *FEBS Lett.* 270:24–29

118. Madsen KM, Tisher CC. 1986. Structure function relationships along the distal nephron. *Am. J. Physiol.* 250 (19):F1–15

119. Manganiello VC, Smith CJ, Degerman E, Belfrage P. 1990. Cyclic GMP-inhibited cyclic nucleotide phosphodieterases. In *Cyclic Nucleotide Phosphodiesterases: Structure, Regulation and Drug Action,* ed. J Beavo, MD Houslay, pp. 87–116. New York: Wiley & Sons

120. Marunaka Y, Eaton DC. 1991. Effects of vasopressin and cAMP on single amiloride-blockable Na channels. *Am. J. Physiol.* 260:C1071–84

121. Masur SK, Sapirstein V, Rivero D. 1985. Phorbol myristate acetate induces endocytosis as well as exocytosis and hydroosmosis in toad urinary bladder. *Biochem. Biophys. Acta.* 821: 286–96

122. Miller M, Moses AM. 1972. Urinary antidiuretic hormone in polyuric disorders and in inappropriate ADH syndrome. *Ann. Intern. Med.* 77:715–21

123. Miller RT. 1991. Transmembrane signalling through G proteins. *Kidney Int.* 39:421–29

124. Morel A, O'Carroll A-M, Brownstein MJ, Lolait SJ. 1992. Molecular cloning and expression of a rat V1a arginine vasopressin receptor. *Nature* 356:523–26

125. Morel F, Doucet A. 1986. Hormonal control of kidney functions at the cell level. *Physiol. Rev.* 66:377–468

126. Moriarty TM, Padrell E, Carty DJ, Omri G, Landau EM, Iyengar R. 1990. G$_o$ protein as signal transducer

in the pertussis toxin-sensitive phosphatidylinositol pathway. *Nature* 343: 79–82

127. Moses A, Steciak E. 1986. Urinary and metabolic clearances of arginine vasopressin in normal subjects. *Am. J. Physiol.* 251:R365–70

128. Muller J, Kachadorian WA, DiScala VA. 1980. Evidence that ADH-stimulated intramembranous particle aggregates are transfered from cytoplasmic to luminal membranes in toad bladder epithelial cells. *J. Cell Biol.* 85:83–95

129. Murayama T, Ui M. 1983. Loss of the inhibitory function of the guanine nucleotide regulatory component of adenylate cyclase due to its ADP ribosylation by islet-activating protein, pertussis toxin, in adipocyte membranes. *J. Biol. Chem.* 258:3319–26

130. Nadler SP, Zimpelmann JA, Hebert RL. 1992. Endothelin inhibits vasorpessin-stimulated water permeability in rat terminal inner medullary collecting duct. *J. Clin. Invest.* 90:1458–66

131. Nagamine Y, Reich E. 1985. Gene expression and cAMP. *Proc. Natl. Acad. Sci. USA* 82:4606–10

132. Nakamura T, Gold GH. 1987. A cyclic nucleotide-gated conductance in olfactory receptor cilia. *Nature* 325:442–44

133. Natochin YV, Shakhmatova EI. 1992. Vasopressin V1-antagonist increases the hydroosmotic response to arginine vasopressin in frog urinary bladder. *Pflügers Arch.* 421:406–8

134. Nemenoff RA, Sinitz S, Qian N-X, Van Putten V, Johnson GL, Heasley LE. 1993. Phosphorylation and activation of a high molecular weight form of phospholipase A2 by p42 microtubule-associated protein 2 kinase and protein kinase C. *J. Biol. Chem.* 268(3):1960–64

135. Nesterova MV, Glukhov AI, Severin ES. 1982. Effect of regulatory subunit of cAMP-dependent protein kinase on the genetic activity of eukaryotic cells. *Mol. Cell. Biochem.* 49:53–61

136. Nishizuka Y. 1992. Intracellular signaling by hydrolysis of phospholipids and activation of protein kinase C. *Science* 258:607–14

137. Nonoguchi H, Sands JM, Knepper MA. 1988. Atrial natriuretic factor inhibits vasopressin-stimulated osmotic water permeability in rat inner medullary collecting duct. *J. Clin. Invest.* 82:1383–90

138. Nonoguchi HM, Knepper MA, Manganiello VC. 1987. Effects of atrial natriuretic factor on cyclic guanosine

monophosphate and cyclic adenosine monophosphate accumulation in microdissected nephron segments from rats. *J. Clin. Invest.* 79:500–7

139. Ohuchi K, Levine L. 1978. Stimulation of prostaglandin synthesis by tumor promoting phorbol-12,13-diesters in canine kidney (MDCK) cells. *J. Biol. Chem.* 253:4783–90

140. O'Neil RG, Hayhurst RH. 1985. Functional differentiation of cell types of the cortical collecting duct. *Am. J. Physiol.* 248:F449–53

141. Orloff J, Handler JS. 1962. The similarity of effects of vasopressin, adenosine-3',5'-phosphate (cyclic AMP) and theophylline on the toad bladder. *J. Clin. Invest.* 41:702–9

142. Palmer LG. 1992. Epithelial Na channels: function and diversity. *Annu. Rev. Physiol.* 54:51–66

143. Palmer LG, Frindt G. 1986. Amiloride-sensitive Na channels from the apical membrane of the rat cortical collecting tubule. *Proc. Natl. Acad. Sci. USA* 83:2767–70

144. Palmer LG, Frindt G. 1987. Effects of cell Ca and pH on Na channels from rat cortical collecting tubule. *Am. J. Physiol.* 253:F333–39

145. Pelech SL, Sanghera JS. 1992. MAP kinases: charting the regulatory pathways. *Science* 257:1355–56)

146. Peterson MW, Walter ME. 1992. Calcium-activated phosphatidylcholine-specific phospholipase C and D in MDCK epithelial cells. *Am. J. Physiol.* 263:C1216–24

147. Phillips ME, Taylor A. 1989. Effect of nocodazole on the water permeability response to vasopressin in rabbit collecting tubules perfused in vitro. *J. Physiol.* 411:529–44

148. Premont RT, Chen J, Ma H-W, Ponnapalli M, Iyengar R. 1992. Two members of a widely expressed subfamily of hormone-stimulated adenylyl cyclases. *Proc. Natl. Acad. Sci. USA* 89:9809–13

149. Preston BM, Agre P. 1991. Isolation of the cDNA for erythrocyte integral membrane protein of 28 kilodaltons: member of an ancient channel family. *Proc. Natl. Acad. Sci. USA* 88:11110–14

150. Preston BM, Carroll TP, Guggino WB, Agre P. 1992. Appearance of water channels in *Xenopus* oocytes expressing red cell CHIP28 protein. *Science* 256: 385–87

151. Rabkin R, Share L, Payne PA, Young J, Crofton J. 1979. The handling of immunoreactive vasopressin by the iso-

lated perfused rat kidney. *J. Clin. Invest.* 63:6–13

152. Reif MC, Troutman SL, Schafer JA. 1984. Sustained response to vasopressin in isolated rat cortical collecting tubule. *Kidney Int.* 26:725–32

153. Repaske DR, Swinnen JV, Jin S-LC, Van Wyk JJ, Conti M. 1992. A polymerase chain reaction strategy to identify and clone cyclic nucleotide phosphodiesterase cDNAs. *J. Biol. Chem.* 267:18683–88

154. Rhee SG, Choi KD. 1992. Regulation of inositol phospholipid-specific phospholipase C isozymes. *J. Biol. Chem.* 267(18):12393–96

155. Ribeiro C-P, Ribeiro-Neto F, Field JB, Suki WN. 1987. Prevention of α2-adrenergic inhibition on ADH action by pertussis toxin in rabbit CCT. *Am. J. Physiol.* 253:C105–12

156. Rick R, Spancken G, Dorge A. 1988. Differential effects of aldosterone and ADH on intracellular electrolytes in the toad urinary bladder epithelium. *J. Membr. Biol.* 101:275–82

157. Robertson GL. 1977. The regulation of vasopressin function in health and disease. *Recent Prog. Horm. Res.* 33:333–85

158. Rocha AS, Kudo LH. 1990. Atrial peptide and cGMP effects on NaCl transport in inner medullary collecting duct. *Am. J. Physiol.* 259:F258–68

159. Rocha AS, Kudo LH. 1990. Effect of atrial natriuretic factor and cyclic guanosine monophosphate on water and urea transport in the inner medullary collecting duct. *Pflügers Arch.* 417:84–90

160. Rouch AJ, Chen L, Kudo L, Corbitt BD, Schafer JA. 1991. Changes in intracellular Ca^{2+} or PKC activity do not alter AVP-dependent Na^+ or H_2O transport in the rat cortical collecting duct (CCD). *J. Am. Soc. Nephrol.* 2:740 (Abstr.)

161. Rouch AJ, Chen L, Troutman SL, Schafer JA. 1991. Na^+ transport in isolated rat CCD: effects of bradykinin, ANP, clonidine, and hydrochlorothiazide. *Am. J. Physiol.* 260:F86–95

162. Sabolic I, Valenti G, Verbavatz J-M, Van Hoek AN, Verkman AS, et al. 1992. Localization of the CHIP28 water channel in rat kidney. *Am. J. Physiol.* 263:C1225–33

163. Sariban-Sohraby S, Sorscher EJ, Brenner BM, Benos DJ. 1988. Phosphorylation of a single subunit of the epithelial Na channel protein following vasopressin treatment of A6 cells. *J. Biol. Chem.* 263:13875–79

164. Sasaki S, Fushimi K, Uchida S, Marumo F. 1992. Regulation and localization of two types of water channel in the rat kidney. *J. Am. Soc. Nephrol.* 3:798 (Abstr.)

165. Satoh T, Cohen HT, Kats AI. 1992. Intracellular signaling in the regulation of renal Na-K-ATPase. I. role of cyclic AMP and phospholipase A2. *J. Clin. Invest.* 89:1496–1500

166. Schafer JA, Hawk CT. 1992. Regulation of Na^+ channels in the cortical collecting duct by AVP and mineralocorticoids. *Kidney Int.* 41:255–68

167. Schafer JA, Troutman SL. 1990. cAMP mediates the increase in apical membrane Na^+ conductance produced in rat CCD by vasopressin. *Am. J. Physiol.* 259(28):F823–31

168. Schafer JA, Troutman SL, Schlatter E. 1990. Vasopressin and mineralocorticoid increase apical membrane driving force for K^+ secretion in rat CCD. *Am. J. Physiol.* 258:F199–210

169. Schlondorff D, Levine SD. 1985. Inhibition of vasopressin stimulated water flow in toad bladder by phorbol myristate acetate, dioctanoylglycerol, and RHC-80267. *J. Clin. Invest.* 76:1071–78

170. Schlondorff D, Satriano JA, Schwartz GJ. 1985. Synthesis of prostaglandin E2 in different segments of isolated collecting tubules from adult and neonatal rabbits. *Am. J. Physiol.* 248:F134–44

171. Schuster VL. 1985. Mechanism of bradykinin, ADH, and cAMP interaction in rabbit cortical collecting duct. *Am. J. Physiol.* 249:F645–53

172. Schuster VL. 1993. Function and regulation of collecting duct intercalated cells. *Annu. Rev. Physiol.* 55:267–88

173. Scott JD. 1991. Cyclic nucleotide-dependent protein kinases. *Pharmacol. Ther.* 50:123–45

174. Scott JD, Stofko RE, McDonalds JR, Comer JD, Vitalis EA, Mangili JA. 1990. Type II regulatory subunit dimerization determines the subcellular localization of the cAMP-dependent protein kinase. *J. Biol. Chem.* 265:21561–66

175. Senkfor SI, Johnson GL, Berl T. 1993. Molecular map of G protein α chains in microdissected rat nephron segments. *J. Clin. Invest.* 92:786–90

176. Shacter E, Stadtman ER, Jurgensen SR, Chock PB. 1988. Role of cAMP in cyclic cascade regulation. See Ref. 16, pp. 3–19

177. Shariff A, Luna E. 1992. Diacylglycerol-stimulated formation of actin

nucleation sites at plasma membranes. *Science* 256(256):245–47

178. Shayman JA, Morrissey JJ, Morrison AR. 1987. Islet activating protein inhibits kinin-stimulated inositol phosphate production, calcium mobilization, and prostaglandin E2 synthesis in renal papillary collecting tubule cells independent of cyclic AMP. *J. Biol. Chem.* 262:17083–87

179. Shimizu T, Yoshitomi K, Nakamura M, Imai M. 1988. Site and mechanism of action of trichlormethiazide in rabbit distal nephron segments perfused in vitro. *J. Clin. Invest.* 82:721–30

180. Skorecki KL, Verkman AS, Ausiello DA. 1987. Cross talk between stimulatory and inhibitory guanosine 5'-triphosphate binding proteins: role in activation and desensitization of the adenylate cyclase response to vasopressin. *Biochemistry.* 26:639–45

181. Slivka SR, Insel PA. 1987. α1-Adrenergic receptor-mediated phosphoinositide hydrolysis and prostaglandin E₂ formation in Madin-Darby canine kidney cells: possible parallel activation of phospholipase C and phospholipase A₂. *J. Biol. Chem.* 262(9):4200–7

182. Smrck AV, Hepler JR, Brown KO, Sternweis PC. 1991. Regulation of polyphosphoinositide-specific phospholipase C activity by purified Gq. *Science* 804:804–7

183. Snowdowne KW, Borle AB. 1985. Effect of low extracellular sodium on cytosolic ionized calcium:Na⁺-Ca²⁺ exchange as a major calcium influx pathway in kidney cells. *J. Biol. Chem.* 260:14998–5007

184. Snyder HM, Fredin DM, Breyer MD. 1991. Muscarinic receptor activation inhibits AVP-induced water flow in rabbit cortical collecting ducts. *Am. J. Physiol.* 260:F283–36

185. Snyder HM, Noland TD, Breyer MD. 1992. cAMP-dependent kinase mediates hydroosmotic effect of vasopressin in collecting duct. *Am. J. Physiol.* 263:C147–53

186. Sonnenburg WK, Mullaney PJ, Beavo JA. 1991. Molecular cloning of a cyclic GMP-stimulated cyclic nucleotide phosphodiesterase cDNA: identification and distribution of isozyme variants. *J. Biol. Chem.* 266(26):17655–61

187. Sonnenburg WK, Smith WL. 1988. Regulation of cyclic AMP metabolism in rabbit cortical collecting tubule cells by prostaglandins. *J. Biol. Chem.* 263: 6155–60

188. Sonnenburg WK, Zhu J, Smith WL. 1990. A prostglandin E receptor coupled to a pertussis toxin-sensitive guanine nucleotide regulatory protein in rabbit cortical collecting tubule cells. *J. Biol. Chem.* 265:8479–83

189. Stanton BA. 1991. Molecular mechanisms of ANP inhibition of renal sodium transport. *Can. J. Physiol. Pharmacol.* 69:1546–52

190. Star RA, Nonoguchi H, Balaban RB, Knepper MA. 1988. Calcium and cyclic adenosine monophosphate as second messengers for vasopressin in the rat inner medullary collecting duct. *J. Clin. Invest.* 81:1879–88

191. Stassen FL, Heckman G, Schmidt D, Papadopoulos MT, Nambi P, et al. 1988. Oxytocin induced a transient increase in cytosolic free [Ca²⁺] in renal tubular epithelial cells: evidence for oxytocin receptors on LLC-PK1 cells. *Mol. Pharmacol.* 33:218–24

192. Stoos BA, Carretero OA, Farhy RD, Scicili G, Garvin JL. 1992. Endothelium-derived relaxing factor inhibits transport and increases cGMP content in cultured mouse cortical collecting duct cells. *J. Clin. Invest.* 89:761–65

193. Stow JL, Sabolic I, Brown D. 1991. Heterogeneous localization of G protein α-subunits in rat kidney. *Am. J. Physiol.* 1991:F831–40

194. Strange K, Spring KR. 1987. Cell membrane water permeability of rabbit cortical collecting duct. *J. Membr. Biol.* 96:27–43

195. Sweadner KJ. 1989. Isozymes of the Na⁺/K⁺-ATPase. *Biochem. Biophys. Acta* 988:185–220

196. Takeda S, Lin C-T, Morgano PG, McIntyre SJ, Dousa TP. 1991. High activity of low-Michaelis-Menten constant 3',5'-cyclic adenosine monophosphate-phosphodiesterase isozymes in renal inner medula of mice with hereditary nephrogenic diabetes insipidus. *Endocrinology.* 129:287–94

197. Taussig R, Qaurmby LM, Gilman AG. 1993. Regulation of purified type I and type II adenylylcyclases by G protein bg subunits. *J. Biol. Chem.* 268:9–12

198. Taylor A, Mamelak M, Reaven E, Maffly R. 1973. Vasopressin: possible role of microtubules and microfilaments in its action. *Science* 181:347–50

199. Taylor SJ, Chae HZ, Rhee SG, Exton JH. 1991. Activation of the β1 isozyme of phospholipase C by α subunits of the Gq class of G proteins. *Nature* 350:516–18

200. Teitelbaum I. 1990. The epidermal growth factor receptor is coupled to a phospholipase A2-specific, pertussis

toxin inhibitable guanine nucleotide-binding regulatory protein in cultured rat inner medullary collecting tubule cells. *J. Biol. Chem.* 265:4218–22

201. Tereda Y, Knepper MA. 1990. Thiazide sensitive NaCl absorption in rat cortical collecting duct. *Am. J. Physiol.* 259:F519–28

202. Tereda Y, Moriyama T, Martin BM, Knepper MA, Garcia PA. 1991. RT-PCR microlocalization of mRNA for guanylyl cyclase-coupled ANF receptor in rat kidney. *Am. J. Physiol.* 261:F1080–87

203. Tereda Y, Tomita K, Nonoguchi H, Marumo F. 1992. Polymerase chain reaction localization of constitutive nitric oxide synthase and soluble guanylate cyclase messenger RNAs in micro dissected rat nephron segments. *J. Clin. Invest.* 90:659–65

204. Tetsuka T, Kusano E, Takeda S, Homma S, Ando Y, Asano Y. 1992. Phorbol myristate acetate (PMA) activates rolipram sensitive cyclic AMP phosphodiesterase (PDIE) in medullary collecting tubules (MCT) of the rat kidney. *J. Am. Soc. Nephrol.* 3:510

205. Torikai S, Kurokawa K. 1983. Effect of PGE2 on vasopressin-dependent cell cAMP in isolated single nephron segments. *Am. J. Physiol.* 249:F58-F66

206. Ujiie K, Drewett JG, Yuen ST, Star RA. 1993. Differential expression of mRNA for guanylyl cyclase-linked endothelium derived relaxing factor receptor subunits in rat kidney. *J. Clin. Invest.* 91:730–34

207. Vehaskari VM, Hering-Smith KS, Moskowitz DW, Weiner ID, Hamm LL. 1989. Effect of epidermal growth factor on sodium transport in the cortical collecting tubule. *Am. J. Physiol.* 256:F803–9

208. Vehaskari VM, Herndon J, Hamm LL. 1991. Mechanism of sodium transport inhibition by epidermal growth factor in cortical collecting ducts. *Am. J. Physiol.* 261:F896–903

209. Verkman AS, Lencer WI, Brown D, Ausiello DA. 1988. Endosomes from kidney collecting tubule cells contain the vasopressin-sensitive water channel. *Nature* 333:268–69

210. Wade JB, Kachadorian WA. 1988. Cytochalasin B inhibition of toad bladder apical membrane responses to ADH. *Am. J. Physiol.* 255:C526

211. Walker LA, Whorton AR, Smigel M, France R, Frölich JC. 1978. Antidiuretic hormone increases renal prostaglandin synthesis in vivo. *Am. J. Physiol.* 234:F180–85

212. Wang W, Giebisch G. 1991. Dual effect of adenosine triphosphate on the apical small conductance K^+ channel of the rat cortical collecting duct. *J. Gen. Physiol.* 98:35–61

213. Wang W, Giebisch G. 1991. Dual modulation of renal ATP-sensitive K^+ channel by protein kinases A and C. *Proc. Natl. Acad. Sci. USA* 88:9722–25

214. Wang W, Sackin H, Giebisch G. 1992. Renal potassium channels and their regulation. *Annu. Rev. Physiol.* 54:81–96

215. Warden DH, Stokes JB. 1993. EGF and PGE_2 inhibit rabbit CCD Na^+ transport by different mechanisms: PGE_2 inhibits the Na^+/K^+-ATPase. *Am. J. Physiol.* 264:F670–77

216. Wilke TM, Scherle PA, Strathmann MP, Slepak VZ, Simon MI. 1991. Characterization of G-protein α subunits in the Gq class: Expression in murine tissues and in stromal and hematopoietic cell lines. *Proc. Natl. Acad. Sci. USA* 88:10049–53

217. Wong S-K-F, Garbers DL. 1992. Receptor guanylyl cyclases. *J. Clin. Invest.* 90:299–305

218. Xing M, Mattera R. 1992. Phosphorylation-dependent regulation of phospholipase A2 by G-proteins and Ca^{2+} in HL-60 granulocytes. *J. Biol. Chem.* 267(36):25966–75

219. Yagil Y. 1992. Differential effect of basolateral and apical adenosine on AVP-stimulated cAMP formation in primary culture of IMCD. *Am. J. Physiol.* 263:F268–76

220. Yanese M, Handler JS. 1986. Activators of protein kinase C inhibit sodium transport in A6 epithelia. *Am. J. Physiol.* 250:C517–22

221. Yoshimura M, Cooper DMF. 1992. Cloning and expression of a Ca^{2+} inhibitable adenylyl cyclase from NCB-20 cells. *Proc. Natl. Acad. Sci. USA* 89:6716–20

222. Zeidel ML, Brady HR, Kone BC, Gullans SR, Brenner BM. 1989. Endothelin, a peptide inhibitor of Na^+-K^+-ATPase in intact renal tubular epithelial cells. *Am. J. Physiol.* 257:C1101–07

Annu. Rev. Physiol. 1994. 56:741–61
Copyright © 1994 by Annual Reviews Inc. All rights reserved

COMPLEX MODELS FOR THE STUDY OF GENE FUNCTION IN CARDIOVASCULAR BIOLOGY

E. G. Nabel and G. J. Nabel

Departments of Internal Medicine and Biological Chemistry, Howard Hughes
Medical Institute, University of Michigan, Ann Arbor, Michigan 48109

KEY WORDS: gene transfer, gene expression, vectors, vascular cells, myocytes

INTRODUCTION

Advances in molecular genetics have fostered powerful new approaches to
animal models of human disease and to potential molecular genetic treatments. The introduction of recombinant DNA into recipient cells provides
an opportunity to evaluate gene function in vivo (75). For several years, it
has been possible to introduce genes into the germ line of animals. Such
transgenic animals gain new genetic information from the addition of foreign
DNA to cells, which can be maintained in the germ line and subsequently
expressed in somatic tissues (74). More recently, it has been possible to
introduce recombinant DNA into somatic cells of animals without introduction into the germ line (32, 67, 68). Both of these methods may be employed
to examine gene expression and regulation in cells or tissues in vivo. At
the same time, gene transfer may also be employed to deliver an exogenous
gene to an animal to replace or complement a missing or defective gene.
The new gene product may provide a therapeutic effect for the host animal,
i.e. gene therapy (3, 61). In this review, we discuss strategies for gene
transfer relevant to cardiovascular diseases. The relative advantages and
limitations of vectors, as well as animal models of vascular and myocardial

741

diseases created by gene transfer, and potential applications to cardiovascular disease treatment are reviewed.

STRATEGIES FOR GENE TRANSFER

Strategies for gene transfer can potentially utilize three different approaches: (*a*) replacement of a mutant gene sequence from the genome with a functional genomic sequence that differs from its normal counterpart; (*b*) correction of a mutant genomic sequence to the normal, wild-type structure in the host genome; and (*c*) augmentation of the correct gene in defective cells by introducing cDNA expression vectors that encode the normal gene product (Figure 1). At the present time, the techniques of gene replacement and gene correction remain limited to the laboratory. Such genetic alterations

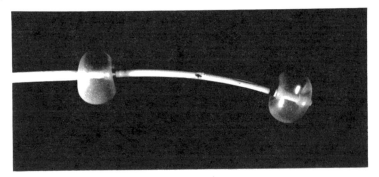

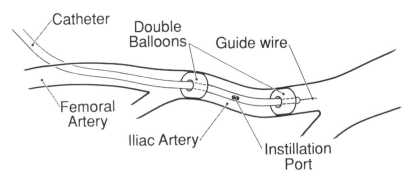

Figure 1   Method of introduction of recombinant gene. A double-balloon catheter is inserted into an artery. Inflation of a proximal and distal balloon creates a central protected space into which the modified cells or vector can be directly instilled. Vascular cells in the adjacent area are transfected to express the recombinant gene [Nabel et al (67) with permission. Copyright 1990 by the AAAS].

of genomic DNA have been demonstrated in several mammalian systems by homologous recombination in which foreign DNA sequences are targeted to cells, which result in gene sequence modification (12, 23, 33, 58). In lower eukaryotic cells, recombination between homologous segments on different DNAs is used to construct new genetic variants. For example, yeast DNA fragments inserted in a bacterial plasmid are routinely introduced into yeast cells, where they recombine with and replace its chromosomal homologue by homologous recombination. Although this phenomenon can be deliberately exploited to alter endogenous genes with homologous recombination constructs in which the coding sequence may be interrupted in mammalian cells, DNA generally integrates at random sites, and the likelihood of inactivating a specific gene is low ($\sim 10^{-6}$) (33).

Another approach to gene correction is targeting with pluripotent embryonic stem (ES) cell lines (12). ES cells from normal embryos are manipulated in vitro, injected into a host embryo, and undergo normal embryonic development during incubation in a foster mother. These chimeric animals gain new genetic information in the germ line and in somatic tissues. Homologous recombination has been employed to introduce gene sequence modifications in ES cells in order to generate mouse strains carrying the mutant allele.

Gene augmentation is the major gene transfer strategy utilized in the development of animal models for human gene therapy protocols. A number of vectors efficiently introduce new sequences into recipient cells, thus leaving the host genes intact. Gene function is acquired by the addition of nontargeted sequences into the host genome. It is theoretically possible that random insertion of foreign DNA sequences will result in mutagenesis (16). However, this complication appears to be rare and has not occurred in human studies to date. Gene augmentation may provide a missing or defective gene in a genetic disorder, or stimulate or suppress gene function in an acquired disease, like cancer or cardiovascular disease.

VECTOR SYSTEMS

Viral Vectors

RETROVIRUS   Historically, transfection systems in cultured cells employed chemical methods, such as calcium phosphate-mediated DNA transfection (97) and encapsulation of DNA in lipid vesicles (85), or physical means, such as microinjection (36) or electroporation (83), to introduce gene sequences into cells. Viral vectors have received considerable attention because of their efficient infection of host cells. Several types of viruses are used as tools for genetic manipulations including retrovirus, adenovirus, adeno-associated virus, and herpes virus.

Retroviruses have served as model systems for studying eukaryotic gene expression for several reasons. The retrovirus life cycle involves several steps that facilitate the uptake and expression of foreign genes in eukaryotic cells including reverse transcription, integration of viral DNA into host chromosomes, and the use of host mechanisms for gene expression in response to viral signals (5, 93). Cell lineage studies have been performed by transduction of retroviral DNA into host chromosomes in order to study developmental processes (78). Retroviral oncogenesis provides insight into the control of normal growth and human cancers (10). Retroviruses are important human pathogens and include the causative agent of the acquired immunodeficiency syndrome (7, 34). Finally, retroviruses provide efficient genetic vectors for experimental studies and human therapies (13).

Retroviruses contain an RNA genome that replicates through a DNA intermediate. The extracellular virus particle is composed of two identical single strands of RNA (the genome) and viral enzymes (reverse transcriptase, integrase, and protease), which form a core of viral protein and are surrounded by an envelope comprised of host membranes and viral glyco-proteins. Retroviruses attach to cells by cell surface proteins, which specif-ically recognize viral envelope proteins, and enter a cell by receptor-mediated endocytosis (64). Entry into a cell initiates uncoating to form a nucleoprotein complex in which viral RNA is copied by reverse transcriptase into DNA. The complex migrates to the nucleus and integrates into host chromosomes. Viral RNA and proteins are synthesized in the cytoplasm, and viral particles exit the cell by budding through the plasma membrane.

Viral regulatory sequences, located at the ends of the RNA, include signals for initiation and progression of viral DNA synthesis, integration, transcription of the provirus into RNA, RNA processing, and packaging RNA into progeny particles (96). Long terminal repeats (LTRs), several hundred base pairs in length and located at the ends of the proviral DNA, contain many of the regulatory signals in the viral sequence. Between the regulatory regions are coding sequences (open reading frames) for the major viral structural proteins, including *gag,* which encodes the core proteins, *env,* which encodes the envelope glycoproteins, *pol,* which encodes reverse transcriptase and integrase, and other proteins, which have specialized, intracellular functions (52).

Because retroviruses with viral oncogenes are naturally occurring genetic vectors, the mechanisms by which oncogenes are incorporated into genomes can be employed to design vectors to deliver genes to cultured cells and animals. Most retroviral vectors encode two genes, an experimental gene and a gene for a selectable marker. The selectable marker permits identification of individually infected clones, and populations consisting entirely of transduced cells can be generated, thus allowing evaluation of the activity of the experimental gene in a defined cell. Vectors with internal promoters can be generated that contain a cDNA regulated by an independent promoter and a selectable marker gene regulated by viral LTR. Several murine strains have been used to construct double-gene vectors, including the Moloney murine leukemia virus (MoMuLV) (8), the Harvey murine mammary tumor virus (MuMTV) (38), and the murine myeloproliferative sarcoma virus (MuMPSV) (46).

A retroviral vector consists of two parts, the genetic sequence and the structure, which acts as the vehicle to introduce genes into cells. Retroviral vectors are replication-incompetent in order to prevent infection in the host. Naturally occurring defective retroviruses require "help" to produce infectious vector particles, and this help is provided by a helper virus containing intact structural genes. When a cell is simultaneously infected with the defective retrovirus and the helper virus, a productive infection follows because the helper virus provides the structural proteins needed for the genome to be packaged. The same concept applies to the design of replication-incompetent vectors, with the exception that developed cell lines provided help without the generation of wild-type retroviruses (15). Packaging cell lines were developed that contained plasmids encoding all of the structural genes of a retrovirus under control of the regulatory sequences of the LTR and no packaging signal (15, 20). Without the packaging signal, the cell lines produce empty or genome-deficient virions. When a retroviral vector, in which the structural genes are removed but the packaging signal remains intact, is introduced into a packaging cell line, transcripts of the vector are recognized by the packaging mechanism and a vector virion is produced.

To reduce the likelihood of generating wild-type viruses, additional modifications have been made in packaging cell lines. In addition to deletion of the packaging signal, the LTR of the helper provirus has been modified (deletion of sequences in the 5' end of the 5' LTR and the 3' LTR) so that more than one recombinational event is required to generate a wild-type virus (62). With these changes, two recombinations are necessary to regenerate wild-type virus.

Retroviral vectors have been employed in numerous animal gene transfer studies of multiple target cells including bone marrow (25, 39, 43), fibroblasts (35, 65, 91), lymphocytes (42), liver cells (48, 100), and in recent human gene therapy trials (81). These studies employ cell-mediated gene transfer in which autologous cell lines are developed and infected with a retroviral vector in culture, and the genetically modified cells are returned to the host. There has been a single report of a complication from retroviral gene transfer (45). Three of eight immunosuppressed monkeys developed a T cell lymphoma 6 months following gene transfer into bone marrow stem cells. The complication arose from contamination of the vector with replication-competent MoMuLV. Theoretically, helper virus could have inserted into the thymic cell DNA in such a way to activate a pro- tooncogene, or knock out a tumor suppressor gene. However, other studies have not detected mutagenic or oncogenic complications following retroviral gene transfer in which no replication-competent virus can be detected, including a human gene marking protocol (81). Retroviral gene transfer has been performed directly in pig arteries without detection of helper virus activity for up to 5 months following transduction (68), which suggests that this vector is relatively safe, but retroviral vectors may not be suitable to express genes in postmitotic cells such as cardiac myo- cytes. Previous studies have shown that retroviral infection can be in- hibited in nonreplicating cells in culture and suggest that infected cells must be replicating at the time of infection for successful gene transfer (63).

ADENOVIRUS   Recombinant adenoviruses have several properties that make them attractive vectors for in vivo gene delivery, which include high efficiency gene transfer. This results from efficient propagation of adenovirus to high titer, the promiscuity and tissue tropism of adenoviral infection of cells, and the infectivity of adenovirus for replicating and nonreplicating cells. Several laboratories have reported gene transfer of foreign genes using adenoviral vectors into liver (41, 88), lung (59, 82), muscle (80, 88), brain (2, 4, 49), and endothelial and smooth muscle cells (50, 51). However, several issues relevant to application to human therapies including stability of gene expression, host cell immune responses, transmission to germline cells, and toxicity have not been systematically studied.

   Human adenovirus is a nonenveloped, icosahedral, double-stranded DNA virus, approximately 35–40 kb genome size. Adenoviruses infect a broad range of mammalian cells by attachment to a cell surface glycoprotein receptor (76), probably through the fiber protein component of its capsid (37). The mechanism(s) by which the adenovirus enters a cell is not completely known and presumably occurs via receptor-mediated endocytosis into the lyosomal compartment. The viral genome escapes degradation from digestion by terminal proteins covalently linked to the ends of the genome (40). Following release from the cytoplasm, the viral genome translocates to the nucleus. In dividing cells, adenoviral sequences integrate at low frequency into host chromosomes. However, in nondividing somatic cells in vivo, the adenoviral genome appears to be maintained as an episome

(40). Expression of adenoviral genes proceeds by interactions with host cell transcription factors and requires expression of adenoviral early region 1, which encodes *trans*-activators of viral gene expression. The adenoviral genome may replicate to several thousand copies per cell. The genome associates with core proteins, is packaged into capsids, and then is released by the cell.

Foreign genes can be inserted into adenoviral genomes in three locations; as replacements in the early regions 1 or 3 (E1, E3), or as an insertion between the E4 region and the end of the genome (9). The E1 region is required for adenoviral replication, and replacement of the early E1 region with a foreign gene results in a replication-defective virus. Vectors based on substitution of the E3 or E4 regions are replication-competent. Recombinant, replication-incompetent adenovirus is produced with a helper cell line, similar in concept to retroviral packaging. A bacterial plasmid containing the foreign gene and sequences from the adenovirus genome are transfected into 293 cells (a human embryonic kidney cell line), or other efficient cell lines that contain an integrated copy of adenovirus E1 region in *trans*. Homologous recombination between the two DNAs generates a packaged recombinant viral genome. Recombinant adenoviruses can be generated in very high titer, often ($>10^9$ plaque-forming units per ml.

Adenoviruses, in general, are high titer, efficient vectors. However, several parameters related to gene expression in vivo must be examined. First, the stability of gene expression is unknown. In dividing cells in culture, adenoviral sequences integrate into host chromosomes at low frequency; however, in nondividing cells in vivo, adenovirus sequences probably persist transiently as episomes (40). Expression of reporter genes have been noted for up to 12 months in murine muscle and liver following intravenous injection of adenovirus (88). In other systems, reporter gene expression is lost by 4 weeks in vascular cells (51), and low density lipoprotein receptor expression in murine liver persists for only several weeks (38a). Whether this is due to extinction of the promoter or loss of genome is not currently known.

Second, the safety of direct adenoviral gene transfer is under investigation. Inhalation of human adenovirus 5 has been associated with rodent interstitial pneumonitis (79), and a lymphocytic infiltration in murine livers has been observed following intravenous administration of virus (38a). The inflammatory reaction and spread to reproductive tissue may be a function of the titer of virus administered. Human adenoviruses are ubiquitous viruses. Neutralizing antibodies to different adenoviral serotypes are present in most adults. Whether host immune responses will limit their efficacy, particularly after multiple administrations of adenovirus, is being examined.

Nonviral Vectors

CATIONIC LIPOSOMES   Transfection employing chemical carriers, including calcium-phosphate and DEAE dextran, have commonly been used to achieve high levels of gene transfer in cultured cells. However, following the demonstration that viruses efficiently infect mammalian cells, there was an interest in identifying synthetic systems that would mimic viral delivery and avoid infectious complications (31). Liposomes were attractive vehicles of gene delivery (26). In theory, liposomal fusion with cell membranes could lead to polynucleotide delivery to the cytoplasm, bypassing the lysosomal compartment (and degradation) by a protein-mediated and pH-sensitive fusion mechanism (89), but there were several technical difficulties that slowed the development of liposomes as carriers. Encapsulation efficiency of DNA into conventional liposomes was low because the internal volume of liposomes is usually smaller than the foreign gene (90), and transfection efficiency was low since conventional liposomes did not bypass lysosomal degradation.

Cationic liposomes were developed in the late 1980s to overcome the deficiencies of conventional liposomes. Since their initial description, cationic liposomes have been employed to deliver DNA, RNA, antisense molecules, and proteins to cells in vitro and in vivo. The commercially available cationic lipid, Lipofectin (BRL, Gaithersburg, MD), is a member of a class of cationic lipids called cytofectins. The first cationic lipid, and a prototype for this approach, is DOTMA (N[1-(2,3-dioleyloxy)propyl]-N,N,N-trimethylammonium) (29). When mixed with an equimolar amount of DOPE (dioleoyl phosphatidylethanolamine), DOTMA forms liposomes that interact spontaneously with DNA or RNA, which result in a liposome/polynucleotide complex. Cytofectins overcome some of the difficulties of conventional liposomes. Cationic lipid vesicles condense with DNA to form complexes in which nearly all of the DNA is trapped (57). Virtually all biological surfaces have a net negative charge and, thus, positively charged lipid vesicles containing polynucleotide interact spontaneously with these surfaces and deliver polynucleotide to the cell. Cationic lipid/polynucleotide fuses with cell membranes in such a manner that the entrapped DNA avoids degradation in the lysosomal compartment (24). Following delivery to the cytoplasm, plasmid DNA translocates to the nucleus and persists in the nucleus predominantly as an episome. Integration into host chromosome occurs at low frequency. Transient expression levels and stable transformation efficiencies depend upon the expression vector and cell line (28).

The ratio of DOTMA/DOPE to DNA is important for optimal transfection efficiency. Theoretically, the optimal ratio occurs when the amount of positive charges contributed by DOTMA liposomes exceeds the number of negative charges on the DNA. The liposome complexes have a net positive charge that facilitates interaction with the negatively charged target cell surface. In our experience, the ratio of DOTMA/DOPE to DNA must be optimized for cell type, plasmid and lot of DOTMA/DOPE. In addition, serum-free conditions are important in liposomal transfections in order to avoid inhibition from polyvalent negatively charged serum components (27). Unlike calcium-phosphate transfection, the efficiency of cationic liposomes is unaffected by pH between 6.0 and 8.0, and large DNA molecules can be successfully transfected.

The advantages of cationic liposomal transfection include safety, reproducibility, and ease of preparation. Safety concerns about the use of retrovirus or adenovirus in humans are largely mitigated by nonviral vectors. In our studies of direct gene transfer using cationic liposomes, gene expression is limited to the site of gene introduction, and we have not observed biochemical, hemodynamic, or cardiac toxicities. Construction of plasmid DNA expression vectors requires less technology than viral vectors. Scale-up manufacturing considerations are more complex for potentially infectious than lipid-polynucleotide complexes. (66, 84, 87).

POLYLYSINE LIGAND CONJUGATES   Another polycation/polynucleotide delivery system employs specific ligands conjugated to polylysine, which spontaneously condense with DNA through disassociable ionic interactions. The condensate is taken up by receptor-mediated endocytosis into cells containing the receptor for the conjugated ligand (17, 18, 103). For example, macromolecular complexes can be taken up by cells, such as endothelial cells and hepatocytes, by endocytosis, using ligands that are specific for cell surface receptors or nuclear proteins (103). The addition of chloroquine or adenovirus coat proteins can also be used to disrupt the lysosome compartment and release DNA into the cell (17).

PLASMID INJECTION   One of the most promising developments in myocyte transfection during recent years has been the introduction of foreign genes into cardiac and skeletal muscle by direct injection. In skeletal muscle, no gene delivery vector was necessary to achieve significant levels of transgene expression (101). In these initial studies, reporter gene expression, including luciferase, chloramphenicol acetyl transferase (CAT), and β-galactosidase genes, was detected in mouse skeletal muscle for up to 6 months following direct injection (101). Since skeletal myocytes are nondividing, fully differentiated cells, integration was not expected, and further studies suggested that gene sequences persisted as nuclear episomes (102). Additional studies have demonstrated the usefulness of this approach for cardiac muscle and the introduction of transduced myoblasts (6, 55).

PARTICLE-MEDIATED GENE DELIVERY   Particle-mediated gene delivery can also be employed to deliver recombinant DNA into cells in vivo. In this instance, plasmid DNA is precipitated on to the surface of microscopic metal beads (1 μm in diameter), and the microprojectiles are accelerated with a wave of expanding helium gas and penetrate tissues to a depth of several cell layers. The approach delivers foreign DNA to the skin or internal organs of anesthetized animals. Expression of the gene is high for several days, and expression falls off but is detectable for several weeks (98). This approach may be useful for situations in which transient expression is required within a localized region of tissue, such as genetic immunization of mice against foreign antigens (92).

ANIMAL MODELS OF VASCULAR CELL GENE TRANSFER

Two strategies are employed to introduce foreign genes into vascular cells: cell-mediated and direct gene transfer. Cell transfer is a multistep process in which autologous target cells are removed from the animal, gene transduction and selection are performed in culture, and genetically modified cells are reimplanted into the animal (Figure 1). Cell-mediated gene transfer permits the analysis of a gene product in a specific target cell. The disadvantages of cell transfer include utilization of resources, time delay during transduction and selection of autologous cells, and cost. In addition, cell lines cannot be grown from some tissues or animals. Direct gene transfer eliminates transduction of cell lines in vitro and potentially simplifies gene transfection, although it can be limited by lack of cell-specific and regulated gene expression at the present time.

Vascular cell seeding has been performed on the surface of arteries (56, 60, 67, 77), synthetic grafts (99), or stents (22). These studies have examined the feasibility of cell seeding with endothelial (67) and smooth muscle cells (77). In these experiments, endothelial cell seeding was optimized by partial denudation of the artery and/or perfusion of the artery with serum or adhesive proteins prior to cell transplantation. Endothelial cell seeding of capillary beds has also been demonstrated using autologous cell lines in a canine model of the microcirculation (60). While it has been presumed that endothelial cells would attach to denuded surfaces only, these investigators showed that endothelial cells can attach to intact endothelial surfaces, at least in the microcirculation. The ability of smooth muscle cells to attach to denuded arterial surfaces has been confirmed in several models, including rat (56) and porcine (77) experiments. Human adenosine deaminase activity was detected 6 months following implantation of transduced vascular smooth muscle cells in denuded carotid arteries (56). Autologous endothelial cells transduced with reporter genes have also been seeded into canine carotid arteries with expression of the foreign transgene persisting for at least 5 weeks (99). Endothelial cells have also been seeded on synthetic metallic stents in vitro (22), but persistence of gene expression following implantation in vivo has not been demonstrated. Whether these modified transduced cells retain their smooth muscle cell phenotype remains to be determined. Also, the usefulness of these models for addressing questions about gene expression and regulation in vivo needs exploration. It is possible, but unlikely, that cell-mediated gene transfer of vascular cells will have widespread clinical utility for cardiovascular diseases.

The direct introduction of recombinant DNA into the vasculature in situ is compelling for several reasons. Direct gene transfer is less complex and requires less technology compared with cell-mediated gene transfer. Direct gene transfer is less disruptive to the normal architecture of the vessel since denudation is not performed prior to transfection. The initial demonstrations that recombinant DNA can be expressed directly in arteries in vivo was made with retroviral vectors and DNA liposome complexes expressing reporter genes (68). In this model, gene expression was limited to the site of gene delivery and was not observed in other organs, including liver, lung, spleen and kidney. Importantly, while the retroviral vector was administered directly into the artery, helper virus was not detected in the serum, which suggests that in these limited studies, retroviral vectors may be safe for gene delivery.

Direct gene transfer in situ has been developed in several animal models using different reporter genes, vectors, and sites in the circulation. Lim and colleagues reported expression of a luciferase gene in nine of ten canine coronary arteries using DNA liposome conjugates (54). The luciferase marker permits quantification of protein, but because antibodies are not available, cell localization could not be determined. Additional percutaneous approaches to gene delivery were developed by Stack and co-workers, who used an autoperfusion porous balloon catheter to deliver high quantities of DNA liposome conjugates to canine coronary and iliofemoral arteries (14). These investigators noted a higher rate of gene delivery in arteries transfected under direct visualization (100%), compared to vessels transfected percutaneously (67%). While these findings suggest that percutaneous gene delivery is feasible, further technical developments are required to optimize the procedure.

While the above studies examined gene delivery into normal arteries, Isner and colleagues have developed methods for transfection into balloon-injured and atherosclerotic rabbit arteries (47). In situ hybridization of transfected atherosclerotic arteries revealed luciferase mRNA in neointimal cells. Current studies are examining whether proliferating endothelial and

A.

B.

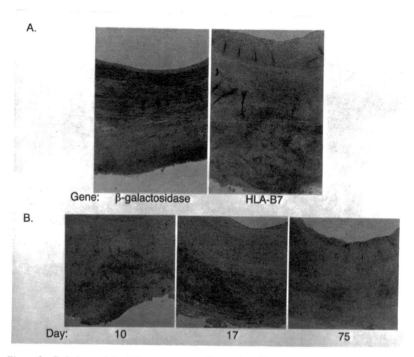

Figure 2 Pathology of the inflammatory reaction produced by the expression of recombinant human HLA-B7 gene in porcine vascular cells in vivo. (*A*) Porcine arteries transduced with a reporter gene, *E. coli* β-galactosidase (*left*) or human HLA-B7 gene (*right*) 17 days after transfection. (*B*) Time course of inflammatory response in the adventitia, media, and intima: 10 (*left*), 17 (*middle*), and 75 (*right*) days following transfection [Nabel et al (69) with permission]. (Magnification ×100)

vascular smooth muscle cells are transfected at higher percentages than normal, quiescent vascular cells.

Following development of methods for cell-mediated and direct gene transfer into the vasculature, subsequent studies examined whether expression of recombinant genes would alter biological function. To test this hypothesis, we studied a potent biological modifier, a class I major histocompatibility (MHC) gene, HLA-B7 (69). We reasoned that expression of a human HLA-B7 gene in porcine arteries should produce xenogeneic tissue rejection (Figure 2). Following transfection of plasmid DNA encoding human HLA-B7 into porcine iliofemoral arteries using retroviral vectors and DNA liposomes conjugates, gene transfer and expression were confirmed by PCR and immunohistochemistry. Expression of recombinant HLA-B7 antigen stimulated vascular inflammation, characterized by a mononuclear infiltration in the adventitia, associated with medial and intimal thickening. Expression of the recombinant protein generated HLA-B7-specific cytolytic T cells, determined by a ^{51}Cr release assay and suggested a cell-mediated immune response as a mechanism for the vascular inflammation. These studies suggested that expression of recombinant DNA can modify arterial function.

Vascular cell gene transfer has also been employed to study the mechanisms of intimal cell proliferation following expression of growth factor genes in vivo. Our laboratory has had an interest in examining the effects of growth factors, including PDGF B (71), FGF-1 (72), and TGF-β1 (70), on the development of neointima in arteries. Recent data from human atherosclerosis specimens (53, 73) and gene targeting studies (86) suggest an important role for these growth factors in human vascular disease, including atherosclerotic and restenosis. However, the direct effects of these growth factors in arteries in vivo are poorly understood. In these studies, we have used DNA liposomes to avoid possible biological hazards associated with viral vectors encoding proto-oncogenes. Prior to initiating these experiments, we developed a model of gene transfection into porcine arteries using low pressures (150 mmHg), which minimized arterial injury and possible stimulation of endogenous growth factors that could limit interpretation of the biological response to introduced growth factor genes (71). In each set of experiments, a plasmid expression vector encoding human PDGF B secreted FGF-1 (acidic FGF), secreted active TGF-β1, or a reporter gene (control) was transfected into porcine peripheral arteries using a double-balloon catheter (Figure 3). Transfer of plasmid DNA was documented by PCR, and gene expression was confirmed by analysis of recombinant mRNA (reverse transcriptase PCR) and recombinant protein (immunohistochemistry). Expression of the PDGF B gene was associated with intimal thickening, characterized by increased cellularity and smooth muscle proliferation, in contrast to control arteries transfected with a reporter gene (71). The expression of a secreted form of FGF-1 also was associated with intimal thickening; however, in vessels with expanded intima, neocapillaries were observed within the intima (72). These findings have not been observed in vessels transduced with other growth factor genes, including PDGF and TGF, and suggest a role for FGF-1 in stimulating vascular angiogenesis in vivo. TGF-β1 expression produced significant increases in procollagen synthesis in the intima and media that resulted in intimal and medial thickening (70). Other matrix proteins, including reticulin and proteoglycans, were also synthesized in different patterns compared to control arteries transfected with a reporter gene. These data suggest that three growth factor genes may have overlapping but distinct effects on arterial pathology and may guide the development of molecular genetic interventions to limit intimal hyperplasia following balloon injury.

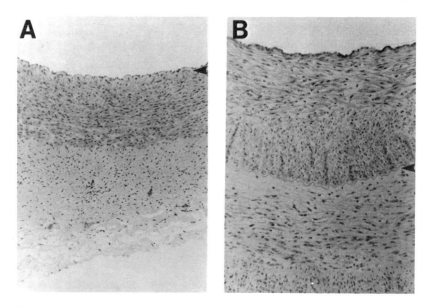

Figure 3   Expression of a recombinant growth factor gene in porcine arteries in vivo. Intimal thickening was produced following transfection of a human PDGF B gene into porcine iliofemoral arteries (*B*) compared with no intimal proliferation following transfection with a control gene, *E. coli* β-galactosidase (A). The arrow denotes the internal elastic lamina [Nabel et al (71) with copyright permission Am. Soc. Clin. Invest.]. (Magnification ×100)

Several issues are important to the establishment of animal models of vascular cell gene transfer and potential application for human therapy. First, retroviral vectors and DNA liposome conjugates are low efficiency vectors, transfecting 0.1–5% of vascular endothelial and smooth muscle cells in most studies (30, 47, 68, 83). Reports of adenoviral infection of arteries in situ suggest higher efficiencies. Adenoviral conjugate vectors have not been systematically studied in the vasculature. Optimal vectors for vascular cell gene transfer, which combine high efficiency with long term expression and adequate safety, are being developed. Second, the goal of gene transfer is to achieve a biological (or therapeutic) effect in situ. However, how many cells must be transfected in a vessel segment in order to produce a particular response may vary. Only a small percentage of cells may secrete a recombinant protein, and the secreted gene product may have local paracrine effects that in turn amplify a biological response. The pharmacology and dose response properties of recombinant proteins have not been addressed. Methods must be developed to target genes to endothelial cells or smooth muscle cells using cell-specific promoters, and gene expression should ideally be regulated through inducible or repressible promoters. Finally, appropriate catheters that permit efficient atraumatic delivery of a vector into an artery and/or vein without compromising the native circulation are being developed.

Technical factors must be considered for successful gene delivery into the vasculature. These factors account for minor differences observed between species, delivery systems, and reporter genes. For example, there has been concern about the use of the reporter gene *E. coli* β-galactosidase as a marker for foreign gene expression. The bacterial gene encodes for a cytoplasmic enzyme that produces a perinuclear blue stain when exposed to an X-gal chromagen. Macrophages in the adventitia of arteries may stain blue when exposed to the same X-gal chromagen. In our porcine model, endogenous β-galactosidase-like staining is observed only if the arteries are injured during the in situ transfection, or if the arteries are exposed to the chromagen for an extended time period (generally more than 8–12 hours). To address this issue, we performed experiments in porcine arteries in which we introduced a transgene or saline at increasing pressures using two different catheters (66a, 84). We found that infusion of saline or transfection with a control plasmid at pressures ranging from 130 mmHg to 3 atmospheres in a double-balloon catheter did not produce endogenous blue staining, which suggests that under controlled conditions, transfection of a gene at low pressures using a double-balloon catheter does not produce endogenous β-galactosidase activity. The choice of catheter will also influence vessel injury and levels of transfection. Several investigators have noted that delivery of foreign genes through porous balloon catheters produces jet-like streaming of the solution through the artery, which results in vessel injury and low transfection efficiency (30).

ANIMAL MODELS FOR CARDIAC AND SKELETAL MUSCLE GENE TRANSFER

Cardiac and skeletal muscle gene transfer are also performed using cell-mediated and direct approaches. Cellular gene transfer using myoblasts injected into skeletal muscle has been an effective strategy for expressing reporter genes (6), or genes encoding for therapeutic proteins (6, 21) secreted into the circulation. Transplantation of cardiac myocytes has been limited by difficulty in growing and manipulating cardiac myocytes in vivo.

Several groups have demonstrated that foreign genes can be directly introduced into skeletal (101) or cardiac myocytes (11, 44, 55, 94). Because myocytes are fully differentiated cells, transfection with retroviral or liposomal vectors has limited effectiveness. Purified DNA and RNA have been injected and expressed in murine skeletal myofibers for at least 2 months

(101). Other investigators have expressed recombinant genes in rat hearts for several months following direct plasmid DNA injection (44, 55). In these experiments, plasmid DNA in saline was directly injected by needle and syringe into the apical portion of beating left ventricles. Several reporter genes were studied, including β-galactosidase, CAT, and luciferase, and gene expression was observed in greater than 75% of skeletal and cardiac muscles injected (1). Gene expression was limited to the site of injection and was not observed in adjacent vascular cells, fibroblasts, or other systemic organs. Inflammatory reactions and fibrous scars in areas of needle insertion were noted in control and experimental animals, probably caused by the insertion of the needle rather than plasmid DNA (55). Immune responses against plasmid DNA have not been established. Data from Southern blot experiments indicate that recombinant DNA persists primarily as an episome in closed circular and linear forms and does not integrate into the host genome (1). These findings suggest that the risk of mutagenesis is low. However, the duration of expression is also unknown.

Recent promising studies have demonstrated that genetically modified myoblasts injected into skeletal muscle can secrete proteins into the systemic circulation at physiological levels. Stable clones of transfected myoblasts have been isolated from muscle biopsies and expanded in cell culture to large number. Injected myoblasts were observed to fuse with adjacent normal muscle, and presumably secrete protein into local capillaries. Several investigators have infected a human growth hormone gene into murine C2C12 myoblasts, using retroviral vectors, and selected for transduced cells with a neomycin gene and antibiotic resistance (6, 21). Human growth hormone secreting myoblasts were injected into the hind limb of mice and physiological levels of hGH were detected in the serum for 3 weeks (6) and 3 months (21), respectively. The transduced myoblasts fused into vascularized, multinucleated myofibers, which accounted for the survival and systemic delivery of foreign protein (19).

Adenoviral vectors have been successfully deployed for cardiac and skeletal gene transfer. Intravenous or intramuscular injection of adenoviral vectors expressing the *E. coli* β-galactosidase gene has resulted in gene expression in multiple organs, including lung, liver, intestine, heart, and skeletal muscle (88). Intravenous delivery resulted in wide dissemination of reporter gene in cardiac and skeletal muscle, while intramuscular injection produced a circumscribed region of gene product. Adenovirus delivered into the coronary arteries resulted in expression of reporter genes in adjacent vascular and myocardial cells. Gene expression following adenoviral transfer is short, approximately several weeks, and widespread, thus suggesting the promiscuous nature of the virus. These results demonstrate the feasibility of direct adenoviral gene transfer in cardiac and skeletal muscle, but the duration of expression and lack of tissue specificity require further investigation.

These animal models afford an opportunity to examine the regulation of muscle gene expression, for example, the rat alpha myosin heavy chain reporter (11, 94, 103). Lineage studies can be performed by following reporter gene expression in developing cardiac tissues. The introduction of genes encoding angiogenic proteins has been undertaken to investigate the development of myocardial collateral circulation. Gene transfer in skeletal and cardiac muscle complements other genetic technologies, such as transgenics and gene targeting, and provides new avenues for investigation of the growth and development of cardiac and skeletal tissues.

CONCLUSIONS

Gene transfer technology has evolved from the simple introduction of reporter genes into cardiovascular tissues to complex animal models of cardiac and vascular diseases. These animal models afford the opportunity to investigate the pathophysiology of disease, the development of cardiac and vascular structures, and molecular treatments of certain cardiovascular diseases. Technical hurdles related to optimization of vectors, regulated gene expression, and cell-specific expression remain; however, new opportunities exist for investigating gene expression and function in cardiovascular tissues that should provide fresh insight into the biology of the cardiovascular system and novel approaches to the treatment of cardiovascular diseases.

Literature Cited

1. Acsadi G, Jiao SS, Jani A, Duke D, Williams P, et al. 1991. Direct gene transfer and expression into rat heart in vivo. *New Biol.* 3:71–81
2. Akli S, Caillaud C, Vigne E, Stratford-Perricaudet LD, Poenaru L, et al. 1993. Transfer of a foreign gene into the brain using adenovirus vectors. *Nature Genet.* 3:224–28
3. Anderson WF. 1992. Human gene therapy. *Science* 256:808–13
4. Bajocchi G, Feldman SH, Crystal RG, Mastrangeli A. 1993. Direct in vivo gene transfer to ependymal cells in the central nervous system using recombinant adenovirus vectors. *Nature genetics* 3:229–34
5. Baltimore D. 1970. RNA-dependent DNA polymerase in virions of RNA tumor viruses. *Nature* 226:1209–11
6. Barr E, Leiden JM. 1991. Systemic delivery of recombinant proteins by genetically modified myoblasts. *Science* 254:1507–9
7. Barre-Sinoussi F, Chermann JC, Rey F, Nugeyre MT, Chamaret S, et al. 1983. Isolation of a T-lymphotropic retrovirus from a patient at risk for acquired immune deficiency syndrome (AIDS). *Science* 220:868–71
8. Berger SA, Bernstein A. 1985. Characterization of a retrovirus shuttle vector capable of either proviral integration or extra-chromosomal replication in mouse cells. *Mol. Cell. Biol.* 5:305–12
9. Berkner KL. 1988. Development of adenovirus vectors for the expression of heterologous genes. *BioTechniques* 6:616–29
10. Bishop JM. 1983. Cellular oncogenes and retroviruses. *Annu. Rev. Biochem.* 52:301–54

11. Buttrick PM, Kass A, Kitsis RN, Kaplan ML, Leinwand LA. 1992. Behavior of genes directly injected into the rat heart in vivo. *Circ. Res.* 70:193–98

12. Capecchi MR. 1989. Altering the genome by homologous recombination. *Science* 244:1288–92

13. Cepko CL, Roberts BE, Mulligan RC. 1984. Construction and applications of a highly transmissible murine retrovirus shuttle vector. *Cell* 37:1053–62

14. Chapman GD, Lim CS, Gammon RS, Culp SC, Desper S, et al. 1992. Gene transfer into coronary arteries of intact animals with a percutaneous balloon catheter. *Circ. Res.* 71:27–33

15. Cone RD, Mulligan RC. 1984. High-efficiency gene transfer into mammalian cells: Generation of helper-free recombinant retrovirus with broad mammalian host range. *Proc. Natl. Acad. Sci. USA* 81:6349–53

16. Cornetta K, Morgan RA, Anderson WF. 1991. Safety issues related to retroviral-mediated gene transfer in humans. *Hum. Gene Ther.* 2:5–14

17. Cotten M, Wagner E, Zatloukal K, Phillips S, Curiel DT, et al. 1992. High-efficiency receptor-mediated delivery of small and large (48 kilobase) gene constructs using the endosome-disruption activity of defective or chemically inactivated adenovirus particles. *Proc. Natl. Acad. Sci. USA* 89:6094–98

18. Curiel DT, Agarwal S, Wagner E, Cotten M. 1991. Adenovirus enhancement of transferrin-polylysine-mediated gene delivery. *Proc. Natl. Acad. Sci. USA* 88:8850–54

19. Dai Y, Roman M, Naviaux RK, Verma IM. 1992. Gene-therapy via primary myoblasts: long-term expression of factor IX protein following transplantation in vivo. *Proc. Natl. Acad. Sci. USA* 89:10892–95

20. Danos O, Mulligan RC. 1988. Safe and efficient generation of recombinant retroviruses with amphotropic and ecotropic host ranges. *Proc. Natl. Acad. Sci. USA* 85:6460–64

21. Dhawan J, Pan LC, Pavlath GK, Travis MA, Lanctot AM, et al. 1991. Systemic delivery of human growth hormone by injection of genetically engineered myoblasts. *Science* 254:1509–12

22. Dichek DA, Neville RF, Zwiebel JA, Freeman SM, Leon MB, et al. 1989. Seeding of intravascular stents with genetically engineered endothelial cells. *Circulation* 80:1347–53

23. Doetschman T, Gregg RG, Maeda N, Hooper ML, Melton DW, et al. 1987. Targetted correction of a mutant HPRT gene in mouse embryonic stem cells. *Nature* 330:576–78

24. Duzgunes N, Goldstein JA, Friend DS, Felgner PL. 1989. Fusion of liposomes containing a novel cationic lipid, N-[2,3-(dioleyloxy)propyl]-N,N,N-trimethylammonium: Induction by multivalent anions and asymmetric fusion with acidic phospholipid vesicles. *Biochemistry* 28:9179–84

25. Eglitis NM, Kantoff PW, Gilboa E, Anderson WF. 1985. Gene expression in mice after high efficiency retroviral-mediated gene transfer. *Science* 230: 1395–98

26. Felgner PL. 1990. Particulate systems and polymers for in vitro and in vivo delivery of polynucleotides. *Adv. Drug Delivery Rev.* 5:163–87

27. Felgner PL, Holm M, Chan H. 1989. Cationic liposome mediated transfection. *Proc. W. Pharmacol. Soc.* 32: 115–21

28. Felgner PL, Rhodes O. 1991. Gene therapeutics. *Nature* 349:351–52

29. Felgner PL, Ringold GM. 1989. Cationic liposome-mediated transfection. *Nature* 337:387–88

30. Flugelman MY, Jaklitsch MT, Newman KD, Casscells W, Bratthauer GL, et al. 1992. Low level in vivo gene transfer into the arterial wall through a perforated balloon catheter. *Circulation* 3:1110–17

31. Fraley R, Subramani S, Berg P, Papahadjopoulos D. 1980. Introduction of liposome-encapsulated SV40 DNA into cells. *J. Biol. Chem.* 255:10431–35

32. Friedman T. 1989. Progress toward human gene therapy. *Science* 244: 1275–81

33. Frohman MA, Martin GR. 1989. Cut, paste, and save: New approaches to altering specific genes in mice. *Cell* 56:145–47

34. Gallo RC, Salahuddin SZ, Popovic M, Shearer GM, Kaplan M, et al. 1984. Frequent detection and isolation of cytopathic retrovirus (HTLV-III) from patients with AIDS and at risk for AIDS. *Science* 224:500–3

35. Garver RI Jr, Chytil A, Courtney M, Crystal RG. 1987. Clonal gene therapy: transplanted mouse fibroblast clones express human a₁-antitrypsin gene in vivo. *Science* 237:762–64

36. Graessman A, Graessman K, Topp WC, Botchan M. 1979. Retransformation of a simian virus 40 revertant cell line, which is resistant to viral and DNA infections, by microinjection of viral DNA. *J. Virol.* 32:989–94

37. Green NM, Wrigley NG, Russell WC, Martin SR, McLachlan AD. 1983. Evidence for a repeating cross-b structure in the adenovirus fibre. *EMBO J.* 2:1357–65

38. Gunzburg WH, Salmons B. 1986. Mouse mammary tumor virus mediated transfer and expression of neomycin resistance to infected cultured cells. *Virology* 155:236–48

38a. Herz J, Gerard RD. 1993. Adenovirus-mediated transfer of low density lipoprotein receptor gene acutely accelerates cholesterol clearance in normal mice. *Proc. Natl. Acad. Sci. USA* 90:2812–16

39. Hock RA, Miller AD. 1986. Retrovirus-mediated transfer and expression of drug resistance genes in human haematopoietic progenitor cells. *Nature* 320:275–77

40. Horwitz, MS. 1985. Adenoviruses and their replication. In *Virology,* ed. BN Fields, pp. 433–76. New York: Raven

41. Jaffe HA, Danel C, Longenecker G, Metzger M, Setoguchi Y, et al. 1992. Adenovirus-mediated in vivo gene transfer and expression in normal rat liver. *Nature Genet.* 1:372–78

42. Kasid A, Morecki S, Aebersold P, Cornetta K, Culver K, et al. 1990. Human gene transfer: characterization of human tumor-infiltrating lymphocytes as vehicles for retroviral mediated gene transfer in man. *Proc. Natl. Acad. Sci. USA* 87:473–77

43. Keller G, Paige C, Gilboa E, Wagner EF. 1985. Expression of a foreign gene in myeloid and lymphoid cells derived from multipotent haematopoietic precursors. *Nature* 318:149–54

44. Kitsis RN, Buttrick PM, McNally EM, Kaplan ML, Leinwand LA. 1991. Hormonal modulation of a gene injected into rat heart in vivo. *Proc. Natl. Acad. Sci. USA* 88:4138–42

45. Kolberg R. 1992. Gene transfer virus contaminant linked to monkeys' cancer. *J. NIH Res.* 4:43–44

46. Laker C, Stocking C, Bergholz U, Hess N, De Lamarter JF, et al. 1987. Autocrine stimulation after transfer of the granulocyte-macrophage colony stimulating factor gene and autonomous growth are distinct by interdependent steps in the oncogenic pathway. *Proc. Natl. Acad. Sci. USA* 84:8458–62

47. Leclerc G, Gal D, Takeshita S, Nikol S, Weir L, et al. 1992. Percutaneous arterial gene transfer in a rabbit model. Efficiency in normal and balloon-dilated atherosclerotic arteries. *J. Clin. Invest.* 90:936–44

48. Ledley FD, Darlington GJ, Tahn T, Woo SLC. 1987. Retrovirus gene transduction into primary hepatocytes: Implications for genetic therapy of liver-specific functions. *Proc. Natl. Acad. Sci. USA* 84:5335–39

49. Le Gal La Salle G, Robert JJ, Berrard S, Ridoux V, Stratford-Perricaudet LD, et al. 1993. An adenovirus vector for gene transfer into neurons and glia in the brain. *Science* 259:988–90

50. Lemarchand P, Jaffe HA, Danel C, Cid MC, Kleinman HK, et al. 1992. Adenovirus-mediated transfer of a recombinant human a_1-antitrypsin cDNA to human endothelial cells. *Proc. Natl. Acad. Sci. USA* 89:6482–86

51. Lemarchand P, Jones M, Yamada I, Crystal RG. 1993. In vivo gene transfer and expression in normal uninjured blood vessels using replication-deficient recombinant adenovirus vectors. *Circ. Res.* 72:1132–38

52. Lewin, B. 1990. *Genes* IV:672–90. New York: Oxford Univ. Press

53. Libby P, Warner SJ, Salomon RN, Birinyi LK. 1988. Production of platelet-derived growth factor-like mitogen by smooth-muscle cells from human atheroma. *N. Engl. J. Med.* 318:1493–98

54. Lim CS, Chapman GD, Gammon RS, Muhlestein JB, Bauman RP, et al. 1991. Direct in vivo gene transfer into the coronary and peripheral vasculatures of the intact dog. *Circulation* 83:2007–11

55. Lin H, Parmacek MS, Morle G, Bolling S, Leiden JM. 1990. Expression of recombinant genes in myocardium in vivo after direct injection of DNA. *Circulation* 82:2217–21

56. Lynch CM, Clowes MM, Osborne WR, Clowes AW, Miller AD. 1992. Long-term expression of human adenosine deaminase in vascular smooth muscle cells of rats: a model for gene therapy. *Proc. Natl. Acad. Sci. USA* 89:1138–42

57. Malone RW, Felgner PL, Verma IM. 1989. Lipofectin mediated RNA transfection. *Proc. Natl. Acad. Sci. USA* 86:6077–81

58. Mansour SL, Thomas KR, Capecchi MR. 1988. Disruption of the proto-oncogene int-2 in mouse embryo-derived stem cells: a general strategy for targeting mutations; to nonselectable genes. *Nature* 336:348–52

59. Mastrangeli A, Danel C, Rosenfeld MA, Stratford-Perricaudet L, Perricaudet M, et al. 1993. Diversity of airway epithelial cell targets for in vivo

recombinant adenovirus-mediated gene transfer. *J. Clin. Invest.* 91:225–34

60. Messina LM, Podrazik RM, Whitehill TA, Ekhterae D, Brothers TE, et al. 1992. Adhesion and incorporation of lac-Z-transduced endothelial cells into the intact capillary wall in the rat. *Proc. Natl. Acad. Sci. USA* 89:12018–22

61. Miller AD. 1992. Human gene therapy comes of age. *Nature* 357:455–60

62. Miller AD, Buttimore C. 1986. Redesign of retrovirus packaging cell lines to avoid recombination leading to helper virus production. *Mol. Cell. Biol.* 6:2895–902

63. Miller DG, Adam MA, Miller AD. 1990. Gene transfer by retrovirus vectors occurs only in cells that are actively replicating at the time of infection. *Mol. Cell. Biol.* 10:4239–42

64. Mims CA. 1986. Virus receptors and cell tropisms. *J. Infect.* 12:199–203

65. Morgan JR, Barrandon Y, Green H, Mulligan RC. 1987. Expression of an exogenous growth hormone gene by transplantable epidermal cells. *Science* 237:1476–79

66. Nabel EG, Gordon D, Xang Z-Y, Xu L, San H, et al. 1992. Gene transfer in vivo with DNA-liposome complexes: lack of autoimmunity and gonadal localization. *Hum. Gene Ther.* 3:649–56

66a. Nabel EG, Nabel GJ. 1993. Molecular genetic interventions for cardiovascular diseases. In *Textbook of Interventional Cardiology*, ed. EJ Topol, pp. 1006–18. Philadelphia: Saunders

67. Nabel EG, Plautz G, Boyce FM, Stanley JC, Nabel GJ. 1989. Recombinant gene expression in vivo within endothelial cells of the arterial wall. *Science* 244:1342–44

68. Nabel EG, Plautz G, Nabel GJ. 1990. Site-specific gene expression in vivo by direct gene transfer into the arterial wall. *Science* 249:1285–88

69. Nabel EG, Plautz G, Nabel GJ. 1992. Transduction of a foreign histocompatibility gene into the arterial wall induces vasculitis. *Proc. Natl. Acad. Sci. USA* 89:5157–61

70. Nabel EG, Shum L, Pompili VJ, Yang ZY, San H, et al. 1993. Direct gene transfer of transforming growth factor β1 into arteries stimulates fibrocellular hyperplasia. *Proc. Natl. Acad. Sci. USA.* 90:10759–63

71. Nabel EG, Yang Z, Liptay S, San H, Gordon D, et al. 1993. Recombinant platelet-derived growth factor B gene expression in porcine arteries induces

intimal hyperplasia in vivo. *J. Clin. Invest.* 91:1822–29

72. Nabel EG, Yang Z, Plautz G, Forough R, Zhan X, et al. 1993. Recombinant fibroblast growth factor-1 promotes intimal hyperplasia and angiogenesis in arteries in vivo. *Nature* 362:844–46

73. Nikol S, Isner JM, Pickering JG, Kearney M, Leclerc G, et al. 1992. Expression of transforming growth factor-β1 is increased in human vascular restenosis lesions. *J. Clin. Invest.* 90: 1582–92

74. Palmiter RD, Brinster RL. 1985. Transgenic mice. *Cell* 41:343–54

75. Pellicer A, Robins D, Wold B, Sweet R, Jackson J, et al. 1980. Altering genotype and phenotype by DNA-mediated gene transfer. *Science* 209:1414–22

76. Philipson L, Lonberg-Holm K, Pettersson U. 1968. Virus-receptor interaction in an adenovirus system. *J. Virol.* 2:1064–75

77. Plautz G, Nabel EG, Nabel GJ. 1991. Introduction of vascular smooth muscle cells expressing recombinant genes in vivo. *Circulation* 83:578–83

78. Price J, Turner D, Cepko C. 1987. Lineage analysis in the vertebrate nervous system by retrovirus-mediated gene transfer. *Proc. Natl. Acad. Sci. USA* 84:156–60

79. Prince GA, Porter DD, Jenson AB, Horswood RL, Chanock RM, et al. 1993. Pathogenesis of adenovirus type 5 pneumonia in cotton rats (*Sigmodon hispidus*). *J. Virol.* 67:101–11

80. Ragot T, Vincent N, Chafey P, Vigne E, Gilgenkrantz H, et al. 1993. Efficient adenovirus-mediated transfer of a human minidystrophin gene to skeletal muscle of mdx mice. *Nature* 361: 647–50

81. Rosenberg SA, Aebersold P, Cornetta K, Kasid A, Morgan RA, et al. 1990. Gene transfer into humans—immunotherapy of patients with advanced melanoma, using tumor-infiltrating lymphocytes modified by retroviral gene transduction. *N. Engl. J. Med.* 323:570–78

82. Rosenfeld MA, Yoshimura K, Trapnell BC, Yoneyama K, Rosenthal ER, et al. 1992. In vivo transfer of the human cystic fibrosis transmembrane conductance regulator gene to the airway epithelium. *Cell* 68:143–55

83. Sambrook J, Fritsch EF, Maniatis, T. 1989. *Molecular Cloning: A Laboratory Manual*, 16:54–55. Cold Spring Harbor NY: Cold Spring Harbor Press

84. San H, Yang ZY, Pompili VJ, Xu L,

Felgner P, et al. 1993. Safety and short-term toxicity of a novel cationic lipid formulation for human gene therapy. *Hum. Gene Ther.* 4:781–88

85. Schaefer-Ridder M, Wang Y, Hofschneider PH. 1982. Liposomes as gene carriers: Efficient transformation of mouse L cells by thymidine kinase gene. *Science* 215:166–68

86. Shull MM, Ormsby L, Kier AB, Pawlowski S, Diebold RJ, et al. 1992. Targeted disruption of the mouse transforming growth factor-β1 gene results in multifocal inflammatory disease. *Nature* 359:693–99

87. Stewart MJ, Plautz GE, Del Buono L, Yang ZY, Xu L, et al. 1992. Gene transfer in vivo with DNA-liposome complexes: safety and acute toxicity in mice. *Hum. Gene Ther.* 3:267–75

88. Stratford-Perricaudet LD, Makeh I, Perricaudet M, Briand P. 1992. Widespread long-term gene transfer to mouse skeletal muscles and heart. *J. Clin. Invest.* 90:626–30

89. Straubinger RM, Papahadjopoulos D. 1983. Liposomes as carriers for intracellular delivery of nucleic acids. *Methods Enzymol.* 101:512–27

90. Szoka F, Paphadjopoulos D. 1978. Procedure for preparation of liposomes with large internal aqueous space and high capture by reverse-phase evaporation. *Proc. Natl. Acad. Sci. USA* 75:4194–98

91. Tabin CJ, Hoffman JW, Goff SP, Weinberg RA. 1982. Adaptation of a retrovirus as a eucaryotic vector transmitting the herpes simplex virus thymidine kinase gene. *Mol. Cell. Biol.* 2:426–36

92. Tang D, DeVit M, Johnston SA. 1992. Genetic immunization is a simple method for eliciting an immune response. *Nature* 356:152–54

93. Temin HM, Mizutani S. 1970. RNA-dependent DNA polymerase in virions of Rous sarcoma virus. *Nature* 226:1211

94. von Harsdorf R, Schott RJ, Shen YT, Vatner SF, Mahdavi V, et al. 1993. Gene injection into canine myocardium as a useful model for studying gene expression in the heart of large mammals. *Circ. Res.* 72:688–95

95. Wagner E, Zatloukal K, Cotten M, Kirlappos H, Mechtler K, et al. 1992. Coupling of adenovirus to transferrin-polylysine/DNA complexes greatly enhances receptor-mediated gene delivery and expression of transfected genes. *Proc. Natl. Acad. Sci. USA* 89:6099–103

96. Watson JD, Hopkins NH, Roberts JW, Steitz JA, Weiner AM. 1988. *Molecular Biology of the Gene*, pp. 936–49. Menlo Park: Benjamin-Cummings

97. Wigler M, Silverstein S, Lee L-S, Pellicer A, Cheng Y-C, et al. 1977. Transfer of purified herpes virus thymidine kinase gene to cultured mouse cells. *Cell* 11:223–32

98. Williams RS, Johnston SA, Reidy M, Devitt MJ, McElligott SG, et al. 1991. Introduction of foreign genes into tissues of living mice by DNA-coated microprojectiles. *Proc. Natl. Acad. Sci. USA* 88:2726–30

99. Wilson JM, Birinyi LK, Salomon RN, Libby P, Callow AD, et al. 1989. Implantation of vascular grafts lined with genetically modified endothelial cells. *Science* 244:1344–46

100. Wilson JM, Jefferson DM, Chowdhury JR, Novikoff PM, Johnston DE, et al. 1988. Retrovirus-mediated transduction of adult hepatocytes. *Proc. Natl. Acad. Sci. USA* 85:3014–18

101. Wolff JA, Malone RW, Williams P, Chong W, Acsadi G, et al. 1990. Direct gene transfer into mouse muscle in vivo. *Science* 247:1465–68

102. Wolff JA, Williams P, Acsadi G, Jiao S, Jani A, et al. 1991. Conditions affecting direct gene transfer into rodent muscle in vivo. *BioTechniques* 11:474–85

103. Wu GY, Wilson JM, Shalaby F, Grossman M, Shafritz DA, et al. 1991. Receptor-mediated gene delivery in vivo. Partial correction of genetic analbuminemia in Nagase rats. *J. Biol. Chem.* 266:14338–42

Annu. Rev. Physiol. 1994. 56:763–96
Copyright © 1994 by Annual Reviews Inc. All rights reserved

MOLECULAR GENETIC APPROACHES TO THE STUDY OF HUMAN CARDIOVASCULAR DISEASE

Harry C. Dietz, III and Reed E. Pyeritz

Center for Medical Genetics and Departments of Pediatrics and Medicine, Johns Hopkins University School of Medicine, Baltimore, Maryland 21205

KEY WORDS: linkage analysis, positional cloning, candidate genes, developmental biology, Marfan syndrome

INTRODUCTION

For most of the twentieth century, disorders of the cardiovascular system have been the leading cause of death in developed countries; this burden will be magnified as traditional cultures become more westernized. Cardiovascular disorders, like those that affect virtually all other organs systems, are comprised of many rare conditions and far fewer relatively common ones. The rare disorders become evident over a wide age spectrum, but often emerge early in life, and many are congenital. Teratogen exposures, defects in single genes and chromosome aberrations, account for the majority of early-onset cardiovascular diseases. The common disorders, on the other hand, are more likely to be diagnosed in adulthood and to have no single identifiable cause. For decades the familial predisposition to common disorders such as hypertension, atherosclerosis, and diabetes mellitus has been well appreciated. While relatives share environment and experiences, which could account for exaggerated familial risks, considerable evidence from studies of nuclear pedigrees and twins has pointed to genes as the principal determinants of familial predispositions. Given that about 500 genes, or nearly 10% of all human genes catalogued, have been associated with human cardiovascular phenotypes (76), it is likely that all diseases of the heart and blood vessels have one or more genetic factors important to their development (96).

This review focuses on some molecular genetic approaches to cardiovascular physiology and pathophysiology. Clinical applications employing molecular techniques are burgeoning (95), and these are surveyed briefly. Our major focus is on normal embryology and physiology, and cause and pathogenesis of disease. We outline the general principles that guide the design, conduct, interpretation, and application of molecular genetic techniques, describe the various approaches available, and illustrate in detail the progress made in a number of diverse conditions.

AREAS OF INVESTIGATION

Etiology

For two terms that have distinct meanings, it is suprising how often etiology and pathogenetics are used as if they were synonymous. Etiology is the systematic study of the cause(s) of a pathologic process. To date, molecular genetics has had its most notable successes in uncovering causes such as the mutations in cystic fibrosis, Duchene muscular dystrophy, neurofibromatosis I and II, and Huntington disease. In each of these instances, a previously unrecognized gene was discovered as well. Nearly half a century ago, the discovery of the cause of sickle cell disease at the level of a protein, specifically a defect in β-globin, was itself a seminal accomplishment. But it was the recognition that all patients with sickle cell disease had the same nucleotide change at the sixth codon of the β-globin gene that ultimately solved etiology, by defining cause at the highest resolution possible. The causes of many hereditary cardiovascular diseases are now known in the same detail (Table 1).

Pathogenetics

The pathogenesis of a condition consists of the various mechanisms through which pathology develops, and pathogenetics is the study of these mechanisms and how they interact. To use a culinary analogy, if etiology is the list of ingredients that go into a soufflé, then pathogenetics is the recipe. The pathogenetics of sickle cell disease, Marfan syndrome, familial hypertrophic cardiomyopathy, and so forth, involves the study of both how—at molecular, cellular, tissue and organismal levels—the various clinical manifestations arise, and which factors are involved in modulating expression of the basic cause. There is often striking disparity between how little is known about pathogenesis and complete understanding of etiology. It is not at all clear, for example, how physical growth is stunted in children

Table 1 The morbid anatomy of the human genome—representative disorders of the cardiovascular system

Disorder	OMIM # (Reference 76)	Gene		
		Symbol	Locus	Product
Mapped disorders of known cause				
Metabolic disorders				
Glycogen storage disease II	232300	GAA	17q23	α-1,4-glucosidase (acid maltase)
Pompe disease and late onset form				
Mucopolysaccharidosis I	252800	IDVA	4p16.3	α-L-iduronidase
Hurler and Scheie syndrome				
Fabry disease	301500	GLA	Xq22	α-galactosidase A
Kearns-Sayre	530000			Various mitochondrial proteins and tRNAs
Lipid metabolism and arterial disease				
↓ LDL and ↑ LDL	107730	APOB	2p23-p24	Apolipoprotein B
↑ LDL	143890	LDLR	19p13.2-p13.12	LDL receptor
↓ HDL	107680	APOA1	11q23	Apolipoprotein A-1
↑ Lp(a)	152200	LPA	6q26-q27	Lp(a) lipoprotein
Homocystinuria	236200	CBS	21q22.3	Cystathione β-synthase
Structural				
Familial hypertrophic cardiomyopathy	192600			
	160760	CHMI	14q12	Cardiac β-myosin heavy chain
	115195	CHM2	1q3	?
	115196	CHM3	15q2	
	115197	CHM4	11	
Marfan syndrome	154700			
	134797	FBN1	15q21	Fibrillin
Ehlers-Danlos IV	130050			
	120180	COL3A1	2q24.3-q31	Type III collagen

Table 1 (*continued*)

Disorder	OMIM # (Reference 76)	Gene		
		Symbol	Locus	Product
Supravalvular aortic stenosis	185500	ELN	7q11.2	Elastin
Duchenne muscular dystrophy	310200	DMD	Xp21	Dystrophin
Electrical				
Ward-Romano (long QT syndrome)	192500	LQT	11p14	?
Myotonic dystrophy	160900	MD	19q13.2	Myotonin
Mapped disorders of unknown cause				
Arterio-hepatic dysplasia (Alagille syndrome)	118450	AHD	20p11.2	?
DiGeorge sequence	188400		22q11.21-q11.23	
Velocardiofacial syndrome	192430		22q11.21-q11.23	
Hemochromatosis	235200		6p21.3	Iron accumulation
Amyloidosis	176300		18q11.2-q12.1	Thyroxine-binding prealbumin

homozygous β^S/β^S, how pulmonary infarcts arise, what triggers painful crises, etc. While certain other loci are known to modulate expression of the disease phenotype, such as the α-globin genes and the gene(s) controlling production of fetal hemoglobin, there may well be additional genetic and nongenetic factors that are important. To cite another example, knowing that certain defects in the β-myosin heavy chain cause familial hypertrophic cardiomyopathy does little to explain how hypertrophy develops in the heart, why skeletal muscle is rarely clinically involved, how electrophysiological aberrations emerge, how the extensive intrafamilial variation in expression arises, and so on. Without minimizing the importance of etiology, to the patient and the clinician, understanding pathogenetics may be more relevant, and studying pathogenetics is almost always more challenging to investigators of both clinical and basic science. Studying pathogenesis also sheds considerable light on normal developmental, metabolic, and cellular processes, which until the cause of a particular disease was found, were not even known to exist.

Investigations of cause and pathogenetics can be complementary, especially at the molecular level. The traditional view has most autosomal recessive disorders resulting from enzyme deficiencies, witness most of the classic inborn errors of metabolism. Similarly, autosomal-dominant human traits often affect organ or tissue development through defects in structural proteins. However, thinking in terms of homeostasis, it was unclear until the past decade why a patient with an autosomal-dominant disorder could not get by with the product of the normal allele. In humans, it was first demonstrated convincingly in osteogenesis imperfecta (92), and more recently in Marfan syndrome (22), that the normal product, in the most severe cases of these conditions, is disrupted by the product of the mutant allele (Figure 1). This phenomenon represents a dominant-negative effect (47). The basic pathogenetic mechanism involves a mutant protein combining with its normal analogue to generate a dysfunctional multimer. One result of this model is that the product of loci other than the one in which the mutation resides can be drawn into the pathogenesis if it helps to form or interact with the multimer. Another result seems paradoxical: a mutation so overwhelming as to totally disrupt production of a peptide product will have the least effect on phenotype because only normal peptide will be available, albeit at 50% quantity. Both situations are exemplified by Marfan syndrome, described below.

Homeostasis

Virtually all human biology occurs in the context of homeostatic systems. On the one hand is physiological homeostasis, such as control of plasma glucose concentration, blood pressure, core temperature, heart rate etc. On

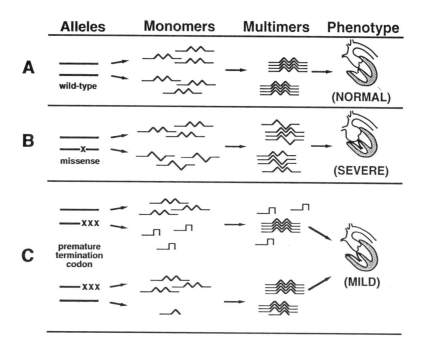

Figure 1   A dominant-negative model for Marfan syndrome. (*A*) Two wild-type alleles produce a homogeneous population of normal monomers, which form normal multimers (microfibrils), and the phenotype is normal. (*B*) Heterozygosity for a missense mutation (X) produces equal amounts of normal and mutant monomers. Because all multimers will contain some mutant monomers, all microfibrils will be defective, and the phenotype will be severe (indicated by aortic root dilatation and atrioventricular valve redundancy. (*C*) A mutation that causes a premature signal for termination of translation (XXX) might produce a truncated monomer incapable of multimer formation (*upper panel*). Alternatively, a reduction in mutant allele transcripts might produce few defective monomers capable of forming multimers (*lower panel*). Both situations predict a relative preponderance of normal microfibrils, and the phenotype will be mild (shown by isolated atriventricular valve redundancy) (adapted from 22).

the other hand is developmental homeostasis, which is most evident during embryogenesis but still pertinent during growth and repair. Both types of regulatory systems have long intellectual histories, stimulated mightily by Bernard and Cannon in physiological homeostasis and Waddington in developmental homeostasis. Both are appropriate constructs for studying etiology and pathogenetics of processes that, at our current level of under-standing, seem quite complex. When reduced to mathematical terms, how-ever, both forms of homeostasis can potentially be controlled by a suprisingly small number of parameters (81). Moreover, genetic specification of these parameters would provide explanations for subtle variations in how humans respond to physiological perturbations, for overt pathology, and for refinement of homeostatic mechanisms through evolution (82, 99).

AUGMENTATION OF PEDIGREE ANALYSIS BY MOLECULAR TECHNIQUES

The Importance of Phenotyping

The importance of careful attention to accurate and complete characterization of clinical, pathological, biochemical and ancestral details cannot be emphasized enough. The most refined linkage or segregation analyses are doomed to reduced power, if not outright misinformation, if all members of a pedigree are not assessed accurately. The difficulties are compounded when pedigrees with presumably the same clinical diagnosis are combined in analyses, and in complex, subtle, or age-dependent conditions.

Biochemical and Physiological Investigations

All of the publicity about positional cloning, much of it well deserved, should not detract from the benefit of knowing something about the pathogenesis of a disease, preferably at the cell biological, physiological, or biochemical level, before embarking on a project to map the defective gene(s). For example, knowledge of glucose homeostasis suggested straightaway that defects in the insulin molecule, the islet β-cell, the insulin receptor, the second messenger pathways, glucose transporters, and glycolosis might all present as hyperglycemia. That none of these classes of Mendelian disorders, most of which having been identified likely account for but a fraction of familial diabetes, should not detract from the considerable insight into physiology and pathophysiology that has been gained.

Table 2 lists some cardiovascular disorders that are reasonably well understood at various levels short of etiology and seem likely to be mapped in the near future.

Segregation Patterns of Disorders Caused Predominantly by Single Genes

MENDELIAN INHERITANCE   The first clue that a disorder is due to a mutation at a single genetic locus is the pattern of recurrence of the condition in families. Two clinical points are essential. First the diagnosis must be secure, or in the case of a new disorder, the phenotype must be completely described in the proband. Second, all family members must be evaluated as thoroughly as possible. Accurate phenotyping may reveal that the disorder in one family is not exactly the same, in terms of age of onset, severity, or specific

Table 2 Prominent chromosomal and Mendelian diseases poised for discovery of cause

Disorder	OMIM # (Reference 76)
Familial dilated cardiomyopathy	115200
Noonan syndrome	163950
Holt-Oram syndrome	142900
Mitral valve prolapse syndrome	157700
Jervell and Lange-Nielsen syndrome	220400
Primary pulmonary hypertension	178600
Ellis-van Creveld syndrome	225500
Ivemark syndrome	208530
Hypoplastic left heart syndrome	241550
Pseudoxanthoma elasticum	264800
Williams syndrome	194050
Hereditary hemorrhagic telangiectasia (Osler-Weber-Rendu syndrome)	187300
Situs inversus	207010

features, as in other families, and suggests either variable expression or genetic heterogeneity.

The basic principles of Mendelian inheritance in humans are reviewed elsewhere (94, 96). For clarity of thought and precision in language, recessive and dominant should be descriptors of phenotypes, not genotypes or alleles.

MITOCHONDRIAL INHERITANCE   Thirteen peptides are encoded by the mitochondrial genome; each functions in one of the five complexes that constitute the respiratory chain (5, 121). Mutations of one or more of these genes, or of the other mitochondrial genes that specify mitochondrion-specific tRNAs and rRNAs, can disrupt oxidative phosphorylation and cellular energy generation. A variety of disorders, which involve the eye, nerves, skeletal muscle, cardiac muscle, and kidney singly or in various combinations, have been found to be caused by mitochondrial DNA mutations (100, 118). These mutations are passed through the cytoplasm of the ovum, and their associated phenotypes show maternal inheritance. Most of the disorders are highly variable and pleiotropic, in part due to some of the unique characteristics of mitochondrial inheritance (heteroplasmy and a high rate of somatic mutation), but also because of organ variation in oxidative capacity and a threshold phenomenon arising from differential tissue susceptibility to hypoxia (121).

The mitochondrial genome is small enough (16,569 bp) that mutations are relatively easy to discover. However, because there can exist tremendous variation in both the type of mutations and their abundance relative to normal mitochondria in individual organs, assessing a patient fully may involve assaying the mitochondrial DNA from multiple invasive biopsies.

In a small pedigree, inheritance of a mitochondrial DNA mutation is difficult to distinguish from autosomal-dominant inheritance. One key is the absence of transmission through affected males to either sons or daughters. Also confusing is the fact that most defects of the mitochondrial respiratory chain are from mutations of nuclear genes, whose products are transported into the cytoplasmic organelle, and are inherited as Mendelian traits.

SOMATIC MUTATION   Mutations occurring after conception are traditionally separated into somatic and germinal ones, but the distinction can be blurred by mutations that occur in the early embryo in a progenitor cell that gives rise to both somatic and germinal tissue. Somatic mutations can involve entire chromosomes (anaphase lag-producing aneuploidy), chromosomal translocations or other aberrations, or mutations of one or a few genes. A congenital phenotype depends largely on how many mutated cells are distributed into specific organs. To a first approximation, distribution of somatic mutations is determined by how early in zygotic or fetal development the mutational event occurs.

For years embryologists have been studying normal development by physically ablating specific regions of animal embryos. For example, microsurgery of the neural crest performed on chick embryos has yielded information on the normal migration of these progenitor cells and the types of cardiovascular malformations that result. Refinement of this approach is now possible by selective introduction of embryonic somatic mutations. A number of molecular techniques can be used. Reporter genes such as the *lac* gene can be attached to tissue-specific promoters to follow cellular migration. Alternatively, a gene that produces a cellular poison such as diphtheria toxin can be linked with a specific promoter, and the effect of ablating an embryonic anlage can be observed. Homologous recombination is another transgenic approach that can enable the knock out of a gene known to be expressed in a specific embryonic tissue (12). All of these approaches that shed light on animal embryology are feasible in mice, difficult for technical and economic reasons in nonhuman primates, and not feasible in humans. But studies of induced somatic mutations in lower animals have the potential for providing understanding of general principles of developmental homeostasis and some insight to human congenital anomalies and hereditary diseases.

Factors that Confound Segregation Analysis

Molecular analyses have clarified some of the many reasons that Mendelian conditions do not always follow the rules of segregation.

ISOLATED CASES AND GERMINAL MOSAICISM   For both autosomal dominant and X-linked phenotypes, parental germinal mutations are the source of both isolated cases and multiple occurrences when (a) the ancestral history is negative, (b) neither parent is affected, and (c) the mutation cannot be detected in somatic tissue of either parent. The more severe the disorder (precisely, the lower the genetic fitness meaning the less likely the patient will reproduce), the higher the percentage of total cases represented by new mutations. Isolated cases are often called sporadic, but this term implies a specific mechanism—germinal mutation (113). Given the small family sizes in the developed world, autosomal recessive conditions are often present in only one of a sibship; this proband will also be an isolated case, but not sporadic; and if there is no consanguinity and the inheritance pattern of the phenotype is otherwise unknown, then genetic counseling will be difficult. For previously undescribed disorders, or those for which molecular etiology is uncertain, analysis of neither the pedigree nor parental genome has much to offer the isolated occurrence in a family.

PLEIOTROPY   The ability of a single mutation to be expressed in a number of ways in the same patient is known as pleiotropy. An increasing array of molecular mechanisms—multifunctional proteins, alternative splicing of mRNA, multifunctional genes—can account for this characteristic of many Mendelian conditions (93, 97). However, when pleiotropy is extensive, explaining pathogenesis can be a formidable task, but investigators can use pleiotropy to their advantage in searching for cause. For example, Marfan syndrome was traditionally described in terms of involvement of the eye, heart, and skeleton. Many components of the extracellular matrix common to these three tissues were suggested as possible causes, but when more extensive pleiotropy emerged, the task became easier, not harder. First, the culprit molecule had to be present in lung, skin, muscle, and dura. Second, recognition of skin involvement yielded a readily accessible tissue for study (49, 97).

VARIABLE EXPRESSION   In strict terms, variable expression, or variability, refers to qualitatively or quantitatively distinctive expression of identical mutations in different people. More commonly, the term refers to phenotypes caused by different mutations at the same locus. But a host of environmental, stochastic, and genetic factors affect expression of any given allele. Variability is best investigated in inbred animals, in which nutrition, temperature, maternal exposures, genetic background, modifying (epistatic) loci, and so on can be held constant or varied at will.

The level at which variation occurs can be explored in molecular terms by examining transcription, translation, post-translational modification, macromolecular aggregation, and physiological function. Within a pedigree, some mechanisms may pertain to all affected individuals, while others will show Mendelian segregation independent of the pathologic mutation. While understanding an individual's potential for variable expression is highly pertinent to prognosis, only rarely can such information be obtained now.

Some autosomal dominant and X-linked traits show a specific type of variability termed anticipation. In, for example, myotonic muscular dystrophy and the fragile X mental retardation syndrome, the phenotype may worsen through successive generations. Until recently, this characteristic was thought to be an epiphenomenon, due largely to biases of ascertainment (45). However, the discovery of the causes of both disorders in the past two years provides a biologic explanation for the clinical observations. Both genes, that for myotonic dystrophy at 19q13.2 and for fragile X at Xq28, contain a trinucleotide sequence repeated a variable number of times. This type of repetitive sequence is prone to expansion, by a molecular mechanism not yet understood, during mitosis in somatic cells and meiosis in gamete formation. In these disorders (44, 115), as well as in Huntington disease (51), the severity of the phenotype is directly related to the number of repeats of the trinucleotide. Anticipation is not a one-way street; in rare instances, the number of repeats decreases one generation to the next, and the phenotype is milder or even nonpenetrant (i.e. not evident) (7), a phenomenon we term reversion. Knowledge of this type of mutation and its association with extreme phenotypic variability can identify the cause of a disorder that also shows anticipation; searching specifically for trinucleotide repeats led one group to the myotonic dystrophy gene (36).

Mendelian conditions typically show variable expression. The most common reasons for unrelated patients with the same condition to show phenotypic differences are intra- and interlocus genetic heterogeneity. These are well illustrated by a number of the conditions discussed subsequently. With regard to a single locus, molecular dissection of the specific mutations causing a particular condition nearly always show considerable heterogeneity.

Interlocus heterogeneity is usually revealed by either linkage analysis or mutation searching. Familial hypertrophic cardiomyopathy is caused by mutations at four loci (30, 52, 60, 76, 110, 112). Tuberous sclerosis, which can produce cardiac rhabdomyomas, is caused by at least two different mutant genes (76).

Sorting out genetic heterogeneity can be highly enlightening about normal physiology, especially when disease loci are found by positional cloning. Usually, the identified mutation resides in a gene whose function, indeed its existence, was previously unknown. By identifying all of the genes that cause, for example, hypertrophic cardiomyopathy, additional components of the myofibril may well be discovered.

The challenging aspects of variable expression go well beyond differences in the principal gene. A host of other factors, including some genetic ones, determine how an individual expresses a given mutation; the range may span lethality to no overt disease. Sorting out variability, understanding how gene action is modified, and controlling such modulation should be the most expeditious means to treat a great many Mendelian disorders. Manipulating expression by pharmacologic or somatic genetic means affords alternative gene therapies that do not depend on introduction of a functioning copy of the mutant allele (35, 90). A good example is increasing the production of fetal hemoglobin (by phenylbutyrate or hydroxyurea) to ameliorate the effects of sickle hemoglobin (86, 102).

When extreme, variable expression can result in nonpenetrance, such that a mutant allele is not evident phenotypically. An autosomal-dominant disease appears to skip generations, and sorting out the pedigree may be confusing. Fortunately, as more sensitive means are brought to bear on the phenotype (such as echocardiography in Marfan syndrome, electromyography in myotonic dystrophy, etc), fewer people with mild manifestations escape detection. Of course, knowledge of the gene involved permits linkage analysis or direct mutational analysis to determine accurately who has the mutant allele.

IMPRINTING   Mendel's first law, which holds that it makes no phenotypic difference whether an allele is inherited from mother or from father, has been proven incorrect in humans for loci subject to imprinting. Some loci are modified as they pass through either gonad during gametogenesis (29, 41). Imprinting, which may involve DNA methylation, is specific for the sex of the parent and independent of the sex of the offspring. Thus for an autosomal-dominant trait, expression of a mutant allele may be different depending on the sex of the affected parent.

The phenomenon has been studied best in experimental mice strains bred for retention of chromosome translocations, and only certain regions of certain mouse chromosomes seem susceptible to imprinting (11). By locus homology and comparative gene mapping, the human chromosome regions can be implicated (109). Variability can be a manifestation of imprinting (13).

UNIPARENTAL DISOMY   For some autosomal loci, it is important that mother and father each contribute an allele to the zygote. The chromosomal regions at issue overlap substantially with those that undergo imprinting. When one parent contributes both alleles the situation is termed uniparental disomy; if the alleles are identical because of duplication of an originally haploid gamete, the situation is termed uniparental isodisomy (29). It has long been suspected that some autosomal-recessive disorders might arise when a heterozygous parent contributes two mutant alleles to an offspring while the other parent contributes none. However, the offspring may have additional problems (growth retardation is a common one) in addition to the phenotype associated with the mutant locus. The best studied example involves Prader-Willi syndrome and Angelman syndrome, both of which map to the same region of chromosome 15q11.3. If father contributes both alleles, or if mother fails to contribute one, Prader-Willi syndrome results, while the opposite situation leads to the Angelman syndrome (76).

Segregation Patterns of Disorders Caused by Multiple Genes

GENETIC HETEROGENEITY   Some disorders, such as familial hypertrophic cardiomyopathy and familial dilated cardiomyopathy, can be caused by mutations at one of a number of genes. In the former case, at least four loci have been implicated; in each case, the phenotype is autosomal-dominant, so segregation analysis adjusted for age-dependency gives the same result in every family. The causes of dilated cardiomyopathy have not yet been discovered, but at least two loci must be capable of producing the phenotype because both X-linked and autosomal-dominant forms are known.

CONTIGUOUS GENE DELETION SYNDROMES   Some phenotypes are so complex that extreme pleiotropy must be in effect, or multiple genes must be contributing simultaneously. The identification of small chromosomal deletions associated with some of these phenotypes (Prader-Willi syndrome, DiGeorge sequence, Miller-Dieker syndrome, to name a few) suggested that defects (i.e. absence of one allele) in multiple contiguous genes, each with a separate function, were the cause. In a few instances, some of the genes involved have been identified, but most disorders are not understood in molecular terms. Imprinting is clearly at work in some. Many of the phenotypes are so severe that reproduction of affected patients is impossible. However, autosomal deletions segregate to half the gametes at meiosis, and the phenotype is formally dominant at the level of the individual.

POLYGENIC PHENOTYPES   Most of the common diseases of mid-life—atherosclerosis, hypertension, obesity, etc—run in families. A percentage of cases, how large is still undetermined, are due to Mendelian phenotypes, relatively rare but severe defects of one or another component of homeostasis. Disease will develop unless considerable adjustment of the environment is accomplished, or even in spite of such efforts. Dysfunction of the LDL receptor, pseudoxanthoma elasticum, and multiple endocrine neoplasia with pheochromocytoma are examples.

The prevailing wisdom holds that most patients develop disease because of the interaction of environmental and stochastic factors on several or perhaps many separate genetic loci. One goal of quantitative genetics is to devise methods for teasing evidence out of families and populations for the role of these loci; how many there are, and where they might be. Numerous molecular approaches have broadened the inquiry in several ways (8, 64, 77, 122). First, by providing an increasingly dense and informative matrix of markers for linkage analysis, the disease phenotype in some families can be found to segregate with a specific marker, and the genetic locus identified through positional cloning. Second, this same approach can be applied to animals in which the disease appears spontaneously, or can be readily induced; any locus identified as important to the disease in the animal thus becomes a candidate for study in humans. Recombinant congenic strains of mice can be especially informative when analyzing polygenic traits (40). Third, human candidate genes can be inserted into animals, or used to knock out the endogenous gene of interest in the animal, and the resulting phenotype can be observed (34, 42, 88, 122).

MOLECULAR APPROACHES TO ETIOLOGY AND PATHOGENETICS

The golden age of human gene mapping began in the 1970's and was spurred by the development of, first, somatic cell hybrids and, second, simplified methods for cloning genes encoding protein molecules of known function. The golden age of the discovery of human genes involved in Mendelian disorders began in the mid-1980's with the extensive application of recombinant DNA techniques, positional cloning, and direct sequencing of mutant alleles. Nearly all the techniques that led to the increase in mapped disease loci from under 200 in 1986 to nearly 750 in 1992 (76) have either been enormously improved or totally supplanted. The next sections review in broad outline the most useful current techniques.

The Classical Approach

Traditionally, biochemistry, physiology, pathology, and medicine were parallel endeavors; interactions occurred when it made sense to test patients with a disease for inactivity of a particular enzyme. If the disorder were recessive, then parents could be checked for reduced levels of the enzyme. Eventually, the gene encoding the enzyme was cloned, and mutations were found. This approach has not disappeared entirely, and Table 3 lists some proteins that are in search of a disorder.

Table 3 Candidate proteins and genes looking for diseases

Protein or locus	OMIM # (Reference 76)	Symbol	Map locus
α-actin, cardiac muscle	102540	ACTC	15q21
Na-Ca exchanger, sarcolemma	182305	NCX1	2p23-p21
Atrial natiuretic peptide	108780	ANF	1p36.2
Atrial natiuretic peptide receptor, type C	108962	ANPRC	5p14-p12
Angiotensin II receptor, vascular type I	106165	AGTRI	3q21-q25
cAMP phosphodiesterase, myocardial	123805		
Epoxide hydrolase	132810	EPHX	1p11-qter
Nitrous oxide synthase (endothelium-derived relaxing factor)	163729	NOS	
6-phosphofructo-2-kinase, cardiac isozyme	171835	PFKB2	1q31
Utrophin	128240	DMDL	6q24
Ca channel, 1 type, α-1 polypeptide	114206	CACNL1A2	3p14.3
Homeobox 7	142983	HOC7	4p16.1

Cytogenetics

At the coarsest level, the high prevalence of cardiovascular anomalies in trisomies 13, 18, and 21 has long suggested that genes important to embryology of the heart and blood vessels reside on those chromosomes. However, an alternative hypothesis holds that trisomy itself disrupts developmental homeostasis in both general and specfic ways, and so leads to the entire spectrum of anomalies found in these conditions. This remains an area of unresolved controversy and active research. More refined methods for observing chromosomes using light microscopy include high-resolution banding of prometaphase nuclei and fluorescent in situ hybridization (FISH) of DNA probes (120). These techniques have been useful in both detecting subtle chromosome aberrations and in performing phenotype-genotype correlations. For example, it now appears that only a small portion of chromosome 21 needs to be present in triplicate for the Down syndrome to emerge (61). There is some suggestion that the region critical for defects of the endocardial cushions resides at 21q22.2 (62).

The following example illustrates how a cytogenetic aberration can provide the key to unlocking both etiology and pathogenesis of a range of disorders.

DiGEORGE SEQUENCE AND DEVELOPMENT OF THE CONOTRUNCUS   The conotruncal cushions are specialized regions of the developing heart, composed largely of mesenchymal cells of neuroectodermal origin and connective tissue elements, that participate extensively in the process of ventricular and great vessel septation. This is largely accomplished through a complex sequence of cellular migration, growth, death, and differentiation. Aberration of this phase of cardiac morphogenesis can produce a spectrum of congenital cardiac defects, so-called conotruncal malformations, including interrupted aortic arch, tetralogy of Fallot, pulmonary atresia with ventricular septal defect, and persistent truncus arteriosus. Although often seen in isolation, these lesions also occur in the context of a developmental field defect of the third and fourth pharyngeal pouches and occasionally show autosomal-dominant segregation.

In addition to conotruncal cardiac malformations, the DiGeorge sequence includes craniofacial and skeletal anomalies and aplasia or hypoplasia of the thymus and parathyroid glands with secondary immunologic deficiency and altered calcium homeostasis. The velo-cardio-facial (VCF) syndrome is defined by cleft palate, facial dysmorphism, and cognitive impairment, in addition to conotruncal malformations. The diverse inheritance patterns of these disorders suggest genetic heterogeneity.

The first insight into the molecular genetic basis of the DiGeorge sequence came from cytogenetics. A balanced translocation between chromosome 20 and 22, causing monosomy 22pter-22q11, was found to segregate with disease in a kindred with multiple affected relatives (19). High-resolution chromosome banding studies showed that between 20 and 40% of patients with the DiGeorge sequence have monosomy for 22q11 (2, 9, 18, 20, 27, 70, 72, 89, 125). However, what can be seen by standard cytogenetic analysis represents only the tip of the iceberg in terms of chromosomal deletions. Studies to detect submicroscopic deletions—loss of heterozygosity of DNA polymorphisms or FISH—have produced a more accurate frequency of monosomy for 22q11 sequences in DiGeorge sequence and unexpected extension to VCF and other phenotypes (9, 10). Multiple independent investigations have identified monosomy for markers at 22q11 in 94–100% of patients with DiGeorge sequence and refined the boundaries of the critical DiGeorge chromosome region (DGCR) (9, 10, 20, 33, 83, 107).

These molecular tools have been used to study the inheritance of DiGeorge sequence and the pathogenesis of related phenotypes. While all affected family members carried a 22q11 deletion, phenotypes varied widely, and microdeletions have been discovered in apparently unaffected relatives. For example, in one family Wilson, Burn, and colleagues found a 22q11 interstitial deletion in a proband with classic DiGeorge sequence in one sibling with isolated ventricular septal defect, in one sibling with coarctation of the aorta, and in their mother, whose cardiovascular evaluation was normal (126). Although monosomy at 22q11 may be sufficient to produce DiGeorge sequence, any model must account for variable expression and for involvement of other loci. Possible explanations include the presence of genes that modify or participate in the clinical expression of 22q11 deletions, or a dynamic process at the site of deletion with variable disruption of one or more genes in different individuals in the same family. The former hypothesis is supported by two findings. First, cytogenetic abnormalities of the short arm of chromosome 10 occur in a subset of patients with DiGeorge sequence (79, 84). Second, a mouse strain with a phenotype remarkably similar to DiGeorge sequence was generated by disrupting the murine *Hox*-1.5 gene (12); the homologous human gene localizes to chromosome 7p14-p21 (101).

Recently, the vast majority of patients with the VCF syndrome have been found to have interstitial deletions at 22q11 (28, 58, 108). In addition, similar molecular defects have been identified in a subset of patients with isolated conotruncal outflow tract lesions (126, 127). These data suggest that conotruncal heart malformations occur in the context of a phenotypic continuum involving extracardiac tissues and that the pathogenic pathways for these clinical entities must converge.

Ongoing investigations are attempting to identify candidate genes in the DGCR. Relevant coding sequences should be expressed at the appropriate developmental stage in cardiac morphogenesis and should play a role in the migration and differentiation of neural crest-derived cells from the third and fourth pharyngeal pouches and the conotruncal cushions. Recent studies have demonstrated that the embryopathy associated with retinoic acid exposure has considerable overlap with both the DiGeorge and VCF syndromes (63). Many transcriptional control genes that are influential in early developmental patterning, including selected homeobox genes, are retinoic acid-responsive, and their expression pattern can be altered by exogenous administration of high levels of retinoids with morphologic consequence (14). If localized to 22q11, such genes would be attractive candidates for the site of defect in the DiGeorge sequence and related syndromes.

Linkage Analysis

The goal of any linkage analysis is to discover a rate of recombination between two loci less than expected if the loci were assorting independently. If two loci are linked, then they (*a*) must be on the same chromosome, and (*b*) must be physically close enough that recombination between them is occurring in less than half of the meioses; that is, when the parental genome is passed to an offspring. If one of the loci is already placed on the gene map, then the position of the linked locus becomes identified to within no more than 50 centiMorgans (cM) of genetic distance, corresponding roughly to 50 million base pairs (mb). About 300 polymorphic markers, spaced at about 10 cM intervals, are needed to cover the entire human genome for a linkage search.

In medical genetics, the usual goal of linkage analysis is to link a phenotype (often a disease thought to be Mendelian) with a marker already mapped. Initially, markers were blood groups and proteins that showed subtle, nonpathologic variations that were genetically determined and that were readily assayed by immunologic or electrophoretic methods. The field received a tremendous boost in the early 1980's by exploitation of restriction fragment length polymorphisms (RFLPs), wherein the two alleles of a given piece of cloned DNA (cDNA) could be distinguished. Over the past decade, a large number of such markers were cloned and mapped. An even greater stimulus to linkage analysis has been the recent discovery of variable number tandem repeats (VNTRs, short tandem repeats, and microsatellites) scattered randomly throughout the entire human genome. These VNTR regions consist of a 2, 3, or 4 nucleotide sequence repeated a number of times. The actual number of repeats is reasonably faithfully transmitted between generations, so the length of any specific VNTR marker (easily assayed by PCR) can be tracked through a pedigree. If a particular length of a specific VNTR is found to be linked to a disease also present in a pedigree, then the gene causing the disease is located in proximity to the VNTR.

An increasing number of DNA probes exist for expressed sequences. These so-called cDNA probes may identify either genes of known function or genes in search of a function. In the former case, they can serve as candidate gene probes for disorders whose causes have not been discovered. Some candidate genes potentially relevant to the cardiovascular system are listed in Table 3. The following examples illustrate the effectiveness of this approach.

SUPRAVALVULAR AORTIC STENOSIS   Supravalvular aortic stenosis (SVAS) can be inherited as an autosomal-dominant trait. Manifestations most often involve the ascending aorta, but other large elastic vessels, including the pulmonary, coronary, and carotid arteries can be affected. All of these vascular problems occur in the Williams syndrome, which also includes neonatal hypercalcemia, elfin facies, and mental retardation. Recently, linkage analysis using random DNA probes established a locus for SVAS at chromosome 7q11 in selected families (31). The likely importance of this region was reinforced by detecting a chromosomal rearrangement at this site in one patient. Because the gene for tropoelastin (ELN) was known to map to this region, it became a candidate for the cause of SVAS. In fact, the translocation breakpoint interrupts ELN (17). The reason why a defect in tropoelastin would cause isolated vascular pathology, leaving other elastic tissues apparently unaltered, remains to be elucidated. The described rearrangement would be expected to result in decreased RNA from the mutant allele and hence little if any mutant peptide. If wild-type tropoelastic monomers are allowed to associate normally, perhaps only the elastic tissues that are exposed to extreme mechanical stress, like the aortic root, will express this molecular defect at the clinical level. Such issues will only be resolved after the identification of additional mutations associated with these vascular defects.

THE LONG QT SYNDROME   The long QT (Ward-Romano) syndrome is characterized by autosomal-dominant inheritance of a prolonged QT interval and predisposition to ventricular arrhythmia and sudden death. Prolongation of the QT interval can be mild, overlapping with the normal range, or intermittent, both of which make clinical detection of heterozygotes problematic. Ventricular arrhythmia can be managed with medication or an implanted defibrillator. Inability to assess presymptomatic risk accurately has been a major limitation to optimal medical care.

Using a comprehensive panel of DNA markers, Keating, Leppert, and co-investigators established linkage between a locus on the short arm of chromosome 11 and the long QT syndrome (56, 57). Specifically, polymorphic alleles of the Harvey ras-1 gene (HRAS1), a proto-oncogene, showed linkage at no recombination and lod score of 16.4 in a single large kindred. Subsequent analysis of six additional and unrelated families showed consistent linkage to this locus at 11p15.5 (57), but genetic heterogeneity in this disorder is suggested by absence of linkage in some families (59). No mutation in HRAS1 or any other sequence in an affected patient has yet been detected, so the actual defect must be approached by positional cloning.

FAMILIAL HYPERTROPHIC CARDIOMYOPATHY   This disorder (FHC) is a common form of heritable heart disease and can present with primary asymmetric thickening of the ventricular myocardium, heart failure, arrhythmia or sudden death. The left ventricle and ventricular septum are disproportionately, albeit variably, affected. Cellular pathology shows a defect in myocardiocyte growth and hypertrophy with myocyte disorganization and enlargement, myocardial scarring, and abnormalities of small caliber intramural coronary arteries, which serve as histologic hallmarks of disease.

Most families with multiple relatives with FHC show autosomal-dominant inheritance. A large number of patients have no affected relative and appear to be sporadic cases. The age of onset, progression, and outcome in heterozygotes vary widely, both among and within families. In the absence of a sensitive or specific clinical or histologic marker with prognostic significance (32), it was hoped that delineation of the molecular basis for HCM would allow for presymptomatic diagnosis and would guide risk assessment and intervention in this complex population of patients.

Initially, the Seidmans and their colleagues used linkage analysis to position the disease locus in large multiplex families that segregated this disorder. Linkage was established between anonymous DNA marker D14S26 and the disease phenotype in a subset of families at no recombination (52), thereby mapping the defective gene in these families to 14q11–12. Furthermore, linkage analysis demonstrated that about half of families from the United States and the United Kingdom segregated with 14q1 markers; in the remaining half, this locus could be excluded (lod score less than or equal to −2.0) (30, 60, 112).

In order to determine the precise genetic defect in the families showing linkage to 14q1 markers, a candidate gene approach was first considered. Because patients with FHC show isolated cardiac pathology, the obvious goal was to determine whether any genes that had been mapped near the disease locus showed a cardiac-specific pattern of expression. The genes encoding the two isoforms of cardiac myosin heavy chain, α and β, were clear suspects. A causal association between the MYHCB gene, which produces the predominant isoform in adult ventricular myocardium, and FHC was strongly supported by the detection of mutations that segregated with the disease phenotype in families where linkage had previously been established. A variety of missense mutations have been identified (37, 71, 110, 116, 123, 124). Already genotype-phenotype correlations are emerging. First, all missense mutations are located in the head or head-rod junction region of the myosin heavy chain (123). None substitute head residues critical to ATPase activity, actin binding, or myosin light-chain binding (123); perturbation of these functions, or mutations occurring in the rod region may be associated with a different phenotype or may be incompatible with life. Second, mutations that alter the charge of residues in the head region of βCMHC appear to be associated with a shorter life expectancy than more conservative substitutions (123). This influence on survival occurs despite no apparent difference in the distribution or severity of hypertrophy associated with the different classes of mutations. It seems likely that the change of charge in the head domain will alter local, and perhaps distant, polypeptide structure, which may result in faulty chain aggregations and hence expression of the disease phenotype. Such a dominant-negative model, where mutant peptides disrupt the function of wild-type counterparts, would account for autosomal-dominant inheritance of FHC.

Illegitimate transcription of the MYHCB locus produces β-myosin heavy chain mRNA in circulating blood lymphocytes and raises the prospects for a simple and efficient method for preclinical DNA diagnosis in selected families (103). The screening of cDNA, reverse-transcribed from mRNA, for new mutations is now possible without the need for invasive cardiac biopsy. In addition, when a family's mutation is known, lymphocyte mRNA can be assayed to diagnose presymptomatic family members. Linkage analyses have now defined three additional loci for FHC, thereby accounting for disease in virtually all families tested. Delineation of the defective genes, additional genotype-phenotype correlations, expression of mutant proteins (87), transgenic animals, and structure-function studies will define the molecular basis for the variable natural history and prognosis of this common heritable disorder of cardiac growth and development (110).

Expression of Mutations

A powerful proof of etiology is obtained when expression of a putative mutation either in vitro or in transgenic mice, produces the phenotype found in the affected patients. For most metabolic disorders, in vitro expression of the mutant cDNA permits sufficient quantitative and qualitative assessment of the mutant enzyme, peptide hormone, receptor, or so forth. For developmental defects and highly pleiotropic Mendelian conditions, however, cellular assays are usually inadequate to assess whether the mutation is capable of producing a complex phenotype. Here insertion of the mutation into fertilized eggs or embryonic stem cells of mice has become a standard approach. The following example illustrates in vitro expression, while animal models are discussed below.

LIPOPROTEIN LIPASE DEFICIENCY   Hayden and co-workers have described more than two-dozen mutations in the lipoprotein lipase (LPL) gene, which maps to 8p22, all of which cause hypertriglyceridemia in a pattern known as familial hyperchylomicronemia (46). Recently they studied a female patient who had marked variability in plasma triglycerides in association with pregnancy (68). She was found to be homozygous for a point mutation, Ser172Cys, in one exon of the LPL gene. This mutation was introduced into the wild-type LPL cDNA, the mutant cDNA was transfected into a cell line maintained in vitro, and cells that incorporated the human LPL cDNA were selected for further culture. The cells transfected with the mutant LPL gene secreted less LPL protein into the medium, and what was produced had a reduced enzymatic activity. However, this particular mutation did not abolish completely LPL activity in either the patient or the in vitro system, which provided the likely explanation for her milder phenotype, albeit one prone to worsening during times of metabolic stress.

The Unified Approach

The foregoing examples illustrate that the etiology of many disorders has been solved by one or another approach. But determining the cause of some was difficult enough that a coalition of distinct approaches proved necessary.

The Marfan syndrome was the first to be solved by a number of streams of evidence converging on the same idea at roughly the same time.

THE MARFAN SYNDROME   The Marfan syndrome is an autosomal-dominant disorder of connective tissue characterized by marked variability in the age of onset, tissue distribution, and severity of manifestations. Cardinal features involve the eye (lens dislocation, myopia), skeleton (dolichostenomelia, joint laxity, chest and spine deformity), and cardiovascular system (aortic root dilatation and dissection, mitral valve prolapse, mitral and aortic valve regurgitation) (97). A subset of patients show ventricular impairment out of proportion to valvular disease, suggestive of a primary cardiomyopathy. Other features include spontaneous pneumothorax, striae distensae, dural ectasia, and learning disability with or without hyperactivity. Involvement of the cardiovascular system is the leading cause of functional morbidity and early mortality in Marfan syndrome. Features include dilatation of the aortic root, often progressing to dissection, aortic regurgitation, mitral valve prolapse, mitral regurgitation, and pulmonary artery dilatation (97).

The search for the molecular basis of Marfan syndrome was long and arduous, and epitomizes both the classical and the molecular genetic approaches to gene identification. Progress began with the classification of Marfan syndrome as a distinct clinical entity, a founding member of the heritable disorders of connective tissue. Commencing in the 1950's, McKusick and colleagues undertook large clinical studies of Marfan syndrome thereby describing natural history, pleiotropy, clinical variability, and inheritance of the phenotype. These early observations suggested that a gene encoding a structural component of connective tissue, prone to new mutation, and expressed in many and diverse tissues was the site of defect.

The classical approach   Histologic and biochemical studies variously suggested abnormalities in tropoelastin, elastin cross-linking, collagen, collagen cross-linking, and hyaluronic acid metabolism, but none of the presumptive defects could be proven conclusively (reviewed in 97). The first defect shown to be consistent in a large number of patients was described by Hollister and colleagues who focused on the extracellular microfibril (39, 49). This 10–12 nm structure is found clustered around the amorphous core of maturing elastic fibers and has been proposed to play a regulatory role in the deposition and organization of newly added tropoelastin molecules. Moreover, the fibrillin-containing microfibril is an abundant component of the many tissues altered in the Marfan phenotype including vascular wall, skin, cartilage and tendon, suspensory ligament of the ocular lens, and alveolar wall (104). The abundance of fibrillin in fibroblast culture and in tissues from patients with Marfan syndrome and controls were assessed with fluorescent-labeled monoclonal antibodies. Hollister and co-workers found quantitative and qualitative abnormalities in the majority of patient samples tested, and these defects segregated with the disease phenotype within families (39, 49). Specificity of the assay was not complete, however, as evidence by the erroneous assignment of affected status to a subset of patients with other connective tissue disorders including pseudoxanthoma elasticum, homocystinuria, ectodermal dysplasia, and cutis laxa. Next, pulse-chase analysis of fibrillin synthesis and processing by cultured dermal fibroblasts was examined (74). Normal samples demonstrated that the 350-kd fibrillin is secreted in monomeric form within 4 hr of synthesis and is processed into a smaller (320 kd) form prior to incorporation into the extracellular matrix. Patient samples showed a spectrum of abnormalities including reduced synthesis (27% of patients), delayed secretion (27%), or defective matrix (31%). Approximately 15% of samples were indistinguishable from controls.

Linkage analysis   The ability to test hypotheses generated by biochemistry and cytochemistry became a reality when the genes for many connective tissue components were cloned and characterized and with the advent of linkage analysis using RFLPs. With these methods, a large group of independent investigators excluded over 80% of the human genome as the site of defect in Marfan syndrome (4). Polymorphic variations in both anonymous DNA fragments and in multiple candidate genes, including those encoding fibronectin, tropoelastin, and multiple procollagens, were excluded.

Linkage between anonymous markers on the long arm of chromosome 15 and the Marfan phenotype was achieved in 1990 (53). Further study placed the disease locus in the close physical proximity to anonymous marker D15S1 at 15q15–21.3 and demonstrated the apparent absence of genetic heterogeneity in families from diverse ethnic backgrounds (23, 55, 106, 117).

Because fibrillin and other potential components of the microfibril were leading candidates for the cause of Marfan syndrome, there was intense interest to map the gene for fibrillin. Sakai and colleagues succeeded in cloning and sequencing approximately 6.9 kb of the 10 kb fibrillin coding sequence (73). This cDNA was largely composed of tandemly repeated epidermal growth-factor (EGF)-like domains with a second cysteine-rich domain with homology to transforming growth factor β-1 binding protein occurring at irregular intervals. Both domains have been implicated in intramolecular and intermolecular interactions.

We used fibrillin cDNA clones to identify an intragenic polymorphism and performed linkage analysis in large families with Marfan syndrome (21). No recombination was seen between the fibrillin gene and the Marfan

.

phenotype or anonymous marker D15S1. Simultaneously, using in situ hybridization, Magenis and colleagues mapped the fibrillin gene to 15q21.1 (69). In addition, a team led by Lee & Ramirez independently cloned a portion of two distinct fibrillin genes, one on chromosome 15 (FBN1) and the other on chromosome 5 (FBN2) (66). These genes proved to be linked to Marfan syndrome and congenital contractural arachnodactyly, a related phenotype without cardiovascular involvement, respectively (66).

Mutation detection   Substantial proof of causality between fibrillin gene defects and Marfan syndrome came with identification of a recurrent de novo missense mutation in the fibrillin gene in two unrelated patients with sporadic and infantile onset of classic and severe disease (21). This mutation substituted proline for arginine at codon 239 within one of the EGF-like repeats in the partially characterized FBN1 cDNA. The insertion of proline usually induces protein bending and can alter local and remote protein conformation.

Correlations of phenotype with genotype   By mid 1993, a total of 13 fibrillin (FBN1) mutations in patients with Marfan syndrome have been reported (21, 22, 24–26, 48, 54, 98). When genotype is correlated with clinical phenotype, a number of patterns emerge. First, with the exception of the first mutation, all others have been family-specific. This probably reflects the high rate of sporadic mutation in this gene and an impairment in reproductive fitness in Marfan syndrome due to early morbidity and mortality. Second, a wide range of phenotypic severity occurs among family members carrying the identical mutant allele. In one family studied, the only two members with identical manifestations were monozygotic twins (24). These data suggest the presence of tissue-specific genetic modifiers to the phenotypic expression of mutant FBN1 alleles.

All missense mutations are associated with moderate or severe disease phenotypes, and most occur at residues with putative roles in calcium binding to EGF-like domains (15, 22, 43, 111), an event that may be necessary to stabilize secondary structure, for protein-protein interactions, and to resist the activity of proteases. The study of other proteins containing EGF-like domains has demonstrated that specific amino acids are crucial to this process. These include the six highly conserved and predictably spaced cysteine residues (C), negatively charged aspartic acid (D), and glutamic acid (E) residues at the amino terminus, and an asparagine (N) or aspartic acid (D) residue and an aromatic residue (F or Y) in the context of the subsequence CXD/NXXXXF/YXCXC (X is any amino acid). This consensus subsequence promotes the β-hydroxylation of N or D at internal position

3. The FBN1 gene has now nearly been characterized in entirety, and 43 EGF-like domains that satisfy this calcium-binding consensus have been identified (16, 85). In addition, Corson, Sakai, and colleagues have demonstrated high affinity calcium binding to fibrillin (16). Of the missense mutations reported to date, all occur within EGF-like domains, 4 of 8 substitute cysteine residues, 7 of 8 occur within the β-hydroxylation consensus sequence, 2 of 8 substitute the N residue that is proposed to undergo β-hydroxylation, and 1 substitutes a highly conserved D residue at the amino terminus. These data argue strongly that calcium binding to EGF-like domains is vital to normal fibrillin structure and function and that perturbation of this process is a common pathogenetic mechanism in Marfan syndrome.

Figure 2 displays the domain organization of the cDNA for FBN1. Interestingly, the position of mutations along the 5′ to 3′ expanse of the gene does not correlate with phenotypic severity. This is in contrast to type I collagen defects causing osteogenesis imperfect, where mutations in the region that encodes the carboxy terminal regions of the triple helical domain are associated with the most severe disease.

Three mutations have been identified that create premature signals for the termination of translation of messenger RNA (mRNA) and are associated with severely reduced amounts of mutant allele transcript (22, 26). The association between nonsense or frameshift mutations that creates premature stop codons prior to the penultimate exon and impairs RNA stability and/or trafficking is well documented. Two patients with mutant transcript levels of 16 and 25% of the amount observed from the wild-type allele, respectively, have classic and severe disease (22, 26). In striking contrast, a patient with a frameshift mutation and only 6% mutant transcript has much milder disease phenotype, in the category of the MASS phenotype (22, 38). These data demonstrate that a deficiency of wild-type transcript and a predicted deficiency of wild-type monomer are not sufficient for expression

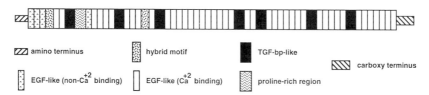

Figure 2   Domain organization of the FBN1 cDNA. Note that 43 EGF-like domains satisfy the consensus for Ca^{2+} binding. Abbreviations: EGF-like = epidermal growth factor-like motif; TGF-bp-lole = transforming growth factor β1-binding protein-like motif (adapted from references 16, 85).

of classic Marfan syndrome. This observation lends support to a dominant-negative model of molecular pathogenesis (Figure 1).

The dominant-negative model implies that the presence of an abnormal peptide (change in function), in contrast to a deficiency of wild-type protein (loss of function), is the primary determinant of phenotypic expression (47). The abnormal peptide can interfere with multimer assembly or impair interactions between the normal protein and receptors or trafficking machinery. The fact that normal microfibrillar assembly requires disulfide bond-mediated aggregation of fibrillin monomers makes this an attractive pathogenic mechanism for Marfan syndrome (104). In light of this model, the mild disease of the patient with only 6% mutant transcript can be resolved in two ways. Either the abnormal (truncated) predicted peptide product from the mutant allele can no longer efficiently interact with the normal gene product in multimer formation, or the reduction in level of transcript from the mutant allele predicts a preponderance of normal fibrillin monomer. Both possibilities predict the formation of structurally and functionally intact microfibrils and hence mild manifestations of disease.

The fact that two patients with mutant transcript levels of 16 and 25%, respectively, have severe disease suggests that some critical threshold of mutant transcript and monomer, between 6 and 16% of wild-type levels, is necessary for expression of classic disease (22, 26). Genetic background and the character and stability of mutant peptides must be considered. Finally, one patient with deletion of an extremely 5' exon and a premature termination codon shortly downstream has severe disease (22). This suggests that the amino terminus, in isolation, can participate in a dominant-negative fashion with wild-type monomer and is in keeping with the head-to-tail model for fibrillin monomer assembly into microfibrils (104).

Future directions   Substantiation of the dominant-negative model awaits application of transfection and/or transgenic technologies that mimic the complexity of the human system. Expression of truncated peptides, encoded by the extreme 5' end of the fibrillin gene, might be sufficient for the creation of an animal model. Successful creation of a transgenic animal expressing the Marfan phenotype will allow for testing of traditional or genetic interventions. Verification of a dominant-negative pathogenic mechanism would offer selective knock out of the mutant allele as a potential strategy for genetic intervention, perhaps using an antisense approach. The ideal animal model would mimic the human pattern of developmental and tissue-specific expression of fibrillin, would be suitable to assess different surgical approaches, and would be of sufficient size to allow for the application of established catheter-based technologies to deliver therapeutic gene constructs to the cardiovascular system (35, 90).

Animal Models

Three types of animal models are in common use. The first consists of those phenotypically abnormal animals that are detected, bred to insure that the phenotype is hereditary and can be perpetuated, and then investigated by genetic and molecular approaches. One example is the only model of Marfan syndrome, which arose spontaneously in limousin cattle (3). Recent biochemical and molecular genetic work by Potter and colleagues strongly points to a defect in bovine fibrillin as the cause, thereby solidifying the importance of this model to the human disease (91). Unfortunately, bovine models have a number of disadvantages (long generation time, small litters, the size of facilities needed) that limit their utility. Another example, discovered several decades ago by alert animal care workers at the Jackson Laboratory, is the *iv* mouse strain, which has a defect in situs determination (50, 65, 114). This mutation, which has been mapped but not fully characterized (6), abolishes the usual control of situs determination, so that organ rotation is random; one-half of *iv/iv* mice have situs solitus and one-half have situs inversus. This mutation, then, is an example of an inborn error of developmental homeostasis with relevance to a human disease. In Kartegener syndrome, control of situs is also abolished (80); the role of defects in cilia and their components needs to be elucidated (1, 78).

The baseline mutation rate in laboratory animals can be increased by a number of methods. One that has proven extremely, if serendipitously, useful is insertional mutagenesis. A piece of DNA is randomly inserted into the mouse genome by one of the standard transgenic techniques. In rare instances, the foreign DNA will disrupt a native gene and produce a phenotype, either directly or after breeding to homozygosity. The mutant obtained may not even be the expected result, if the investigator was really attempting to have the transgenic animal express the foreign DNA. For example, Yokoyama and colleagues (128) were attempting to produce various pigmentary defects, but generated a mouse mutant (*inv*) that always has situs inversus. Thus the phenotype of the *inv/inv* mouse, and possibly the locus, are different from the *in/in* model. Molecular analysis of these two models will help to solve one of the long-standing problems in developmental biology: how asymmetry is specified and maintained.

In most transgenic models, the goal is either to insert and express a specific mutation or to abolish expression of an endogenous gene. The latter approach, commonly called knock out, generally involves homologous recombination of foreign DNA with the gene of interest, to create a heterozygote for a loss-of-function allele, and then breed the heterozygotes to generate homozygotes who completely lack the functional sequence. This approach does not always produce a phenotype analogous to humans with the same gene mutated, and there is a requirement for careful clinical, biochemical, and pathological assessment of mutants who begin life with their genomes understood in exquisite detail.

Animals created by transgenic and homologous recombination techniques have proven useful in the study of a variety of human Mendelian disorders and increasingly are shedding light on complex, polygenic traits, as described by J Breslow and by M Paul et al in this volume.

CLINICAL APPLICATIONS

When a specific gene is known to be the cause of a disorder, analysis of mutations can be helpful in validating a diagnosis in a given patient, proving that the mutation arose de novo or, alternatively, is present in a parent, screening other relatives who are at risk and, in some cases, providing counseling about prognosis. In addition, population studies can be done to track specific mutations [geographic epidemiology (75)] and suggest when mutations arose. In a few cases, population screening for disease-producing alleles is being conducted using DNA-based screening; common mutations at the CFTR locus (that produce cystic fibrosis) and the β-globin locus (for sickle cell disease) are currently implemented in some regions, and screening for mutations at breast cancer susceptibility genes on chromosome 17 and elsewhere is likely to be set up as soon as the genes are characterized. Using DNA technology in diagnosing individual cases or in population screening has a major requirement, which has not often been met. Either the entire coding and regulatory sequences need to be studied in every case, or a relatively small number of mutations need to cause the preponderance of the cases. The former approach is feasible for diagnosing the vast majority of β-thalassemia (the entire gene and most 5' and 3' regulatory sequences occupy only about 5 kb of DNA), whereas with the CFTR gene, it is feasible now to screen for only the 6–10 most common mutations, which depending on the ethnic background of the population, will detect 85–95% of heterozygotes (75).

Some molecular advances find prompt application. For example, comprehensive genotype and phenotype assessment of a single large kindred with the long QT syndrome revealed that the duration of the QT interval was neither a sensitive nor specific marker of heterozygosity. While the mean corrected QT (QT_c) interval was 0.49 in gene carriers and 0.42 in noncarriers, the range for one group showed substantial overlap with the other (0.41 to 0.59 vs 0.38 to 0.47, respectively) (119). In fact, no diagnostic criterion based solely upon the QT_c could be established that did not result in either false negative or false positive classification. Therefore, linkage analysis quickly proved to be the most reliable method of risk assessment in this family, and would be useful in any informative family where cosegregation between marker alleles and the disease phenotype can be established.

ACKNOWLEDGMENTS

Supported by grants from the National Institutes of Health (RR00722, AR41135, HL02815, and HL35877), the National Marfan Foundation, and the Smilow Family Foundation.

Literature Cited

1. Aitken J. 1991. A clue to Kartagener's. *Nature* 353:306
2. Anneren G, Gustafsson J, Sunnegardh J. 1989. DiGeorge syndrome in a child with partial monosomy of chromosome 22. *Uppsala J. Med. Sci.* 94:47–53
3. Besser TE, Potter KA, Bryan GM, Knowlen GG. 1990. An animal model for the Marfan syndrome. *Am. J. Med. Genet.* 37:159–65
4. Blanton SH, Sarfarazi M, Eiberg H, Degroote J, Farndon PA, et al. 1990. An exclusion map of Marfan syndrome. *J. Med. Genet.* 27:73–77
5. Brown MD, Voljavec AS, Lott MT, MacDonald I, Wallace DC. 1992. Leber's hereditary optic neuropathy: a model for mitochondrial neurodegenerative diseases. *FASEB J.* 6:2791–99
6. Brueckner M, D'Eustachio P, Horwich AL. 1989. Linkage mapping of a mouse gene, *iv*, that controls left-right asymmetry of the heart and viscera. *Proc. Natl. Acad. Sci. USA* 86:5035–38
7. Brunner HG, Jansen G, Nillesen W, Nelen MR, Christine EM, et al. 1993. Brief report: Reverse mutation in myotonic dystrophy. *N. Engl. J. Med.* 328:476–80
8. Burke W, Motulsky AG. 1992. Molecular genetics of hypertension. See Ref 67, pp. 228–236
9. Carey AH, Kelly D, Halford S, Wadey R, Wilson D, et al. 1992. Molecular genetic study of the frequency of monosomy 22q11 in DiGeorge syndrome. *Am. J. Hum. Genet.* 51:964–70
10. Carey AH, Roach S, Williamson R, Dumanski JP, Nordenskjold M, et al. 1990. Localization of 27 DNA markers to the region of human chromosome 22q11-pter deleted in patients with DiGeorge syndrome and duplicated in the der22 syndrome. *Genomics* 7:299–306
11. Cattanach BM, Kirk M. 1985. Differential activity of maternally and paternally derived chromosome regions in mice. *Nature* 315:496–98
12. Chisaka O, Capecchi M. 1991. Regionally restricted developmental defects resulting from targeted disruption of the mouse homeobox gene *hox*-1.5. *Nature* 350:473–79
13. Clarke LA, Eistein E, Sole MJ, Hayden MR. 1992. Genomic imprinting in a family with dominant hypertrophic cardiomyopathy. *Am. J. Hum. Genet.* 51:A93 (Abstr.)
14. Conlon RA, Rossant J. 1992. Exogenous retinoic acid rapidly induces anterior ectopic expression of murine *Hox*-2 genes in vivo. *Development* 116:357–68
15. Cooke RM, Wilkinson AJ, Baron M, Pastore A, Tappin MJ, et al. 1987. The solution structure of human epidermal growth factor. *Nature* 327:339–41
16. Corson GM, Chalberg SC, Dietz HC, Charbonneau N, Sakai LY. 1993. Fibrillin binds calcium and is encoded by cDNAs that reveal a multidomain structure and alternatively spliced exons at the 5' end. *Genomics* 17:476–84
17. Curran ME, Atkinson DL, Ewart AK, Morris CA, Leppert MF, Keating MT. 1993. The elastin gene is disrupted by a translocation associated with supravalvular aortic stenosis. *Cell* 73:159–68
18. Dallapiccola B, Marino B, Giannotti A, Valorani G. 1989. DiGeorge anomaly associated with partial deletion of chromosome 22. Report of a case with X/22 translocation and review of the literature. *Ann. Genet.* 32:92–96
19. de la Chapelle A, Herva R, Koivisto M, Aula O. 1981. A deletion in chromosome 22 can cause diGeorge syndrome. *Hum. Genet.* 57:253–56

20. Desmaze C, Scambler P, Prieur M, Halford S, Sidi D, et al. 1993. Confirmation that the velo-cardio-facial syndrome is associated with haplo-insufficiency of genes at chromosome 22q11. *Am. J. Med. Genet.* 45:308–12

21. Dietz HC, Cutting GR, Pyeritz RE, Maslen CL, Sakai LY, et al. 1991. Marfan syndrome caused by a recurrent de novo missense mutation in the fibrillin gene. *Nature* 352:337–39

22. Dietz HC, McIntosh I, Sakai LY, Corson GM, Chalberg SC, et al. 1993. Four novel FBN1 mutations: significance for mutant transcript level and EGF-like domain calcium binding in the pathogenesis of Marfan syndrome. *Genomics.* 17:468–75

23. Dietz HC, Pyeritz RE, Hall BD, Cadle RG, Hamosh A, et al. 1991. The Marfan syndrome locus: confirmation of assignment to chromosome 15 and identification of tightly linked markers at 15q15-q21.3. *Genomics* 9: 355–61

24. Dietz HC, Pyeritz RE, Puffenberger EG, Kendzior RJ Jr, Corson GM, et al. 1992. Marfan phenotype variability in a family segregating a missense mutation in the epidermal growth factor-like motif of the fibrillin gene. *J. Clin. Invest.* 89:1674–80

25. Dietz HC, Saraiva J, Pyeritz RE, Cutting GR, Francomano CA. 1992. Clustering of fibrillin (FBN1) missense mutations in Marfan syndrome patients at cysteine residues in EGF-like domains. *Hum. Mutat.* 1:366–74

26. Dietz HC, Valle D, Francomano CA, Kendzior RJ Jr, Pyeritz RE, Cutting GR. 1993. The skipping of constitutive exons in vivo induced by nonsense mutations. *Science* 259:680–83

27. Driscoll DA, Budarf ML, Emanuel BS. 1992. A genetic etiology for DiGeorge syndrome: consistent deletions and microdeletions of 22q11. *Am. J. Hum. Genet.* 50:924–33

28. Driscoll DA, Spinner NB, Budarf ML, McDonald-McGinn DM, Zackai EH, et al. 1992. Deletions and microdeletions of 22q11 in velo-cardio-facial syndrome. *Am. J. Med. Genet.* 44:261–68

29. Engel E, Delozier-Blanchet CD. 1991. Uniparental disomy, isodisomy, and imprinting: probable effects in man and strategies for their detection. *Am. J. Med. Genet.* 40:432–39

30. Epstein ND, Fananapazir L, Lin HJ, Mulvihill J, White R, et al. 1992. Evidence of genetic heterogeneity in five kindreds with familial hypertrophic

cardiomyopathy. *Circulation* 85:635–47

31. Ewart AK, Morris CA, Ensing GJ, Loker J, Moore C, et al. 1993. A human vascular disorder, supravalvular aortic stenosis, maps to chromosome 7. *Proc. Natl. Acad. Sci. USA* 90: 3226–30

32. Fananapazir L, Chang AC, Epstein SE, McAreavey D. 1992. Prognostic determinants in hypertrophic cardiomyopathy: prospective evaluation of a therapeutic strategy based on clinical, holter, hemodynamic, and electrophysical findings. *Circulation* 86:730–40

33. Fibison WJ, Budarf M, McDermid H, Greenberg F, Emanuel BS. 1990. Molecular studies of DiGeorge syndrome. *Am. J. Hum. Genet.* 46:888–95

34. Field LJ. 1993. Transgenic mice in cardiovascular research. *Annu. Rev. Physiol.* 55:97–114

35. Flugelman MY, Jaklitsch MT, Newman KD, Casscells W, Bratthauer GL, Dichek DA 1992. Low level in vivo gene transfer into the arterial wall through a perforated balloon catheter. *Circulation* 85:1110–17

36. Fu Y-H, Pizzoti A, Fenwick RG Jr, King J, Rajnarayan S, et al. 1992. An unstable triplet repeat in a gene related to myotonic muscular dystrophy. *Science* 255:1256–58

37. Geisterfer-Lowrance AA, Kass S, Tanigawa G, Vosberg HP, McKenna W, et al. 1990. A molecular basis for familial hypertrophic cardiomyopathy: a beta cardiac myosin heavy chain gene missense mutation. *Cell* 62:999–1006

38. Glesby MJ, Pyeritz RE. 1989. Association of mitral valve prolapse and systemic abnormalities of connective tissue: a phenotypic continuum. *J. Am. Med. Assoc.* 262:523–28

39. Godfrey M, Menashe V, Weleber RH, Koler RD, Bigley RH, et al. 1990. Cosegregation of elastin-associated microfibrillar abnormalities with the Marfan phenotype in families. *Am. J. Hum. Genet.* 46:652–60

40. Groot PC, Moen CJA, Dietrich W, Stoye JP, Lander ES, Demant P. 1992. The recombinant congenic strains for analysis of multigenic traits: genetic composition. *FASEB J.* 6:2826–35

41. Hall JG. 1990. Genomic imprinting: review and relevance to human diseases. *Am. J. Hum. Genet.* 46:857–73

42. Hanahan D. 1989. Transgenic mice as probes into complex systems. *Science* 246:1265–75

43. Handford PA, Mayhew M, Baron M,

Winship PR, Campbell ID, Brownlee GG. 1991. Key residues involved in calcium binding motifs in EGF-like domains. *Nature* 351:164–67

44. Harley HG, Brook JD, Rundle SA, Crow S, Reardon W, et al. 1992. Expansion of an unstable DNA region and phenotypic variation in myotonic dystrophy. *Nature* 355:545–46

45. Harper PS, Harley HG, Reardon W, Shaw DJ. 1992. Anticipation in myotonic dystrophy: new light on an old problem. *Am. J. Hum. Genet.* 51:10–16

46. Hayden MR, Ma Y. 1992. Molecular genetics of human lipoprotein lipase deficiency. *Mol. Cell. Biochem.* 113:171–76

47. Herskowitz I. 1987. Functional inactivation of genes by dominant negative mutations. *Nature* 329:219–22

48. Hewett DR, Lynch JR, Smith R, Sykes BC. 1993. A novel fibrillin mutation in the Marfan syndrome which could disrupt calcium binding of the epidermal growth factor-like module. *Hum. Mol. Genet.* 2:475–77

49. Hollister DW, Godfrey M, Sakai LY, Pyeritz RE. 1990. Immunohistologic abnormalities of the microfibrillar-fiber system in the Marfan syndrome. *N. Engl. J. Med.* 323:152–59

50. Hummel KP, Chapman DB. 1959. Visceral inversion and associated anomalies in the mouse. *J. Hered.* 50:9–13

51. Huntington Disease Collaborative Research Group. 1993. A novel gene containing a trinucleotide repeat that is expanded and unstable on Huntington's disease chromosomes. *Cell* 72:971–83

52. Jarcho JA, McKenna W, Pare JA, Solomon SD, Holcombe RF, et al. 1989. Mapping a gene for familial hypertrophic cardiomyopathy to chromosome 14q1. *N. Engl. J. Med.* 321:1372–78

53. Kainulainen K, Pulkkinen L, Savolainen A, Kaitila I, Peltonen L. 1990. Location on chromosome 15 of the gene defect causing Marfan syndrome. *N. Engl. J. Med.* 323:935–39

54. Kainulainen K, Sakai LY, Child A, Pope FM, Puhakka L, et al. 1992. Two mutations in Marfan syndrome resulting in truncated fibrillin polypeptides. *Proc. Natl. Acad. Sci. USA* 89:5917–21

55. Kainulainen K, Steinmann B, Collins F, Dietz HC, Francomano CA, et al. 1991. Marfan syndrome: no evidence for heterogeneity in different populations, and more precise mapping of the gene. *Am. J. Hum. Genet.* 49:662–67

56. Keating M, Atkinson D, Dunn C, Timothy K, Vincent GM, Leppert M. 1991. Linkage of a cardiac arrhythmia, the long QT syndrome, and the Harvey *RAS-1* gene. *Science* 252:704–6

57. Keating M, Dunn C, Atkinson D, Timothy K, Vincent GM, Leppert M. 1991. Consistent linkage of the long-QT syndrome to the Harvey *Ras-1* locus on chromosome 11. *Am. J. Hum. Genet.* 49:1335–39

58. Kelly D, Goldberg R, Wilson D, Lindsay E, Carey A, et al. 1993. Confirmation that the velo-cardio-facial syndrome is associated with haplo-insufficiency of genes at chromosome 22q11. *Am. J. Med. Genet.* 45:308–12

59. Kerem B, Benhorin J, Kalman YM, Medina A, Dyer TD, et al. 1992. Evidence for genetic heterogeneity in the long QT syndrome. *Am. J. Hum. Genet.* 51:A192 (Abstr.)

60. Ko Y-L, Lien W-P, Chen J-J, Wu C-W, Tang T-K, et al. 1992. No evidence for linkage of familial hypertrophic cardiomyopathy and chromosome 14q1 locus D14S26 in a Chinese family: evidence for genetic heterogeneity. *Hum. Genet.* 89:597–601

61. Korenberg JR. 1991. Down syndrome phenotypic mapping. *Prog. Clin. Biol. Res.* 373:43–52

62. Korenberg JR, Bradley C, Disteche CM. 1992. Down syndrome: molecular mapping of the congenital heart disease and duodenal stenosis. *Am. J. Hum. Genet.* 50:294–302

63. Lammer EJ, Chen DT, Hoar RM, Agnish ND, Benke PJ, et al. 1985. Retinoic acid embryopathy. *N. Engl. J. Med.* 313:837–41

64. Lander ES, Botstein D. 1989. Mapping Mendelian factors underlying quantitative traits using RFLP linkage maps. *Genetics* 121:185–99

65. Layton WM Jr. 1976. Random determination of a developmental process: reversal of normal visceral asymmetry in the mouse. *J. Hered.* 67:336–38

66. Lee B, Godfrey M, Vitale E, Hori H, Mattei M-G, et al. 1991. Linkage of Marfan syndrome and a phenotypically related disorder to two different fibrillin genes. *N. Engl. J. Med.* 352:330–34

67. Lusis AJ, Rotter JI, Sparkes RS eds. 1992. *Molecular Genetics of Coronary Artery Disease. Candidate Genes and Processes in Atherosclerosis.* Monogr. Hum. Genet. Basel: Karger

68. Ma Y, Liu M-S, Ginzinger D, Frohlich J, Brunzell JD, Hayden MR. 1993.

Gene-environment interaction in the conversion of a mild-to-severe phenotype in a patient homozygous for a Ser172→Cys mutation in the lipoprotein lipase gene. *J. Clin. Invest.* 91: 1953–58

69. Magenis RE, Maslen CL, Smith L, Allen L, Sakai LY. 1991. Localization of the fibrillin gene to chromosome 15, band 15q21.1. *Genomics* 11:346–51

70. Magnani I, Larizza L, Doneda L, Weitnauer L, Rizzi R, Di Lernia R. 1989. Malformation syndrome with t(2;22) in a cancer family with chromosome instability [published erratum appears in *Cancer Genet. Cytogenet.* 1990 44:following 141]. *Cancer Genet. Cytogenet.* 38:223–27

71. Marian AJ, Yu Q-T, Mares A Jr, Hill R, Roberts R, Perryman MB. 1992. Detection of a new mutation in the β-myosin heavy chain gene in an individual with hypertrophic cardiomyopathy. *J. Clin. Invest.* 90:2156–65

72. Mascarello JT, Bastian JF, Jones MC. 1989. Interstitial deletion of chromosome 22 in a patient with the DiGeorge malformation sequence. *Am. J. Med. Genet.* 32:112–14

73. Maslen CL, Corson GM, Maddox BK, Glanville RW, Sakai LY. 1991. Partial sequence for a candidate gene for the Marfan syndrome. *Nature* 352:334–37

74. McGookey Milewicz D, Pyeritz RE, Crawford ES, Byers PH. 1991. Marfan syndrome: defective synthesis, secretion, and extracellular matrix formation of fibrillin by cultured dermal fibroblasts. *J. Clin. Invest.* 88:79–86

75. McIntosh I, Cutting GR. 1992. Cystic fibrosis transmembrane conductance regulator and the etiology and pathogenesis of cystic fibrosis. *FASEB J.* 6:2775–82

76. McKusick VA. 1992. *Mendelian Inheritance in Man.* Baltimore: Johns Hopkins Univ. Press. 10th ed.

77. Mehrabian M, Lusis, AJ. 1992. Molecular genetics of hypertension. See Ref. 67, pp. 363–418

78. Mierau GW, Agostini R, Beals TF, Carlen B, Dardick I, et al. 1992. The role of electron microscopy in evaluating ciliary dysfunction: report of a workshop. *Ultrastruct. Pathol.* 16:245–54

79. Monaco G, Pignata C, Rossi E, Mascellaro O, Cocozza S, Ciccimarra F. 1991. DiGeorge anomaly associated with 10p deletion. *Am. J. Med. Genet.* 39:215–16

80. Moreno A, Murphy EA. 1981. Inher-itance of Kartagener syndrome. *Am. J. Med. Genet.* 8:305–13

81. Murphy EA, Pyeritz RE. 1986. Homeostasis. VII. A conspectus. *Am. J. Med. Genet.* 24:735–51

82. Murphy EA, Rhee S, Pyeritz RE, Berger KR. 1991. Angular homeostasis VIII. Pursuit of a slowly moving target in a plane: relevance to lateralization in cardiovascular ontogeny. *Am. J. Med. Genet.* 41:362–70

83. Nukina S, Nishimura Y, Kinugasa A, Sawada T, Hamaoka K, et al. 1989. A case of incomplete DiGeorge syndrome associated with partial monosomy 22q11.1 due to maternal 14;22 translocation. *Jpn. J. Hum. Genet.* 34:235–41

84. Obregon MG, Mingarelli R, Giannotti A, di Comite A, Spedicato FS, Dallapiccola B. 1992. Partial deletion 10p syndrome. Report of two patients. *Ann. Genet.* 35:101–4

85. Pereira L, D'Alessio M, Ramirez F, Lynch JR, Sykes B, et al. 1993. Genomic organization of the sequence coding for fibrillin, the defective gene product in Marfan syndrome. *Hum. Mol. Genet.* In press

86. Perrine SP, Ginder DG, Faller DV, Dover GH, Ikuta T, et al. 1993. A short-term trial of butyrate to stimulate fetal-globin-gene expression in the β-globin disorders. *N. Engl. J. Med.* 328:81–86

87. Perryman MB, Yu Q-T, Marian AJ, Mares A Jr, Czernuszewicz G, et al. 1992. Expression of a missense mutation in the messenger RNA for β-myosin heavy chain in myocardial tissue in hypertrophic cardiomyopathy. *J. Clin. Invest.* 90:271–77

88. Peters J, Münter K, Bader M, Hackenthal E, Mullins JJ, Ganten D. 1993. Increased adrenal renin in transgenic hypertensive rats, TGR(mREN2) 27 and its regulation by cAMP, angiotensin II, and calcium. *J. Clin. Invest.* 91:742–47

89. Pivnick EK, Wilroy RS, Summitt JB, Tucker B, Herrod HG, Tharapel AT. 1990. Adjacent-2 disjunction of a maternal t(9;22) leading to duplication 9pter-q22 and deficiency of 22pter-q11.2. *Am. J. Med. Genet.* 37:92–96

90. Plautz G, Nabel EG, Nabel GJ. 1991. Introduction of vascular smooth muscle cells expressing recombinant genes in vivo. *Circulation* 83:578–83

91. Potter KA, Hoffman Y, Sakai LY, Byers PH, Besser TE, Milewicz DM. 1993. Abnormal fibrillin metabolism

in bovine Marfan syndrome. *Am. J. Pathol.* 142:803–10

92. Prockop DJ. 1984. Osteogenesis imperfecta: phenotypic heterogeneity, protein suicide, short and long collagen. *Am. J. Hum. Genet.* 36:499–505

93. Pyeritz RE. 1989. Pleiotropy revisited: molecular explanations of a classic concept. *Am. J. Med. Genet.* 34:124–34

94. Pyeritz RE. 1991. Formal genetics in humans: Mendelian and nonMendelian inheritance. In *Genes, Brain and Behavior*, ed. PR McHugh, VA McKusick, pp. 47–73. New York: Raven

95. Pyeritz RE. 1992. A revolution in medicine like no other. *FASEB J.* 6:2761–66

96. Pyeritz RE. 1992. Genetics and cardiovascular disease. In *Heart Disease*, ed. E Braunwald pp. 1622–55. Philadelphia: Saunders

97. Pyeritz RE. 1993. The Marfan syndrome. In *Connective Tissue and Its Heritable Disorders: Molecular, Genetic and Medical Aspects*, ed. PM Royce, B Steinmann, pp. 437–68. New York: Wiley-Liss

98. Pyeritz RE, Francke U. 1993. The Second Int. Symp. Marfan Syndrome. *Am. J. Med. Genet.* 47:127–35

99. Pyeritz RE, Murphy EA. 1989. The genetics of congenital heart disease: perspectives and prospects. *J. Am. Col. Cardiol.* 13:1458–68

100. Remes AM, Peukhurinen KJ, Herva R, Majamaa K, Hassinen IE. 1993. Kearns-Sayre syndrome case presenting a mitochondrial DNA deletion with unusual direct repeats and a rudimentary RNAase mitochrondrial ribonucleotide processing target sequence. *Genomics* 16:256–58

101. Robin M, Ferguson-Smith A, Hart CP, Ruddle FH. 1986. Cognate homeobox loci mapped on homologous human and mouse chromosomes. *Proc. Natl. Acad. Sci. USA* 83:9104–8

102. Rodgers GP, Dover GJ, Uyesaka N, Noguchi CT, Schechter AN, Nienhuis AW. 1993. Augmentation by erythropoietin of the fetal-hemoglobin response to hydroxyurea in sickle cell disease. *N. Engl. J. Med.* 328:73–80

103. Rosenzweig A, Watkins H, Hwang D-S, Miri M, McKenna W, et al. 1991. Preclinical diagnosis of familial hypertrophic cardiomyopathy by genetic analysis of blood lymphocytes. *N. Engl. J. Med.* 325:1753–60

104. Sakai LY, Keene DR, Glanville, RW, Bächinger HP. 1991. Purification and partial characterization of fibrillin, a cysteine-rich structural component of connective tissue microfibrils. *J. Biol. Chem.* 266:14763–70

105. Sakuraba H, Eng CM, Desnick RJ, Bishop OF. 1992. Invariant exon skipping in the human α-galactosidase: A pre-mRNA. *Genomics* 12:643–50

106. Sarfarazi M, Tsipouras P, Del Mastro R, Kilpatrick M, Farndon P, et al. 1992. A linkage map of 10 loci flanking the Marfan locus on 15q: results of an international consortium study. *J. Med. Genet.* 29:75–80

107. Scambler PJ, Carey AH, Wyse RK, Roach S, Dumanski JP, et al. 1991. Microdeletions within 22q11 associated with sporadic and familial DiGeorge syndrome. *Genomics* 10:201–6

108. Scambler PJ, Kelly D, Lindsay E, Williamson R, Goldberg R, et al. 1992. Velo-cardio-facial syndrome associated with chromosome 22 deletions encompassing the DiGeorge locus. *Lancet* 339:1138–39

109. Searle AG, Peters J, Lyon MF, Hall JG, Evans EP, et al. 1989. Chromosome maps of man and mouse. IV. *Ann. Hum. Genet.* 53:89–140

110. Seidman, CE, Seidman JG. 1991. Mutations in cardiac myosin heavy chain genes cause familial hypertrophic cardiomyopathy. *Mol. Biol. Med.* 8:159–66

111. Selander-Sunnerhagen M, Ullner M, Persson E, Teleman O, Stenflo J, Drakenberg T. 1992. How an epidermal growth factor (EGF)-like domain binds calcium. *J. Biol. Chem.* 267:19642–49

112. Solomon SD, Jarcho JA, McKenna W, Geisterfer-Lowrance A, Germain R, et al. 1990. Familial hypertrophic cardiomyopathy is a genetically heterogeneous disease. *J. Clin. Invest.* 86:993–99

113. Sommer SS. 1992. Assessing the underlying pattern of human germline mutations: lessons from the factor IX gene. *FASEB J.* 6:2767–74

114. Sundberg JP, Collins RL. 1992. Animal models of human disease: situs inversus. *Comp. Pathol. Bull.* 24:2,6

115. Sutherland GR, Richards RI. 1992. Anticipation legitimized: unstable DNA to the rescue. *Am. J. Hum. Genet.* 51:7–9

116. Tanigawa G, Jarcho JA, Kass S, Solomon SD, Vosberg HP, et al. 1990. A molecular basis for familial hypertrophic cardiomyopathy: an alpha/beta cardiac myosin heavy chain hybrid gene. *Cell* 62:991–98

117. Tsipouras P, Sarfarazi M, Devi A, Weiffenbach B, Boxer M. 1991. Mar-

fan syndrome is closely linked to a marker on chromosome 15q15 to q21. *Proc. Natl. Acad. Sci. USA* 88:4486–88

118. Tulinius MG, Holme E, Kristiansson B, Larsson N-G, Oldfors A. 1991. Mitochondrial encephalomyopathies in childhood. I. Biochemical and morphologic investigations. *J. Pediatr.* 119:242–50

119. Vincent GM, Timothy KW, Leppert M, Keating M. 1992. The spectrum of symptoms and QT intervals in carriers of the gene for the long-QT syndrome. *N. Engl. J. Med.* 327:846–52

120. Vooijs M, Yu L-C, Tkachuk D, Pinkel D, Johnson D, Gray JW. 1993. Libraries for each human chromosome, constructed from sorter-enriched chromosomes by using linker-adaptor PCR. *Am. J. Hum. Genet.* 52:586–97

121. Wallace DC. 1992. Mitochondrial genetics: a paradigm for aging and degenerative diseases. *Science* 256:628–32

122. Warden CH, Daluiski A, Lusis AJ. 1992. Identification of new genes contributing to atherosclerosis: the mapping of genes contributing to complex disorders in animal models. See Ref 67, pp. 419–41

123. Watkins H, Rosenzweig A, Hwang D-S, Levi T, McKenna W, et al. 1992. Characteristics and prognostic implications of myosin missense mutations in familial hypertrophic cardio- myopathy. *N. Engl. J. Med.* 326: 1108–14

124. Watkins H, Thierfelder L, Hwang DS, McKenna W, Seidman JG, Seidman CE. 1992. Sporadic hypertrophic cardiomyopathy due to de novo myosin mutations. *J. Clin. Invest.* 90: 1666–71

125. Wilson DI, Cross IE, Goodship JA, Brown J, Scambler PJ, et al. 1992. A prospective cytogenetic study of 36 cases of DiGeorge syndrome. *Am. J. Hum. Genet.* 51:957–63

126. Wilson DI, Cross IE, Goodship JA, Coulthard S, Carey AH, et al. 1991. DiGeorge syndrome with isolated aortic coarctation and isolated ventricular septal defect in three sibs with a 22q11 deletion of maternal origin. *Brit. Heart J.* 66:308–12

127. Wilson DI, Goodship JA, Burn J, Cross IE, Scambler PJ. 1992. Deletions within chromosome 22q11 in familial congenital heart disease. *Lancet* 340: 573–75

128. Yokoyama T, Copeland NG, Jenkins NA, Montgomery CA, Elder FFB, et al. 1993. Reversal of left-right asymmetry: a situs inversus mutation. *Science* 260:679–82

Annu. Rev. Physiol. 1994. 56:797–810
Copyright © 1994 by Annual Reviews Inc. All rights reserved

INSIGHTS INTO LIPOPROTEIN METABOLISM FROM STUDIES IN TRANSGENIC MICE

Jan L. Breslow

Laboratory of Biochemical Genetics and Metabolism, The Rockefeller University, New York, New York 10021–6399

KEY WORDS: transgenic mice, lipoprotein, apolipoprotein, atherosclerosis, LDL receptor

INTRODUCTION

Lipoproteins are complex particles composed of various lipids and proteins that transport endogenous and dietary fats in the blood stream. There are five types of lipoprotein particles that range from smallest to largest: HDL, LDL, IDL, VLDL, and chylomicrons. Abnormal lipoprotein levels are associated with several human diseases, most commonly atherosclerosis. Individuals with atherosclerotic coronary heart disease almost invariably have one or more of four lipoprotein abnormalities: increased LDL-C; decreased HDL-C, usually associated with increased levels of triglyceride-rich lipoproteins (VLDL); increased levels of IDL-C and chylomicron remnants; and high levels ·of an abnormal lipoprotein Lp(a), which is a complex of LDL and a large glycoprotein called apo(a).

In the last decade genes have been isolated that code for proteins that directly interact with plasma lipids, thus enabling us to better understand lipoprotein metabolism and its abnormalities. There are approximately 17 such lipoprotein transport proteins including apolipoproteins that coat lipoprotein particles, lipoprotein processing proteins, and lipoprotein receptors (Figure 1). The genes coding for these proteins are all single copy in the human genome. They have been sequenced, mapped, and used as candidate

797

Apolipoproteins	A-I, A-II, A-IV, B CI, CII, CIII, D, E, apo(a)
Processing Proteins	Lipoprotein Lipase Hepatic Lipase Lecithin Cholesterol Acyl Transferase Cholesterol Ester Transfer Protein
Receptors	LDL Receptor Chylomicron Remnant Receptor Scavenger Receptor

Figure 1   Lipoprotein transport proteins.

genes to identify mutations underlying each of the lipoprotein phenotypes associated with coronary heart disease susceptibility (3). The lipoprotein transport genes have also been used to make transgenic animals, principally mice, that have provided new insights into the control of lipoprotein transport gene expression as well as the effects of over or under expression of these genes on lipoprotein metabolism. Finally, either singly or in combination, these transgenes have been used to make the mouse a better model for human lipoprotein disorders and atherosclerosis.

LIPOPROTEIN TRANSPORT GENE EXPRESSION

Cis-acting regions controlling transcriptional regulation of lipoprotein transport genes have been studied in transgenic mice. This approach has been particularly helpful in identifying the regions controlling tissue-specific expression of two clusters of apolipoprotein genes. One cluster located on chromosome 11q23 consists of the A-I, CIII, and A-IV genes in that order. Transcription of the CIII gene occurs in the opposite orientation from that of the A-I or A-IV genes (Figure 2). The A-I and CIII genes are expressed primarily in liver and intestine, whereas the A-IV gene is expressed primarily in intestine. In early experiments, human A-I transgenes extending from as little as 256bp 5' to 80bp 3' of the gene achieved high level liver expression, whereas this construction and others extending from 5kb 5' to 4kb 3' of the gene failed to give any intestinal expression (37). Subsequent experiments revealed a region approximately 6kb 3' to the A-I gene between −0.2 and −1.4kb 5' of the CIII gene required for A-I gene intestinal expression (36). The intestinal expression region was active either in its natural context, or

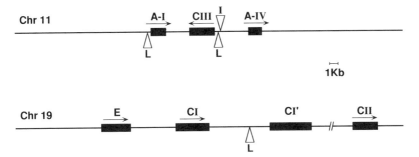

Figure 2   Apoliprotein gene tissue-specific transcriptional regulation.

when placed 3′ to the A-I gene in either orientation. These experiments clearly showed that the *cis*-acting regions required for A-I gene expression in liver and intestine were physically distinct. Further studies at this locus showed that the region between the CIII and A-IV genes, which contains the A-I gene intestinal control element, also controls the intestinal expression of these genes (16). Although it must be formally proven, these experiments suggest that a single DNA element may control intestinal expression of this entire apolipoprotein gene locus.

The second cluster of apolipoprotein genes that has been studied in transgenic mice is located on chromosome 19q13 and consists of the E, CI, and CII genes in that order. The genes are transcribed in the same orientation, and there is a CI pseudo gene between the CI and CII genes (Figure 2). The E gene is expressed primarily in the liver, and also in most body tissues, but at lower levels. The initial studies of human E transgene expression with constructions extending from 5kb 5′ to 2kb 3′ of the gene gave low level liver expression, but high level kidney expression (32, 34). Subsequently, it was found that a region 14kb 3′ to the E gene, in a region between the CI gene and CI pseudo gene, was required for high level liver expression (33). This region, which also dampens out kidney expression, has been narrowed to 154bp (28, 31). There is also some evidence that this element may control liver expression of the other two apolipoprotein genes in this cluster, CI and CII. Thus the transgenic studies of both apolipoprotein gene clusters have revealed previously unsuspected, but qualitatively different, regulatory elements: an intestinal control element for the A-I, CIII, A-IV locus, and a liver control element for the E, CI, CII locus.

Transgenic mice have also been used to identify a *cis*-acting region controlling transcription of the CETP gene in response to diet (15). A high fat, high cholesterol diet is known to increase plasma CETP levels and liver

CETP mRNA. A CETP mini gene extending from 138bp 5' to 121bp 3' to the gene and including the coding sequences and introns 1 and 12–15 has been expressed in transgenic mice. When this mini gene is driven by the mouse metallothionein I promoter, it is not diet-responsive. However, when the mini gene is driven by 3.2kb of 5' and 2kb of 3' natural flanking sequence, diet induces a four to fivefold increase in mRNA levels, the result of increased transcription. Cholesterol is the main dietary constituent responsible for this increase. Thus the transgenic experiments have defined a region containing a novel transcriptional element that is up-regulated by dietary cholesterol, in contrast to the well known sterol response element, which down regulates the transcription of several genes in response to cholesterol.

LIPOPROTEIN TRANSPORT GENE PHYSIOLOGY

The early transgenic mouse experiments involving the A-I gene were designed to identify *cis*-acting regions controlling tissue-specific gene expression (37). Since A-I is present at such high concentrations in plasma (140 mg/dl), it was not expected that there would be sufficient expression of the transgene to affect the A-I pool size and thereby be of physiological significance. However, the initial results indicated that, even with genomic constructions containing relatively small amounts of natural flanking sequences, enough A-I was produced to increase plasma levels. This observation opened up a whole new area of lipoprotein research in which it is possible to study the consequences of over expression of lipoprotein transport genes on lipoprotein metabolism in vivo. Transgenic mouse lines have now been established that over express several of the lipoprotein transport genes, and new information about how these genes function has been produced in almost every case. Recently the technique of homologous recombination in embryonic stem cells was used to knock out lipoprotein transport genes. This has also made it possible to study the consequences of gene under expression in lipoprotein metabolism and has provided other insights into lipoprotein transport gene function.

A-I Transgenic Mice

A-I is the major HDL protein, comprising 70% of total HDL protein, and transgenic animals expressing the human A-I protein have been produced (24, 35–37). In transgenic mice and rats, A-I over expression was found to selectively increase HDL-C levels. This is compatible with studies in humans, which show that HDL-C levels correlate with A-I levels, and suggests that pharmacological interventions that increase A-I production may raise HDL-C levels in humans and improve the lipoprotein profile. Human A-I expression in the mouse also resulted in a decrease in levels of mouse A-I, with some transgenic lines having 80–90% of plasma A-I of the human variety (4, 24). Coincident with the expression of human A-I in the mouse, changes were also noted in the physical properties of HDL. Mouse HDL normally consists of a single major size distribution of particles approximately 10 nm in diameter. In human A-I transgenic mice, there are two major size distributions of particles, with diameters approximately 10.3 and 8.8 nm. This corresponds to the two major size distributions of HDL particles in human plasma, HDL 2b and 3a, respectively. The transgenic mouse studies show that the structure of A-I is an important determinant of HDL particle size distribution and, for the first time, suggest an explanation for HDL subspeciation in humans. Human A-I transgenic mice have also been used to study the developmental regulation of A-I levels and HDL particle size distribution (7). This work revealed that post-transcriptional factors are important in regulating A-I levels and that developmental changes in A-I concentrations are associated with changes in HDL particle size distribution.

Human A-I transgenic mice have served as a model system to examine the mechanisms whereby diet and drugs alter HDL-C and A-I levels. A high fat diet increases HDL-C and A-I levels in humans, and this was mimicked in transgenic mice (10). In these animals, the main metabolic effect was to increase HDL cholesterol ester and A-I transport rates without an increase in A-I mRNA levels. In contrast, probucol decreases HDL-C and A-I levels, and this effect could also be reproduced in transgenic mice (9). In probucol-treated mice, the HDL cholesterol ester fractional catabolic rate increased, but the A-I transport rate decreased. The latter was not accompanied by a change in A-I mRNA levels. Thus over the wide range of A-I levels observed in the high fat diet and probucol experiments, there were no changes observed in the A-I fractional catabolic rates or in the A-I mRNA levels. Two interesting implications can be drawn from these studies. The first is that over the physiological range of A-I levels, there is no saturable A-I or HDL receptor. The second is that previously unrecognized, potent post-transcriptional regulation exists that regulates A-I production in relevant clinical situations.

Human A-I transgenic mice have been used to test a possible nonlipid transport function of HDL. *Trypanosoma brucei brucei* fatally infect livestock, but humans are resistant, apparently because human HDL lyse the organism. Human A-I is fully trypanolytic, whereas cattle and sheep A-I are not. Plasma from human A-I transgenic mice was found to be less trypanolytic than human plasma in vitro, and the transgenic mice were fully susceptible to infection with this organism (19). The difference between the lytic activity of human A-I in human and mouse plasma was shown to result from inhibition by mouse HDL apolipoproteins. Thus it appears that mouse A-I can antagonize the trypanolytic effect of human A-I.

Recently, A-I gene knockout mice were created and, as expected, these animals have reduced levels of HDL-C, but the consequences of this for lipoprotein metabolism have not yet been reported (38).

A-II Transgenic Mice

A-II is the second most abundant HDL protein, comprising 20% of the total. Transgenic mice expressing human A-II have been produced (26). Unlike the human A-I transgenics, these animals do not have elevated HDL-C levels, nor do they have diminished levels of mouse A-I or A-II. The lack of effect of excess A-II production on HDL-C levels is compatible with clinical studies that fail to show a correlation between plasma A-II and HDL-C levels and the relatively normal HDL-C levels reported in an A-II-deficient patient. The human A-II transgenics did show an alteration of HDL particle size with the appearance of a population of 8.0 nm diameter particles along with the normal-sized mouse HDL particles. The protein composition of the smaller HDL consisted almost entirely of human A-II, whereas the larger particles consisted of mouse A-I and human A-II. Thus A-II appears to affect the quality rather than the quantity of HDL particles.

CIII Transgenic Mice

CIII is a protein in VLDL and HDL. In the course of making transgenic mice to study the *cis*-acting regions responsible for the tissue-specific expression of the A-I gene, a DNA construction was used that contained the A-I gene plus the neighboring CIII gene (36). These mice were found to have massive hypertriglyceridemia, whereas mice made with the A-I gene alone had normal triglyceride levels. Subsequently, several transgenic mouse lines were made with only the CIII gene, and triglyceride levels were proportional to CIII gene expression as measured by human CIII plasma concentrations (14). In one transgenic line, there was a single copy of the transgene and only 30–40% extra C-III in plasma, yet these mice had more than twice normal triglyceride levels. The human CIII transgenic mice are the first animal model of primary hypertriglyceridemia.

The mechanism of the hypertriglyceridemia has been studied in the human CIII transgenic mice (1). These animals accumulate VLDL that is slightly larger than normal. The VLDL composition is appropriately triglyceride-rich, but there is altered apolipoprotein content with increased CIII and diminished E. The transgenic mice also have increased free fatty acid levels. Metabolic studies indicate the primary abnormality to be decreased VLDL fractional catabolic rate with a small increase in VLDL triglyceride, but not B production rate. In vitro the transgenic VLDL showed decreased LDL receptor-mediated uptake by tissue culture cells, but normal lipolysis by purified lipoprotein lipase. Thus the hypertriglyceridemia appears to result from a prolonged VLDL residence time, but without the accumulation of remnant particles. This implies decreased in vivo lipolysis and tissue uptake, presumably secondary to altered surface apolipoprotein composition and/or elevated free fatty acid levels. Human CI transgenic mice are also mildly hypertriglyceridemic (33). Although this model has not been studied in detail, it raises the question of whether other apolipoproteins besides CIII might also act in this manner.

The human CIII transgenic mouse experiments prove that CIII over expression can cause hypertriglyceridemia and suggest that CIII gene expression may regulate triglyceride levels in humans. Hypertriglyceridemia is common in humans with one third of middle-aged males affected, yet the known genetic abnormalities, lipoprotein lipase and CII deficiency, are quite rare, less than one in a million (3). Evidence for the involvement of the CIII gene in human hypertriglyceridemia has come from association studies. These have repeatedly shown that CIII alleles with an SstI cutting site in the 3' untranslated region are more common in affected Caucasians with hypertriglyceridemia than in controls. More recently, five new sites of genetic variation have been identified in the CIII gene promoter, and haplotype analysis utilizing these and the SstI site has revealed three classes of CIII alleles: susceptible, neutral, and protective with regard to hypertriglyceridemia (6). Further efforts are underway to identify the causative mutations and prove that CIII expression influences human triglyceride levels. If this line of research proves successful, the use of transgenic animals to provide clues to the genes underlying complex human traits may become an important paradigm in human genetics.

E Transgenic Mice

E, a protein in VLDL and HDL, is a ligand for the LDL and chylomicron remnant receptors and plays an important role in the clearance of lipoprotein particles from the plasma. The initial E transgenic mice were made with human E gene constructions that contained limited amounts of natural flanking sequences (32, 34). These constructions lacked the liver control element discussed above and, as a result, the animals produced had relatively low levels of E expression with no significant effect of transgene expression on lipoprotein levels. Recently, transgenic mice have been made with the rat E gene driven by the metallothionein promoter (29, 30). After zinc induction, these animals had a fourfold increase in E levels accompanied by a significant decrease in VLDL and LDL cholesterol levels. Metabolic studies indicated a several-fold increase in the clearance rate of radiolabeled

VLDL and LDL. In addition, these animals were resistant to diet-induced hypercholesterolemia. These studies indicate that E over expression lowers fasting levels of atherogenic lipoproteins and decreases diet response.

Recently, E knockout mice with a true null mutation have been created (22, 23, 40). Homozygous-deficient animals are viable and fertile. On a chow diet, which is very low in cholesterol, 0.01%, and low in fat, 4.5%, they have cholesterol levels of 400 to 500 mg/dl. Most of this is in the VLDL plus IDL lipoprotein fractions. When the homozygous E knockout mice are fed a Western-type diet (WTD), which has moderate amounts of cholesterol, 0.15%, and fat, 20%, they respond with cholesterol levels of approximately 1800 mg/dl, also mostly in the VLDL plus IDL lipoprotein fractions (23). On both diets triglyceride levels are minimally elevated, which suggests the presence of cholesterol-enriched particles, probably similar to B-VLDL. Metabolic studies indicate a severe defect in lipoprotein clearance from plasma, as predicted from the known function of E as a ligand for lipoprotein receptors. Heterozygous E knockout mice have diminished plasma E levels, normal fasting lipoprotein levels, and slightly delayed postprandial lipoprotein clearance. Thus half normal E expression in the mouse is nearly sufficient for normal lipoprotein metabolism.

Apo(a) Transgenic Mice

Apo(a) is a large glycoprotein that is disulfide-bonded to the B moiety of LDL to form Lp(a). Lp(a) is found in humans, old world primates, and hedge hogs, but not in other species, and its function is unknown. Apo(a) resembles plasminogen with domains of plasminogen-like kringle IV in multiple copies, and has plasminogen-like kringle V and protease in single copies. Apo(a) alleles specify proteins that differ in size due to variation in the number of kringle IV-like domains. Mice do not express apo(a), and transgenic animals were made with a human apo(a) gene construction consisting of a cDNA containing 17 kringle IVs, kringle V, and protease coding regions driven by the transferrin promoter (5). Expression was achieved in all tissues analyzed, whereas the gene is normally expressed only in liver. Mean plasma levels equivalent to 9 mg/dl of Lp(a) were achieved but, in contrast to humans, apo(a) was found in the lipoprotein-free fraction. Infusion of human LDL into these transgenic mice resulted in binding of apo(a) to lipoproteins of the LDL density class. These experiments suggest that human apo(a) can not bind to mouse B, perhaps because there is no conservation of a crucial cysteine.

CETP Transgenic Mice

CETP exchanges cholesterol ester in HDL for triglycerides in VLDL and IDL. CETP activity is lacking in mouse plasma. As mentioned above, a human CETP mini gene driven by the mouse metallothionein I promoter was used to make a transgenic line with human-like levels of activity in plasma, which could be doubled by feeding zinc (2, 8). After zinc treatment, compared to control mice, these mice had lower levels of HDL-C and A-I, 35 and 24%, respectively, and a smaller HDL particle size (10 to 9.7 nm mean particle diameter). These effects of CETP were less than expected based on studies comparing normal and CETP-deficient humans. Subsequently, CETP was found to be more potent in mice expressing the human A-I transgene (8). In these experiments, human CETP transgenic mice were crossed with human A-I transgenic mice. After zinc treatment, compared to the human A-I transgenic mice, the doubly transgenic mice had a large reduction in HDL-C and A-I levels, 66 and 42%, respectively, with an even smaller HDL particle size (10.4, 8.8, and 7.4 nm to 9.7, 8.5, and 7.3 nm mean particle diameter). In the doubly transgenic mice it was also found that 100% of the CETP was HDL-associated vs 22% in the singly transgenic animals. Thus CETP over expression can reduce HDL-C levels and particle size, and the effect is much more dramatic on the human A-I background. This implies a specific interaction of human CETP with human A-I or the particles it produces.

Recently, a cynomolgus monkey CETP cDNA driven by the mouse metallothionein-I promoter was used to make a CETP transgenic mouse (18). These animals had considerably higher levels of CETP than the human CETP transgenic mice previously studied. The monkey CETP transgenic mice showed a strong inverse correlation of CETP activity with HDL-C and A-I levels and HDL size, as previously shown, and also showed a positive correlation of CETP activity with B levels and the size of B-containing lipoproteins. The monkey CETP transgenic mice were also more diet-responsive than control animals. These experiments confirm the proposed role of CETP in lipoprotein metabolism deduced from other systems and will make it possible to test the effect of CETP on cholesterol homeostasis, particularly reverse cholesterol transport, and atherosclerosis.

LDL Receptor Transgenic Mice

The LDL receptor mediates lipoprotein clearance from plasma through recognition of B and E on the surface of lipoprotein particles. LDL receptor transgenic mice were made with a human cDNA construction driven by the mouse metallothionein-I promoter (13). After heavy metal induction, transgenic mice cleared injected radiolabeled LDL eight to ten times faster than control mice, and the plasma concentrations of LDL receptor ligands, B and E, declined by more than 90%. The increase in LDL clearance was primarily the result of increased liver removal of LDL, mainly by parenchymal cells. This study shows that inappropriate over expression of a receptor can lower plasma levels of its ligand. In addition, the authors suggest that inappropriate over expression of a receptor in one tissue might result in decreased ligand uptake by another tissue with pathophysiological consequences. These LDL receptor transgenic mice were also used to suggest that Lp(a) particles are cleared from plasma by LDL receptors (12). However, this is controversial, since other lines of evidence suggest that LDL receptors do not play a physiologically important role in Lp(a) clearance.

LDL receptor transgenic mice were also made with a human mini gene construction driven by the transferrin promoter, which resulted in animals with chronically elevated levels of LDL receptors (39). When the transgenic mice were challenged with a high fat, high cholesterol diet they did not increase IDL or LDL levels and only slightly increased VLDL levels, whereas control mice significantly increased the levels of all three of these lipoprotein fractions. Thus it appears that unregulated expression of LDL receptors can affect diet response. This suggests one possible mechanism for the variation in diet response in humans. Finally, LDL receptor transgenic mice have been used to demonstrate that receptor sorting to the surfaces of epithelial cells varies between tissues (21). In hepatocytes and intestinal epithelium, transgenic LDL receptors localize to the basolateral surface, whereas in renal tubular epithelium, these receptors are on the apical surface. A signal presumably present in the coding sequence of the transgene apparently controls tissue-specific sorting to cell membrane surfaces.

LDL Receptor-Related Protein (LRP) Transgenic Mice

LRP is presumed to be the chylomicron remnant receptor, but it also functions in the cellular uptake of protease-inhibitor complexes. A knockout of the LRP gene has been accomplished, but homozygous deficiency is nonviable, and heterozygous-deficient mice are normal (11). Therefore, this model has not been useful in confirming the role of LRP in chylomicron remnant metabolism in vivo.

MOUSE MODELS OF ATHEROSCLEROSIS

The mouse is the best mammalian system for the study of genetic contributions to disease. This is because of the easy breeding, short generation time, and availability of inbred strains, many of which have interesting heritable phenotypes. Unfortunately, the mouse is highly resistant to atherosclerosis, which makes it difficult to use this animal model to identify the genes controlling this complex disease. In an attempt to overcome this problem and produce atherosclerotic lesions, mice have been fed an unphysiological diet consisting of 1.25% cholesterol, 15% fat, and 0.5% cholic acid. This diet contains 10–20 times the amount of cholesterol of a human diet and an unnatural constituent, cholic acid. The diet is toxic. However, it produces a cholesterol level of 200 to 300 mg/dl with the increase in cholesterol in the non-HDL lipoprotein fractions. This is in contrast to a chow diet, which produces cholesterol levels of 60 to 80 mg/dl, mostly in HDL. When certain strains of mice are fed the high cholesterol diet for four to five months, they develop foam cell lesions in the region of the aortic sinus. In this model, crosses between resistant and susceptible mouse strains have been used to identify atherosclerosis susceptibility loci (20).

Transgenic techniques have now been used to further exploit this model. In these studies, lipoprotein transport genes have been introduced into one of the susceptible strains, C57BL6, to evaluate their effect on diet-induced atherosclerosis. In one study, human A-I gene expression reduced the aortic sinus foam cell lesion area (25). These results suggest that A-I expression with its attendant increase in HDL-C levels can protect against atherosclerosis. In a second study, human A-I and A-II transgenic mice were crossed, and there was less protection when both genes were expressed than with just human A-I gene expression (27). Since A-II gene expression does not increase HDL-C levels, but rather increases the A-I plus A-II HDL particles and decreases the A-I only HDL particles, this experiment suggests that not all HDL particles are equally antiatherogenic. Finally, in a variation on this study, the apo(a) transgene was introduced into outbred mice that do not get atherosclerosis (17). In response to diet, the apo(a) transgenic mice developed aortic sinus lesions. As previously noted, Lp(a) does not form in these mice, which implies that apo(a) is itself atherogenic.

The homozygous E knockout mice have provided a new model of atherosclerosis (23, 40). These animals are outbred, representing a mixture of C57BL6 and 129 strain genetic backgrounds. When the animals are fed a chow diet they show lesions in the aortic sinus at 10 weeks of age. When these mice are fed a WTD for 4 weeks the lesion area increases threefold in 10 week old mice (23). This indicates that lesion formation is diet-responsive. Wild-type and heterozygous E knockout mice show no lesions under either condition. Closer examination of the lesions in these young E-deficient animals indicates, in addition to foam cells, smooth muscle or fibroblastic-like cells and collagen deposition. This suggests the potential for progression to more complicated human-like atherosclerotic lesions in this animal model. Thus the single genetic lesion causing E absence and severe hypercholesterolemia is sufficient to convert the mouse from a species that is highly resistant to atherosclerosis to one that is highly susceptible. These animals should be of great assistance in studies of diets, genes, and drugs that influence atherosclerosis, which should greatly accelerate research in this field.

Literature Cited

1. Aalto-Setälä K, Fisher EA, Chen X, Chajek-Shaul, T, Hayek T, et al. 1992. Mechanism of hypertriglyceridemia in human apo CIII transgenic mice: Diminished VLDL fractional catabolic rate associated with increased apo CIII and reduced apo E on the particles. *J. Clin. Invest.* 90:1889–900
2. Agellon LB, Walsh A, Hayek T, Moulin P, Jiang XC, et al. 1991. Reduced high density lipoprotein cholesterol in human cholesteryl ester transfer protein transgenic mice. *J. Biol. Chem.* 266:10796–801
3. Breslow JL. 1991. Lipoprotein transport gene abnormalities underlying coronary heart disease susceptibility. *Annu. Rev. Med.* 42:357–71
4. Chajek-Shaul T, Hayek T, Walsh A, Breslow JL. 1991. Expression of the human apolipoprotein A-I gene in transgenic mice alters high density lipoprotein (HDL) particle size distribution and diminishes selective uptake of HDL cholesteryl esters. *Proc. Natl. Acad. Sci. USA* 88:6731–35
5. Chiesa G, Hobbs HH, Koschinsky ML, Lawn RM, Maika SD, Hammer RE. 1992. Reconstitution of lipoprotein(a) by infusion of human low density lipoprotein into transgenic mice expressing human apolipoprotein(a). *J. Biol. Chem.* 267:24369–74
6. Dammerman M, Sandkuijl LA, Halaas J, Chung W, Breslow JL. 1993. An apo CIII haplotype protective against hypertriglyceridemia is specified by novel promoter polymorphisms and a known 3' untranslated region polymorphism. *Proc. Natl. Acad. Sci. USA.* 90:4562–66
7. Golder-Novoselsky E, Forte TM, Nichols AV, Rubin EM. 1992. Apolipoprotein AI expression and high density lipoprotein distribution in transgenic mice during development. *J. Biol. Chem.* 267:20787–90
8. Hayek T, Chajek-Shaul T, Walsh A, Agellon LB, Moulin P, et al. 1992. An interaction between the human cholesteryl ester transfer protein (CETP) and apolipoprotein A-I genes in transgenic mice results in a profound CETP-mediated depression of high density lipoprotein cholesterol levels. *J. Clin. Invest.* 90:505–10
9. Hayek T, Chajek-Shaul T, Walsh A, Azrolan N, Breslow JL. 1991. Probucol decreases apolipoprotein A-I transport rate and increases high density lipo-

protein cholesteryl ester fractional catabolic rate in control and human apolipoprotein A-I transgenic mice. *Arterioscler. Thromb.* 11:1295–302
10. Hayek T, Ito Y, Azrolan N, Verdery RB, Aalto-Setälä K, et al. 1993. Dietary fat increases high density lipoprotein (HDL) levels both by increasing the transport rates and decreasing the fractional catabolic rates of HDL cholesterol ester and apolipoprotein (apo) A-I. *J. Clin. Invest.* 91:1665–71
11. Herz J, Clouthier DE, Hammer RE. 1992. LDL receptor-related protein internalizes and degrades uPA-PA-1 complexes and is essential for embryo implantation. *Cell* 71:411–21
12. Hofmann SL, Eaton DL, Brown MS, McConathy WJ, Goldstein JL, Hammer RE. 1990. Overexpression of human low density lipoprotein receptors leads to accelerated catabolism of Lp(a) lipoprotein in transgenic mice. *J. Clin. Invest.* 85:1542–47
13. Hofmann SL, Russell DW, Brown MS, Goldstein JL, Hammer RE. 1988. Overexpression of low density lipoprotein (LDL) receptor eliminates LDL from plasma in transgenic mice. *Science* 239:1277–81
14. Ito Y, Azrolan N, O'Connell A, Walsh A, Breslow JL. 1990. Hypertriglyceridemia as a result of human apolipoprotein CIII gene expression in transgenic mice. *Science* 249:790–93
15. Jiang XC, Agellon LB, Walsh A, Breslow JL, Tall A. 1992. Dietary cholesterol increases transcription of the human cholesteryl ester transfer protein gene in transgenic mice. Dependence on natural flanking sequences. *J. Clin. Invest.* 90:1290–95
16. Lauer SJ, Simonet WS, Bucay N, de Silva HV, Taylor JM. 1991. Tissue-specific expression of the human apolipoprotein A-IV gene in transgenic mice. *Circulation* 84:17 (Suppl. II)
17. Lawn RM, Wade DP, Hammer RE, Chiesa G, Verstuyft JG, Rubin EM. 1992. Atherogenesis in transgenic mice expressing human apolipoprotein(a). *Nature* 360:670–71
18. Marotti KR, Castle CK, Murray RW, Rehberg EF, Polites HG, Melchior GW. 1992. The role of cholesteryl ester transfer protein in primate apolipoprotein A-I metabolism. Insights from studies with transgenic mice. *Arterioscler. Thromb.* 12:736–44
19. Owen JS, Gillett MPT, Hughes TE.

1992. Transgenic mice expressing human apolipoprotein A-I have sera with modest trypanolytic activity in vitro but remain susceptible to infection by *Trypanosoma brucei brucei*. *J. Lipid Res.* 33:1639–46

20. Paigen B, Mitchell D, Reue K, Morrow A, Lusis A, LeBoeuf RC. 1987. *Ath-1*, a gene determining atherosclerosis susceptibility and high density lipoprotein levels in mice. *Proc. Natl. Acad. Sci. USA* 84:3763–67

21. Pathak RK, Yokode M, Hammer RE, Hofmann SL, Brown MS, et al. 1990. Tissue-specific sorting of the human LDL receptor in polarized epithelia of transgenic mice. *J. Cell Biol.* 111:347–59

22. Piedrahita JA, Zhang SH, Hagaman JR, Oliver PM, Maeda N. 1992. Generation of mice carrying a mutant apolipoprotein E gene inactivated by gene targeting in embryonic stem cells. *Proc. Natl. Acad. Sci. USA* 89:4471–75

23. Plump AS, Smith JD, Hayek T, Aalto-Setälä K, Walsh A, et al. 1992. Severe hypercholesterolemia and atherosclerosis in apolipoprotein E-deficient mice created by homologous recombination in ES cells. *Cell* 71:343–53

24. Rubin EM, Ishida BY, Clift SM, Krauss RM. 1991. Expression of human apolipoprotein A-I in transgenic mice results in reduced plasma levels of murine apolipoprotein A-I and the appearance of two new high density lipoprotein size subclasses. *Proc. Natl. Acad. Sci. USA* 88:434–38

25. Rubin EM, Krauss RM, Spangler EA, Verstuyft JG, Clift SM. 1991. Inhibition of early atherogenesis in transgenic mice by human apolipoprotein AI. *Nature* 353:265–67

26. Schultz JR, Gong EL, McCall MR, Nichols AV, Clift SM, Rubin EM. Expression of human apolipoprotein A-II and its effect on high density lipoproteins in transgenic mice. *J. Biol. Chem.* 267:21630–36

27. Schultz JR, Verstuyft JG, Gong EL, Nichols AV, Rubin EM. 1992. ApoAI and ApoAI + ApoAII transgenic mice: A comparison of atherosclerotic susceptibility. *Circulation* 86(4):I-473 (Abstr.; Suppl.)

28. Shachter NS, Zhu Y, Walsh A, Breslow JL, Smith JD. 1993. Localization of a liver-specific enhancer in the apolipoprotein E/CI/CII gene locus. *J. Lipid Res.* 34:1699–1707

29. Shimano H, Yamada N, Katsuki M, Shimada M, Gotoda T, et al. 1992.

Overexpression of apolipoprotein E in transgenic mice: Marked reduction in plasma lipoproteins except high density lipoprotein and resistance against diet-induced hypercholesterolemia. *Proc. Natl. Acad. Sci. USA* 89:1750–54

30. Shimano H, Yamada N, Katsuki M, Yamamoto K, Gotoda T, et al. 1992. Plasma lipoprotein metabolism in transgenic mice overexpressing apolipoprotein E. *J. Clin. Invest.* 90: 2084–91

31. Simonet WS, Bucay N, Lauer SJ, Taylor JM. 1993. A far-downstream hepatocyte-specific control region directs expression of the linked human apolipoprotein E and C-I genes in transgenic mice. *J. Biol. Chem.* 268: 8221–29

32. Simonet WS, Bucay N, Lauer SJ, Wirak DO, Stevens ME, et al. 1990. In the absence of a downstream element, the apolipoprotein E gene is expressed at high levels in kidneys of transgenic mice. *J. Biol. Chem.* 265: 10809–12

33. Simonet WS, Bucay N, Pitas RE, Lauer SJ, Taylor JM. 1991. Multiple tissue-specific elements control the apolipoprotein E/C-I gene locus in transgenic mice. *J. Biol. Chem.* 265:8651–54

34. Smith JD, Plump AS, Hayek T, Walsh A, Breslow JL. 1990. Accumulation of human apolipoprotein E in the plasma of transgenic mice. *J. Biol. Chem.* 265:14709–12

35. Swanson ME, Hughes TE, St Denny I, France DS, Paterniti JR Jr, et al. 1992. High level expression of human apolipoprotein A-I in transgenic rats raises total serum high density lipoprotein cholesterol and lowers rat apolipoprotein A-I. *Transgenic Res.* 1: 142–47

36. Walsh A, Azrolan N, Wang K, Marcigliano A, O'Connell A, Breslow JL. 1993. Intestinal expression of the human apoA-I gene in transgenic mice is controlled by a DNA region 3' to the gene in the promoter of the adjacent convergently transcribed apo C-III gene. *J. Lipid Res.* 34:617–23

37. Walsh A, Ito Y, Breslow JL. 1989. High levels of human apolipoprotein A-I in transgenic mice result in increased plasma levels of small high density lipoprotein (HDL) particles comparable to human HDL3. *J. Biol. Chem.* 264:6488–94

38. Williamson R, Lee D, Hagaman J, Maeda N. 1992. Marked reduction of

high density lipoprotein cholesterol in mice genetically modified to lack apolipoprotein A-I. *Proc. Natl. Acad. Sci. USA* 89:7134–38

39. Yokode M, Hammer RE, Ishibashi S, Brown MS, Goldstein JL. 1990. Diet-induced hypercholesterolemia in mice:

Prevention by overexpression of LDL receptors. *Science* 250:1273–75

40. Zhang SH, Reddick RL, Piedrahita JA, Maeda N. 1992. Spontaneous hypercholesterolemia and arterial lesions in mice lacking apolipoprotein E. *Science* 258:468–71

Annu. Rev. Physiol. 1994. 56:811–29
Copyright © 1994 by Annual Reviews Inc. All rights reserved

TRANSGENIC RATS: New Experimental Models for the Study of Candidate Genes in Hypertension Research

Martin Paul and Jürgen Wagner

Department of Pharmacology, University of Heidelberg, Im Neuenheimer Feld 366, 69120 Heidelberg, Germany

Sigrid Hoffmann, Hidenori Urata, and Detlev Ganten

Max-Delbrück Center for Molecular Medicine, Robert-Rössle Strasse 10, 13125 Berlin-Buch, Germany

KEY WORDS: transgenic techniques, hypertension, cardiovascular disease, renin-angiotensin-system, mice, rats, candidate genes

INTRODUCTION

Primary hypertension is a disease with a significant genetic background. Although we do not know exactly which genes are involved, present studies link sections of the genome to the hypertensive phenotype in genetically hypertensive rats (SHRsp). In addition, several candidate genes have been proposed to be related to this disorder. They include components of vaso-active regulatory systems, long considered to be involved in the pathogenesis of high blood pressure.

The capability to modify the expression of specific gene products in intact animals provides a powerful experimental approach to study cardiovascular pathophysiology. Such animal models can be generated using transgenic technology. Transgenic animals are useful for the production of defined alterations in the germ line that result in specific pathophysiologic changes. These changes can be induced not only in a systemic but also in a tissue-specific manner by studying the functional aspects of organ- or cell-

811

specific promoter function. Based on these developments of transgene technology, we can approach important problems that are directly related to cardiovascular pathophysiology.

In recent years, many genes related to cardiovascular disease have been cloned and analyzed. These include the genes of the renin-angiotensin system (RAS), atrial natriuretic peptide (ANP), brain natriuretic peptide (BNP), C-natriuretic peptide (CNP), vasopressin, endothelin, genes of the adrenergic system, and others. Several of these genes are sufficiently well characterized to permit experiments in vivo by introducing genomic fragments or constructs into transgenic animals, which could then become novel and valuable animal models for cardiovascular research.

In general, transgenic techniques can be applied in many species, but until now mice have been used most extensively. In transgenic hypertension research, however, rats may be the more appropriate models because they offer several advantages over mice. One is that rats can be easily characterized using the methodological approaches of whole animal physiology and pharmacology. In addition, there are several genetically hypertensive rat lines already available that can be used as a reference.

METHODS FOR GENERATING TRANSGENIC RATS

Several methods are used to generate transgenic animals. Most common are (a) retroviral infection of preimplantative blastocysts (32, 35, 69), (b) use of embryonic stem cells previously transfected with the DNA of interest to produce chimeras via microinjection into blastocysts (16, 58, 81), and (c) direct microinjection of the foreign DNA into the pronucleus of fertilized oocytes (3, 22, 54).

The microinjection of foreign DNA into the pronucleus of fertilized oocytes is widely used and is considered the most efficient way for construction of transgenic animals. Whereas this method has become a routine procedure in mice during the last ten years, its application for production of transgenic rats developed only recently (24, 29, 30, 46). The steps for producing transgenic rats are summarized in Figure 1. Since detailed methodological descriptions for the construction of transgenic mice via microinjection are already available (11, 22, 32, 55), only those aspects that specifically apply to the production of transgenic rats are described here.

Choice of Strain

Superovulation can be induced in mature and immature (1, 37, 43, 64) rats. The optimum age for superovulation varies between strains (Table 1). This is in contrast to mice, where the optimum age is 2–3 weeks of age

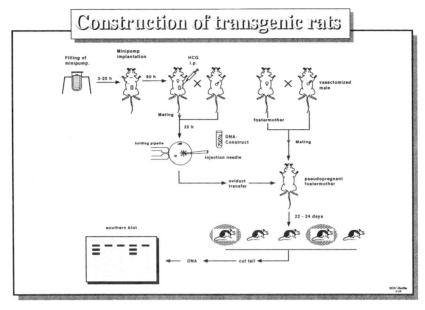

Figure 1   Flowsheet for the generation of transgenic rats.

irrespective of the strain chosen. The average number of oocytes obtained after superovulation varies between 20 to 30 (low responder strain) and 60 to more than 100 (high responder strain) (Table 1). In general, outbred strains of rats and F-1 hybrids produce the highest numbers of zygotes after superovulation.

Superovulation

Superovulation is essential to obtain a sufficient number of oocytes with normal developmental potential. Difficulties in inducing an efficient super-ovulation have long prevented the application of transgenic technology to the rat. In mice, a single dose of pregnant mare serum gonadotropin (PMSG) usually is sufficient for induction of superovulation. The use of PMSG in rats, in contrast, is connected with a high variation in the ovulatory response (80, 83), a low fertilization rate (17), and a high percentage of degenerated oocytes, and oocytes that do not develop normally (1, 37, 43, 64). Since PMSG shows both follicle stimulating hormone (FSH) and luteinizing hormone (LH) activity (53), the relatively high percentage of LH activity in PMSG is thought be the reason for the low efficiency of superovulation in rats after treatment with PMSG (15). High LH activity could induce an

Table 1   Schedule for production of transgenic rats

Time	Day	Procedure
9 A.M.	−3	Implant of minipumps into immature female rats. Pump rate is 1 U FSH and 0.2 IE human choriogonadotropin (HCG)
11 A.M.	−1	Administer 30 IE HCG by intraperitoneal injection
4 P.M.	−1	Place hormone-treated female with fertile male for mating; place mature females with vasectomized males for mating
2 A.M.	0	Ovulation and mating completed
7–9 A.M.	0	Examine immature and mature females for the presence of a copulatory (vaginal) plug
9–11 A.M.	0	Kill immature females and harvest oocytes
1–4 P.M.	0	Microinjection
6 P.M.	0	Reimplant surviving oocytes into pseudopregnant females
		or
7–9 A.M.	1	Reimplant surviving two-cell eggs into day 1 or day 0 pseudopregnant females

excessive synthesis of androgens in the ovaries 36 hr after PMSG application, which may cause degeneration of the oocytes (84).

The means for obtaining large amounts of normally developed rat oocytes have been studied by Armstrong and co-workers (2). Using high purified FSH preparations from the porcine pituitary, they showed that a specified ratio of LH/FSH for a given FSH amount is necessary to achieve appropriate superovulation in the rat. The optimal dose is 1 U FSH-NIH S1 and 0.2 IU HCG, given 24 hr after administration of gonadotropin. Use of a minipump system (implanted subcutaneously) is necessary (2) because of the short half-life of purified FSH (8, 40). According to the protocol of Armstrong et al (2), a combination of 1 U FSH and 0.2 IU HCG/24 hr is applied to immature rats over a 72 hr period. Fifty hours after implantation of the minipump, 30 IU are injected for induction and timing the ovulation. The subcutaneous implantation of the minipump is performed on day 3, between 8:30 and 9:30 a.m., under light ether anesthesia. 30 IU of human choriogonadotropin (HCG) are injected 50–52 hours after implantation of the minipump. In the evening of day 1, the females are placed with fertile males for mating. At the same time, mature females are mated with vasectomized males for induction of pseudopregnancy. Up to 15 mature females are needed to obtain 2–3 pseudopregnant foster mothers. Using females selected to be in estrus before mating will increase the yield of recipients. On the next morning between 7:00 and 8:00 a.m., egg donors and mature females are checked for the presence of copulatory plugs.

Microinjection

Fertilized oocytes are collected on day 1 between 9.00 and 11.00 a.m. After cervical dislocation of the donor animals, oviducts are excised and opened under a microscope. Since oocytes are found in a conglomerate with cumulus cells, they are placed into M2 medium (32) with 4000 IU hyaluronidase/ml M2 medium. After the conglomerate has been dissolved, the oocytes are washed two or three times in M2 medium and transferred to M16 (32) in a humidified tissue culture incubator under 5% CO_2 and at 37°C. The microinjection itself is performed when the pronuclei are well visible. The procedure is, in principle, not different from that described for mice (32).

Oviduct Transfer

The successful embryo-transfer is dependent on synchronization between embryo development and timing of pseudopregnancy. The pseudopregnant rat is anesthetized with a combination of Ketavet (ketamine hydrochloride)/Rompun (5,6-dihydro-2(2,6-xylindo)-4H-1,3 thiatin) (0.1/0.01 mg per 100 g body weight). We have found this mixture superior to ether anesthesia for this procedure in the rat. After opening the body wall through a midline incision at the lower back, the ovaries and the oviducts are surgically exposed. Contrary to oviduct transfer in mice, hemorrhage from ruptured vessels of the ovarian capsule is a frequent problem. In rats, therefore, a few drops of epinephrine are applied to the bursa ovaria. A glass transfer capillary is then inserted into the infundibulum and fixed in position using a micro-forceps, and the embryos are placed in the oviduct. To obtain a sufficient number of progeny 30–40 one-cell oocytes or 15–30 two-cell oocytes are typically transferred bilaterally.

TRANSGENIC RATS IN HYPERTENSION RESEARCH

As of this writing several transgenic rat lines expressing candidate genes for hypertension have been produced. These animals exclusively express components of the renin-angiotensin system. There are a number of reasons for this as discussed elsewhere (20). Genetic linkage studies have recently demonstrated that the components of RAS are associated with hypertension. Linkage has been described for the angiotensinogen gene in human hypertension, for example. Molecular variants of angiotensinogen, which result in significant differences in plasma concentrations among hypertensive subjects, have been interpreted as an inherited predisposition to the development of essential hypertension (36). Interestingly, angiotensin-converting enzyme in humans does not appear to be associated with hypertension, but with myocardial infarction (12). A deletion (D) polymorphism of the gene has been found in conjunction with increased plasma levels of the enzyme. The homozygous (DD) genotype for this polymorphism appears to be associated with an increased risk for myocardial infarction in the absence of other risk factors. This suggests that the RAS may not only be involved in the elevation of blood pressure, but also in the sequellae of hypertension such as cardiovascular end-organ damage. For renin, a restriction length polymorphism has been linked to hypertension in the Dahl salt-sensitive rat (6), whereas no linkage could be demonstrated in humans (48). Transgenic animals have been applied to test these candidate genes in vivo. Initially a number of transgenic mouse lines were established to express genes of the renin-angiotensin system, but transgenic rats have been the species of choice more recently.

The Hypertensive Transgenic Rat TGR(mREN2)27

The first transgenic rat lines in hypertension research have been established by microinjecting a genomic construct of the mouse *Ren-2* gene (46) into oocytes of normotensive rats. The transgenic rats developed fulminant hypertension. The identical construct had been used previously to generate transgenic mice (47, 73). Several transgenic lines with this construct have now been characterized [transgenic rat lines TGR(mRen2) 25, 26, and 27]. In heterozygous male TGR(mREN2)27 rats, blood pressure increases shortly after weaning at 5 weeks of age, and maximum systolic values of about 240 mm Hg are reached at 10 weeks of age (5). Homozygous TGR(mREN2)-27 rats develop even higher blood pressure and show a high mortality rate if they are not treated with angiotensin-converting enzyme (ACE) inhibitors or other antihypertensive medication (5). Both homozygous and heterozygous TGR(mREN2)27 rats exhibit a marked sexual dimorphism with respect to blood pressure, with higher blood pressure in males, which reflects the higher prevalence of hypertension in males in human hypertension. Androgens and their stimulatory effect on tissue RAS are probably the main cause for this gender discrepancy, since dihydrotestosterone treatment of females elevated blood pressure to the level of males, whereas castration of males had the opposite effect (5). The highest expression of the *Ren-2* gene was found in the adrenal gland, whereas the kidney (which expresses highest renin levels in rats) showed only low renin levels, which were probably influenced by feedback inhibition (57). Tissue renin protein concentrations parallel the mRNA measurements, i.e. tissue renin is low in the kidney and high in the adrenal gland. Hypertension in TGR(mREN2)27 rats is dependent on angiotensin (ANG) II since treatment with low-dose ACE inhibitors or ANG II antagonists normalized blood pressure (5). Preliminary experiments

(M Böhm et al, unpublished) show that the animals are extremely sensitive to ANG II receptor (AT_1) antagonists. The plasma RAS is not stimulated and the concentrations of active renin, angiotensin I (ANG I), ANG II, and angiotensinogen are unchanged or even suppressed when compared to control animals (5, 46, 59), which characterizes these rats as a low-renin-hypertension model. In contrast, the concentration of plasma inactive renin (prorenin) is much higher in TGR(mREN2)27 rats than in control animals. The main source of plasma inactive renin in TGR(mREN2)27 rats is probably the adrenal gland because its concentration was reduced by 80% after bilateral adrenalectomy (57). Moreover, isolated adrenal cells of these transgenic rats secrete considerable amounts of inactive, but also active, renin (59). The physiological significance of the high plasma inactive renin is currently under investigation. The fact that the elevated blood pressure decreased to nearly normotensive values after adrenalectomy supports an important role of this organ in the hypertensinogenic process. The potential role of the adrenal gland for hypertension in these animals was further investigated by measuring the concentrations of adrenal steroids. Results indicate that the urinary excretion of deoxycorticosterone, corticosterone, and aldosterone was significantly elevated in young TGR(mREN2)27 animals during the developmental phase of hypertension, but not in adult animals (20). ACTH treatment caused a dramatic increase of corticosterone excretion as compared to control rats, which indicates that the adrenal glands of TGR(mREN2)27 animals react more sensitively to ACTH stimulation than do the glands of other rats. These data support the hypothesis that the adrenal expression of the transgene stimulates corticosteroid production and sensitivity to ACTH. However, hypertension in these animals is probably not dependent on mineralocorticoids, since spironolactone treatment does not reduce blood pressure (4). The possibility exists, however, that there is an interaction between increased renin and production of adrenal steroids, since dexamethasone treatment effectively lowered blood pressure in these animals (13).

Although the role of the adrenal gland has generated the most interest in the investigation of hypertensive mechanisms in this transgenic model, increased production of renin or ANG II in other organs may equally contribute to the phenotypic alterations. Recently, studies investigating the cardiovascular system in these animals have been carried out. Hilgers et al (27) used an isolated hindlimb preparation to demonstrate that the vasculature of the transgenic animals produced increased amounts of ANG II, which is most likely the result of overexpression of the transgene in the vascular wall. Indeed, sensitive RNAse protection assays show that *Ren-2* expression is markedly increased in blood vessels (27). The hearts of the transgenic animals show marked pathological changes including hypertrophy and fibrosis (4). This can be partially explained by the dramatically altered blood pressure levels, but there are clearly additional effects. Current studies focus on the investigation of the cardiac function in these animals and its cellular basis.

Transgenic Animals Expressing the Human Renin Gene

The human renin gene initially was expressed in transgenic mice (C57BL/6) using a genomic construct of the gene with 3.0 kb of 5'-flanking regions and 1.2 kb of downstream sequences (19, 66). The transgene in these animals was correctly spliced and showed a tissue-specific expression pattern in the kidney and also in cardiovascular organs. Human renin protein was detected in the juxtaglomerular apparatus of the kidney with the use of a monoclonal antibody specific to human renin that demonstrated not only correct tissue-, but also cell-specific expression (18).

A construct containing the entire human renin gene was microinjected into pronuclei of fertilized rat oocytes from outbred Sprague-Dawley/WKY hybrids. The construct comprised a total length of 17.6 kb after stripping it from vector-encoded sequences (21). Two rat lines were obtained that transmitted the transgene to their progeny. These transgenic rats produced and secreted active human renin into their plasma, as has been determined by an immunoradiometric assay using monoclonal antibodies specific for human renin. The plasma levels of active human renin in one line were slightly less than in humans, whereas active human renin was more than twelve times the levels found in humans in the other. Transgene expression was found to be highest in the kidney, but was also present in extrarenal tissues such as the lung or the gastrointestinal tract (21). On the cellular level, in situ hybridization showed that human renin expression under basal conditions is confined to the juxtaglomerular apparatus.

The question of whether the presence of the transgene would interfere with the production of the endogenous renin, plasma rat renin concentration, was also examined, but no significant differences were found between transgenic rats and negative controls. Also, no alteration in other components of the RAS such as angiotensin II or angiotensinogen could be detected. In addition, both rats strains were normotensive. These negative findings can be explained by the fact that human renin does not interact with rat angiotensinogen except at very high levels. To investigate how the human renin transgene responds to physiological stimuli of renin secretion, animals were sodium-depleted with a low-sodium diet for 3 days. In plasma, active human renin levels increased by about 11-fold, similar to those of rat renin. This indicates that the transgene is regulated by sodium-depletion and does not interfere with rat renin production even under stimulated conditions.

Transgenic Animals Expressing the Human Angiotensinogen Gene

A genomic human angiotensinogen gene construct comprised of five exons, four introns, a 1.3 kb of 5'-flanking region, and a 2.4 kb of 3'-flanking region was used to generate transgenic mice as well as rats carrying the human angiotensinogen transgene (21, 49, 71). In transgenic mice, expression of the transgene could be detected predominantly in the liver, but also in a number of organs including the brain, kidney, and the heart (21). By generating transgenic rats, four lines could be obtained. Human angiotensinogen was secreted into the plasma in all rats, but the levels markedly varied between the lines and ranged from 120 μg/ml up to 5 mg/ml. All four lines exceeded plasma angiotensinogen levels in humans, which amounts to about 60 μg/ml. Despite the high plasma levels, these animals were normotensive, which indicates that human angiotensinogen did not interact with rat renin at the concentration found in these animals (21). Compared to transgene-negative controls, rat angiotensinogen levels as well as angiotensin II levels were not significantly different in transgenics. Transgene expression was highest at the appropriate sites in the liver, where it was expressed in the parenchyma as demonstrated by in situ hybridization (21). Transgene expression was also detected about tenfold lower in the kidney and the gastrointestinal tract. These findings are in contrast to a previously described transgenic mouse strain carrying the human angiotensinogen gene. Here, human angiotensinogen was expressed as high in the kidney as in the liver in contrast to humans, where kidney angiotensinogen is low (71, 72). Human renin and angiotensinogen in transgenic rats have been shown to be expressed highest in the kidney or the liver, but expression can also be demonstrated in extrarenal or extrahepatic tissues, respectively. The coexpression of the human transgenes in crossbred transgenic animals carrying both genes in these organs supports the possibility of local angiotensin I production from the interaction of the human proteins. The functional role of such human-dependent tissue-specific RAS remains to be established.

Species-specificity of the Human Renin Substrate Reaction in Transgenic Rats

Despite the high expression of human transgenes, rats carrying either the human renin or human angiotensinogen gene remained normotensive as an indication of the species-specificity of the human renin substrate reaction. As demonstrated by the unaltered levels of angiotensin II in both human renin and angiotensinogen transgenic rats, rat renin did not react with human angiotensinogen nor did human renin react with rat angiotensinogen. Blood pressure remained unaltered when the human-specific renin inhibitor Ro

42-5892 was given as a bolus injection to sodium-depleted TGR(hREN)1936 rats, whereas the angiotensin II receptor antagonist lowered blood pressure by about 20 mmHg. The species-specificity of the human renin substrate reaction in the transgenic rats could further be demonstrated by injection of recombinant human renin into rats carrying the human angiotensinogen gene. Here, at a dosage of 5 μg ANG I/ml/h, blood pressure rapidly increased from 142 ± 4 mmHg to 192 ± 8 mmHg. Addition of the human renin inhibitor Ro 42-5892 rapidly normalized the blood pressure to pretreatment values. Human renin at this dosage did not elicit a hypertensive response in transgene negative controls, which indicates that the blood pressure increase was due to the interaction of human renin with human angiotensinogen. Infusion of rat renin in equipressor doses raised blood pressure as well, but in this case, Ro 42-5892 remained without any effect, whereas DuP 753 (10 mg/kg) normalized blood pressure rapidly, which supports the finding that angiotensin II formation in this case originated from the reaction of rat renin with rat angiotensinogen.

FUTURE PERSPECTIVES OF HYPERTENSION RESEARCH IN TRANSGENIC RATS

Future directions of hypertension research in transgenic rats will focus on the investigation of new genes as well on the establishement of new and better methods for generating transgenic animals. In several cases, candidate genes have already been expressed and characterized in transgenic mice, and the information provided by these studies can now be applied to the rat model. Particular emphasis is given to genes expressed predominantly in the organs of the cardiovascular system, namely the heart and the vasculature. In the following, several of the most prominent targets for future research in transgenic rats are discussed.

New Candidate Genes

Atrial natriuretic peptide (ANP) is a peptide hormone synthesized predominantly by atrial cardiomyocytes. The biological responses to acute ANP administration include a rapid natriuretic and diuretic effect, as well as a reduction in arterial blood pressure. Despite extensive information concerning the acute biological responses to ANP, it remains to be determined whether ANP chronically regulates the cardiovascular system. Seidman et al (67) have introduced transgenic mice for the characterization of the ANP promoter that demonstrate the tissue specificity of ANP expression. To investigate the chronic regulatory effects of ANP in vivo, Steinhelper et al (70) developed transgenic mice harboring mouse ANP, driven with a transthyretin promoter, which targets expression of the fusion gene to the liver. Hepatic expression of atrial natriuretic peptide was detectable as early as embryonic day 15 in transgenic animals. In adult mice, plasma immunoreactive atrial natriuretic factor concentration was elevated at least eightfold as compared with that in nontransgenic litter mates. The mean arterial pressure of conscious transgenic mice was 75.5 ±0.9 mmHg, significantly less than that of nontransgenic siblings (103.9 ±2.0 mmHg). This relative hypotension in the transgenic mice was not correlated with a difference in heart rate and was not associated with significant changes in fluid or electrolyte balance as compared with nontransgenic controls. Thus transgenic mice with chronically elevated plasma ANP have significantly lower arterial blood pressure.

Arginine vasopressin (AVP) is a potent neuroactive and vasoactive non-apeptide encoded and processed from a precursor, preproarginine vasopressin-neurophysin II. To study the physiological consequences of a genetic model of chronic hypervasopressinemia, Habener et al (23) developed transgenic mice harboring a rat pre-pro-AVP-neurophysin II gene driven by mouse metallothionein promoter. Levels of immunoreactive AVP and neurophysin in sera, liver, kidney, intestine, pancreas, and brain were markedly elevated and serum osmolalities were elevated, consistent with a state of mild nephrogenic diabetes insipidus.

The status of the blood vessel wall in animals with growth hormone excess is interesting because of the high incidence of hypertension in acromegaly and gigantism. Despite the many endocrine modulations caused by excess growth hormones, there is no apparent endocrine explanation for the increased blood pressure in these individuals. To address this problem, researchers utilized transgenic mice expressing the metallothionein-growth hormone fusion genes (51). Although there was no elevation of blood pressure in transgenic mice, wall to lumen ratios were significantly increased only in mesenteric resistance artery after normalization for body and organ weight. They suggested that this increased wall to lumen ratio in the mesenteric artery in transgenic mice may partially contribute to the increase of peripheral vascular resistance and could result in hypertension for one third of patients with acromegaly or gigantism. Thus the use of transgenic technology as a means to deliver cardiovascular hormones provides a new and exciting experimental approach to the study of the long-term regulation of cardiovascular homeostasis.

Hormones and other ligands are known to regulate their own receptors, but we have only recently recognized that the converse is also true, i.e. receptors can determine the concentrations of their own ligands. The latter is true because the receptors transport their ligands into cells by receptor-mediated endocytosis, thereby removing them from the blood. The most clear-cut example occurs in the low density lipoprotein (LDL) receptor system. LDL receptors, located predominantly in the liver, mediate the rapid removal of LDL from plasma. When LDL receptors are deficient as a result of genetic or acquired status, the concentration of LDL in plasma rises. When the number of LDL receptors is increased by drug or hormone therapy, plasma LDL declines. A complimentary DNA encoding the human LDL receptor under control of the mouse metallothionein-I promoter was injected into fertilized mouse oocytes, and a strain of mice expressing high levels of LDL receptors was established (31). After administration of cadmium, these mice cleared intravenously injected ^{125}I-labeled LDL from blood eight to ten times more rapidly than did normal mice. Since it is well known that the increased plasma LDL level by the genetic LDL receptor defect is associated with the augmentation of atherosclerosis in the systemic and cardiac vessels, the normal gene transfer of LDL receptor to these patients could be a therapeutic approach in the future.

Experiments involving the biochemical mechanisms for cardiac hypertrophy or myopathy invoke great interest. Such experiments are possible through the use of transgenic technology since several genes have been identified related to the pathophysiological condition of the hypertrophic heart or cardiomyopathy (44, 55). Recently, transgenic mice expressing v-fps, one of the cytosolic protein tyrosine kinase genes, driven with β-globin promoter was developed (82). v-fps expression was detected in several tissues of transgenic mice including heart (most abundant), brain, thymus, lymph node, testis, and spleen. The expression of v-fps and protein-tyrosine kinase activity in the heart were directly correlated with cardiac enlargement. This cardiomegaly was accompanied by severe myocardial and endocardial damage, which was concentrated in the left ventricular wall, and characterized by a progressive atrophy and necrosis of cardiac muscle fibers with concomitant fibrosis. This pathology was associated with congestive heart failure. To our knowledge, this is the first successful transgenic model targeting cardiac hypertrophy.

Transgenic mice have also proven to be quite useful for developing models of targeted oncogenesis. One of the direct offshoots of these experiments has been the ability to derive tumor cell lines from the targeted cell type. Typically, a fusion gene is constructed with use of a cell-type-specific promoter fused to a potent oncogene. The SV40 large T-antigen oncogene (T ag) has proven to be particularly useful for this purpose and has produced tumors in a wide variety of cell types. Frequently, these tumors retain many of the differentiated phenotypes of the targeted cell type. Such tumors provide an ideal resource for generating tumor cell lines (65, 67, 68). Unfortunately, cell lines are not usually obtained by simply culturing cells derived from the transgenic tumor. Extensive effort to define optimal conditions of cell isolation, culture, and passage to generate a useful tumor cell line resource are usually required.

In order to examine the susceptibility of haploid, round spermatids to neoplastic transformation by simian virus 40 (SV40) large tumor (T) antigen, this gene, fused to the 5′ and 3′ flanking sequences of the mouse protamine 1 gene, was used to develop transgenic animal models (7). In addition to expression in the round spermatids and temporal bones, unexpectedly, the transgene was expressed in the heart. This expression resulted in rhabdomyosarcomas in the right atrium. The availability of an animal model for cardiac tumorigenesis may contribute to an understanding of the basic development and physiology of this organ and its susceptibility to transformation. The atrial tumors expressed ANP mRNA, and levels of ANP in plasma were up to 50-fold higher than those in control animals. Subpopulations of cells from a cardiac atrial tumor display features characteristic of differentiated cardiac myocytes and contain ANP immunoreactivity. A similar but more specific approach has been achieved by Field et al, using the cardiac-specific ANP promoter to produce transgenic mice harboring the SV40-T antigen gene (17). The right atrium of the transgenic mice contain hyperplastic tumors with severe abnormalities in the atrial conduction system. Differentiated myocytes from the atrial tumor can proliferate in culture and can be passaged. Thus transgenic strains and cultured cell lines from the cardiac tumor would be useful models for studying the mechanisms and consequences of ANP expression.

Recent experimental data support the existence of the cardiac renin-angiotensin system (renin, angiotensinogen, ACE, chymase, and angiotensin II receptors) in the human heart (28, 55, 60, 62, 74, 76).

Human heart chymase is a cardiac serine protease isolated from the human heart and is the most potent and specific ANG II-forming enzyme described thus far (39, 77, 78). ANG II formation from ANG I by human heart chymase is not inhibited by ACE inhibitors, but is inhibited by soybean trypsin inhibitor, chymostatin, or α2-macroglobulin. In the particulate left ventricular membrane, a major (80%) ANG II formation from ANG I was due to human heart chymase, while a minor (10%) was due to ACE (75). Recently, the cDNA and gene of human heart chymase have been cloned and characterized (79). Since ACE expression is higher in the atria than in the ventricles (75), the atrial ANG II formation under ACE inhibitor therapy may be significantly decreased, and this could contribute to the antiarrhythmogenic effect of ACE inhibitors. However, in the ventricles, chymase-dependent ANG II formation under ACE inhibitor therapy could be active and supportive as a inotropic substance in the failing heart. Although this clinical hypothesis is interesting, appropriate animal models are not available to test. Since the hearts from rat, mice, dog, or hamster do not express chymase-like activity (H Urata, unpublished observation), development of a transgenic rat expressing human heart chymase is of great interest and is on-going in our laboratory.

Another important target for transgenic hypertension research is the investigation of the endothelin peptide family and their receptors. The members of this family (endothelin I, II, and III) are thought to play an important role in cardiovascular regulation. The endothelin system has been extensively characterized by biochemical, pharmacological, physiological, and molecular biological methods, but its ultimate role in vivo still remains elusive. Recently, the establishment of transgenic rats expressing the human endothelin-2 gene has been reported (56). These animals will provide important tools for the study of endothelin function and regulation.

An important target for transgenic research in the cardiovascular system is the identification of tissue- and cell-specific sequences that will allow the directed expression of genes in the cardiovascular system. Research has focused on the identification of promoter sequences specific for expression of genes in cells of the heart or the vascular wall. Indeed, functional analysis of promoter sequences was one of the first applications of transgenic technology. Correctly targeted expression in an intact animal provides the ultimate proof that a given sequence can suffice as a promoter. In addition, these sequences can be used for directing gene expression into specific cells and tissues. In designing experiments to test a promoter in transgenic animals, the transgene product must be readily distinguishable from the host gene products. Many investigators use an easily discernible enzymatic reporter to monitor promoter activity in transgenic animals. Activity assays for these reporters are simple to perform and the quantitative data are readily obtained. Alternatively, if the gene under study is derived from a species different from the host (or from a different strain within the same species), it may be possible to generate allele-specific probes to distinguish between transgene and host gene products. Assays based on Northern blot, primer extension, RNAse protection, or PCR amplification have been successfully employed to this end. When interpreting promoter function in transgenic animals, it is important to be aware of potential experimental artifacts that may contribute to the observed pattern of expression. Such a targeting attempt of cardiac-specific expression has been achieved using the reporter genes [chloramphenicol acetyltransferase (CAT) or luciferase] driven by ANF or myosin-light chain-2 promoters, respectively (42, 63). These promoter sequences will be useful for future studies to produce new animal models overexpressing the particular gene only in the heart.

New Methods

The microinjection of DNA into fertilized oocytes has been a widely used technique for more than ten years. Since the integration of the transgene is random, other transgenic techniques are sought. One focus is the improvement of the established techniques and the introduction of foreign DNA into the germ line (52). An approach to obtain reliable position and copy number of the transgene, to regulate the level of expression, and to make the transgene independent of the neighboring chromosome could be the use of a recombinant yeast artificial chromosome (YAC), which allows the introduction of large gene constructs into the germ line (61). Alternative methods to time-consuming microinjection, such as the use of sperm as a vehicle for transgene transport (41), or the transfer of DNA into the mouse oocyte by electroporation, have yet to provide convincing results.

Another route for studying the function of genes and creating animal models is the so-called knockout approach, which uses homologous recombination of embryonic stem cells (16, 45, 58). As of this writing no rat embryonic stem cell line is available, so this powerful technique has not been used for knockout of genes in rats. The search for and the development of embryonic stem cell technology in the rat, therefore, has become an important aim in transgenic research.

Other approaches for the inactivation or inhibition of gene expression, however, are available in rats. These include suppression of gene expression by microinjection of antisense or ribozyme constructs. To date there are only few reports of successful antisense targeting in vivo (38). An alternative strategy is the genetic ablation of certain cell types, which are specialized for the expression of a desired gene, by microinjection of cytotoxic genes such as the diphtheria toxin A gene (7, 50) under the regulatory control of tissue-specific promoters. The expression of these genes results in cell death of the target cell. The early expression of a toxin gene during embryonic development may have lethal consequences. Using the thymidine kinase (*tk*) gene from herpes simplex virus, whose expression is only toxic in the presence of certain nucleoside analogues such as FIAU or gancyclovir, it is possible to provide a conditional or inducible system for killing cells in vitro (9, 25).

In summary, the introduction of genes into the rat that results in the establishement of transgenic rat lines has opened new avenues for hypertension research. The application of these techniques and the targeting of new candidate genes will provide important information on the etiology and pathophysiology of primary hypertension. The identification of the genetic basis of this disease will, without doubt, have important implications for the diagnosis, prevention, and future therapy of this disorder.

Literature Cited

1. Armstrong DT, Opavsky MA. 1988. Superovulation of immature rats by continuous infusion of follicle-stimulating hormone. *Biol. Reprod.* 39:511–18

2. Armstrong DT, Siuda A, Opavsky MA, Chandrasekhar Y. 1989. Bimodal effects of luteinizing hormone and role of androgens in modifying superovulatory responses of rats to infusion with purified porcine follicle stimulating hormone. *Biol. Reprod.* 41:54–62

3. Babinet C, Morello D, Renard JP. 1989. Transgenic mice. *Genome* 31:938–49

4. Bachmann S, Peters J, Engler E, Ganten D, Mullins J. 1992. Transgenic rats carrying the mouse renin gene—morphological characterization of a low renin hypertension model. *Kidney Int.* 41:24–36

5. Bader M, Zhao Y, Sander M, Lee M, Bachmann J, et al. 1992. Role of tissue renin in the pathophysiology of hypertension in TGR(mREN2)27. *Hypertension* 19:681–86

6. Beermann F, Ruppert S, Hummler E, Schütz G. 1991. Tyrosinase as a marker for transgenic mice. *Nucleic Acids Res.* 19:958

7. Behringer RR, Mathews LS, Palmiter RD, Brinster RL. 1988. Dwarf mice produced by genetic ablation of growth hormone-expressing cells. *Genes Dev.* 2:453–61

8. Bogdanove EM, Gay VL. 1969. Studies on the disappearance of LH and FSH in the rat, a quantitative approach to adenohypophyseal secretory kinetics. *Endocrinology* 84:1118–38

9. Borrelli E, Heyman RA, Sawchenko PE, Evans RM. 1989. Transgenic mice with inducible dwarfism. *Nature* 339:538–41

10. Deleted in proof

11. Brinster RL, Chen HY, Trumbauer ME, Yagle MK, Palmiter RD. 1985. Factors affecting the efficiency of introducing foreign DNA into mice by microinjecting oocytes. *Proc. Natl. Acad. Sci. USA* 82:4438–42

12. Cambien F, Poirier O, Lecerf L, Evans A, et al. 1992. Deletion polymorphism in the gene for angiotensin-converting enzyme is a potent risk factor for myocardial infarction. *Nature* 359:641–45

13. Djavidani B, Sander M, Böhm M, Kreutz R, Bader M, et al. 1992. Dexamethasone suppresses development of fulminant hypertension in TGR(mRen2)27. *J. Hypertens.* 10(Suppl. 4):S10 (Abstr.)

14. Deleted in proof

15. Evans G, Armstrong DT. 1984. Reduction in fertilization rate in vitro of oocytes from immature rats induced to superovulate. *J. Reprod. Fertil.* 70:131–35

16. Evans MJ. 1989. Potential for genetic manipulation of mammals. *Mol. Biol. Med.* 6:557–65

17. Field LJ. 1991. Cardiovascular research in transgenic animals. *Trends Cardiovasc. Med.* 1:141–46

18. Fukamizu A, Hatae T, Kon Y, Sugimura T, Hasegawa M, et al. 1991. Human renin in transgenic mouse kidney is localized to juxtaglomerular cells. *Biochem. J.* 278:601–3

19. Fukamizu A, Seo MS, Hatae T, Yokoyama M, Nomura T, et al. 1989. Tissue-specific expression of the human renin gene in transgenic mice. *Biochem. Biophys. Res. Commun.* 165:826–32

20. Ganten D, Takahashi S, Lindpaintner K, Mullins JJ. 1991. Genetic basis of hypertension: The renin-angiotensin paradigm. *Hypertension* 18:III:108–14

21. Ganten D, Wagner J, Zeh K, Bader M, Michel JB, et al. 1992. Species-specificity of renin kinetics in transgenic rats harboring the human renin and angiotensinogen gene. *Proc. Natl Acad Sci USA* 89:7806–10

22. Gordon JW, Ruddle FH. 1983. Gene transfer into mouse embryos: production of transgenic mice by pronuclear injection. *Meth. Enzymol.* 101:411–33

23. Habener JF, Cwikel BJ, Herman H, Hammer RE, Palmiter RD, Brinster RL. 1991. Metallothionein-vasopressin transgenic mice. *J. Biol. Chem.* 264:18844–52

24. Hammer RE, Maika SD, Richardson JA, Tang JP, Taurog JD. 1990. Spontaneous inflammatory disease in transgenic rats expressing HLA-B27 and human beta 2m: an animal model of HLA-B27-associated human disorders. *Cell* 63:1099–112

25. Heyman RA, Borelli E, Lesley J, Anderson D, Richman DD, et al. 1989. Thymidin kinase obliteration: creation of transgenic mice with controlled immune deficiency. *Proc. Natl. Acad. Sci. USA* 86:2698–702

26. Hilbert P, Lindpainter K, Beckmann JS, Serikawa T, Soubrier F, et al.

1991. Chromosomal mapping of two genetic loci associated with blood pressure regulation in hereditary hypertensive rats. *Nature* 353:521–29

27. Hilgers KF, Peters J, Sommer M, Rupprecht G, Ganten D, et al. 1992. Local vascular angiotensin formation in female rats harboring the mouse Ren-2 gene. *Hypertension* 19:687–91

28. Hirsch AT, Talsness CE, Schunkert H, Paul M, Dzau VJ. 1991. Tissue-specific activation of cardiac angiotensin converting enzyme in experimental heart failure. *Circ. Res.* 69:475–82

29. Hochi SI, Ninomiyta T, Honma M, Yuki A. 1990. Successful production of transgenic rats. *Anim. Biotechnol.* 1:175–84

30. Hochi SI, Ninomiya T, Waga-Homma M, Sagara J, Yuki A. 1992. Secretion of bovine beta lactalbumin into the milk of transgenic rats. *Mol. Reprod. Dev.* 33:160–64

31. Hofmann SL, Russell DW, Brown MS, Goldstein JL, Hammer RE. 1988. Overexpression of low density lipoprotein receptor eliminates LDL from plasma in transgenic mice. *Science* 239:1277–81

32. Hogan B, Costantini F, Lacy E. 1986. *Manipulating the mouse embryo. A Laboratory Manual.* pp. 52–75. Cold Spring Harbor: Cold Spring Harbor Lab. Press

33. Huszar D, Balling B, Kothary R, Magl MC, Hozumi N, et al. 1985. Insertion of a bacterial gene into the mouse germ line using an infectious retrovirus vector. *Proc. Natl. Acad. Sci. USA* 82:8587–91

34. Jacob HJ, Lindpaintner K, Lincoln SE, Kusumi K, Bunker RK, et al. 1991. Genetic mapping of a gene causing hypertension in the stroke-prone spontaneously hypertensive rat. *Cell* 67:213–24

35. Jaenisch R, Jahner D, Nobis P, Simon T, Lohler J, et al. 1981. Chromosomal position and advance of retroviral genomes inserted into germ line of mice. *Cell* 24:519

36. Jeunemaitre X, Soubrier F, Kotelevtsev YV, Lifton RP, Williams CS, et al. 1992. Molecular basis of human hypertension: role of angiotensinogen. *Cell* 71:169–80

37. Jong-Ho L, Kang DJ, Park CS. 1988. Ovulation in timing and PMSG dose response in superovulation of immature rats. *Korean J. Anim. Sci.* 30:714–19

38. Katsuki M, Sato M, Kimura M, Yokoyama M, Kobayashi K, et al. 1988. Conversion of normal behavior to shiverer by myelin basic proteins antisense cDNA in transgenic mice. *Science* 241:593–95

39. Kinoshita A, Urata H, Bumpus FM, Husain A. 1991. Multiple determinants for the high substrate specificity of an angiotensin II-forming chymase from the human heart. *J. Biol. Chem.* 266:19192–97

40. Laster DB. 1972 Disappearance and uptake of 125 J-FSH in the rat, rabbit, ewe and cow. *J. Reprod. Fertil.* 30:407–15

41. Lavitrano M, Camaioni A, Fazio VM, Dolci S, Farace MG, Spadafora C. 1989. Sperm cells as vectors for introducing foreign DNA into oocytes: genetic transformation of mice. *Cell* 57:717–23

42. Lee KJ, Ross RS, Rockman HA, Harris AN, O'Brien TX, et al. 1992. Myosin light chain-2 luciferase transgenic mice reveal distinct regulatory programs for cardiac and skeletal muscle-specific expression of a single contractile protein gene. *J. Biol. Chem.* 267:15875–85

43. Leveille MC, Armstrong DT. 1989. Preimplantation embryo development and serum steroid levels in immature rats induced to ovulate or superovulate with pregnant mares serum gonadotropin injection or FSH infusion. *Gamete Res.* 23:127–38

44. Lindpaintner K, Jin MW, Niedermaier N, Wilhelm MJ, Ganten D. 1990 Cardiac angiotensinogen and its local activation in the isolated perfused beating heart. *Circ. Res.* 67:564–73

45. Mansour SL. 1990. Gene targeting in murine embryonic stem cells: introduction of specific alterations into the mammalian genome. *Genet. Anal. Tech. Appl.* 7:219–27

46. Mullins JJ, Peters J, Ganten D. 1990. Fulminant hypertension in transgenic rats harbouring the mouse Ren-2 gen. *Nature* 344:541–44

47. Mullins JJ, Sigmund CD, Kane-Haas C, McGowan RA, Gross KW. 1989. Expression of the murine Ren-2 gene in the adrenal gland of transgenic mice. *EMBO J.* 8:4065–72

48. Naftilan AJ, Williams R, Burt D, Paul M, Pratt RE, et al. 1989. A lack of genetic linkage of renin gene restriction length polymorphisms with human hypertension. *Hypertension* 14:614–18

49. Ohkubo H, Kawakami H, Takumi T, Arai H, Yokota Y, et al. 1990. Generation of transgenic mice with elevated blood pressure by introduction of the rat renin and angiotensinogen genes.

Proc. Nat.l Acad. Sci. USA 87:5153–57

50. Palmiter RD, Behringer RR Quaife CJ, Maxwell F, Maxwell IH, Brinster RL. 1987. Cell lineage ablation in transgenic mice by cell-specific expression of a toxin gene. Cell 50:435–43

51. Palmiter RD, Brinster RL. 1986. Germline transformation of mice. Annu. Rev. Genet. 20:465–99

52. Palmiter RD, Sandgren EP, Avarbrock MR, Allen D, Brinster R. 1991. Heterologous introns can enhance expression of transgenes in mice. Proc. Natl. Acad. Sci. USA 88:478–82

53. Papkoff H. 1974. Chemical and biological properties of the subunits of pregnant mare serum gonadotrophin. Biochem. Biophys. Res. Commun. 58: 397–404

54. Pattengale PK, Steart TA, Leder A, Sinn E, Muller W, et al. 1989. Animal models of human disease. Am. J. Pathol. 135:39–61

55. Paul M, Ganten D. 1992. The molecular basis of cardiovascular hypertrophy: The role of the renin-angiotensin system. J. Cardiovasc. Pharmacol. 19: S51–58

56. Paul M, Zimmermann F, Ruf P, Zintz M, Maier D, Yanagisawa M. 1993. Transgenic rats expressing the human endothelin-2 gene. Naunyn-Schmiedebergs Arch. Pharmacol. 347(Suppl.): R93 (Abstr.)

57. Peters J, Münter K, Bader M, Hackenthal E, Mullins JJ, Ganten D. 1992. Increased adrenal renin in transgenic hypertensive rats, TGR(mREN2) 27, and its regulation by cAMP, angiotensin II, and calcium. J. Clin. Invest. 91:251–57

58. Robertson EJ. 1991. Using embryonic stem cells to introduce mutations into mouse germ line. Biol. Reprod. 44: 238–45

59. Sander M, Bader M, Djavidani B, Maser-Gluth C, Vecsei P, et al. 1992. The role of the adrenal gland in the hypertensive transgenic rats TGR (mREN2)27. Endocrinology 131:807–14

60. Sawa H, Tokuchi F, Mochizuki N, Endo Y, Furuta Y, et al. 1992. Expression of the angiotensinogen gene and localization of its protein in the human heart. Circulation 86:138–46

61. Schedle A, Beerman F, Thies E, Montoliu L, Kelsey G, Schutz G. 1992. Transgenic mice generated by pronuclear injection of a yeast artificial chromosome. Nucleic Acids Res. 20: 3073–77

62. Schunkert H, Dzau VJ, Tang SS, Hirsh AT, Apstein CS, Lorell BH. 1990. Increased rat cardiac angiotensin converting enzyme activity and mRNA expression in pressure overload ventricular hypertrophy: Effects on coronary resistance, contractility, and relaxation. J. Clin. Invest. 86:1913–20

63. Seidman CE, Bloch KD, Klein JA, Smith JA, Seidman JG. 1984. Nucleotide sequences of the human and mouse atrial natriuretic factor genes. Science 226:1206–9

64. Seong HH, Yun CH. 1987. Study on the transfer of embryos in mature rats I. induction of superovulation by PMSG and HCG treatment in mature rats. Korean J. Anim. Sci. 29:112–17

65. Sigmund CD, Jones CA, Fabian JR, Mullins J, Gross KW. 1990 Tissue and cell-specific expression of a renin promoter T-antigen reporter gene construct in transgenic mice. Biochem. Biophys. Res. Commun. 170:344–50

66. Sigmund CD, Jones CA, Kane CM, WU C, Lang JA, Gross KW. 1992. Regulated tissue- and cell-specific expression of the human renin gene in transgenic mice. Circ. Res. 70:1070–79

67. Sigmund CD, Okuyama K, Ingelfinger J, Jones CA, Mullins J, et al. 1990. Isolation and characterization of renin expressing cell lines from transgenic mice containing a renin promoter viral oncogene fusion construct. J. Biol. Chem. 265:19916–22

68. Sola C, Tronik D, Dreyfus M, Babiner C, Rougeon F. 1989. Renin-promoter SV40 large T-antigen transgenes induce tumors irrespective of normal cellular expression of renin genes. Oncogene Res. 5:149–53

69. Soriano P, Cone RD, Mulligan RC, Jaenisch R. 1986. Tissue-specific and ectopic expression of genes introduced into transgenic mice by retroviruses. Science 234:1409

70. Steinhelper ME, Cochrane KL, Field LJ. 1990. Hypotension in transgenic mice expressing atrial natriuretic factor genes. Hypertension 16:301–7

71. Takahashi S, Fukamizu A, Hasegawa T, Yokoyama M, Nomura T, et al. 1991. Expression of the human angiotensinogen gene in transgenic mice and transfected cells. Biochem. Biophys. Res. Commun. 180:1103–9

72. Takahashi S, Fukamizu A, Hatae T, Yamda Y, Sugiyama F, et al. 1992. Species-specific kinetics of mouse renin contribute to maintenance of normal blood pressure in transgenic mice with overexpressed human angiotensinogen. J. Vet. Med. Sci. 54:1191–93

73. Tronik D, Dreyfus M, Babiner C, Rougeon F. 1987. Regulated expression of the ren-2 gene in transgenic mice derived from parental strains carrying only the Ren-1 gene. *EMBO J.* 6:983–87

74. Unger T, Ganten D, Lang RE. 1986. Tissue converting enzyme and cardiovascular actions of converting enzyme inhibitors. *J Cardiovasc. Pharmacol.* 8:S75–81

75. Urata H, Healy B, Stewart RW, Bumpus FM, Husain A. 1989. Angiotensin II receptors in normal and failing human hearts. *J. Clin. Endocrinol. Metab.* 69:54–66

76. Urata H, Healy B, Stewart RW, Bumpus FM, Husain A. 1990. Angiotensin II-forming pathways in normal and failing human hearts. *Circ. Res.* 66:883–90

77. Urata H, Kinoshita A, Bumpus FM, Graham RM, Husain A. 1992. Tissue specific expression of human heart chymase. *J. Hypertens.* 10(Suppl. 4): S9

78. Urata H, Kinoshita A, Misono KS, Bumpus FM, Husain A. 1990. Identification of a highly specific chymase as the major angiotensin II-forming enzyme in the human heart. *J. Biol. Chem.* 265:22348–57

79. Urata H, Kinoshita A, Perez DM, Misono KS, Bumpus FM, et al. 1991. Cloning of the gene and cDNA for human heart chymase. *J. Biol. Chem.* 266:17173–79

80. Walton EA, Evans G, Armstrong DT. 1983. Ovulation response and fertilization failure in immature rats induced to superovulate. *J. Reprod. Fertil.* 67:91–96

81. Williams DA. 1990. Embryonic stem cells as targets for gene transfer: a new approach to molecular manipulation of the murine hematopoietic system. *Bone Marrow Transpl.* 5:141–44

82. Yee SP, Mock D, Maltby V, Silver M, Rossant J, et al. 1989. Cardiac and neurological alterations in *v-fps* transgenic mice. *Proc. Natl. Acad. Sci. USA* 86:5873–77

83. Young WY, Yuen BH, Moon YS. 1987. Effects of superovulatory doses of pregnant mare serum gonadotropin on oozyte quality and ovulatory and steroid responses in rats. *Gamete Res.* 16:109–20

84. Yun YW, Yuen BH, Moon YS. 1988. Effects of antiandrogen flutamide on oocyte quality and embryo development in rats superovulated with pregnant mare's serum gonadotropin. *Biol. Reprod.* 39:279–86

SUBJECT INDEX

CUMULATIVE INDEXES

CONTRIBUTING AUTHORS, VOLUMES 52–56

CUMULATIVE TITLES
CHAPTER TITLES, VOLUMES 51–55

SPECIAL TOPICS

CAGED COMPOUNDS IN CELLULAR PHYSIOLOGY

ANNUAL REVIEWS

a nonprofit scientific publisher
4139 El Camino Way
P.O. Box 10139
Palo Alto, CA 94303-0139 • USA

ORDER FORM

**ORDER TOLL FREE
1.800.523.8635
from USA and Canada**

Fax: 1.415.855.9815

Annual Reviews publications may be ordered directly from our office; through booksellers and subscription agents, worldwide; and through participating professional societies. **Prices are subject to change without notice. We do not ship on approval.**

- **Individuals:** Prepayment required on new accounts. in US dollars, checks drawn on a US bank.

- **Institutional Buyers:** Include purchase order. Calif. Corp. #161041 • ARI Fed. I.D. #94-1156476

- **Students / Recent Graduates:** $10.00 discount from retail price, per volume. *Requirements:* 1. be a degree candidate at, or a graduate within the past three years from, an accredited institution;   2. present proof of status (photocopy of your student I.D. or proof of date of graduation);   3. Order direct from Annual Reviews;   4. prepay. This discount **does not** apply to standing orders, *Index on Diskette,* Special Publications, ARPR, or institutional buyers.

- **Professional Society Members:** Many Societies offer *Annual Reviews* to members at reduced rates. Check with your society or contact our office for a list of participating societies.

- **California orders** add applicable sales tax. • **Canadian orders** add 7% GST. Registration #R 121 449-029.

- **Postage paid** by Annual Reviews (4th class bookrate/surface mail). UPS ground service is available at S2.00 extra per book within the contiguous 48 states only. UPS air service or US airmail is available to any location at actual cost. UPS requires a street address. P.O. Box, APO, FPO, not acceptable.

- **Standing Orders:** Set up a standing order and the new volume in series is sent automatically each year upon publication. Each year you can save 10% by prepayment of prerelease invoices sent 90 days prior to the publication date. Cancellation may be made at any time.

- **Prepublication Orders:** Advance orders may be placed for any volume and will be charged to your account upon receipt. Volumes not yet published will be shipped during month of publication indicated.

N O T E	For copies of individual articles from any *Annual Review,* or copies of any article cited in an *Annual Review,* call **Annual Reviews Preprints and Reprints (ARPR)** toll free 1-800-347-8007 (fax toll free 1-800-347-8008) from the USA or Canada. From elsewhere call 1-415-259-5017.

ANNUAL REVIEWS SERIES *Volumes not listed are no longer in print*	**Prices, postpaid, per volume.** **USA/other countries**	Regular Order Please send Volume(s):	Standing Order Begin with Volume:
❏ *Annual Review of* **ANTHROPOLOGY**			
Vols. 1-20	(1972-91)....................$41 / $46		
Vols. 21-22	(1992-93)....................$44 / $49		
Vol. 23	(avail. Oct. 1994).....................$47 / $52	Vol(s). _____	Vol. _____
❏ *Annual Review of* **ASTRONOMY AND ASTROPHYSICS**			
Vols. 1, 5-14, 16-29	(1963, 67-76, 78-91) ....$53 / $58		
Vols. 30-31	(1992-93)....................$57 / $62		
Vol. 32	(avail. Sept. 1994).....................$60 / $65	Vol(s). _____	Vol. _____
❏ *Annual Review of* **BIOCHEMISTRY**			
Vols. 31-34, 36-60	(1962-65,67-91)....................$41 / $47		
Vols. 61-62	(1992-93) ....$46 / $52		
Vol. 63	(avail. July 1994).....................$49 / $55	Vol(s). _____	Vol. _____
❏ *Annual Review of* **BIOPHYSICS AND BIOMOLECULAR STRUCTURE**			
Vols. 1-20	(1972-91)....................$55 / $60		
Vols. 21-22	(1992-93)....................$59 / $64		
Vol. 23	(avail. June 1994).....................$62 / $67	Vol(s). _____	Vol. _____

<table>
<tr><td colspan="3">ANNUAL REVIEWS SERIES
Volumes not listed are no longer in print</td><td>Prices, postpaid, per volume.
USA/other countries</td><td>Regular
Order
Please send
Volume(s):</td><td>Standing
Order
Begin with
Volume:</td></tr>
</table>

❏ *Annual Review of* **CELL BIOLOGY**
Vols.	1-7	(1985-91).....................................$41 / $46		
Vols.	8-9	(1992-93).....................................$46 / $51		
Vol.	10	(avail. Nov. 1994).....$49 / $54	Vol(s). _____	Vol. _____

❏ *Annual Review of* **COMPUTER SCIENCE** (Series suspended)
Vols.	1-2	(1986-87).....................................$41 / $46	
Vols.	3-4	(1988-89/90).................................$47 / $52	Vol(s). _____

Special package price for
Vols.	1-4	(if ordered together)....... ....$100 / $115	❏ Send all four volumes.

❏ *Annual Review of* **EARTH AND PLANETARY SCIENCES**
Vols.	1-6, 8-19	(1973-78, 80-91)..............$55 / $60		
Vols.	20-21	(1992-93).....................................$59 / $64		
Vol.	22	(avail. May 1994).....$62 / $67	Vol(s). _____	Vol. _____

❏ *Annual Review of* **ECOLOGY AND SYSTEMATICS**
Vols.	2-12, 14-17, 19-22..(1971-81, 83-86, 88-91)...$40 / $45			
Vols.	23-24	(1992-93).....................................$44 / $49		
Vol.	25	(avail. Nov. 1994).....$47 / $52	Vol(s). _____	Vol. _____

❏ *Annual Review of* **ENERGY AND THE ENVIRONMENT**
Vols.	1-16	(1976-91).....................................$64 / $69		
Vols.	17-18	(1992-93).....................................$68 / $73		
Vol.	19	(avail. Oct. 1994).....$71 / $76	Vol(s). _____	Vol. _____

❏ *Annual Review of* **ENTOMOLOGY**
Vols.	10-16, 18, 20-36 (1965-71, 73, 75-91)...........$40 / $45			
Vols.	37-38	(1992-93).....................................$44 / $49		
Vol.	39	(avail. January 1994).....$47 / $52	Vol(s). _____	Vol. _____

❏ *Annual Review of* **FLUID MECHANICS**
Vols.	2-4, 7	(1970-72, 75)		
	9-11, 16-23	(1977-79, 84-91).........................$40 / $45		
Vols.	24-25	(1992-93).....................................$44 / $49		
Vol.	26	(avail. January 1994).....$47 / $52	Vol(s). _____	Vol. _____

❏ *Annual Review of* **GENETICS**
Vols.	1-12, 14-25	(1967-78, 80-91).........................$40 / $45		
Vols.	26-27	(1992-93).....................................$44 / $49		
Vol.	28	(avail. Dec. 1994).....$47 / $52	Vol(s). _____	Vol. _____

❏ *Annual Review of* **IMMUNOLOGY**
Vols.	1-9	(1983-91).....................................$41 / $46		
Vols.	10-11	(1992-93).....................................$45 / $50		
Vol.	12	(avail. April 1994).....$48 / $53	Vol(s). _____	Vol. _____

❏ *Annual Review of* **MATERIALS SCIENCE**
Vols.	1, 3-19	(1971, 73-89) ....$68 / $73		
Vols.	20-23	(1990-93) ....$72 / $77		
Vol.	24	(avail. August 1994).....$75 / $80	Vol(s). _____	Vol. _____

❏ *Annual Review of* **MEDICINE: Selected Topics in the Clinical Sciences**
Vols.	9, 11-15, 17-42 (1958, 60-64, 66-42) ....$40 / $45			
Vols.	43-44	(1992-93) ....$44 / $49		
Vol.	45	(avail. April 1994).....$47 / $52	Vol(s). _____	Vol. _____

From:

Name

Address

Zip

ANNUAL REVIEWS
4139 EL CAMINO WY
PO BOX 10139
PALO ALTO CA 94303-0139

Place
Stamp
Here

ANNUAL REVIEWS SERIES Volumes not listed are no longer in print	Prices, postpaid, per volume. USA/other countries	Regular Order Please send Volume(s):	Standing Order Begin with Volume:

☐ *Annual Review of* SOCIOLOGY

Vols. 1-17	(1975-91)...................................$45 / $50		
Vols. 18-19	(1992-93)...................................$49 / $54		
Vol. 20	(avail. August 1994)...............$52 / $57	Vol(s). _____	Vol. _____

> Student discount prices are $10, per volume, off the prices listed above.

ANNUAL REVIEWS SERIES Volumes not listed are no longer in print	Prices, postpaid, per volume. USA/other countries	Regular Order Please send:

☐ THE EXCITEMENT AND FASCINATION OF SCIENCE:

Vol. 1	(1965) softcover.......................$25 / $29	_____ copy(ies)
Vol. 2	(1978) softcover.......................$25 / $29	_____ copy(ies)
Vol. 3	(1990) hardcover.....................$90 / $95	_____ copy(ies)

(Volume 3 is published in two parts with complete indexes for Volumes 1, 2 and both parts of Volume 3. **Sold as a two part set only.**)

☐ INTELLIGENCE AND AFFECTIVITY: Their Relationship During Child Development, by Jean Piaget   (1981) hardcover. ....$8 / $9   _____ copy(ies)

☐ ANNUAL REVIEWS INDEX on Diskette for DOS
single copy..$45
one year subscription (4 quarterly editions).................$120

A complete, searchable listing of titles, authors, keywords, and more for all *Annual Review* articles published since 1984.

Send to: **ANNUAL REVIEWS INC.**
a nonprofit scientific publisher
4139 El Camino Way • P. O. Box 10139
Palo Alto, CA 94303-0139 • USA

For individual articles from any *Annual Review*, call **Annual Reviews Preprints and Reprints (ARPR)** toll free 1-800-347-8007 from USA or Canada. From elsewhere call 1-415-259-5017.

☐ Please enter my order for the volumes indicated above.

Please note: Advance orders for volumes not yet published will be charged to your account upon receipt. Volumes will not be shipped before the month of publication indicated. Prices are subject to change without notice.

☐ Add applicable CA sales tax ☐ Add 7% Canadian GST

☐ Check or money order enclosed or ☐ Charge my:

☐ VISA ☐ MasterCard ☐ American Express

Signature _____

☐ Apply Student/Recent graduate discount. $10 off, per volume. Proof of status enclosed.

☐ Optional UPS ground service, $2 extra per volume in the 48 contiguous states only. UPS requires street address.

☐ Optional UPS air service or US airmail to anywhere in the world. Charged at actual cost and added to invoice.

Account Number _____ Exp. Date _____/_____

Name _____
  Please print

Address_____
  Please print

_____ Zip Code _____

Daytime telephone _____ Fax _____

☐ Send a free copy of the current *Prospectus* or catalog. Area(s) of interest: _____

ARI Federal ID #94-1156476